enVision™ Algebra 1

Teacher's Edition

Volume 2

SAVVAS
LEARNING COMPANY

Savvas Learning Company LLC, 15 East Midland Avenue, Paramus, NJ 07652

SAVVAS
LEARNING COMPANY

ISBN-13: 978-0-328-93185-9
ISBN-10: 0-328-93185-3
10 21

Contents in Brief

enVision™ Algebra 1

Reviewers & Consultants

Mathematicians

David Bressoud, Ph.D.
Professor Emeritus of Mathematics
Macalester College
St. Paul, MN

Karen Edwards, Ph.D.
Mathematics Lecturer
Harvard University
Cambridge, MA

Teacher Reviewers

Jennifer Barkey
K–12 Math Supervisor
Gateway School District
Monroeville, PA

Miesha Beck
Math Teacher/Department Chair
Blackfoot School District
Blackfoot, ID

Joseph Brandell, Ph.D.
West Bloomfield High School
West Bloomfield Public Schools
West Bloomfield, MI

Andrea Coles
Mathematics Teacher
Mountain View Middle School
Blackfoot, ID

Julie Johnson
Mathematics/CS teacher (9–12)
Williamsville Central Schools
Williamsville, NY

Tamar McPherson
Plum Sr HS/Math Teacher
Plum School District
Pittsburgh, PA

Melisa Rice
Math Department Chairperson
Shawnee Public Schools
Shawnee, OK

Erin Zitka
6–12 Math Coordinator
Forsyth County
Cumming, GA

Jeff Ziegler
Teacher
Pittsburgh City Schools
Pittsburgh, PA

About the Authors

Authors

Dan Kennedy, Ph.D

- Classroom teacher and the Lupton Distinguished Professor of Mathematics at the Baylor School in Chattanooga, TN
- Co-author of textbooks *Precalculus: Graphical, Numerical, Algebraic* and *Calculus: Graphical, Numerical, Algebraic, AP Edition*
- Past chair of the College Board's AP Calculus Development Committee.
- Previous Tandy Technology Scholar and Presidential Award winner

Eric Milou, Ed.D

- Professor of Mathematics, Rowan University, Glassboro, NJ
- Member of the author team for Savvas' **enVision**math**2.0** 6-8
- Member of National Council of Teachers of Mathematics (NCTM) feedback/advisory team for the Common Core State Standards
- Author of *Teaching Mathematics to Middle School Students*

Christine D. Thomas, Ph.D

- Professor of Mathematics Education at Georgia State University, Atlanta, GA
- Past-President of the Association of Mathematics Teacher Educators (AMTE)
- Past NCTM Board of Directors Member
- Past member of the editorial panel of the NCTM journal *Mathematics Teacher*
- Past co-chair of the steering committee of the North American chapter of the International Group of the Psychology of Mathematics Education

Rose Mary Zbiek, Ph.D

- Professor of Mathematics Education, Pennsylvania State University, College Park, PA
- Series editor for the NCTM *Essential Understanding* project

Contributing Author

Al Cuoco, Ph.D

- Lead author of CME Project, a National Science Foundation (NSF)-funded high school curriculum
- Team member to revise the Conference Board of the Mathematical Sciences (CBMS) recommendations for teacher preparation and professional development
- Co-author of several books published by the Mathematical Association of America and the American Mathematical Society
- Consultant to the writers of the Common Core State Standards for Mathematics and the PARCC Content Frameworks for high school mathematics

About This Program

enVision™ Algebra 1 offers an innovative instructional model that offers maximum flexibility with implementation options supporting student learning in print, digital, or blended classrooms.

Overview of Components

SavvasRealize.com is your gateway to all digital resources for planning, teaching, and progress monitoring. Each lesson provides instructional content with embedded interactives and visual examples, lesson explorations, formative assessment, and more. It's easy to navigate, assign resources, search, customize, plan, assess, and analyze data.

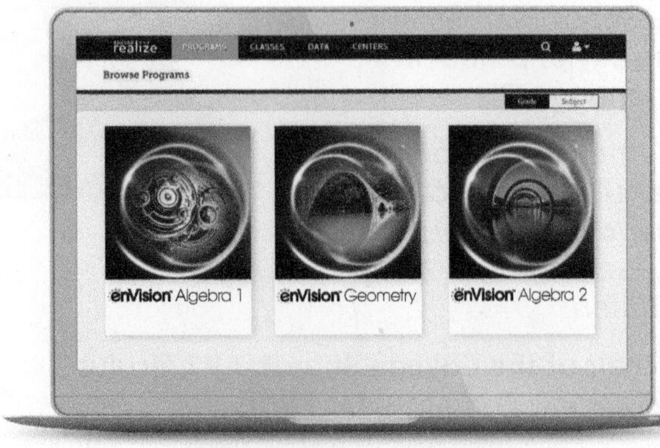
realize
Browse Programs
enVision Algebra 1
enVision Geometry
enVision Algebra 2

Teacher's Edition provides comprehensive teaching support to help all students be successful.

Teacher's Edition
VOLUME 1
enVision Algebra 1

Teacher's Edition Program Overview offers an overview of the program and a comprehensive user's guide.

Teacher's Edition
PROGRAM OVERVIEW
enVision Algebra 1

Assessment Resources Book provides all diagnostic, formative, and summative assessments in one convenient place. Assessments are also available online via SavvasRealize.com.

- Course Readiness Assessment
- Topic Readiness Assessment
- Lesson Quizzes
- Topic Assessments
- Topic Performance Assessments
- Benchmark / Cumulative Assessment
- Mid-Course Assessment
- End-of-Course Assessment

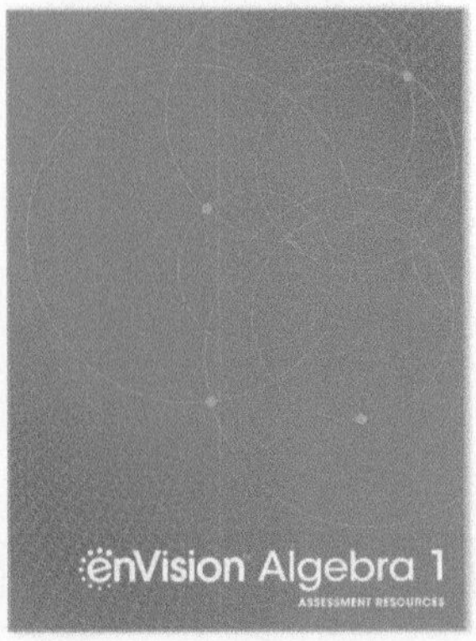
enVision Algebra 1
ASSESSMENT RESOURCES

Student Edition provides all instructional content in a four-color visually engaging format.

enVision Algebra 1

Write-in Student Companion encourages students' active engagement during in-class instruction. Students take ownership of their learning as they take notes, work out problems on their own, and strengthen their math thinking skills.

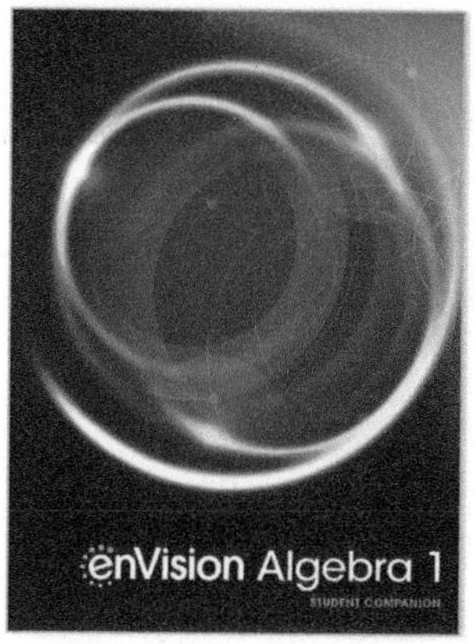
enVision Algebra 1
STUDENT COMPANION

Assessment Readiness Workbook provides standards-based practice and tests to help students prepare for high-stakes assessments.

enVision Algebra 1
ASSESSMENT READINESS WORKBOOK

Additional digital resources:

- Additional digital examples for explicit instruction
- Editable Teacher Resource Masters that offer vocabulary support, remediation, enrichment, additional practice, and more!
- enVision STEM projects and videos
- Answers & Solutions to all Student Edition answers and solutions
- ExamView to build assessments and worksheets in seconds

realize
PROGRAMS
CLASSES
DATA
Programs
Classes
Data

How to Use Your Teacher's Edition

Your Teacher's Edition is a comprehensive resource that offers you easy-to-navigate teaching support for both planning and in-class instruction. Look for these topic-level resources.

Topic and Lesson Resources

At the beginning of each topic are resources to help you plan efficiently and effectively.

Math Background: Focus presents an overview of the math content in the topic.

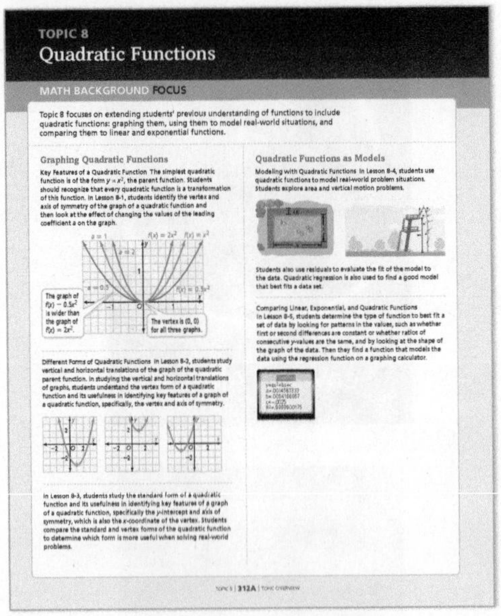
TOPIC 8
Quadratic Functions
MATH BACKGROUND FOCUS

Math Background: Coherence summarizes the content connections throughout the course and program by highlighting what students were presented previously and what student will encounter in future studies.

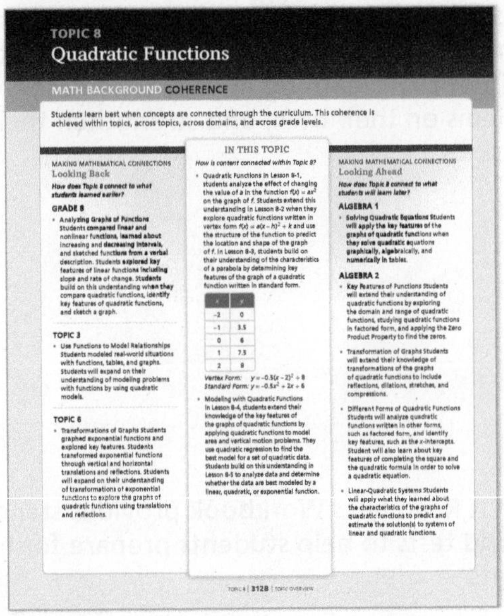
TOPIC 8
Quadratic Functions
MATH BACKGROUND COHERENCE

Math Background: Rigor highlights the three aspects of rigor—conceptual understanding, procedural fluency, and application—that students encounter in the topic.

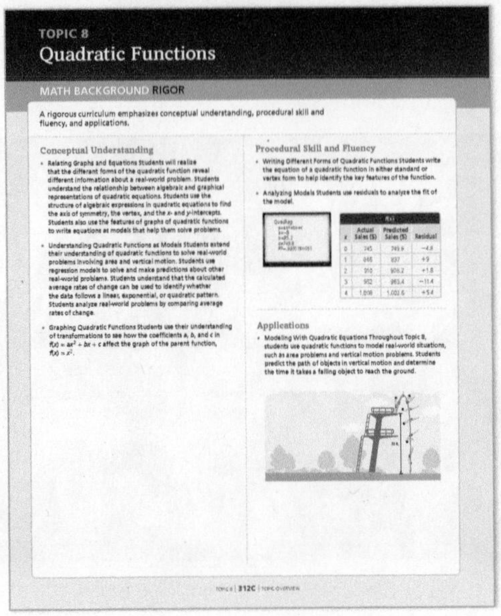
TOPIC 8
Quadratic Functions
MATH BACKGROUND RIGOR

Math Practices & Processes describe behaviors and habits of mind within the context of the topic content.

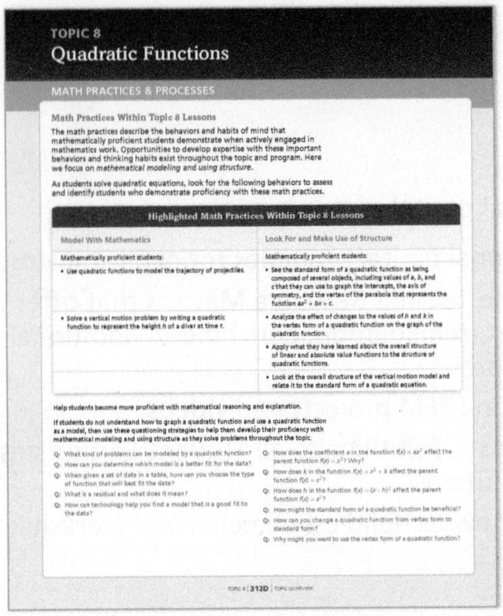
TOPIC 8
Quadratic Functions
MATH PRACTICES & PROCESSES

Topic Planner provides an at-a-glance view of all of the lessons, including pacing recommendations, key vocabulary, objectives, essential understanding, and standards alignment.

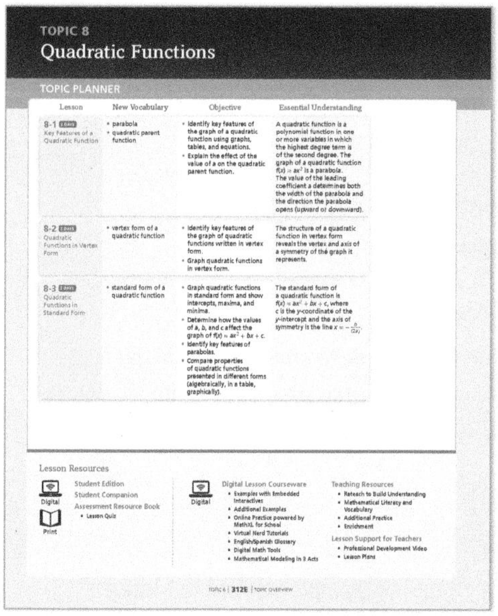
TOPIC 8
Quadratic Functions
TOPIC PLANNER

Topic Readiness Assessment helps you assess students' understanding of prerequisite concepts and skills.

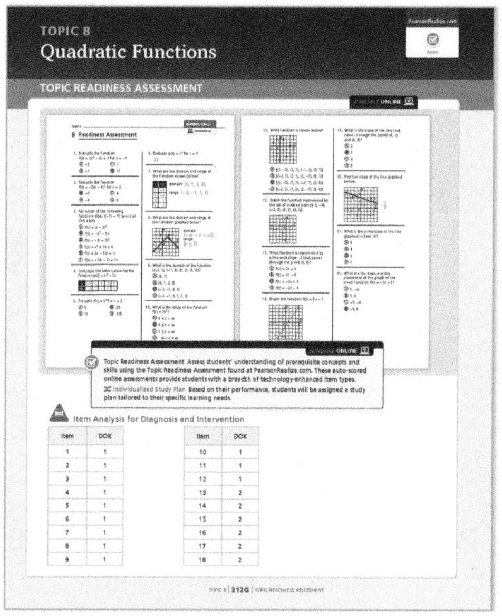
TOPIC 8
Quadratic Functions
TOPIC READINESS ASSESSMENT

Mathematical Modeling in 3 Acts engages students through authentic mathematical modeling and real-world scenarios.

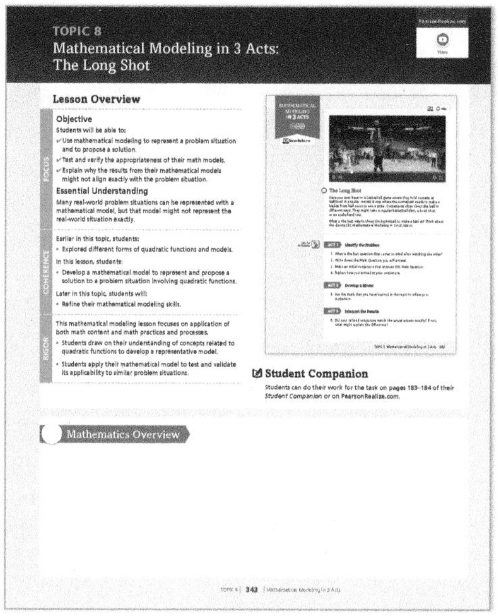
TOPIC 8
Mathematical Modeling in 3 Acts:
The Long Shot
Lesson Overview
Student Companion
Mathematics Overview

enVision™ STEM projects provide opportunities to make meaningful mathematical connections across topics.

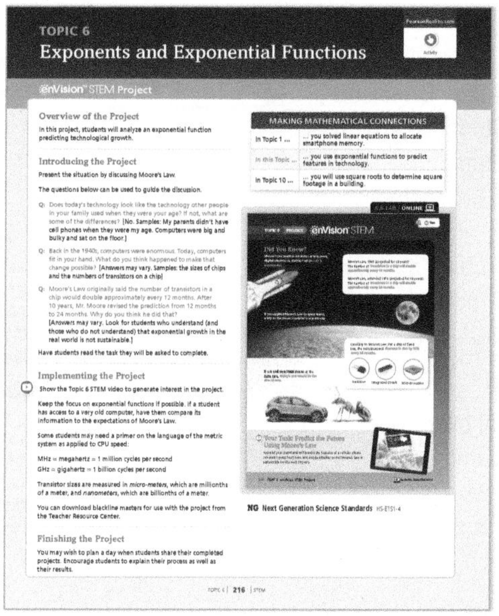
TOPIC 6
Exponents and Exponential Functions
enVision STEM Project
MAKING MATHEMATICAL CONNECTIONS

Navigating a Lesson in your Teacher's Edition

Overview: Each lesson begins with comprehensive overview of the lesson.

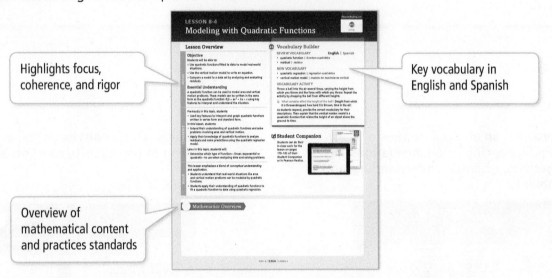

Highlights focus, coherence, and rigor

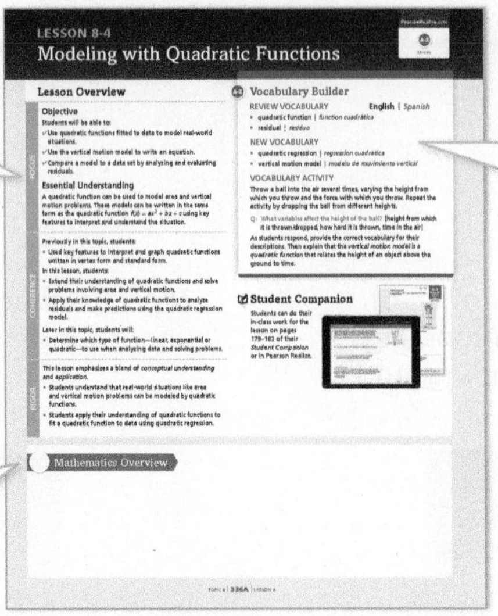

LESSON 8-4
Modeling with Quadratic Functions
Lesson Overview
Vocabulary Builder
Student Companion
Mathematics Overview

Key vocabulary in English and Spanish

Overview of mathematical content and practices standards

Steps 1 & 2: Each lesson begins with a lesson–opening exploration followed by guided instruction.

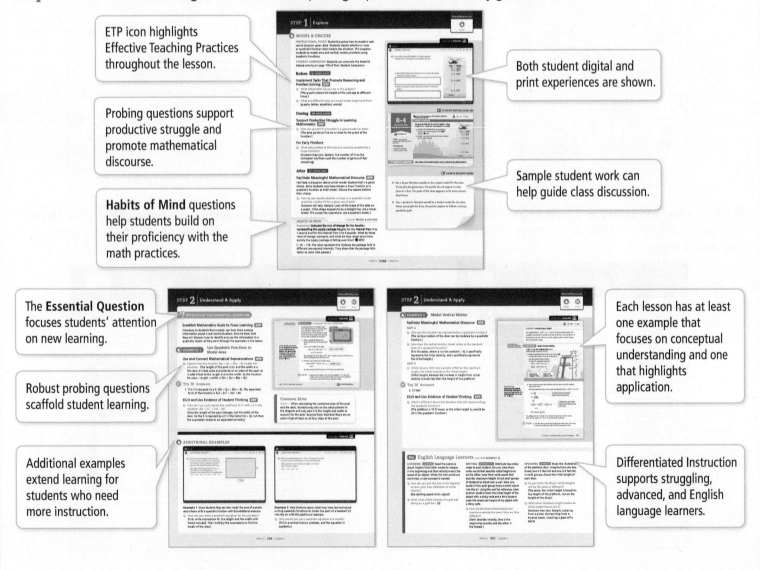

ETP icon highlights Effective Teaching Practices throughout the lesson.

Probing questions support productive struggle and promote mathematical discourse.

Habits of Mind questions help students build on their proficiency with the math practices.

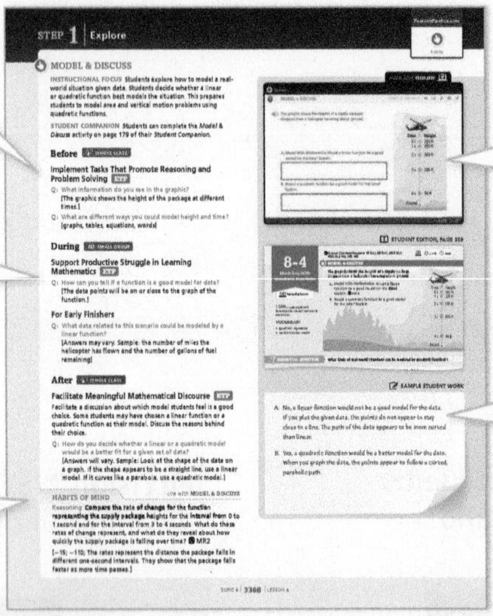

STEP 1 Explore
MODEL & DISCUSS

Both student digital and print experiences are shown.

Sample student work can help guide class discussion.

The **Essential Question** focuses students' attention on new learning.

Robust probing questions scaffold student learning.

Additional examples extend learning for students who need more instruction.

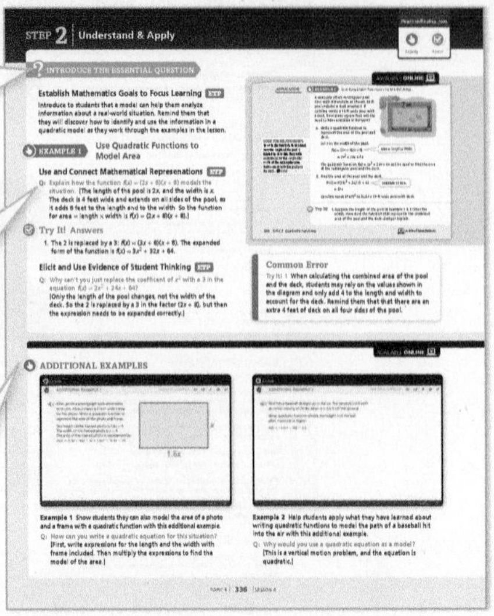

STEP 2 Understand & Apply
ADDITIONAL EXAMPLES

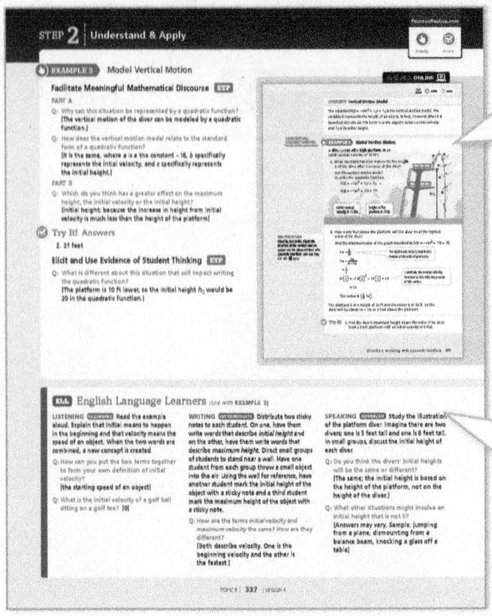

STEP 2 Understand & Apply
Model Vertical Motion
English Language Learners

Each lesson has at least one example that focuses on conceptual understanding and one that highlights application.

Differentiated Instruction supports struggling, advanced, and English language learners.

Do You Understand? and **Do You Know How?** offer students opportunities to check their understanding of the lesson.

Common Error callouts point out errors to look for and strategies to support students.

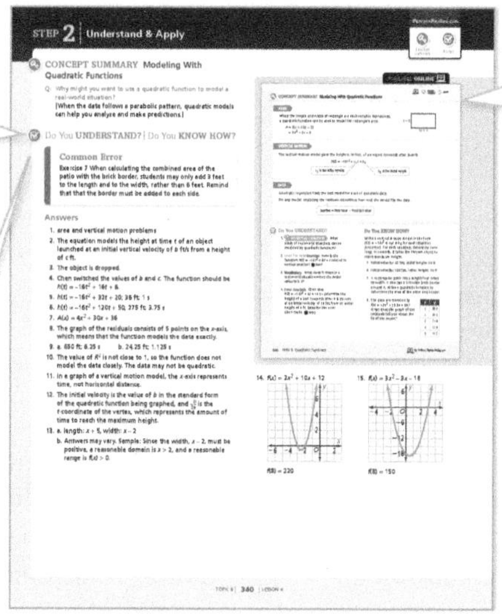

Concept Summaries provide a concise summary of the main lesson concepts.

Step 3: Practice and Problem Solving exercises help your students practice newly learned content.

Digital practice that corresponds to the Practice & Problem Solving assignment is available and it is auto-graded.

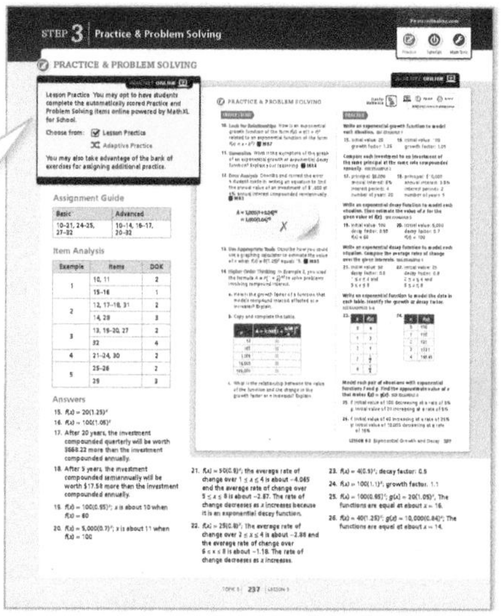

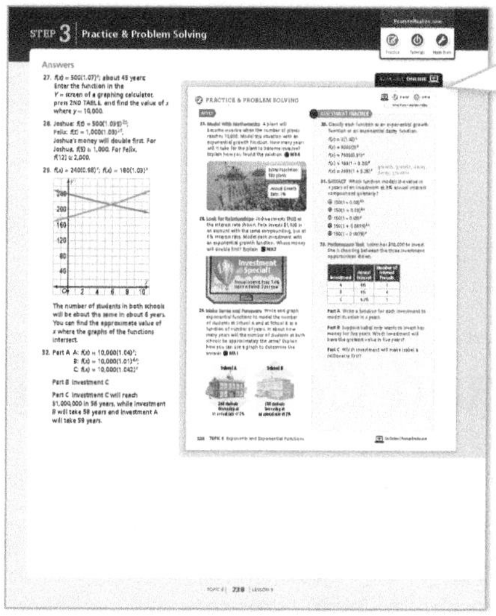

Additional practice exercises can be found online at SavvasRealize.com

Step 4: Check for student understanding and provide remediation.

Lesson Quiz is available for print and digital administration. The digital version is auto-scored.

Robust differentiation intervention resources can be assigned based on students' quiz scores. If students take the quiz online, differentiation is auto-assigned.

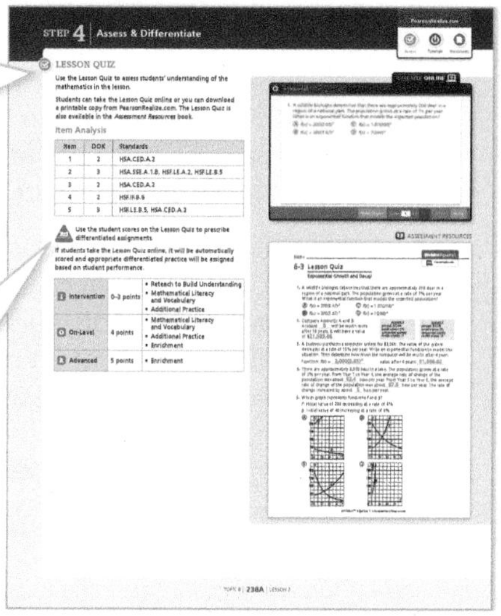

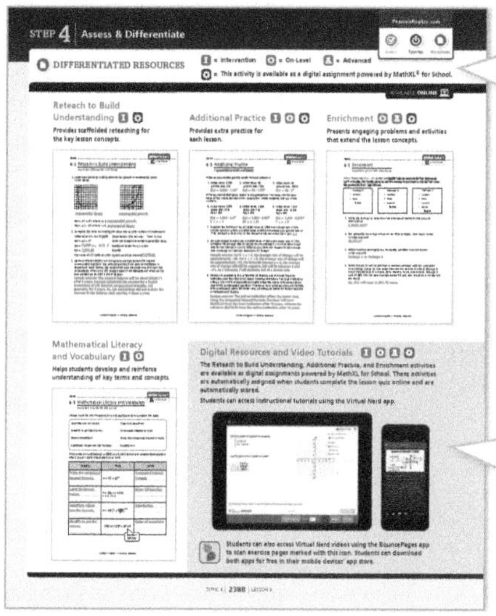

Differentiated Resources Library provides an array of resources to support needs of all students. Some are available as digital activities powered by MathXL® for School.

Video Tutorials are available for every lesson.

Problem Solving

Make sense of problems and persevere in solving them.

Proficient math thinkers read through a problem situation and put together a workable solution path to solve the problem posed. They analyze the information provided and identify constraints and dependencies. Proficient math thinkers identify multiple entries to a problem solution and will choose an efficient and effective entry point.

To help students develop proficiency with this standard, teachers should provide enough time for students to explore problem situations. As needed, teachers can facilitate students' discussion by asking them to identify the problem they are asked to solve, to think about similar problems that they have previously solved, and to describe their solution plan.

Attend to precision.

Proficient math thinkers communicate clearly and precisely the approach they are using. They identify the meaning of symbols that they use and always remember to specify units of measure and to label graphical models accurately. They use mathematical terms precisely and express their answers with the appropriate degree of accuracy.

To help students develop proficiency with this standard, teachers should encourage clear and precise mathematical discourse in the classroom. As needed, teachers can help students attend to precision by asking them to identify the symbols that they use in their mathematical models, to specify the units of measures called for in the problem, and to explain mathematical terms and expressions. Ask students to describe an alternate strategy or method that they can use to check their solutions to problems.

Reasoning and Communicating

Reason abstractly and quantitatively.

Proficient math thinkers make sense of quantities in problem situations. They are able to both represent a problem situation using symbols or equations and explain what the symbols or equation represent in relationship to a problem situation. As they model a situation symbolically or mathematically, they can explain the meaning of the quantities.

To help students develop proficiency with this standard, teachers should help students break down a problem situation and analyze options for modeling or representing the problem situation mathematically. Teachers can ask students what the quantities or variables in an equation represent and how they relate to each other.

Construct viable arguments and critique the reasoning of others.

Proficient math thinkers communicate clearly and convincingly their problem solutions. They construct sound mathematical arguments and develop and defend conjectures to explain mathematical situations. They make use of examples and counterexamples to support their arguments and justify their conclusions. When asked, they respond clearly and logically to the positions and conclusions of others, and compare two arguments, identifying any flaws in logic or reasoning that the arguments may contain. They ask questions to clarify or improve the position of a classmate.

To help students develop proficiency with this standard, teachers can provide frequent opportunities for students to engage in mathematical discourse. Teachers should have students share their solution strategies, explain what their solution means, and defend their selected strategies. Teachers can also encourage students to compare and contrast different strategies. Teachers can ask students to explain how they know their solutions are correct or those of classmates may not be correct.

Representing and Connecting

Model with mathematics.

Proficient math thinkers use mathematics to represent a problem situation and make connections between a real-world problem situation and mathematics. They see the applicability of mathematics to solve every-day problems and can explain how geometry can be used to solve a carpentry problem or algebra to solve a proportional relationship problem. They define and map relationships among quantities in a problem, using appropriate tools to do so. They analyze the relationships and draw conclusions about the solutions.

To help students develop proficiency with this standard, teachers can provide a variety of contexts for students to apply mathematics. For each problem situation, teachers can ask students to think of an equation or a graphical representation that describes the problem. Teachers can also ask students to identify what quantities they should use to solve the problem and what the numbers in the solution represent. Teachers should also ask students to defend their solutions, explaining how they know their solutions are correct.

Use appropriate tools strategically.

Proficient math thinkers strategize about which tools are more helpful to solve a problem situation. They consider all tools, from paper and pencil to protractors and rulers, to calculators and software applications. They articulate the appropriateness of different tools and recognize which would best serve the needs for a given problem. They are especially insightful about technological tools and use them in ways that deepen or extend their understanding of concepts. They also make use of mental tools, such as estimation, to determine the appropriateness of a solution.

To help students develop proficiency with this standard, teachers can encourage students to think about the range of tools that might be used to solve a given problem and then to justify their selection of a tool. Teachers should have students articulate the strengths and weaknesses of different tools as part of their selection process. Teachers should also encourage students to estimate a solution before they begin to solve the problem to help them monitor whether their solution path is helping them reach an accurate solution.

Seeing Patterns and Generalizing

Look for and make use of structure.

Proficient math thinkers go beyond simply solving problems presented to see the structure of mathematics in these problems and to generalize mathematics principles from this structure. They see complicated expressions or equations as single objects composed of many parts.

To help students develop proficiency with this standard, teachers should spend time having students look at the structure of an equation or expression. Teachers can ask students to talk about what they notice about a given solution and what would change if different numbers or quantities were used. Teachers should also encourage students to analyze an expression, asking what each term in an expression or equation represents.

Look for and express regularly in repeated reasoning.

Proficient math thinkers notice when calculations are repeated and can uncover both general methods and shortcuts for solving similar problems.

To help students develop proficiency with this standard, teachers can encourage students to engage in mathematical discourse about solutions to find and express regularity in reasoning about concepts. As students uncover regularity in mathematical behavior, teachers should ask students to propose shortcuts or generalized methods for solving similar types of problems.

Key Concepts in Algebra 1

Proficiency with key concepts and skills of Algebra I is often cited as a requisite for college- and career-readiness. These foundational concepts of algebraic thinking provide the gateway to advanced mathematics.

At the heart of **enVision™ Algebra 1** is the study of functions. Through the study of specific functions: notably linear, exponential, quadratic functions, you will be able to see the structure of functions, to make generalization about all functions, and to describe the uniqueness of specific functions. Within the study of functions, you will work with various types of real numbers, from rational and radicals, to irrational. You will apply properties of numbers and equality to carry out operations within different functions, all with the goal of seeing the applicability of mathematics to describe and model a wide range of natural or man-made events. The focus on transforming functions will help you build connections between the algebraic and graphical representations of functions.

Listed below are the key concepts that you will be studying in **enVision Algebra 1**.

Number and Quantities

- A monomial consists of a single term made up of a number, a variable, an exponent, or any combination thereof.
- A polynomial is made up of monomials.
- Polynomials can be added, subtracted, and multiplied.
- Polynomials form a system that is closed under the operations of addition, subtraction, and multiplication. This system is analogous to the integers.
- Polynomials can be factored to reveal zeros. The zeros can be used to construct a rough graph of the function defined by the polynomial.
- A rational exponent can be rewritten as a radical expression. A radical expression can be rewritten as a rational exponent.
- Properties of integer exponents can be applied when rewriting expressions with rational and radical exponents.
- Properties of rational and irrational numbers can explain sums and products of rational and irrational numbers.

Solving Equations and Inequalities

- Equations and inequalities in two or more variables represent relationships between quantities. They can be used to model real-world situations.
- Rearranging an equation, using the same reasoning as in solving equations, reveals key information about a quantity of interest.
- Each step in solving an equation can be explained and justified mathematically.
- Properties of real numbers and equality hold for all types of equations. These properties, along with properties of inequality, can be applied to solve any equation or inequality.
- Equations and inequalities in two or more variables can represent constraints of the context they represent.
- A system of equations can have no solutions, one solution, or infinitely many solutions.
- A system of inequalities has infinitely many solutions.
- The solutions to equations and inequalities in two or more variables can be graphed in a coordinate plane.
- The solutions to equations and inequalities in two or more variables can be interpreted as viable or non-viable in relationship to the context represented.
- The graph of an equation in two variables is the set of all its solutions plotted in the coordinate plane.
- The graph of the solution to a linear inequality in two variables is a half-plane on a coordinate plane.
- The graph of the solution to a system of linear inequalities in two variables is the intersection of the corresponding half-planes.
- A system of linear equations can be solved by graphing the system or through algebraic manipulation.
- Linear equations can be solved algebraically through substitution or elimination.

Key Concepts in Algebra 1

A Study of Functions

- A function describes a relationship between two quantities. A function consists of inputs, called the domain, and outputs, called the range.
- A function can be written using function notation.
- A function can be rewritten in different forms. Each form reveals different information about the context it models.
- A function can be evaluated for inputs in its domain.
- A function can be represented in different ways: algebraically, in a graph, in a table, or by a verbal description.
- A function has parameters that can be interpreted in terms of the context it models.
- The domain and range of a function may be restricted based on the contextual situation.
- Key features of the graph of a function reveal information about the relationship between the two quantities that the function models.
- A table of values of a function has key features that reveal information about the relationship between the two quantities that the function models.
- The properties of two (or more) functions of the same type can be compared even when the functions are represented in different ways (algebraically, graphically, numerically in tables, or by verbal descriptions).
- The average rate of change of a function can be estimated from a graph or calculated algebraically.
- The average rate of change of a function over a given interval reveals information about the relationship between the two quantities that the model represents.
- The domain of a function can be determined from its graph.
- Standard functions can be combined using arithmetic operations.
- The graph of a function reveals the type of the function. For example, the graph of these functions is easily recognizable: square root, cube root, and piecewise-defined functions, which include step functions and absolute value functions.
- Changing parameters of a function leads to transformations in the graph of the function.
- The graphs of functions can be transformed in similar and predictable ways.
- A function can be classified as even or odd. An even or odd function is recognizable from its graph or the algebraic expression that represents the function.
- A function can have an inverse function.

Linear Functions and Equations

- A linear function represents a situation in which one quantity changes at a constant rate per unit interval relative to another quantity.
- A linear function grows by equal differences over equal intervals.
- The graph of a linear function is a straight line that can show x- and y-intercepts.
- An arithmetic sequence is a type of linear function. It can be defined recursively or explicitly. It can be used to model a real-world situation.
- The domain of an arithmetic sequence is a subset of the integers.
- In a linear function, the slope represents the rate of change and the y-intercept represents a constant term. These parameters have meaning in the context of a situation or data set.
- Linear equations or functions can be used to represent and solve real-world and mathematical problems.
- A correlation coefficient represents the goodness of fit of a data set to a linear model.

Quadratic Functions and Equations

- A quadratic function or equation can be solved by inspection (e.g., for $x^2 = 49$), taking square roots, completing the square, using the quadratic formula, or by factoring.
- Factoring a quadratic expression reveals the zeros of the function it defines.
- Completing the square in a quadratic expression reveals the maximum or minimum value and the symmetry of the function it defines.
- The parameters of a quadratic function, a, b, c, reveal important information about the graph of the function.
- The graph of a quadratic function shows x- and y-intercepts, when appropriate, the vertex, intervals of increase and decrease, and the maxima, or minima.
- A system of equations can consist of a linear equation and a quadratic equation in two variables. The system can be solved graphically or algebraically.
- The method of completing the square can be used to transform any quadratic equation in x into an equation of the form $(x - p)^2 = q$ that has the same solutions.
- The quadratic formula can be derived from the equation $(x - p)^2 = q$.
- At times, the quadratic formula gives complex solutions in the form $a \pm bi$ for real numbers a and b.
- A quadratic equation can have two solutions, one solution, or no real solutions.
- The discriminant can be used to determine the number of solutions of a quadratic function.

Key Concepts in Algebra 1

Exponential Functions and Equations

- An exponential function grows by equal factors over equal intervals.
- An exponential function represents a situation in which a quantity grows or decays by a constant rate per unit interval relative to another.
- A geometric sequence is a type of exponential function. It can be defined recursively or explicitly. It can be used to model a real-world situation.
- The domain of a geometric sequence is a subset of the integers.
- The graph of an exponential function shows x- and y-intercepts, when appropriate, and end behavior.
- A quantity that increases exponentially eventually exceeds a quantity increasing linearly or quadratically.
- The parameters of an exponential function reveal important information about the context that the function represents.
- The properties of exponents can be used to interpret expressions for exponential functions.
- The properties of exponents can be used to transform expressions for exponential functions.

Statistics

- Data can be represented using a variety of displays. Some data can be plotted on the real number line to create dot plots, histograms, and box plots.
- The shape of the data distribution reveals key information about the center and spread of the data set. It can also reveal extreme outliers in the data set.
- Comparing the shapes of the data distribution for two different data sets reveals important information about the data sets.
- Two-way frequency tables can be used to summarize categorical data for two categories.
- The relative frequencies – joint, marginal, and conditional relative frequencies – of a data set can be interpreted to reveal possible associations or trends in the data.
- Data on two quantitative variables can be represented in a scatter plot. The scatter plot can show how the variables are related.
- A function can be fit to a data set. The function fitted to a data set can be used to solve problems in the context of the data. The function is often linear or exponential.
- The context of a data set may suggest the type of function that fits the data.
- The fit of a function to a data set can be informally assessed by plotting and analyzing residuals.
- Correlation suggests that the behavior of one variable is linked to the behavior of a second variable. Causation indicates that the behavior of one variable is caused by the behavior of a second variable.

TOPIC 1

Solving Equations and Inequalities

TOPIC 2

Linear Equations

TOPIC 3

Linear Functions

TOPIC 4

Systems of Linear Equations and Inequalities

TOPIC 5

Piecewise Functions

TOPIC 6

Exponents and Exponential Functions

TOPIC 7

Polynomials and Factoring

TOPIC 8

Quadratic Functions

TOPIC 9

Solving Quadratic Equations

TOPIC 10

Working with Functions

MATH BACKGROUND FOCUS

Topic 7 focuses on extending polynomials. Students identify the parts and factors of polynomials. Students understand how to factor trinomials using the greatest common factor, binomial factors, and special patterns. Students learn methods to add, subtract, and multiply polynomials.

Operations of Polynomials

Add and Subtract Polynomials In Lesson 7-1, students learn that a monomial is a real number, a variable, or the product of a real number and one or more variables, and a polynomial is a monomial or the sum or difference of two or more monomials (terms). Students learn that polynomials are closed under the operations of addition and subtraction. They add and subtract polynomials by combining like terms.

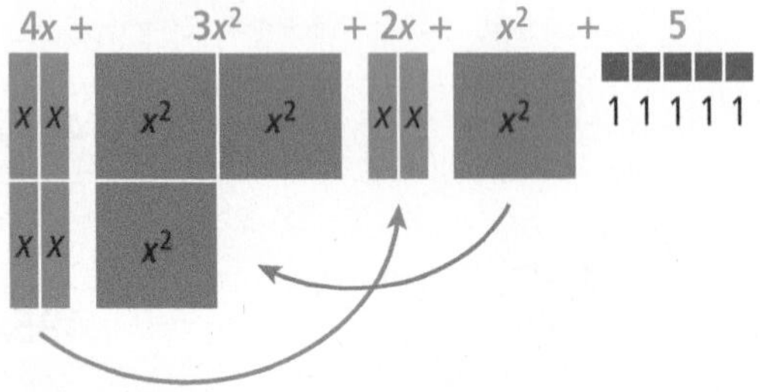

4x + 3x² + 2x + x² + 5
x x
x²
x²
x x
x²
1 1 1 1 1
x x
x²

Multiply Polynomials In Lesson 7-2, students understand that polynomials form a system similar to integers when they recognize that polynomials are also closed under multiplication. Students multiply polynomials by applying the Distributive Property or by using tables and area models.

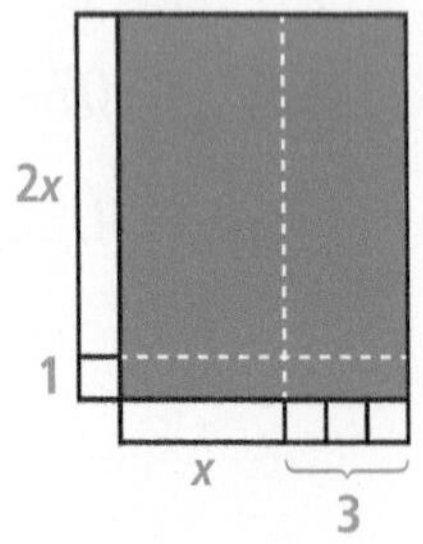

2x
1
x
3

Product of Binomials In Lesson 7-3, students see that the product of the square of a binomial $(a + b)^2$ always follows the same pattern: the square of the first term, plus twice the product of the first and last terms, plus the square of the last term. Students recognize that the product of two binomials in the form $(a + b)(a - b)$ results in the difference of the two squares.

Factoring Polynomials

Greatest Common Factor In Lesson 7-4, students learn that the greatest common factor of a polynomial is the greatest common factor of the coefficients combined with the variables that are common factors of each term.

Quadratic Trinomials (when $a = 1$) In Lesson 7-5, students recognize and understand that when a trinomial is in the form $x^2 + bx + c$, the factors are found by identifying a pair of integer factors of c that have a sum of b. Students then use the factors to write binomials that have a product equal to the trinomial.

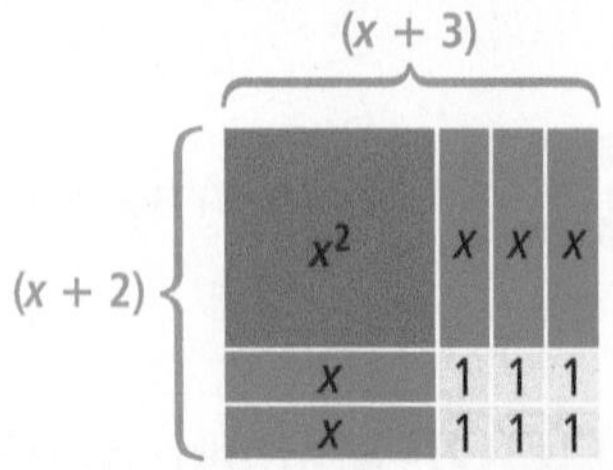

(x + 3)
(x + 2)
x²
x x x
x
1 1 1
x
1 1 1

Quadratic Trinomials (when $a \neq 1$) In Lesson 7-6, students recognize and understand that when a trinomial is in the form $ax^2 + bx + c$, the factors are found by identifying a factor pair of ac that have a sum of b. When ac and b are positive, the second terms in the binomial factors are also positive. When ac is negative, the second terms in the binomial factors have opposite signs.

Special Cases In Lesson 7-7, students identify patterns that are used to factor a perfect-square trinomial and a difference of two squares.

Factoring a Perfect-Square Trinomial

$a^2 + 2ab + b^2 = (a + b)^2$

$a^2 - 2ab + b^2 = (a - b)^2$

Factoring a Difference of Two Squares

$a^2 - b^2 = (a + b)(a - b)$

TOPIC 7
Polynomials and Factoring

MATH BACKGROUND COHERENCE

Students learn best when concepts are connected through the curriculum. This coherence is achieved within topics, across topics, across domains, and across grade levels.

MAKING MATHEMATICAL CONNECTIONS
Looking Back

How does Topic 7 connect to what students learned earlier?

GRADE 8

- **Factoring** Students factored expressions by identifying the greatest common factor and using the Distributive Property. Students apply this knowledge in Topic 7 when factoring polynomials, including trinomials with binomial factors.
- **Operations and Properties** Students learned that operations with integers and exponents were similar to the concept of adding and subtracting digits with the same place value. In Topic 7, students recognize that polynomials form a system that is similar to integers and use the same properties of equality to add, subtract, and multiply polynomials.

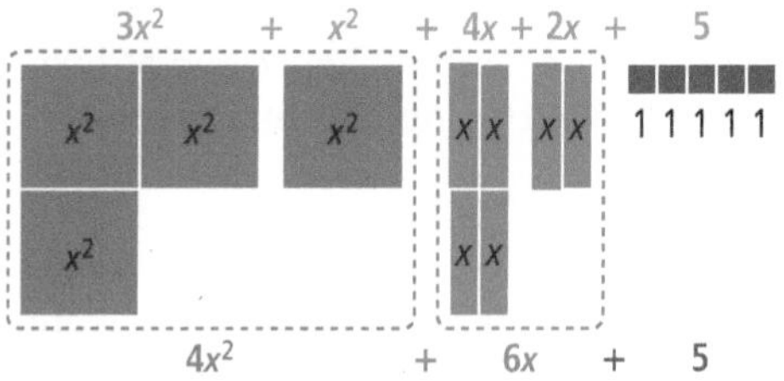

3x² + x² + 4x + 2x + 5
x²
x²
x²
x²
x x
x x
x x
1 1 1 1 1
4x² + 6x + 5

- **Polynomials** Students were previously introduced to polynomials and identified different types of polynomials. In Topic 7, students extend this understanding of polynomials by adding, subtracting, multiplying, and factoring polynomials.

ALGEBRA 1

- **Multiply Exponents** In Topic 6, students learned about multiplication properties of exponents and solved exponential equations. In Topic 7, students apply these properties of exponents when multiplying polynomials and finding products of binomials.

IN THIS TOPIC

How is content connected within Topic 7?

- **Addition, Subtraction, and Multiplication** Students recognize that the operations of addition, subtraction, and multiplication are closed for polynomials (Closure Property). In Lesson 7-1, students add and subtract polynomials by combining like terms. In Lesson 7-2, students multiply polynomials using different methods.
- **Products** In Lesson 7-3, students identify patterns in the square of a binomial, $(a + b)^2$ or $(a - b)^2$, and in the products of two binomials in the form $(a + b)(a - b)$. Students apply these patterns to simplify expressions and solve problems.
- **Factors of Polynomials** In Lesson 7-4, students factor polynomials by finding the greatest common factor of the terms. In Lesson 7-5, students factor a trinomial in the form $x^2 + bx + c$ by finding a pair of integer factors of c that have a sum of b and then using the factors of c to write the binomial factors. In Lesson 7-6, students factor a trinomial in the form $ax^2 + bx + c$ by finding a factor pair of ac that has a sum of b. In Lesson 7-7, students factor special cases of polynomials such as a perfect-square trinomial and a difference of two squares.

Factors of −6	Sum of Factors
1 and −6	−5
−1 and 6	5

MAKING MATHEMATICAL CONNECTIONS
Looking Ahead

How does Topic 7 connect to what students will learn later?

ALGEBRA 1

- **Quadratics** In Topic 7, students recognize that a quadratic trinomial in the form $ax^2 + bx + c$ is factored by finding a factor pair of ac that has a sum of b. In Topic 8, students will identify the key features of a quadratic function and use quadratic functions in various forms to model real-world problems. Then, in Topic 9, students will solve quadratic equations using tables, graphs, and factoring.

ALGEBRA 2

- **Operations on Polynomials** In Topic 7, students learn how to add, subtract, and multiply polynomials. In Algebra 2, students will expand their knowledge of operations on polynomials to include division of polynomials.

$(x + 5)(x + 8)$

	x	8
x	x^2	$8x$
5	$5x$	40

CALCULUS

- **Procedures with Exponents** In Topic 7, students apply their understanding of multiplying exponents to multiplying and factoring polynomials. In Calculus, students will extend their knowledge of multiplying and factoring polynomials and expressions containing exponents to find derivatives of powers of x.

MATH BACKGROUND RIGOR

A rigorous curriculum emphasizes conceptual understanding, procedural skill and fluency, and applications.

Conceptual Understanding

- **Identify Polynomials** Students understand that polynomials are composed of monomials, each of which is a term of the polynomial. Students identify the degree of the polynomial as the largest sum of the exponents of the variables of a monomial.

- **Multiply Polynomials** Students understand that polynomials are closed under multiplication. Students recognize that they can use the Distributive Property or a table to find the product of polynomials. The degree of the product is larger than the degree of the factors when the factors include variables.

  Area of phone $= (x + 1)(1.8x + 3)$
  $= x(1.8x + 3) + 1(1.8x + 3)$
  $= 1.8x^2 + 3x + 1.8x + 3$
  $= 1.8x^2 + 4.8x + 3$

- **Factor Quadratic Trinomials** Students understand that when factoring a quadratic trinomial in the form $ax^2 + bx + c$, there is a pair of factors *ac* that have a sum of *b*. If *ac* and *b* are both positive, the second terms in the binomial factors are positive, and if *ac* is negative, the second terms in the binomial factors have opposite signs.

- **Patterns** Students learn to conceptualize patterns that represent a perfect-square trinomial and a difference of two squares.

  $(a + b)(a - b) = a^2 - b^2$

  difference of two squares

Procedural Skill and Fluency

- **Add and Subtract Polynomials** Students add and subtract polynomials by combining like terms.

- **Greatest Common Factor** Students factor a polynomial using a process that is similar to factoring integers, using the Distributive Property and the GCF.

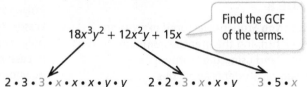

  $18x^3y^2 + 12x^2y + 15x$ — Find the GCF of the terms.

  $2 \cdot 3 \cdot 3 \cdot x \cdot x \cdot x \cdot y \cdot y$ $2 \cdot 2 \cdot 3 \cdot x \cdot x \cdot y$ $3 \cdot 5 \cdot x$

  The greatest common factor of $18x^3y^2 + 12x^2y + 15x$ is $3x$.

  $3x(6x^2y^2 + 4xy + 5)$ — Identify the remaining factors of the polynomial after factoring out the GCF, then write it in factored form.

- **Factoring $x^2 + bx + c$** Students factor a trinomial in the form $x^2 + bx + c$ by first finding a factor pair of *c* that has a sum of *b*. Students use the factors they found to write binomials that have a product equal to the trinomial.

- **Factoring $ax^2 + bx + c$** Students factor a trinomial in the form $ax^2 + bx + c$ by either grouping or using substitution. When grouping, students find a factor pair of *ac* that has a sum of *b* and rewrite *bx* as the sum of those factors. Then group as two binomials, factor out the GCF of each binomial, and use the Distributive Property.

- **Products of Factors** Students rewrite a perfect-square trinomial and a difference of two squares as products of factors. Students recognize when they can repeatedly apply factoring patterns until an expression is factored completely.

Applications

- **Squaring a Binomial** Students apply the process of squaring a binomial to solve real-world problems, such as finding the area of an image within a border.

- **Finding the Greatest Common Factor** Students apply the process of finding the GCF of a polynomial to factor a polynomial model, such as the area of photos in various arrangements on a page.

- **Factoring Trinomials** Students apply factoring trinomials to solve real-world problems, such as finding the dimension of the largest amount of wall space needed for a closet system that has three different sizes of storage units.

Polynomials and Factoring

MATH PRACTICES & PROCESSES

Math Practices Within Topic 7 Lessons

The math practices describe the behaviors and habits of mind that mathematically proficient students demonstrate when actively engaged in mathematics work. Opportunities to develop expertise with these important behaviors and thinking habits exist throughout the topic and program. Here we focus on constructing arguments and using structure.

As students add, subtract, multiply, and factor polynomials look for the following behaviors to assess and identify students who demonstrate proficiency with these math practices.

Highlighted Math Practices Within Topic 7 Lessons

Construct Viable Arguments **MP.3**	Look For and Make Use of Structure **MP.7**
Mathematically proficient students:	Mathematically proficient students:
• Explain and justify the steps of combining like terms to add or subtract polynomials.	• Apply general rules to specific situations when they determine that the degree of the product is greater than the degree of the factors when multiplying polynomials.
• Craft an argument that compares factoring trinomials in the form $ax^2 + bx + c$ when $a = 1$ versus when $a \neq 1$.	• Use the structure of the factors to identify a polynomial as a square of a binomial or a difference of two squares.
• Justify their solution pathway by explaining how they chose which method to use for factoring a polynomial.	• Extend their understanding of factors and common factors to include monomials and binomials. They use the structure of a trinomial, including the signs and values of the coefficients, to factor a trinomial completely.
• Use stated mathematical assumptions about the relationships between the terms in a trinomial to explain the flawed logic in a student's thinking about the relationship between the terms in a trinomial and whether the trinomial is factorable.	• See a polynomial as being composed of terms whose greatest common factor is the greatest common factor of the coefficients, as well as the greatest common factor of the variables of each term.

Help students become more proficient with constructing arguments and using structure.

If students do not understand how to identify and use appropriate strategies for understanding and solving problems involving polynomials and factoring, then use these questioning strategies to help them develop their proficiency with constructing arguments and using structure as they solve problems throughout the topic.

Q: What mathematical evidence supports your decision to combine like terms when adding or subtracting polynomials?

Q: How can you prove that a factorization is correct?

Q: What should you consider when you decide whether a trinomial is factorable?

Q: What patterns can you use to multiply binomials?

Q: How do you know that you have factored a trinomial completely?

Q: What observations can you make about the greatest common factor of a polynomial?

TOPIC PLANNER

Lesson	New Vocabulary	Objective	Essential Understanding	Standards
7-1 2 DAYS Adding and Subtracting Polynomials	• Closure Property, degree of a monomial, degree of a polynomial, monomial, polynomial, standard form of a polynomial	• Identify the parts of a polynomial. • Classify polynomials by number of terms and by degree. • Write a polynomial in standard form. • Add or subtract two polynomials.	A polynomial is a monomial or the sum or differences of two or more monomials (terms). Polynomials can be added or subtracted by combining like terms. Polynomials are closed under addition or subtraction, similar to integers.	HSA.APR.A.1 **Mathematical Practices** MP.2, MP.3, MP.7
7-2 2 DAYS Multiplying Polynomials	none	• Use the Distributive Property with polynomials, recognizing that polynomials are closed under multiplication. • Multiply polynomials using a table and an area model.	Polynomials can be multiplied by applying the Distributive Property or by using a table. They form a system similar to integers. Therefore, polynomials are closed under multiplication.	HSA.APR.A.1 **Mathematical Practices** MP.1, MP.3, MP.7
7-3 2 DAYS Multiplying Special Cases	• difference of two squares	• Determine the square of a binomial. • Find the product of a sum and difference of two squares. • Solve real-world problems involving the square of a binomial.	The product of the square of a binomial in the form $(a + b)^2$ is always the square of the first term, plus twice the product of the first and last terms, plus the square of the last term. The product of a sum and a difference of two binomials in the form $(a + b)(a - b)$ is always the difference of the two squares.	HSA.APR.A.1 **Mathematical Practices** MP.3, MP.7, MP.8
7-4 2 DAYS Factoring Polynomials	none	• Find the greatest common factor of the terms of a polynomial. • Use the structure of a polynomial to rewrite it in factored form. • Factor polynomials that represent real-world problems.	The greatest common factor of the terms of a polynomial is the greatest common factor of the coefficients and the variable or variables, using the number of instances of the variable that are common to each term.	HSA.APR.A.1, HSA.SSE.A.2 **Mathematical Practices** MP.1, MP.4, MP.7

Lesson Resources

Digital

Print

Student Edition

Student Companion

Assessment Resource Book

- Lesson Quiz

Digital

Digital Lesson Courseware

- Examples with Embedded Interactives
- Additional Examples
- Online Practice powered by MathXL for School
- Virtual Nerd Tutorials
- English/Spanish Glossary
- Digital Math Tools
- Mathematical Modeling in 3 Acts

Teaching Resources

- Reteach to Build Understanding
- Mathematical Literacy and Vocabulary
- Additional Practice
- Enrichment

Lesson Support for Teachers

- Professional Development Video
- Lesson Plans

The suggested pacing for each lesson is shown for a 45-minute class.
In addition, allow 1 day for the Topic Review and 1 day for the Topic Assessment.

TOPIC PLANNER

Lesson	New Vocabulary	Objective	Essential Understanding	Standards
7-5 2 DAYS Factoring $x^2 + bx + c$	none	• Factor a trinomial in the form $x^2 + bx + c$ by finding two binomial factors whose product is equal to the trinomial. • Identify and use patterns in the signs of the coefficients of the terms of a trinomial expression.	When a trinomial is in the form $x^2 + bx + c$, the factors are found by identifying a pair of integer factors of *c* that have a sum of *b* and then using the factors to write binomials that have a product equal to the trinomial.	HSA.SSE.A.1.A **Mathematical Practices** MP.2, MP.5, MP.7
Mathematical Modeling in 3 Acts: Who's Right? 1 DAY	none	• Use mathematical modeling to represent a problem situation and to propose a solution. • Test and verify the appropriateness of their math models. • Explain why the results from their mathematical models might not align exactly with the problem situation.	Many real-world problem situations can be represented with a mathematical model, but that model might not represent the real-world situation exactly.	HSA.APR.A.1 **Mathematical Practices** MP.4
7-6 2 DAYS Factoring $ax^2 + bx + c$	none	• Identify the common factor of the coefficients in the terms of a trinomial expression when $a \neq 1$. • Write a quadratic trinomial as a product of two binomial factors.	A quadratic trinomial in the form $ax^2 + bx + c$ when $a \neq 1$ can either be factored by grouping or factored by substitution.	HSA.SSE.A.1.A **Mathematical Practices** MP.1, MP.2, MP.7
7-7 2 DAYS Factoring Special Cases	• perfect-square trinomial	• Identify and factor a trinomial that is a perfect square or a binomial that is a difference of two squares. • Factor special cases of polynomials within the context of real-world problems.	When a trinomial has the pattern $a^2 + 2ab + b^2$ or $a^2 - 2ab + b^2$, then it can be factored as $(a + b)^2$ or $(a - b)^2$ respectively. If a binomial has the pattern $a^2 - b^2$, then it can be factored as $(a + b)(a - b)$.	HSA.SSE.A.1, HSA.SEE.A.2 **Mathematical Practices** MP.1, MP.2, MP.7

Topic Resources

Digital

Print

Student Edition
- enVision STEM
- Mathematical Modeling in 3 Acts
- Topic Review

Digital Lesson Courseware
- Topic Readiness Assessment
- Topic Assessment
- Topic Performance Assessment

Digital

Teaching Resources
- enVision STEM
- Graphing Technology Activities

Topic Support for Teachers
- Mathematical Modeling in 3 Acts
- ExamView
- Answers and Solutions

AVAILABLE ONLINE

Name ____________

enVision Algebra 1
PearsonRealize.com

7 Readiness Assessment

For Items 1–5, what property of real numbers does each statement demonstrate?

1. $a + (-a) = 0$
   - (A) Additive Inverse
   - (B) Commutative Property of Addition
   - (C) Associative Property of Addition
   - (D) Distributive Property
2. $a + b = b + a$
   - (A) Additive Inverse
   - (B) Commutative Property of Addition
   - (C) Associative Property of Addition
   - (D) Distributive Property
3. $2(x + 6) = 2(x) + 2(6)$
   - (A) Additive Inverse
   - (B) Commutative Property of Addition
   - (C) Associative Property of Multiplication
   - (D) Distributive Property
4. $(3 + 4) + 1 = 3 + (4 + 1)$
   - (A) Associative Property of Addition
   - (B) Multiplicative Identity
   - (C) Commutative Property of Addition
   - (D) Distributive Property
5. $a \cdot 1 = a$
   - (A) Associative Property of Multiplication
   - (B) Multiplicative Identity
   - (C) Commutative Property of Multiplication
   - (D) Distributive Property

6. List all of the factors of 36.
   1, 2, 3, 4, 6, 9, 12, 18, 36

For Items 7–9, evaluate each expression for the given value.

7. $4x - 3$; $x = -2$
   -11
8. $-w^2 + 5$; $w = -3$
   -4
9. $3y^2 - 7y + 1$; $y = 2$
   -1

10. Simplify $(-2x^3)^4$.
    $16x^{12}$
11. Simplify $(3w^3)(-5w)^2$.
    $75w^5$
12. Rewrite the expression in exponential form.
    $x \cdot x \cdot x =$ x^3

For Items 13–15, simplify each expression.

13. $3d + 4 - d + 8$
    $2d + 12$
14. $2x^2 - 5 - 5x^2 + 4$
    $-3x^2 - 1$
15. $2(w + 3) - (w - 1)$
    $w + 7$

16. What is the greatest common factor of 36 and 48?
    - (A) 4
    - (B) 12
    - (C) 36
    - (D) 144

17. What is the area of the rectangle below in square units?

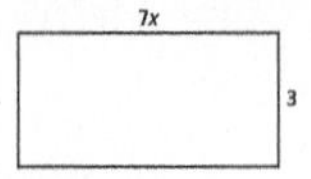

7x
3

   - (A) $7x + 3$
   - (B) $21x$
   - (C) $14x + 6$
   - (D) 21

18. What is the total area of the figure below in square units?

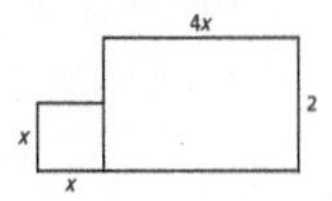

4x
2
x
x

   - (A) $x^2 + 8x$
   - (B) $8x$
   - (C) $6x + 2$
   - (D) $8x^2$

AVAILABLE ONLINE

Topic Readiness Assessment Assess students' understanding of prerequisite concepts and skills using the Topic Readiness Assessment found at **SavvasRealize.com.** These auto-scored online assessments provide students with a breadth of technology-enhanced item types.

Individualized Study Plan Based on their performance, students will be assigned a study plan tailored to their specific learning needs.

RtI

Item Analysis for Diagnosis and Intervention

Item	DOK	Standard	Item	DOK	Standard
1	1	7.NS.A.1, 7.NS.A.2, 7.EE.A.1	10	1	HSN.RN.A.2
2	1	7.NS.A.1, 7.NS.A.2, 7.EE.A.1	11	1	HSN.RN.A.2
3	1	7.NS.A.1, 7.NS.A.2, 7.EE.A.1	12	1	HSN.RN.A.2
4	1	7.NS.A.1, 7.NS.A.2, 7.EE.A.1	13	1	HSN.SSE.A.2
5	1	7.NS.A.1, 7.NS.A.2, 7.EE.A.1	14	1	HSN.SSE.A.2
6	1	6.NS.B.4	15	1	HSN.SSE.A.2
7	1	6.EE.A.2.C	16	1	6.NS.B.4
8	1	6.EE.A.2.C	17	2	8.EE.A.1
9	1	6.EE.A.2.C	18	2	8.EE.A.1

TOPIC 7
Polynomials and Factoring

TOPIC OPENER

AVAILABLE ONLINE

TOPIC 7

Polynomials and Factoring

TOPIC ESSENTIAL QUESTION

How do you work with polynomials to rewrite expressions and solve problems?

Topic Overview

Topic Vocabulary

- Closure Property
- degree of a monomial
- degree of a polynomial
- difference of two squares
- monomial
- perfect-square trinomial
- polynomial
- standard form of a polynomial

Go online | PearsonRealize.com

Digital Experience

INTERACTIVE STUDENT EDITION Access online or offline.

ACTIVITIES Complete ***Explore & Reason, Model & Discuss,*** and ***Critique & Explain*** activities. Interact with Examples and Try Its.

ANIMATION View and interact with real-world applications.

PRACTICE Practice what you've learned.

MATHEMATICAL MODELING IN 3 ACTS

Who's Right?

People often approach a problem in different ways. Sometimes their solutions are the same, but other times different approaches lead to very different, but still valid, solutions.

Suppose you had to solve a system of linear equations. You might solve it by graphing while a classmate might use substitution. Is one way of solving a problem always better than another? Think about this during the Mathematical Modeling in 3 Acts lesson.

VIDEOS Watch clips to support ***Mathematical Modeling in 3 Acts Lessons*** and **enVision™ *STEM Projects***.

CONCEPT SUMMARY Review key lesson content through multiple representations.

ASSESSMENT Show what you've learned.

GLOSSARY Read and listen to English and Spanish definitions.

TUTORIALS Get help from ***Virtual Nerd***, right when you need it.

MATH TOOLS Explore math with digital tools and manipulatives.

Topic Essential Question

How do you work with polynomials to rewrite expressions and solve problems?

Revisit the Topic Essential Question throughout the topic. See page 307 (Topic Review) for notes about answering the Topic Essential Question.

Mathematical Modeling in 3 Acts

Generate excitement about the upcoming Mathematical Modeling in 3 Acts lesson by having students read about the math modeling problem for this topic.

See pages 294, 294A, and 294B for notes about how to use the lesson video in your classroom.

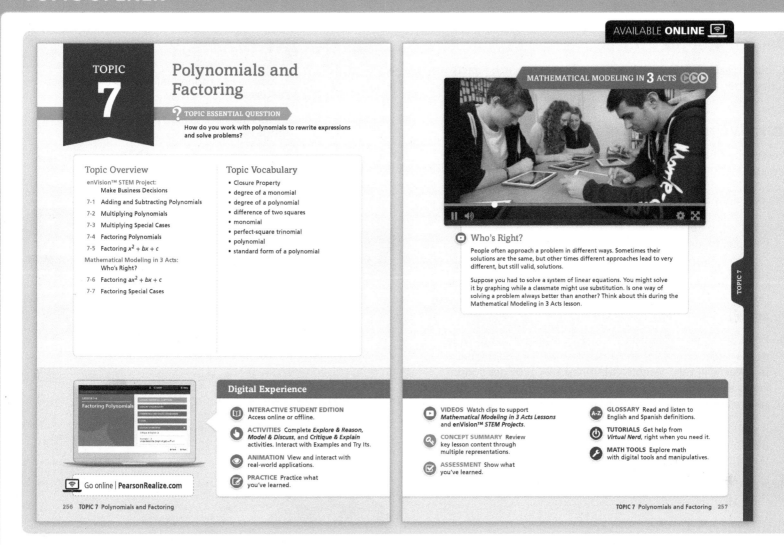

Overview of the Project

In this project, students will learn how market research affects business decisions.

Introducing the Project

Present the situation by discussing business revenue and market research.

The questions below can be used to guide the discussion.

Q: What is the goal of a business?
[Sample: to make money]

Q: How do you think the population of a town influences the success or failure of a new business in that town?
[Answers will vary. Look for students who are aware of buying power.]

Q: What are some differences between a business that provides goods (objects for sale) and a business that provides services?
[Answers will vary. Sample: A business that provides goods keeps an inventory of goods to sell; a business that provides services needs equipment to provide the services.]

Q: If you were to go into business, would that business provide goods (objects) or provide services?
[Encourage a variety of answers.]

Have students read the task they will be asked to complete.

Implementing the Project

Show the Topic 7 STEM video to generate interest in the project.

You can download blackline masters for use with the project from the Teacher Resource Center.

Encourage students to set up situations that allow all functions to have integer coefficients. While it is still possible to do the work otherwise, it is recommended that students use integer coefficients.

Finishing the Project

You may wish to plan a day when students share their completed business plans. Encourage students to explain their process as well as their results.

MAKING MATHEMATICAL CONNECTIONS	
In Topic 6 ...	... you used exponential functions to predict features in technology.
In this Topic ...	... you use polynomials to model business decisions.
In Topic 8 ...	... you will use quadratic functions to estimate business profits.

AVAILABLE **ONLINE**

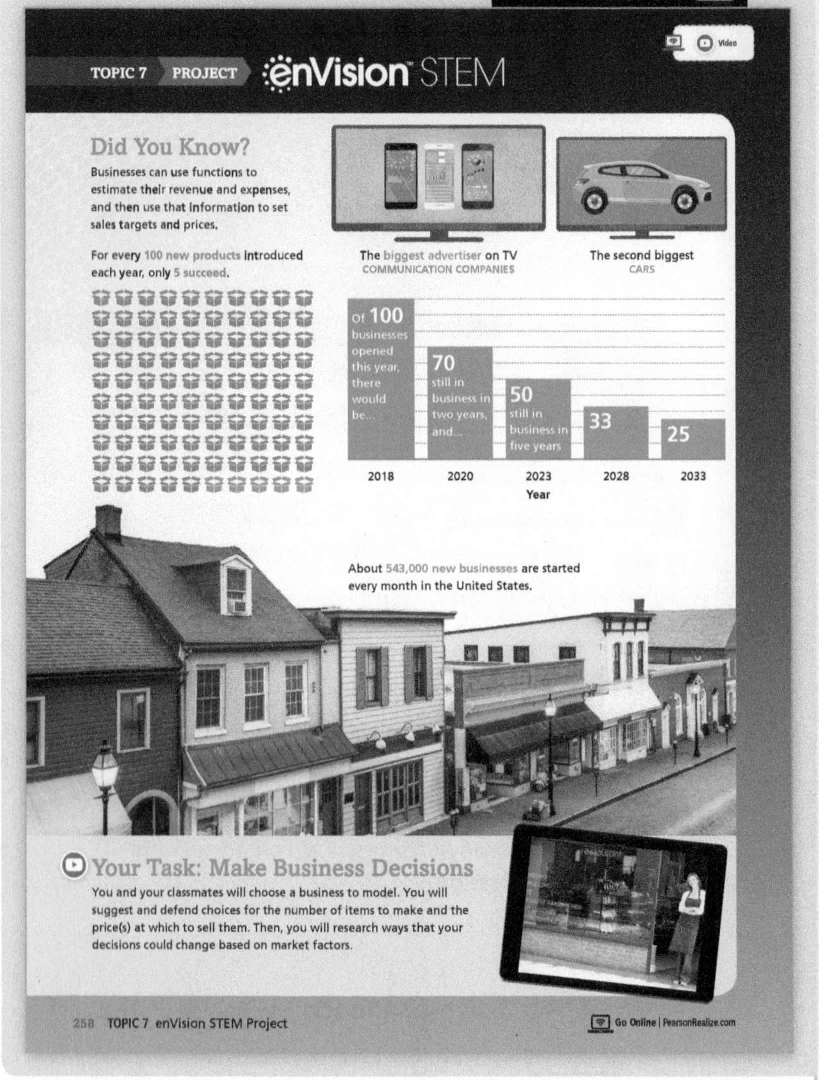
Video
TOPIC 7
PROJECT
ënVision™ STEM
Did You Know?
Businesses can use functions to estimate their revenue and expenses, and then use that information to set sales targets and prices.
For every 100 new products introduced each year, only 5 succeed.
The biggest advertiser on TV
COMMUNICATION COMPANIES
The second biggest
CARS
of 100 businesses opened this year, there would be...
70 still in business in two years, and...
50 still in business in five years
33
25
2018
2020
2023
2028
2033
Year
About 543,000 new businesses are started every month in the United States.
Your Task: Make Business Decisions
You and your classmates will choose a business to model. You will suggest and defend choices for the number of items to make and the price(s) at which to sell them. Then, you will research ways that your decisions could change based on market factors.
258 TOPIC 7 enVision STEM Project
Go Online | PearsonRealize.com

Common Core Standards HSA.APR.A.1, HSA.SSE.B.3, HSA.CED.A.2

Mathematical Practices MP.4, MP.7

SavvasRealize.com

A-Z Glossary

LESSON 7-1
Adding and Subtracting Polynomials

Lesson Overview

FOCUS

Objective

Students will be able to:

✔ Identify the parts of a polynomial, such as coefficients, variables, and constants.

✔ Classify polynomials by number of terms and by degree.

✔ Write a polynomial in standard form.

✔ Add or subtract two polynomials and recognize that polynomials are closed under addition and subtraction, just as the integers are.

Essential Understanding

A polynomial is a monomial or the sum or differences of two or more monomials (terms). Polynomials can be added or subtracted by combining like terms. Polynomials are closed under addition or subtraction, similar to integers.

COHERENCE

Previously in this course, students:

- Performed mathematical operations on monomials and binomials.
- Applied the Distributive Property to combine like terms.

In this lesson, students:

- Identify parts of polynomials, including degrees and terms.
- Add or subtract polynomials by combining like terms.

Later in this topic, students will:

- Use the Distributive Property to multiply polynomials.

RIGOR

This lesson emphasizes a blend of *conceptual understanding* and *procedural skill and fluency*.

- Students describe polynomials and identify the terms and degree of a polynomial.
- Students practice naming polynomials by degree and number of terms.

A-Z Vocabulary Builder

NEW VOCABULARY — **English** | *Spanish*

- **Closure Property** | *propiedad de cierre*
- **degree of a monomial** | *grado de un monomio*
- **degree of a polynomial** | *grado de un polinomio*
- **monomial** | *monomio*
- **polynomial** | *polinomio*
- **standard form of a polynomial** | *forma normal de un polonomio*

VOCABULARY ACTIVITY

As preparation for combining like terms, ask students to work through and discuss these exercises.

1. When two terms are like terms, what parts of the terms must be the same? What parts can be different? Give examples. [Same: variables and exponents; different: coefficient; in the expression $5x^4 + 2x + 3 - 5x^3 - 10x$, the terms $2x$ and $-10x$ are like terms.]
2. Write three like terms for each given term.

   a. $15x^3$ **b.** -17 **c.** $-12y^5$

   [Answers may vary. Samples:

   a. $x^3, -2x^3, -100x^3$ **b.** 0, 5, −3 **c.** $12y^5, -y^5, 200y^5$]

Student Companion

Students can do their in-class work for the lesson on pages 137–140 of their *Student Companion* or in Savvas Realize.

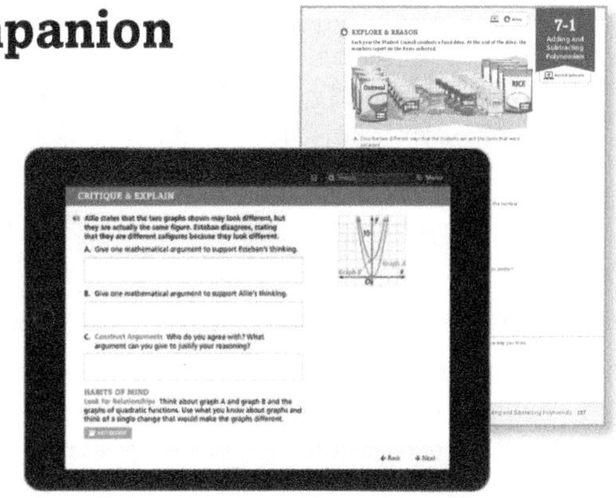

© Mathematics Overview — COMMON CORE STANDARDS

Content Standards

In this lesson, students focus on this standard:

HSA.APR.A.1 Understand that polynomials form a system analogous to the integers, namely, they are closed under the operations of addition, subtraction, and multiplication; add, subtract, and multiply polynomials.

Mathematical Practice Standards

These standards are highlighted in this lesson:

MP.2 Reason Abstractly and Quantitatively

Students describe quantities by identifying the degrees of polynomials, writing them in standard form, and combining like terms.

MP.3 Critique the Reasoning of Others

Students present and justify the steps in combining like terms to add or subtract polynomials.

Activity

EXPLORE & REASON

INSTRUCTIONAL FOCUS Students explore several ways to sort and describe a collection of items. They explain how different algebraic expressions can describe the same collection, preparing them to work with polynomials in one or more variables.

STUDENT COMPANION Students can complete the *Explore & Reason* activity on page 137 of their *Student Companion*.

Before WHOLE CLASS

Implement Tasks that Promote Reasoning and Problem Solving ETP

Q: How would you describe the food collected in words?
[3 packages of oatmeal, 6 cans of peas, 3 cans of meat, 5 cans of beans, 6 cans of corn, and 4 bags of rice]

During SMALL GROUP

Support Productive Struggle in Learning Mathematics ETP

Q: How many different variables are needed?
[One variable is needed for each category of food. If you sort by the type of food, you would need 6 variables.]

For Early Finishers

Q: If the Student Council distributes one of each item to a food bank, what is an expression for what remains? What is an expression for what remains if the Student Council distributes two of each item? Three of each item?
[Representing oatmeal, peas, meat, beans, corn, and rice with t, p, m, b, c, and r, respectively, $2t + 5p + 2m + 4b + 5c + 3r$; $t + 4p + m + 3b + 4c + 2r$; $3p + 2b + 3c + r$.]

After WHOLE CLASS

Facilitate Meaningful Mathematical Discourse ETP

Q: Suppose the food drive is extended and additional food is collected. When would you be able to use the same method to sort all the items?
[If the new food items fell into the same food categories, then the same sorting method could be used.]

HABITS OF MIND *Use with* **EXPLORE & REASON**

Use Structure How does the structure of each expression relate to the way you think about the items? MP.7

[Answers may vary. Sample: The structure indicates a sum, and each term represents a quantity of food.]

AVAILABLE **ONLINE**

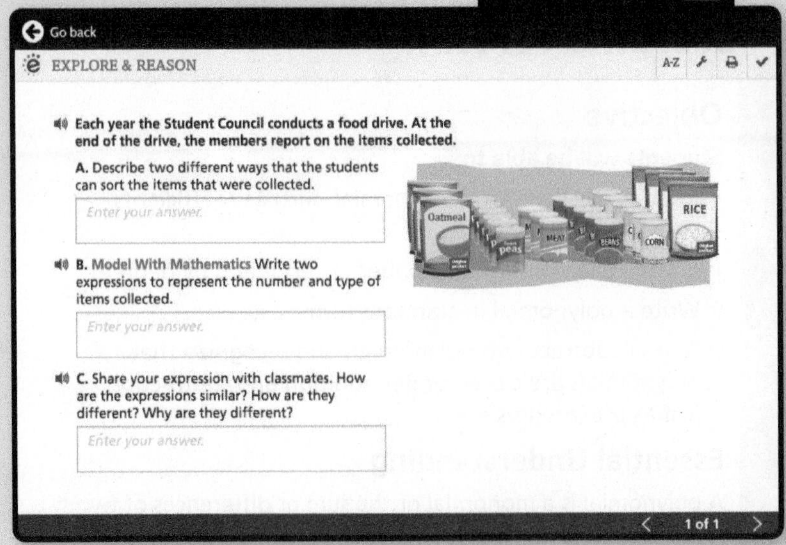
Go back
EXPLORE & REASON
Each year the Student Council conducts a food drive. At the end of the drive, the members report on the items collected.
A. Describe two different ways that the students can sort the items that were collected.
Enter your answer.
B. Model With Mathematics Write two expressions to represent the number and type of items collected.
Enter your answer.
C. Share your expression with classmates. How are the expressions similar? How are they different? Why are they different?
Enter your answer.
1 of 1

STUDENT EDITION, PAGE 259

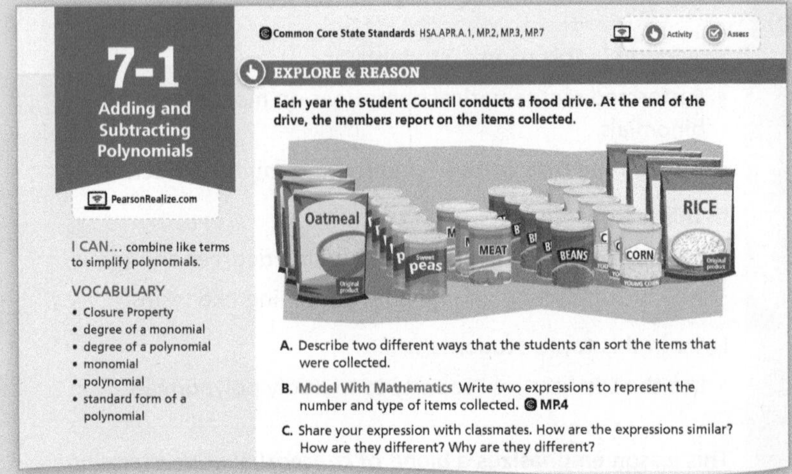
Common Core State Standards HSA.APR.A.1, MP.2, MP.3, MP.7

Activity Assess

7-1 Adding and Subtracting Polynomials

PearsonRealize.com

I CAN… combine like terms to simplify polynomials.

VOCABULARY
- Closure Property
- degree of a monomial
- degree of a polynomial
- monomial
- polynomial
- standard form of a polynomial

EXPLORE & REASON

Each year the Student Council conducts a food drive. At the end of the drive, the members report on the items collected.

Oatmeal
peas
MEAT
BEANS
CORN
RICE

A. Describe two different ways that the students can sort the items that were collected.

B. Model With Mathematics Write two expressions to represent the number and type of items collected. MP.4

C. Share your expression with classmates. How are the expressions similar? How are they different? Why are they different?

SAMPLE STUDENT WORK

A. The food could be sorted by each category of food: oatmeal, peas, etc. or the food could be sorted by the type of container it comes in: cans, bags, etc.

B. Let t = oatmeal, m = meat, b = beans, c = corn, and r = rice, or let c = cans and b = bags.
Then the students' contribution could be written as $3t + 6p + 3m + 5b + 6c + 4r$ or as $20c + 7b$

C. Our expressions use different variables and the terms have different coefficients because we classified our items differently.

INTRODUCE THE ESSENTIAL QUESTION

Establish Mathematics Goals to Focus Learning ETP

Introduce students to polynomials and the individual terms of polynomials. Explain that they need to look at polynomials from two perspectives: as an entire entity, and as individual terms.

EXAMPLE 1 Understand Polynomials

Build Procedural Fluency From Conceptual Understanding ETP

Q: In Part A, why is a variable to the zero power equal to 1? [Start with the expression $\frac{a^m}{a^m}$, $a \neq 0$. Exponent properties state that $\frac{a^m}{a^m} = a^{m-m} = a^0$. Also, an expression such as $\frac{a^m}{a^m}$, $a \neq 0$, represents a nonzero number divided by itself, so it is 1. By the Transitive Property of Equality, $a^0 = 1$ for $a \neq 0$.]

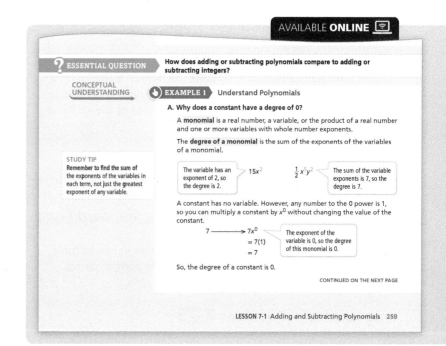

AVAILABLE ONLINE

ESSENTIAL QUESTION **How does adding or subtracting polynomials compare to adding or subtracting integers?**

CONCEPTUAL UNDERSTANDING

EXAMPLE 1 Understand Polynomials

A. Why does a constant have a degree of 0?

A **monomial** is a real number, a variable, or the product of a real number and one or more variables with whole number exponents.

The **degree of a monomial** is the sum of the exponents of the variables of a monomial.

STUDY TIP
Remember to find the sum of the exponents of the variables in each term, not just the greatest exponent of any variable.

The variable has an exponent of 2, so the degree is 2. $15x^2$

$\frac{1}{2}x^5y^2$ The sum of the variable exponents is 7, so the degree is 7.

A constant has no variable. However, any number to the 0 power is 1, so you can multiply a constant by x^0 without changing the value of the constant.

$$7 \longrightarrow 7x^0 = 7(1) = 7$$

The exponent of the variable is 0, so the degree of this monomial is 0.

So, the degree of a constant is 0.

CONTINUED ON THE NEXT PAGE

LESSON 7-1 Adding and Subtracting Polynomials 259

ADDITIONAL EXAMPLES

AVAILABLE ONLINE

Go back

ADDITIONAL EXAMPLE 5 | ESSENTIAL QUESTION | ES | A-Z

Use the three polynomials below.

A: $5x^3 - 2x^2 + 3x - 7$
B: $-2x^3 + 3x^2 - 5x + 3$
C: $x^3 - 4x^2 - 2x + 8$

a. Find $C - B$ by lining up like terms vertically.
b. Find $A - C$ by organizing the terms horizontally.

a.
$$\begin{array}{r} x^3 - 4x^2 - 2x + 8 \\ \underline{-(-2x^3 + 3x^2 - 5x + 3)} \end{array} \rightarrow \begin{array}{r} x^3 - 4x^2 - 2x + 8 \\ \underline{2x^3 - 3x^2 + 5x - 3} \\ 3x^3 - 7x^2 - 3x + 5 \end{array}$$

b. $(5x^3 - 2x^2 + 3x - 7) - (x^3 - 4x^2 - 2x + 8)$
$= (5x^3 - x^3) + (-2x^2 - (-4x^2)) + (3x - (-2x)) + (-7 - 8)$
$= 4x^3 + 2x^2 + 5x - 15$

1 of 2

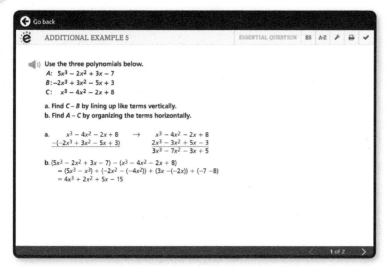

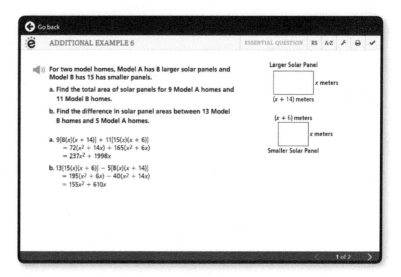

Example 5 Help students practice subtracting polynomials.

Q: When you use the method of vertical alignment, how do you indicate subtraction?
[The second polynomial appears in parentheses, with a subtraction sign in front of the left parenthesis.]

Q: When you organize the terms horizontally, how do you use parentheses?
[Answers may vary. Sample: Each set of like terms goes into its own set of parentheses.]

Go back

ADDITIONAL EXAMPLE 6 | ESSENTIAL QUESTION | ES | A-Z

For two model homes, Model A has 8 larger solar panels and Model B has 15 has smaller panels.

a. Find the total area of solar panels for 9 Model A homes and 11 Model B homes.
b. Find the difference in solar panel areas between 13 Model B homes and 5 Model A homes.

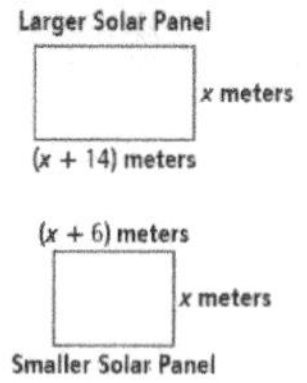
Larger Solar Panel
x meters
(x + 14) meters
(x + 6) meters
x meters
Smaller Solar Panel

a. $9[8(x)(x + 14)] + 11[15(x)(x + 6)]$
$= 72(x^2 + 14x) + 165(x^2 + 6x)$
$= 237x^2 + 1998x$

b. $13[15(x)(x + 6)] - 5[8(x)(x + 14)]$
$= 195(x^2 + 6x) - 40(x^2 + 14x)$
$= 155x^2 + 610x$

1 of 2

Example 6 Help students practice writing, adding, and subtracting polynomial expressions in a real-world context.

Q: How are parts a and b similar to each other? How are they different?
[Similar: both deal with polynomial expressions. Different: Part (a) involves addition and part (b) involves subtraction.]

Q: Suppose x is given several values. What parts of the questions do not change for those values? What parts of the questions do change?
[The polynomial expressions do not change. If the polynomial expressions are evaluated for the values of x, the calculated values change.]

Activity Assess

EXAMPLE 1 CONTINUED

Q: In Part B, how is finding the degree of a monomial with one variable different from finding the degree of a monomial with more than one variable?
[For a monomial with one variable the degree is the exponent of the variable, while for a monomial with more than one variable the degree is the sum of the degrees of the variables.]

Try It! Answers

1. **a.** cubic monomial

   b. quadratic trinomial

EXAMPLE 2 Write Polynomials in Standard Form

In Example 1, students worked with polynomials in two or more variables. For Example 2, and the rest of the lessons, students focus on understanding polynomials in one variable.

Pose Purposeful Questions ETP

Q: If a polynomial in one variable is written in standard form, can it have two terms with the same degree?
[No, if a polynomial has one variable, then two terms with the same degree are like terms and should be combined into a single term.]

Try It! Answers

2. **a.** $-3x^3 + 6x^2 + 7$ **b.** $-8y^2 + 2y - 3$

Elicit and Use Evidence of Student Thinking ETP

Q: If two students start with the same polynomial and rewrite it in standard form, should they always get the same result?
[Yes; the standard form for a given polynomial is unique.]

AVAILABLE **ONLINE**

Activity Assess

EXAMPLE 1 CONTINUED

B. Why is $5x^3 - 4$ called a cubic binomial?

A **polynomial** is a monomial or the sum or difference of two or more monomials, called terms.

Polynomials are named according to their degree. The **degree of a polynomial** is the greatest degree of any term of the polynomial.

Polynomial	Degree	Name Based on Degree
7	0	Constant
$4x$	1	Linear
$3x^2 + 2x + 1$	2	Quadratic
$-5x^2y$	3	Cubic
$4x^2y^2 + 5x - 2y + 6$	4	Fourth Degree

Polynomials with a degree greater than 3 are named by their degree—fourth degree, fifth degree, and so on.

Polynomials are also named according to how many terms they have.

Polynomial	Number of Terms	Name Based on Number of Terms
$4x$	1	Monomial
$x + 7$	2	Binomial
$-5x^2y + x^2 + x$	3	Trinomial
$4x^2y^2 + 5x - 2y + 6$	4	Polynomial

Polynomials with more than 3 terms do not have special names.

$5x^3 - 4$ is called a cubic binomial because it has a degree of 3 and two terms.

Try It! 1. Name each polynomial based on its degree and number of terms.

a. $-2xy^2$ **b.** $6xy - 3x + y$

EXAMPLE 2 Write Polynomials in Standard Form

What is the standard form of the polynomial $7x - 5 - x^3 + 6x^4 - 3x^2$?

The **standard form of a polynomial** is the form of a polynomial in which the terms are written in descending order according to their degree.

LOOK FOR RELATIONSHIPS
Why is writing polynomials in standard form important? How will it be useful? MP.7

Rewrite the polynomial in standard form.

$7x - 5 - x^3 + 6x^4 - 3x^2$

$6x^4 - x^3 - 3x^2 + 7x - 5$

$6x^4$ has the greatest degree, 4, so write it first.

The standard form of the polynomial is $6x^4 - x^3 - 3x^2 + 7x - 5$.

Try It! 2. Write each polynomial in standard form.

a. $7 - 3x^3 + 6x^2$ **b.** $2y - 3 - 8y^2$

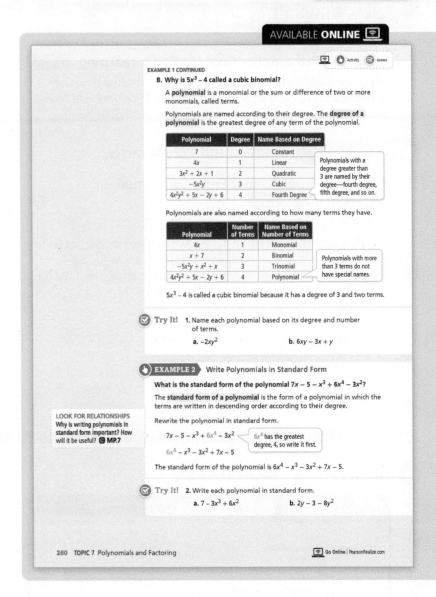

ELL English Language Learners *(Use with* **EXAMPLE 2***)*

WRITING BEGINNING In order to understand *polynomials*, students must first understand the definitions of *monomial* and *term*. Have students write the definitions for those three words in their journals.

Q: Make a T-chart in your journal showing examples and non-examples of *monomials*.
[Check students' work.]

Q: Although the prefix *poly-* means many, by definition, a polynomial may consist of only one term (a monomial). Make a T-chart in your journal showing examples and non-examples of *polynomials* and circle each of the terms.
[Check students' work.]

READING INTERMEDIATE Have students read this definition of *standard*: something considered by an authority or by general consent as a basis of comparison. Then have students read the example.

Q: How can you apply the definition of standard to help understand the meaning of *standard form of a polynomial*?
[It is easier to compare polynomials when they are all written in the same form.]

Q: Describe a polynomial written in standard form. Provide an example.
[The terms are written in descending order according to their degree. Sample: $4x^6 + 2x^4 - 5x + 7$]

LISTENING ADVANCED Have students listen as you read the following sentences:

- The number of tickets available for the opening night of the play steadily *decreased* throughout the day.
- The maid started her work by *decluttering* the room.
- A *dehumidifier* helps to remove humidity from the air.

Q: Given these contexts, what do you think the prefix *de-* means?
[Sample: to lessen the amount of something]

Q: In the definition of standard form of a polynomial, what does *descending* mean?
[to order from greatest to least]

EXAMPLE 3 Add and Subtract Monomials

Use and Connect Mathematical Representations ETP

Q: How are like terms represented in the diagrams?
[Like terms are shown as rectangles with the same dimensions and colors.]

Q: How can you describe *combining like terms* using the Distributive Property?
[The Distributive Property, in the form $ab + cb = (a + c)\,b$, describes the process of adding the like terms ab and cb.]

Q: What do you notice after the terms of a polynomial are combined?
[The variables and their exponents do not change; the coefficients for the terms change.]

Try It! Answers

3. a. $3x^2$

b. $12y^3 - 5y + 7$

Elicit and Use Evidence of Student Thinking ETP

Q: When a polynomial has two like terms, how do you know whether the combined term is positive or negative?
[Compare the coefficients of the like terms. The combined term has the sign of the coefficient with the greater absolute value.]

HABITS OF MIND

Use with **EXAMPLES 1–3**

Reason Why is it important to combine like terms and rewrite the polynomial in standard form before determining the name and number of terms of a polynomial? **MP.2**

[If like terms are not combined, then counting the number of terms does not indicate whether it is a binomial or trinomial; if the polynomial is not in standard form, it is not easy to identify the leading term and thus harder to identify the degree of the polynomial.]

EXAMPLE 4 Add Polynomials

Build Procedural Fluency From Conceptual Understanding ETP

Q: In Part A, how is adding multi-digit numbers similar to and different from adding like terms?
[Similar: With multi-digit numbers, only like place values can be added just as only like terms can be added.
Different: Parts of the like terms—the variables and exponents—are not changed.]

AVAILABLE **ONLINE**

Activity Assess

EXAMPLE 3 Add and Subtract Monomials

VOCABULARY
Remember, *like terms* are terms with exactly the same variable factors in an expression.

LOOK FOR RELATIONSHIPS
Which terms in a polynomial are like terms? How does combining them change the polynomial? MP.7

How can you use the properties of operations to combine like terms and write the expression $4x + 3x^2 + 2x + x^2 + 5$ in standard form?

Use algebra tiles to model the expression.

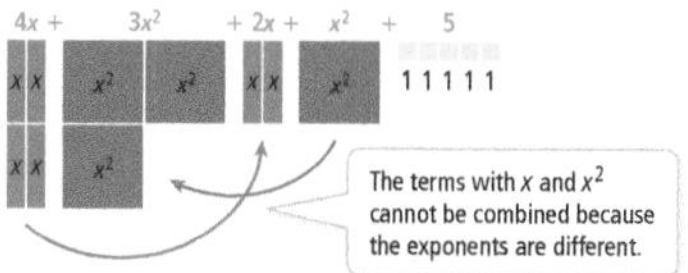
4x + 3x2 + 2x + x2 + 5
x x
x2
1 1 1 1 1
The terms with x and x2 cannot be combined because the exponents are different.

Rearrange the tiles to group like terms together.

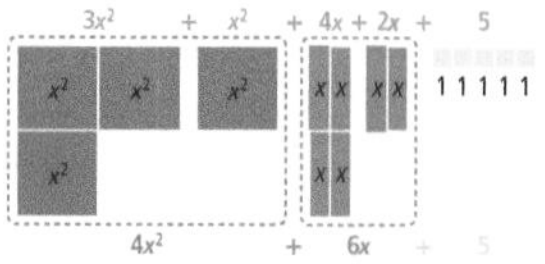
3x2 + x2 + 4x + 2x + 5
x2
x x
1 1 1 1 1
4x2 + 6x + 5

The expression $4x + 3x^2 + 2x + x^2 + 5$ written in standard form is $4x^2 + 6x + 5$.

You can also rewrite the expression in standard form using the properties of operations.

$4x + 3x^2 + 2x + x^2 + 5$
$= (3x^2 + x^2) + (4x + 2x) + 5$
$= 4x^2 + 6x + 5$

You can apply the same properties of operations for real numbers to operations with monomials.

Try It! **3.** Combine like terms and write each expression in standard form.

a. $4x^2 - 3x - x^2 + 3x$ **b.** $7y^3 - 3y + 5y^3 - 2y + 7$

EXAMPLE 4 Add Polynomials

A. How is adding polynomials like adding whole numbers?

Consider the expressions $123 + 405$ and $(x^2 + 2x + 3) + (4x^2 + 5)$.

$$\begin{array}{r} 123 \\ +\,405 \\ \hline 528 \end{array}$$

Only like place values can be added.

Only like terms can be added.

$$\begin{array}{rrr} x^2 & +\,2x & +\,3 \\ +\,4x^2 & & +\,5 \\ \hline 5x^2 & +\,2x & +\,8 \end{array}$$

Before you add polynomials, the terms must be aligned with like terms. This is similar to how, before adding whole numbers, the numbers must be aligned according to their place value.

CONTINUED ON THE NEXT PAGE

LESSON 7-1 Adding and Subtracting Polynomials 261

EXAMPLE 4 CONTINUED

Q: In Part B, if you add two binomials, is the sum always a binomial? [No, depending on the variables and exponents in each term, adding binomials could result in 0, 1, 2, 3, or 4 terms.]

Q: When you add two polynomials, can the sum have a greater degree than the original polynomials? A lesser degree? [When adding polynomials, the powers of terms do not change, so you cannot end up with a greater degree. If the leading terms of the two polynomials have coefficients that are opposites, then the leading terms are eliminated when combined, and the degree of the sum is less than the degree of the original polynomials.]

Try It! Answers

4. a. $3x^2 + x + 9$ **b.** $-2x^2 + 8x$

EXAMPLE 5 Subtract Polynomials

Pose Purposeful Questions ETP

Q: Compare adding and subtracting polynomials. [They are the same because both combine like terms. They are different because the first step for subtracting polynomials is to multiply each term of the second polynomial by −1 before combining like terms.]

Try It! Answers

5. a. $3x^2 + 5x - 2$ **b.** $-4x^2 - 5x - 12$

Common Error

Try It! 5 Some students may not change the sign of each term in the subtracted polynomial expression. Ask students to think of the problem $(A) - (B)$ as $A + (-1)(B)$ and use the Distributive Property by distributing −1 to each term of the second polynomial.

AVAILABLE ONLINE

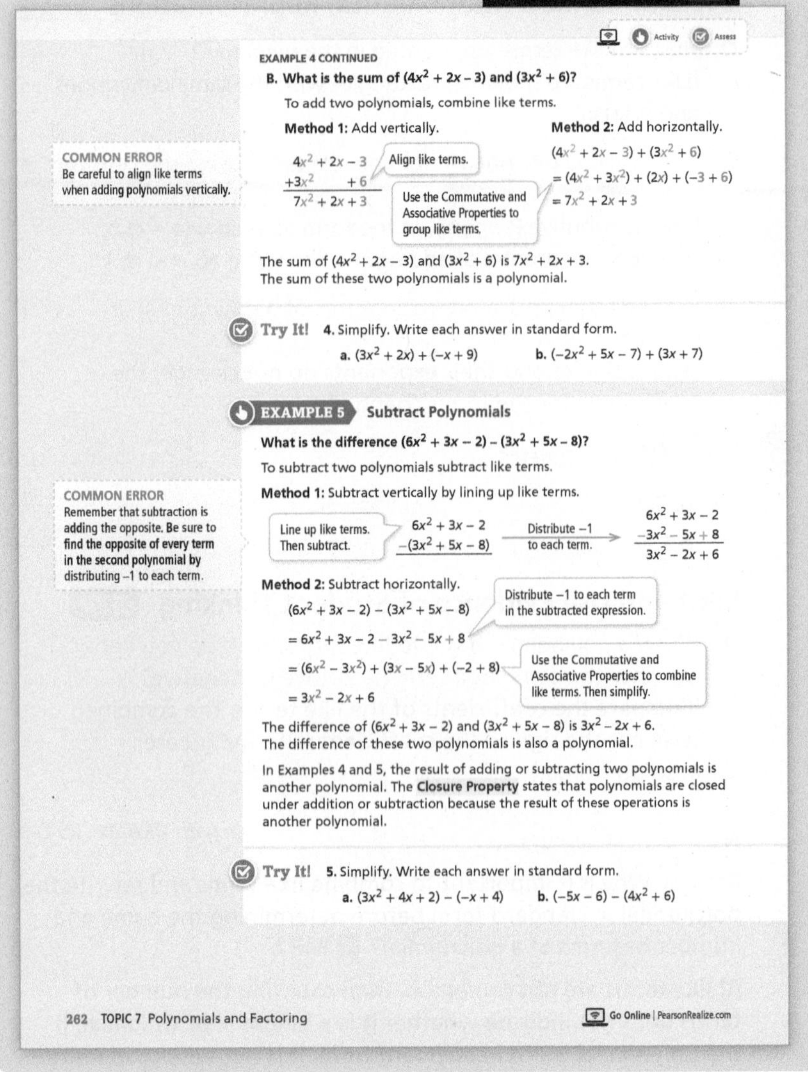

Activity Assess

EXAMPLE 4 CONTINUED

B. What is the sum of $(4x^2 + 2x - 3)$ and $(3x^2 + 6)$?

To add two polynomials, combine like terms.

Method 1: Add vertically.

$$\begin{array}{r} 4x^2 + 2x - 3 \\ +3x^2 \quad\quad + 6 \\ \hline 7x^2 + 2x + 3 \end{array}$$

Align like terms.

Use the Commutative and Associative Properties to group like terms.

Method 2: Add horizontally.

$(4x^2 + 2x - 3) + (3x^2 + 6)$

$= (4x^2 + 3x^2) + (2x) + (-3 + 6)$

$= 7x^2 + 2x + 3$

COMMON ERROR
Be careful to align like terms when adding polynomials vertically.

The sum of $(4x^2 + 2x - 3)$ and $(3x^2 + 6)$ is $7x^2 + 2x + 3$.
The sum of these two polynomials is a polynomial.

Try It! **4.** Simplify. Write each answer in standard form.

a. $(3x^2 + 2x) + (-x + 9)$ **b.** $(-2x^2 + 5x - 7) + (3x + 7)$

EXAMPLE 5 Subtract Polynomials

What is the difference $(6x^2 + 3x - 2) - (3x^2 + 5x - 8)$?

To subtract two polynomials subtract like terms.

Method 1: Subtract vertically by lining up like terms.

Line up like terms. Then subtract.

$$\begin{array}{r} 6x^2 + 3x - 2 \\ -(3x^2 + 5x - 8) \\ \hline \end{array} \xrightarrow[\text{to each term.}]{\text{Distribute } -1} \begin{array}{r} 6x^2 + 3x - 2 \\ -3x^2 - 5x + 8 \\ \hline 3x^2 - 2x + 6 \end{array}$$

COMMON ERROR
Remember that subtraction is adding the opposite. Be sure to find the opposite of every term in the second polynomial by distributing −1 to each term.

Method 2: Subtract horizontally.

$(6x^2 + 3x - 2) - (3x^2 + 5x - 8)$

$= 6x^2 + 3x - 2 - 3x^2 - 5x + 8$

$= (6x^2 - 3x^2) + (3x - 5x) + (-2 + 8)$

$= 3x^2 - 2x + 6$

Distribute −1 to each term in the subtracted expression.

Use the Commutative and Associative Properties to combine like terms. Then simplify.

The difference of $(6x^2 + 3x - 2)$ and $(3x^2 + 5x - 8)$ is $3x^2 - 2x + 6$.
The difference of these two polynomials is also a polynomial.

In Examples 4 and 5, the result of adding or subtracting two polynomials is another polynomial. The **Closure Property** states that polynomials are closed under addition or subtraction because the result of these operations is another polynomial.

Try It! **5.** Simplify. Write each answer in standard form.

a. $(3x^2 + 4x + 2) - (-x + 4)$ **b.** $(-5x - 6) - (4x^2 + 6)$

262 TOPIC 7 Polynomials and Factoring Go Online | PearsonRealize.com

ADV Advanced Students

USE WITH EXAMPLE 5 To extend their skills in adding and subtracting polynomials, have students substitute polynomials into a literal equation and then solve for a missing polynomial.

- In equations 1–3, p, q, and r represent polynomials. Rewrite each equation to isolate p, q, or r. Then use polynomials A, B, and C below to find the missing polynomial.

  A: $5x^3 - 2x^2 + 7x - 11$

  B: $-3x^3 + 3x^2 - x + 7$

  C: $-2x^3 + x^2 - 8x - 5$

1. $A + p = B$ [$p = B - A$; $-8x^3 + 5x^2 - 8x + 18$]

2. $B + q = -C$ [$q = -B - C$; $5x^3 - 4x^2 + 9x - 2$]

3. $C + r = B - A$ [$r = B - A - C$; $-6x^3 + 4x^2 + 23$]

Q: What property is used to isolate p, q, and r? [Addition Property or Subtraction Property]

EXAMPLE 6 Apply Polynomials

Pose Purposeful Questions ETP

Q: How do you know what operations to use in the expression?
[You are given expressions for three different areas and are asked to find the total area, which implies addition.]

Q: Explain why the Commutative and Associative Properties are helpful in simplifying the expression.
[Using the properties to re-order and group like terms together helps reduce confusion and computational errors when simplifying the expression.]

Try It! Answer

6. $28x^2 + 360x$

Elicit and Use Evidence of Student Thinking ETP

Q: What language in the question indicates the operation to perform?
[The phrase "the difference" indicates that the operation is subtraction.]

HABITS OF MIND

Use with **EXAMPLES 4–6**

Communicate Precisely A student claims that the difference of the expression $(3x^2 + 5x - 2) - (3x^2 + 5x - 2x)$ is zero. Is the student correct? Explain. MP.6

[No; The expression $(3x^2 + 5x - 2)$ is not the same as the expression $(3x^2 + 5x - 2x)$, so their difference is not 0.]

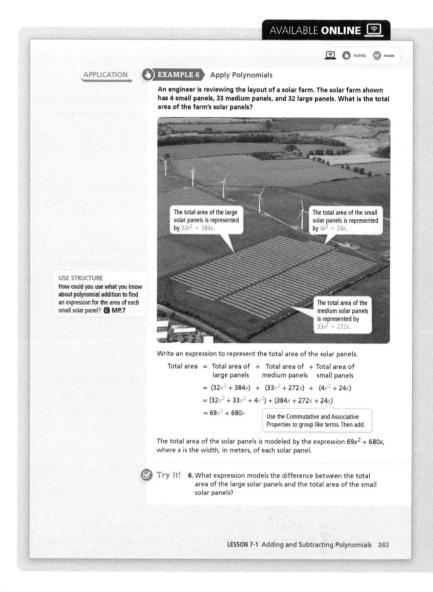

AVAILABLE **ONLINE**

Activity Assess

APPLICATION

EXAMPLE 6 Apply Polynomials

An engineer is reviewing the layout of a solar farm. The solar farm shown has 4 small panels, 33 medium panels, and 32 large panels. What is the total area of the farm's solar panels?

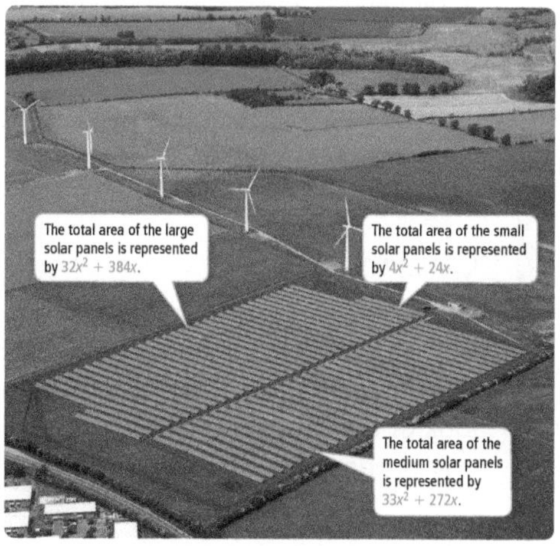
The total area of the large solar panels is represented by $32x^2 + 384x$.
The total area of the small solar panels is represented by $4x^2 + 24x$.
The total area of the medium solar panels is represented by $33x^2 + 272x$.

USE STRUCTURE
How could you use what you know about polynomial addition to find an expression for the area of each small solar panel? MP.7

Write an expression to represent the total area of the solar panels.

Total area = Total area of large panels + Total area of medium panels + Total area of small panels

$= (32x^2 + 384x) + (33x^2 + 272x) + (4x^2 + 24x)$

$= (32x^2 + 33x^2 + 4x^2) + (384x + 272x + 24x)$

$= 69x^2 + 680x$

Use the Commutative and Associative Properties to group like terms. Then add.

The total area of the solar panels is modeled by the expression $69x^2 + 680x$, where x is the width, in meters, of each solar panel.

Try It! **6.** What expression models the difference between the total area of the large solar panels and the total area of the small solar panels?

LESSON 7-1 Adding and Subtracting Polynomials 263

Struggling Students

USE WITH EXAMPLE 6 Have students practice writing polynomial expressions that represent areas.

1. A rectangle has sides represented by $x + 3$ and 5. What is the area of the rectangle? What is the total area of 8 of the same size rectangles?
[$5x + 15$; $40x + 120$]
2. A rectangle has sides represented by $2x + 1$ and $3x$. What is the area of the rectangle? What is the total area of 6 of the same size rectangles?
[$6x^2 + 3x$; $36x^2 + 18x$]

Q: Other than variables and numbers, what are some of the key phrases in the problems? What do those key phrases suggest?
[The key phrase *area of a rectangle* suggests using the area formula $A = \ell \times w$. The key phrase *total area of 8 of the same size rectangles* suggests using multiplication to find the total area.]

CONCEPT SUMMARY Adding and Subtracting Polynomials

Q: How does standard form help name a polynomial? How does standard form help add or subtract polynomials?
[When a polynomial is in standard form, it is easy to identify the leading term and the number of terms so the polynomial can be named. Also, it is easy to identify like terms so the polynomials can be added or subtracted.]

Do You UNDERSTAND? | Do You KNOW HOW?

Common Error

Exercises 6–7 Some students may assume a polynomial is in standard form and use the first term of a polynomial as its leading term. Suggest to students that they always look at the exponents of ALL the terms in the polynomial before they identify the leading term.

Answers

1. Adding or subtracting polynomials is similar to adding or subtracting integers, because adding or subtracting two polynomials results in another polynomial and adding or subtracting two integers results in another integer.
2. The prefix *mono-* means one; *bi-* means two; *tri-* means three. Therefore, a *mono*mial has one term; *bi*nomial has two terms; *tri*nomial has three terms.
3. The standard form of a polynomial arranges the variables in order from term with highest degree to term with lowest degree. The degree of the terms (monomials) determine the order.
4. $x + x$ is similar to combining two of the same item, which is $2x$. The term, x^2, can be interpreted as $x \cdot x$, which refers to the area of a square.
5. Answers may vary. Sample: To be like terms, terms must have the same degree AND the same variable.
6. linear binomial
7. cubic trinomial
8. $-y^2 + 2y - 3$
9. $x^3 + 3x^2 - 2x + 6$
10. $3x^2 - 3x - 7$
11. $7x^2 - 3x - 7$
12. $10x^2 + 76x + 144$

AVAILABLE ONLINE

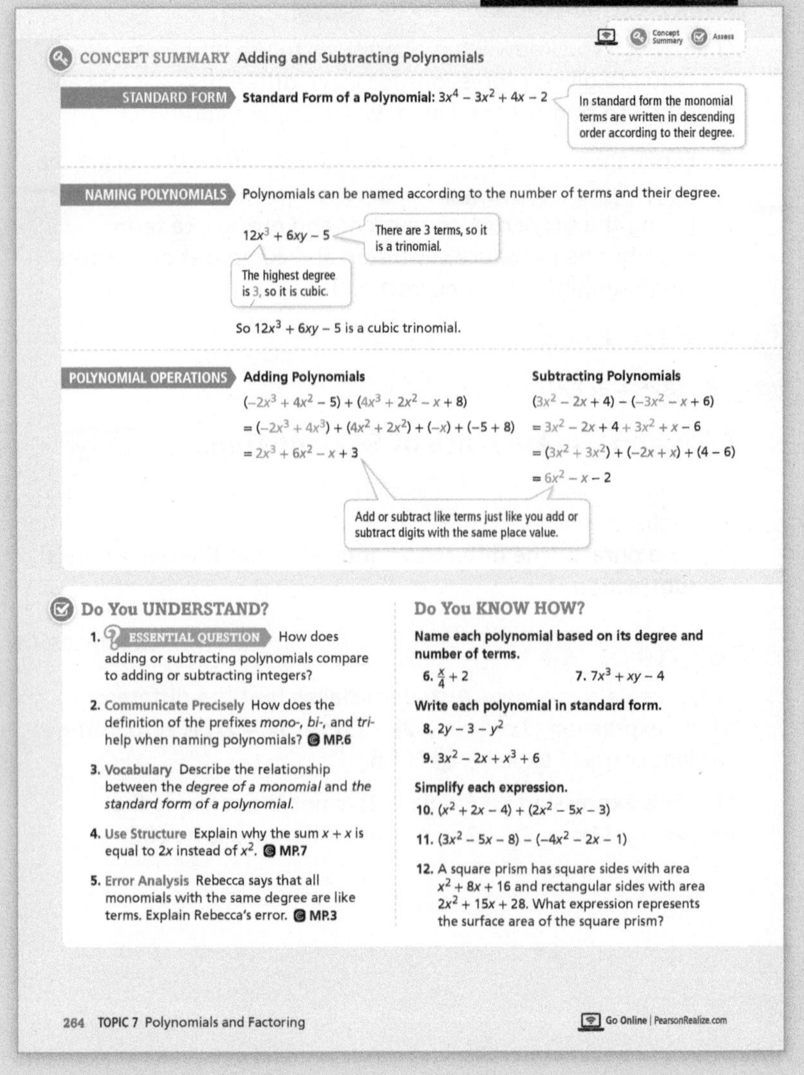

Concept Summary Assess

CONCEPT SUMMARY Adding and Subtracting Polynomials

STANDARD FORM **Standard Form of a Polynomial:** $3x^4 - 3x^2 + 4x - 2$

In standard form the monomial terms are written in descending order according to their degree.

NAMING POLYNOMIALS Polynomials can be named according to the number of terms and their degree.

$12x^3 + 6xy - 5$

There are 3 terms, so it is a trinomial.

The highest degree is 3, so it is cubic.

So $12x^3 + 6xy - 5$ is a cubic trinomial.

POLYNOMIAL OPERATIONS

Adding Polynomials

$(-2x^3 + 4x^2 - 5) + (4x^3 + 2x^2 - x + 8)$
$= (-2x^3 + 4x^3) + (4x^2 + 2x^2) + (-x) + (-5 + 8)$
$= 2x^3 + 6x^2 - x + 3$

Subtracting Polynomials

$(3x^2 - 2x + 4) - (-3x^2 - x + 6)$
$= 3x^2 - 2x + 4 + 3x^2 + x - 6$
$= (3x^2 + 3x^2) + (-2x + x) + (4 - 6)$
$= 6x^2 - x - 2$

Add or subtract like terms just like you add or subtract digits with the same place value.

Do You UNDERSTAND?

1. ESSENTIAL QUESTION How does adding or subtracting polynomials compare to adding or subtracting integers?
2. Communicate Precisely How does the definition of the prefixes *mono-*, *bi-*, and *tri-* help when naming polynomials? MP.6
3. Vocabulary Describe the relationship between the *degree of a monomial* and *the standard form of a polynomial.*
4. Use Structure Explain why the sum $x + x$ is equal to $2x$ instead of x^2. MP.7
5. Error Analysis Rebecca says that all monomials with the same degree are like terms. Explain Rebecca's error. MP.3

Do You KNOW HOW?

Name each polynomial based on its degree and number of terms.

6. $\frac{x}{4} + 2$
7. $7x^3 + xy - 4$

Write each polynomial in standard form.

8. $2y - 3 - y^2$
9. $3x^2 - 2x + x^3 + 6$

Simplify each expression.

10. $(x^2 + 2x - 4) + (2x^2 - 5x - 3)$
11. $(3x^2 - 5x - 8) - (-4x^2 - 2x - 1)$
12. A square prism has square sides with area $x^2 + 8x + 16$ and rectangular sides with area $2x^2 + 15x + 28$. What expression represents the surface area of the square prism?

264 TOPIC 7 Polynomials and Factoring Go Online | PearsonRealize.com

PRACTICE & PROBLEM SOLVING

AVAILABLE ONLINE

Lesson Practice You may opt to have students complete the automatically scored Practice and Problem Solving items online powered by MathXL for School.

Choose from: **Lesson Practice**

Adaptive Practice

You may also take advantage of the bank of exercises for assigning additional practice.

Assignment Guide

Basic	Advanced
13–27, 30–32, 34–37, 39–45	13–20, 25-45

Item Analysis

Example	Items	DOK
1	19–22	2
	13, 14, 23–26	3
	17	4
2	27, 28	2
3	29, 30	2
4	31, 32	2
	16, 35, 40, 41, 44	3
5	33, 34	2
	15, 18, 39, 43	3
6	36–38, 42, 45	3

AVAILABLE ONLINE

PRACTICE & PROBLEM SOLVING

Scan for Multimedia

Practice Tutorial

Additional Exercises Available Online

UNDERSTAND

13. Reason How is it possible that the sum of two quadratic trinomials is a linear binomial? MP.2

14. Error Analysis Describe and correct the error a student made when naming the polynomial. MP.3

$-2x^3 + 5x^4 - 3x$ is a cubic trinomial. ✗

15. Error Analysis Describe and correct the error a student made when subtracting the polynomials. MP.3

$(-5x^2 + 2x - 3) - (3x^2 - 2x - 6)$
$-5x^2 + 2x - 3 - 3x^2 - 2x - 6$
$-8x^2 - 9$ ✗

16. Reason What is the missing term in the equation? MP.2

a. $(\_\_\_ + 7) + (2x - 6) = -4x + 1$

b. $(a^2 + \_\_\_ + 1) - (\_\_\_ + 5a + \_\_\_) = 4a^2 - 2a + 7$

17. Higher Order Thinking Describe each statement as *always, sometimes,* or *never* true.

a. A linear binomial has a degree of 0.

b. A trinomial has a degree of 2.

c. A constant has a degree of 1.

d. A cubic monomial has a degree of 3.

18. Make Sense and Persevere Consider the set of linear binomials $ax + b$, where a and b are positive integers, $a > 0$ and $b > 0$. MP.1

a. Does the set have closure for addition? Explain.

b. Does the set have closure for subtraction? Explain.

PRACTICE

Find the degree of each monomial. SEE EXAMPLE 1

19. $\frac{x}{4}$ 1 **20.** $-7xy$ 2

21. 21 0 **22.** $4x^2y$ 3

Name each polynomial based on its degree and number of terms. SEE EXAMPLE 1

23. $17yx^2 + xy - 5$ cubic trinomial

24. $5x^3 + 2x - 8$ cubic trinomial

25. $100x^2 + 3$ quadratic binomial

26. $-9x^4 + 8x^3 - 7x + 1$ fourth degree polynomial

Simplify each expression. Write the answer in standard form. SEE EXAMPLES 2 AND 3

27. $3x + 2x^2 - 4x + 3x^2 - 5x$ $5x^2 - 6x$

28. $5 + 8y^2 - 12y^2 + 3y$ $-4y^2 + 3y + 5$

29. $3z - 7z^2 - 5z + 5z^2 + 2z^2$ $-2z$

30. $7 - 2x + 3 + 5x + 4x^2$ $4x^2 + 3x + 10$

Add or subtract. Write each answer in standard form. SEE EXAMPLES 4 AND 5

31. $(3b - 8) + (7b + 4)$ $10b - 4$

32. $(2x^2 - 7x^3 + 8x) + (-8x^3 - 3x^2 + 4)$ $-15x^3 - x^2 + 8x + 4$

33. $(5y^2 - 2y + 1) - (y^2 + y + 3)$ $4y^2 - 3y - 2$

34. $(-7a^4 - a + 4a^2) - (-8a^2 + a - 7a^4)$ $12a^2 - 2a$

35. $(4m^2 - 2m + 4) + (2m^2 + 2m - 5)$ $6m^2 - 1$

Write an expression to represent each situation. SEE EXAMPLE 6

36. Find the perimeter of the rectangle. $8x$

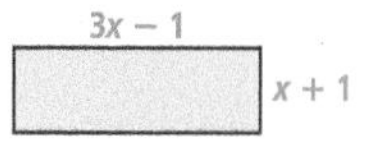
3x − 1
x + 1

37. A cube has square sides with area $x^2 + 24x + 144$. What expression represents the surface area of the cube? $6x^2 + 144x + 864$

38. A rectangle has a length of $5x + 2$ in. and a width of $4x + 6$ in. What is the perimeter of the rectangle? $18x + 16$ in.

LESSON 7-1 Adding and Subtracting Polynomials 265

Answers

13. The terms with exponents of 2 would become zero, so the trinomial would become a binomial. Since the square terms are zero, only exponents of degree one (linear) remain (e.g., a quadratic trinomial plus a quadratic trinomial can be a linear binomial): $(3x^2 + 2x + 9) + (-3x^2 - 5x - 8) = -3x + 1$

14. The student did not put the polynomial in standard form before naming it and named it by the first term. Written in order, the polynomial is $5x^4 - 2x^3 - 3x$, so the name is a fourth degree trinomial.

15. The student did not distribute the (–1) to all terms in the second polynomial, they only distributed it to the first term. The second line should read $-5x^2 + 2x - 3 - 3x^2 + 2x + 6$. And the answer should be $-8x^2 + 4x + 3$.

16. **a.** $(-6x + 7) + (2x - 6) = -4x + 1$

b. $(a^2 + 3a + 1) - (-3a^2 + 5a + (-6))$

17. **a.** never

b. sometimes

c. never

d. always

18. **a.** Yes; the integers are closed under addition.

b. No; the positive integers are not closed for subtraction.

Answers

39. $6x - 20$

40. $2x^2 + 17x + 36$

41. a. sum and difference: degree 4, trinomial

b. sum and difference: degree 4; The number of terms in each would depend on the degrees of the second terms in Polynomials A and B.

42. $20x^2 + 22x + 30$ sq. units

45. Part A $18x + 8$

Part B 10 ft, 9 ft, 14 ft, 7 ft, 24 ft, 16 ft

AVAILABLE **ONLINE**

Practice Tutorial

Mixed Review Available Online

PRACTICE & PROBLEM SOLVING

APPLY

39. Mathematical Connections The perimeters of the two figures are equal.

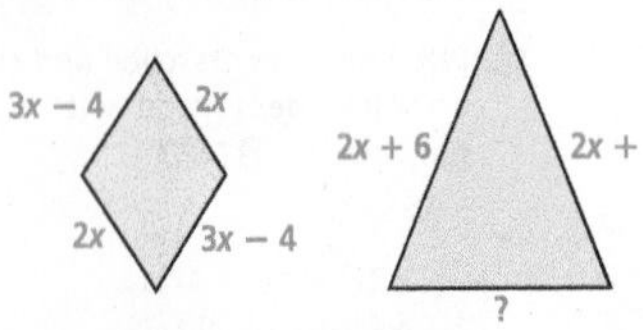

3x − 4
2x
2x
3x − 4
2x + 6
2x + 6
?

What expression represents the missing side length?

40. Make Sense and Persevere The owners of a house want to knock down the wall between the kitchen and family room. MP.1

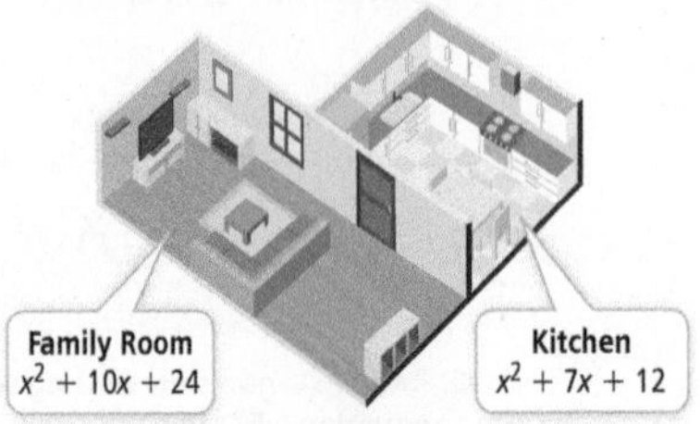

Family Room
x² + 10x + 24
Kitchen
x² + 7x + 12

What expression represents the area of the new combined open space?

41. Reason Polynomial A has degree 2; Polynomial B has degree 4. What can you determine about the name and degree of the sum of the polynomials and the difference of the polynomials if

a. Polynomial A is a binomial and Polynomial B is a monomial?

b. Both Polynomial A and Polynomial B are binomials? MP.2

42. Model With Mathematics A large indoor market is set up with 4 rows of booths. There are large booths with an area of x^2 sq. units, medium booths with an area of x sq. units, and small booths with an area of 1 sq. unit. In the marketplace, two of the rows contain 7 large booths, 6 medium booths, and 5 small booths each. The other two rows each contain 3 large booths, 5 medium booths, and 10 small booths. What is the total area of the booths in the marketplace? MP.4

ASSESSMENT PRACTICE

43. Which expression is equivalent to $(x^2 + 3x - 5) - (4x^2 + 3x - 6)$?

Ⓐ $5x^2 + 6x - 11$

Ⓑ $-3x^4 + 6x^2 + 1$

Ⓒ $-3x^2 + 1$

Ⓓ $-3x^2 + 6x - 11$

44. SAT/ACT What is the sum of $-2x^2 + 3x - 4$ and $3x^2 - 4x + 6$?

Ⓐ $x^4 - x^2 + 2$

Ⓑ $5x^4 + 7x^2 + 10$

Ⓒ 2

Ⓓ $x^2 - x + 2$

Ⓔ $2x^6$

45. Performance Task A room has the dimensions shown below. Molding was installed around the edge of the ceiling.

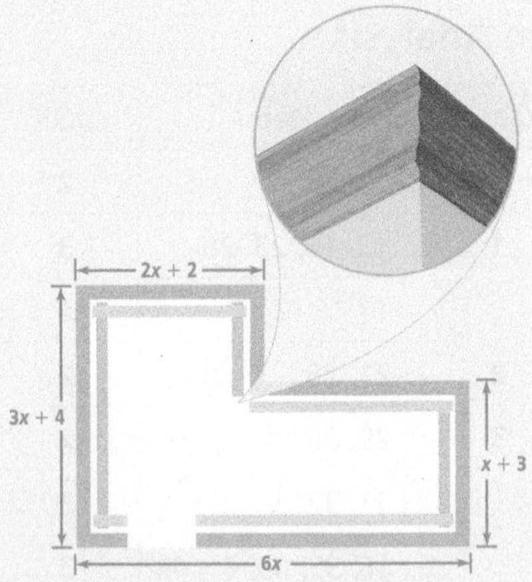

2x + 2
3x + 4
x + 3
6x

Part A Write an expression to represent the amount of molding needed.

Part B Sam used 80 feet of molding. What is the measurement of each edge of the ceiling?

Go Online | PearsonRealize.com

LESSON QUIZ

Use the Lesson Quiz to assess students' understanding of the mathematics in the lesson.

Students can take the Lesson Quiz online or you can download a printable copy from **SavvasRealize.com**. The Lesson Quiz is also available in the *Assessment Resources* book.

Item Analysis

Item	DOK	Standards
1	1	HSA.SSE.A.1.A
2	1	HSA.SSE.A.1.A
3	1	HSA.APR.A.1
4	2	HSA.APR.A.1
5	2	HSA.APR.A.1

RtI Use the student scores on the Lesson Quiz to prescribe differentiated assignments.

If students take the Lesson Quiz online, it will be automatically scored and appropriate differentiated practice will be assigned based on student performance.

I Intervention	0–3 points	• Reteach to Build Understanding • Mathematical Literacy and Vocabulary • Additional Practice
O On-Level	4 points	• Mathematical Literacy and Vocabulary • Additional Practice • Enrichment
A Advanced	5 points	• Enrichment

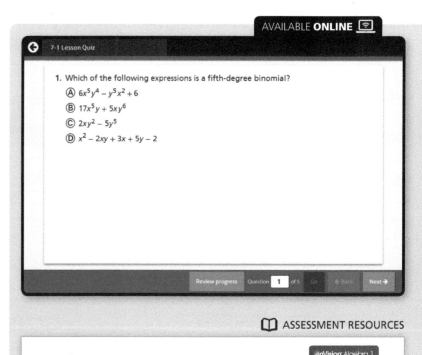

AVAILABLE **ONLINE**

7-1 Lesson Quiz

1. Which of the following expressions is a fifth-degree binomial?

Ⓐ $6x^5y^4 - y^5x^2 + 6$

Ⓑ $17x^5y + 5xy^6$

Ⓒ $2xy^2 - 5y^5$

Ⓓ $x^2 - 2xy + 3x + 5y - 2$

Review progress Question 1 of 5 Go Back Next

ASSESSMENT RESOURCES

Name

enVision Algebra 1

PearsonRealize.com

7-1 Lesson Quiz

Adding and Subtracting Polynomials

1. Which of the following expressions is a fifth-degree binomial?

Ⓐ $6x^5y^4 - y^5x^2 + 6$

Ⓑ $17x^5y + 5xy^6$

Ⓒ $2xy^2 - 5y^5$

Ⓓ $x^2 - 2xy + 3x + 5y - 2$

2. Write $7x^2 - 4 + 6x^3 - 4x - x^4$ in standard form.

$-x^4 + 6x^3 + 7x^2 - 4x - 4$

3. Combine like terms and write $4y + 5y^2 - 6 - 5y + 27 - y^2$ in standard form.

$4y^2 - y + 21$

4. Simplify. Write your answer in standard form.

$(4x^3 + 6x - 7) + (3x^3 - 5x^2 - 5x + 9)$

$7x^3 - 5x^2 + x + 2$

5. Which of the following is $(-5x + 4) - (3x^2 - 7x + 4)$ simplified and written in standard form?

Ⓐ $3x^2 - 12x + 8$

Ⓑ $2x - 3x^2$

Ⓒ $-3x^2 + 7x - 5x$

Ⓓ $-3x^2 + 2x$

enVision™ **Algebra 1** • Assessment Resources

DIFFERENTIATED RESOURCES

I = Intervention O = On-Level A = Advanced

= This activity is available as a digital assignment powered by MathXL® for School.

AVAILABLE **ONLINE**

Reteach to Build Understanding I

Provides scaffolded reteaching for the key lesson concepts.

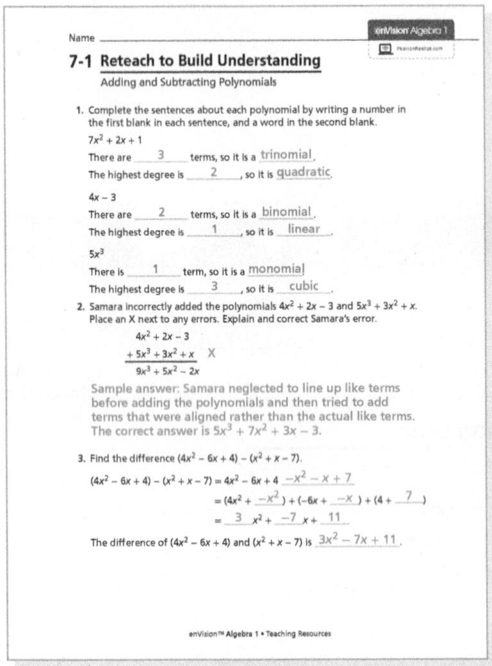

Name

enVision Algebra 1

7-1 Reteach to Build Understanding

Adding and Subtracting Polynomials

1. Complete the sentences about each polynomial by writing a number in the first blank in each sentence, and a word in the second blank.

$7x^2 + 2x + 1$

There are 3 terms, so it is a trinomial.

The highest degree is 2, so it is quadratic.

$4x - 3$

There are 2 terms, so it is a binomial.

The highest degree is 1, so it is linear.

$5x^3$

There is 1 term, so it is a monomial.

The highest degree is 3, so it is cubic.

2. Samara incorrectly added the polynomials $4x^2 + 2x - 3$ and $5x^3 + 3x^2 + x$. Place an X next to any errors. Explain and correct Samara's error.

$4x^2 + 2x - 3$

$+ 5x^3 + 3x^2 + x$ X

$9x^3 + 5x^2 - 2x$

Sample answer: Samara neglected to line up like terms before adding the polynomials and then tried to add terms that were aligned rather than the actual like terms. The correct answer is $5x^3 + 7x^2 + 3x - 3$.

3. Find the difference $(4x^2 - 6x + 4) - (x^2 + x - 7)$.

$(4x^2 - 6x + 4) - (x^2 + x - 7) = 4x^2 - 6x + 4\ \underline{-x^2 - x + 7}$

$= (4x^2 + \underline{-x^2}) + (-6x + \underline{-x}) + (4 + \underline{7})$

$= \underline{3}\,x^2 + \underline{-7}\,x + \underline{11}$

The difference of $(4x^2 - 6x + 4)$ and $(x^2 + x - 7)$ is $3x^2 - 7x + 11$.

enVision™ Algebra 1 • Teaching Resources

Additional Practice I O

Provides extra practice for each lesson.

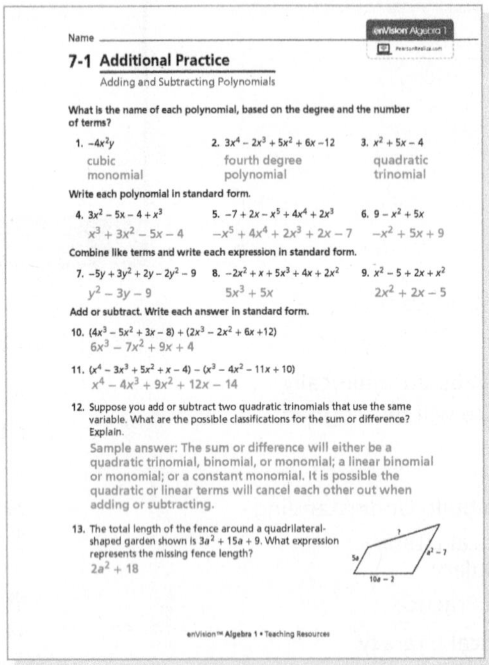

Name

enVision Algebra 1

7-1 Additional Practice

Adding and Subtracting Polynomials

What is the name of each polynomial, based on the degree and the number of terms?

1. $-4x^2y$ — cubic monomial
2. $3x^4 - 2x^3 + 5x^2 + 6x - 12$ — fourth degree polynomial
3. $x^2 + 5x - 4$ — quadratic trinomial

Write each polynomial in standard form.

4. $3x^2 - 5x - 4 + x^3$ — $x^3 + 3x^2 - 5x - 4$
5. $-7 + 2x - x^5 + 4x^4 + 2x^3$ — $-x^5 + 4x^4 + 2x^3 + 2x - 7$
6. $9 - x^2 + 5x$ — $-x^2 + 5x + 9$

Combine like terms and write each expression in standard form.

7. $-5y + 3y^2 + 2y - 2y^2 - 9$ — $y^2 - 3y - 9$
8. $-2x^2 + x + 5x^3 + 4x + 2x^2$ — $5x^3 + 5x$
9. $x^2 - 5 + 2x + x^2$ — $2x^2 + 2x - 5$

Add or subtract. Write each answer in standard form.

10. $(4x^3 - 5x^2 + 3x - 8) + (2x^3 - 2x^2 + 6x + 12)$ — $6x^3 - 7x^2 + 9x + 4$

11. $(x^4 - 3x^3 + 5x^2 + x - 4) - (x^3 - 4x^2 - 11x + 10)$ — $x^4 - 4x^3 + 9x^2 + 12x - 14$

12. Suppose you add or subtract two quadratic trinomials that use the same variable. What are the possible classifications for the sum or difference? Explain.

Sample answer: The sum or difference will either be a quadratic trinomial, binomial, or monomial; a linear binomial or monomial; or a constant monomial. It is possible the quadratic or linear terms will cancel each other out when adding or subtracting.

13. The total length of the fence around a quadrilateral-shaped garden shown is $3a^2 + 15a + 9$. What expression represents the missing fence length?

$2a^2 + 18$

enVision™ Algebra 1 • Teaching Resources

Enrichment O A

Presents engaging problems and activities that extend the lesson concepts.

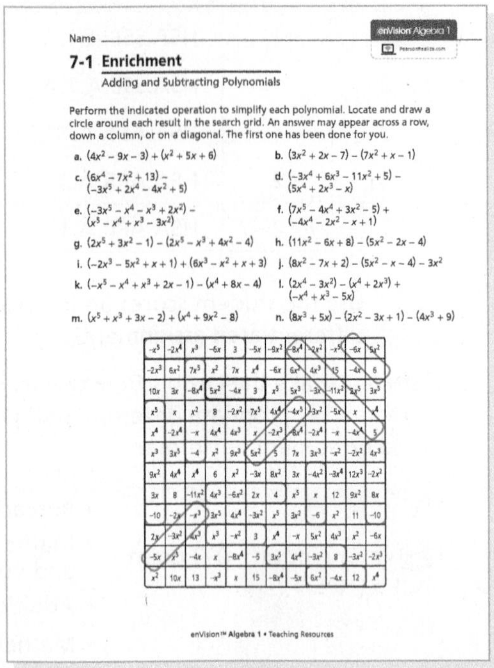

Name

enVision Algebra 1

7-1 Enrichment

Adding and Subtracting Polynomials

Perform the indicated operation to simplify each polynomial. Locate and draw a circle around each result in the search grid. An answer may appear across a row, down a column, or on a diagonal. The first one has been done for you.

a. $(4x^2 - 9x - 3) + (x^2 + 5x + 6)$

b. $(3x^2 + 2x - 7) - (7x^2 + x - 1)$

c. $(6x^4 - 7x^2 + 13) - (-3x^3 + 2x^4 - 4x^2 + 5)$

d. $(-3x^4 + 6x^3 - 11x^2 + 5) - (5x^4 + 2x^3 - x)$

e. $(-3x^3 - x^4 - x^3 + 2x^2) - (x^3 - x^4 + x^3 - 3x^2)$

f. $(7x^5 - 4x^4 + 3x^2 - 5) + (-4x^4 - 2x^2 - x + 1)$

g. $(2x^5 + 3x^2 - 1) - (2x^5 - x^3 + 4x^2 - 4)$

h. $(11x^2 - 6x + 8) - (5x^2 - 2x - 4)$

i. $(-2x^3 - 5x^2 + x + 1) + (6x^3 - x^2 + x + 3)$

j. $(8x^2 - 7x + 2) - (5x^2 - x - 4) - 3x^2$

k. $(-x^5 - x^4 + x^3 + 2x - 1) - (x^4 + 8x - 4)$

l. $(2x^4 - 3x^2) - (x^4 + 2x^3) + (-x^4 + x^3 - 5x)$

m. $(x^5 + x^3 + 3x - 2) + (x^4 + 9x^2 - 8)$

n. $(8x^3 + 5x) - (2x^2 - 3x + 1) - (4x^3 + 9)$

enVision™ Algebra 1 • Teaching Resources

Mathematical Literacy and Vocabulary I O

Helps students develop and reinforce understanding of key terms and concepts.

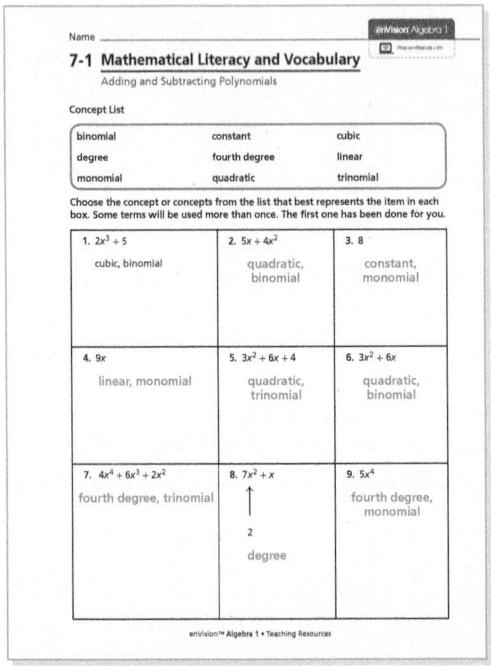

Name

enVision Algebra 1

7-1 Mathematical Literacy and Vocabulary

Adding and Subtracting Polynomials

Concept List

binomial	constant	cubic
degree	fourth degree	linear
monomial	quadratic	trinomial

Choose the concept or concepts from the list that best represents the item in each box. Some terms will be used more than once. The first one has been done for you.

1. $2x^3 + 5$ cubic, binomial	2. $5x + 4x^2$ quadratic, binomial	3. 8 constant, monomial
4. $9x$ linear, monomial	5. $3x^2 + 6x + 4$ quadratic, trinomial	6. $3x^2 + 6x$ quadratic, binomial
7. $4x^4 + 6x^3 + 2x^2$ fourth degree, trinomial	8. $7x^2 + x$ 2 degree	9. $5x^4$ fourth degree, monomial

enVision™ Algebra 1 • Teaching Resources

Digital Resources and Video Tutorials I O A

The **Reteach to Build Understanding, Additional Practice,** and **Enrichment** activities are available as digital assignments powered by MathXL for School. These activities are automatically assigned when students complete the lesson quiz online and are automatically scored.

Students can access instructional tutorials using the **Virtual Nerd app.**

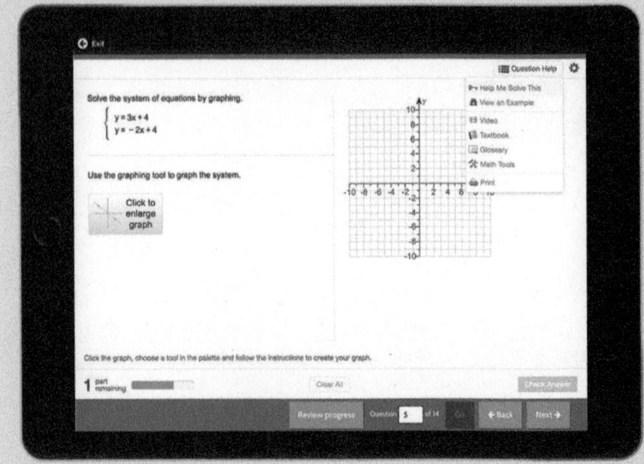
Solve the system of equations by graphing.
y = 3x + 4
y = −2x + 4
Use the graphing tool to graph the system.
Click to enlarge graph
Question Help
Review progress
Back
Next

Tutorial
SLOPE-INTERCEPT FORM
y = mx + b
What's Slope-Intercept Form of a Linear Equation?
SAVVAS

Students can also access Virtual Nerd videos using the **BouncePages app** to scan exercise pages marked with this icon. Students can download both apps for free in their mobile devices' app store.

SavvasRealize.com

A-Z Glossary

LESSON 7-2

Multiplying Polynomials

Lesson Overview

FOCUS

Objective

Students will be able to:

✔ Use the Distributive Property with polynomials, recognizing that polynomials are closed under multiplication.

✔ Multiply polynomials using a table and an area model.

✔ Apply the product of polynomials to solve real-world problems.

Essential Understanding

Polynomials can be multiplied by applying the Distributive Property or by using a table. They form a system similar to integers. Therefore, polynomials are closed under multiplication.

COHERENCE

Previously in this course, students:

- Added and subtracted polynomials, understanding that they are closed under the operations of addition and subtraction.

In this lesson, students:

- Multiply polynomials, recognizing that polynomials are also closed under the operation of multiplication.

Later in this topic, students will:

- Factor polynomials, including quadratic trinomials, perfect-square trinomials, and the difference of two squares.

RIGOR

This lesson emphasizes a blend of *conceptual understanding* and *application.*

- Students understand that the polynomials are closed under multiplication and that when the factors include variables, the degree of the product is larger than the degree of the factors.
- Students apply multiplication of binomials to solve real-world problems, such as finding the area of a phone that is not occupied by a screen.

Vocabulary Builder

REVIEW VOCABULARY English | *Spanish*

- **binomial** | *binomio*
- **closure** | *cierre*
- **polynomial** | *polinomio*
- **term** | *término*
- **trinomial** | *trinomio*

VOCABULARY ACTIVITY

Review the term *polynomial* and two specific types of polynomials, *binomial* and *trinomial*. Discuss the term *closure* and what it means for operations to be closed by relating it to the system of integers.

Q: What kind of number is the sum, difference, or product of two integers? [integer]

Because the sum, difference, and product of integers are always integers, the system of integers is closed for each of these operations.

Q: *Closure* also applies to *polynomials*. Therefore, what do we know about the sum, difference, or product of two polynomials? [Each one is also a polynomial.]

Student Companion

Students can do their in-class work for the lesson on pages 141–144 of their *Student Companion* or in Savvas Realize.

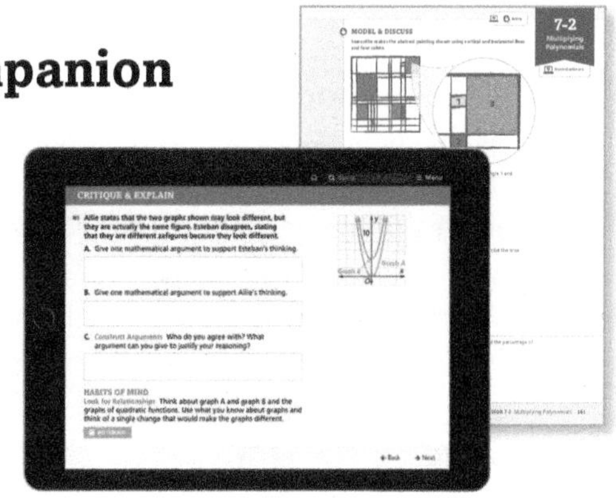

Mathematics Overview COMMON CORE STANDARDS

Content Standards

In this lesson, students focus on this standard:

HSA.APR.A.1 Understand that polynomials form a system analogous to the integers, namely, they are closed under the operations of addition, subtraction, and multiplication; add, subtract, and multiply polynomials.

Mathematical Practice Standards

These standards are highlighted in this lesson:

MP.1 Make Sense of Problems and Persevere in Solving Them

Students identify a starting point for a problem about rectangles with side lengths expressed as polynomials when they recognize that they can use the formula for the area of a rectangle to solve the problem.

MP.7 Look For and Make Use of Structure

Students apply general rules of polynomials to specific situations when they determine that the degree of the product is different from the degree of the factors, because when two variable terms are multiplied, the degree of the product increases.

Activity

MODEL & DISCUSS

INSTRUCTIONAL FOCUS Students explore using the formula for the area of a rectangle to describe the given areas. This helps them make the connection to the process of multiplying polynomials when they find the area of a rectangle given sides represented by binomial expressions.

STUDENT COMPANION Students can complete the *Model & Discuss* activity on page 141 of their *Student Companion*.

Before WHOLE CLASS

Implement Tasks that Promote Reasoning and Problem Solving ETP

Q: How do you find the area of a rectangle?
[Multiply the length by the width.]

During SMALL GROUP

Support Productive Struggle in Learning Mathematics ETP

Q: What does each rectangle in the figure represent?
[Each individual rectangle represents a piece of the entire rectangular figure.]

Q: Since there is more than one rectangle, how do you find the area of the entire figure?
[Find the area of each individual rectangle and then add them together.]

For Early Finishers

Q: Draw the blue figure, and extend the length by x and the width by $2x$. Describe the area of the new rectangle.
[The area of the new figure is $(\ell + x)(w + 2x)$.]

Q: Draw the blue figure, and decrease the length by x and the width by $2x$. Describe the area of the new rectangle.
[The area of the new figure is $(\ell - x)(w - 2x)$.]

After WHOLE CLASS

Facilitate Meaningful Mathematical Discourse ETP

Discuss the area model for multiplication as an organizational process to multiply variable expressions.

Q: How can you use the formula for the area of a rectangle to show the area when side lengths are unknown and represented with a variable expression?
[The area formula serves as a guideline for multiplying the expression for the length by the expression for the width.]

HABITS OF MIND *Use with* **MODEL & DISCUSS**

Communicate Precisely What information would you need to find the percentage of the painting that is red? Explain. **MP.6**

[You would need to know the total area of the red rectangles and the total area of the painting.]

AVAILABLE **ONLINE**

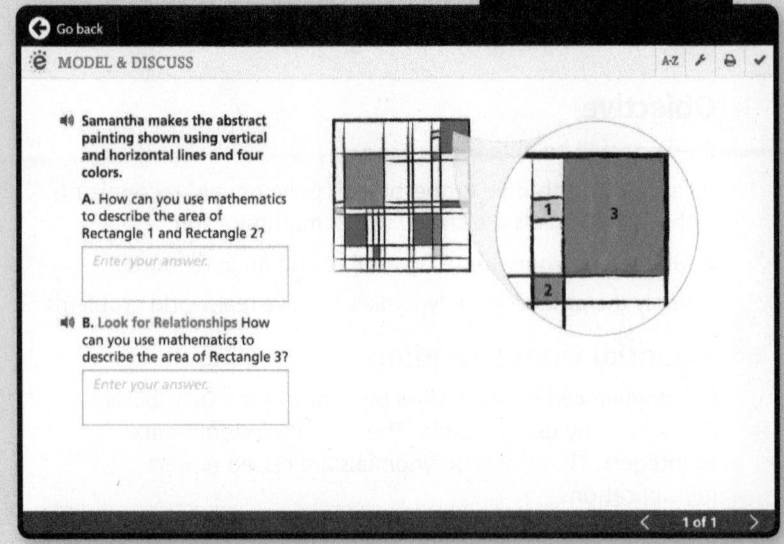

Go back
MODEL & DISCUSS
A-Z
Samantha makes the abstract painting shown using vertical and horizontal lines and four colors.
A. How can you use mathematics to describe the area of Rectangle 1 and Rectangle 2?
Enter your answer.
B. Look for Relationships How can you use mathematics to describe the area of Rectangle 3?
Enter your answer.
1
2
3
1 of 1

STUDENT EDITION, PAGE 267

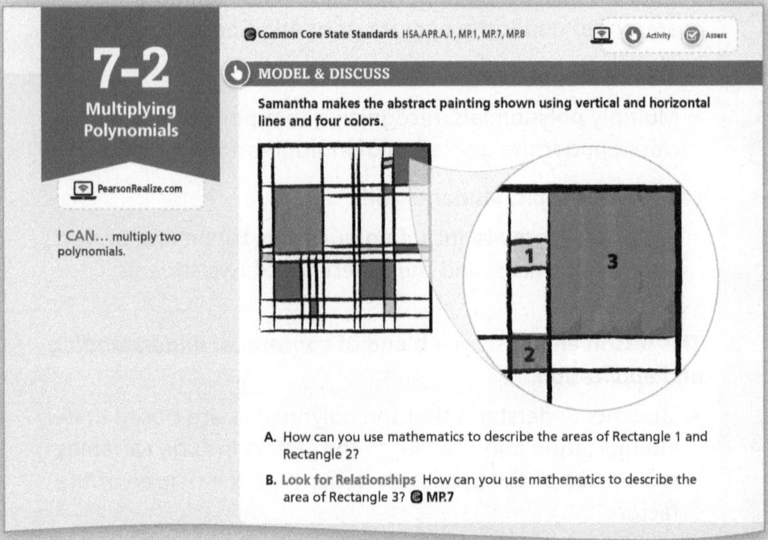

7-2
Multiplying Polynomials
PearsonRealize.com
I CAN… multiply two polynomials.
Common Core State Standards HSA.APR.A.1, MP.1, MP.7, MP.8
Activity
Assess
MODEL & DISCUSS
Samantha makes the abstract painting shown using vertical and horizontal lines and four colors.
1
2
3
A. How can you use mathematics to describe the areas of Rectangle 1 and Rectangle 2?
B. Look for Relationships How can you use mathematics to describe the area of Rectangle 3? MP.7

SAMPLE STUDENT WORK

A. Find the length and width of the rectangle and multiply.
B. The length of the blue rectangle is composed of three segments. Add these segments and multiply the sum by the width to find the area.

INTRODUCE THE ESSENTIAL QUESTION

Establish Mathematics Goals to Focus Learning ETP

Introduce students to multiplication of polynomials. Remind them that the multiplication of rational coefficients includes working with negatives and positives and using the Product Property of Exponents. Explain that each polynomial term must be identified by its variable, degree, and sign in order to correctly multiply it by another polynomial term.

EXAMPLE 1 Multiply a Monomial and a Trinomial

Pose Purposeful Questions ETP

Q: Why is the Distributive Property used when multiplying a monomial and a trinomial?
[The Distributive Property ensures that the term outside the parenthesis (monomial) is multiplied by each term of the trinomial. The Distributive Property works for polynomial in the same way it works for real numbers.]

Q: How do you multiply monomials that have coefficients, variables, and exponents?
[When you multiply two monomials together, you multiply the coefficients and add the exponents of the variables with the same bases.]

Try It! Answers

1. a. $-2x^4 - 6x^3 - 8x^2$
   b. $-8x^3 + 12x^2 - 20x$

AVAILABLE ONLINE

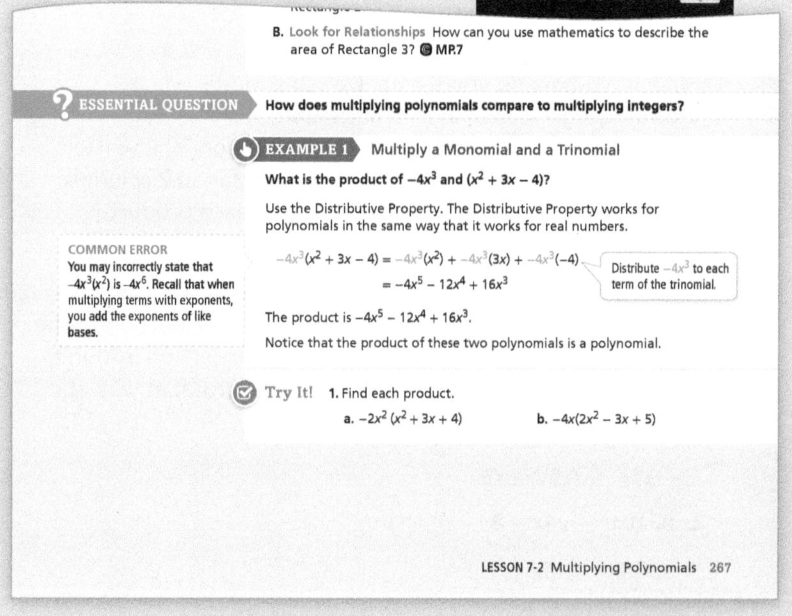
B. Look for Relationships How can you use mathematics to describe the area of Rectangle 3? MP.7

ESSENTIAL QUESTION How does multiplying polynomials compare to multiplying integers?

EXAMPLE 1 Multiply a Monomial and a Trinomial

What is the product of $-4x^3$ and $(x^2 + 3x - 4)$?

Use the Distributive Property. The Distributive Property works for polynomials in the same way that it works for real numbers.

COMMON ERROR You may incorrectly state that $-4x^3(x^2)$ is $-4x^6$. Recall that when multiplying terms with exponents, you add the exponents of like bases.

$-4x^3(x^2 + 3x - 4) = -4x^3(x^2) + -4x^3(3x) + -4x^3(-4)$
$= -4x^5 - 12x^4 + 16x^3$

Distribute $-4x^3$ to each term of the trinomial.

The product is $-4x^5 - 12x^4 + 16x^3$.

Notice that the product of these two polynomials is a polynomial.

Try It! 1. Find each product.
a. $-2x^2(x^2 + 3x + 4)$ b. $-4x(2x^2 - 3x + 5)$

LESSON 7-2 Multiplying Polynomials 267

Elicit and Use Evidence of Student Thinking ETP

Q: When multiplying a monomial by a trinomial, are there any like terms to combine?
[If the trinomial is in standard form, the multiplication results in a product that has no like terms and the product is in standard form.]

AVAILABLE ONLINE

ADDITIONAL EXAMPLES

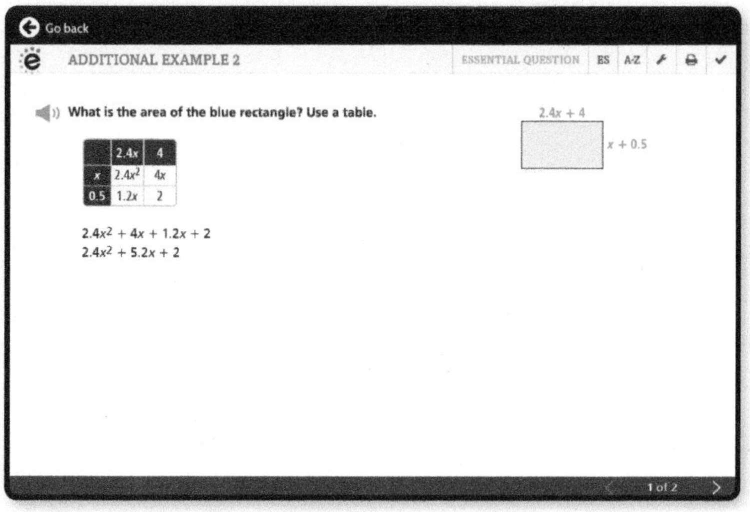
Go back
ADDITIONAL EXAMPLE 2
ESSENTIAL QUESTION ES A-Z
What is the area of the blue rectangle? Use a table.
2.4x + 4
x + 0.5
2.4x 4
x 2.4x² 4x
0.5 1.2x 2
2.4x² + 4x + 1.2x + 2
2.4x² + 5.2x + 2
1 of 2

Example 2 Students relate the area model to a table with coefficients and constants that are not whole numbers.

Q: How is a table helpful when multiplying polynomials?
[The table helps you stay organized during the process of multiplying polynomials.]

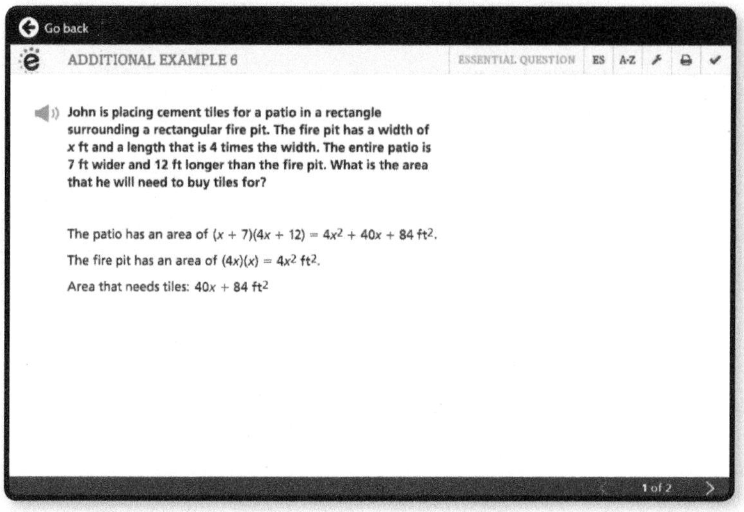
Go back
ADDITIONAL EXAMPLE 6
ESSENTIAL QUESTION ES A-Z
John is placing cement tiles for a patio in a rectangle surrounding a rectangular fire pit. The fire pit has a width of x ft and a length that is 4 times the width. The entire patio is 7 ft wider and 12 ft longer than the fire pit. What is the area that he will need to buy tiles for?
The patio has an area of (x + 7)(4x + 12) = 4x² + 40x + 84 ft².
The fire pit has an area of (4x)(x) = 4x² ft².
Area that needs tiles: 40x + 84 ft²
1 of 2

Example 6 Students write and solve word problems involving multiplication of polynomials.

Q: How can you represent the area of the patio in the problem?
[The area of the patio will be a binomial times a binomial.]

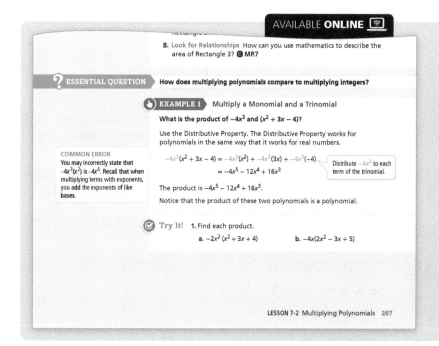

EXAMPLE 2 Use a Table to Find the Product of Polynomials

Pose Purposeful Questions ETP

Q: In Part A, how do you set up the table model when multiplying a binomial by a binomial?
[Each binomial has two terms, the first binomial is written in 2 rows and the second binomial is written in 2 columns, creating 4 empty spaces in the table for each product.]

Q: In Part B, how is the table model related to the area model?
[In the area model, each rectangular section represents an area created by a portion of the length and a portion of the width. When the area of each rectangular section is found, all of them are added together to get the total as with the table model.]

Try It! Answers

2. a. $10x^2 + 24x + 8$

b. $14x^2 + 11x + 2$

Elicit and Use Evidence of Student Thinking ETP

Q: What do you do after the area of each section of the table has a product?
[Combine like terms.]

Common Error

Try It! 2 Students may multiply the two lengths or the two widths together. Show them how the table creates empty spaces for each piece of the product while reinforcing that they are using the concept of length times width to find the area of each section of the rectangle.

AVAILABLE ONLINE

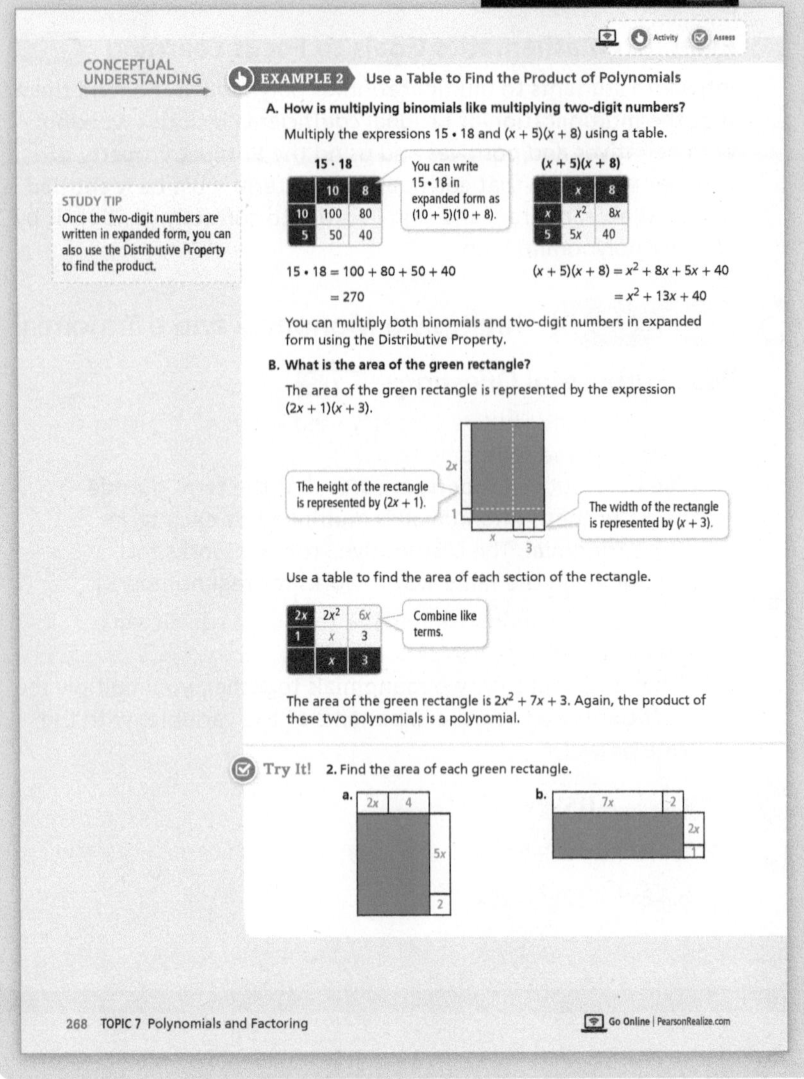

Activity Assess

CONCEPTUAL UNDERSTANDING

EXAMPLE 2 Use a Table to Find the Product of Polynomials

A. How is multiplying binomials like multiplying two-digit numbers?

Multiply the expressions $15 \cdot 18$ and $(x + 5)(x + 8)$ using a table.

$15 \cdot 18$

	10	8
10	100	80
5	50	40

You can write $15 \cdot 18$ in expanded form as $(10 + 5)(10 + 8)$.

$(x + 5)(x + 8)$

	x	8
x	x^2	$8x$
5	$5x$	40

STUDY TIP
Once the two-digit numbers are written in expanded form, you can also use the Distributive Property to find the product.

$15 \cdot 18 = 100 + 80 + 50 + 40$
$= 270$

$(x + 5)(x + 8) = x^2 + 8x + 5x + 40$
$= x^2 + 13x + 40$

You can multiply both binomials and two-digit numbers in expanded form using the Distributive Property.

B. What is the area of the green rectangle?

The area of the green rectangle is represented by the expression $(2x + 1)(x + 3)$.

The height of the rectangle is represented by $(2x + 1)$.

The width of the rectangle is represented by $(x + 3)$.

Use a table to find the area of each section of the rectangle.

$2x$	$2x^2$	$6x$
1	x	3
	x	3

Combine like terms.

The area of the green rectangle is $2x^2 + 7x + 3$. Again, the product of these two polynomials is a polynomial.

Try It! 2. Find the area of each green rectangle.

a. $2x$, 4, $5x$, 2

b. $7x$, 2, $2x$, 1

268 TOPIC 7 Polynomials and Factoring

Go Online | PearsonRealize.com

ADV Advanced Students

USE WITH EXAMPLE 2A Students investigate how the number of terms in each polynomial determines the number of terms that result from multiplying.

- Use a table to multiply the polynomials.

1. $(4x - 7)(x^2 + 2)$
$[4x^3 - 7x^2 + 8x - 14]$

Q: How many products result from a binomial multiplied by a trinomial?
[6 products]

Q: How can you use the table to determine the number of products that result from the multiplication?
[When you draw the table, the blank spaces represent a place for each product; therefore, you can count the blank spaces.]

Q: How do you find the number of individual products from looking at the polynomials before drawing a table?
[The number of individual products is the number of terms in the first polynomial times the number of terms in the second polynomial.]

EXAMPLE 3 Multiply Binomials

Use and Connect Mathematical Representations ETP

Q: How is the table model similar to using the Distributive Property?
[Both are organized approaches to ensure that each term in the first polynomial is multiplied by each term in the second polynomial.]

Try It! Answers

3. a. $10x^2 - 3x - 4$

b. $6x^2 + 2x - 20$

HABITS OF MIND

Use with **EXAMPLES 1–3**

Reason Could you use an area model to find the product of polynomials that have subtracted terms? Explain. **MP.2**

[No, because there is no way to physically represent negative length or negative area.]

EXAMPLE 4 Multiply a Trinomial and a Binomial

Use and Connect Mathematical Representations ETP

Q: In Part A, how does multiplying a trinomial and a binomial compare to multiplying two binomials?
[You need to multiply each term in the binomial by 3 terms instead of 2 terms. The result will be 6 products instead of 4. You need to combine any like terms in both multiplication problems.]

Q: How does the table help organize and focus the multiplication?
[For each product to be found, there is an empty space. The number of spaces depends on how many terms are in each polynomial.]

AVAILABLE **ONLINE**

Activity Assess

EXAMPLE 3 Multiply Binomials

How can you use the Distributive Property to rewrite $(2x + 4)(x - 5)$ as a polynomial?

Distribute each term in the first binomial to each term in the second binomial.

$(2x + 4)(x - 5) = 2x(x - 5) + 4(x - 5)$	Distribute $2x$ and 4 to the second binomial.
$= 2x(x) + 2x(-5) + 4(x) + 4(-5)$	Distribute $2x$ and 4 to each term in the second binomial.
$= 2x^2 - 10x + 4x - 20$	Multiply.
$= 2x^2 - 6x - 20$	Combine like terms.

The product of $(2x + 4)$ and $(x - 5)$ is $2x^2 - 6x - 20$.

Again, the product of these two polynomials is a polynomial.

GENERALIZE
Compare the factors and the final product. What generalizations can you make from this example? **MP.8**

Try It! **3.** Find each product.

a. $(5x - 4)(2x + 1)$ **b.** $(3x - 5)(2x + 4)$

EXAMPLE 4 Multiply a Trinomial and a Binomial

A. How can you use a table to find the product of $(x^2 + 2x - 1)$ and $(3x + 4)$?

Write the terms for each polynomial in the first row and column of the table. Multiply to find each product.

$3x + 4$ | $x^2 + 2x - 1$

	x^2	$2x$	-1
$3x$	$3x^3$	$6x^2$	$-3x$
4	$4x^2$	$8x$	-4

Combine the like terms.

	x^2	$2x$	-1
$3x$	$3x^3$	$6x^2$	$-3x$
4	$4x^2$	$8x$	-4

$$(x^2 + 2x - 1)(3x + 4) = 3x^3 + 6x^2 + 4x^2 + 8x + (-3x) + (-4)$$
$$= 3x^3 + 10x^2 + 5x - 4$$

So $(x^2 + 2x - 1)(3x + 4) = 3x^3 + 10x^2 + 5x - 4$. When you multiply a trinomial by a binomial, the result is six individual products. Using a table is one method you can use to help organize these products.

CONTINUED ON THE NEXT PAGE

ELL English Language Learners *(Use with* **EXAMPLE 4***)*

LISTENING BEGINNING Have students listen as you read the following sentences:

- At one time, tobacco was a main *product* of southern plantations.
- Bread is the *product* that results from mixing flour, yeast, salt, and water together and then baking.
- The *product* of 3 and 8 is 24.

Q: What word is used in each of these sentences? [product]

Q: Compare the meaning of the word *product* in each sentence.
[In each sentence, *product* describes the result of putting things together: the result of farming land, the result of baking ingredients that were mixed together, and the result of multiplying two numbers.]

SPEAKING INTERMEDIATE Explain that *rows* are horizontal, or go from left to right, and *columns* are vertical, or go up and down. In small groups, have students discuss ways to distinguish the two terms and remember them easily.

Q: How can you remember that rows run horizontally?
[Use a phrase like **R**ed **H**ot to remember that **R**ows are **H**orizontal. Picture rows of corn going from left to right across a field.]

Q: How can you remember that columns run vertically?
[Both the words *column* and *vertical* have the letter *c* in them. Think of famous architecture with pillars, or columns, running vertically.]

WRITING ADVANCED One definition of a *table* is a flat surface supported by legs that people often sit around to complete various activities, such as eating or writing. Ask students to write the definition of table in their journals along with three complete sentences that use the word *table*.

Q: When the example says, "How can you use a table to find the product...," is it referring to a piece of furniture?
[No, in the example, *table* refers to a rectangle split into rows and columns used to display information.]

Q: Write the mathematical definition of table in your journals and draw an example of a table to support your definition.
[Check students' work.]

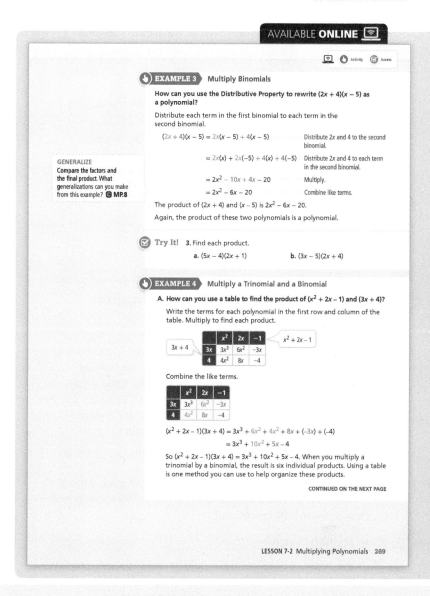

Activity Assess

EXAMPLE 4 CONTINUED

Use and Connect Mathematical Representations ETP

Q: In Part B, since polynomials are made up of different terms, what must be included when setting up the multiplication process?
[Each term must have its sign included when multiplying so that like terms are combined correctly.]

Q: How can you be sure to line up like terms during the multiplication?
[Just like multiplying a 3-digit number by a 2-digit number, a space must be skipped for the second row of products.]

Try It! Answers

4. a. $-6x^3 + 23x^2 - 34x + 35$

b. $-6x^4 - 9x^3 + 14x^2 + 3x - 4$

EXAMPLE 5 Closure and Multiplication

Pose Purposeful Questions ETP

Q: When multiplying two polynomials, is it possible to have a product with an exponent that is not a whole number?
[No, if the two factors are polynomials, they have whole number exponents. The Product Property of Exponents states to add exponents of the same base when multiplying. Adding two whole numbers results in a whole number.]

Q: How can you generalize a closure statement for multiplying polynomials?
[Since the exponents of each product are whole numbers, the product of two polynomials is always a polynomial and is closed under multiplication.]

Try It! Answer

5. If the product does not have only whole numbers, then it is not a polynomial. This means that polynomials would not be closed under multiplication, which is not true.

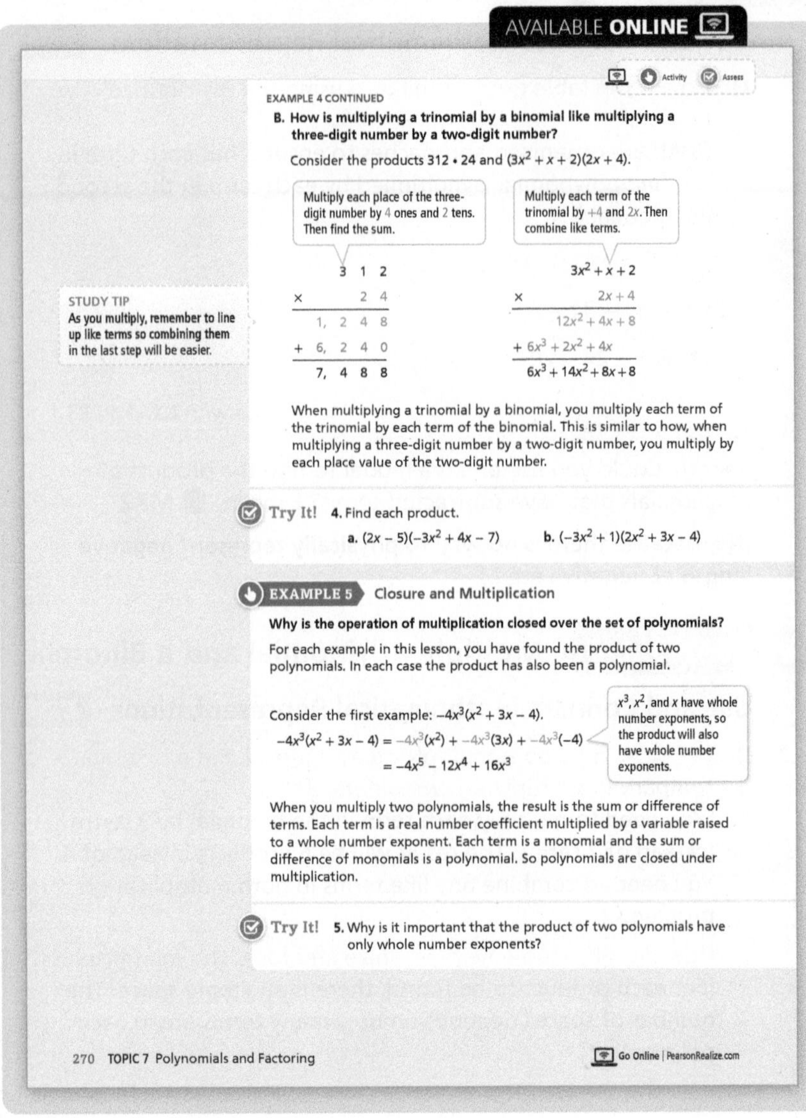
AVAILABLE ONLINE

Activity Assess

EXAMPLE 4 CONTINUED

B. How is multiplying a trinomial by a binomial like multiplying a three-digit number by a two-digit number?

Consider the products $312 \cdot 24$ and $(3x^2 + x + 2)(2x + 4)$.

Multiply each place of the three-digit number by 4 ones and 2 tens. Then find the sum.

Multiply each term of the trinomial by +4 and 2x. Then combine like terms.

$$\begin{array}{r} 3\ 1\ 2 \\ \times \quad 2\ 4 \\ \hline 1,\ 2\ 4\ 8 \\ +\ 6,\ 2\ 4\ 0 \\ \hline 7,\ 4\ 8\ 8 \end{array} \qquad \begin{array}{r} 3x^2 + x + 2 \\ \times \quad 2x + 4 \\ \hline 12x^2 + 4x + 8 \\ +\ 6x^3 + 2x^2 + 4x \\ \hline 6x^3 + 14x^2 + 8x + 8 \end{array}$$

STUDY TIP
As you multiply, remember to line up like terms so combining them in the last step will be easier.

When multiplying a trinomial by a binomial, you multiply each term of the trinomial by each term of the binomial. This is similar to how, when multiplying a three-digit number by a two-digit number, you multiply by each place value of the two-digit number.

Try It! 4. Find each product.

a. $(2x - 5)(-3x^2 + 4x - 7)$ b. $(-3x^2 + 1)(2x^2 + 3x - 4)$

EXAMPLE 5 Closure and Multiplication

Why is the operation of multiplication closed over the set of polynomials?

For each example in this lesson, you have found the product of two polynomials. In each case the product has also been a polynomial.

Consider the first example: $-4x^3(x^2 + 3x - 4)$.

$$-4x^3(x^2 + 3x - 4) = -4x^3(x^2) + -4x^3(3x) + -4x^3(-4)$$
$$= -4x^5 - 12x^4 + 16x^3$$

x^3, x^2, and x have whole number exponents, so the product will also have whole number exponents.

When you multiply two polynomials, the result is the sum or difference of terms. Each term is a real number coefficient multiplied by a variable raised to a whole number exponent. Each term is a monomial and the sum or difference of monomials is a polynomial. So polynomials are closed under multiplication.

Try It! 5. Why is it important that the product of two polynomials have only whole number exponents?

270 TOPIC 7 Polynomials and Factoring

Go Online | PearsonRealize.com

Struggling Students

USE WITH EXAMPLE 5 Students may struggle with adding exponents when multiplying terms.

- Have students practice multiplying the following terms.

1. $(4x^2)(3x^4)$ $[12x^7]$
2. $(2x)(3x^2)$ $[6x^3]$
3. $(-6x^3)(4x^2)$ $[-24x^5]$

Q: How do you multiply terms that have coefficients, variables, and exponents?
[You multiply the coefficients and add the exponents of the variables that are the same.]

EXAMPLE 6 Apply Multiplication of Binomials

Use and Connect Mathematical Representations ETP

Q: How can you use a table to help solve the area problem?
[Since the phone has a width of $x + 1$ and a height of $1.8x + 3$, you can write the terms of each binomial in the first row and column of the table and multiply the product.]

Q: If a rectangle is set within another rectangle, how can you find the area of the space surrounding the smaller rectangle?
[The area of the space surrounding the rectangle inside the other is found by subtracting the area of the smaller rectangle from the area of the larger rectangle.]

Try It! Answer

6. $4.9x + 3$

Use with **EXAMPLES 4, 5, & 6**

HABITS OF MIND

Generalize Does closure of polynomial multiplication depend on closure of polynomial addition and subtraction? Explain. **MP.8**

[No; closure under addition, subtraction, and multiplication depends on the definition of a polynomial, which states that for an expression to be a polynomial, each term must have a whole number exponent and no variable can be in the denominator.]

AVAILABLE **ONLINE**

Activity Assess

APPLICATION

EXAMPLE 6 Apply Multiplication of Binomials

A smartphone has a screen that has a width of x and a height that is 1.8 times the width. The outer dimensions of the phone are shown.

Write an expression for the portion of the phone that is not occupied by the screen. Assume that the phone is rectangular.

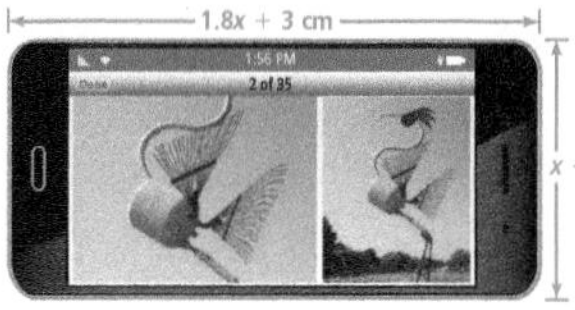
1.8x + 3 cm
x + 1 cm

Formulate ◀ Write expressions to represent the area of the screen and the area of the phone.

Area of screen = $x(1.8x)$

Area of phone = $(x + 1)(1.8x + 3)$

Compute ◀ Express each area in standard form.

Area of screen = $x(1.8x) = 1.8x^2$

Area of phone = $(x + 1)(1.8x + 3)$

$= x(1.8x + 3) + 1(1.8x + 3)$

$= 1.8x^2 + 3x + 1.8x + 3$

$= 1.8x^2 + 4.8x + 3$

Subtract the area of the screen from the area of the phone.

Non-screen Area = Area of Phone − Area of Screen

$= (1.8x^2 + 4.8x + 3) - 1.8x^2$

$= 4.8x + 3$

Interpret ◀ The expression $4.8x + 3$ represents the portion of the phone's surface not occupied by the screen.

Try It! **6.** Suppose the height of the phone in Example 6 were 1.9 times the width but all of the other conditions were the same. What expression would represent the area of the phone's surface not occupied by the screen?

LESSON 7-2 Multiplying Polynomials 271

CONCEPT SUMMARY Multiplying Polynomials

Q: When multiplying polynomials, what methods can help you organize your work?
[Multiplying polynomials involves the process of using the Distributive Property. Using the Distributive Property can be carried out by multiplying polynomials horizontally, using a table, or stacking the polynomials vertically as with multi-digit numbers.]

Do You UNDERSTAND? | Do You KNOW HOW?

Common Error

Exercise 10 Students may stack the two binomials and multiply only like terms. Reinforce the connection between the table method and the area model to give students a strategy for finding the area of a rectangle with polynomial dimensions.

Answers

1. When two polynomials are multiplied together the result is another polynomial. When two integers are multiplied together the result is another integer. So, like the integers, polynomials are closed under multiplication.
2. When using the Distributive Property, each term of a second polynomial is multiplied by the terms in the first polynomial. This is similar to using a table since each term in the columns is multiplied by every term in a row.
3. The error is that Mercedes also multiplied the exponents. When multiplying terms with variables, the exponents are added, so the answer should be: $4x^6 + 8x^5 - 12x^3$.
4. The exponents are added when multiplying, resulting in a degree of the product that is different from either of the factors.
5. $-6x^5 + 8x^4 - 14x^3$
6. $2x^2 - 2x - 24$
7. $3x^2 - 2x - 8$
8. $20y^3 + 7y^2 - 11y + 2$
9. $6x^3 - 5x^2 - 16x + 15$
10. $8x^2 + 12x - 8$
11. $(x + 7)(x + 4)$

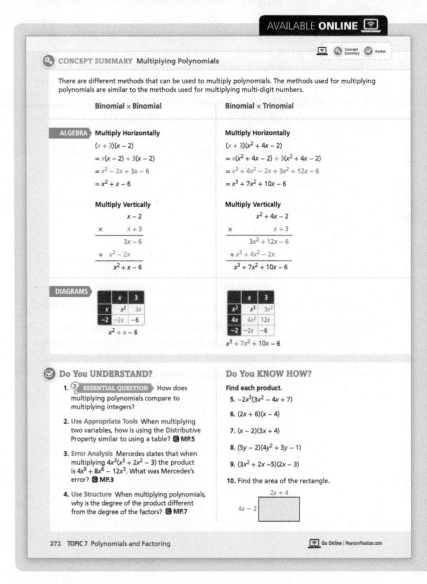

AVAILABLE **ONLINE**

Concept Summary | Assess

CONCEPT SUMMARY Multiplying Polynomials

There are different methods that can be used to multiply polynomials. The methods used for multiplying polynomials are similar to the methods used for multiplying multi-digit numbers.

	Binomial × Binomial	Binomial × Trinomial
ALGEBRA	**Multiply Horizontally** $(x + 3)(x - 2)$ $= x(x - 2) + 3(x - 2)$ $= x^2 - 2x + 3x - 6$ $= x^2 + x - 6$	**Multiply Horizontally** $(x + 3)(x^2 + 4x - 2)$ $= x(x^2 + 4x - 2) + 3(x^2 + 4x - 2)$ $= x^3 + 4x^2 - 2x + 3x^2 + 12x - 6$ $= x^3 + 7x^2 + 10x - 6$
	Multiply Vertically $x - 2$ $\times\ x + 3$ $3x - 6$ $+\ x^2 - 2x$ $x^2 + x - 6$	**Multiply Vertically** $x^2 + 4x - 2$ $\times\ x + 3$ $3x^2 + 12x - 6$ $+\ x^3 + 4x^2 - 2x$ $x^3 + 7x^2 + 10x - 6$

DIAGRAMS

	x	3
x	x^2	$3x$
-2	$-2x$	-6

$x^2 + x - 6$

	x	3
x^2	x^3	$3x^2$
$4x$	$4x^2$	$12x$
-2	$-2x$	-6

$x^3 + 7x^2 + 10x - 6$

Do You UNDERSTAND?

1. ESSENTIAL QUESTION How does multiplying polynomials compare to multiplying integers?
2. **Use Appropriate Tools** When multiplying two variables, how is using the Distributive Property similar to using a table? MP.5
3. **Error Analysis** Mercedes states that when multiplying $4x^3(x^3 + 2x^2 - 3)$ the product is $4x^9 + 8x^6 - 12x^3$. What was Mercedes's error? MP.3
4. **Use Structure** When multiplying polynomials, why is the degree of the product different from the degree of the factors? MP.7

Do You KNOW HOW?

Find each product.

5. $-2x^3(3x^2 - 4x + 7)$
6. $(2x + 6)(x - 4)$
7. $(x - 2)(3x + 4)$
8. $(5y - 2)(4y^2 + 3y - 1)$
9. $(3x^2 + 2x - 5)(2x - 3)$
10. Find the area of the rectangle.

$2x + 4$

$4x - 2$

272 TOPIC 7 Polynomials and Factoring

Go Online | PearsonRealize.com

12. The first term of the product is the product of the first terms in each binomial.
The coefficient of the second term of the product is the sum of the second terms in the binomial.
The last term of the product is the product of the last terms in each binomial.
13. The student multiplied the first terms of each binomial and the second terms of each binomial together instead of distributing each term of the first binomial to each term of the second binomial.
$2x(4x) + 2x(-1) + 2(4x) + 2(-1)$

SavvasRealize.com

Practice Tutorials Math Tools

PRACTICE & PROBLEM SOLVING

AVAILABLE **ONLINE**

Lesson Practice You may opt to have students complete the automatically scored Practice and Problem Solving items online powered by MathXL for School.

Choose from: **Lesson Practice**

Adaptive Practice

You may also take advantage of the bank of exercises for assigning additional practice.

Assignment Guide

Basic	Advanced
11–25, 29–40	11–19, 23–40

Item Analysis

Example	Items	DOK
1	18–21	1
	15	2
2	22, 23	1
	14, 32	2
3	12, 24–26, 38, 39	1
	11, 13, 16, 33	2
	36, 37	2
4	27–31	1
	35	2
6	34	1
	17, 40	2

AVAILABLE **ONLINE**

PRACTICE & PROBLEM SOLVING

Scan for Multimedia

Practice Tutorial

Additional Exercises Available Online

UNDERSTAND

11. Make Sense and Persevere The area of a rectangle is given. Identify the missing terms in the length and width. MP.1

$(x + \_\_)$

$x^2 + 11x + 28$ $(\_\_ + 4)$

12. Use Structure The table shows the product when multiplying two binomials. What is the relationship between the numbers in the factors and the terms in the product? MP.7

Binomials	Products
$(x + 3)(x + 4)$	$x^2 + 7x + 12$
$(x + 2)(x - 5)$	$x^2 - 3x - 10$
$(x - 3)(x - 5)$	$x^2 - 8x + 15$

13. Error Analysis Describe and correct the error a student made when multiplying two binomials. MP.3

$(2x + 2)(4x - 1)$
$8x^2 - 2$
X

14. Use Appropriate Tools Use a table to find the product of $(3x + 4)(x^2 + 3x - 2)$. How are the like terms in a table arranged? MP.5

15. Higher Order Thinking Is it possible for the product of a monomial and trinomial to be a binomial? Explain.

16. Mathematical Connections A triangle has a height of $2x + 6$ and a base length of $x + 4$. What is the area of the triangle? $x^2 + 7x + 12$

17. Communicate Precisely Explain how to find the combined volume of the two rectangular prisms described. One has side lengths of $3x$, $2x + 1$, and $x + 3$. The other has side lengths of $5x - 2$, $x + 9$, and 8. MP.6

PRACTICE

Find each product. SEE EXAMPLE 1

18. $6x(x^2 - 4x - 3)$ $6x^3 - 24x^2 - 18x$

19. $-y(-3y^2 + 2y - 7)$ $3y^3 - 2y^2 + 7y$

20. $3x^2(-x^2 + 2x - 4)$ $-3x^4 + 6x^3 - 12x^2$

21. $-5x^3(2x^3 - 4x^2 + 2)$ $-10x^6 + 20x^5 - 10x^3$

Use a table to find each product. SEE EXAMPLE 2

22. $(x - 6)(3x + 4)$

23. $(2x + 1)(4x + 1)$

Use the Distributive Property to find each product. SEE EXAMPLE 3

24. $(x - 6)(x + 3)$ $x^2 - 3x - 18$

25. $(3x - 4)(2x + 5)$ $6x^2 + 7x - 20$

26. $(x - 8)(2x + 3)$ $2x^2 - 13x - 24$

Find each product. SEE EXAMPLE 4

27. $(y + 3)(2y^2 - 3y + 4)$ $2y^3 + 3y^2 - 5y + 12$

28. $(2x - 7)(3x^2 - 4x + 1)$ $6x^3 - 29x^2 + 30x - 7$

29. $(2x^2 - 3x)(-3x^2 + 4x - 2)$ $-6x^4 + 17x^3 - 16x^2 + 6x$

30. $(-2x^2 + 1)(2x^2 - 3x - 7)$ $-4x^4 + 6x^3 + 16x^2 - 3x - 7$

31. $(x^2 + 3x)(3x^2 - 2x + 4)$ $3x^4 + 7x^3 - 2x^2 + 12x$

32. Find the area of the shaded region. SEE EXAMPLE 6

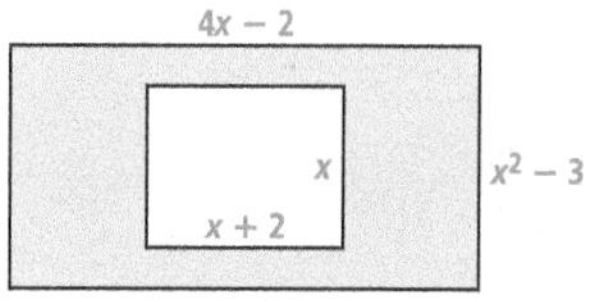
4x − 2
x
x + 2
x² − 3

33. A rectangular park is $6x + 2$ ft long and $3x + 7$ ft wide. In the middle of the park is a square turtle pond that is 8 ft wide. What expression represents the area of the park not occupied by the turtle pond? SEE EXAMPLE 6 $18x^2 + 48x - 50$

LESSON 7-2 Multiplying Polynomials 273

Answers

11–13. See previous page.

14.

	x^2	$+3x$	-2
$3x$	$3x^3$	$9x^2$	$-6x$
$+4$	$4x^2$	$12x$	-8

The product is $3x^3 + 13x^2 + 6x - 8$.

The like terms are on the diagonals of the table from bottom left to top right.

15. No; The product of a monomial and trinomial can never be a binomial. The product will be a trinomial.

17. Answers may vary. Sample: Find the volume of each rectangular prism by first multiplying the binomials. Then multiply the resulting trinomials by the monomial side. Finally, combine like terms to find the combined volume of the two prisms.

22.

	x	-6
$3x$	$3x^2$	$-18x$
$+4$	$4x$	-24

The product is $3x^2 - 14x - 24$.

23.

	$4x$	$+1$
$2x$	$8x^2$	$2x$
$+1$	$4x$	$+1$

The product is $8x^2 + 6x + 1$.

32. $(4x^3 - 2x^2 - 12x + 6) - (x^2 + 2x) = 4x^3 - 3x^2 - 14x + 6$

Answers

34. $27x^3 + 54x^2 + 36x + 8$

35. Answers may vary. Sample: Change $x^2 + 2x - 4$ to $x^2 + 4x - 4$. The new product is: $(2x + 2)(x^2 + 4x - 4) = 2x^3 + 8x^2 - 8x + 2x^2 + 8x - 8 = 2x^3 + 10x^2 - 8$.

36. $4x^2 + 24x + 32$

37. $10x^2 + 16x - 24$

40. **Part A** $10x^2 + 38x + 30$

Part B 6 cm

AVAILABLE **ONLINE**

PRACTICE & PROBLEM SOLVING

Practice Tutorial

Mixed Review Available Online

APPLY

34. **Model With Mathematics** The volume of a cube is calculated by multiplying the length, width, and height. What is the volume of this cube? **MP.4**

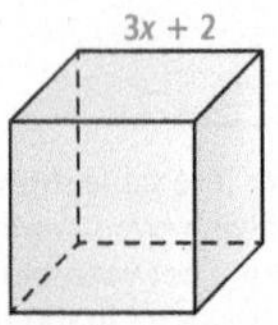

3x + 2

35. **Reason** The product of the binomial and the trinomial shown is a polynomial with four terms. Change one of the terms of the binomial or the trinomial so the product is also a trinomial. **MP.2**

$(2x + 2)(x^2 + 2x - 4) = 2x^3 + 7x^2 - 2x - 12$

36. **Make Sense and Persevere** What is the area of the painting shown? **MP.1**

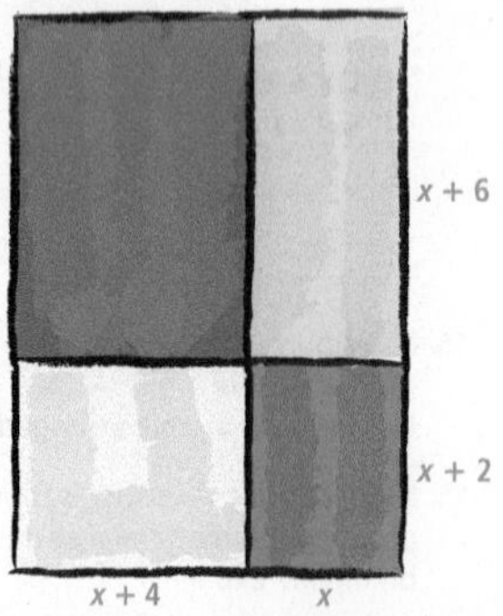

x + 6
x + 2
x + 4
x

37. **Make Sense and Persevere** A dance teacher wants to expand her studio to fit more classes. What is the combined area of Studio A and Studio B? **MP.1**

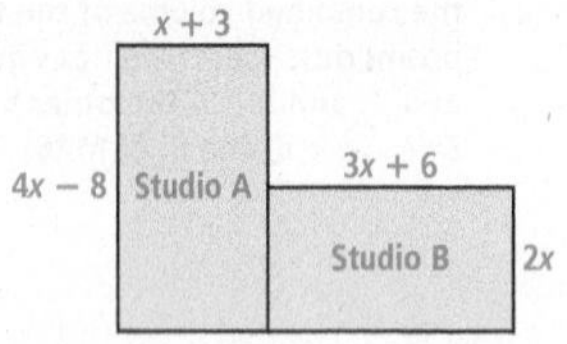

x + 3
4x − 8
Studio A
3x + 6
Studio B
2x

ASSESSMENT PRACTICE

38. Write the expression as a sum of monomials.

$(x + 4)(2x + 1) - [(x - 5)(x + 3)] + 3x^2$

$4x^2 + 11x + 19$

39. **SAT/ACT** What is the product of $-2x + 2$ and $x - 5$?

Ⓐ $-2x^2 - 10$

Ⓑ $-2x^2 + 12x - 10$

Ⓒ $-x - 3$

Ⓓ $-2x^2 - 12x - 10$

40. **Performance Task** The net of a rectangular box and its dimensions are shown.

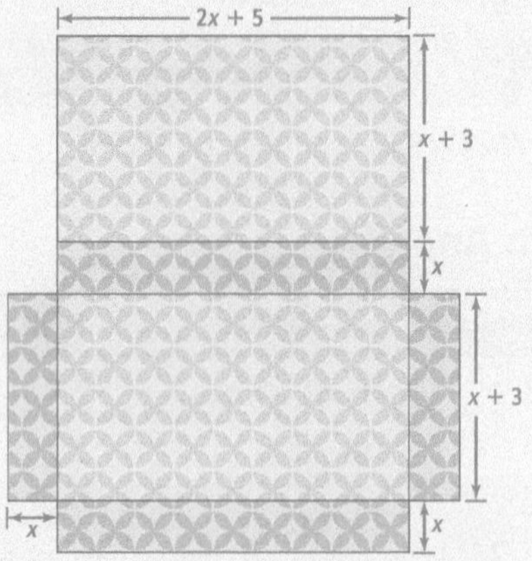

2x + 5
x + 3
x
x + 3
x
x

Part A Write an expression for the surface area of the box in terms of x.

Part B Evaluate the polynomial expression you found in Part A. What integer value of x would give the prism a surface area of about 600 cm²?

SavvasRealize.com

Assess | Tutorials | Worksheets

LESSON QUIZ

Use the Lesson Quiz to assess students' understanding of the mathematics in the lesson.

Students can take the Lesson Quiz online or you can download a printable copy from **SavvasRealize.com**. The Lesson Quiz is also available in the *Assessment Resources* book.

Item Analysis

Item	DOK	Standards
1	1	HSA.APR.A.1
2	2	HSA.APR.A.1
3	1	HSA.APR.A.1
4	2	HSA.APR.A.1
5	2	HSA.APR.A.1

RtI Use the student scores on the Lesson Quiz to prescribe differentiated assignments.

If students take the Lesson Quiz online, it will be automatically scored and appropriate differentiated practice will be assigned based on student performance.

I Intervention	0–3 points	• Reteach to Build Understanding • Mathematical Literacy and Vocabulary • Additional Practice
O On-Level	4 points	• Mathematical Literacy and Vocabulary • Additional Practice • Enrichment
A Advanced	5 points	• Enrichment

AVAILABLE **ONLINE**

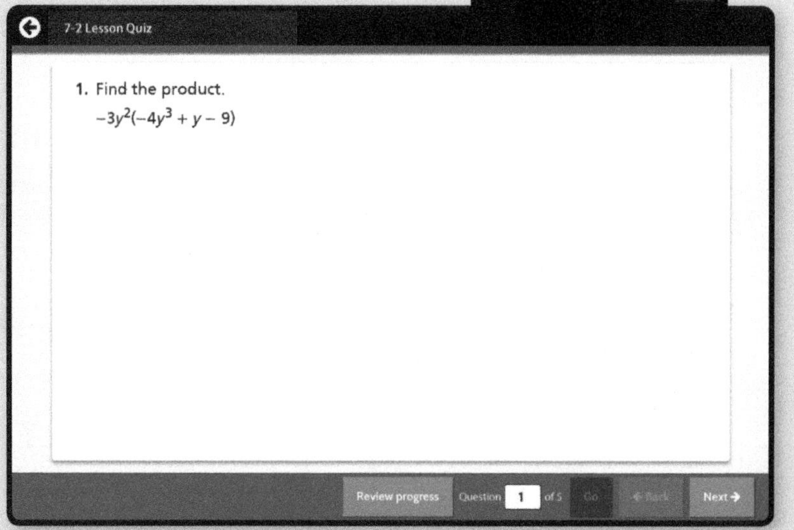
7-2 Lesson Quiz
1. Find the product.
$-3y^2(-4y^3 + y - 9)$
Review progress
Question 1 of 5
Go
Back
Next

ASSESSMENT RESOURCES

Name ____________

enVision Algebra 1

PearsonRealize.com

7-2 Lesson Quiz

Multiplying Polynomials

1. Find the product.
   $-3y^2(-4y^3 + y - 9)$
   $12y^5 - 3y^3 + 27y^2$

2. Which of the following is the product of $(7x + 2)$ and $(5x - 11)$?
   Ⓐ $12x^2 - 10x - 77x - 22$
   Ⓑ $35x^2 - 67x - 22$
   Ⓒ $12x^2 - 67x - 22$
   Ⓓ $35x^2 + 67x + 22$

3. Complete the table to multiply $x^2 - 4x + 4$ and $6x + 3$.

	x^2	$-4x$	4
$6x$	$6x^3$	$-24x^2$	$24x$
3	$3x^2$	$-12x$	12

   $= 6x^3 - 21x^2 + 12x + 12$

4. Find the product.
   $(3x^2 + 7)(6x^2 - 4x + 5)$
   $18x^4 - 12x^3 + 57x^2 - 28x + 35$

5. A portrait without its frame has a height 1.5 times its width w, in inches. The width of the frame is 3 inches. Which of the following is an expression for the area of the framed portrait in terms of w?
   Ⓐ $5w + 24$
   Ⓑ $1.5w^2$
   Ⓒ $1.5w^2 + 7.5w + 9$
   Ⓓ $1.5w^2 + 15w + 36$

enVision™ **Algebra 1** • Assessment Resources

DIFFERENTIATED RESOURCES

I = Intervention   O = On-Level   A = Advanced

= This activity is available as a digital assignment powered by MathXL® for School.

AVAILABLE ONLINE

Reteach to Build Understanding I

Provides scaffolded reteaching for the key lesson concepts.

Name ______ enVision Algebra 1

7-2 Reteach to Build Understanding
Multiplying Polynomials

1. Complete each product table using monomials. Then write the product for each table as a polynomial in standard form.

$(x+4)(x-5)$ | $(x+4)(x^2+3x-1)$

The product is $x^2 - x - 20$. The product is $x^3 + 7x^2 + 11x - 4$.

2. Xavier said the product of a monomial and a binomial will always be a trinomial. Explain the error in his reasoning.
Sample answer: The product of a monomial and a binomial will be a binomial because you are not increasing the number of terms in the polynomial, just multiplying the monomial by the two terms in the binomial.

3. Complete the steps to find the product $(5x+2)(x-3)$ by writing expressions or numbers in the blanks.

$(5x+2)(x-3) = 5x(x-3) + 2(x-3)$ Distribute $5x$ and 2 to the second binomial.
$= 5x(x) + 5x(-3) + 2(x) + 2(-3)$ Distribute $5x$ and 2 to each term in the second binomial.
$= 5x^2 - 15x + 2x - 6$ Multiply.
$= 5x^2 - 13x - 6$ Combine like terms.
The product is $5x^2 - 13x - 6$.

enVision™ Algebra 1 • Teaching Resources

Additional Practice I O

Provides extra practice for each lesson.

Name ______ enVision Algebra 1

7-2 Additional Practice
Multiplying Polynomials

Find each product.
1. $2y^2(y^2 - 6y + 5)$ $2y^4 - 12y^3 + 10y^2$
2. $-x(2x^3 - x^2 + 6x - 8)$ $-2x^4 + x^3 - 6x^2 + 8x$
3. $-3x(x^2 - 7x - 6)$ $-3x^3 + 21x^2 + 18x$

Use a table to find each product.
4. $(2x-4)(3x+5)$ $6x^2 - 2x - 20$
5. $(x-3)(3x-6)$ $3x^2 - 15x + 18$
6. $(x+3)(5x-4)$ $5x^2 + 11x - 12$

Find each product.
7. $(x-7)(x-2)$ $x^2 - 9x + 14$
8. $(2x+3)(3x-2)$ $6x^2 + 5x - 6$
9. $(x-6)(3x-4y)$ $3x^2 - 4xy - 18x + 24y$
10. $(x-4)(x^2+7x-8)$ $x^3 + 3x^2 - 36x + 32$
11. $(3x-4)(2x^2+5x+4)$ $6x^3 + 7x^2 - 8x - 16$
12. $(-2x^2+5)(x^3-8x-6)$ $-2x^5 + 21x^3 + 12x^2 - 40x - 30$

13. When multiplying two polynomials of degrees m and n, will the product always be a polynomial? If so, explain, and state the degree.
Sample answer: Yes, since polynomials always have whole-number exponents, when multiplying the terms with like bases, the exponents will be added together, resulting in different whole-number exponents. The degree will be $m + n$.

14. A circular flower garden surrounds a sculpture on a square base as shown. What is an expression for the area of the flower garden?
$36\pi x^2 - 16x^2$

enVision™ Algebra 1 • Teaching Resources

Enrichment O A

Presents engaging problems and activities that extend the lesson concepts.

Name ______ enVision Algebra 1

7-2 Enrichment
Multiplying Polynomials

An architect is preparing to design an office building. She creates a sketch of the basic shape of the structure and the relative dimensions of each piece shown. The angles in the sketch are all right angles.

Find the volume of the structure using each approach. Draw lines on the sketches and record your expressions.

1. Divide the structure into two different rectangular prisms. Add the volumes of the two prisms to create an expression for the total volume.
Prism 1 volume: $(x-8)(x+4)(x-5) = x^3 - 9x^2 - 12x + 160$
Prism 2 volume: $x(x-5)(3x-2) = 3x^3 - 17x^2 + 10x$
Total volume: $4x^3 - 26x^2 - 2x + 160$

2. Divide the structure into three prisms. Write expressions for the three volumes and add them to represent the total volume.
Prism 1 volume: $x(x-3)(x-5) = x^3 - 8x^2 + 15x$
Prism 2 volume: $(x+4)(2x-8)(x-5) = 2x^3 - 10x^2 - 32x + 160$
Prism 3 volume: $x(x-3)(x-5) = x^3 - 8x^2 + 15x$
Total volume: $4x^3 - 26x^2 - 2x + 160$

3. View the structure as one prism with two equal-sized prisms. Find the volume of the large prism and subtract the volumes of the smaller pieces to find the expression for total volume.
Big prism volume: $(2x-8)(x-5)(3x-2) = 6x^3 - 58x^2 + 156x - 80$
Each cutout volume: $(x-3)(x-8)(x-5) = x^3 - 16x^2 - 79x - 120$
Total volume: $4x^3 - 26x^2 - 2x + 160$

enVision™ Algebra 1 • Teaching Resources

Mathematical Literacy and Vocabulary I O

Helps students develop and reinforce understanding of key terms and concepts.

Name ______ enVision Algebra 1

7-2 Mathematical Literacy and Vocabulary
Multiplying Polynomials

Problem
Use the Distributive Property to find $(3x+2)(4x-3)$.

$(3x+2)(4x-3)$	Write the problem.
$3x(4x-3) + 2(4x-3)$	Distribute $3x$ and 2 to the second binomial.
$3x(4x) + 3x(-3) + 2(4x) + 2(-3)$	Distribute $3x$ and 2 to each term.
$12x^2 - 9x + 8x - 6$	Multiply.
$12x^2 - x - 6$	Combine like terms.

Exercises
Use the Distributive Property to find $(5x+6)(2x-4)$.

$(5x+6)(2x-4)$	Write the problem.
$5x(2x-4) + 6(2x-4)$	Distribute $5x$ and 6 to the second binomial.
$5x(2x) + 5x(-4) + 6(2x) + 6(-4)$	Distribute $5x$ and 6 to each term.
$10x^2 - 20x + 12x - 24$	Multiply.
$10x^2 - 8x - 24$	Combine like terms.

Use the Distributive Property to find $(7x-3)(4x+6)$.

$(7x-3)(4x+6)$	Write the problem.
$7x(4x+6) - 3(4x+6)$	Distribute $7x$ and -3 to the second binomial.
$7x(4x) + 7x(6) - 3(4x) - 3(6)$	Distribute $7x$ and -3 to each term.
$28x^2 + 42x - 12x - 18$	Multiply.
$28x^2 + 30x - 18$	Combine like terms.

enVision™ Algebra 1 • Teaching Resources

Digital Resources and Video Tutorials I O A

The **Reteach to Build Understanding, Additional Practice,** and **Enrichment** activities are available as digital assignments powered by MathXL for School. These activities are automatically assigned when students complete the lesson quiz online and are automatically scored.

Students can access instructional tutorials using the **Virtual Nerd app.**

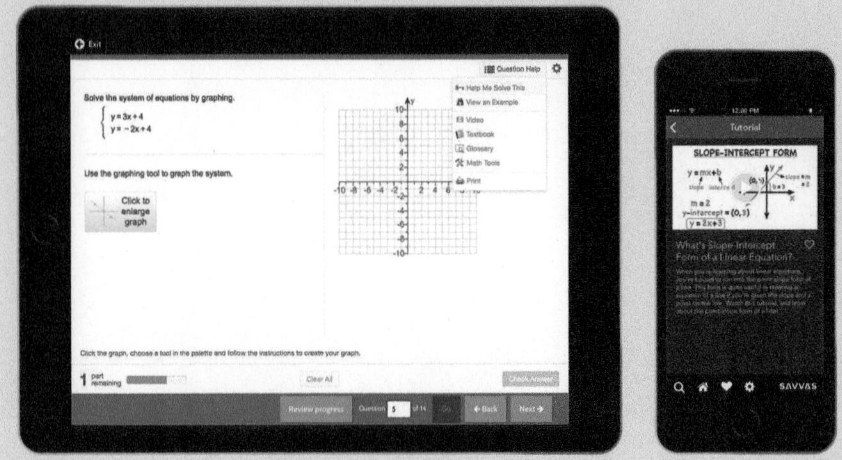

Solve the system of equations by graphing.
Use the graphing tool to graph the system.
Click to enlarge graph
Question Help
Tutorial
SLOPE-INTERCEPT FORM
What's Slope-Intercept Form of a Linear Equation?
SAVVAS

Students can also access Virtual Nerd videos using the **BouncePages app** to scan exercise pages marked with this icon. Students can download both apps for free in their mobile devices' app store.

A-Z Glossary

LESSON 7-3

Multiplying Special Cases

Lesson Overview

FOCUS

Objective

Students will be able to:

✔ Determine the square of a binomial.

✔ Find the product of a sum and difference of two squares.

✔ Solve real-world problems involving the square of a binomial.

Essential Understanding

The product of the square of a binomial in the form $(a + b)^2$ is always the square of the first term, plus twice the product of the first and last terms, plus the square of the last term. The product of a sum and a difference of two binomials in the form $(a + b)(a - b)$ is always the difference of the two squares.

COHERENCE

Previously in this course, students:

- Solved problems, including those that involve real-world situations, by adding, subtracting, and multiplying polynomials.

In this lesson, students:

- Identify patterns in the square of a binomial and in the product of a sum and a difference of two squares and use them to simplify expressions and solve real-world problems.

Later in this topic, students will:

- Solve real-world problems by factoring polynomials, including perfect square trinomials and the difference of two squares.

RIGOR

This lesson emphasizes a blend of *conceptual understanding* and *application*.

- Students understand that there are patterns in the product of perfect square binomials and in the product of a sum and difference of two squares that can be used to simplify expressions.
- Students apply the process of squaring a binomial to solve real-world problems, such as finding the area of an image within a border.

Vocabulary Builder

REVIEW VOCABULARY — **English** | *Spanish*

- **binomial** | *binomio*
- **polynomial** | *polinomio*
- **square of a binomial** | *cuadrado de un binomio*

NEW VOCABULARY

- **difference of two squares** | *diferencia de dos cuadrados*

VOCABULARY ACTIVITY

Review the terms *polynomial* and *binomial* by having students identify which of the following polynomials are binomials.

$4x^2 + 3x + 9$ ($3x + 9$)   18   ($x + 3$) $x^3 + 2x^2 + x + 2$

Explain that the square of a binomial is in the form $(a + b)^2$ and the difference of two squares is in the form $(a + b)(a - b)$. Have students use the binomials they identified above to write a square of a binomial and a difference of two squares.

square of a binomial: $[(3x + 9)^2; (x + 3)^2]$

difference of two squares: $[(3x + 9)(3x - 9); (x + 3)(x - 3)]$

Student Companion

Students can do their in-class work for the lesson on pages 145–148 of their *Student Companion* or in Savvas Realize.

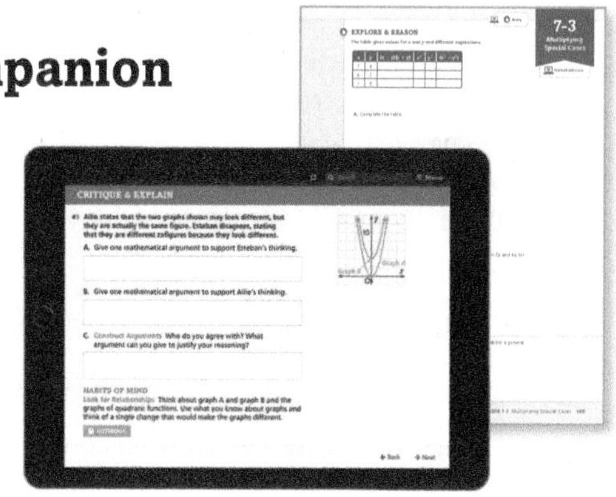

Mathematics Overview — COMMON CORE STANDARDS

Content Standards

In this lesson, students focus on this standard:

HSA.APR.A.1 Understand that polynomials form a system analogous to the integers, namely, they are closed under the operations of addition, subtraction, and multiplication; add, subtract, and multiply polynomials.

Mathematical Practice Standards

These standards are highlighted in this lesson:

MP.7 Look For and Make Use of Structure

Students recognize the patterns in the product of the square of a binomial and the product of two binomials that results in the difference of two squares.

MP.8 Look For and Express Regularity in Repeated Reasoning

Students generalize by using the terms in the binomial factors when squaring a binomial or finding the product of a sum and difference to quickly determine the products.

Activity

EXPLORE & REASON

INSTRUCTIONAL FOCUS Students use patterns to identify equivalent expressions containing variables. This prepares students to recognize and use patterns when multiplying special cases of binomials such as the square of a binomial and the product of a sum and difference.

STUDENT COMPANION Students can complete the *Explore & Reason* activity on page 145 of their *Student Companion.*

Before WHOLE CLASS

Implement Tasks that Promote Reasoning and Problem Solving ETP

Q: What do you notice about the table?
[Multiple expressions are to be evaluated for the same values of x and y.]

During SMALL GROUP

Support Productive Struggle in Learning Mathematics ETP

Q: How is the table helpful?
[When the various expressions have been evaluated for the same values of x and y, the table shows that $(x - y)(x + y)$ is equivalent to $(x^2 - y^2)$.]

For Early Finishers

Q: Use the pattern demonstrated in the table to explain how to mentally calculate $26^2 - 24^2$ without squaring the two-digit numbers. Then, create two more problems that can be simplified the same way.
[Rewrite $26^2 - 24^2$ as $(26 - 24)(26 + 24)$, which simplifies to 2(50), or 100. Check students' work.]

After WHOLE CLASS

Facilitate Meaningful Mathematical Discourse ETP

Ask students to add two additional columns to their tables, one for $(x + y)^2$ and one for $x^2 + 2xy + y^2$ and have them evaluate those expressions for the same values of x and y.

Q: $(x + y)^2$ is called the square of a binomial. How can you use the pattern shown in the table to describe an expression equivalent to the square of a binomial?
[The square of a binomial is the first term squared, plus two times the product of the first and last terms, plus the last term squared.]

HABITS OF MIND *Use with* **EXPLORE & REASON**

Generalize Did your exploration provide enough information to establish a general rule? Explain. **MP.8**

[Yes; it appears that for any x and y, $(x + y)(x - y) = x^2 - y^2$.]

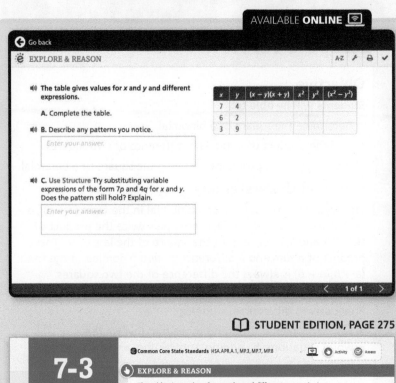

AVAILABLE **ONLINE**

Go back

EXPLORE & REASON

The table gives values for x and y and different expressions.

A. Complete the table.

B. Describe any patterns you notice.

Enter your answer.

C. Use Structure Try substituting variable expressions of the form $7p$ and $4q$ for x and y. Does the pattern still hold? Explain.

Enter your answer.

x	y	$(x - y)(x + y)$	x^2	y^2	$(x^2 - y^2)$
7	4				
6	2				
3	9				

1 of 1

STUDENT EDITION, PAGE 275

7-3 Multiplying Special Cases

PearsonRealize.com

I CAN… use patterns to multiply binomials.

VOCABULARY
- difference of two squares

Common Core State Standards HSA.APR.A.1, MP.3, MP.7, MP.8

Activity Assess

EXPLORE & REASON

The table gives values for x and y and different expressions.

x	y	$(x - y)(x + y)$	x^2	y^2	$(x^2 - y^2)$
7	4				
6	2				
3	9				

A. Copy and complete the table.

B. Describe any patterns you notice.

C. Use Structure Try substituting variable expressions of the form $7p$ and $4q$ for x and y. Does the pattern still hold? Explain. MP.7

SAMPLE STUDENT WORK

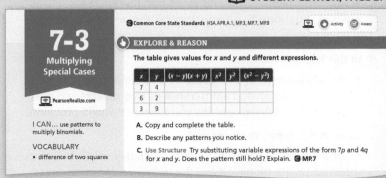

Explore and Reason

A.

x	y	$(x - y)(x + y)$	x^2	y^2	$(x^2 - y^2)$
7	4	33	49	16	33
6	2	32	36	4	32
3	9	-72	9	81	-72

B. The answers for $(x - y)(x + y)$ and $(x^2 - y^2)$ are equal.

C. The pattern will be the same.

Activity | Assess

INTRODUCE THE ESSENTIAL QUESTION

Establish Mathematics Goals to Focus Learning ETP

Introduce students to the square of a binomial. Remind them how to use the Distributive Property and what it means to square a number. Explain that you can use the Distributive Property to find a pattern to calculate the product of the square of a binomial and the product of a sum and a difference.

EXAMPLE 1 Determine the Square of a Binomial

Build Procedural Fluency From Conceptual Understanding ETP

Q: In Part A, explain how the model represents an expression equivalent to $(a + b)^2$. [Answers may vary. Sample: The model shows that each side of the large square is $a + b$. Then, the large square is broken into 4 sections with areas a^2, ab, ab, and b^2. So, the sum of these areas, $a^2 + 2ab + b^2$, is equivalent to $(a + b)^2$.]

Q: In Part B, why do you substitute –3 for b when simplifying $(5x – 3)^2$? [The pattern shows the square of a sum, so rewrite $(5x – 3)^2$ as the sum $[5x + (–3)]^2$ to see that $b = –3$.]

Q: In Part C, can you use another sum or difference to easily find the product of 29^2? [Yes; Answers may vary. Sample: Use two values whose squares you know such as (25 + 4) or (40 – 11) for 29.]

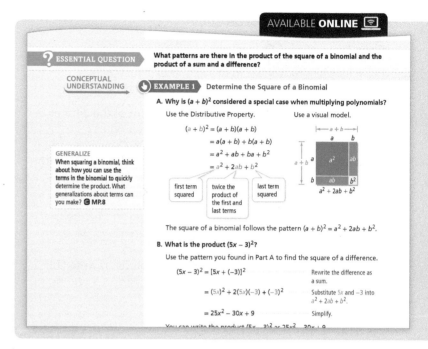

AVAILABLE ONLINE

ESSENTIAL QUESTION What patterns are there in the product of the square of a binomial and the product of a sum and a difference?

CONCEPTUAL UNDERSTANDING

EXAMPLE 1 Determine the Square of a Binomial

A. Why is $(a + b)^2$ considered a special case when multiplying polynomials?

Use the Distributive Property.

$(a + b)^2 = (a + b)(a + b)$

$= a(a + b) + b(a + b)$

$= a^2 + ab + ba + b^2$

$= a^2 + 2ab + b^2$

first term squared | twice the product of the first and last terms | last term squared

Use a visual model.

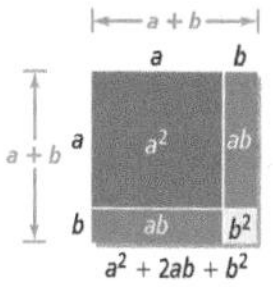

a + b
a
b
a + b
a
a^2
ab
b
ab
b^2
$a^2 + 2ab + b^2$

GENERALIZE
When squaring a binomial, think about how you can use the terms in the binomial to quickly determine the product. What generalizations about terms can you make? MP.8

The square of a binomial follows the pattern $(a + b)^2 = a^2 + 2ab + b^2$.

B. What is the product $(5x – 3)^2$?

Use the pattern you found in Part A to find the square of a difference.

$(5x – 3)^2 = [5x + (–3)]^2$ — Rewrite the difference as a sum.

$= (5x)^2 + 2(5x)(–3) + (–3)^2$ — Substitute $5x$ and –3 into $a^2 + 2ab + b^2$.

$= 25x^2 – 30x + 9$ — Simplify.

You can write the product $(5x – 3)^2$ as $25x^2 – 30x + 9$

Try It! Answers

1. a. $9x^2 – 24x + 16$
   b. 5,041

ADDITIONAL EXAMPLES

AVAILABLE ONLINE

Go back

ADDITIONAL EXAMPLE 1C — ESSENTIAL QUESTION | ES | A-Z

Use the square of a binomial to find the $(–18)^2$ mentally.

$(–18)^2 = (–20 + 2)^2 = (–20)^2 + 2(–20)(2) + (2)^2 = 400 – 80 + 4 = 324$

1 of 2

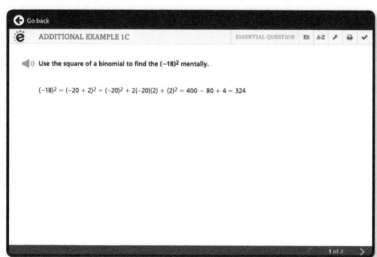

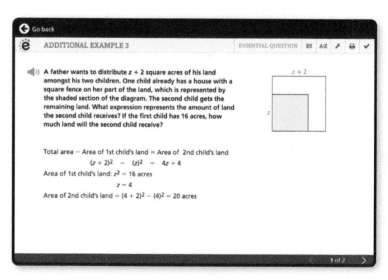

Example 1 Students explore using the square of a binomial to find the square of a negative number.

Q: How does the process of finding the product of $(–18)^2$ and the solution compare to finding the product and solution of $(18)^2$? [$(–18)^2 = (–20 + 2)^2$ and $(18)^2 = (20 – 2)^2$. Although the values substituted for –18 and 18 are different, the process of finding the products and the solutions are the same.]

Go back

ADDITIONAL EXAMPLE 3 — ESSENTIAL QUESTION | ES | A-Z

A father wants to distribute $z + 2$ square acres of his land amongst his two children. One child already has a house with a square fence on her part of the land, which is represented by the shaded section of the diagram. The second child gets the remaining land. What expression represents the amount of land the second child receives? If the first child has 16 acres, how much land will the second child receive?

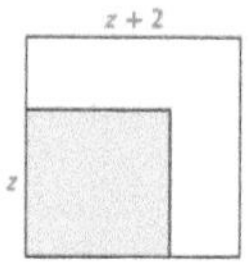

z + 2
z

Total area – Area of 1st child's land = Area of 2nd child's land

$(z + 2)^2 - (z)^2 = 4z + 4$

Area of 1st child's land: $z^2 = 16$ acres

$z = 4$

Area of 2nd child's land $= (4 + 2)^2 – (4)^2 = 20$ acres

1 of 2

Example 3 Students solve real-world problems by finding the square of binomials and determining their area.

Q: If you are told the total number of acres (total area) the father has but do not know how much land either child has, how can you find the acreage of land for each child?
[Total area = $(z + 2)^2$, so solve for z. Substitute the solution for z into the equations for the area of each child's land.]

EXAMPLE 2 Find the Product of a Sum and a Difference

Pose Purposeful Questions ETP

Q: In Part A, why is the sum of $-ab$ and ba equal to 0?
[They are opposite terms, so $-ab + ba = -(ab) + ab = 0$.]

Q: In Part B, how does recognizing the pattern of the difference of two squares make it easier to write the product?
[Recognizing the pattern results in less work. Otherwise, you would have to multiply each term of the first binomial by each term of the second binomial, only to discover that the two middle terms drop out because they are opposites.]

Q: In Part C, how can you use the same strategy to rewrite the product of 16 and 24 as the sum and difference of the same two numbers?
[16 and 24 are each 4 units from 20, so you can rewrite (16)(24) as $(20 - 4)(20 + 4)$.]

Try It! Answers

2. a. $4x^2 - 16$

b. 2,464

Common Error

Try It! 2a Some students may forget to square the 2 in $(2x)^2$ and state that the product is $2x^2 - 16$. Encourage students to evaluate both the original expression and their answer for the same value of x to determine whether the expressions are actually equivalent.

HABITS OF MIND

Use with **EXAMPLES 1 & 2**

Use Appropriate Tools How do area models and algebraic expressions help you understand the patterns for the square of a binomial and for the product of a sum and a difference? **MP.5**

[Area models and algebraic expressions help you see the general patterns for squares of binomials and for products of a sum and difference.]

AVAILABLE **ONLINE**

Activity Assess

EXAMPLE 1 CONTINUED

C. How can you use the square of a binomial to find the product 29^2?

Rewrite the product as a difference of two values whose squares you know, such as $(30 - 1)^2$. Then use the pattern for the square of a binomial to find its square.

$$(30 - 1)^2 = (30)^2 + 2(30)(-1) + (-1)^2$$
$$= 900 - 60 + 1$$
$$= 841$$

(30 − 1) is the same as 29. So, $(30 - 1)^2$ is the same as 29^2.

So, $29^2 = 841$. In general, you can use the square of a binomial to find the square of a large number by rewriting the number as the sum or difference of two numbers with known squares.

Try It! 1. Find each product.

a. $(3x - 4)^2$

b. 71^2

EXAMPLE 2 Find the Product of a Sum and a Difference

A. What is the product $(a + b)(a - b)$?

Use the Distributive Property to find the product.

$$(a + b)(a - b) = a(a - b) + b(a - b)$$
$$= a^2 - ab + ba - b^2$$
$$= a^2 - b^2$$

The middle terms drop out because they are opposites.

first term squared

last term squared

The product of two binomials in the form $(a + b)(a - b)$ is $a^2 - b^2$. The product of the sum and difference of the same two values results in the **difference of two squares**.

B. What is the product $(5x + 7)(5x - 7)$?

Use the pattern you found in Part A.

$$(5x + 7)(5x - 7) = (5x)^2 - (7)^2$$ Substitute $5x$ and 7 into $a^2 - b^2$.

$$= 25x^2 - 49$$ Simplify.

The product of $(5x + 7)(5x - 7)$ is $25x^2 - 49$. It is the difference of two squares, $(5x)^2 - 7^2$.

COMMON ERROR
Remember that the last terms of each binomial are opposites. So, the product of the last terms will always be negative.

CONTINUED ON THE NEXT PAGE

ADV Advanced Students

USE WITH EXAMPLE 1 Students extend using the square of a binomial to find the square of a large number to now find the square of a positive number times −1.

Q: Explain how to use the square of a binomial to find the product of -16^2.
$[-16^2 = -(20 - 4)^2 = -[(20)^2 + 2(20)(-4) + (-4)^2] = -1(256) = -256]$

Q: Explain how to use the square of a binomial to find the product of $(-16)^2$.
$[(-16)^2 = (-20 + 4)^2 = (-20)^2 + 2(-20)(4) + (4)^2) = 256]$

Q: Why are the two products different?
[For -16^2 the 16 is squared first and then multiplied by −1. For $(-16)^2$, the −16 is squared, resulting in a positive value.]

RtI Struggling Students

USE WITH EXAMPLE 2 When finding the product of a sum and a difference, some students may struggle with understanding that the mixed terms drop out because they are opposites. Have students practice finding opposite terms.

Q: Write the product of $(2x + 3)(2x - 3)$ using the Distributive Property. Show your work.
$[2x(2x - 3) + 3(2x - 3) = (2x)^2 - 2x(3) + (3)2x - (3)^2 = (2x)^2 - (3)^2 = 4x^2 - 9]$

Q: What are the mixed terms in the product?
$[-2x(3)$ and $(3)2x]$

Q: What happens to the mixed terms?
[They drop out because they are opposites.]

EXAMPLE 3 Apply the Square of a Binomial

Pose Purposeful Questions ETP

Q: What does x represent in this scenario?
[The variable x represents the length and width of the image.]

Q: How can you represent the area of the image?
[The area of the image is x^2 because each side of the image is x.]

Q: Explain how can you represent the total area.
[The side of the image is x and the border adds two pixels on all sides of the image. Two pixels added to the top and two pixels added to the bottom makes the total length $x + 4$. Two pixels added to the left and two pixels added to the right makes the total width $x + 4$. Then, the total area is $(x + 4)^2$.]

Try It! Answers

3. 1600 square pixels

Elicit and Use Evidence of Student Thinking ETP

Q: What equation represents the area of the square image?
[$(x + 8)^2 - x^2 = 704$; $(x + 8)^2$ is the area of the image and the border; x^2 is the area of the image; 704 is the area of the border.]

HABITS OF MIND

Use with **EXAMPLE 3**

Communicate Precisely What mathematical terms apply in this situation? MP.6

[Answers may vary. Sample: Square of a binomial]

AVAILABLE ONLINE

Activity Assess

EXAMPLE 2 CONTINUED

C. How can you use the difference of two squares to find the product of 43 and 37?

Rewrite the product as the sum and difference of the same two numbers *a* and *b*.

43 and 37 are each 3 units from 40.

$$(40 + 3)(40 - 3) = (40)^2 - (3)^2$$
$$= 1{,}600 - 9$$
$$= 1{,}591$$

$(40 + 3)(40 - 3)$ is of the form $(a + b)(a - b)$, so it is equivalent to the difference of two squares.

You can use the difference of two squares to mentally find the product of large numbers when the numbers are the same distance from a known square.

USE APPROPRIATE TOOLS
What types of practical limitations are there on using the product of a sum and difference to find the product of two numbers? MP.5

Try It! **2.** Find each product.

a. $(2x - 4)(2x + 4)$ **b.** $56 \cdot 44$

APPLICATION

EXAMPLE 3 Apply the Square of a Binomial

A graphic designer is developing images for icons. The square pixelated image is placed inside a border that is 2 pixels wide on all sides. If the area of the border of the image is 176 square pixels, what is the area of the image?

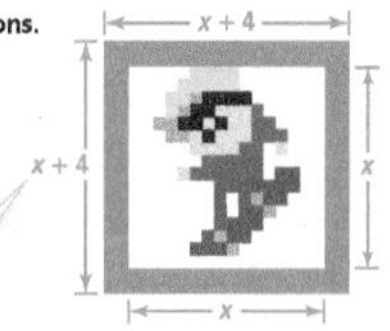
x + 4
x + 4
x
x

Let x represent the length and width of the image.

Formulate The area of the image and the border is represented by the expression $(x + 4)^2$.

Total area	−	Area of Image	=	Area of Border
$(x + 4)^2$	−	x^2	=	176

Compute

$$(x + 4)^2 - x^2 = 176$$
$$x^2 + 8x + 16 - x^2 = 176$$
$$8x + 16 = 176$$
$$8x = 160$$
$$x = 20$$

Find the product of the squared binomial first.

Interpret The image will be 20 pixels by 20 pixels. The area of the image is $20 \cdot 20$, or 400 square pixels.

Try It! **3.** What is the area of the square image if the area of the border is 704 square pixels and the border is 4 pixels wide?

LESSON 7-3 Multiplying Special Cases 277

ELL English Language Learners *(Use with* **EXAMPLE 3***)*

READING BEGINNING Together with students, read first the sentence of the example: *A graphic designer is developing images for icons.* Ask students to identify three words in the sentence that are related to each other (graphic, images, icon). Display the definitions of these words and help students read them. Then identify each word, have them reread its definition, and talk about its meaning.

Q: What type of work does a graphic designer do?
[A graphic designer uses computers to draw pictures and designs.]

Q: What are icons used for?
[as symbols that stand for a computer program, file, or app]

LISTENING INTERMEDIATE Have students listen as you explain what the words *pixel* and *pixelated* mean. Explain that adding –ated to some nouns can make them adjectives. For example, the noun caffeine becomes caffeinated as an adjective. Have students break into pairs and practice making and using adjectives with other words like: origin/originated; hyphen/hyphenated; alien/alienated; mature/maturated.

Q: What happens when a noun that you want to add "–ated" to has an "e" on the end?
[The "e" is omitted.]

Q: How are adjectives used in sentences?
[They are used to describe nouns.]

SPEAKING ADVANCED Have students take turns, line by line, describing the mathematical steps being taken in the Compute section of the example. Encourage them to use the appropriate terminology, including square binomial, product, and like terms.

Q: How is the equation in the first line determined?
[It is the total area of the image and the border minus the area of the image set equal to the known area of the border.]

Q: What does x represent in the equation?
[the side length of the icon]

Q: After the binomial is squared, what happens to the like terms?
[They add to zero.]

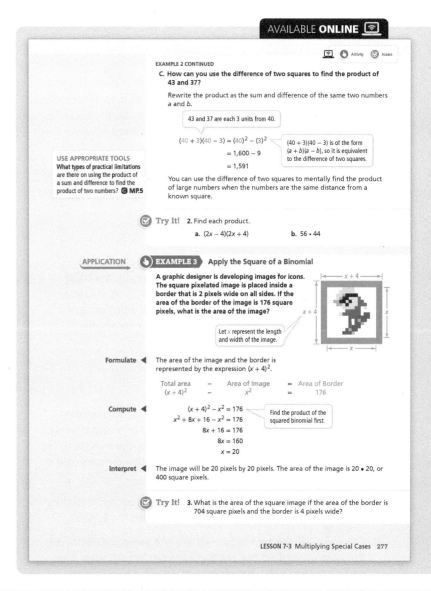

CONCEPT SUMMARY Multiplying Special Cases

Q: How do the patterns of the square of a binomial and the product of two binomials compare?
[Both patterns square the first and last terms. However, the square of a binomial has a middle term that is twice the product of the first and last terms, while in the product of two binomials, the middle terms are eliminated because they are opposites.]

Do You UNDERSTAND? | Do You KNOW HOW?

Common Error

Exercise 6 Some students may forget the product of $(2x + 5)^2$ contains a middle term of $20x$ and write their solution as $4x^2 + 25$. Have students check their solution by substituting an integer for x into their solution and into $(2x + 5)^2$ to determine whether the expressions are equivalent.

Answers

1. For the product of the square of a binomial, the middle term is always equal to twice the product of a and b, while for the product of a sum and a difference, the middle terms always cancel, leaving only two terms in the product of the expression, a^2 and b^2.
2. She did not multiply 3 and x and -3 and x correctly so they would become zero. The correct answer is $x^2 - 9$.
3. The terms of the two binomials are the same so that when they are multiplied the products are perfect squares. The middle terms with x becomes zero, leaving two perfect squares. The second term of the product is always negative. So, the final product is a difference of two perfect squares.
4. When the terms are distributed, the middle term becomes zero when the first term of each binomial is multiplied by the second term of each binomial. This eliminates one of the terms so instead of a trinomial, the product is a binomial.
5. $x^2 - 14x + 49$
6. $4x^2 + 20x + 25$
7. $x^2 - 16$
8. $9y^2 - 25$
9. 2,916 cm^2
10. 864 cm^2

AVAILABLE ONLINE

Concept Summary Assess

CONCEPT SUMMARY Multiplying Special Cases

	Square of a Binomial	Product of a Sum and Difference
WORDS	The square of a binomial, $(a + b)^2$, always follows the same pattern: the square of the first term, plus twice the product of the first and last term, plus the square of the last term.	The product of two binomials in the form $(a + b)(a - b)$ results in the difference of two squares.
ALGEBRA	$(a + b)^2 = a^2 + 2ab + b^2$ or $(a - b)^2 = a^2 - 2ab + b^2$	$(a + b)(a - b) = a^2 - b^2$ (difference of two squares)
NUMBERS	$(x + 4)^2 = (x + 4)(x + 4) = x^2 + 4x + 4x + 16 = x^2 + 8x + 16$	$(x - 7)(x + 7) = x^2 - 7x + 7x - 49 = x^2 - 49$

Do You UNDERSTAND?

1. ESSENTIAL QUESTION What patterns are there in the product of the square of a binomial and the product of a sum and a difference?
2. **Error Analysis** Kennedy multiplies $(x - 3)(x + 3)$ and gets an answer of $x^2 - 6x - 9$. Describe and correct Kennedy's error. MP.3
3. **Vocabulary** The product $(x + 6)(x - 6)$ is equivalent to an expression that is called the *difference of two squares*. Explain why the term *difference of two squares* is appropriate.
4. **Use Structure** Explain why the product of two binomials in the form $(a + b)(a - b)$ is a binomial instead of a trinomial. MP.7

Do You KNOW HOW?

Write each product in standard form.

5. $(x - 7)^2$
6. $(2x + 5)^2$
7. $(x + 4)(x - 4)$
8. $(3y - 5)(3y + 5)$

Use either the square of a binomial or the difference of two squares to find the area of each rectangle.

9. 

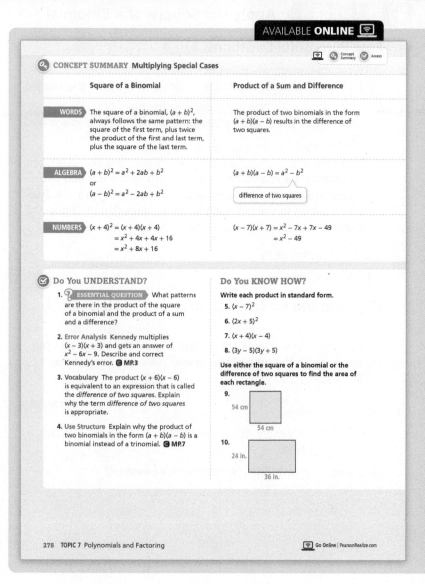

54 cm
54 cm

10. 

24 in.
36 in.

SavvasRealize.com

Practice | Tutorials | Math Tools

PRACTICE & PROBLEM SOLVING

AVAILABLE ONLINE

Lesson Practice You may opt to have students complete the automatically scored Practice and Problem Solving items online powered by Math XL for School.

Choose from: **Lesson Practice**

Adaptive Practice

You may also take advantage of the bank of exercises for assigning additional practice.

Assignment Guide

Basic	Advanced
11–31, 35–43	11–23, 27–43

Item Analysis

Example	Items	DOK
1	16–27, 41	1
	13	2
	15	3
2	28–35, 42	1
	11, 12, 14, 43	2
3	36, 37	1
	38, 39	2
	40	3

AVAILABLE ONLINE

PRACTICE & PROBLEM SOLVING

Scan for Multimedia

Practice | Tutorial

Additional Exercises Available Online

UNDERSTAND

11. Generalize Find each product. MP.8

- $(x + 9)(x + 9)$
- $(x - 7)(x - 7)$
- $(2x - 1)^2$

a. What do all products of the square of a binomial have in common?

b. Will the third term of the square of a binomial always be positive? Explain.

c. What is the relationship between the sign of the binomial and the sign of the second term in the product?

d. What is true about the exponents representing perfect square variables?

12. Look for Relationships Find a value for m or n to make a true statement. MP.7

a. $mx^2 - 36 = (3x + 6)(3x - 6)$ $m = 9$

b. $(mx + ny)^2 = 4x^2 + 12xy + 9y^2$ $m = 2; n = 3$

13. Error Analysis Describe and correct the error a student made when squaring $(x + 5)$. MP.3

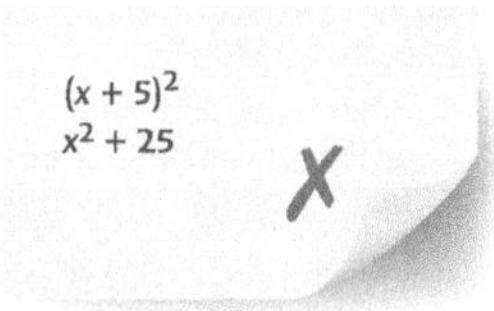

(x + 5)²
x² + 25
X

14. Use Structure The expression $96^2 - 95^2$ is a difference of two squares. How can you use the factors $(96 - 95)(96 + 95)$ to make it easier to simplify this expression? MP.7

15. Construct Arguments Jacob makes the following conjectures. Is each conjecture correct? Provide arguments to support your answers. MP.3

a. The product of any two consecutive even numbers is 1 less than a perfect square.

b. The product of any two consecutive odd numbers is 1 less than a perfect square.

PRACTICE

Write each product in standard form. SEE EXAMPLE 1

16. $(y + 9)(y + 9)$ $y^2 + 18y + 81$

17. $(5x - 3)(5x - 3)$ $25x^2 - 30x + 9$

18. $(a + 11)(a + 11)$ $a^2 + 22a + 121$

19. $(x - 13)(x - 13)$ $x^2 - 26x + 169$

20. $(p + 15)^2$ $p^2 + 30p + 225$

21. $(3k + 8)^2$ $9k^2 + 48k + 64$

22. $(x - 4y)^2$ $x^2 - 8xy + 16y^2$

23. $(2a + 3b)^2$ $4a^2 + 12ab + 9b^2$

24. $\left(\frac{2}{5}x + \frac{1}{5}\right)^2$

25. $(0.4x + 1.2)^2$

Use the square of a binomial to find each product. SEE EXAMPLE 1

26. 56^2 3,136

27. 72^2 5,184

Write each product in standard form. SEE EXAMPLE 2

28. $(x - 12)(x + 12)$ $x^2 - 144$

29. $(2x + 5)(2x - 5)$ $4x^2 - 25$

30. $(3a - 4b)(3a + 4b)$

31. $(x^2 - 2y)(x^2 + 2y)$ $x^4 - 4y^2$

32. $\left(\frac{1}{4}x - \frac{2}{3}\right)\left(\frac{1}{4}x + \frac{2}{3}\right)$ $\frac{1}{16}x^2 - \frac{4}{9}$

33. $(x + 2.5)(x - 2.5)$ $x^2 - 6.25$

Use the product of sum and difference to find each product. SEE EXAMPLE 2

34. $32 \cdot 28$ 896

35. $83 \cdot 97$ 8,051

36. Consider the figure shown. SEE EXAMPLE 3

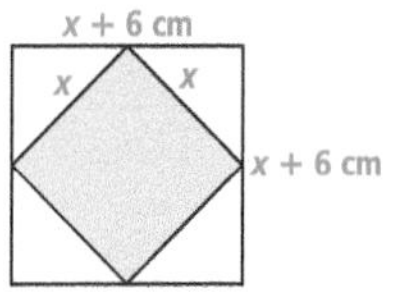

x + 6 cm
x
x
x + 6 cm

a. What expression represents the total area of the four white triangles? $(x + 6)^2 - x^2$

b. If the length of each side of the shaded square is 12 cm, what is the total area of the four white triangles? 180 cm^2

37. What is the area of the shaded region? SEE EXAMPLE 3

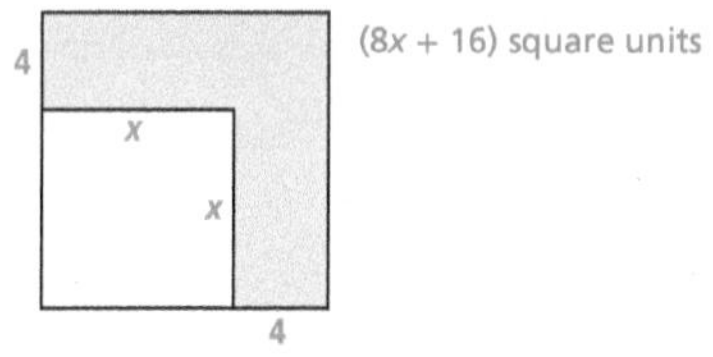

(8x + 16) square units
4
x
x
4

LESSON 7-3 Multiplying Special Cases 279

Answers

11. $(x + 9)(x + 9) = x^2 + 18x + 81$
$(x - 7)(x - 7) = x^2 - 14x + 49$
$(2x - 1)^2 = 4x^2 - 4x + 1$

a. All are a trinomial; the first and third terms are perfect squares.

b. Yes; because the factors are the same, either two negatives or two positives are being multiplied, resulting in a positive answer.

c. The second term in the product is the same as the sign of the binomial being squared.

d. All the exponents are even.

13. The student only multiplied the first terms together and the last terms together. He did not multiply the first and last terms together. The correct answer is $x^2 + 10x + 25$.

14. $(96 - 95) = 1$, so you will be multiply the sum of the two numbers by 1, which will equal the sum.

15. a. Yes; consecutive even numbers are 1 away from an odd number, which is the average between them. You can write their product as the sum and difference of their average and 1. For example; $6 \bullet 8 = (7 - 1)(7 + 1) = 7^2 - 1 = 49 - 1$. So 48 is one less than the perfect square 49.

b. Yes; Consecutive odd numbers are 1 away from an even number, which is the average between them. You can write their product as the sum and difference of their average and 1. Their product will be one less that the square of their average.

24. $\frac{4}{25}x^2 + \frac{4}{25}x + \frac{1}{25}$

25. $0.16x^2 + 0.96x + 1.44$

30. $9a^2 - 16b^2$

Answers

38. $A = 12\pi x + 36\pi$

39. **a.** x by $(x - y)$ and y by $(x - y)$

b. $x^2 - xy$ and $xy - y^2$

c. The remaining figure is the result of finding the difference between the larger x^2 and the smaller y^2.

40. **a.** $1176x^2 + 1344x + 384$

b. $2{,}744x^3 + 4{,}704x^2 + 2{,}688x + 512$ ft^3

43. **Part A** Answers may vary. Sample: the answers are odd numbers.

Part B 22, 23

Part C The answers are even numbers that increase by 8.

Part D 24, 26

AVAILABLE **ONLINE**

Practice Tutorial

Mixed Review Available Online

PRACTICE & PROBLEM SOLVING

APPLY

38. Mathematical Connections The radius of the inner circle of a tile pattern shown is x inches. Write a polynomial in standard form to represent the area of the space between the inner and outer circle.

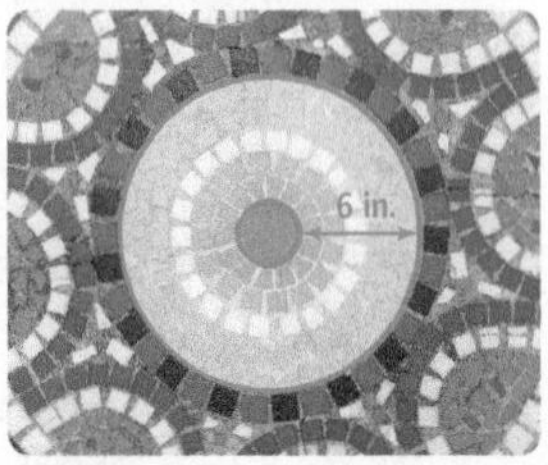
6 in.

39. Make Sense and Persevere In the figure shown, the darker square is removed. MP.1

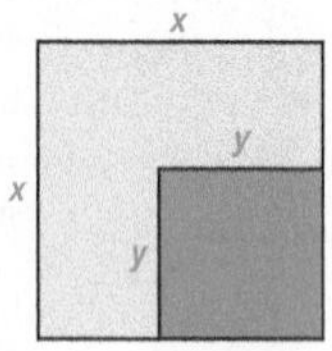
x
x
y
y

a. Divide the remaining figure into two rectangles. What are the dimensions of each rectangle?

b. What is the area of each rectangle?

c. What is the total area of the remaining figure? How does this figure represent the difference of two squares?

40. Higher Order Thinking The sculpture shown contains a large cube.

The length of each side of the cube is 14x + 8 feet.

a. Write a polynomial in standard form to represent the surface area of the cube.

b. Write a polynomial in standard form to represent the volume of the cube.

ASSESSMENT PRACTICE

41. Consider each expression. Can you use the expression to find the product 53^2? Select *Yes* or *No* in each row.

	Yes	No
$(50 + 3)^2$	☑	☐
$(50 - 3)^2$	☐	☑
$(60 + 7)^2$	☐	☑
$(60 - 7)^2$	☑	☐
$(50 + 3)(50 - 3)$	☐	☑

42. SAT/ACT What is the product of $(3x^2 - 4y)(3x^2 + 4y)$?

Ⓐ $9x^4 - 24x^2y - 16y^2$
Ⓑ $3x^2 - 4y^2$
● $9x^4 - 16y^2$
Ⓓ $3x^2 + 14x^2y - 4y$

43. Performance Task Consider the difference of squares $a^2 - b^2$, for integer values of a and b.

Part A Make a table of the difference of squares using consecutive integers for a and b. What pattern do you notice?

Part B Use the pattern from Part A to find pair of consecutive integers that generates a difference of squares of –45.

Part C Make a table of the difference of squares using consecutive even integers for a and b. What pattern do you notice?

Part D Use the pattern from Part C to find a pair of consecutive even integers that generates a difference of squares of –100.

SavvasRealize.com

Assess Tutorials Worksheets

LESSON QUIZ

Use the Lesson Quiz to assess students' understanding of the mathematics in the lesson.

Students can take the Lesson Quiz online or you can download a printable copy from **SavvasRealize.com**. The Lesson Quiz is also available in the *Assessment Resources* book.

Item Analysis

Item	DOK	Standards
1	1	HSA.APR.A.1
2	1	HSA.APR.A.1
3	1	HSA.APR.A.1
4	1	HSA.APR.A.1
5	2	HSA.APR.A.1

RtI Use the student scores on the Lesson Quiz to prescribe differentiated assignments.

If students take the Lesson Quiz online, it will be automatically scored and appropriate differentiated practice will be assigned based on student performance.

I Intervention	0–3 points	• Reteach to Build Understanding • Mathematical Literacy and Vocabulary • Additional Practice
O On-Level	4 points	• Mathematical Literacy and Vocabulary • Additional Practice • Enrichment
A Advanced	5 points	• Enrichment

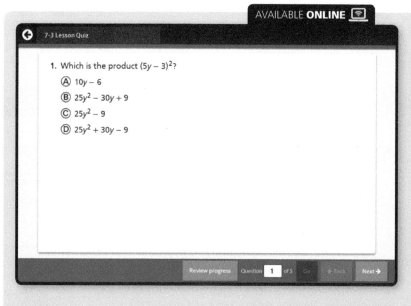

AVAILABLE **ONLINE**

7-3 Lesson Quiz

1. Which is the product $(5y - 3)^2$?

Ⓐ $10y - 6$
Ⓑ $25y^2 - 30y + 9$
Ⓒ $25y^2 - 9$
Ⓓ $25y^2 + 30y - 9$

Review progress Question 1 of 5 Go ← Back Next →

ASSESSMENT RESOURCES

Name ______

enVision Algebra 1
PearsonRealize.com

7-3 Lesson Quiz

Multiplying Special Cases

1. Which of the following is the product $(5y - 3)^2$?

Ⓐ $10y - 6$
Ⓑ $25y^2 - 30y + 9$
Ⓒ $25y^2 - 9$
Ⓓ $25y^2 + 30y - 9$

2. Complete the following to use the Distributive Property to find the product.

$(x + y)(x - y) = \underline{x^2} - \underline{xy} + \underline{xy} - \underline{y^2} = \underline{x^2} - \underline{y^2}$

3. Which of the following is the product of $(3x - 5)$ and $(3x + 5)$?

Ⓐ $9x^2 - 25$
Ⓑ $9x^2 - 30x - 25$
Ⓒ $9x - 10$
Ⓓ $9x^2 + 25$

4. Complete the following to use the difference of two squares to find the product of 22 and 18.

$(\underline{20} + \underline{2})(\underline{20} - \underline{2}) = (\underline{20})^2 - (\underline{2})^2 = 396$

5. A square picture has a 1-in. frame around it. If the area of the frame alone is 48 in.^{2}, what is the area of the picture?

121 in.^{2}

enVision™ **Algebra 1** • Assessment Resources

Assess | Tutorials | Worksheets

DIFFERENTIATED RESOURCES

I = Intervention O = On-Level A = Advanced

⚙ = This activity is available as a digital assignment powered by MathXL® for School.

AVAILABLE ONLINE

Reteach to Build Understanding I ⚙

Provides scaffolded reteaching for the key lesson concepts.

Name ______ enVision Algebra 1

7-3 Reteach to Build Understanding
Multiplying Special Cases

1. Label each item as *square of a binomial* or *product of a sum and difference*.
$(a+b)(a-b)=a^2-b^2$ product of a sum and difference
$(x+7)^2=x^2+14x+49$ square of a binomial
Square of the first term plus twice the product of the first and last terms plus the square of the last term square of a binomial
$(a-b)^2=a^2-2ab+b^2$ square of a binomial
Results in the difference of two squares product of a sum and difference
$(x-4)(x+4)=x^2-16$ product of a sum and difference
$(a+b)^2=a^2+2ab+b^2$ square of a binomial

2. Brian incorrectly identified two of the features of the product $(x-5)^2$. Put an X next to any incorrect statements. Correct his errors.
a. Use the square of a binomial pattern to find the product.
b. The result is a difference of two squares. X — The result is a perfect square trinomial, $x^2-10x+25$.
c. The first term of the product is x^2.
d. The last term of the product is -25. X — The last term is positive 25, because $-5(-5)=25$.
e. The middle term of the product is $-10x$.

3. Find the product of $(2x+6)$ and $(2x-6)$.
Use the Distributive Property to find the product.
$(2x+6)(2x-6)=$ 2x $(2x-6)+$ 6 $(2x-6)$
$=4x^2-12x+12x-36$
$=4x^2-36$
The product of $(2x+6)$ and $(2x-6)$ is $4x^2-36$.

enVision™ Algebra 1 • Teaching Resources

Additional Practice I O ⚙

Provides extra practice for each lesson.

Name ______ enVision Algebra 1

7-3 Additional Practice
Multiplying Special Cases

Find each product.
1. $(x+4)^2$ — $x^2+8x+16$
2. $(2x-3)^2$ — $4x^2-12x+9$
3. $(4y+7)^2$ — $16y^2+56y+49$
4. 32^2 — 1,024
5. 57^2 — 3,249
6. 45^2 — 2,025

Write each product in standard form.
7. $(x+7)(x-7)$ — x^2-49
8. $(3x+4)(3x-4)$ — $9x^2-16$
9. $(5y-1)(5y+1)$ — $25y^2-1$

Use the difference of two squares to find each product.
10. $34\cdot26$ — $(30-4)(30+4)$, $900-16$, 884
11. $22\cdot28$ — $(25-3)(25+3)$, $625-9$, 616
12. $17\cdot7$ — $(12+5)(12-5)$, $144-25$, 119

13. Why is the middle term $2ab$ in $(a+b)^2$ and $-2ab$ in $(a-b)^2$ when written in standard form?
Sample answer: When evaluating $(a+b)^2$, you can rewrite as $(a+b)(a+b)$. Applying the Distributive Property will yield $a^2+ab+ab+b^2$. Since ab occurs twice, you can rewrite the sum as $2ab$. A similar argument may be used with $(a-b)^2$.

14. A hole is punched in a piece of metal to make a part for a machine. What is the area of the metal part, or the shaded region shown?
$18x+45$

$x-2$, $x+7$

enVision™ Algebra 1 • Teaching Resources

Enrichment O A ⚙

Presents engaging problems and activities that extend the lesson concepts.

Name ______ enVision Algebra 1

7-3 Enrichment
Multiplying Special Cases

There are three binomial products that deserve special attention.
Perfect Square of a Sum $(a+b)^2=a^2+2ab+b^2$
Perfect Square of a Difference $(a-b)^2=a^2-2ab+b^2$
Difference of Squares $(a+b)(a-b)=a^2-b^2$

You already know that understanding these patterns makes it easier to multiply binomials. It also makes it easier to multiply large numbers!

Suppose you are challenged to find the square of 78. You can quickly perform the calculation without technology by applying the special formulas.

First notice that $78=80-2$. Then use the formula for the perfect square of a difference.
$78^2=(80-2)^2=80^2-2(80)(2)+2^2=6{,}400-320+4=6{,}084$

You could also use the formula for the perfect square of a sum.
$78^2=(70+8)^2=70^2-2(70)(8)+8^2=4{,}900+1{,}120+64=6{,}084$

Find the following products, performing all calculations by hand. Show your strategy.
1. 36×22 $(40-4)(20+2)=800-80+80-8=800-8=792$
2. 29×33 $(30-1)(30+3)=900-30+90-3=900+60-3=957$
3. 59×61 $(60-1)(60+1)=60^2-1^2=3{,}600-1=3{,}599$
4. 103×103 $(100+3)^2=100^2+2(100)3+3^2=10{,}000+600+9=10{,}609$
5. 48×48 $(50-2)^2=50^2-2(50)(2)+2^2=2{,}500-200+4=2{,}304$
6. 85×95 $(90-5)(90+5)=90^2-5^2=8{,}100-25=8{,}075$
7. 37×37 $(40-3)^2=40^2-2(40)(3)+3^2=1{,}600-240+9=1{,}369$
8. 91×91 $(90+1)^2=90^2+2(90)(1)+1^2=8{,}100+180+1=8{,}281$
9. 72×68 $(70+2)(70-2)=70^2-2^2=4{,}900-4=4{,}896$
10. 206×194 $(200+6)(200-6)=200^2-6^2=40{,}000-36=39{,}964$

enVision™ Algebra 1 • Teaching Resources

Mathematical Literacy and Vocabulary I O

Helps students develop and reinforce understanding of key terms and concepts.

Name ______ enVision Algebra 1

7-3 Mathematical Literacy and Vocabulary
Multiplying Special Cases

Consider each phrase or expression. Determine whether it is the *square of a binomial* or the *product of a sum and difference*.

1. $(9x^2-81)$ — product of a sum and difference	2. The product of the sum and difference of the same two terms is the difference of two squares. — product of a sum and difference	3. $(2x+5)^2$ — square of a binomial
4. the square of the first term plus twice the product of the two terms plus the square of the last term — square of a binomial	5. $(x-15)^2$ — square of a binomial	6. $(a-b)^2=a^2-2ab+b^2$ — square of a binomial
7. $(a+b)(a-b)=a^2-b^2$ — product of a sum and difference	8. $(a+b)^2=a^2+2ab+b^2$ — square of a binomial	9. $(x+3)(x-3)=(x^2-9)$ — product of a sum and difference

enVision™ Algebra 1 • Teaching Resources

Digital Resources and Video Tutorials I O A ⚙

The **Reteach to Build Understanding, Additional Practice**, and **Enrichment** activities are available as digital assignments powered by MathXL for School. These activities are automatically assigned when students complete the lesson quiz online and are automatically scored.

Students can access instructional tutorials using the **Virtual Nerd app**.

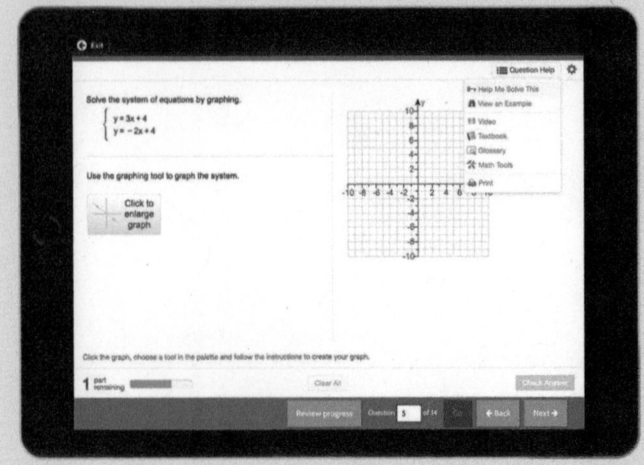

Solve the system of equations by graphing.
Use the graphing tool to graph the system.
Click to enlarge graph
Question Help
Help Me Solve This
View an Example
Video
Textbook
Glossary
Math Tools
Print
Clear All
Check Answer
Review progress
Back
Next

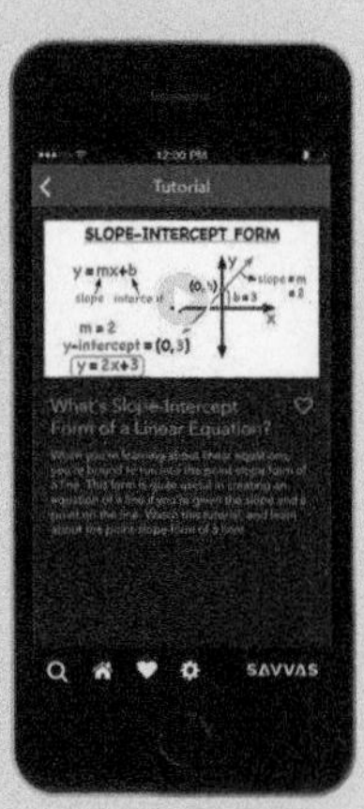

Tutorial
SLOPE-INTERCEPT FORM
SAVVAS

Students can also access Virtual Nerd videos using the **BouncePages app** to scan exercise pages marked with this icon. Students can download both apps for free in their mobile devices' app store.

LESSON 7-4

Factoring Polynomials

Lesson Overview

FOCUS

Objective

Students will be able to:

✔ Find the greatest common factor of the terms of a polynomial.

✔ Use the structure of a polynomial, and the understanding that polynomials form a system similar to integers, to rewrite it in factored form.

✔ Factor polynomials that represent real-world problems.

Essential Understanding

The greatest common factor of the terms of a polynomial is the greatest common factor of the coefficients and the variable or variables, using the number of instances of the variable that are common to each term.

COHERENCE

Previously in this course, students:

- Used their understanding of the system of integers to understand the system formed by polynomials, and used that understanding to add, subtract, and multiply polynomials.

In this lesson, students:

- Use the understanding that polynomials form a system similar to integers to factor polynomials by finding the greatest common factor of the terms.

Later in this topic, students will:

- Factor trinomials in the form $x^2 + bx + c$ and $ax^2 + bx + c$.

RIGOR

This lesson emphasizes a blend of *procedural skill and fluency* and *application*.

- Students factor a polynomial using the Distributive Property and the GCF, similar to the process for factoring integers.
- Students apply the process of finding the GCF of a polynomial to factor a polynomial model that represents a real-world problem, such as the area of photos in various arrangements on a page.

A-Z Vocabulary Builder

REVIEW VOCABULARY — **English** | *Spanish*

- **coefficient** | *coeficiente*
- **factor** | *factor*
- **greatest common factor** | *máximo común divisor*
- **polynomial** | *polinomio*

VOCABULARY ACTIVITY

Review the terms *factor* and *greatest common factor* as they apply to integers. Ask students to find the greatest common factor of 18 and 45 [9].

Now apply the same terms to *polynomials*. Have students identify the *coefficients* in the polynomial shown below. Then have them find the greatest common factor of the coefficients.

$$16x^6 + 4x^5 + 2x^4$$

The coefficients of the terms are ________ [16, 4, 2].

The greatest common factor of the coefficients is ________ [2].

Student Companion

Students can do their in-class work for the lesson on pages 149–152 of their *Student Companion* or in Savvas Realize.

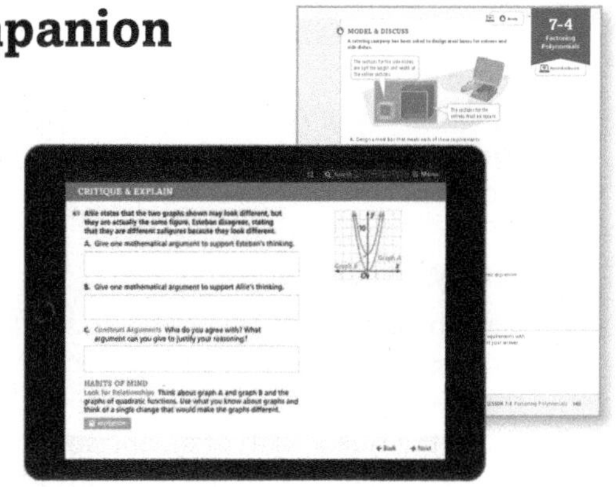

Mathematics Overview — COMMON CORE STANDARDS

Content Standards

In this lesson, students focus on these standards:

HSA.APR.A.1 Understand that polynomials form a system analogous to the integers, namely, they are closed under the operations of addition, subtraction, and multiplication; add, subtract, and multiply polynomials.

HSA.SSE.A.2 Use the structure of an expression to identify ways to rewrite it.

Mathematical Practice Standards

These standards are highlighted in this lesson:

MP.4 Model With Mathematics

Students use mathematics to describe a situation when they recognize how finding the GCF of the terms in a polynomial is useful for solving problems, such as writing an expression in factored form to represent the volume of an empty tennis ball canister.

MP.7 Look For and Make Use of Structure

Students see a polynomial as being composed of terms whose greatest common factor is the greatest common factor of the coefficients, as well as, the variable that is common to each of the terms.

Activity

MODEL & DISCUSS

INSTRUCTIONAL FOCUS Students experiment with possible configurations of different size squares having side lengths that are multiples of a single factor. Students write equations for the area of these configurations. The activity prepares students to learn how to factor polynomials and factor a polynomial model.

STUDENT COMPANION Students can complete the *Model & Discuss* activity on page 149 of their *Student Companion*.

Before WHOLE CLASS

Implement Tasks that Promote Reasoning and Problem Solving ETP

Q: How does the size of the side dish sections compare to the size of the entrée sections?
[The side dish sections are half the size of the entrée sections on each side, so a quarter of the area.]

During SMALL GROUP

Support Productive Struggle in Learning Mathematics ETP

Q: What do you know about the relationship between the length and width of each section?
[Since the entrée sections are square, the length and width are equal. The length and width of the side dish sections are also equal since they are half the length and width of the entrée sections.]

For Early Finishers

Q: Explain how to determine the maximum value for the side lengths of entrée and side dish sections if the overall size of the meal box is 8 in. × 6 in.
[Since the side length of an entrée plus side dish is $3x$, and the smallest dimension of the meal box is 6 in., let $3x = 6$ or $x = 2$. So side dishes are 2 in. and entrée sections are 4 in.]

After WHOLE CLASS

Facilitate Meaningful Mathematical Discourse ETP

Q: What do all the terms of your equations for area have in common?
[The variable for the side length of the sections.]

Q: How is the formula for area affected when there is more than one of a particular section?
[The area is multiplied by the number of sections.]

HABITS OF MIND *Use with* **MODEL & DISCUSS**

Construct Arguments Can you meet more than one of the three requirements with the same-sized meal box? Use a mathematical argument to support your answer. **MP.3**

[Yes, a meal with more sides than entrées and a meal with more entrées than sides could fit in the same box. A box with 8 sides and 4 entrées has the same area as a box with 5 entrées and 4 sides.]

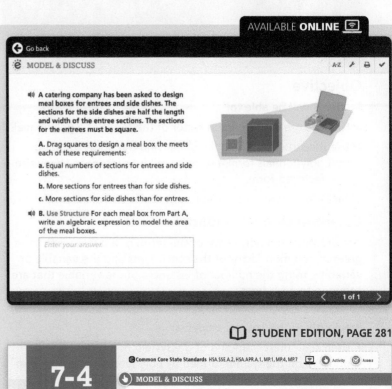

AVAILABLE **ONLINE**

Go back

MODEL & DISCUSS

A catering company has been asked to design meal boxes for entrees and side dishes. The sections for the side dishes are half the length and width of the entree sections. The sections for the entrees must be square.

A. Drag squares to design a meal box the meets each of these requirements:

a. Equal numbers of sections for entrees and side dishes.

b. More sections for entrees than for side dishes.

c. More sections for side dishes than for entrees.

B. Use Structure For each meal box from Part A, write an algebraic expression to model the area of the meal boxes.

Enter your answer

1 of 1

STUDENT EDITION, PAGE 281

7-4 Factoring Polynomials

PearsonRealize.com

I CAN… factor a polynomial.

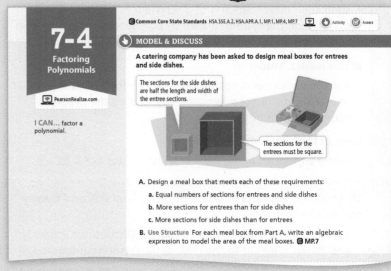

Common Core State Standards HSA.SSE.A.2, HSA.APR.A.1, MP.1, MP.4, MP.7 Activity Assess

MODEL & DISCUSS

A catering company has been asked to design meal boxes for entrees and side dishes.

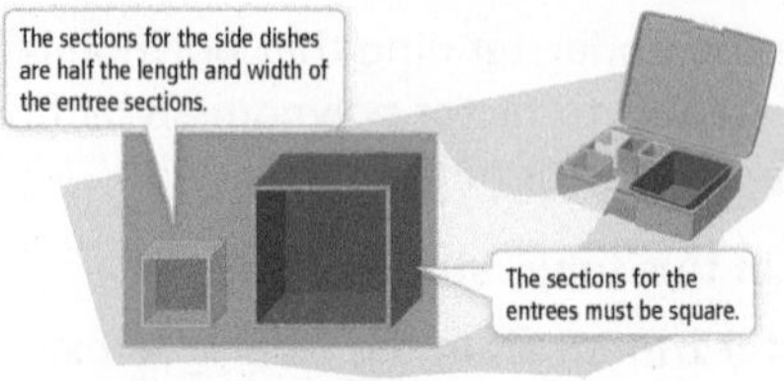

The sections for the side dishes are half the length and width of the entree sections.
The sections for the entrees must be square.

A. Design a meal box that meets each of these requirements:

a. Equal numbers of sections for entrees and side dishes

b. More sections for entrees than for side dishes

c. More sections for side dishes than for entrees

B. Use Structure For each meal box from Part A, write an algebraic expression to model the area of the meal boxes. MP.7

SAMPLE STUDENT WORK

A. a.

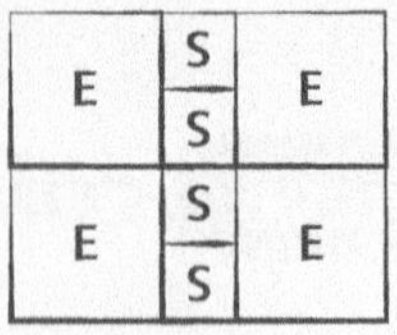

E
S
S
E
E
S
S
E

b.

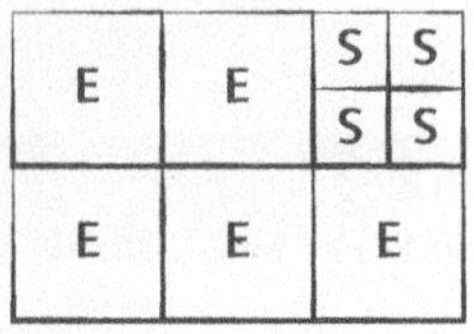

E
E
S S
S S
E
E
E

c.

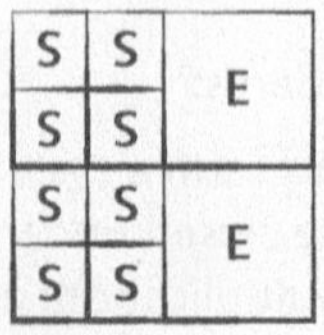

S S
S S
E
S S
S S
E

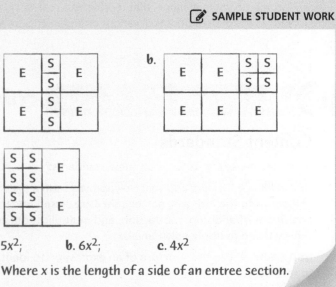

B. a. $5x^2$; b. $6x^2$; c. $4x^2$

Where x is the length of a side of an entree section.

INTRODUCE THE ESSENTIAL QUESTION

Establish Mathematics Goals to Focus Learning ETP

Introduce students to factoring polynomials. Remind them that they have factored integers by writing the prime factorization of the integer. Explain that they can use the same process for variables in order to factor polynomials.

EXAMPLE 1 Find the Greatest Common Factor

Pose Purposeful Questions ETP

Q: Compare finding the common factor of the variables to finding the common factor of the coefficients.
[They are the same process, but the common factor of the variable is the number of occurrences of the variable indicated by the lowest exponent.]

Q: If the prime factorization of all terms in a polynomial only has two instances of 3 in common, what is the GCF? Explain.
[The GCF would be 9, because 3 is a factor twice and $3^2 = 3 \bullet 3 = 9$.]

Q: What do you know about the GCF if one term does not include a variable?
[The GCF does not include a variable.]

AVAILABLE ONLINE

expression to model the area of the meal boxes. MP.7

ESSENTIAL QUESTION How is factoring a polynomial similar to factoring integers?

EXAMPLE 1 Find the Greatest Common Factor

What is the greatest common factor (GCF) of the terms of $12x^5 + 8x^4 - 6x^3$?

STUDY TIP
Recall that finding the prime factorization of a number is expressing the number as a product of only prime numbers.

Step 1 Write the prime factorization of the coefficient for each term to determine if there is a greatest common factor other than 1.

12 → $2 \cdot 2 \cdot 3$ 8 → $2 \cdot 2 \cdot 2$ 6 → $2 \cdot 3$

One instance of 2 is the only common factor of the numbers, so the GCF of the coefficients of this trinomial is 2.

Step 2 Determine the greatest common factor for the variables of each term.

x^5 → $x \cdot x \cdot x \cdot x \cdot x$ x^4 → $x \cdot x \cdot x \cdot x$ x^3 → $x \cdot x \cdot x$

Three instances of x are the only common factors of the terms, so the GCF of the variables is x^3.

The greatest common factor of the terms $12x^5 + 8x^4 - 6x^3$ is $2x^3$.

Try It! 1. Find the GCF of the terms of each polynomial.
a. $15x^2 + 18$ b. $-18y^4 + 6y^3 + 24y^2$

LESSON 7-4 Factoring Polynomials 281

Try It! Answers

1. a. 3
   b. $6y^2$

AVAILABLE ONLINE

ADDITIONAL EXAMPLES

Go back

ADDITIONAL EXAMPLE 2   ESSENTIAL QUESTION ES A-Z

Factor the following polynomials.
a. $16xy^2 + 4x^2y + 8xy$
b. $6x^2y^2 + 18xy + 15x$

a. $16xy^2 + 4x^2y + 8xy$
$4xy(4y + x + 2)$
b. $6x^2y^2 + 18xy + 15x$
$3x(2xy^2 + 6y + 5)$

1 of 2

Go back

ADDITIONAL EXAMPLE 3A   ESSENTIAL QUESTION ES A-Z

Selma is making a stained glass piece for art class. She is using some special glittered glass that is very expensive, so she wants to order only the amount she needs. The sides of the glitter squares are one quarter the sides of the blue squares. The glitter rectangles are the same width as the squares but one half inch longer than twice the width. How can Selma express the amount of glitter glass she would need?

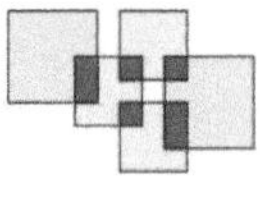

Glitter squares are x by x
Glitter rectangles are x by $2x + 0.5$
Area of glitter glass $= 3x^2 + 2(2x^2 + 0.5x)$
$= 3x^2 + 4x^2 + x$
$= 7x^2 + x$

1 of 2

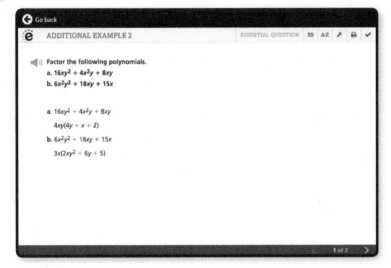

Example 2 Students transition to factoring polynomials that contain multiple variables.

Q: How can you factor a polynomial that has two different variables?
[Find the GCF, which may include two variables.]

Q: How do you factor a polynomial where only some terms have two variables?
[Find the GCF that includes the variable in all the terms.]

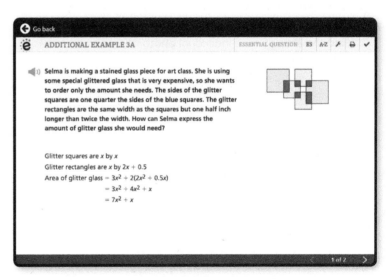

Example 3A Students determine dimensions and write a polynomial equation that represents a stained glass design.

Q: How can the length of the sides of the glitter rectangles be expressed?
[Width is x and height is $2x + 0.5$.]

Q: How can the area of glitter glass for one rectangle be expressed? For two rectangles?
[$2x^2 + 0.5x$; $4x^2 + x$]

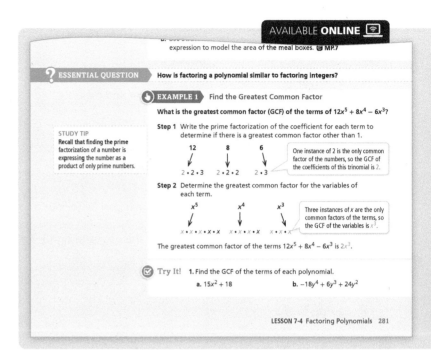

Activity Assess

EXAMPLE 2 Factor Out the Greatest Common Factor

Pose Purposeful Questions ETP

Q: Why is it helpful to factor out the GCF?
[It simplifies the remainder of the expression and makes it easier to further analyze or factor.]

Q: Why can it be helpful to factor out -1 when the first term in the expression is negative?
[It will generally make the factored expression simpler to analyze further.]

Q: What happens to the terms in a polynomial if you factor out a negative number?
[The signs of all the terms are changed to the opposite sign.]

Try It! Answers

2. a. $x(x^2 + 5x - 22)$

   b. $-4y^3(4y^3 - 7y + 5)$

Common Error

Try It! 2b Students may forget to factor out -1 from all terms, since not all the terms are negative. Have students multiply their GCF and resulting factored polynomial to see if their answer is the original polynomial.

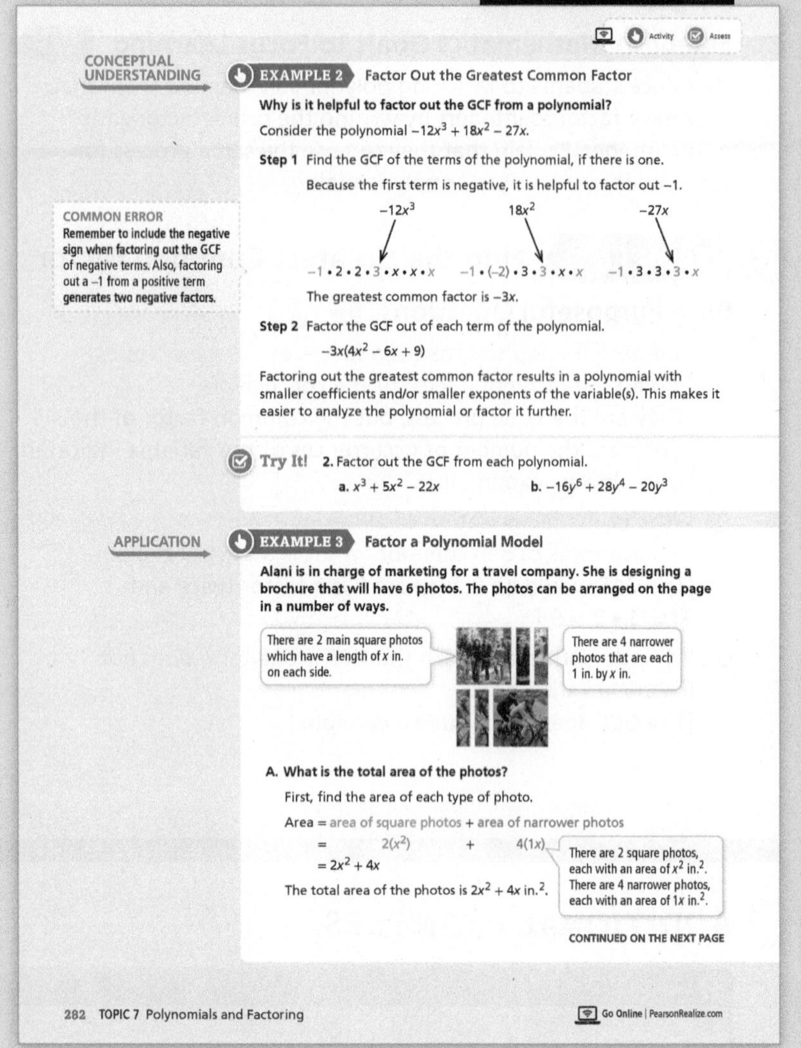

AVAILABLE **ONLINE**

Activity Assess

CONCEPTUAL UNDERSTANDING

EXAMPLE 2 Factor Out the Greatest Common Factor

Why is it helpful to factor out the GCF from a polynomial?

Consider the polynomial $-12x^3 + 18x^2 - 27x$.

Step 1 Find the GCF of the terms of the polynomial, if there is one.

Because the first term is negative, it is helpful to factor out -1.

$-12x^3$ → $-1 \cdot 2 \cdot 2 \cdot 3 \cdot x \cdot x \cdot x$

$18x^2$ → $-1 \cdot (-2) \cdot 3 \cdot 3 \cdot x \cdot x$

$-27x$ → $-1 \cdot 3 \cdot 3 \cdot 3 \cdot x$

The greatest common factor is $-3x$.

COMMON ERROR
Remember to include the negative sign when factoring out the GCF of negative terms. Also, factoring out a -1 from a positive term generates two negative factors.

Step 2 Factor the GCF out of each term of the polynomial.

$-3x(4x^2 - 6x + 9)$

Factoring out the greatest common factor results in a polynomial with smaller coefficients and/or smaller exponents of the variable(s). This makes it easier to analyze the polynomial or factor it further.

Try It! 2. Factor out the GCF from each polynomial.

a. $x^3 + 5x^2 - 22x$

b. $-16y^6 + 28y^4 - 20y^3$

APPLICATION

EXAMPLE 3 Factor a Polynomial Model

Alani is in charge of marketing for a travel company. She is designing a brochure that will have 6 photos. The photos can be arranged on the page in a number of ways.

There are 2 main square photos which have a length of x in. on each side.

There are 4 narrower photos that are each 1 in. by x in.

A. What is the total area of the photos?

First, find the area of each type of photo.

Area = area of square photos + area of narrower photos
$= 2(x^2) + 4(1x)$
$= 2x^2 + 4x$

There are 2 square photos, each with an area of x^2 in.^{2}. There are 4 narrower photos, each with an area of $1x$ in.^{2}.

The total area of the photos is $2x^2 + 4x$ in.^{2}.

CONTINUED ON THE NEXT PAGE

Go Online | PearsonRealize.com

HABITS OF MIND

Use with **EXAMPLES 1 & 2**

Use Appropriate Tools If you model a trinomial $ax^2 + bx + c$ using algebra tiles how can you tell if it has common factor? MP.5

[If the number of x^2 tiles, x tiles, and constant tiles has a common factor, then the trinomial has a common factor.]

EXAMPLE 3 Factor a Polynomial Model

Connect and Use Mathematical Representations ETP

Q: In Part A, how would you calculate the total area?
[Find the area of each individual photo, then add the areas of all the photos to get the total.]

Q: How are the areas of the individual photos expressed?
[The area is length times width, so the main photos are $x \cdot x$, or x^2 and the thinner photos are $1 \cdot x$, or $1x$.]

RtI Struggling Students

USE WITH EXAMPLE 2 Students may struggle finding the GCF of integers and variables. Help students practice finding the GCF with these exercises.

- Find the GCF.

1. 15 and 12 [3]
2. 4, 8, and 12 [4]
3. $3x$ and $3x^2$ [$3x$]
4. $6x$ and $8x^2$ [$2x$]

Q: How is finding the greatest common factor of variable terms similar to finding the greatest common factor of integers?
[In both cases you are identifying the greatest common factor that can divide into both terms.]

ADV Advanced Students

USE WITH EXAMPLE 3 Students extend factoring polynomials skills to solving an engineering problem.

- The plan for the original dimensions of a rectangular pool was a length 8 ft more than twice the width. A change in the design of the building means the maximum area of the pool is $2w^2 - 4w$, where w is the original width of the pool.

Q: How can you determine the maximum length of the pool in the redesigned building?
[Factor the width of the pool w out of the expression for the area of the pool to get $2w - 4$ as the new length.]

Q: How much is the length of the pool reduced in the redesigned building? [The length is reduced by 12 ft; $[8 - (-4)]$.]

Q: In Part B, explain why the length of the other side is $2x + 4$?
[If the height component of area x is factored out, you are left with the width component, $2x + 4$.]

Q: In Part C, what does the GCF represent in this configuration of photos?
[The GCF represents the total height if the main photos were stacked on top of each other and the other photos were stacked on top of each other in two columns of two.]

Q: In Part D, are these two configurations the only possible arrangements for the photos?
[No, since the equation represents only the area of the photos together, these configurations represent the two possibilities if the photos are arranged so that they are bordering each other and there is no blank space.]

Try It! Answer

3. $2x(x + 4)$

Elicit and Use Evidence of Student Thinking ETP

Q: What is the effect of increasing the side length to 2 inches on the GCF?
[The area of the narrower photos increases by a factor of two but, since the main photos do not change, the GCF does not change.]

HABITS OF MIND

Use with **EXAMPLE 3**

Reason If none of the terms of a polynomial have the same variable, what will be true about the GCF? **MP.2**

[If none of the terms have the same variable, then the GCF will be less than or equal to the smallest constant term.]

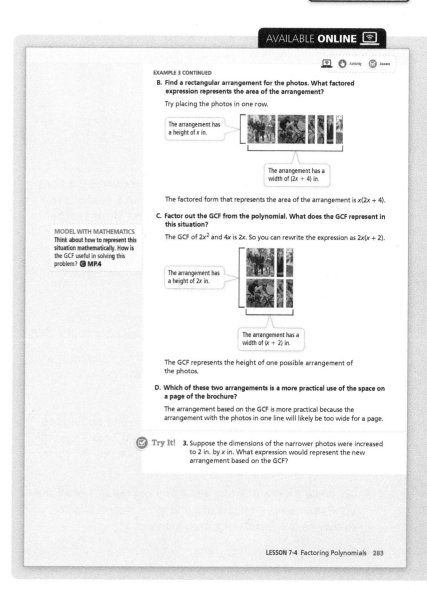

AVAILABLE **ONLINE**

Activity Assess

EXAMPLE 3 CONTINUED

B. Find a rectangular arrangement for the photos. What factored expression represents the area of the arrangement?

Try placing the photos in one row.

The arrangement has a height of x in.
The arrangement has a width of (2x + 4) in.

The factored form that represents the area of the arrangement is $x(2x + 4)$.

C. Factor out the GCF from the polynomial. What does the GCF represent in this situation?

The GCF of $2x^2$ and $4x$ is $2x$. So you can rewrite the expression as $2x(x + 2)$.

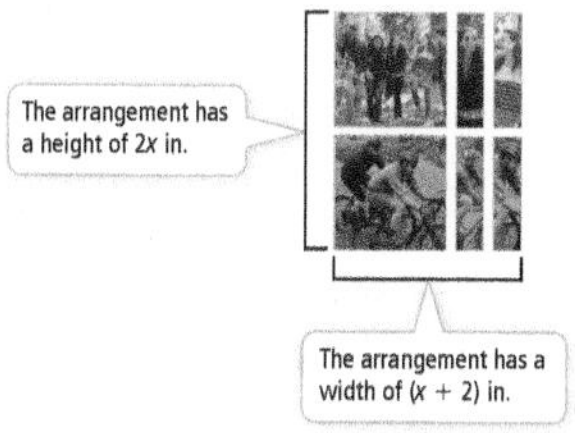

The arrangement has a height of 2x in.
The arrangement has a width of (x + 2) in.

The GCF represents the height of one possible arrangement of the photos.

MODEL WITH MATHEMATICS
Think about how to represent this situation mathematically. How is the GCF useful in solving this problem? MP.4

D. Which of these two arrangements is a more practical use of the space on a page of the brochure?

The arrangement based on the GCF is more practical because the arrangement with the photos in one line will likely be too wide for a page.

Try It! **3.** Suppose the dimensions of the narrower photos were increased to 2 in. by x in. What expression would represent the new arrangement based on the GCF?

LESSON 7-4 Factoring Polynomials 283

ELL English Language Learners *(Use with* **EXAMPLE 3***)*

WRITING BEGINNING To make *arrangements* means to make plans. But an *arrangement* is also when a group of items is put together in a particular way, or order. Indicate which meaning of arrangement is used, to make plans or a particular order.

Q: The tables at the banquet hall were covered with flower *arrangements*.
[particular order]

Q: My mom had to make funeral *arrangements* when my grandpa died.
[make plans]

Q: Which meaning of arrangement is used in the example?
[particular order.]

SPEAKING INTERMEDIATE In Part C, the phrase *greatest common factor* is used. Have students discuss with a partner synonyms for each word in the phrase in order to help them better understand its meaning.

Q: What words mean the same thing as *great*? [large, important, big]

Q: What words mean the same thing as *common*? [general, regular, shared]

Q: What words mean the same thing as *factor*? [part, portion, consideration]

Q: What words can you use to convey the mathematical meaning of the phrase *greatest common factor*?
[the largest shared part]

READING ADVANCED Distribute brochures from the nurse's office to small groups of students and ask them to take turns reading through them. Have each group summarize the main idea of their brochure.

Q: What does each brochure have in common?
[Answers may vary. Sample: Each one tries to convey important information in a small amount of space.]

Q: Read the first paragraph of the example. Do you think a brochure is a good marketing strategy for the company?
[Yes; Answers may vary. Sample: The pictures can entice people to a particular destination.]

CONCEPT SUMMARY Factoring Polynomials

Q: How do you know that a polynomial can be factored?
[All of the terms in the polynomial can be divided by the same common factor.]

Do You UNDERSTAND? | Do You KNOW HOW?

Common Error

Exercise 13 Some students may forget to change the signs of terms when factoring out a negative GCF. Students can check their work by multiplying the terms of the factored polynomial by the GCF to see if they get the original polynomial back.

Answers

1. In both instances, the product of the common factors between either the integers or polynomials become the GCF.
2. The variable with the least exponent will be included in any common variables with greater exponents.
3. 1
4. Andrew is removing a $3xy$ from each term and putting the remainder as the second factor. Multiplying $3xy(x - 2y)$ will not give the third term of the original equation. The correct answer is $3xy(x - 2y + 1)$.
5. No, while 2 is the GCF of 6 and 8, it is not the GCF of x^6 and x^8; x^6 represents 6 factors of x and x^8 represents 8 factors of x, so they have 6 factors of x in common, or x^6.
6. 5
7. x^3y
8. $4a^2$
9. 1
10. $4a^4b$
11. x^6y^8
12. $2ab(5a + 6b)$
13. $-3x^2(x^2 - 4x + 7)$
14. $5x^2y(3x - 2y^2)$
15. $x^8(x^2 + x - 1)$
16. $1(3x^3y^2 - 9xz^4 + 8y^2z)$
17. $50a^7b^3(2b^2 - 3a)$

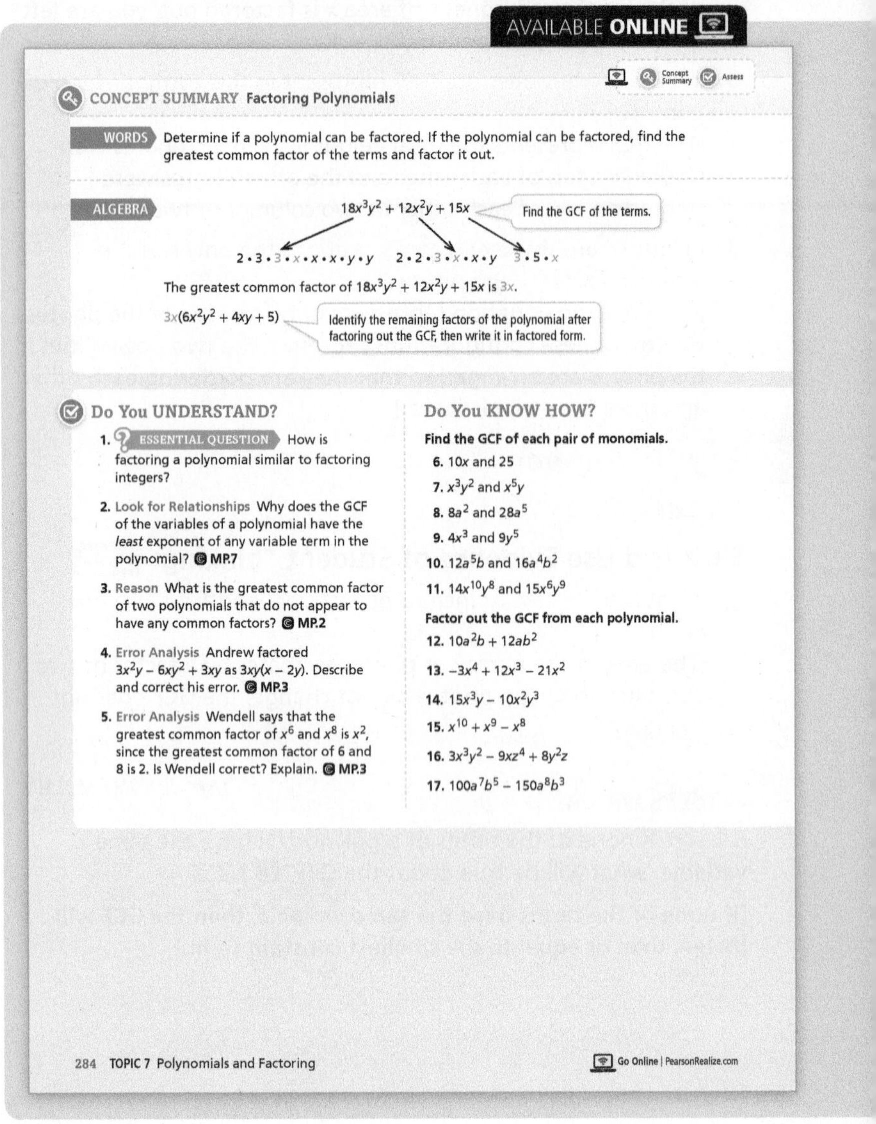
AVAILABLE ONLINE

Concept Summary Assess

CONCEPT SUMMARY Factoring Polynomials

WORDS Determine if a polynomial can be factored. If the polynomial can be factored, find the greatest common factor of the terms and factor it out.

ALGEBRA $18x^3y^2 + 12x^2y + 15x$ — Find the GCF of the terms.

$2 \cdot 3 \cdot 3 \cdot x \cdot x \cdot x \cdot y \cdot y$ $\quad 2 \cdot 2 \cdot 3 \cdot x \cdot x \cdot y$ $\quad 3 \cdot 5 \cdot x$

The greatest common factor of $18x^3y^2 + 12x^2y + 15x$ is $3x$.

$3x(6x^2y^2 + 4xy + 5)$ — Identify the remaining factors of the polynomial after factoring out the GCF, then write it in factored form.

Do You UNDERSTAND?

1. ESSENTIAL QUESTION How is factoring a polynomial similar to factoring integers?
2. Look for Relationships Why does the GCF of the variables of a polynomial have the *least* exponent of any variable term in the polynomial? MP.7
3. Reason What is the greatest common factor of two polynomials that do not appear to have any common factors? MP.2
4. Error Analysis Andrew factored $3x^2y - 6xy^2 + 3xy$ as $3xy(x - 2y)$. Describe and correct his error. MP.3
5. Error Analysis Wendell says that the greatest common factor of x^6 and x^8 is x^2, since the greatest common factor of 6 and 8 is 2. Is Wendell correct? Explain. MP.3

Do You KNOW HOW?

Find the GCF of each pair of monomials.

6. $10x$ and 25
7. x^3y^2 and x^5y
8. $8a^2$ and $28a^5$
9. $4x^3$ and $9y^5$
10. $12a^5b$ and $16a^4b^2$
11. $14x^{10}y^8$ and $15x^6y^9$

Factor out the GCF from each polynomial.

12. $10a^2b + 12ab^2$
13. $-3x^4 + 12x^3 - 21x^2$
14. $15x^3y - 10x^2y^3$
15. $x^{10} + x^9 - x^8$
16. $3x^3y^2 - 9xz^4 + 8y^2z$
17. $100a^7b^5 - 150a^8b^3$

284 TOPIC 7 Polynomials and Factoring

Go Online | PearsonRealize.com

PRACTICE & PROBLEM SOLVING

AVAILABLE ONLINE

Lesson Practice You may opt to have students complete the automatically scored Practice and Problem Solving items online powered by MathXL for School.

Choose from: **Lesson Practice**
Adaptive Practice

You may also take advantage of the bank of exercises for assigning additional practice.

Assignment Guide

Basic	Advanced
18–31, 34–43	18–25, 28–43

Item Analysis

Example	Items	DOK
1	20, 26–29	1
	19, 23	2
	22, 25	3
2	21, 30–33, 39, 41	1
	18, 24	2
3	34–38, 42	2
	40, 43	3

Answers

18. $8xy^2$ The answer has a coefficient that is a multiple of 4 but not 12. It must have both an x and y variable. The exponent for x must be 1; however the exponent for y can be any whole number.

19. Answers may vary. Sample: $12x^4 + 32x^3 - 24x^2$

20. The student did not take out the correct GCF. All terms of the trinomial also have a b. The correct answer is $5ab(2a^2 - ab - 3)$.

21. $2x(7x^3 - 10x + 5)$

22. Sometimes; an example of when it would not be a multiple of 6 is $4x^2 + 6x + 9y^2 + 12y$.

25. Answers may vary.
1: {2x, 3x, 4x, 5xy, 7x, 9y, 12xy, 13x, 15x};
2x: {2x, 4x, 12xy}; 3: {3x, 9y, 12xy, 15x};
4x: {4x, 12xy}; 5x: {5xy, 15x}; y: {5xy, 9y}

AVAILABLE ONLINE

PRACTICE & PROBLEM SOLVING

Scan for Multimedia | Practice | Tutorial
Additional Exercises Available Online

UNDERSTAND

18. Use Structure What term and $12x^2y$ have a GCF of $4xy$? Write an expression that shows the monomial factored out of the polynomial. MP.7

19. Look for Relationships Write a trinomial that has a GCF of $4x^2$. MP.7

20. Error Analysis Describe and correct the error a student made when factoring $10a^3b - 5a^2b^2 - 15ab$. MP.3

$10a^3b - 5a^2b^2 - 15ab$
$5a(2a^2b - ab^2 - 3b)$ ✗

21. Make Sense and Persevere Write the difference in factored form. MP.1

$(24x^4 - 15x^2 + 6x) - (10x^4 + 5x^2 - 4x)$

22. Higher Order Thinking In the expression $ax^2 + b$, the coefficients of a and b are multiples of 2. The coefficients c and d in the expression $cx^2 + d$ are multiples of 3. Will the GCF of $ax^2 + b$ and $cx^2 + d$ *always*, *sometimes*, or *never* be a multiple of 6? Explain.

23. Make Sense and Persevere What is the GCF in the expression $x(x + 5) - 3x(x + 5) + 4(x + 5)$? MP.1 $(x + 5)$

24. Look for Relationships Find the greatest common factor of the terms $x^{n+1}y^n$ and x^ny^{n-2}, where n is a whole number greater than 2. How can you factor the expression $x^{n+1}y^n + x^ny^{n-2}$? MP.7
x^ny^{n-2}; $x^ny^{n-2}(xy^2 + 1)$

25. Mathematical Connections consider the following set of monomials.

$A = \{2x, 3x, 4x, 5xy, 7x, 9y, 12xy, 13x, 15x\}$

The GCF the elements in subset $B = \{2x, 3x\}$ is x. Create 6 different subsets of A, such the GCFs of the elements are 1, $2x$, 3, $4x$, $5x$, and y.

PRACTICE

Find the GCF of each group of monomials.
SEE EXAMPLE 1

26. $8y^3$ and $28y$
$4y$

27. $9a^2b^3$, $15ab^2$, and $21a^4b^3$
$3ab^2$

28. $18m^2$ and 25
1

29. x^2y^3 and x^3y^5
x^2y^3

Factor out the GCF from each polynomial.
SEE EXAMPLE 2

30. $12x^2 - 15x$
$3x(4x - 5)$

31. $-4y^4 + 6y^2 - 14y$
$-2y(2y^3 - 3y + 7)$

32. $3m^2 - 10m + 4$
$1(3m^2 - 10m + 4)$

33. $24x^3y^2 - 30x^2y^3 + 12x^2y^4$
$6x^2y^2(4x - 5y + 2y^2)$

The areas of the rectangles are given. Use factoring to find expressions for the missing dimensions.
SEE EXAMPLE 3

34.

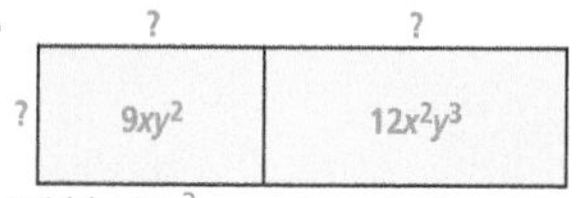
?
?
?
9xy²
12x²y³

Width: $3xy^2$ Length: 3 and $4xy$

35.

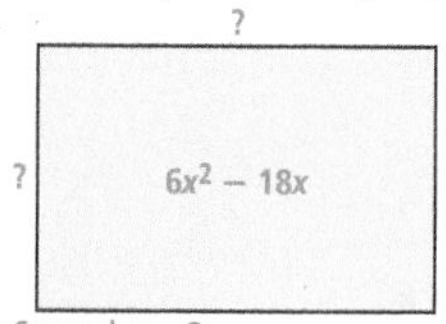
?
?
6x² − 18x

$6x$ and $x - 3$

36.

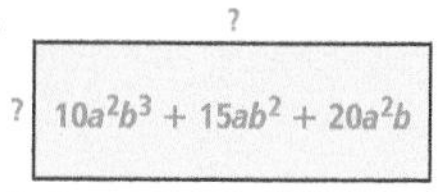
?
?
10a²b³ + 15ab² + 20a²b

$5ab$ and $2ab^2 + 3b + 4a$

37. A farmer wants to plant three rectangular fields so that the widths are the same. The areas of the fields, in square yards, are given by the expressions $12x^2y$, $9xy^2$, and $21xy$. What is the width of the fields if $x = 3$ and $y = 4$?
SEE EXAMPLE 3 36 yd

Answers

38. $V = \pi r^2 h - \left[3\left(\frac{4}{3}\pi r^3\right)\right]$

$V = \pi r^2 h - [4\pi r^3]$

$V = \pi r^2 (h - 4r)$

39. $10x^2 - 4x$

$2x(5x - 2)$

40. $24x^2 - 6\pi x^2$. Yes, $24x^2 - 6\pi x^2 > \pi x^2$, so there is enough dough

43. **Part A** Face A: $3x + 1$ by x; Face B: $x + 1$ by x; Face C: $3x + 1$ by $x + 1$

Part B $3x^2 + 4x + 1$

Part C $14x^2 + 12x + 2$

Part D $3x^3 + 4x^2 + x$

AVAILABLE **ONLINE**

Practice Tutorial

Mixed Review Available Online

PRACTICE & PROBLEM SOLVING

APPLY

38. Model With Mathematics Write an expression in factored form to represent the volume in the canister not occupied by the tennis balls. Assume the canister is cylinder with volume $V = \pi r^2 h$. MP.4

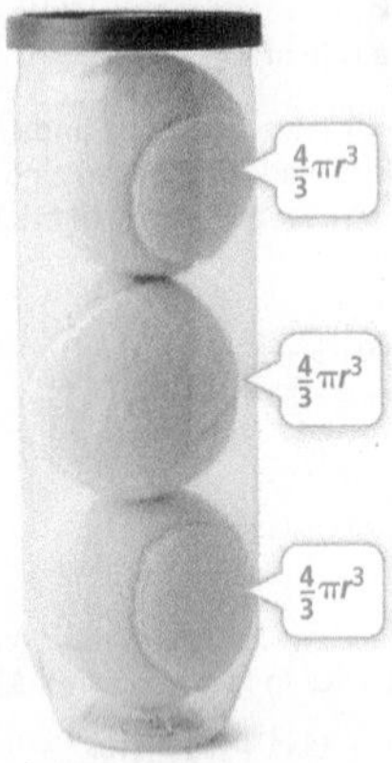

$\frac{4}{3}\pi r^3$
$\frac{4}{3}\pi r^3$
$\frac{4}{3}\pi r^3$

39. Use Structure Determine the GCF and write the expression in factored form. MP.7

$(6x^2 + 4x) + (4x^2 - 8x)$

40. Make Sense and Persevere A sheet of dough has six identical circles cut from it. Write an expression in factored form to represent the approximate amount of dough that is remaining. Is there enough dough for another circle? MP.1

x

ASSESSMENT PRACTICE

41. Fill in the blanks to find the factor pairs for $18x^4 + 12x^3 - 24x^2$.

$\square$	$6x^2 + 4x - 8$
$2x$	$\square x^{\square} + \square x^{\square} - \square x$
$x^{\square}$	$18x^2 + 12x - 24$
$\square x^{\square}$	$3x^2 + 2x - 4$

$3x^2$; 9; 3; 6; 2; 12; 2; 6; 2

42. SAT/ACT The area of a rectangle is $12x^3 - 18x^2 + 6x$. The width is equal to the GCF. What could the dimensions of the rectangle be?

Ⓐ $6x(2x^2 - 3x)$

Ⓑ $3(4x^3 - 6x^2 + 2x)$

Ⓒ $x(12x^2 - 18x + 6)$

Ⓓ $6x(2x^2 - 3x + 1)$

43. Performance Task Camilla is designing a platform for an athletic awards ceremony. The areas for two of the three faces of a platform are given.

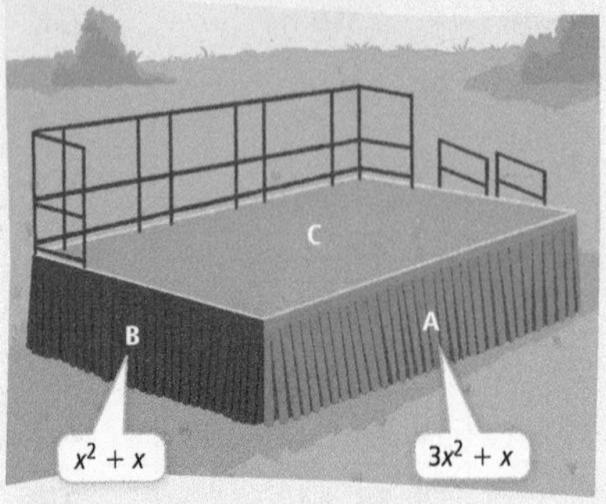

C
B
A
$x^2 + x$
$3x^2 + x$

Part A What are the dimensions of each face of the platform?

Part B What is the area of the top of the platform?

Part C What expression represents the surface area of the entire platform, including the bottom?

Part D What expression represents the volume of the platform?

LESSON QUIZ

Use the Lesson Quiz to assess students' understanding of the mathematics in the lesson.

Students can take the Lesson Quiz online or you can download a printable copy from **SavvasRealize.com**. The Lesson Quiz is also available in the *Assessment Resources* book.

Item Analysis

Item	DOK	Standards
1	2	HSA.APR.A.1
2	1	HSA.APR.A.1
3	2	HSA.APR.A.1
4	2	HSA.APR.A.1
5	2	HSA.APR.A.1

RtI Use the student scores on the Lesson Quiz to prescribe differentiated assignments.

If students take the Lesson Quiz online, it will be automatically scored and appropriate differentiated practice will be assigned based on student performance.

I Intervention	0–3 points	• Reteach to Build Understanding • Mathematical Literacy and Vocabulary • Additional Practice
O On-Level	4 points	• Mathematical Literacy and Vocabulary • Additional Practice • Enrichment
A Advanced	5 points	• Enrichment

AVAILABLE **ONLINE**

7-4 Lesson Quiz

1. What is the prime factorization of 60?

Review progress Question 1 of 5 Go Back Next

ASSESSMENT RESOURCES

Name ________

enVision Algebra 1

PearsonRealize.com

7-4 Lesson Quiz

Factoring Polynomials

1. Which expression(s) have a greatest common factor (GCF) of $3xy^2$ with $42xy^4$? Select all that apply.
   - Ⓐ $6x^2y^2$
   - Ⓑ $15xy^2z$
   - Ⓒ $27x^3y^2$
   - Ⓓ $9xy^3$
2. What is the GCF of the terms of the polynomial $-15y^4 + 12y^2 - 9y$?
   $3y$
3. Factor out the GCF from the terms of the polynomial $-2x^5 - 6x^3 - 16x^2$.
   - Ⓐ $-2x(x^4 + 3x^2 + 8x)$
   - Ⓑ $-2x^2(x^3 + 3x + 8)$
   - Ⓒ $-2x^2(-x^3 - 3x - 8)$
   - Ⓓ The polynomial is already fully factored.
4. Factor out the GCF from the terms of the polynomial $2x^3 - 5x^2 + 25$.
   - Ⓐ $x^2(2x - 5) + 25$
   - Ⓑ The polynomial is already fully factored.
   - Ⓒ $2x^3 - 5(x^2 - 5)$
   - Ⓓ $2(x^3 - 2.5x^2 + 12.5)$
5. Factor out the GCF from the terms of the polynomial $-4y^5 + 6y^3 + 8y^2 - 2y$.
   $-2y(2y^4 - 3y^2 - 4y + 1)$

enVision™ **Algebra 1** • Assessment Resources

Assess | Tutorials | Worksheets

DIFFERENTIATED RESOURCES

I = Intervention O = On-Level A = Advanced

= This activity is available as a digital assignment powered by MathXL® for School.

AVAILABLE ONLINE

Reteach to Build Understanding I

Provides scaffolded reteaching for the key lesson concepts.

Name

7-4 Reteach to Build Understanding

Factoring Polynomials

enVision Algebra 1 — PearsonRealize.com

1. For the polynomial, circle the common factors to determine the GCF and write it in the blank. Use the GCF to write the factored form of the polynomial.

$12x^3y^3 - 8x^2y + 30x$

$2 \times 2 \times 3 \times x \times x \times x \times y \times y \times y$ $\quad -1 \times 2 \times 2 \times 2 \times x \times x \times y$ $\quad 2 \times 3 \times 5 \times x$

GCF: $2x$

Factored polynomial: $2x$ $(6x^2y^3 - 4xy + 15)$

2. Circle the GCF of the polynomial $15x^2y^3 + 10xy^2 + 5y$.
Use the GCF to write the factored form of the polynomial.

$15x^2y^3 + 10xy^2 + 5y$

$3 \times 5 \times x \times x \times y \times y \times y$ $\quad 2 \times 5 \times x \times y \times y$ $\quad 5 \times y$

GCF: $5y$

Factored polynomial: $5y(3x^2y^2 + 2xy + 1)$

3. James incorrectly factored the polynomial. Find and correct his error.

$14x^3y^2 + 42x^2y^2 - 10xy^2$

$2 \times 7 \times x \times x \times x \times y \times y$ $\quad 2 \times 3 \times 7 \times x \times x \times y \times y$ $\quad -2 \times 5 \times x \times y \times y$

The greatest common factor is xy^2.

The factored form of the polynomial is $xy^2(14x^2 + 42x - 10)$.

James should have factored the last term as $-1 \times 2 \times 5 \times x \times y \times y$. The correct greatest common factor is $2xy^2$, and the correct factored form is $2xy^2(7x^2 + 21x - 5)$.

enVision™ Algebra 1 • Teaching Resources

Additional Practice I O

Provides extra practice for each lesson.

Name

7-4 Additional Practice

Factoring Polynomials

enVision Algebra 1 — PearsonRealize.com

Find the GCF of the terms of each polynomial.

1. $6x^2 + 10$ — 2
2. $12x^2 - 16x$ — $4x$
3. $-24y^4 + 30y^3$ — $6y^3$
4. $4x^2y - 8xy^2$ — $4xy$
5. $6x^2y^3 + 9xy^2$ — $3xy^2$
6. $-15x^4y^2 - 25x^3y^3$ — $-5x^3y^2$

Factor out the GCF from each polynomial.

7. $4x^2 - 8x - 6$ — $2(x^2 - 4x - 3)$
8. $8x^3 + 12x^2 - 4x$ — $4x(2x^2 + 3x - 1)$
9. $-3y^2 + 9y - 3$ — $-3(y^2 - 3y + 1)$
10. $2x^2y - 4xy + 6xy^2$ — $2xy(x - 2 + 3y)$
11. $12x^4 - 16x^3 + 8x^2 - 28x$ — $4x(3x^3 - 4x^2 + 2x - 7)$
12. $4x^2 + 6xy - 14y^2$ — $2(2x^2 + 3xy - 7y^2)$
13. Explain why the terms of the polynomial $y^2 + 7$ are said to be relatively prime.
Sample answer: The two terms of the polynomial share no common factors other than 1.
14. Write a trinomial of degree 3 in standard form with a GCF of $6x$. Factor out the GCF from your trinomial.
Sample answer: $12x^3 + 18x^2 + 24x$; $6x(2x^2 + 3x + 4)$
15. A rectangle has an area of $14y^3 - 35y$.
a. What are expressions for the length and width where one dimension is the GCF?
Sample answer: $7y$ and $2y^2 - 5y$
b. Does a rectangle exist with the given dimensions if $y = 2$? Explain.
Sample answer: No, the dimensions would be 14 and −2, and dimensions of a rectangle cannot be zero or negative.

enVision™ Algebra 1 • Teaching Resources

Enrichment O A

Presents engaging problems and activities that extend the lesson concepts.

Name

7-4 Enrichment

Factoring Polynomials

enVision Algebra 1 — PearsonRealize.com

The expressions given in the table are either the greatest common factor or a factor of each polynomial. Use the GCF to factor each of the following polynomials. Some expressions may be used more than once. If the polynomial cannot be factored, enter PRIME in the GCF column.

x^3y	$(3x^3 + x^3y^2 + 5y)$	$(x - 8)$	$11x^2y$
$(4 + 7x - 7y)$	$6xy^2$	$(5x^2y^7 + 6)$	$18y$
$5x$	$(3x + y - 2x^2y^4)$	$7x^3$	$(2x^3 - 3xy + 4y^5)$
$(1 + 5y)$	$-7x^3$	$(x - y)$	$(3xy + y^2 - 2x^2y^5)$

	GCF	Polynomial Factored
1. $5x^2 - 40x$	$5x$	$5x(x - 8)$
2. $3x^4y + x^3y^2 - 2x^5y^5$	x^3y	$x^3y(3x + y - 2x^2y^4)$
3. $12x^2 - 11y$	PRIME	
4. $12x^4y^2 - 18x^2y^3 + 24xy^7$	$6xy^2$	$6xy^2(2x^3 - 3xy + 4y^5)$
5. $54x^3y + 18x^3y^3 + 90y^2$	$18y$	$18y(3x^3 + x^3y^2 + 5y)$
6. $4(x - y) + 7(x - y)^2$	$(x - y)$	$(x - y)(4 + 7x - 7y)$
7. $-35x^5y^7 - 42x^3$	$-7x^3$	$-7x^3(5x^2y^7 + 6)$
8. $11x^2y + 55x^2y^2$	$11x^2y$	$11x^2y(1 + 5y)$
9. $30x^3y^9 + 36xy^2$	$6xy^2$	$6xy^2(5x^2y^7 + 6)$
10. $21x^4y + 7x^3y^2 - 14x^5y^5$	$7x^3$	$7x^3(3xy + y^2 - 2x^2y^5)$

enVision™ Algebra 1 • Teaching Resources

Mathematical Literacy and Vocabulary I O

Helps students develop and reinforce understanding of key terms and concepts.

Name

7-4 Mathematical Literacy and Vocabulary

Factoring Polynomials

enVision Algebra 1 — PearsonRealize.com

There are two sets of note cards that show how Brittany factored the polynomial $(5x^5 + 15x^3 + 4x^2)$. The set on the left explains her thinking. The set on the right shows her steps. Write her thinking and her steps in the correct order on the blank cards.

Think Cards	Write Cards
Factor each term of the polynomial.	$x^2(5x^3 + 15x + 4)$
Simplify.	The GCF is $x \cdot x$, or x^2.
Find the GCF of the three terms.	$5x^5 + 15x^3 + 4x^2 = x^2(5x^3) + x^2(15x) + x^2(4)$
Factor out the GCF from each term.	$5x^5 = 5 \cdot x \cdot x \cdot x \cdot x \cdot x$ $15x^3 = 3 \cdot 5 \cdot x \cdot x \cdot x$ $4x^2 = 2 \cdot 2 \cdot x \cdot x$

Think	Write
First, she should factor each term of the polynomial.	Step 1: $5x^5 = 5 \cdot x \cdot x \cdot x \cdot x \cdot x$ $15x^3 = 3 \cdot 5 \cdot x \cdot x \cdot x$ $4x^2 = 2 \cdot 2 \cdot x \cdot x$
Second, she should find the GCF of the three terms.	Step 2: The GCF is $x \cdot x$, or x^2.
Next, she should factor out the GCF from each term.	Step 3: $5x^5 + 15x^3 + 4x^2 = x^2(5x^3) + x^2(15x) + x^2(4)$
Finally, she should simplify.	Step 4: $x^2(5x^3 + 15x + 4)$

enVision™ Algebra 1 • Teaching Resources

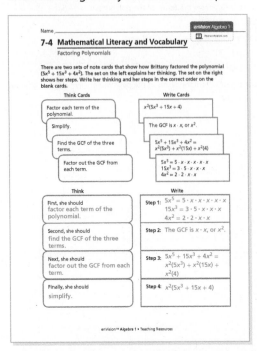

Digital Resources and Video Tutorials I O A

The **Reteach to Build Understanding, Additional Practice**, and **Enrichment** activities are available as digital assignments powered by MathXL for School. These activities are automatically assigned when students complete the lesson quiz online and are automatically scored.

Students can access instructional tutorials using the **Virtual Nerd app.**

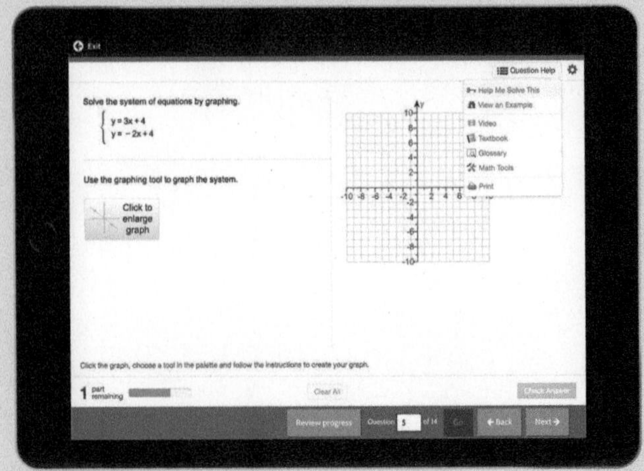
Solve the system of equations by graphing.
Use the graphing tool to graph the system.
Click to enlarge graph
Question Help
Clear All
Check Answer
Review progress
Back
Next

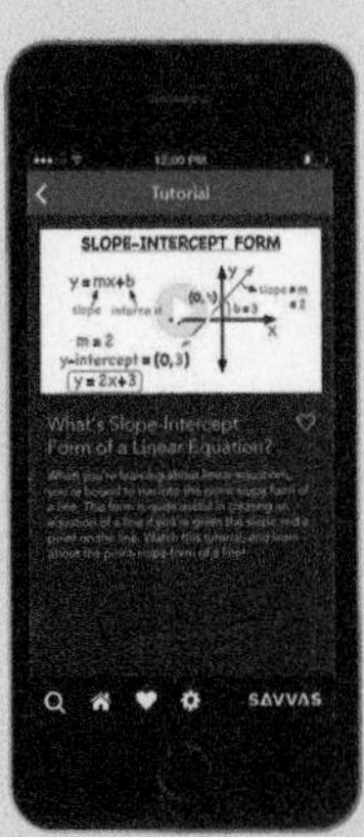
Tutorial
SLOPE-INTERCEPT FORM
SAVVAS

Students can also access Virtual Nerd videos using the **BouncePages app** to scan exercise pages marked with this icon. Students can download both apps for free in their mobile devices' app store.

SavvasRealize.com

A-Z Glossary

LESSON 7-5
Factoring $x^2 + bx + c$

Lesson Overview

FOCUS

Objective

Students will be able to:

✔ Factor a trinomial in the form $x^2 + bx + c$ by finding two binomial factors whose product is equal to the trinomial.

✔ Identify patterns in the signs of the coefficients of the terms of a trinomial expression and use those patterns to determine the signs of the second terms in the binomial factors.

✔ Factor trinomials in the context of solving real-world problems.

Essential Understanding

When a trinomial is in the form $x^2 + bx + c$, the factors are found by identifying a pair of integer factors of c that have a sum of b and then using the factors to write binomials that have a product equal to the trinomial.

COHERENCE

Previously in this course, students:

- Factored polynomials by finding the greatest common factor of the terms.

In this lesson, students:

- Factor a trinomial in the form $x^2 + bx + c$ by finding a pair of integer factors of c that have a sum of b and then using the factors of c to write the binomial factors of $x^2 + bx + c$.

Later in this topic, students will:

- Find the factors of a quadratic trinomial by first factoring out a common factor and then factoring out a binomial.

RIGOR

This lesson emphasizes a blend of *procedural skill and fluency* and *application*.

- Students use patterns in the signs of the coefficients for the terms in the polynomial to determine the signs of the second terms of the binomials; for example, when c is negative, the second terms of the binomials have opposite signs.
- Students apply factoring trinomials to solve real-world problems, such as finding the dimensions of the largest amount of wall space that is needed for a closet system that has three different sizes of storage units.

Vocabulary Builder

REVIEW VOCABULARY — **English** | *Spanish*

- **binomial factor** | *factor binomio*
- **Distributive Property** | *propiedad distributiva*
- **factor** | *factor*
- **greatest common factor** | *máximo comuún divisor*
- **monomial** | *monomio*
- **polynomial** | *polinomio*

VOCABULARY ACTIVITY

Review the term *factor* with students. Up to this point, students have thought of factors as *monomials*, such as in the case of integer factors, or the *greatest common factor* of a *polynomial*. In this lesson, students expand their understanding of the term factor to include *binomial factors*.

Have students identify the monomial and binomial factors in the factored form of the polynomials shown.

$12xy + 8x = 4x(3y + 8)$ [monomial factor: $4x$; binomial factor: $3y + 8$]

$x^2 + 6x + 9 = (x + 3)(x + 3)$ [binomial factor: $x + 3$]

$x^2 - 4 = (x - 2)(x + 2)$ [binomial factors: $x - 2$, $x + 2$]

Student Companion

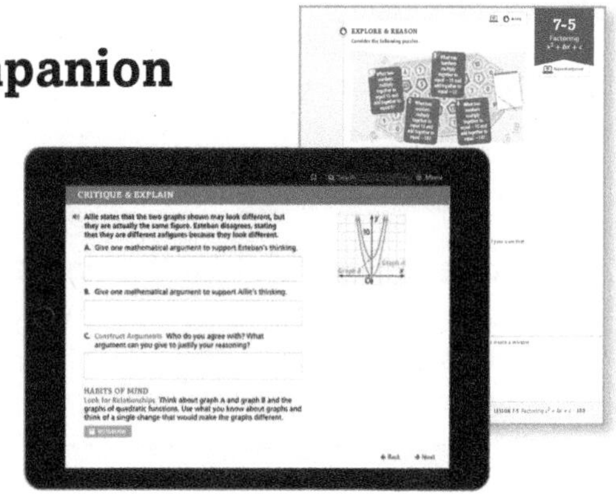

Students can do their in-class work for the lesson on pages 153–156 of their *Student Companion* or in Savvas Realize.

Mathematics Overview — COMMON CORE STANDARDS

Content Standards

In this lesson, students focus on this standards:

HSA.SSE.A.1.A Interpret parts of an expression, such as terms, factors, and coefficients.

Mathematical Practice Standards

This standard is highlighted in this lesson:

MP.5 Use Appropriate Tools Strategically

Students identify when to use tools, such as tables to organize factors and their sums and algebra tiles to verify that they have found the correct factor pairs.

Activity

EXPLORE & REASON

INSTRUCTIONAL FOCUS Students discover patterns while finding the product of a pair of numbers and then the sum of the same pair of numbers. This leads students to use these patterns to determine whether the factors should be positive or negative.

STUDENT COMPANION Students can complete the *Explore & Reason* activity on page 153 of their *Student Companion*.

Before WHOLE CLASS

Implement Tasks that Promote Reasoning and Problem Solving ETP

Q: What do you notice about all of the puzzle questions?
[The puzzle questions involve multiplying two numbers and then adding the same numbers together.]

During SMALL GROUP

Support Productive Struggle in Learning Mathematics ETP

Q: What patterns are similar and what patterns are different amongst the puzzles?
[The products of puzzles A and B and puzzles C and D are the same. The sums of the two numbers cause puzzles A and C and puzzles B and D to each have numbers with opposite signs.]

For Early Finishers

Q: Create 4 additional number puzzles.
Solve your puzzles and describe the patterns.
[Check students' work.]

After WHOLE CLASS

Facilitate Meaningful Mathematical Discourse ETP

Q: How can you use the patterns you discovered?
[The patterns can help you recognize whether the numbers you are trying to find should be positive or negative. For example, when the product of two numbers are positive but their sum is negative, then you know both numbers should be negative.]

Use with **EXPLORE & REASON**

HABITS OF MIND

Make Sense and Persevere Can you choose any pair of integers to create a solvable puzzle? Explain. **MP.1**

[Yes, as long as you state both the sum of the integers and the product of the integers.]

AVAILABLE **ONLINE**

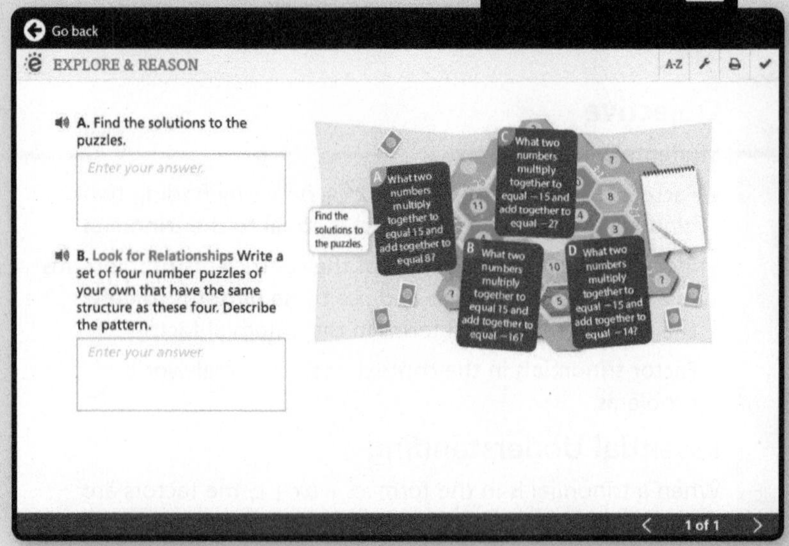

Go back
EXPLORE & REASON
A. Find the solutions to the puzzles.
Enter your answer.
B. Look for Relationships Write a set of four number puzzles of your own that have the same structure as these four. Describe the pattern.
Enter your answer.
1 of 1

STUDENT EDITION, PAGE 287

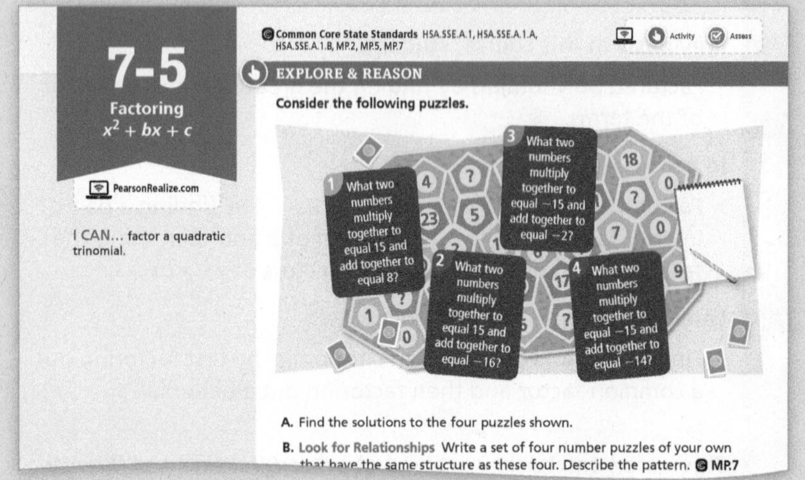

7-5
Factoring $x^2 + bx + c$
PearsonRealize.com
I CAN… factor a quadratic trinomial.
Common Core State Standards HSA.SSE.A.1, HSA.SSE.A.1.A, HSA.SSE.A.1.B, MP.2, MP.5, MP.7
EXPLORE & REASON
Consider the following puzzles.
What two numbers multiply together to equal 15 and add together to equal 8?
What two numbers multiply together to equal 15 and add together to equal −16?
What two numbers multiply together to equal −15 and add together to equal −2?
What two numbers multiply together to equal −15 and add together to equal −14?
A. Find the solutions to the four puzzles shown.
B. Look for Relationships Write a set of four number puzzles of your own that have the same structure as these four. Describe the pattern. MP.7

SAMPLE STUDENT WORK

A. A: 3 and 5; B: -1 and -15; C: -5 and 3; D: -15 and 1

B. What two numbers multiply together to equal 21 and add together to equal 10?
What two numbers multiply together to equal -21 and add together to equal 4?
What two numbers multiply together to equal 21 and add together to equal -22?
What two numbers multiply together to equal -21 and add together to equal 20?
All of these puzzles ask for factors of 21.

INTRODUCE THE ESSENTIAL QUESTION

Establish Mathematics Goals to Focus Learning ETP

Introduce students to factoring polynomials in the form $x^2 + bx + c$. Remind them that multiplying binomials relates to factoring trinomials. Explain that there are patterns that can help them factor polynomials.

AVAILABLE ONLINE

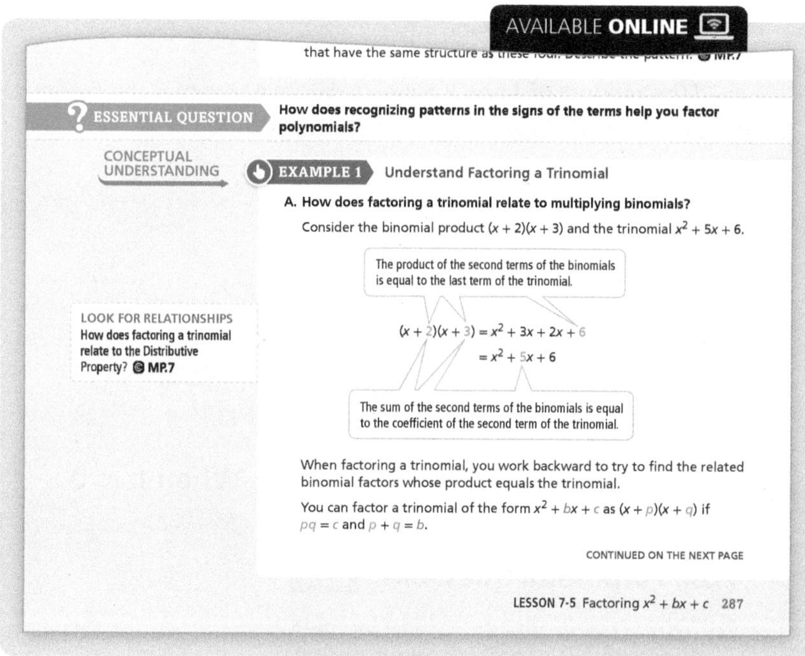
that have the same structure as these four. Describe the pattern. MP.7

ESSENTIAL QUESTION How does recognizing patterns in the signs of the terms help you factor polynomials?

CONCEPTUAL UNDERSTANDING

EXAMPLE 1 Understand Factoring a Trinomial

A. How does factoring a trinomial relate to multiplying binomials?

Consider the binomial product $(x + 2)(x + 3)$ and the trinomial $x^2 + 5x + 6$.

The product of the second terms of the binomials is equal to the last term of the trinomial.

$(x + 2)(x + 3) = x^2 + 3x + 2x + 6$
$= x^2 + 5x + 6$

The sum of the second terms of the binomials is equal to the coefficient of the second term of the trinomial.

LOOK FOR RELATIONSHIPS How does factoring a trinomial relate to the Distributive Property? MP.7

When factoring a trinomial, you work backward to try to find the related binomial factors whose product equals the trinomial.

You can factor a trinomial of the form $x^2 + bx + c$ as $(x + p)(x + q)$ if $pq = c$ and $p + q = b$.

CONTINUED ON THE NEXT PAGE

LESSON 7-5 Factoring $x^2 + bx + c$ 287

EXAMPLE 1 Understand Factoring a Trinomial

Pose Purposeful Questions ETP

Q: In Part A, how can you determine the two numbers that factor the trinomial?
[Find two factors so that the product of the second terms of the binomial factors equals the constant c and the sum of the second terms of the binomial factors equals the coefficient b.]

ADDITIONAL EXAMPLES

AVAILABLE ONLINE

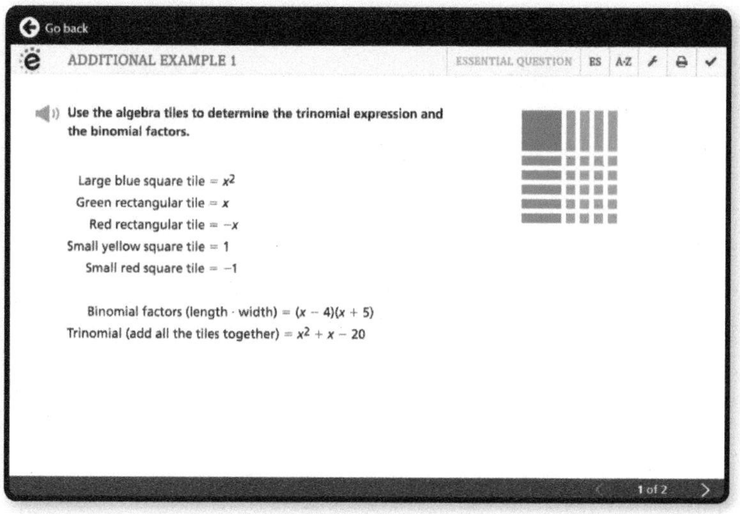
Go back
ADDITIONAL EXAMPLE 1
ESSENTIAL QUESTION ES A-Z
Use the algebra tiles to determine the trinomial expression and the binomial factors.
Large blue square tile = x²
Green rectangular tile = x
Red rectangular tile = −x
Small yellow square tile = 1
Small red square tile = −1
Binomial factors (length · width) = (x − 4)(x + 5)
Trinomial (add all the tiles together) = x² + x − 20
1 of 2

Example 1 Help students transition to using algebra tiles to find trinomial expressions with a negative factor.

Q: How can you use algebra tiles to determine a trinomial expression and the binomial factors of a trinomial?
[Add "like tiles" together to find the trinomial expression. The first term of each binomial factor is x because $x \cdot x = x^2$, which the blue tile represents. Then count the number of green tiles and red tiles to get the second terms of each binomial factor.]

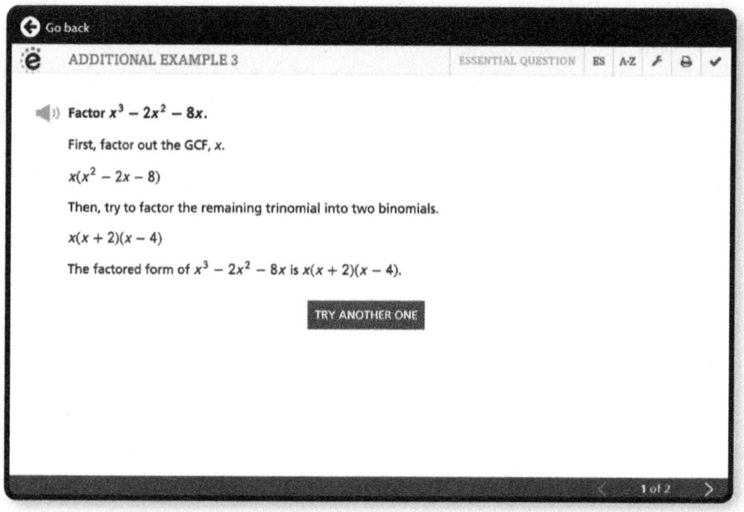
Go back
ADDITIONAL EXAMPLE 3
ESSENTIAL QUESTION ES A-Z
Factor x³ − 2x² − 8x.
First, factor out the GCF, x.
x(x² − 2x − 8)
Then, try to factor the remaining trinomial into two binomials.
x(x + 2)(x − 4)
The factored form of x³ − 2x² − 8x is x(x + 2)(x − 4).
TRY ANOTHER ONE
1 of 2

Example 3 Help students recognize x as a common factor before factoring trinomial expressions.

Q: How do you factor $x^3 - 5x^2 - 6x$? [Factor x out first. Then find the pair of factors whose product equals –6 and sum equals –5.]

EXAMPLE 1 CONTINUED

Q: In Part B, why are 1 and 6 not the correct factor pair of $x^2 + 5x + 6$?
[The product of 1 and 6 equals 6, but the sum of 1 and 6 does not equal 5.]

Try It! Answers

1. a. $(x + 9)(x + 4)$

   b. $(x + 7)(x + 4)$

Elicit and Use Evidence of Student Thinking ETP

Q: How do you decide on the factored form of Try It 1a?
[Find a factor pair of 36 that has a sum of 13.]

EXAMPLE 2 Factor $x^2 + bx + c$, When $b < 0$ and $c > 0$

Pose Purposeful Questions ETP

Q: Why do both factors need to be negative?
[because b is negative and c is positive]

Q: Can there be more than one pair of integers that are factors of c with a sum of b?
[No, the largest exponent in the trinomial is 2, so there can only be two solutions for x. Since factors of $x^2 + bx + c$ help find the solution for x, there can only be one pair of factors.]

Try It! Answers

2. a. $(x - 5)(x - 3)$

   b. $(x - 7)(x - 6)$

Elicit and Use Evidence of Student Thinking ETP

Q: What can you assume about both sets of factors for the Try Its before factoring the trinomials?
[Both factors will be negative because b is negative and c is positive.]

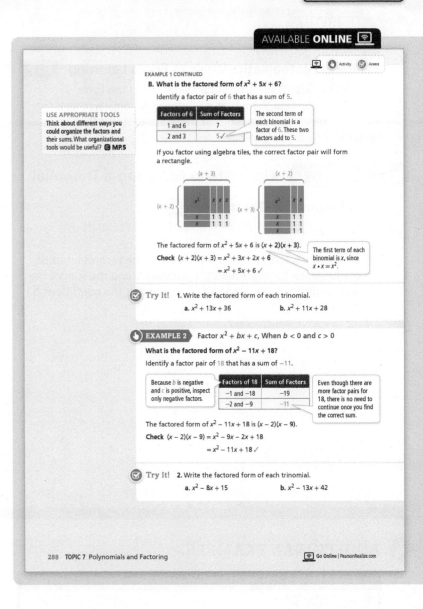

AVAILABLE **ONLINE**

Activity Assess

EXAMPLE 1 CONTINUED

B. What is the factored form of $x^2 + 5x + 6$?

Identify a factor pair of 6 that has a sum of 5.

USE APPROPRIATE TOOLS
Think about different ways you could organize the factors and their sums. What organizational tools would be useful? MP.5

Factors of 6	Sum of Factors
1 and 6	7
2 and 3	5 ✓

The second term of each binomial is a factor of 6. These two factors add to 5.

If you factor using algebra tiles, the correct factor pair will form a rectangle.

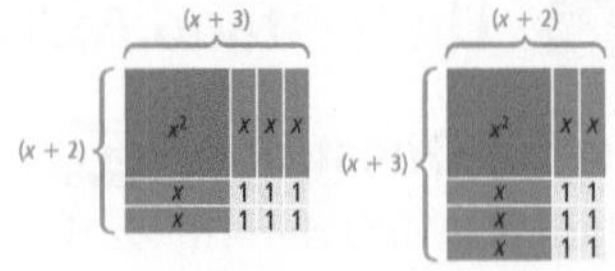

(x + 3)
(x + 2)
x²
x x x
x
x
1 1 1
1 1 1
(x + 2)
(x + 3)
x²
x x
x
x
x
1 1
1 1
1 1

The factored form of $x^2 + 5x + 6$ is $(x + 2)(x + 3)$.

Check $(x + 2)(x + 3) = x^2 + 3x + 2x + 6$
$= x^2 + 5x + 6$ ✓

The first term of each binomial is x, since $x \cdot x = x^2$.

Try It! 1. Write the factored form of each trinomial.

a. $x^2 + 13x + 36$ b. $x^2 + 11x + 28$

EXAMPLE 2 Factor $x^2 + bx + c$, When $b < 0$ and $c > 0$

What is the factored form of $x^2 - 11x + 18$?

Identify a factor pair of 18 that has a sum of −11.

Because b is negative and c is positive, inspect only negative factors.

Factors of 18	Sum of Factors
−1 and −18	−19
−2 and −9	−11

Even though there are more factor pairs for 18, there is no need to continue once you find the correct sum.

The factored form of $x^2 - 11x + 18$ is $(x - 2)(x - 9)$.

Check $(x - 2)(x - 9) = x^2 - 9x - 2x + 18$
$= x^2 - 11x + 18$ ✓

Try It! 2. Write the factored form of each trinomial.

a. $x^2 - 8x + 15$ b. $x^2 - 13x + 42$

288 TOPIC 7 Polynomials and Factoring Go Online | PearsonRealize.com

RtI Struggling Students

USE WITH EXAMPLE 2 Some students struggle with finding the correct factor pairs. Have students practice finding factor pairs and the sum of the factors.

Q: What are the factors of 5, −5, 12, and −12?
[5: −1 and −5, 1 and 5;
−5: −1 and 5, −5 and 1;
12: −1 and −12, 1 and 12, −2 and −6, 2 and 6, −3 and −4, 3 and 4,
−12: −1 and 12, 1 and −12, −2 and 6, 2 and −6, −3 and 4, 3 and −4]

Q: What are the sums for 4 of these factors? [Answers may vary. Sample: $-1 + -5 = -6$; $-1 + 5 = 4$; $2 + 6 = 8$; $3 + -4 = -1$]

EXAMPLE 3 Factor $x^2 + bx + c$, When $c < 0$

Pose Purposeful Questions ETP

Q: Why do the factors have opposite signs?
[because b is positive and c is negative]

Q: Why are 1 and –6 not the correct factor pair of $x^2 + 5x - 6$?
[Although 1 and –6 is a factor pair of –6, it is not a sum of 5 since $1 + (-6) = -5$.]

Try It! Answers

3. a. $(x - 7)(x + 2)$

b. $(x + 8)(x - 2)$

Common Error

Try It! 3a Since b and c are negative, some students may think the factors of the trinomial are both negative. The factors actually have opposite signs. Instead of students trying to memorize which sign the factors have, encourage the students to ask which factor pairs have a product of c and a sum of b.

HABITS OF MIND

Use with **EXAMPLES 1, 2, & 3**

Use Structure If both b and c are negative, will the factors both be negative? Explain. MP.7

[No, if c is negative, then one of the factors must be positive because the product of the two negative numbers is positive.]

EXAMPLE 4 Factor a Trinomial With Two Variables

Pose Purposeful Questions ETP

Q: In Part A, why are there two variables in the middle term of the trinomial?
[The first term of each binomial has an x and the second term of each binomial has a y, so when multiplying the first and last terms and the last and first terms, you get xy in the product.

Q: In Part B, how do you know where y should be placed in the factored form of the trinomial?
[Since the last term of the trinomial is $24y^2$, the product of the second term in each binomial equals $24y^2$.]

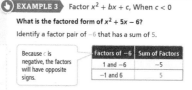

AVAILABLE ONLINE

Activity Assess

EXAMPLE 3 Factor $x^2 + bx + c$, When $c < 0$

What is the factored form of $x^2 + 5x - 6$?

Identify a factor pair of –6 that has a sum of 5.

COMMON ERROR
You may think that the pairs of factors 1, –6 and –1, 6 are the same. However, the sums of the two factors are different.

Because c is negative, the factors will have opposite signs.

Factors of –6	Sum of Factors
1 and –6	–5
–1 and 6	5

The factored form of $x^2 + 5x - 6$ is $(x - 1)(x + 6)$.

Try It! 3. Write the factored form of each trinomial.
a. $x^2 - 5x - 14$ b. $x^2 + 6x - 16$

EXAMPLE 4 Factor a Trinomial With Two Variables

A. How does multiplying binomials in two variables relate to factoring trinomials?

Consider the following binomial products.

$(x + 2y)(x + 4y) = x^2 + 6xy + 8y^2$

$(x - 3y)(x + 5y) = x^2 + 2xy - 15y^2$

$(x - 7y)(x - 9y) = x^2 - 16xy - 63y^2$

Each trinomial has the form $x^2 + bxy + cy^2$. Trinomials of this form are factorable when there is a factor pair of c that has a sum of b.

B. What is the factored form of $x^2 + 10xy + 24y^2$?

Identify a factor pair of 24 that has a sum of 10.

Factors of 24	Sum of Factors
3 and 8	11
4 and 6	10

STUDY TIP
When factoring a trinomial with two variables, make sure the factors contain both variables. Check your answer to determine whether you factored correctly.

The factored form of $x^2 + 10xy + 24y^2$ is $(x + 4y)(x + 6y)$.

Check $(x + 4y)(x + 6y) = x^2 + 6xy + 4xy + 24y^2$
$= x^2 + 10xy + 24y^2$ ✓

Try It! 4. Write the factored form of each trinomial.
a. $x^2 + 12xy + 32y^2$ b. $x^2 - 10xy + 21y^2$

LESSON 7-5 Factoring $x^2 + bx + c$ 289

Try It! Answers

4. a. $(x + 8y)(x + 4y)$

b. $(x - 3y)(x - 7y)$

ADV Advanced Students

USE WITH EXAMPLE 4 Have students extend their knowledge of factoring a trinomial with two variables to factoring trinomials with two variables and a coefficient before x^2.

Q: Factor the trinomial $2x^2 - 22xy - 24y^2$.
[$2(x + y)(x - 12y)$]

Q: What steps can you use to factor this trinomial?
[Sample: Factor 2 out of the trinomial first. Then find the factor pair of –12 and that has a sum of –11. Include y in the second term of each binomial.]

Activity Assess

EXAMPLE 5 Apply Factoring Trinomials

Use and Connect Mathematical Reasoning ETP

Q: What does x represent?
[x represents the height and width of one size storage unit, and the height of another size storage unit.]

Q: What is meant by *wall area*?
[Wall area, or wall space, is the area of the closet wall that is covered by the storage units.]

Q: How does the trinomial compare to the closet storage system?
[The trinomial is the wall area of the closet.]

Q: Why is the trinomial factored?
[in order to find the length and width of the closet wall]

Try It! Answer

5. $(x + 1)$ ft by $(x + 11)$ ft

HABITS OF MIND

Use with **EXAMPLES 4 & 5**

Model With Mathematics How might factoring a trinomial into a pair binomial factors relate to a situation in a physical world? MP.4

[Factoring a trinomial into its binomial factors allows you to find the zeros of the expression, which are important in real-world applications. For instance, trinomials can be used to model vertical motion, and the zeros indicate when the object has reached the ground.]

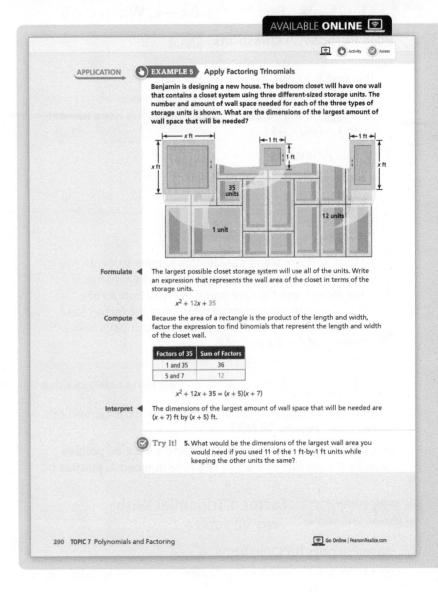

AVAILABLE **ONLINE**

Activity Assess

APPLICATION

EXAMPLE 5 Apply Factoring Trinomials

Benjamin is designing a new house. The bedroom closet will have one wall that contains a closet system using three different-sized storage units. The number and amount of wall space needed for each of the three types of storage units is shown. What are the dimensions of the largest amount of wall space that will be needed?

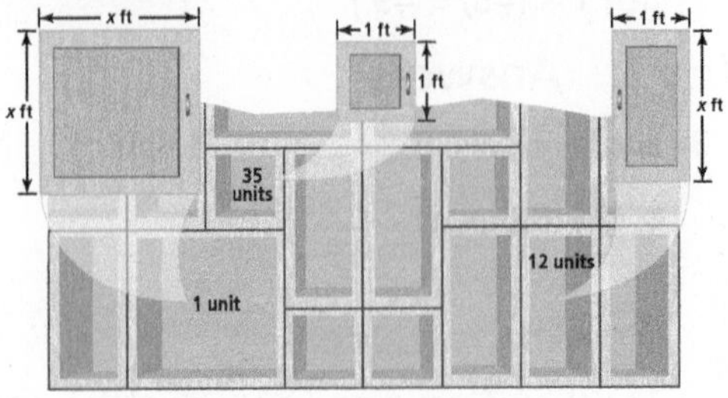

x ft
1 ft
1 ft
1 ft
x ft
x ft
35 units
12 units
1 unit

Formulate ◀ The largest possible closet storage system will use all of the units. Write an expression that represents the wall area of the closet in terms of the storage units.

$x^2 + 12x + 35$

Compute ◀ Because the area of a rectangle is the product of the length and width, factor the expression to find binomials that represent the length and width of the closet wall.

Factors of 35	Sum of Factors
1 and 35	36
5 and 7	12

$x^2 + 12x + 35 = (x + 5)(x + 7)$

Interpret ◀ The dimensions of the largest amount of wall space that will be needed are $(x + 7)$ ft by $(x + 5)$ ft.

Try It! **5.** What would be the dimensions of the largest wall area you would need if you used 11 of the 1 ft-by-1 ft units while keeping the other units the same?

290 TOPIC 7 Polynomials and Factoring

Go Online | PearsonRealize.com

ELL English Language Learners *(Use with* **EXAMPLE 5***)*

WRITING BEGINNING Have students measure their textbooks with a ruler and record the length and the width of their textbook in their journals. Have students repeat the process with a different book found in the room. Explain that the measurements that describe an object are called the *dimensions* of the object.

Q: In your journals, estimate the size of one wall in a walk-in closet.
[Sample: 8 ft by 8 ft]

Q: In your journals, sketch a picture of what a closet system might look like along a wall with the *dimensions* you estimated.
[Check students' work.]

READING INTERMEDIATE Record the following phrases on the board and ask students to read them: a central heating *system*; a computer *system*; the decimal *system*; your body's digestive *system*.

Q: What do all of the *systems* noted on the board have in common?
[They are a group or set of things that all work together.]

Q: Read the first two sentences of the example. What is a closet system?
[a system of shelves and boxes that fit together to provide organized storage in a closet]

LISTENING ADVANCED Many students confuse the terms *expression* and *equation*. Listen to the following definitions. An *expression* is a mathematical phrase that involves variables, numbers, and operations. An *equation* is a mathematical sentence that states that two expressions are equal. Have the students listen to you read the following mathematical phrases aloud. Ask students to identify them as expressions or equations.

Q: $x + 3$ [expression]

Q: $y - 4 = 10$ [equation]

Q: $7 + 8 = 15$ [equation]

Q: $x^2 - 16$ [expression]

CONCEPT SUMMARY Factoring $x^2 + bx + c$

Q: How do the values of b and c in the trinomial $x^2 + bx + c$ affect the factors signs?
[When b and c are positive, then the second terms of the binomials are both positive. When b is negative and c is positive, then the second terms of the binomials are both negative. When c is negative, the second terms of the binomials have opposite signs.]

Do You UNDERSTAND? | Do You KNOW HOW?

Common Error

Exercise 6 Some students may find a pair of factors that have a product −21, such as −7 and 3, but may think that it doesn't matter which factor is negative. Have the students check to make sure the factor pairs equal c and have a sum of b while paying close attention to the signs of both b and c.

Answers

1. You can use patterns to determine whether factors are positive or negative, giving you a starting point.
2. When c is negative in $x^2 + bx + c$, then factors have opposite signs.
3. Factor out any common factors. Factoring out any common factors allows you to more clearly see what patterns to use when factoring.
4. Answers may vary. Sample: Look at the binomial factors of the polynomial $(x + n)$ and $(x + m)$. When you multiply them you get $x^2 + mx + nx + mn$, so c in the trinomial $x^2 + bx + c$ is equivalent to mn.
5. 1 and 16, 2 and 8, 4 and 4
6. −1 and 21, 1 and −21, −3 and 7, 3 and −7
7. both negative
8. opposite signs
9.

Factors of 12	Sum of Factors
−1 and −12	−13
−3 and −4	−7
−2 and −6	−8

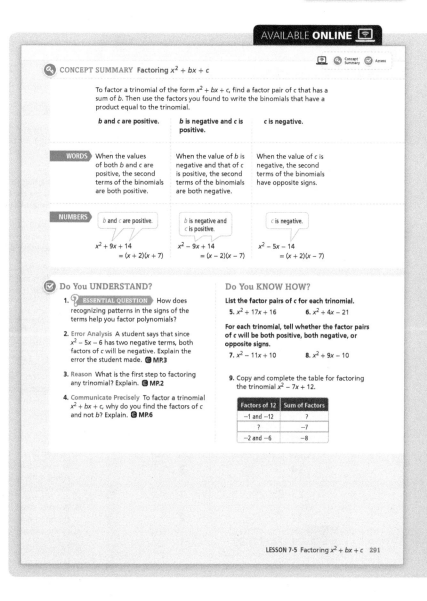

AVAILABLE ONLINE

CONCEPT SUMMARY Factoring $x^2 + bx + c$

To factor a trinomial of the form $x^2 + bx + c$, find a factor pair of c that has a sum of b. Then use the factors you found to write the binomials that have a product equal to the trinomial.

	b and c are positive.	**b is negative and c is positive.**	**c is negative.**
WORDS	When the values of both b and c are positive, the second terms of the binomials are both positive.	When the value of b is negative and that of c is positive, the second terms of the binomials are both negative.	When the value of c is negative, the second terms of the binomials have opposite signs.
NUMBERS	b and c are positive. $x^2 + 9x + 14 = (x + 2)(x + 7)$	b is negative and c is positive. $x^2 - 9x + 14 = (x - 2)(x - 7)$	c is negative. $x^2 - 5x - 14 = (x + 2)(x - 7)$

Do You UNDERSTAND?

1. ESSENTIAL QUESTION How does recognizing patterns in the signs of the terms help you factor polynomials?
2. Error Analysis A student says that since $x^2 - 5x - 6$ has two negative terms, both factors of c will be negative. Explain the error the student made. MP.3
3. Reason What is the first step to factoring any trinomial? Explain. MP.2
4. Communicate Precisely To factor a trinomial $x^2 + bx + c$, why do you find the factors of c and not b? Explain. MP.6

Do You KNOW HOW?

List the factor pairs of c for each trinomial.

5. $x^2 + 17x + 16$
6. $x^2 + 4x - 21$

For each trinomial, tell whether the factor pairs of c will be both positive, both negative, or opposite signs.

7. $x^2 - 11x + 10$
8. $x^2 + 9x - 10$

9. Copy and complete the table for factoring the trinomial $x^2 - 7x + 12$.

Factors of 12	Sum of Factors
−1 and −12	?
?	−7
−2 and −6	−8

LESSON 7-5 Factoring $x^2 + bx + c$ 291

Practice Tutorials Math Tools

PRACTICE & PROBLEM SOLVING

AVAILABLE **ONLINE**

Lesson Practice You may opt to have students complete the automatically scored Practice and Problem Solving items online powered by MathXL for School.

Choose from: **Lesson Practice**

Adaptive Practice

You may also take advantage of the bank of exercises for assigning additional practice.

Assignment Guide

Basic	Advanced
10–31, 36–41	10–18, 21, 24–41

Item Analysis

Example	Items	DOK
1	18–20, 22, 26, 30, 33, 34	1
	10, 11	2
	14	3
2	23, 25, 29	1
	12, 16	2
3	21, 24, 27, 39	1
	13, 40	2
4	28, 31, 32, 35	1
	15	2
5	17, 36, 37, 41	2
	38	3

AVAILABLE **ONLINE**

PRACTICE & PROBLEM SOLVING

Scan for Multimedia

Practice Tutorial

Additional Exercises Available Online

UNDERSTAND

10. Mathematical Connections Explain how factoring a trinomial is like factoring a number. Explain how it is different.

11. Use Appropriate Tools How can you use algebra tiles to factor a trinomial? How do you determine the binomial factors from an algebra tile model? MP.5

12. Look for Relationships How are the binomial factors of $x^2 + 7x - 18$ and $x^2 - 7x - 18$ similar? How are they different? MP.7

13. Error Analysis Describe and correct the error a student made in making a table in order to factor the trinomial $x^2 - 11x - 26$. MP.3

Factors	Sum of Factors
−1 and 11	10
1 and −11	−10

The trinomial $x^2 - 11x - 26$ is not factorable because no factors of b sum to c.

X

14. Higher Order Thinking Given that the trinomial $x^2 + bx + 8$ is factorable as $(x + p)(x + q)$, with p and q being integers, what are four possible values of b?
6, 9, −6, −9

15. Reason What is missing from the last term of the trinomial $x^2 + 5xy + 4$ so that it is factorable as the product of binomials? MP.2
Sample: multiply 4 by y^2.

16. Look for Structure How does the sign of the last term of a trinomial help you know what type of factors you are looking for? MP.7

17. Reason A rectangle has an area of $x^2 + 7x + 12$ in.^{2}. Use factoring to find possible dimensions of the rectangle. Explain why you can use factoring to find the answer. MP.2

PRACTICE

Factor each trinomial represented by the algebra tiles. SEE EXAMPLE 1

18. 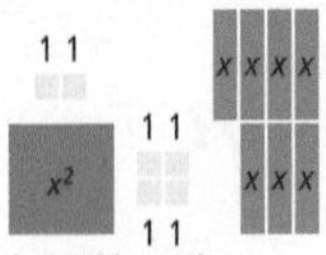
1 1
x^2
1 1
1 1
x x x x
x x x
$(x + 1)(x + 6)$

19. 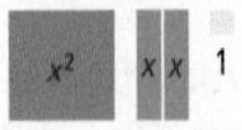
x^2
x x
1
$(x + 1)(x + 1)$

Complete the table to factor each trinomial.
SEE EXAMPLES 1 AND 3

20. $x^2 + 9x + 20$

Factors of c	Sum of Factors
?	?
?	9
?	?

21. $x^2 + 9x - 22$

Factors of c	Sum of Factors
?	?
?	?
?	9
?	?

Write the factored form of each trinomial.
SEE EXAMPLES 1, 2, 3, 4, AND 5

22. $x^2 + 15x + 44$
$(x + 11)(x + 4)$

23. $x^2 - 11x + 24$
$(x - 8)(x - 3)$

24. $x^2 + 2x - 15$
$(x + 5)(x - 3)$

25. $x^2 - 13x + 30$
$(x - 10)(x - 3)$

26. $x^2 + 9x + 18$
$(x + 6)(x + 3)$

27. $x^2 - 2x - 8$
$(x + 2)(x - 4)$

28. $x^2 + 7xy + 6y^2$
$(x + 6y)(x + y)$

29. $x^2 - 12x + 27$
$(x - 9)(x - 3)$

30. $x^2 + 10x + 16$
$(x + 8)(x + 2)$

31. $x^2 - 16xy + 28y^2$
$(x - 14y)(x - 2y)$

32. $x^2 - 10xy - 11y^2$
$(x - 11y)(x + y)$

33. $x^2 + 16x + 48$
$(x + 12)(x + 4)$

34. $x^2 - 13x - 48$

35. $x^2 + 15xy + 54y^2$

292 TOPIC 7 Polynomials and Factoring

Go Online | PearsonRealize.com

Answers

10. Factoring a trinomial is like factoring a number because in both cases you are writing an expression as a product. They are different because the factors of a trinomial are variable expressions and the factors of a number are numbers.

11. The binomial factors correspond to the length and width of the rectangle that can be formed by the algebra tiles that represent the trinomial.

12. $x^2 + 7x - 18$ factors into $(x + 9)(x - 2)$ and $x^2 - 7x - 18$ factors into $(x - 9)(x + 2)$. The signs are opposite.

13. The student found the factors of b rather than the factors of c. The correct factored form of $x^2 - 11x - 26$ is $(x - 13)(x + 2)$.

16. If the sign of the last term is positive you are looking for either two positive or two negative factors. If the sign of the last term is negative you are looking for one positive and one negative factor.

17. $(x + 3)$ inches by $(x + 4)$ inches; Answers may vary. Sample: Because the area of a rectangle is the product of its length and its width, factoring the total area into two factors gives you possible dimensions of the rectangle.

20.

Factors	Sum of Factors
1×20	21
4×5	9
2×10	12

Answers

21.

Factors	Sum of Factors
-1×22	21
1×-22	-21
-2×11	9
2×-11	-9

34. $(x - 16)(x + 3)$

35. $(x + 9)(x + 6y)$

36. x, $(x + 1)$, $(x + 2)$; One dimension is x units. Another dimension is one unit greater and the third dimension is two units greater.

37. b. $3x - 2$; Add $(x + 8)$, $(x - 5)$, and $(x - 5)$ to find the total length of rope. No rope is needed for the side along the beach.

38. Sarah cuts 2 in. from one side and 6 in. from the other.

41. Part A field: $(x + 5)$ by $(x + 90)$; picnic area: $(x + 15)$ by $(x + 30)$; playground: $(x + 15)$ by $(x + 20)$

Part B Find the sum of the areas that are given or use the dimensions you found to find the dimension of the park and then multiply to find the total area.

Part C $(x + 90)$ ft by $(2x + 20)$ ft

Part D Yes; Sample answer: You know that $x + 90$ is the same length as $2x + 50$. Set these expressions equal to one another and then solve for x.

AVAILABLE **ONLINE**

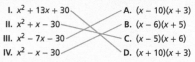

PRACTICE & PROBLEM SOLVING

Practice Tutorial
Mixed Review Available Online

APPLY

36. Make Sense and Persevere The volume of a rectangular box is represented by $x^3 + 3x^2 + 2x$. Use factoring to find possible dimensions of the box. How are the dimensions of the box related to one another? MP.1

37. Model with Mathematics A lake has a rectangular area roped off where people can swim under a lifeguard's supervision. The swimming section has an area of $x^2 + 3x - 40$ square feet, with the long side parallel to the lake shore. MP.4

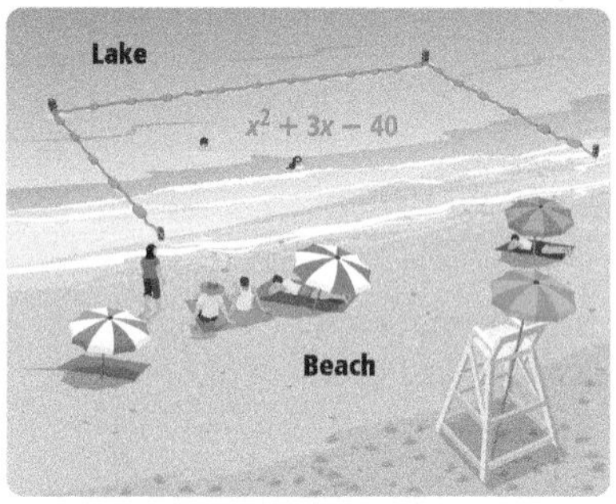
Lake
$x^2 + 3x - 40$
Beach

a. What are possible dimensions of the roped-off area? Use factoring.
$(x + 8)$ feet by $(x - 5)$ feet

b. How much rope is needed for the three sides that are not along the beach? Explain.

c. The rope used to mark the swimming area is 238 ft long. What is x when the total length of rope is 238 ft? 80 ft

38. Make Sense and Persevere Sarah has a large square piece of foam for an art project. The side lengths of the square are x in. To fit her project, Sarah cuts a section of foam from two of the sides so she now has a rectangle. How much foam does Sarah cut from each of the two sides? MP.1

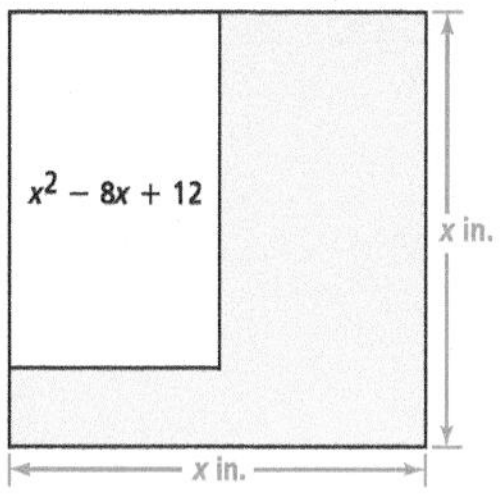
$x^2 - 8x + 12$
x in.
x in.

ASSESSMENT PRACTICE

39. Match each trinomial with its factored form.

I. $x^2 + 13x + 30$ — A. $(x - 10)(x + 3)$
II. $x^2 + x - 30$ — B. $(x - 6)(x + 5)$
III. $x^2 - 7x - 30$ — C. $(x - 5)(x + 6)$
IV. $x^2 - x - 30$ — D. $(x + 10)(x + 3)$

40. SAT/ACT What is the factored form of $4x^3 - 24x^2 - 28x$?

Ⓐ $4x(x - 7)(x + 1)$
Ⓑ $4x(x - 1)(x + 7)$
Ⓒ $x(x - 7)(x + 4)$
Ⓓ $x(x - 4)(x + 7)$
Ⓔ $4(x - 7)(x - 1)$

41. Performance Task A city is designing the layout of a new park. The park will be divided into several different areas, including a field, a picnic area, and a recreation area. One design of the park is shown below.

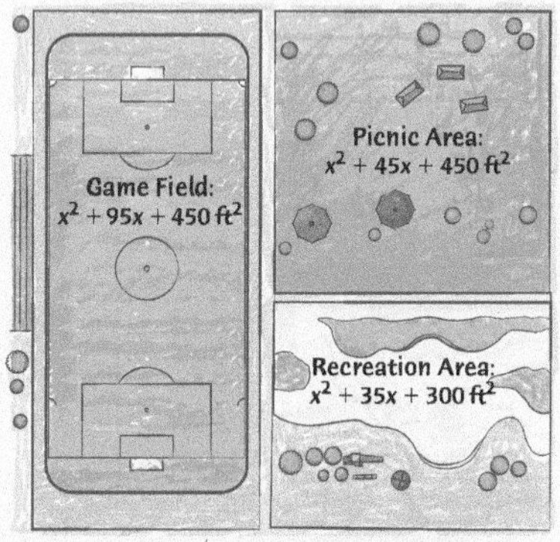
Game Field:
$x^2 + 95x + 450$ ft^2
Picnic Area:
$x^2 + 45x + 450$ ft^2
Recreation Area:
$x^2 + 35x + 300$ ft^2

Part A Use factoring to find the dimensions of each of the three areas of the park shown

Part B Describe two different ways to find the total area of the park.

Part C What are the dimensions of the entire park?

Part D Can you find the value of x? Explain.

LESSON QUIZ

Use the Lesson Quiz to assess students' understanding of the mathematics in the lesson.

Students can take the Lesson Quiz online or you can download a printable copy from **SavvasRealize.com**. The Lesson Quiz is also available in the *Assessment Resources* book.

Item Analysis

Item	DOK	Standards
1	1	HSA.SSE.A.1.A
2	1	HSA.SSE.A.1.A
3	2	HSA.SSE.A.1.A
4	2	HSA.SSE.A.1.A
5	2	HSA.SSE.A.1.A

RtI Use the student scores on the Lesson Quiz to prescribe differentiated assignments.

If students take the Lesson Quiz online, it will be automatically scored and appropriate differentiated practice will be assigned based on student performance.

I Intervention	0–3 points	• Reteach to Build Understanding • Mathematical Literacy and Vocabulary • Additional Practice
O On-Level	4 points	• Mathematical Literacy and Vocabulary • Additional Practice • Enrichment
A Advanced	5 points	• Enrichment

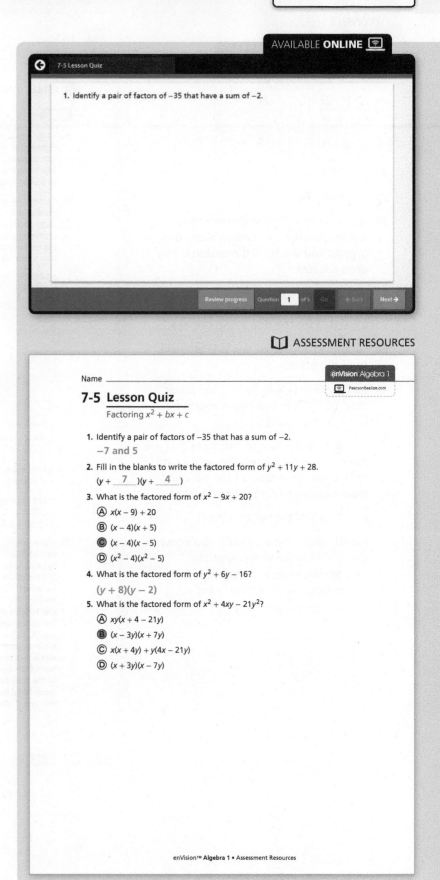

AVAILABLE **ONLINE**

7-5 Lesson Quiz

1. Identify a pair of factors of −35 that have a sum of −2.

Review progress Question 1 of 5 Go ← Back Next →

ASSESSMENT RESOURCES

Name

enVision Algebra 1

PearsonRealize.com

7-5 Lesson Quiz

Factoring $x^2 + bx + c$

1. Identify a pair of factors of −35 that has a sum of −2.

   −7 and 5

2. Fill in the blanks to write the factored form of $y^2 + 11y + 28$.

   $(y + \underline{7})(y + \underline{4})$

3. What is the factored form of $x^2 - 9x + 20$?

   Ⓐ $x(x - 9) + 20$

   Ⓑ $(x - 4)(x + 5)$

   Ⓒ $(x - 4)(x - 5)$

   Ⓓ $(x^2 - 4)(x^2 - 5)$

4. What is the factored form of $y^2 + 6y - 16$?

   $(y + 8)(y - 2)$

5. What is the factored form of $x^2 + 4xy - 21y^2$?

   Ⓐ $xy(x + 4 - 21y)$

   Ⓑ $(x - 3y)(x + 7y)$

   Ⓒ $x(x + 4y) + y(4x - 21y)$

   Ⓓ $(x + 3y)(x - 7y)$

enVision™ **Algebra 1** • Assessment Resources

SavvasRealize.com

Assess | Tutorials | Worksheets

DIFFERENTIATED RESOURCES

I = Intervention O = On-Level A = Advanced

= This activity is available as a digital assignment powered by MathXL® for School.

AVAILABLE ONLINE

Reteach to Build Understanding I

Provides scaffolded reteaching for the key lesson concepts.

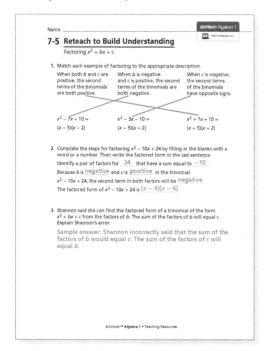

Name

enVision Algebra 1

7-5 Reteach to Build Understanding

Factoring $x^2 + bx + c$

1. Match each example of factoring to the appropriate description.

When both b and c are positive, the second terms of the binomials are both positive. | When b is negative and c is positive, the second terms of the binomials are both negative. | When c is negative, the second terms of the binomials have opposite signs.

$x^2 - 7x + 10 = (x - 5)(x - 2)$ | $x^2 - 3x - 10 = (x - 5)(x + 2)$ | $x^2 + 7x + 10 = (x + 5)(x + 2)$

2. Complete the steps for factoring $x^2 - 10x + 24$ by filling in the blanks with a word or a number. Then write the factored form in the last sentence.
Identify a pair of factors for 24 that have a sum equal to −10.
Because b is negative and c is positive in the trinomial $x^2 - 10x + 24$, the second term in both factors will be negative.
The factored form of $x^2 - 10x + 24$ is $(x - 4)(x - 6)$.

3. Shannon said she can find the factored form of a trinomial of the form $x^2 + bx + c$ from the factors of b. The sum of the factors of b will equal c. Explain Shannon's error.
Sample answer: Shannon incorrectly said that the sum of the factors of b would equal c. The sum of the factors of c will equal b.

enVision™ Algebra 1 • Teaching Resources

Additional Practice I O

Provides extra practice for each lesson.

Name

enVision Algebra 1

7-5 Additional Practice

Factoring $x^2 + bx + c$

Write the factored form of each trinomial.

1. $x^2 + 7x + 10$ — $(x + 5)(x + 2)$
2. $x^2 + 13x + 30$ — $(x + 10)(x + 3)$
3. $x^2 + 12x + 32$ — $(x + 8)(x + 4)$
4. $x^2 - 8x + 15$ — $(x - 5)(x - 3)$
5. $x^2 - 14x + 45$ — $(x - 9)(x - 5)$
6. $x^2 - 17x + 52$ — $(x - 13)(x - 4)$
7. $x^2 + 9x - 10$ — $(x + 10)(x - 1)$
8. $x^2 + x - 42$ — $(x + 7)(x - 6)$
9. $x^2 - 4x - 60$ — $(x - 10)(x + 6)$
10. $x^2 + 12xy + 27y^2$ — $(x + 9y)(x + 3y)$
11. $x^2 - 18xy + 56y^2$ — $(x - 14y)(x - 4y)$
12. $x^2 - xy - 42y^2$ — $(x - 7y)(x + 6y)$
13. $x^2 - 22xy + 85y^2$ — $(x - 17y)(x - 5y)$
14. $x^2 + 15xy - 76y^2$ — $(x + 19y)(x - 4y)$
15. $x^2 + 16xy + 55y^2$ — $(x + 11y)(x + 5y)$
16. Suppose you want to factor the expression $x^2 + 2xn + n^2$. Given that $n > 0$, what are the factors? Explain.
Sample answer: $(x + n)(x + n)$; n can be any positive number.
17. A parallelogram has an area of $x^2 + 9x - 36$.
a. What are expressions for the length and width of the parallelogram?
Sample answer: $(x + 12)$ and $(x - 3)$
b. If x is an integer, what is the least possible value of x for a parallelogram to exist? Explain.
4; Sample answer: Since x is an integer, both dimensions must be positive, so $x > 3$. Hence, $x = 4$ is the least possible integer for a parallelogram to exist.

enVision™ Algebra 1 • Teaching Resources

Enrichment O A

Presents engaging problems and activities that extend the lesson concepts.

Name

enVision Algebra 1

7-5 Enrichment

Factoring $x^2 + bx + c$

To factor the polynomial $x^2 + bx + c$, you need to identify integers with the sum of b and the product of c. Understanding the relationship between b and c is essential to factoring polynomials. When two numbers have a sum of b and a product of c, they are called *factor pairs*.

1. Let $c > 0$. Investigate how c is affected by changes in b. Complete the table.

b	Factor pair	Product (c)	Polynomial	Factored form
2	1, 1	1	$x^2 + 2x + 1$	$(x + 1)(x + 1)$
3	1, 2	2	$x^2 + 3x + 2$	$(x + 1)(x + 2)$
4	1, 3	3	$x^2 + 4x + 3$	$(x + 1)(x + 3)$
	2, 2	4	$x^2 + 4x + 4$	$(x + 2)(x + 2)$
5	1, 4	4	$x^2 + 5x + 4$	$(x + 1)(x + 4)$
	2, 3	6	$x^2 + 5x + 6$	$(x + 2)(x + 3)$
6	1, 5	5	$x^2 + 6x + 5$	$(x + 1)(x + 5)$
	2, 4	8	$x^2 + 6x + 8$	$(x + 2)(x + 4)$
	3, 3	9	$x^2 + 6x + 9$	$(x + 3)(x + 3)$
7	1, 6	6	$x^2 + 7x + 6$	$(x + 1)(x + 6)$
	2, 5	10	$x^2 + 7x + 10$	$(x + 2)(x + 5)$
	3, 4	12	$x^2 + 7x + 12$	$(x + 3)(x + 4)$
8	1, 7	7	$x^2 + 8x + 7$	$(x + 1)(x + 7)$
	2, 6	12	$x^2 + 8x + 12$	$(x + 2)(x + 6)$
	3, 5	15	$x^2 + 8x + 15$	$(x + 3)(x + 5)$
	4, 4	16	$x^2 + 8x + 16$	$(x + 4)(x + 4)$

2. What happens to the number of factor pairs as b increases?
As b increases, the number of factor pairs also increases.
3. Write an expression that provides the number of factor pairs for a value, b. (*Hint*: You need two different expressions describing even and odd values.)
If b is even, there are $\frac{b}{2}$ factor pairs. If b is odd, there are $\frac{b-1}{2}$ factor pairs.
4. Now look at the third column in the table, identifying c. Write an expression for b in terms of c in the case when c is prime.
When c is prime, $b = c + 1$.

enVision™ Algebra 1 • Teaching Resources

Mathematical Literacy and Vocabulary I O

Helps students develop and reinforce understanding of key terms and concepts.

Name

enVision Algebra 1

7-5 Mathematical Literacy and Vocabulary

Factoring $x^2 + bx + c$

For Exercises 1–5, study the equation. Then draw a line from each term in Column A to its definition in Column B. The first one is done for you.

$(x + 4)(x + 8) = x^2 + (8x + 4x) + (4 \cdot 8) = x^2 + 12x + 32$

Column A	Column B
1. 1	coefficient of trinomial's x^2 term
2. 12	binomial
3. 32	coefficient of trinomial's x term
4. $x + 4$	product of $(x + 4)$ and $(x + 8)$
5. $x^2 + 12x + 32$	trinomial's constant term

For Exercises 6–9, complete the definition in Column B that describes the expression in Column A.

$n^2 - 9n - 36 = (n - 12)(n + 3)$

Column A	Column B
6. $(n - 12)(n + 3)$	factored form of $n^2 - 9n - 36$
7. $n^2 - 9n - 36$	three terms; a trinomial
8. −12 and 3	factors of −36
9. −9	sum of −12 and 3

enVision™ Algebra 1 • Teaching Resources

Digital Resources and Video Tutorials I O A

The **Reteach to Build Understanding**, **Additional Practice**, and **Enrichment** activities are available as digital assignments powered by MathXL for School. These activities are automatically assigned when students complete the lesson quiz online and are automatically scored.

Students can access instructional tutorials using the **Virtual Nerd app**.

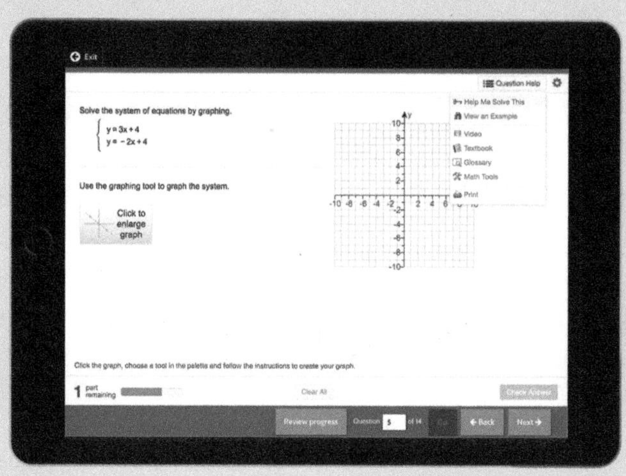

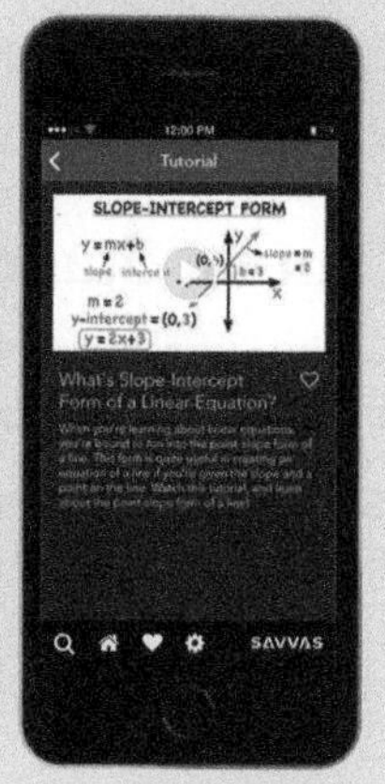

Students can also access Virtual Nerd videos using the **BouncePages app** to scan exercise pages marked with this icon. Students can download both apps for free in their mobile devices' app store.

SavvasRealize.com

Video

TOPIC 7
Mathematical Modeling in 3 Acts: Who's Right?

Lesson Overview

FOCUS

Objective

Students will be able to:

✓ Use mathematical modeling to represent a problem situation and to propose a solution.

✓ Test and verify the appropriateness of their mathematical models.

✓ Explain why the results from their mathematical models might not align exactly with the problem situation.

Essential Understanding

Many real-world problem situations can be represented with a mathematical model, but that model might not represent the real-world situation exactly.

COHERENCE

Earlier in this topic, students:

- Operated with and factored polynomials.

In this lesson, students:

- Develop a mathematical model to represent and propose a solution to a problem situation involving factoring.

Later in this topic, students will:

- Factor quadratic functions in the form $ax^2 + bx + c$ and special cases.

RIGOR

This mathematical modeling lesson focuses on application of both math content and math practices and processes.

- Students draw on their understanding of concepts related to factoring to develop a representative model.
- Students apply their mathematical model to test and validate its applicability to similar problem situations.

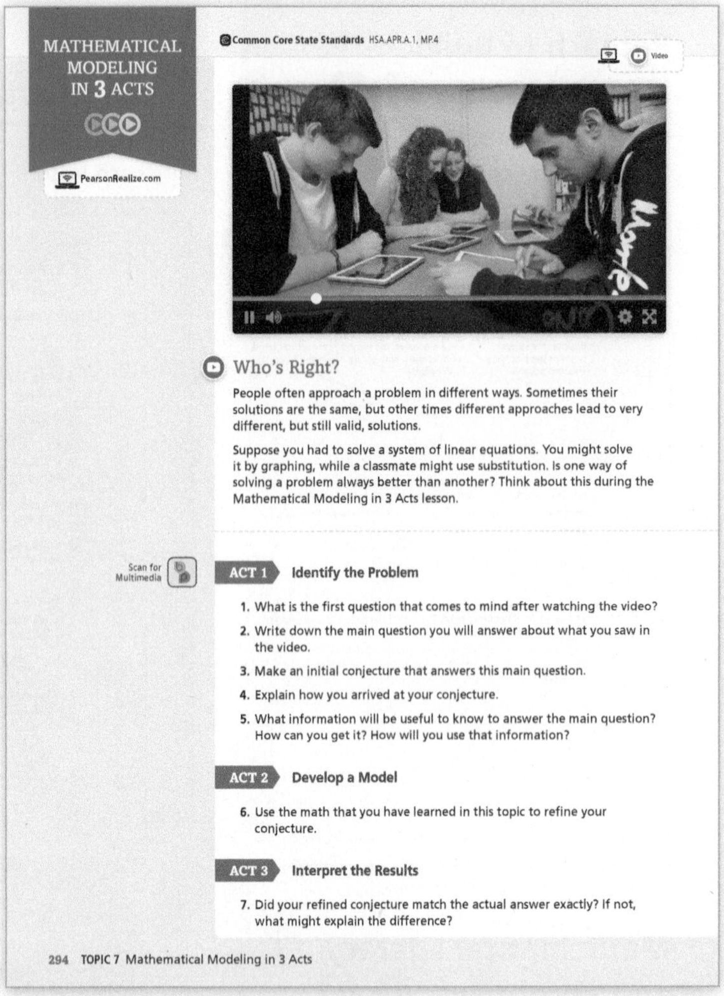
MATHEMATICAL MODELING IN 3 ACTS

PearsonRealize.com

Common Core State Standards HSA.APR.A.1, MP.4

Video

Who's Right?

People often approach a problem in different ways. Sometimes their solutions are the same, but other times different approaches lead to very different, but still valid, solutions.

Suppose you had to solve a system of linear equations. You might solve it by graphing, while a classmate might use substitution. Is one way of solving a problem always better than another? Think about this during the Mathematical Modeling in 3 Acts lesson.

Scan for Multimedia

ACT 1 Identify the Problem

1. What is the first question that comes to mind after watching the video?
2. Write down the main question you will answer about what you saw in the video.
3. Make an initial conjecture that answers this main question.
4. Explain how you arrived at your conjecture.
5. What information will be useful to know to answer the main question? How can you get it? How will you use that information?

ACT 2 Develop a Model

6. Use the math that you have learned in this topic to refine your conjecture.

ACT 3 Interpret the Results

7. Did your refined conjecture match the actual answer exactly? If not, what might explain the difference?

294 TOPIC 7 Mathematical Modeling in 3 Acts

Student Companion

Students can do their work for the task on pages 157–158 of their *Student Companion* or on **SavvasRealize.com.**

Mathematics Overview COMMON CORE STANDARDS

Content Standards

In this lesson, students apply concepts and skills related to Common Core Standards **HSA.APR.A.1**.

HSA.APR.A.1 Understand that polynomials form a system analogous to the integers, namely, they are closed under the operations of addition, subtraction, and multiplication; add, subtract, and multiply polynomials.

Mathematical Practice Standards

MP.4 Model With Mathematics

To solve the problem presented, students identify variables and the relationship among them, develop a model that represents the situation, and use the model to propose a solution. Students interpret their solutions and propose explanations for why their answer may not match the real-world answer.

Students also engage in sense-making **(MP.1)**. In testing their models, students look for patterns in the structure of their models **(MP.7, MP.8)**.

SavvasRealize.com

Video

Who's Right?

In this mathematical modeling task, students will explore and apply concepts related to polynomials and factoring. Students are presented with different algebraic expressions and will be tasked with determining which expression is the factored form. To do so, they apply concepts that they study in Topic 7.

ACT 1 The Hook

Play the video. The video shows four students working on a math problem. The teacher asks them to reveal their answers. The video shows each student's answer, but does not give away which answer is correct.

After the question brainstorming, present to students the Main Question they will be tasked with answering. Remind students to write down their questions and conjectures.

MAIN QUESTION

Which student has the best answer?

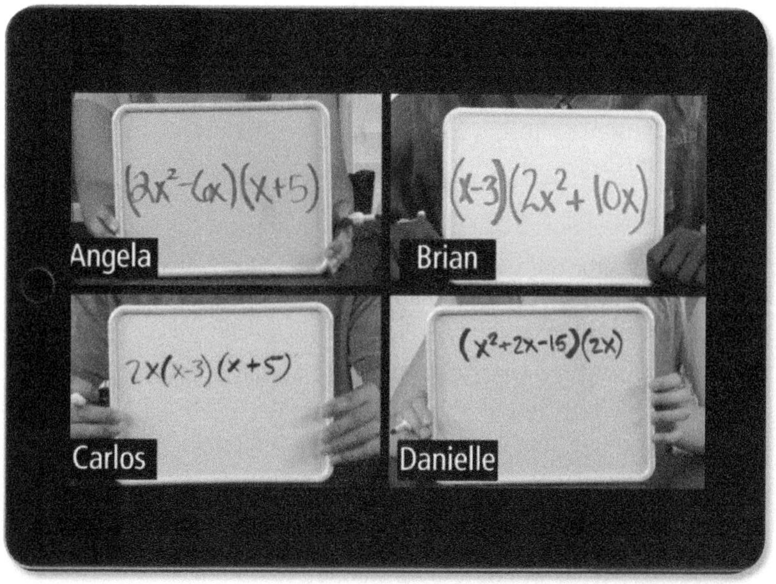

(2x²-6x)(x+5)
Angela
(x-3)(2x²+10x)
Brian
2x(x-3)(x+5)
Carlos
(x²+2x-15)(2x)
Danielle

ACT 2 Modeling With Math

Think about the task. Ask students to speculate how they could determine which answer is best. Then have them think about what information they would need to make a judgment.

Reveal the information. In order to determine which polynomial is best, students will need to know what task the students in the video were given. They will also need the student responses from Act 1.

What's the connection? Give students time to struggle as they think about how their ideas are connected to what they learned in this topic about factoring and polyomials. Ask students how they can determine which responses are equivalent. Can there be more than one completely factored form of the polynomial?

INTERESTING MOMENTS WITH STUDENTS

Students may think that because all of the responses are equivalent, they are all correct. Acknowledge that all four students factored the polynomial correctly. Encourage students to think about why one of the equivalent expressions may be a better answer to the teacher's question than the others are.

Necessary Information

Original question

What is the factored form of $2x^3 + 4x^2 - 30x$?

Student responses

Angela: $(2x^2 - 6x)(x + 5)$

Brian: $(x - 3)(2x^2 + 10x)$

Carlos: $2x(x - 3)(x + 5)$

Danielle: $(x^2 + 2x - 15)(2x)$

Video

ACT 3 The Solution

Play the video. The final video shows that three students did not factor the polynomial completely. The student who factored the polynomial completely is revealed as having the best answer.

Angela
Brian
Carlos
Danielle

MAIN QUESTION ANSWER

Carlos has the best answer because he wrote the only polynomial that is completely in factored form.

Do the "post-game" analysis. Make sure students know that one reason for factoring a polynomial completely is to avoid multiple correct answers. There is only one way to write a polynomial in factored form, just like each number has only one prime factorization. Factoring completely makes it easier to *talk* about polynomials.

ONE POSSIBLE SOLUTION

You can factor the polynomial $2x^3 + 4x^2 - 30x$ by first factoring out 2x from each term, yielding $2x(x^2 + 2x - 15)$, which is Danielle's response.

The factors of the trinomial $x^2 + 2x - 15$ are $(x - 3)(x + 5)$, so the completely factored form of the polynomial is $2x(x - 3)(x + 5)$. Carlos correctly and completely factored the polynomial.

Each of the polynomials is a correctly factored form of $2x^3 + 4x^2 - 30x$. However, Angela, Brian, and Danielle have not completely factored the polynomial. Each of their answers contains a factor that can be further factored.

SEQUEL

As students finish the original task, tell them that the factored form of this polynomial could model the volume of a prism. Ask them to determine the domain of the function $V = 2x^3 + 4x^2 - 30x$. [Sample answer: If $2x$, $x - 3$, and $x + 5$ are the dimensions of the prism, the prism will have positive dimensions and a positive volume for $x > 3$.]

LESSON 7-6
Factoring $ax^2 + bx + c$

SavvasRealize.com

A-Z Glossary

Lesson Overview

FOCUS

Objective

Students will be able to:

✔ Identify the common factor of the coefficients in the terms of a trinomial expression when $a \neq 1$.

✔ Write a quadratic trinomial as a product of two binomial factors.

Essential Understanding

A quadratic trinomial in the form $ax^2 + bx + c$ when $a \neq 1$ can either be factored by grouping or factored by substitution.

COHERENCE

Previously in this topic, students:

- Factored a quadratic trinomial in the form $x^2 + bx + c$.

In this lesson, students:

- Factor a quadratic trinomial in the form $ax^2 + bx + c$ when $a \neq 1$, by grouping and by substitution.

Later in this topic, students will:

- Factor special cases such as perfect square trinomials and the difference of two squares.

RIGOR

This lesson emphasizes a blend of *procedural skill and fluency* and *conceptual understanding*.

- Students factor a trinomial in the form $ax^2 + bx + c$ by finding a factor pair of ac that has a sum of b, rewriting bx as a sum of those factors, factoring out the GCFs twice, and using the Distributive Property to rewrite as the product of two binomials.
- Students understand that when factoring a quadratic trinomial in the form, $ax^2 + bx + c$, if ac and b are both positive, the second terms of the binomials are positive, and if ac is negative, the second terms of the binomials have opposite signs.

Vocabulary Builder

REVIEW VOCABULARY

English | *Spanish*

- **binomial** | *binomio*
- **monomial** | *monomio*
- **quadratic trinomial** | *trinomio cuadrática*
- **trinomial** | *trinomio*

VOCABULARY ACTIVITY

Use prefixes to help students differentiate between the types of polynomials. Ask students to think about words that include the prefixes *mono*, *bi*, and *tri*.

Have students match each of the polynomials to the term that describes them.

$4x^2 + 5x + 1$	monomial
$2x$	binomial
$3x + 4$	trinomial

Students may be confused by the term *quadratic trinomial*. Explain that *trinomial* describes the number of terms in the polynomial and *quadratic* describes an equation in which the highest exponent of a variable is 2.

Student Companion

Students can do their in-class work for the lesson on pages 159–162 of their *Student Companion* or in Savvas Realize.

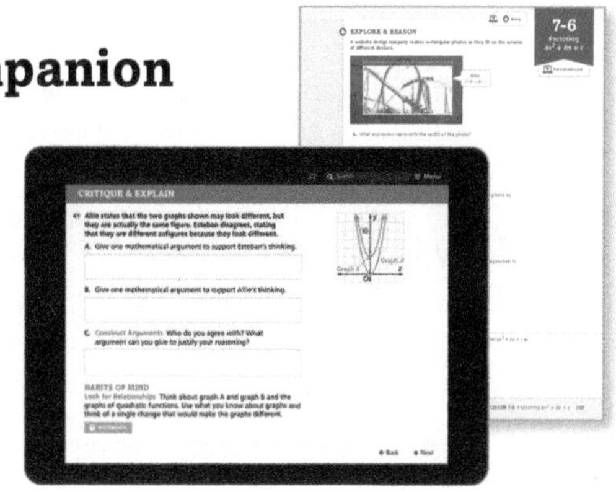

Mathematics Overview — COMMON CORE STANDARDS

Content Standards

In this lesson, students focus on this standard:

HSA.SSE.A.1.A. Interpret parts of an expression, such as terms, factors, and coefficients.

Mathematical Practice Standards

These standards are highlighted in this lesson:

MP.2 Reason Abstractly and Quantitatively

Students make sense of quantities and their relationships when they rule out factor pairs ac that have a sum not equal to the value of the middle coefficient b of the trinomial in the form $ax^2 + bx + c$.

MP.7 Look For and Make Use of Structure

Students recognize that common factors are can be binomials, as well as monomials.

EXPLORE & REASON

INSTRUCTIONAL FOCUS Students will explore finding the expression that represents the width of a photo. This reminds students of the process of factoring trinomials in the form $x^2 + bx + c$, and helps to prepare them to use the process to factor trinomials in the form $ax^2 + bx + c$ when $a \neq 1$.

STUDENT COMPANION Students can complete the *Explore & Reason* activity on page 159 of their *Student Companion*.

Before WHOLE CLASS

Implement Tasks that Promote Reasoning and Problem Solving ETP

Q: Can the expression for the width of the photo be a monomial? [No, a monomial multiplied by a binomial results in a binomial. The area is represented by a trinomial.]

Q: If the expression for the area is a trinomial and the expression for the length is a binomial, what do you know about the expression for the width?
[The expression is a binomial.]

During SMALL GROUP

Support Productive Struggle in Learning Mathematics ETP

Q: What are the restrictions on the values of x for the length and width of the photo?
[The variable can be any number that does not cause the expressions for either the length or width to be less than or equal to zero.]

For Early Finishers

Q: Determine the dimensions of a rectangle with an area of $x^2 + 12x + 35$. Use different values of x to list several possible areas of the rectangle.
[$(x + 5)(x + 7)$; Check students' work.]

After WHOLE CLASS

Facilitate Meaningful Mathematical Discourse ETP

Q: What strategy could you use to factor the trinomial in order to find the width of the photo?
[You could use the value of c to determine what needs to be multiplied by 4 to get 12 and added to 4 to get b, which is 7.]

HABITS OF MIND *Use with* **EXPLORE & REASON**

Make Sense and Persevere Can you factor all trinomials of the form $ax^2 + bx + c$ as $(px + q)(sx + t)$, when a, b, c, p, q, s, and t are integers? Explain. MP.1

[No; even if a, b, and c are integers, they do not always factor.]

AVAILABLE **ONLINE**

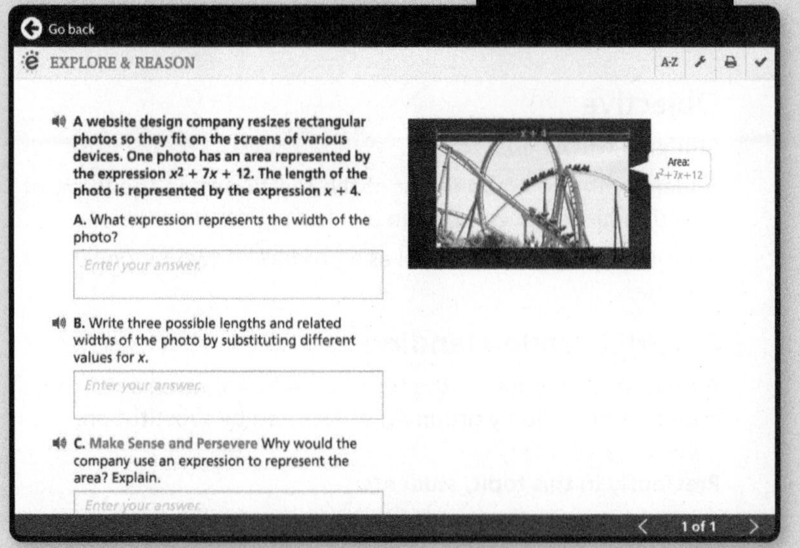

Go back
EXPLORE & REASON
A website design company resizes rectangular photos so they fit on the screens of various devices. One photo has an area represented by the expression $x^2 + 7x + 12$. The length of the photo is represented by the expression $x + 4$.
A. What expression represents the width of the photo?
Enter your answer.
B. Write three possible lengths and related widths of the photo by substituting different values for x.
Enter your answer.
C. Make Sense and Persevere Why would the company use an expression to represent the area? Explain.
Enter your answer.
Area: $x^2+7x+12$
$x + 4$
1 of 1

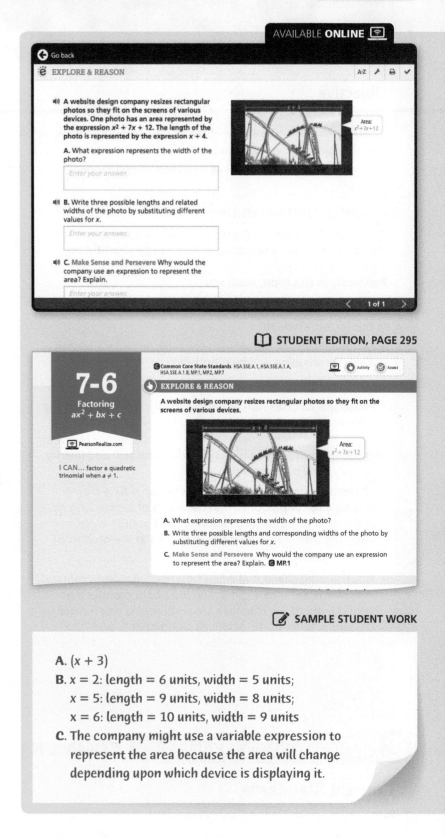

STUDENT EDITION, PAGE 295

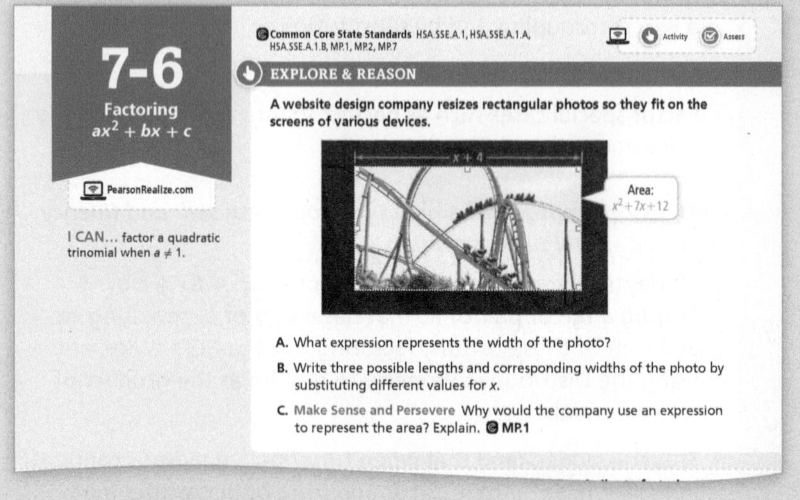

7-6
Factoring $ax^2 + bx + c$
PearsonRealize.com
I CAN… factor a quadratic trinomial when $a \neq 1$.
Common Core State Standards HSA.SSE.A.1, HSA.SSE.A.1.A, HSA.SSE.A.1.B, MP.1, MP.2, MP.7
Activity
Assess
EXPLORE & REASON
A website design company resizes rectangular photos so they fit on the screens of various devices.
$x + 4$
Area: $x^2+7x+12$
A. What expression represents the width of the photo?
B. Write three possible lengths and corresponding widths of the photo by substituting different values for x.
C. Make Sense and Persevere Why would the company use an expression to represent the area? Explain. MP.1

SAMPLE STUDENT WORK

A. $(x + 3)$
B. $x = 2$: length = 6 units, width = 5 units;
$x = 5$: length = 9 units, width = 8 units;
$x = 6$: length = 10 units, width = 9 units
C. The company might use a variable expression to represent the area because the area will change depending upon which device is displaying it.

INTRODUCE THE ESSENTIAL QUESTION

Establish Mathematics Goals to Focus Learning ETP

Introduce students to trinomials in the form $ax^2 + bx + c$ where $a \neq 1$. Remind students that a trinomial is the product of two binomials. Explain that factoring trinomials involves the factors of the product of a and c.

AVAILABLE ONLINE

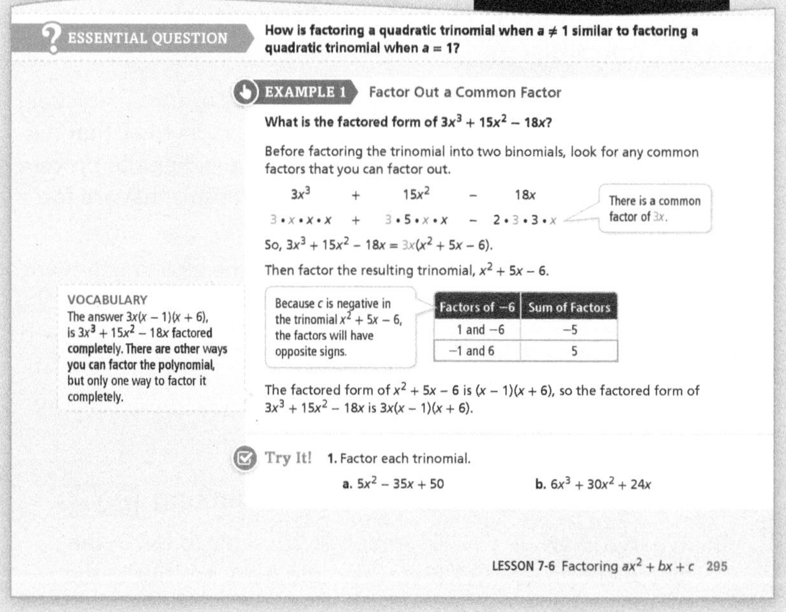

ESSENTIAL QUESTION How is factoring a quadratic trinomial when $a \neq 1$ similar to factoring a quadratic trinomial when $a = 1$?

EXAMPLE 1 Factor Out a Common Factor

What is the factored form of $3x^3 + 15x^2 - 18x$?

Before factoring the trinomial into two binomials, look for any common factors that you can factor out.

$3x^3 \quad + \quad 15x^2 \quad - \quad 18x$

$3 \cdot x \cdot x \cdot x \quad + \quad 3 \cdot 5 \cdot x \cdot x \quad - \quad 2 \cdot 3 \cdot 3 \cdot x$

There is a common factor of $3x$.

So, $3x^3 + 15x^2 - 18x = 3x(x^2 + 5x - 6)$.

Then factor the resulting trinomial, $x^2 + 5x - 6$.

Because c is negative in the trinomial $x^2 + 5x - 6$, the factors will have opposite signs.

Factors of −6	Sum of Factors
1 and −6	−5
−1 and 6	5

The factored form of $x^2 + 5x - 6$ is $(x - 1)(x + 6)$, so the factored form of $3x^3 + 15x^2 - 18x$ is $3x(x - 1)(x + 6)$.

VOCABULARY
The answer $3x(x - 1)(x + 6)$, is $3x^3 + 15x^2 - 18x$ factored completely. There are other ways you can factor the polynomial, but only one way to factor it completely.

Try It! 1. Factor each trinomial.

a. $5x^2 - 35x + 50$ b. $6x^3 + 30x^2 + 24x$

LESSON 7-6 Factoring $ax^2 + bx + c$ 295

EXAMPLE 1 Factor Out a Common Factor

Pose Purposeful Questions ETP

Q: How do you determine whether you can factor out a common factor?
[If each term of the trinomial has a factor in common, it can be factored out.]

Q: Why do you look for and factor out a GCF first?
[If you do not factor out the GCF, one or both of the binomials is still not factored completely.]

Try It! Answers

1. a. $5(x - 5)(x - 2)$ b. $6x(x + 4)(x + 1)$

Elicit and Use Evidence of Student Thinking ETP

Q: How can you check to be sure you factored the GCF out correctly?
[You can multiply the GCF by the factored expression to get the original trinomial expression.]

ADDITIONAL EXAMPLES

AVAILABLE ONLINE

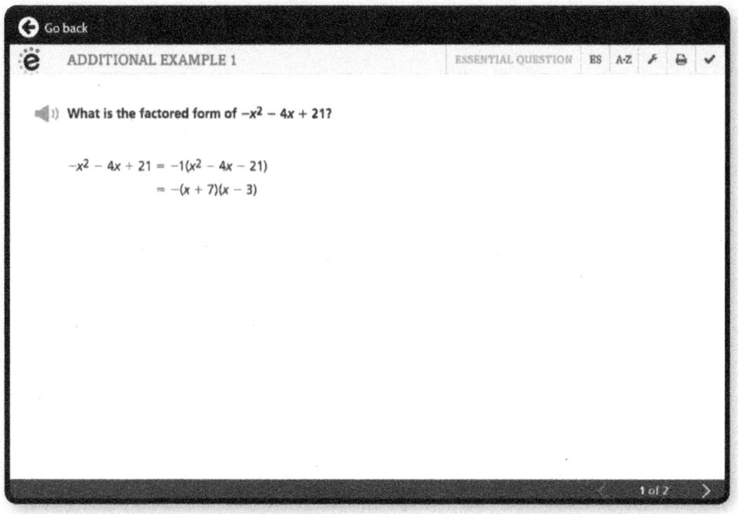

Go back

ADDITIONAL EXAMPLE 1 ESSENTIAL QUESTION ES A-Z

What is the factored form of $-x^2 - 4x + 21$?

$-x^2 - 4x + 21 = -1(x^2 - 4x - 21)$
$= -(x + 7)(x - 3)$

1 of 2

Example 1 Helps students transition to factoring a trinomial where the leading coefficient is negative.

Q: What is an indicator that you need to factor −1 out before factoring the trinomial? [$a = -1$]

Q: What happens when factoring −1 out of a trinomial?
[Each term in the remaining trinomial has the opposite sign.]

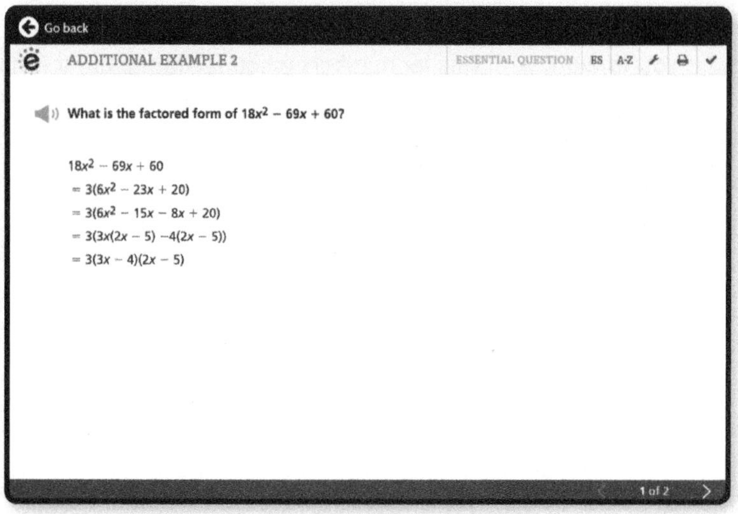

Go back

ADDITIONAL EXAMPLE 2 ESSENTIAL QUESTION ES A-Z

What is the factored form of $18x^2 - 69x + 60$?

$18x^2 - 69x + 60$
$= 3(6x^2 - 23x + 20)$
$= 3(6x^2 - 15x - 8x + 20)$
$= 3(3x(2x - 5) -4(2x - 5))$
$= 3(3x - 4)(2x - 5)$

1 of 2

Example 2 Helps students factor by grouping, after first factoring out a common factor.

Q: What should you always look for first when factoring?
[a common factor]

Q: After the GCF is factored out, how do you begin factoring the trinomial? [You can follow the strategy of multiplying ac to find the factor pair that has a sum of b.]

Activity Assess

EXAMPLE 2 Understand Factoring by Grouping

Build Procedural Fluency From Conceptual Understanding ETP

Q: What is the purpose for finding factor pairs of the product ac?
[To determine whether there is a pair of factors of ac that has a sum of b. It is also a method that helps speed up the process of finding the correct factors by ruling out sums that are far from the target sum of b.]

Q: Why do you group the first two terms and the second two terms?
[By grouping them, you can look for a common factor in each.]

Try It! Answers

2. a. $(5x + 1)(2x + 3)$

   b. $(2x + 7)(x - 3)$

Elicit and Use Evidence of Student Thinking ETP

Q: In part a, how do you determine which signs to use in the binomial expressions? [Because c and b are positive in the trinomial the sign in each binomial must be positive.]

Common Error

Try It! 2b Some students may place the negative sign with the 7 and the positive sign with the 6. Have students mentally combine the middle terms of $2x^2 - 6x + 7x - 21$ and $2x^2 + 6x - 7x - 21$ to see which expression gives them the original trinomial.

HABITS OF MIND

Use with **EXAMPLES 1 & 2**

Use Appropriate Tools Why is it helpful to factor out a GCF from a trinomial before factoring it as the product of binomials? Is it essential? Explain. MP.5

[Factoring out the GCF before factoring the trinomial allows you to work with smaller numbers when factoring, but it is not essential, since the GCF can also be factored out after factoring the trinomial.]

AVAILABLE ONLINE

Activity Assess

CONCEPTUAL UNDERSTANDING

EXAMPLE 2 Understand Factoring by Grouping

A. If $ax^2 + bx + c$ is a product of binomials, how are the values of a, b, and c related?

Consider the product $(3x + 4)(2x + 1)$.

$$\begin{aligned}(3x + 4)(2x + 1) &= (3x)(2x) + (3x)(1) + (4)(2x) + (4)(1)\\ &= 6x^2 + 3x + 8x + 4\\ &= 6x^2 + 11x + 4\end{aligned}$$

The product is $6x^2 + 11x + 4$. Notice that $ac = (6)(4)$ or $(3)(2)(4)(1)$, which is the product of all of the coefficients and constants from $(3x + 4)(2x + 1)$.

In the middle step, the coefficients of the x-terms, 3 and 8, add to form $b = 11$. They are composed of pairs of the coefficients and constants from the original product; $3 = (3)(1)$ and $8 = (4)(2)$.

If $ax^2 + bx + c$ is the product of binomials, there is a pair of factors of ac that have a sum of b.

B. How can you factor $ax^2 + bx + c$ by grouping?

Consider the trinomial $6x^2 + 11x + 4$, $a = 6$ and $c = 4$, so $ac = 24$.

Find the factor pair of 24 with a sum of 11.

Factors of 24	Sum of Factors
2 and 12	14
3 and 8	11

Rewrite $11x$ as $3x$ and $8x$.

$$\begin{aligned}6x^2 + 11x + 4 &= 6x^2 + 3x + 8x + 4\\ &= (6x^2 + 3x) + (8x + 4) && \text{Group as two binomials.}\\ &= 3x(2x + 1) + 4(2x + 1) && \text{Factor out the GCF of each binomial.}\\ &= (3x + 4)(2x + 1) && \text{Use the Distributive Property.}\end{aligned}$$

The factored form of $6x^2 + 11x + 4$ is $(3x + 4)(2x + 1)$.

Check $(3x + 4)(2x + 1) = 6x^2 + 3x + 8x + 4$
$= 6x^2 + 11x + 4$ ✓

STUDY TIP
To speed up your search, when looking for a factor pair that has a sum of b, you can rule out factor pairs with sums that are obviously far from the target.

USE STRUCTURE
Common factors are not limited to monomials. Here the common factors are monomials and binomials. MP.7

Try It! 2. Factor each trinomial.

a. $10x^2 + 17x + 3$

b. $2x^2 + x - 21$

296 TOPIC 7 Polynomials and Factoring

Go Online | PearsonRealize.com

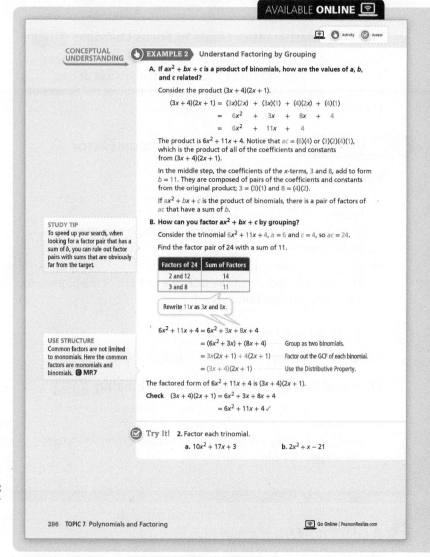

ADV Advanced Students

USE WITH EXAMPLE 2 Have students explore factoring trinomials that have rational coefficients to strengthen the use of this strategy.

- Factor each by using the product ac.

1. $x^2 - 4.5x - 9$ [$(2x + 3)(0.5x - 3)$]
2. $0.25x^2 + 2.25x + 5$ [$(0.25x + 1)(x + 5)$]

Q: What do you know about the factors of −9?
[The factors of −9 will consist of a positive value and a negative value.]

Q: How can you determine that you have factored out the correct number when you have decimal values?
[The product of the two binomials that have rational coefficients is equivalent to the original trinomial.]

RtI Struggling Students

USE WITH EXAMPLE 3 Guide students through STEP 2 of the substitution process as they rewrite the terms.

- Factor each trinomial by substitution.

1. $4x^2 + 16x + 15$ [$(2x + 3)(2x + 5)$]

Q: How can you rewrite $4x^2$ and $16x$ with a common factor?
[$(2x)^2$; $8(2x)$]

2. $2x^2 - 13x - 45$ [$(2x + 5)(x - 9)$]

Q: What must you multiply the trinomial by in order to rename the terms? [2]

Q: What are you creating by multiplying all terms by a when a is not a perfect square?
[You are creating a common factor that can be replaced with a single variable to simplify the expression.]

EXAMPLE 3 Factor a Trinomial Using Substitution

Use and Connect Mathematical Representations ETP

Q: How do you determine whether you need to multiply the trinomial by a?
[If a is not a perfect square, then you need to multiply the trinomial by a to transform x^2 into $(ax)^2$.]

Q: Why does multiplying the trinomial by a allow you to factor the trinomial more easily?
[It creates a common factor that can be replaced by a single variable, in order to write a trinomial where $a = 1$.]

Q: Why do you have to divide by 3 in the final step?
[You must divide by 3 in order to transform the expression back to an equivalent factored form of the original expression.]

Q: Do binomial factors always have to have integer coefficients?
[No, it is possible that in more complicated expressions, the binomial factors could have fractional or decimal coefficients.]

Try It! Answers

3. a. $(x - 2)(2x + 3)$

b. $(5x - 1)(2x + 1)$

HABITS OF MIND

Use with **EXAMPLE 3**

Use Structure How does using substitution help make the process of factoring simpler? MP.7

[Substitution allows you to simplify the first two terms, which makes it easier to factor the expression.]

AVAILABLE **ONLINE**

Activity Assess

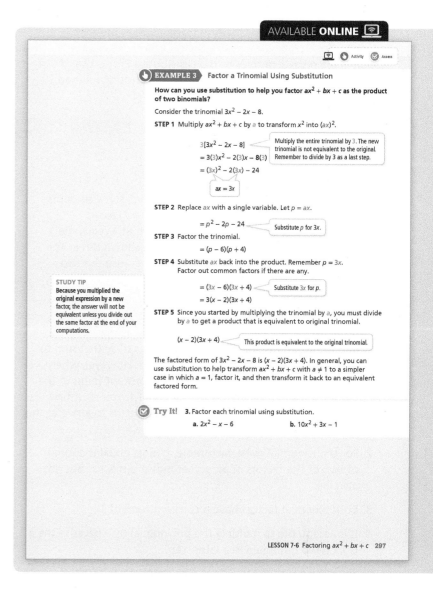

EXAMPLE 3 Factor a Trinomial Using Substitution

How can you use substitution to help you factor $ax^2 + bx + c$ as the product of two binomials?

Consider the trinomial $3x^2 - 2x - 8$.

STEP 1 Multiply $ax^2 + bx + c$ by a to transform x^2 into $(ax)^2$.

$3[3x^2 - 2x - 8]$
$= 3(3)x^2 - 2(3)x - 8(3)$
$= (3x)^2 - 2(3x) - 24$

Multiply the entire trinomial by 3. The new trinomial is not equivalent to the original. Remember to divide by 3 as a last step.

$ax = 3x$

STEP 2 Replace ax with a single variable. Let $p = ax$.

$= p^2 - 2p - 24$

Substitute p for $3x$.

STEP 3 Factor the trinomial.

$= (p - 6)(p + 4)$

STEP 4 Substitute ax back into the product. Remember $p = 3x$. Factor out common factors if there are any.

$= (3x - 6)(3x + 4)$
$= 3(x - 2)(3x + 4)$

Substitute $3x$ for p.

STEP 5 Since you started by multiplying the trinomial by a, you must divide by a to get a product that is equivalent to original trinomial.

$(x - 2)(3x + 4)$

This product is equivalent to the original trinomial.

The factored form of $3x^2 - 2x - 8$ is $(x - 2)(3x + 4)$. In general, you can use substitution to help transform $ax^2 + bx + c$ with $a \neq 1$ to a simpler case in which $a = 1$, factor it, and then transform it back to an equivalent factored form.

STUDY TIP
Because you multiplied the original expression by a new factor, the answer will not be equivalent unless you divide out the same factor at the end of your computations.

Try It! 3. Factor each trinomial using substitution.

a. $2x^2 - x - 6$

b. $10x^2 + 3x - 1$

LESSON 7-6 Factoring $ax^2 + bx + c$ 297

ELL English Language Learners *(Use with* **EXAMPLE 3***)*

SPEAKING BEGINNING *Substitute* is a word used frequently in math. Have students discuss the meaning of the word *substitute* and use it in sentences.

Q: What does *substitute* mean?
[It means to use something in place of something else.]

Q: Use the word substitute in a sentence.
[Percy uses unsweetened applesauce as a substitute for sugar in the recipe.]

Q: What does it mean to substitute p for $3x$ in this example?
[Wherever there is a $3x$ in the expression, it is replaced with p.]

LISTENING INTERMEDIATE Have students listen as you read the following sentences aloud. Ask students which word in the sentence could be replaced with the word *transform*.

Q: In order to change into a butterfly, the caterpillar must first spin itself a cocoon. [change]

Q: Juan is going to convert the garage into an apartment. [convert]

Q: The seamstress is going to alter the old gown into a more modern dress. [alter]

Have the students listen as you read the last sentence of the example.

Q: What does it mean to transform an equation?
[to change it to a different form]

WRITING ADVANCED Display the expression $2x^2 + 7x - 15$ and have students write it in their journals. Then, have students answer the following questions in their journals using complete sentences.

Q: In the term $2x^2$, which part is the coefficient?
[The number 2 in is the coefficient because it is the number placed in front of the variable term.]

Q: Is the coefficient of $2x^2$ a perfect square?
[No, the coefficient is not a perfect square. A perfect square is the product of a rational number multiplied by itself.]

Q: Is the term $7x$ a single variable?
[No; a single variable is just a letter where the coefficient is equal to 1.]

CONCEPT SUMMARY Factoring $ax^2 + bx + c$

Q: How can you describe factoring trinomials in the form $ax^2 + bx + c$?
[It is the reverse process of the Distributive Property and can be done by regrouping or using the substitution method.]

Do You UNDERSTAND? | Do You KNOW HOW?

Common Error

Exercise 12 When factoring the trinomial, some students may incorrectly rewrite $x(5x + 2) + 3(5x + 2)$ as $(x + 3)(5x + 2)(5x + 2)$. Explain to them that a rectangle only has two dimensions and they have shown three. The reason that $(5x + 2)$ is written twice is because the two terms in $(x + 3)$ have to be distributed.

Answers

1. In both situations, you are finding factors of ac that sum to b and using those to factor the trinomial. However, when $a = 1$, those factors correspond to the constant terms in the binomial factors. When a does not equal 1, you must first rewrite b and then factor out common factors to arrive at the two binomial factors of the trinomial.
2. For the trinomial to be factorable, b must equal the sum of two of the factors of ac; sometimes this is $a + c$, but not always.
3. Both binomial factors have a constant term of 1.
4. It is acceptable to multiply the polynomial by a because the a is factored out again in a later step.
5. Since the entire expression can be rewritten in terms of addition, and addition is commutative, the order of the terms do not matter. The factored form will be the same whether Felipe puts $7x$ or $-8x$ first.
6. 1 and 8, 2 and 4, −1 and −8, −2 and −4
7. −1 and 24, 1 and −24, −2 and 12, 2 and −12, −3 and 8, 3 and −8, −4 and 6, 4 and −6
8. yes; 5
9. no
10. $7x + 10x$
11. $18x + 2x$
12. $5x + 2$ and $x + 3$
13. $3x + 5$ and $2x - 1$

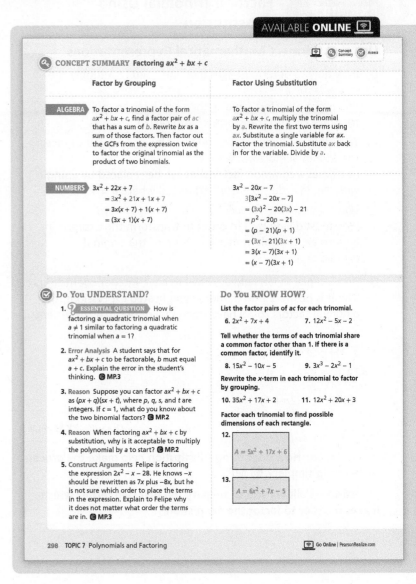

AVAILABLE ONLINE

Concept Summary | Assess

CONCEPT SUMMARY Factoring $ax^2 + bx + c$

	Factor by Grouping	Factor Using Substitution
ALGEBRA	To factor a trinomial of the form $ax^2 + bx + c$, find a factor pair of ac that has a sum of b. Rewrite bx as a sum of those factors. Then factor out the GCFs from the expression twice to factor the original trinomial as the product of two binomials.	To factor a trinomial of the form $ax^2 + bx + c$, multiply the trinomial by a. Rewrite the first two terms using ax. Substitute a single variable for ax. Factor the trinomial. Substitute ax back in for the variable. Divide by a.
NUMBERS	$3x^2 + 22x + 7$ $= 3x^2 + 21x + 1x + 7$ $= 3x(x + 7) + 1(x + 7)$ $= (3x + 1)(x + 7)$	$3x^2 - 20x - 7$ $3[3x^2 - 20x - 7]$ $= (3x)^2 - 20(3x) - 21$ $= p^2 - 20p - 21$ $= (p - 21)(p + 1)$ $= (3x - 21)(3x + 1)$ $= 3(x - 7)(3x + 1)$ $= (x - 7)(3x + 1)$

Do You UNDERSTAND?

1. ESSENTIAL QUESTION How is factoring a quadratic trinomial when $a \neq 1$ similar to factoring a quadratic trinomial when $a = 1$?
2. **Error Analysis** A student says that for $ax^2 + bx + c$ to be factorable, b must equal $a + c$. Explain the error in the student's thinking. MP.3
3. **Reason** Suppose you can factor $ax^2 + bx + c$ as $(px + q)(sx + t)$, where p, q, s, and t are integers. If $c = 1$, what do you know about the two binomial factors? MP.2
4. **Reason** When factoring $ax^2 + bx + c$ by substitution, why is it acceptable to multiply the polynomial by a to start? MP.2
5. **Construct Arguments** Felipe is factoring the expression $2x^2 - x - 28$. He knows $-x$ should be rewritten as $7x$ plus $-8x$, but he is not sure which order to place the terms in the expression. Explain to Felipe why it does not matter what order the terms are in. MP.3

Do You KNOW HOW?

List the factor pairs of ac for each trinomial.

6. $2x^2 + 7x + 4$
7. $12x^2 - 5x - 2$

Tell whether the terms of each trinomial share a common factor other than 1. If there is a common factor, identify it.

8. $15x^2 - 10x - 5$
9. $3x^3 - 2x^2 - 1$

Rewrite the x-term in each trinomial to factor by grouping.

10. $35x^2 + 17x + 2$
11. $12x^2 + 20x + 3$

Factor each trinomial to find possible dimensions of each rectangle.

12. $A = 5x^2 + 17x + 6$
13. $A = 6x^2 + 7x - 5$

298 TOPIC 7 Polynomials and Factoring

Go Online | PearsonRealize.com

PRACTICE & PROBLEM SOLVING

AVAILABLE ONLINE

Lesson Practice You may opt to have students complete the automatically scored Practice and Problem Solving items online powered by MathXL for School.

Choose from: **Lesson Practice**

Adaptive Practice

You may also take advantage of the bank of exercises for assigning additional practice.

Assignment Guide

Basic	Advanced
14–36, 41–51	14–21, 26–51

Item Analysis

Example	Items	DOK
1	21, 22, 37, 40, 41, 44	1
	14, 19, 23–26, 48	2
2	27–33, 42, 43, 52, 53	1
	15, 17, 18, 50, 51	3
3	34–36, 38, 39	1
	16, 20, 45–47	2
	49, 54	3

AVAILABLE ONLINE

PRACTICE & PROBLEM SOLVING

Scan for Multimedia

Practice Tutorial

Additional Exercises Available Online

UNDERSTAND

14. **Mathematical Connections** How is factoring a common factor out of a trinomial like factoring common factors out of the numerator and denominator of a fraction? How is it different?

15. **Make Sense and Persevere** What are all possible values of b for which $7x^2 + bx + 3$ is factorable, if the factors have integer coefficients and constants? MP.1
$-22, -10, 22$ and 10

16. **Look for Relationships** Can you factor the trinomial $3x^2 + 5x + 3$ into linear factors with integer coefficients? Explain. MP.7

17. **Error Analysis** Describe and correct the error a student made in factoring $2x^2 + 11x + 15$. MP.3

$ac = 2 \times 15 = 30; b = 11$

Factors of 30	Sum of Factors
1×30	$1 + 30 = 31$
2×15	$2 + 15 = 17$
3×10	$3 + 10 = 13$
5×6	$5 + 6 = 11$

$2x^2 + 11x + 15 = (x + 5)(x + 6)$ ✗

18. **Higher Order Thinking** Can you factor the trinomial $6x^2 + 7x - 6$ as $(px + q)(sx + t)$, where p, q, s, and t are integers? Explain why or why not.

19. **Reason** Use factoring to arrange the following algebra tiles first into one rectangle and then into two rectangles of equal size. MP.2

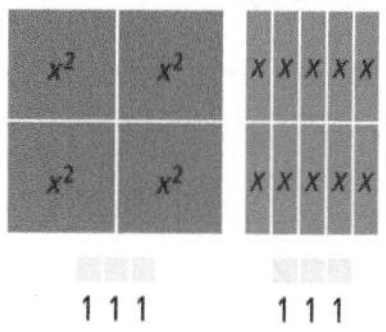

20. **Use Structure** What is the factored form of $pqx^2 + (mp + qn)x + mn$? MP.7
$(px + n)(qx + m)$

PRACTICE

Factor the trinomial represented by the algebra tiles.

21. 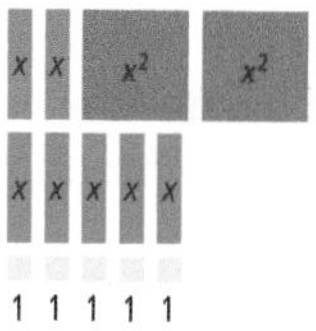
$(x + 1)(2x + 5)$

22. 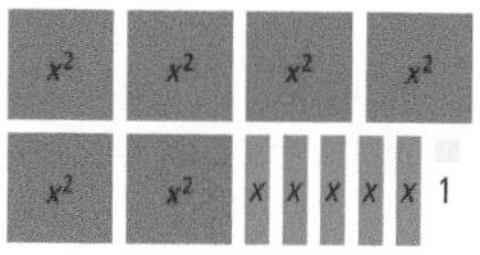
$(3x + 1)(2x + 1)$

Factor each trinomial. SEE EXAMPLE 1

23. $4x^2 + 16x + 12$

24. $2x^2 - 16x + 30$

25. $3x^2 + 12x - 63$

26. $6x^2 + 12x - 48$

Identify the factor pairs of ac you could use to rewrite b to factor each trinomial by grouping. SEE EXAMPLE 2

27. $7x^2 + 9x + 2$
2 and 7

28. $6x^2 + 11x - 2$
-1 and 12

29. $8x^2 - 2x - 1$
-4 and 2

30. $10x^2 + 19x + 6$
4 and 15

31. $15x^2 - 16x - 7$
5 and -21

32. $12x^2 + 11x + 2$
3 and 8

Factor each trinomial completely. SEE EXAMPLES 1, 2, AND 3

33. $4x^2 + 13x + 3$
$(4x + 1)(x + 3)$

34. $6x^2 - 25x - 14$
$(3x - 14)(2x + 1)$

35. $2x^2 + 7x - 4$
$(2x - 1)(x + 4)$

36. $12x^2 + 13x + 3$
$(4x + 3)(3x + 1)$

37. $6x^3 + 9x^2 + 3x$
$3x(2x + 1)(x + 1)$

38. $8x^2 - 10x - 3$
$(4x + 1)(2x - 3)$

39. $12x^2 + 16x + 5$
$(6x + 5)(2x + 1)$

40. $16x^3 + 32x^2 + 12x$
$4x(2x + 1)(2x + 3)$

41. $21x^2 - 35x - 14$
$7(3x + 1)(x - 2)$

42. $16x^2 + 22x - 3$
$(8x - 1)(2x + 3)$

43. $9x^2 + 46x + 5$
$(9x + 1)(x + 5)$

44. $24x^3 - 10x^2 - 4x$
$2x(3x - 2)(4x + 1)$

Factor each trinomial completely.

45. $3x^2 + xy - 2y^2$
$(3x - 2y)(x + y)$

46. $2x^2 + 9xy + 10y^2$
$(2x + 5y)(x + 2y)$

47. $5x^2 - 4xy - y^2$
$(5x + y)(x - y)$

48. $2x^2 + 10xy + 12y^2$
$2(x + 2y)(x + 3y)$

LESSON 7-6 Factoring $ax^2 + bx + c$ 299

Answers

14. In both situations, the common factor must be a factor of all parts. In factoring a trinomial, the parts are the terms of the trinomial. In factoring a fraction, the parts are the numerator and denominator.

16. No; The coefficient of the x term must be the sum of products of factors of the leading coefficient and the constant term.

17. The student used the method for factoring $ax^2 + bx + c$ when $a = 1$ even though a is not equal to 1. The correct factored form of $2x^2 + 11x + 15$ is $(2x + 5)(x + 3)$.

18. No, in this trinomial, $ac = -36$. The factors of -36 are: -1 and 36, 1 and -36, -2 and 18, 2 and -18, -3 and 12, 3 and -12, -4 and 9, 4 and -9, -6 and 6. None of these pairs of factors sum to 7, the value of b.

19. 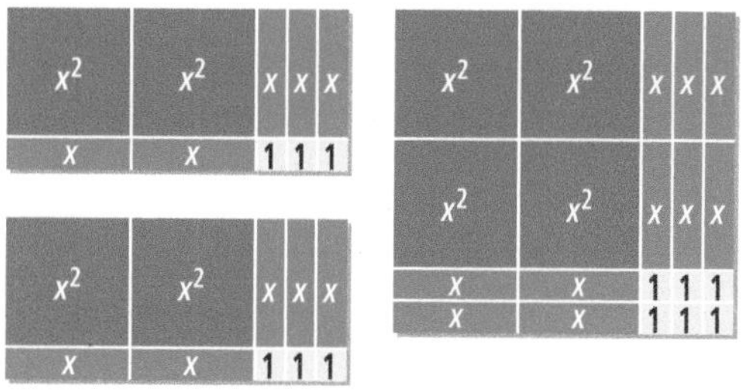

23. $4(x + 1)(x + 3)$

24. $2(x - 5)(x - 3)$

25. $3(x + 7)(x - 3)$

26. $6(x + 4)(x - 2)$

Answers

49. $(2x - 3)$ by $(x + 8)$; $(2x - 1)$ by $(x + 10)$; $2x^2 + 19x - 10$ ft^2

50. $2x$ ft by $(2x + 1)$ ft by $(x + 2)$ ft; 6 ft by 7 ft by 5 ft; 432 ft^3

51. a. $(2x + 8)$ in. by $(2x + 10)$ in.

b. 8 in. by 10 in.

c. The photographer may not know how wide she wants the frames of the photos to be, or she may vary the width of the frame for different photos.

AVAILABLE **ONLINE**

PRACTICE & PROBLEM SOLVING

Practice Tutorial

Mixed Review Available Online

APPLY

49. Reason A rectangular patio has an area of $2x^2 + 13x - 24$ ft^2. Use factoring to find possible dimensions of the patio. The patio is to be enlarged so that each dimension is 2 ft greater than it was originally. What are the new dimensions of the patio? What is the new area of the patio? **MP.2**

50. Make Sense and Persevere Use factoring to find possible dimensions of the container shown. The container is a rectangular prism. What are the dimensions of the container if $x = 3$? What is the volume of the container if $x = 4$? **MP.1**

$V = 4x^3 + 10x^2 + 4x$ ft^3

51. Model With Mathematics A photographer is placing photos in a mat for a gallery show. Each mat she uses is x in. wide on each side. The total area of each photo and mat is shown. **MP.4**

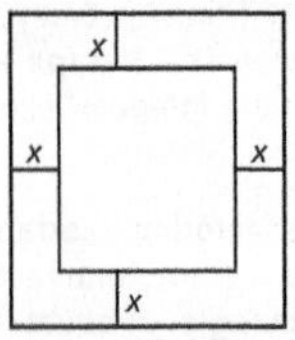
x
x
x
x

Area = $4x^2 + 36x + 80$

a. Factor the total area to find possible dimensions of a photo and mat.

b. What are the dimensions of the photos in terms of x?

c. Explain why the photographer might use x to represent the width of the mat.

ASSESSMENT PRACTICE

52. The trinomial $ax^2 + bx + c$ is factorable when factors of _?_ have a sum of _?_.
ac; b

53. SAT/ACT What is the factored form of $3x^2 - 5x - 12$?

Ⓐ $(x - 4)(3x + 1)$
Ⓑ $(x - 3)(3x + 4)$
Ⓒ $(x + 4)(3x - 9)$
Ⓓ $3(x + 2)(x - 3)$
Ⓔ $3(x - 4)(x + 1)$

54. Performance Task A paint tray has an area of $42x^2 + 135x + 108$ in.^{2}. The square paint compartments that are all the same size and spaced evenly, though the space along the edge of the tray is twice as wide as the space between squares.

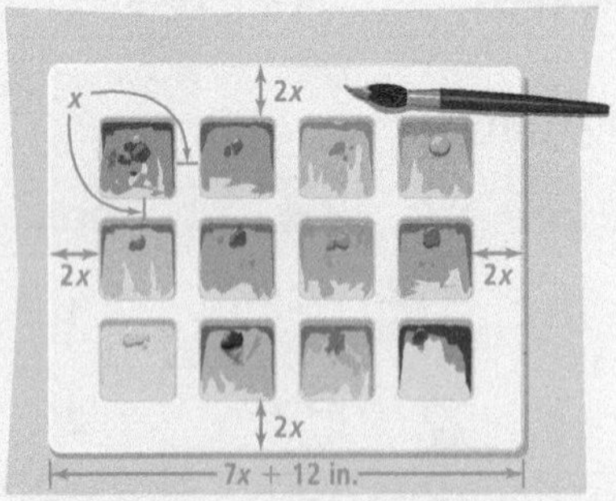
x
2x
2x
2x
2x
7x + 12 in.

Part A What is the width of the paint tray?
6x + 9 inches

Part B What is the area of each of the paint compartments in the tray?
9 in.^{2}

Part C How wide are the edges of the tray if the width of the paint tray is 45 in.?
12 in.

Go Online | PearsonRealize.com

LESSON QUIZ

Use the Lesson Quiz to assess students' understanding of the mathematics in the lesson.

Students can take the Lesson Quiz online or you can download a printable copy from **SavvasRealize.com**. The Lesson Quiz is also available in the *Assessment Resources* book.

Item Analysis

Item	DOK	Standards
1	1	HSA.SSE.A.1.A.
2	1	HSA.SSE.A.1.A.
3	2	HSA.SSE.A.1.A.
4	1	HSA.SSE.A.1.A.
5	2	HSA.SSE.A.1.A.

RtI Use the student scores on the Lesson Quiz to prescribe differentiated assignments.

If students take the Lesson Quiz online, it will be automatically scored and appropriate differentiated practice will be assigned based on student performance.

I Intervention	0–3 points	• Reteach to Build Understanding • Mathematical Literacy and Vocabulary • Additional Practice
O On-Level	4 points	• Mathematical Literacy and Vocabulary • Additional Practice • Enrichment
A Advanced	5 points	• Enrichment

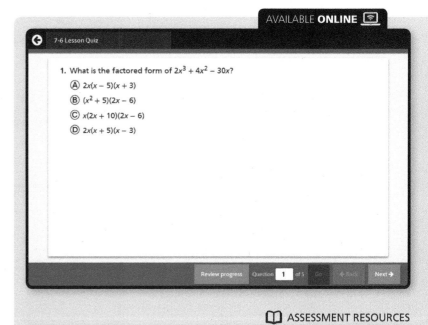

AVAILABLE **ONLINE**

7-6 Lesson Quiz

1. What is the factored form of $2x^3 + 4x^2 - 30x$?
   Ⓐ $2x(x - 5)(x + 3)$
   Ⓑ $(x^2 + 5)(2x - 6)$
   Ⓒ $x(2x + 10)(2x - 6)$
   Ⓓ $2x(x + 5)(x - 3)$

Review progress Question 1 of 5 Go Back Next

ASSESSMENT RESOURCES

Name ____________

enVision Algebra 1 PearsonRealize.com

7-6 Lesson Quiz

Factoring $ax^2 + bx + c$

1. What is the factored form of $2x^3 + 4x^2 - 30x$?
   Ⓐ $2x(x - 5)(x + 3)$
   Ⓑ $(x^2 + 5)(2x - 6)$
   Ⓒ $x(2x + 10)(2x - 6)$
   Ⓓ $2x(x + 5)(x - 3)$

2. Fill in the blanks to factor the trinomial $3x^2 + 13x - 10$ by grouping.
   $3x^2 + 13x - 10 = 3x^2 - \underline{2}\,x + \underline{15}\,x - 10$
   $= \underline{x}\,(3x - 2) + \underline{5}\,(3x - 2)$
   $= (\underline{x} + \underline{5})(3x - 2)$

3. Factor the trinomial $6x^2 + 17x + 5$ by grouping. Show your work.
   $6x^2 + 17x + 5 = 6x^2 + 15x + 2x + 5$
   $= 3x(2x + 5) + 1(2x + 5)$
   $= (3x + 1)(2x + 5)$

4. The area of a rectangular patio is $3x^2 + 17x + 20$ ft^2. Which of the following could be dimensions of the patio?
   Ⓐ $x + 5$ ft by $3x + 4$ ft
   Ⓑ $3x + 5$ ft by $x + 4$ ft
   Ⓒ $x + 5$ ft by $x + 4$ ft
   Ⓓ $3x + 5$ ft by $3x + 4$ ft

5. Factor $2x^2 - 7x - 15$.
   $(2x + 3)(x - 5)$

enVision™ **Algebra 1** • Assessment Resources

DIFFERENTIATED RESOURCES

I = Intervention **O** = On-Level **A** = Advanced

⚙ = This activity is available as a digital assignment powered by MathXL® for School.

AVAILABLE **ONLINE**

Reteach to Build Understanding I ⚙

Provides scaffolded reteaching for the key lesson concepts.

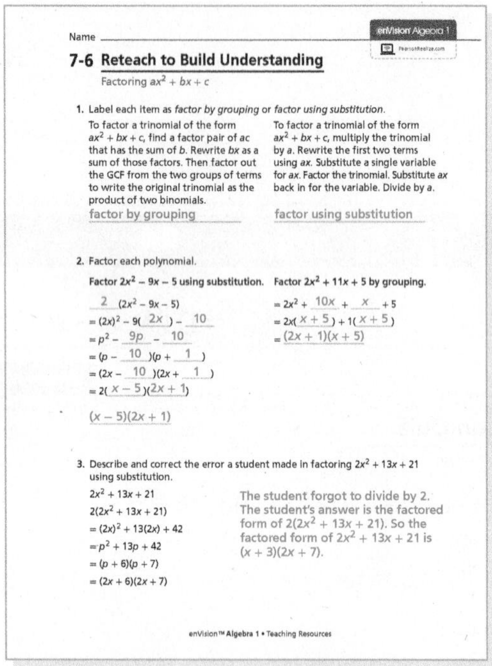
Name

enVision Algebra 1

7-6 Reteach to Build Understanding

Factoring $ax^2 + bx + c$

1. Label each item as *factor by grouping* or *factor using substitution.*

To factor a trinomial of the form $ax^2 + bx + c$, find a factor pair of ac that has the sum of b. Rewrite bx as a sum of those factors. Then factor out the GCF from the two groups of terms to write the original trinomial as the product of two binomials. — factor by grouping

To factor a trinomial of the form $ax^2 + bx + c$, multiply the trinomial by a. Rewrite the first two terms using ax. Substitute a single variable for ax. Factor the trinomial. Substitute ax back in for the variable. Divide by a. — factor using substitution

2. Factor each polynomial.

Factor $2x^2 - 9x - 5$ using substitution.

$\underline{2}\,(2x^2 - 9x - 5)$
$= (2x)^2 - 9(\underline{2x}) - \underline{10}$
$= p^2 - \underline{9p} - \underline{10}$
$= (p - \underline{10})(p + \underline{1})$
$= (2x - \underline{10})(2x + \underline{1})$
$= 2(\underline{x - 5})(2x + 1)$
$(x - 5)(2x + 1)$

Factor $2x^2 + 11x + 5$ by grouping.

$= 2x^2 + \underline{10x} + \underline{x} + 5$
$= 2x(\underline{x + 5}) + 1(\underline{x + 5})$
$= \underline{(2x + 1)(x + 5)}$

3. Describe and correct the error a student made in factoring $2x^2 + 13x + 21$ using substitution.

$2x^2 + 13x + 21$
$2(2x^2 + 13x + 21)$
$= (2x)^2 + 13(2x) + 42$
$= p^2 + 13p + 42$
$= (p + 6)(p + 7)$
$= (2x + 6)(2x + 7)$

The student forgot to divide by 2. The student's answer is the factored form of $2(2x^2 + 13x + 21)$. So the factored form of $2x^2 + 13x + 21$ is $(x + 3)(2x + 7)$.

enVision™ Algebra 1 • Teaching Resources

Additional Practice I O ⚙

Provides extra practice for each lesson.

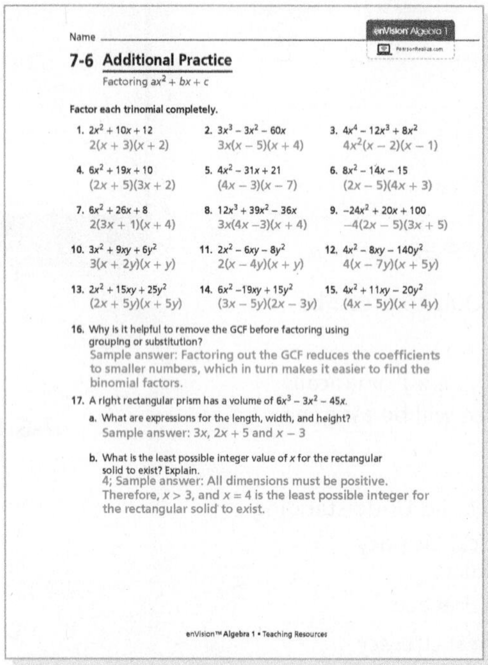
Name

enVision Algebra 1

7-6 Additional Practice

Factoring $ax^2 + bx + c$

Factor each trinomial completely.

1. $2x^2 + 10x + 12$ — $2(x + 3)(x + 2)$
2. $3x^3 - 3x^2 - 60x$ — $3x(x - 5)(x + 4)$
3. $4x^4 - 12x^3 + 8x^2$ — $4x^2(x - 2)(x - 1)$
4. $6x^2 + 19x + 10$ — $(2x + 5)(3x + 2)$
5. $4x^2 - 31x + 21$ — $(4x - 3)(x - 7)$
6. $8x^2 - 14x - 15$ — $(2x - 5)(4x + 3)$
7. $6x^2 + 26x + 8$ — $2(3x + 1)(x + 4)$
8. $12x^3 + 39x^2 - 36x$ — $3x(4x - 3)(x + 4)$
9. $-24x^2 + 20x + 100$ — $-4(2x - 5)(3x + 5)$
10. $3x^2 + 9xy + 6y^2$ — $3(x + 2y)(x + y)$
11. $2x^2 - 6xy - 8y^2$ — $2(x - 4y)(x + y)$
12. $4x^2 - 8xy - 140y^2$ — $4(x - 7y)(x + 5y)$
13. $2x^2 + 15xy + 25y^2$ — $(2x + 5y)(x + 5y)$
14. $6x^2 - 19xy + 15y^2$ — $(3x - 5y)(2x - 3y)$
15. $4x^2 + 11xy - 20y^2$ — $(4x - 5y)(x + 4y)$

16. Why is it helpful to remove the GCF before factoring using grouping or substitution?
Sample answer: Factoring out the GCF reduces the coefficients to smaller numbers, which in turn makes it easier to find the binomial factors.

17. A right rectangular prism has a volume of $6x^3 - 3x^2 - 45x$.
a. What are expressions for the length, width, and height?
Sample answer: $3x$, $2x + 5$ and $x - 3$
b. What is the least possible integer value of x for the rectangular solid to exist? Explain.
4; Sample answer: All dimensions must be positive. Therefore, $x > 3$, and $x = 4$ is the least possible integer for the rectangular solid to exist.

enVision™ Algebra 1 • Teaching Resources

Enrichment O A ⚙

Presents engaging problems and activities that extend the lesson concepts.

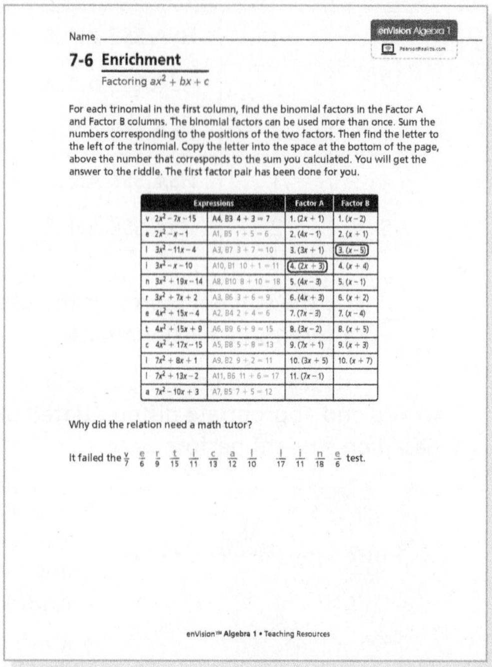
Name

enVision Algebra 1

7-6 Enrichment

Factoring $ax^2 + bx + c$

For each trinomial in the first column, find the binomial factors in the Factor A and Factor B columns. The binomial factors can be used more than once. Sum the numbers corresponding to the positions of the two factors. Then find the letter to the left of the trinomial. Copy the letter into the space at the bottom of the page, above the number that corresponds to the sum you calculated. You will get the answer to the riddle. The first factor pair has been done for you.

Expressions		Factor A	Factor B
v $2x^2 - 7x - 15$	A4, B3 4 + 3 = 7	1. $(2x + 1)$	1. $(x - 2)$
e $2x^2 - x - 1$	A1, B5 1 + 5 = 6	2. $(4x - 1)$	2. $(x + 1)$
l $3x^2 - 11x - 4$	A3, B7 3 + 7 = 10	3. $(3x + 1)$	3. $(x - 5)$
l $3x^2 - x - 10$	A10, B1 10 + 1 = 11	4. $(2x + 3)$	4. $(x + 4)$
n $3x^2 + 19x - 14$	A8, B10 8 + 10 = 18	5. $(4x - 3)$	5. $(x - 1)$
r $3x^2 + 7x + 2$	A3, B6 3 + 6 = 9	6. $(4x + 3)$	6. $(x + 2)$
e $4x^2 + 15x - 4$	A2, B4 2 + 4 = 6	7. $(7x - 3)$	7. $(x - 4)$
t $4x^2 + 15x + 9$	A6, B9 6 + 9 = 15	8. $(3x - 2)$	8. $(x + 5)$
c $4x^2 + 17x - 15$	A5, B8 5 + 8 = 13	9. $(7x + 1)$	9. $(x + 3)$
l $7x^2 + 8x + 1$	A9, B2 9 + 2 = 11	10. $(3x + 5)$	10. $(x + 7)$
l $7x^2 + 13x - 2$	A11, B6 11 + 6 = 17	11. $(7x - 1)$	
a $7x^2 - 10x + 3$	A7, B5 7 + 5 = 12		

Why did the relation need a math tutor?

It failed the v/7 e/6 r/9 t/15 i/11 c/13 a/12 l/10 l/17 i/11 n/18 e/6 test.

enVision™ Algebra 1 • Teaching Resources

Mathematical Literacy and Vocabulary I O

Helps students develop and reinforce understanding of key terms and concepts.

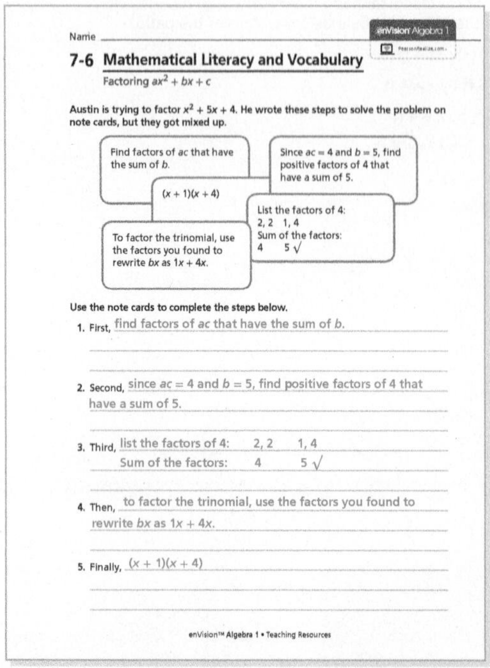
Name

enVision Algebra 1

7-6 Mathematical Literacy and Vocabulary

Factoring $ax^2 + bx + c$

Austin is trying to factor $x^2 + 5x + 4$. He wrote these steps to solve the problem on note cards, but they got mixed up.

Find factors of ac that have the sum of b.

Since $ac = 4$ and $b = 5$, find positive factors of 4 that have a sum of 5.

$(x + 1)(x + 4)$

List the factors of 4: 2, 2 1, 4 Sum of the factors: 4 5 √

To factor the trinomial, use the factors you found to rewrite bx as $1x + 4x$.

Use the note cards to complete the steps below.

1. First, find factors of ac that have the sum of b.
2. Second, since $ac = 4$ and $b = 5$, find positive factors of 4 that have a sum of 5.
3. Third, list the factors of 4: 2, 2 1, 4 Sum of the factors: 4 5 √
4. Then, to factor the trinomial, use the factors you found to rewrite bx as $1x + 4x$.
5. Finally, $(x + 1)(x + 4)$

enVision™ Algebra 1 • Teaching Resources

Digital Resources and Video Tutorials I O A ⚙

The **Reteach to Build Understanding, Additional Practice,** and **Enrichment** activities are available as digital assignments powered by MathXL for School. These activities are automatically assigned when students complete the lesson quiz online and are automatically scored.

Students can access instructional tutorials using the **Virtual Nerd app.**

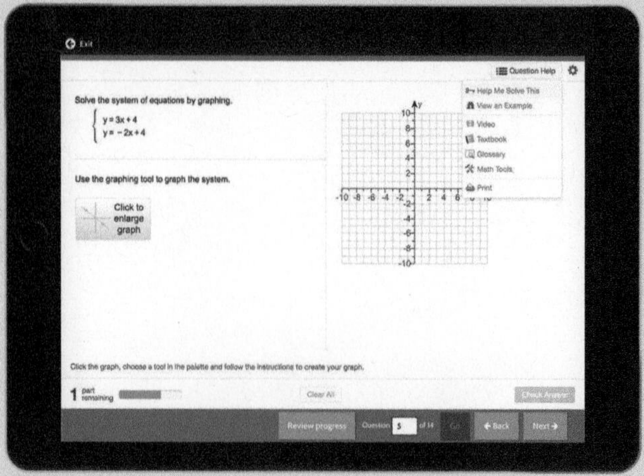
Solve the system of equations by graphing.
Use the graphing tool to graph the system.
Click to enlarge graph
Question Help
Help Me Solve This
View an Example
Video
Textbook
Glossary
Math Tools
Print
Clear All
Check Answer
Review progress
Back
Next

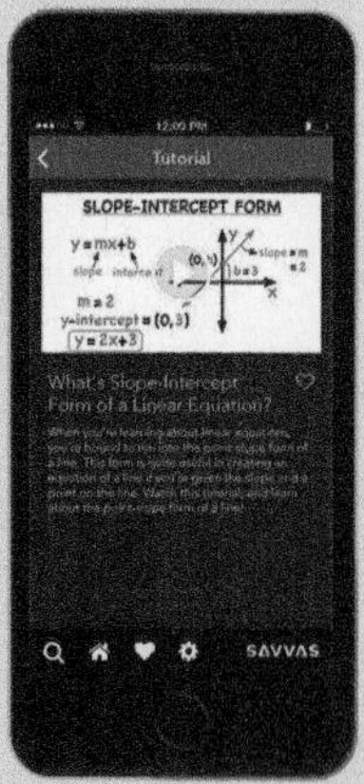
Tutorial
SLOPE-INTERCEPT FORM
What's Slope-Intercept Form of a Linear Equation?
SAVVAS

Students can also access Virtual Nerd videos using the **BouncePages app** to scan exercise pages marked with this icon. Students can download both apps for free in their mobile devices' app store.

LESSON 7-7

Factoring Special Cases

Lesson Overview

FOCUS

Objective

Students will be able to:

✔ Identify and factor a trinomial that is a perfect square or a binomial that is a difference of two squares.

✔ Use a polynomial to represent a measurement in a real-world situation and describe how a factored form of the polynomial relates to that situation.

Essential Understanding

When a trinomial has the pattern $a^2 + 2ab + b^2$, then it can be factored as $(a + b)(a + b)$ or $(a + b)^2$. When a trinomial has the pattern $a^2 - 2ab + b^2$, then it can be factored as $(a - b)(a - b)$ or $(a - b)^2$. When a binomial has the pattern $a^2 - b^2$, then it can be factored as $(a + b)(a - b)$.

COHERENCE

Previously in this topic, students:

- Learned to factor quadratic trinomials in the form $ax^2 + bx + c$ when $a = 1$ and when $a \neq 1$.

In this lesson, students:

- Learn to factor special cases of trinomials such as perfect-square trinomials and the difference of two squares.

Later in this course, students will:

- Use factoring and the Zero Product Property to solve quadratic equations.

RIGOR

This lesson emphasizes a blend of *conceptual understanding* and *procedural skill and fluency*.

- Students understand how to conceptualize patterns that have the structure of a perfect-square trinomial or have the structure of the difference of two squares.
- Students rewrite perfect-square trinomials and difference of two squares as products of binomial factors.
- Students recognize when they can repeatedly apply factoring patterns until a polynomial is factored completely.

A-Z Vocabulary Builder

REVIEW VOCABULARY — **English** | *Spanish*

- **difference of two squares** | *diferencia de dos cuadrados*
- **factor** | *factor*

NEW VOCABULARY

- **perfect-square trinomial** | *trinomio cuadrado perfecto*

VOCABULARY ACTIVITY

As preparation for factoring, help students review how to recognize expressions that model the patterns of a *perfect square trinomial* and a *difference of two squares*.

For each expression, tell whether it is a *perfect square trinomial, a difference of two squares*, or *neither*.

1. $x^2 - 144$

2. $x^2 + 9x + 6$

3. $x^2 - 16x + 64$

4. $x^2 - x + 1$

5. $x^2 + 14x + 49$

6. $25x^2 - 1$

[Answers: 1. difference of two squares; 2. neither; 3. perfect-square trinomial; 4. neither; 5. perfect-square trinomial; 6. difference of two squares]

Student Companion

Students can do their in-class work for the lesson on pages 163–166 of their *Student Companion* or in Savvas Realize.

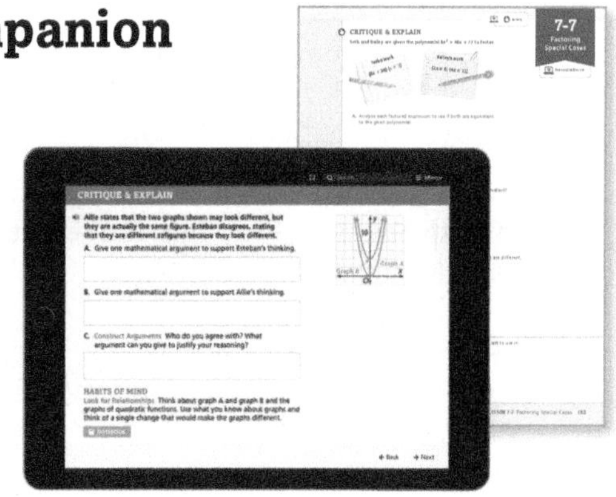

© Mathematics Overview — COMMON CORE STANDARDS

Content Standards

In this lesson, students focus on these standards:

HSA.SSE.A.1 Interpret expressions that represent a quantity in terms of its context.

HSA.SSE.A.2 Use the structure of an expression to identify ways to rewrite it.

Mathematical Practice Standards

These standards are highlighted in this lesson:

MP.2 Reason Abstractly and Quantitatively

Students attend to the meaning of special cases of polynomials. Then they make sense of the meaning of these special cases to factor the resulting expression.

MP.7 Look For and Make Use of Structure

Students identify and use patterns such as the perfect-square trinomial and difference of two squares patterns and their factored forms.

Activity

CRITIQUE & EXPLAIN

INSTRUCTIONAL FOCUS Students explore how a polynomial can be rewritten as a product of binomial factors in different ways and still be equivalent to the given polynomial. Students also see that a *completely factored* sum of terms consists of a unique set of factors. This understanding helps students when factoring special trinomials.

STUDENT COMPANION Students can complete the *Critique & Explain* activity on page 163 of their *Student Companion*.

Before WHOLE CLASS

Implement Tasks that Promote Reasoning and Problem Solving ETP

Q: Why are Seth's and Bailey's expressions called *factored expressions*?
[Each one is a product of factors where the expanded product is the original expression.]

Q: How is the form of a *polynomial* different from the form of a *factored expression*?
[Sample: A *polynomial* is a sum of terms while a *factored expression* is a product of terms.]

During SMALL GROUP

Support Productive Struggle in Learning Mathematics ETP

Q: How can you convert a polynomial from factored form to standard form?
[Use the Distributive Property.]

Q: How do you know when two expressions are equivalent?
[Rewrite one or both so that the rewritten expressions are identical.]

For Early Finishers

Q: Start with the statement $(x + 3)(A)(B) = 24x^2 + 60x - 36$, where A represents a positive integer and B represents a binomial. Write some factored expressions for the left side of the equation that make the statement true.
[Answers may vary. Sample: $(x + 3)(12)(2x - 1)$].

After WHOLE CLASS

Facilitate Meaningful Mathematical Discourse ETP

Q: How can you test whether two sets of factors are equivalent?
[Multiply each set of factors to see if the polynomials are identical.]

Q: How do you know when a factor can be factored further?
[The terms have a common factor or the factor can be rewritten as the product of two polynomials.]

AVAILABLE **ONLINE**

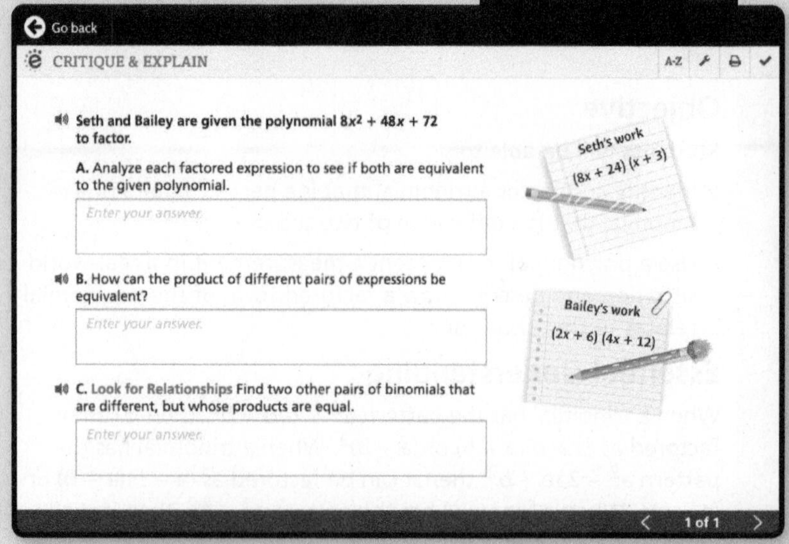
Go back
CRITIQUE & EXPLAIN
Seth and Bailey are given the polynomial 8x2 + 48x + 72 to factor.
A. Analyze each factored expression to see if both are equivalent to the given polynomial.
Enter your answer.
B. How can the product of different pairs of expressions be equivalent?
Enter your answer.
C. Look for Relationships Find two other pairs of binomials that are different, but whose products are equal.
Enter your answer.
Seth's work
(8x + 24) (x + 3)
Bailey's work
(2x + 6) (4x + 12)
1 of 1

STUDENT EDITION, PAGE 301

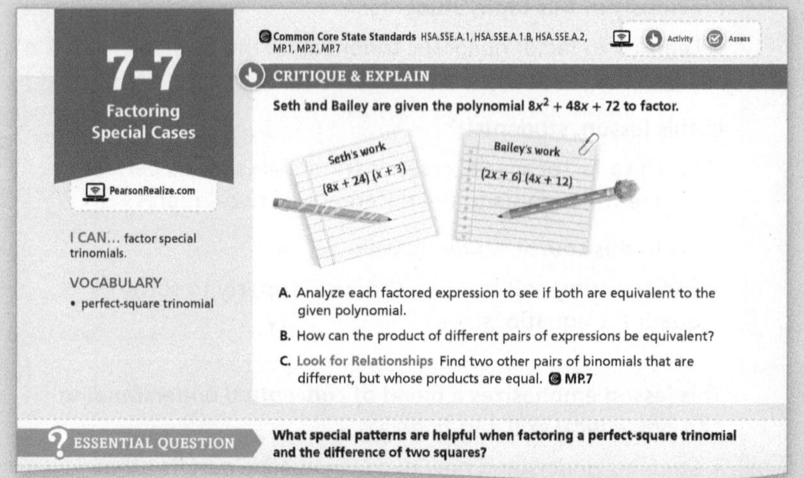
7-7 Factoring Special Cases

PearsonRealize.com

I CAN… factor special trinomials.

VOCABULARY
- perfect-square trinomial

Common Core State Standards HSA.SSE.A.1, HSA.SSE.A.1.B, HSA.SSE.A.2, MP.1, MP.2, MP.7

CRITIQUE & EXPLAIN

Seth and Bailey are given the polynomial $8x^2 + 48x + 72$ to factor.

Seth's work $(8x + 24)(x + 3)$

Bailey's work $(2x + 6)(4x + 12)$

A. Analyze each factored expression to see if both are equivalent to the given polynomial.

B. How can the product of different pairs of expressions be equivalent?

C. Look for Relationships Find two other pairs of binomials that are different, but whose products are equal. MP.7

ESSENTIAL QUESTION What special patterns are helpful when factoring a perfect-square trinomial and the difference of two squares?

SAMPLE STUDENT WORK

A. Both expressions are equivalent to the given polynomial.
B. Both expressions multiply out to the same thing. They just use different factor combinations.
C. $(3x + 3)(x + 5) = 3x^2 + 18x + 15$ and $(x + 1)(3x + 15) = 3x^2 + 18x + 15$

HABITS OF MIND

Use with **CRITIQUE & EXPLAIN**

Communicate Precisely What mathematical language was important to use in explaining the relationship between Seth's and Bailey's work? MP.6

[equivalent factors, equivalent expressions, simplified expressions]

Activity Assess

INTRODUCE THE ESSENTIAL QUESTION

Establish Mathematics Goals to Focus Learning ETP

Discuss with students how to describe key phrases such as *a perfect-square trinomial, the square of a binomial*, and *the difference of two squares* as patterns.

EXAMPLE 1 Understand Factoring a Perfect Square

Pose Purposeful Questions ETP

Q: What is a *perfect square*? What is a *perfect-square trinomial*?
[A perfect square is an expression that can be written in the form a^2; a perfect-square trinomial is a 3-term polynomial of the form $a^2 + 2ab + b^2$ or $a^2 - 2ab + b^2$.]

Q: How can a perfect-square trinomial formed?
[It can be formed by squaring a binomial.]

Q: When a binomial is squared, how are the first and last terms of the product related to the terms of the binomial?
[The first and last terms of the product are the squares of the terms in the original binomial.]

Try It! Answers

1. a. $(2x + 3)^2$
   b. $(x - 4)^2$

AVAILABLE ONLINE

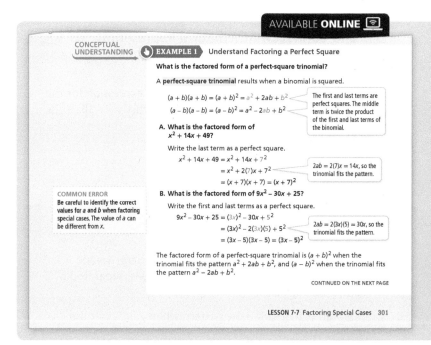

CONCEPTUAL UNDERSTANDING

EXAMPLE 1 Understand Factoring a Perfect Square

What is the factored form of a perfect-square trinomial?

A **perfect-square trinomial** results when a binomial is squared.

$(a + b)(a + b) = (a + b)^2 = a^2 + 2ab + b^2$

$(a - b)(a - b) = (a - b)^2 = a^2 - 2ab + b^2$

The first and last terms are perfect squares. The middle term is twice the product of the first and last terms of the binomial.

A. What is the factored form of $x^2 + 14x + 49$?

Write the last term as a perfect square.

$x^2 + 14x + 49 = x^2 + 14x + 7^2$
$= x^2 + 2(7)x + 7^2$
$= (x + 7)(x + 7) = (x + 7)^2$

$2ab = 2(7)x = 14x$, so the trinomial fits the pattern.

COMMON ERROR
Be careful to identify the correct values for *a* and *b* when factoring special cases. The value of *a* can be different from *x*.

B. What is the factored form of $9x^2 - 30x + 25$?

Write the first and last terms as a perfect square.

$9x^2 - 30x + 25 = (3x)^2 - 30x + 5^2$
$= (3x)^2 - 2(3x)(5) + 5^2$
$= (3x - 5)(3x - 5) = (3x - 5)^2$

$2ab = 2(3x)(5) = 30x$, so the trinomial fits the pattern.

The factored form of a perfect-square trinomial is $(a + b)^2$ when the trinomial fits the pattern $a^2 + 2ab + b^2$, and $(a - b)^2$ when the trinomial fits the pattern $a^2 - 2ab + b^2$.

CONTINUED ON THE NEXT PAGE

LESSON 7-7 Factoring Special Cases 301

Elicit and Use Evidence of Student Thinking ETP

Q: When a binomial is squared, how is the coefficient of the product's middle term related to the original binomial?
[The coefficient of the product's middle term is twice the product of the two terms in the binomial.]

AVAILABLE ONLINE

ADDITIONAL EXAMPLES

Go back

ADDITIONAL EXAMPLE 3 ESSENTIAL QUESTION ES A-Z

Factor the polynomial.

$49y^2 - 9$

This polynomial is a difference of squares.

$(7y + 3)(7y - 3)$

TRY ANOTHER ONE

1 of 2

Go back

ADDITIONAL EXAMPLE 4 ESSENTIAL QUESTION ES A-Z

Factor each expression completely. Which patterns are used, and in what order?

a. $16a^4 - 81b^8$
b. $16a^3 + 48a^2 + 36a$

a. Use the difference of two squares pattern to obtain $(4a^2 + 9b^4)(4a^2 - 9b^4)$. Then use the difference of two squares pattern again to obtain $(4a^2 + 9b^4)(2a + 3b^2)(2a - 3b^2)$.

b. Use the common factor pattern to obtain $4a(4a^2 + 12a + 9)$. Then use the perfect-square trinomial pattern to obtain $4a(2a + 3)^2$.

1 of 2

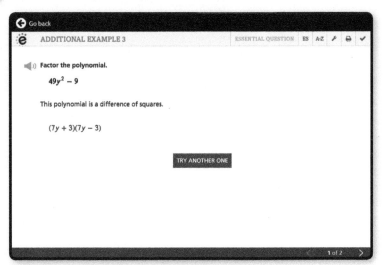

Example 3 Help students understand how to factor perfect-square trinomials or the difference of two squares.

Q: What are the factors of $a^2x^2 + 2abx + b^2$
[$(ax + b)^2$]

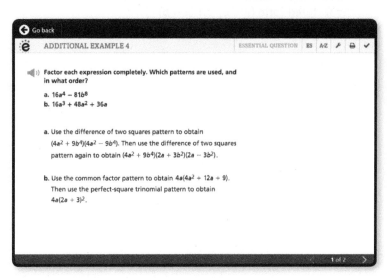

Example 4 Help students learn to apply several factoring patterns to factor an expression completely.

Q: How can you recognize each pattern?
[A perfect-square trinomial can be written as $a^2 + 2ab + b^2$ or $a^2 - 2ab + b^2$; the difference of two squares can be written as $a^2 - b^2$; an expression with a common factor can be written as $ab + ac$.]

EXAMPLE 2 Factor to Find a Dimension

Use and Connect Mathematical Representations ETP

Q: Can you connect the volume of the cylinder to a perfect-square trinomial?
[Yes, after you factor out a 3, part of the expression for the volume of the larger cylinder is the trinomial $x^2 + 10x + 25$, which is a perfect-square trinomial.]

Try It! Answer

2. $(3x + 1)$ in.

EXAMPLE 3 Factor a Difference of Two Squares

Pose Purposeful Questions ETP

Q: What does the term *difference of two squares* mean?
[There are two terms, each a perfect square, separated by a subtraction symbol.]

Q: How can you describe the pattern when you factor the difference of two squares?
[The pattern, $(a + b)(a - b)$, is the product of two binomials that have identical terms except one has an addition sign and the other has a subtraction sign.]

Try It! Answers

3. a. $(x + 8)(x - 8)$ **b.** $(3x + 10)(3x - 10)$

HABITS OF MIND

Use with **EXAMPLES 1 & 2**

Use Structure How can you identify whether a given trinomial is a perfect-square trinomial? MP.7

[Check whether the trinomial has the form $a^2 + 2ab + b^2$ or $a^2 - 2ab + b^2$; or check whether the trinomial can be rewritten in the factored form $(a + b)^2$ or $(a - b)^2$.]

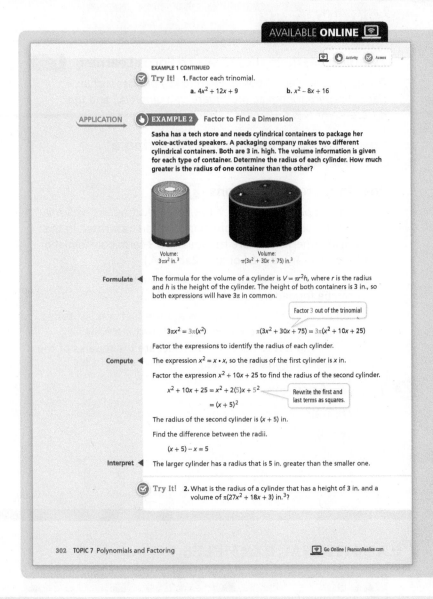

AVAILABLE ONLINE

Activity Assess

EXAMPLE 1 CONTINUED

Try It! **1.** Factor each trinomial.

a. $4x^2 + 12x + 9$ **b.** $x^2 - 8x + 16$

APPLICATION

EXAMPLE 2 Factor to Find a Dimension

Sasha has a tech store and needs cylindrical containers to package her voice-activated speakers. A packaging company makes two different cylindrical containers. Both are 3 in. high. The volume information is given for each type of container. Determine the radius of each cylinder. How much greater is the radius of one container than the other?

Volume: $3\pi x^2$ in.^{3}

Volume: $\pi(3x^2 + 30x + 75)$ in.^{3}

Formulate The formula for the volume of a cylinder is $V = \pi r^2 h$, where r is the radius and h is the height of the cylinder. The height of both containers is 3 in., so both expressions will have 3π in common.

Factor 3 out of the trinomial

$3\pi x^2 = 3\pi(x^2)$ $\pi(3x^2 + 30x + 75) = 3\pi(x^2 + 10x + 25)$

Factor the expressions to identify the radius of each cylinder.

Compute The expression $x^2 = x \cdot x$, so the radius of the first cylinder is x in.

Factor the expression $x^2 + 10x + 25$ to find the radius of the second cylinder.

$$x^2 + 10x + 25 = x^2 + 2(5)x + 5^2$$
$$= (x + 5)^2$$

Rewrite the first and last terms as squares.

The radius of the second cylinder is $(x + 5)$ in.

Find the difference between the radii.

$$(x + 5) - x = 5$$

Interpret The larger cylinder has a radius that is 5 in. greater than the smaller one.

Try It! **2.** What is the radius of a cylinder that has a height of 3 in. and a volume of $\pi(27x^2 + 18x + 3)$ in.^{3}?

302 TOPIC 7 Polynomials and Factoring Go Online | PearsonRealize.com

ELL English Language Learners *(Use with* **EXAMPLE 2***)*

SPEAKING BEGINNING Ask students to talk about the word *cylindrical* and offer some examples of things that are cylindrical. Encourage students to use terms like *round, circles for top and bottom,* etc. Provide paper cutouts of cylinder nets for students to make cylinders to refer to as they give their descriptions.

Q: What shape does the adjective cylindrical describe?
[a cylinder]

Q: How could two cylinders that are the same height have different volumes?
[The size of their circular faces could be different.]

READING INTERMEDIATE Sometimes with word problems, it can be hard for students to pull out the necessary information to solve the problem and overlook the extra information. Have students each read a photocopy of the example problem, crossing out unimportant information and circling important facts as they read.

Q: Is any information in the first sentence important?
[No; it doesn't matter why we're looking at cylindrical containers.]

Q: What important information about the cylinders is given?
[The cylinders are two different sizes; both cylinders are 3 in. high; the expression for volume for each cylinder is given.]

WRITING ADVANCED Point out the word *radii* in the example. Ask students what the difference between *radii* and *radius* is. Explain that some words that come from Latin and end in *-us* have an irregular plural, formed by replacing the *-us* with *-i*. Encourage students to write sentences in their journals with the plural forms of words such as cactus, fungus, and rhombus.

Q: Do all nouns that end in *-us* have a plural form that ends in *-i*?
[No, the plural forms of chorus, bus, and sinus do not end in *-i*.]

Q: Why is the form *radii* used in the sentence "Find the difference between the radii"?
[more than one radius is being compared]

EXAMPLE 4 Factor Out a Common Factor

Use and Connect Mathematical Representations ETP

Q: How do you know when all the terms in an expression have a common factor?
[Identify the GCF by looking at the coefficients of each term and the variables of each term to see if they have any common factors.]

Q: How is the Distributive Property used to factor out a common factor?
[Use the Distributive Property to write $ab + ac$ as $a(b + c)$.]

Try It! Answers

4. a. $4x(x + 3)^2$

b. $2(5x + 4y)(5x - 4y)$

Common Error

Try It! 4 Some students may factor out a common factor that is not the GCF, so the remaining factor is not the difference of two squares. Have students check their factored expression to see if it contains another common factor.

HABITS OF MIND

Use with **EXAMPLES 3 & 4**

Generalize Can you extend the difference of squares factoring pattern to $x^4 - y^4$? Explain. MP.8

[Yes; x^4 and y^4 are both perfect squares, so you can factor them as a difference of two squares, $(x^2 + y^2)(x^2 - y^2)$.]

AVAILABLE ONLINE

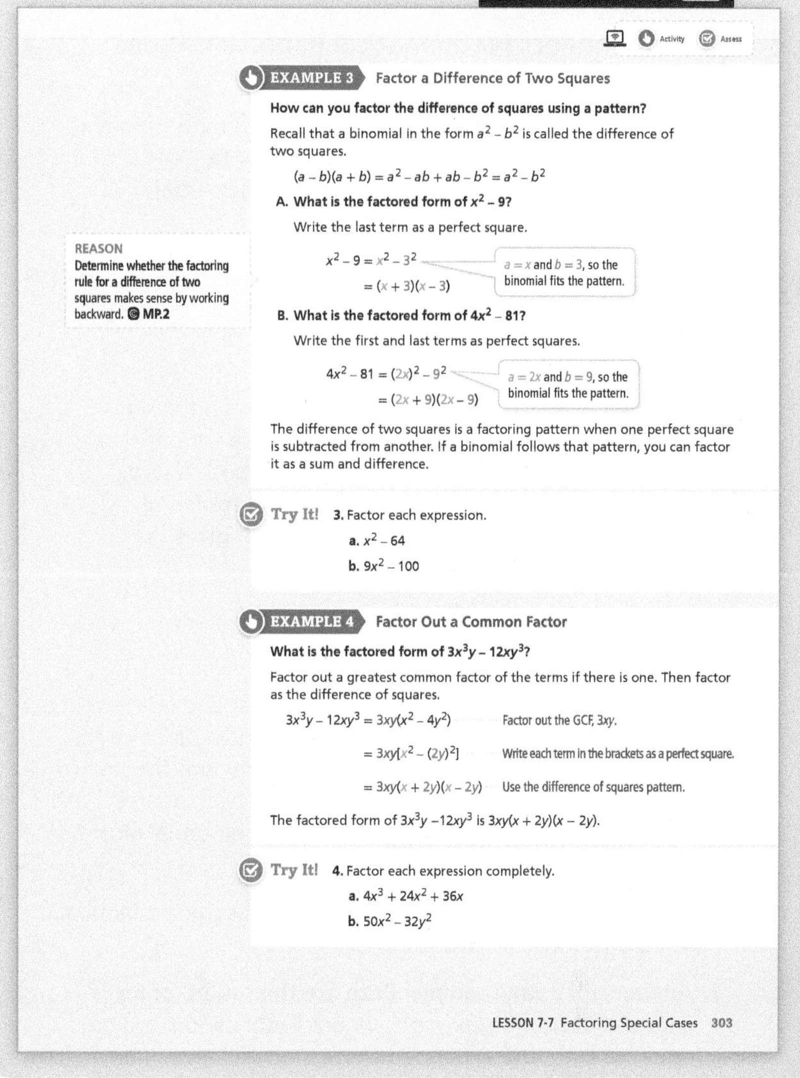

Activity Assess

EXAMPLE 3 Factor a Difference of Two Squares

How can you factor the difference of squares using a pattern?

Recall that a binomial in the form $a^2 - b^2$ is called the difference of two squares.

$(a - b)(a + b) = a^2 - ab + ab - b^2 = a^2 - b^2$

A. What is the factored form of $x^2 - 9$?

Write the last term as a perfect square.

$x^2 - 9 = x^2 - 3^2$ — $a = x$ and $b = 3$, so the binomial fits the pattern.

$= (x + 3)(x - 3)$

REASON
Determine whether the factoring rule for a difference of two squares makes sense by working backward. MP.2

B. What is the factored form of $4x^2 - 81$?

Write the first and last terms as perfect squares.

$4x^2 - 81 = (2x)^2 - 9^2$ — $a = 2x$ and $b = 9$, so the binomial fits the pattern.

$= (2x + 9)(2x - 9)$

The difference of two squares is a factoring pattern when one perfect square is subtracted from another. If a binomial follows that pattern, you can factor it as a sum and difference.

Try It! **3.** Factor each expression.

a. $x^2 - 64$

b. $9x^2 - 100$

EXAMPLE 4 Factor Out a Common Factor

What is the factored form of $3x^3y - 12xy^3$?

Factor out a greatest common factor of the terms if there is one. Then factor as the difference of squares.

$3x^3y - 12xy^3 = 3xy(x^2 - 4y^2)$ — Factor out the GCF, $3xy$.

$= 3xy[x^2 - (2y)^2]$ — Write each term in the brackets as a perfect square.

$= 3xy(x + 2y)(x - 2y)$ — Use the difference of squares pattern.

The factored form of $3x^3y - 12xy^3$ is $3xy(x + 2y)(x - 2y)$.

Try It! **4.** Factor each expression completely.

a. $4x^3 + 24x^2 + 36x$

b. $50x^2 - 32y^2$

LESSON 7-7 Factoring Special Cases 303

Struggling Students

USE WITH EXAMPLE 3 Students may struggle with factoring a difference of two squares.

Q: Have students practice using this pattern to factor the difference of two squares:

$\boxtimes^2 - \odot^2 = (\boxtimes + \odot)(\boxtimes - \odot)$

Using $4x^2 - 81$ from Example 3, $2x$ replaces $\boxtimes$ and 9 replaces $\odot$, so $(\boxtimes + \odot)(\boxtimes - \odot) = (2x + 9)(2x - 9)$.

1. $25x^2 - 64$
[$(5x^2 + 8)(5x^2 - 8)$]

2. $a^2x^2 - b^2y^2$, a and b are constants
[$(ax + by)(ax - by)$]

Q: How do the shapes help focus on the pattern?
[The shapes show the pattern in each binomial factor.]

ADV Advanced Students

USE WITH EXAMPLE 4 Have students extend their knowledge of factoring expressions completely by factoring four-term polynomials. Show students this example of a factorable four-term polynomial where there is no common factor in all four terms:

$8x^3 + 10x + 12x^2y + 15y$

$= (8x^3 + 10x) + (12x^2y + 15y)$ Form two groups.

$= 2x(4x^2 + 5) + 3y(4x^2 + 5)$ Take a common factor from each group.

$= (2x + 3y)(4x^2 + 5)$ Take out the common factor $4x^2 + 5$.

Q: Have students factor the following polynomials:

1. $6x^3 - 9xy - 10x^2y + 15y^2$
[$(2x^2 - 3y)(3x - 5y)$]

2. $20a^4 + 8ab - 35a^3 - 14b$
[$(5a^3 + 2b)(4a - 7)$]

Q: How can you identify which terms to group together?
[The terms in each group should have a common factor.]

CONCEPT SUMMARY Factoring Special Cases of Polynomials

Use and Connect Mathematical Representations ETP

Q: What are the two factoring patterns?
[The two factoring patterns are a perfect-square trinomial, $a^2 + 2ab + b^2 = (a + b)^2$ or $a^2 - 2ab + b^2 = (a - b)^2$, and a difference of two squares $a^2 - b^2 = (a + b)(a - b)$.]

Do You UNDERSTAND? | Do You KNOW HOW?

Common Error

Exercise 8 Students may incorrectly focus on the signs of $9x^2$ and 4 and factor the perfect-square trinomial as $(3x + 2)^2$. Encourage students to look at both $(a + b)^2$ and $(a - b)^2$, substitute the values found for a and b, and multiply the binomial to see which gives the original expression.

Answers

1. In a perfect square trinomial, both the first and last term must be perfect squares and the middle term must be twice the product of the square root of the first term and the square root of the last term. In the difference of two squares, both the first term and the second term in the binomial must be perfect squares.
2. This trinomial fits the pattern of a perfect square trinomial, not a difference of two squares.
3. Answers may vary. Sample: Both are the square of an expression. No, for $(ax + b)^2$, where both a and b are not equal to zero, the expanded expression will always be a trinomial.
4. In both patterns, two of the terms must be perfect squares. In a perfect square trinomial there are three terms and in a difference of two square there are two terms.
5. Factoring out the greatest common factor results in a polynomial with smaller coefficients and/or smaller exponents of the variable(s). This makes it easier to analyze the polynomial or factor it further.
6. difference of two squares
7. perfect-square trinomial
8. perfect-square trinomial
9. perfect-square trinomial
10. difference of two squares
11. perfect-square trinomial
12. $(7x + 5)(7x - 5)$
13. $4(3x + 2)^2$
14. $3x(x - 2)^2$
15. $8(3x + 2)(3x - 2)$
16. $x + 11$
17. Answers may vary. Sample: You can use a difference of two squares to rewrite $50^2 - 45^2$ as $(50 - 45)(50 + 45) = 5(95)$.

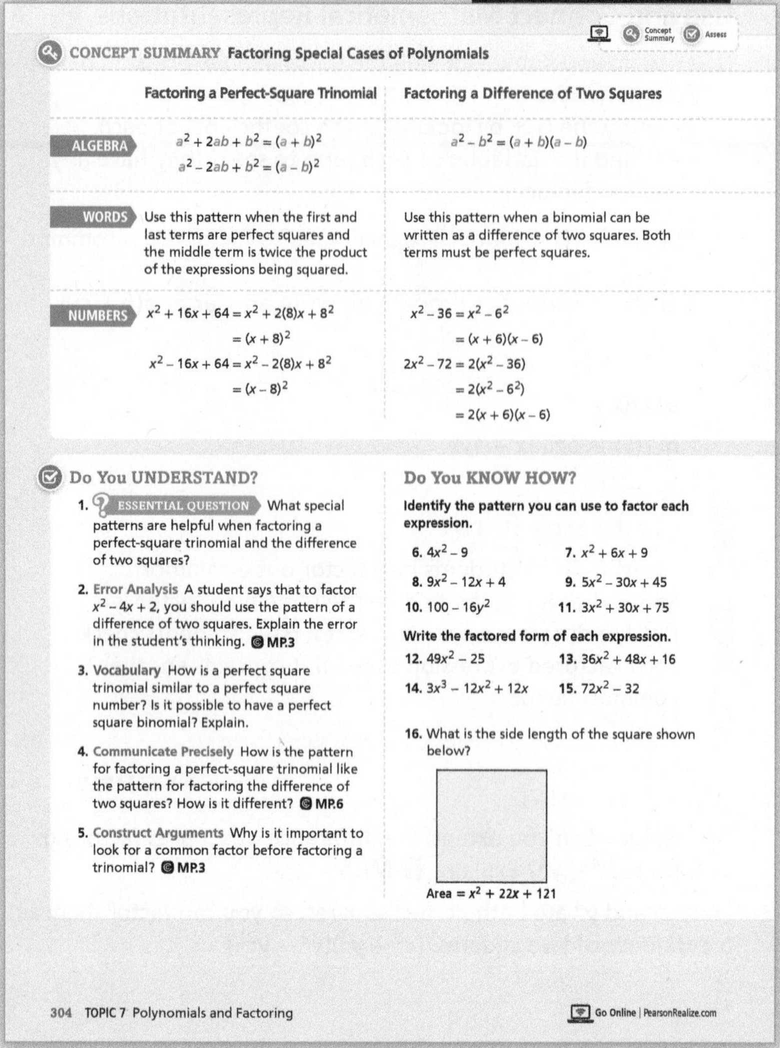
AVAILABLE ONLINE

Concept Summary Assess

CONCEPT SUMMARY Factoring Special Cases of Polynomials

	Factoring a Perfect-Square Trinomial	Factoring a Difference of Two Squares
ALGEBRA	$a^2 + 2ab + b^2 = (a + b)^2$ $a^2 - 2ab + b^2 = (a - b)^2$	$a^2 - b^2 = (a + b)(a - b)$
WORDS	Use this pattern when the first and last terms are perfect squares and the middle term is twice the product of the expressions being squared.	Use this pattern when a binomial can be written as a difference of two squares. Both terms must be perfect squares.
NUMBERS	$x^2 + 16x + 64 = x^2 + 2(8)x + 8^2 = (x + 8)^2$ $x^2 - 16x + 64 = x^2 - 2(8)x + 8^2 = (x - 8)^2$	$x^2 - 36 = x^2 - 6^2 = (x + 6)(x - 6)$ $2x^2 - 72 = 2(x^2 - 36) = 2(x^2 - 6^2) = 2(x + 6)(x - 6)$

Do You UNDERSTAND?

1. ESSENTIAL QUESTION What special patterns are helpful when factoring a perfect-square trinomial and the difference of two squares?
2. **Error Analysis** A student says that to factor $x^2 - 4x + 2$, you should use the pattern of a difference of two squares. Explain the error in the student's thinking. MP.3
3. **Vocabulary** How is a perfect square trinomial similar to a perfect square number? Is it possible to have a perfect square binomial? Explain.
4. **Communicate Precisely** How is the pattern for factoring a perfect-square trinomial like the pattern for factoring the difference of two squares? How is it different? MP.6
5. **Construct Arguments** Why is it important to look for a common factor before factoring a trinomial? MP.3

Do You KNOW HOW?

Identify the pattern you can use to factor each expression.

6. $4x^2 - 9$
7. $x^2 + 6x + 9$
8. $9x^2 - 12x + 4$
9. $5x^2 - 30x + 45$
10. $100 - 16y^2$
11. $3x^2 + 30x + 75$

Write the factored form of each expression.

12. $49x^2 - 25$
13. $36x^2 + 48x + 16$
14. $3x^3 - 12x^2 + 12x$
15. $72x^2 - 32$
16. What is the side length of the square shown below?

Area = $x^2 + 22x + 121$

304 TOPIC 7 Polynomials and Factoring

Go Online | PearsonRealize.com

18. No; Answers may vary. Sample: Because the second term of 50 is not a perfect square, a difference of two squares pattern does not apply. Additionally, the two terms have no common factors.
19. $(2x - y)(2x + y)(4x^2 + y^2)$; difference of two squares followed by difference of two squares.
20. The student used the wrong pattern for factoring. Instead, the student should use the pattern for a difference of two squares. The factored form of the expression is $(x + 6)(x - 6)$.
21.

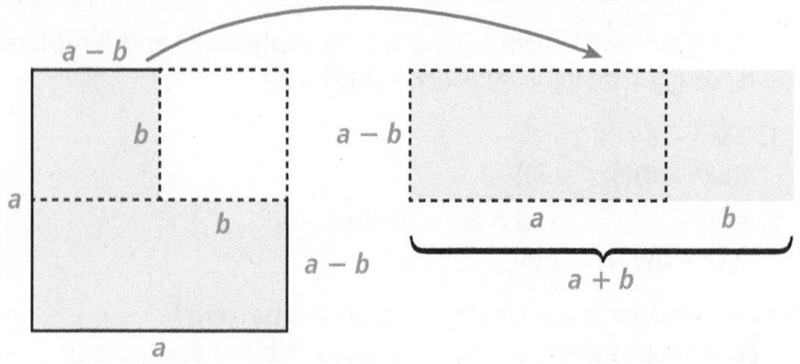

a – b
b
a
b
a – b
a
a – b
a
b
a + b

PRACTICE & PROBLEM SOLVING

AVAILABLE ONLINE

Lesson Practice You may opt to have students complete the automatically scored Practice and Problem Solving items online powered by MathXL for School.

Choose from: **Lesson Practice**

Adaptive Practice

You may also take advantage of the bank of exercises for assigning additional practice.

Assignment Guide

Basic	Advanced
17–38, 43–54	17–26, 31–54

Item Analysis

Example	Items	DOK
1	29–31, 33, 34, 36, 42	2
	25–28	3
2	23, 51	2
	49, 50, 54	3
3	17, 19, 20, 29, 30, 32, 38, 44–48	2
	21, 24	3
4	18, 35, 37, 39, 40, 41, 43, 53	2
	22, 52	3

AVAILABLE ONLINE

PRACTICE & PROBLEM SOLVING

Scan for Multimedia · Practice · Tutorial · Additional Exercises Available Online

UNDERSTAND

17. Mathematical Connections How could you use special factoring patterns to quickly rewrite the difference $50^2 - 45^2$ as a product? Explain.

18. Reason Is the expression $x^2 - 50$ factorable? Explain why or why not. MP.2

19. Look for Relationships What is the completely factored form of the expression $16x^4 - y^4$? Describe the method(s) of factoring you used. MP.7

20. Error Analysis Describe and correct the error a student made in factoring $x^2 - 36$. MP.3

> Use the perfect-square trinomial pattern to factor $x^2 - 36$ because both terms are perfect squares.
>
> $x^2 - 36 = (x - 6)(x - 6)$ ✗

21. Higher Order Thinking Use the visual shown as a starting point. Describe how you can use diagrams to show that $a^2 - b^2 = (a + b)(a - b)$.

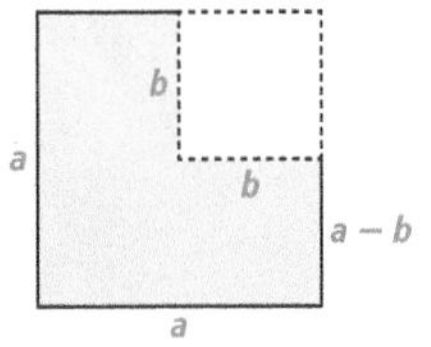
b
a
b
a − b
a

22. Make Sense and Persevere Describe the steps you would use to factor the expression $x^4 - 8x^2 + 16$. MP.1

23. Reason A rectangle has a width that is twice the length. If the area of the rectangle is represented by the expression $18x^2 + 48x + 32$, what expression represents the length of the rectangle? Explain. MP.2

24. Communicate Precisely How can you determine if a binomial of the form $x^2 - \frac{a}{b}$ is factorable using rational constants? MP.6

PRACTICE

Identify the value of c that would make the trinomial factorable using the perfect-square pattern. SEE EXAMPLE 1

25. $x^2 + 24x + c$ 144

26. $x^2 - 10x + c$ 25

27. $6x^2 - 36x + c$ 54

28. $3x^2 + 24x + c$ 48

Given the area of each square, factor to find the side length. SEE EXAMPLES 1 AND 2

29. Area = $36x^2 + 120x + 100$ $(6x + 10)$

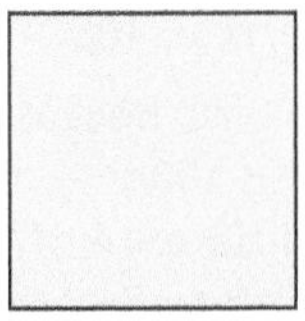

30. Area = $144x^2 - 24x + 1$ $(12x - 1)$

Factor each expression completely.
SEE EXAMPLES 1, 3, and 4

31. $x^2 + 16x + 64$ $(x + 8)^2$

32. $x^2 - 25$ $(x + 5)(x - 5)$

33. $x^2 - 18x + 81$ $(x - 9)^2$

34. $x^2 - 14x + 49$ $(x - 7)^2$

35. $100x^2 - 36$

36. $16x^2 + 40x + 25$ $(4x + 5)^2$

37. $8x^2 - 32x + 32$ $8(x - 2)^2$

38. $16x^2 - 81y^2$ $(4x + 9y)(4x - 9y)$

39. $2x^3 + 32x^2 + 128x$ $2x(x + 8)^2$

40. $7x^3y - 63xy^3$ $7xy(x + 3y)(x - 3y)$

41. $49x^3 - 16xy^2$ $x(7x + 4y)(7x - 4y)$

42. $121x^2 + 110x + 25$ $(11x + 5)^2$

43. $-3x^3 + 18x^2 - 27x$ $-3x(x - 3)^2$

44. $64x^2y^2 - 144z^2$

Factor each expression as the product of binomials.

45. $x^2 - \frac{1}{4}$ $\left(x - \frac{1}{2}\right)\left(x + \frac{1}{2}\right)$

46. $x^2 - \frac{1}{9}$ $\left(x - \frac{1}{3}\right)\left(x + \frac{1}{3}\right)$

47. $p^2 - \frac{49}{100}$ $\left(p - \frac{7}{10}\right)\left(p + \frac{7}{10}\right)$

48. $x^2 + x + \frac{1}{4}$ $\left(x + \frac{1}{2}\right)\left(x + \frac{1}{2}\right)$

Answers

18–21. See previous page.

22. First, use the pattern for a perfect square trinomial to get $(x^2 - 4)^2$. Then apply a difference of two squares pattern to each of the factors to get $(x + 2)(x - 2)(x + 2)(x - 2)$, or $(x + 2)^2(x - 2)^2$.

23. $3x + 4$; Since the width is twice the length, the rectangle is made of two squares side-by-side. If you divide the area by 2, the resulting expression will be the area of each square, $9x^2 + 24x + 16$, which is a perfect-square trinomial. Factor the perfect-square trinomial to find the length of each square, which is also the length of the rectangle.

24. a and b must each be a perfect square, with $b \neq 0$

35. $(10x + 6)(10x - 6)$ or $4(5x + 3)(5x - 3)$

44. $16(2xy + 3z)(2xy - 3z)$ or $(8xy + 12z)(8xy - 12z)$

Answers

49. **a.** $(x + 16)$ by $(x + 16)$; yes; The factors are equal so the side lengths are the same.

b. $(x + 2y)$ by $(x - 2y)$; yes, but only when $y = 0$; The factors are equal when $y = 0$. Other than that, they are not equal.

c. $(x - 10)$ by $(x - 10)$; yes; The factors are equal so the side lengths are the same.

50. $(7x + 5y)$ by $(7x - 5y)$; One side length is $10y$ longer than the other; $5y$

51. **a.** $100p^2 - n^2$

b. $10p$, $10p$, $10p - n$, n, n, $10p - n$

c. $(10p + n)$ by $(10p - n)$; Because the area of the office is $100p^2 - n^2$, you can use the difference of two squares pattern to find the dimensions of a rectangular office with the same area.

52. I. C

II. B

III. D

IV. A

54. **Part A** $12(x + 1)^2$ and $3(x + 13)^2$

Part B Fabric on left: $12(x + 1)$ and $(x + 1)$; $6(x + 1)$ and $2(x + 1)$; or $4(x + 1)$ and $3(x + 1)$

Fabric on right: $3(x + 13)$ and $(x + 13)$

Part C Fabric on left: $6(x + 1)$ and $2(x + 1)$

Fabric on right: $3(x + 13)$ and $(x + 13)$

Part D Fabric on left: 66 in.-by-22 in.

Fabric on right: 69 in.-by-23 in.

AVAILABLE **ONLINE**

PRACTICE & PROBLEM SOLVING

Practice Tutorial

Mixed Review Available Online

APPLY

49. **Reason** In front of a school are several gardens in rectangular raised beds. For each of the areas of a rectangular garden given, use factoring to find possible dimensions. Could the garden be square? If so, explain why. MP.2

a. $x^2 + 32x + 256$

b. $x^2 - 4y^2$

c. $x^2 - 20x + 100$

50. **Make Sense and Persevere** The area of a rectangular rug is $49x^2 - 25y^2$ in.^{2}. Use factoring to find possible dimensions of the rug. How are the side lengths related? What value would you need to subtract from the longer side and add to the shorter side for the rug to be a square? MP.1

51. **Model With Mathematics** A furniture company created an L-shaped table by removing part of a square table. MP.4

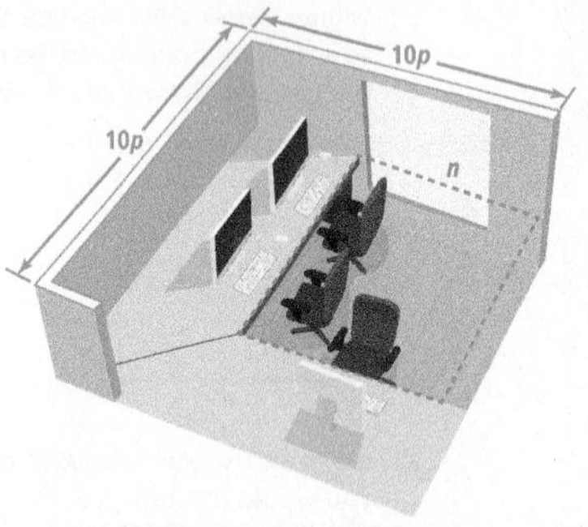
10p
10p
n

a. Write an expression that represents the area of the L-shaped table.

b. What are all the side lengths of the L-shaped table?

c. The furniture company decides to create another table with the same area, but needs this table to be rectangular. What are the possible dimensions of the rectangular table? Explain.

ASSESSMENT PRACTICE

52. Match each expression with its factored form.

I. $25m^2 - 9n^2$	A. $(5m + 3n)^2$
II. $25m^2 - 30mn + 9n^2$	B. $(5m - 3n)^2$
III. $25m^2 - 30mn - 9n^2$	C. $(5m + 3n)(5m - 3n)$
IV. $25m^2 + 30mn + 9n^2$	D. does not factor

53. **SAT/ACT** What is the factored form of $6x^2 - 60x + 150$?

Ⓐ $6(x - 25)^2$
Ⓑ $6(x - 5)(x - 10)$
Ⓒ $6(x - 5)^2$
Ⓓ $6(x - 5)(x + 5)$

54. **Performance Task** Two pieces of fabric are being used for clothing designs for a fashion show at school Expressions for the areas of the rectangular pieces are shown.

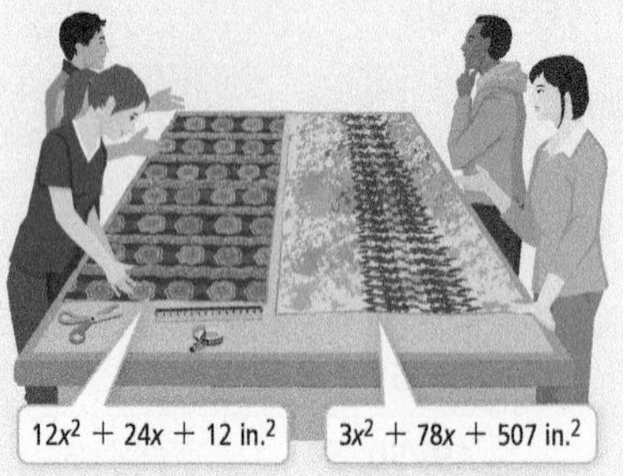
$12x^2 + 24x + 12$ in.^{2}
$3x^2 + 78x + 507$ in.^{2}

Part A Factor the expressions for the areas completely.

Part B Using the factorings from Part A, write all of the possible dimensions of the pieces of fabric as binomials with integer coefficients.

Part C Assume that the table is about 6 ft long. Using integer values for x, which set of binomials yields to most reasonable dimensions based on the picture?

Part D Using your result from Part C what are the dimensions in inches of the two pieces of fabric?

SavvasRealize.com

Assess Tutorials Worksheets

LESSON QUIZ

Use the Lesson Quiz to assess students' understanding of the mathematics in the lesson.

Students can take the Lesson Quiz online or you can download a printable copy from **SavvasRealize.com**. The Lesson Quiz is also available in the *Assessment Resources* book.

Item Analysis

Item	DOK	Standards
1	1	HSA.SSE.A.1
2	2	HSA.SSE.A.1
3	1	HSA.SSE.A.2
4	2	HSA.SSE.A.2
5	2	HSA.SSE.A.2

RtI Use the student scores on the Lesson Quiz to prescribe differentiated assignments.

If students take the Lesson Quiz online, it will be automatically scored and appropriate differentiated practice will be assigned based on student performance.

I Intervention	0–3 points	• Reteach to Build Understanding • Mathematical Literacy and Vocabulary • Additional Practice
O On-Level	4 points	• Mathematical Literacy and Vocabulary • Additional Practice • Enrichment
A Advanced	5 points	• Enrichment

AVAILABLE **ONLINE**

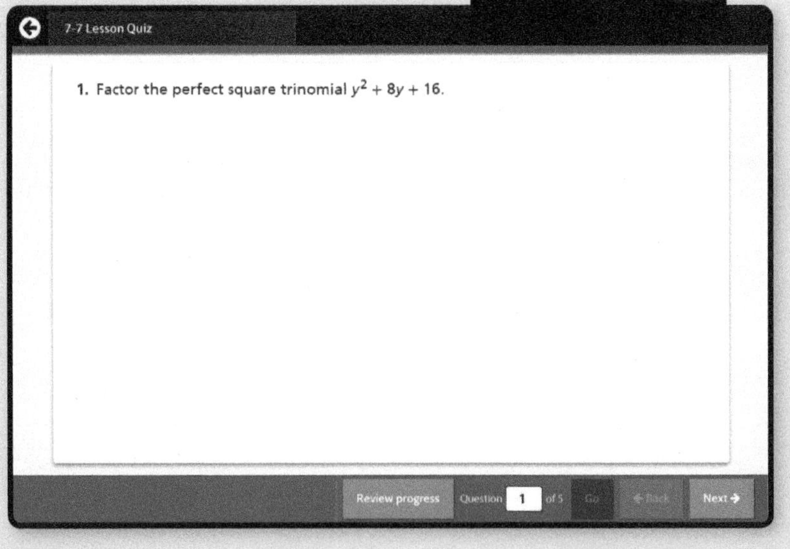
7-7 Lesson Quiz
1. Factor the perfect square trinomial $y^2 + 8y + 16$.
Review progress
Question 1 of 5
Go
Back
Next

ASSESSMENT RESOURCES

Name ____________

enVision Algebra 1

PearsonRealize.com

7-7 Lesson Quiz

Factoring Special Cases

1. Factor the perfect square trinomial $y^2 + 8y + 16$.
   $(y + 4)^2$
2. Factor the perfect square trinomial $25x^2 - 60x + 36$.
   $(5x - 6)^2$
3. Factor the expression $25x^2 - 36$.
   Ⓐ $(5x^2 - 6)(5x^2 + 6)$
   Ⓑ $(5x - 6)^2$
   Ⓒ The expression is already fully factored.
   Ⓓ $(5x - 6)(5x + 6)$
4. A cone with height h and radius r has a volume $V = \frac{1}{3}\pi r^2 h$. If the cone has a height of 6 in. and a volume $V = 8\pi x^2 + 24\pi x + 18\pi$, what is its radius r in terms of x?
   Ⓐ $r = 3x + 2$
   Ⓑ $r = 4x^2 + 12x + 9$
   Ⓒ $r = 2x + 3$
   Ⓓ $r = (2x + 3)(2x - 3)$
5. Factor the expression completely: $2x^4y - 18x^2y^3$.
   $2x^2y(x - 3y)(x + 3y)$

enVision™ **Algebra 1** • Assessment Resources

DIFFERENTIATED RESOURCES

I = Intervention O = On-Level A = Advanced

= This activity is available as a digital assignment powered by MathXL® for School.

AVAILABLE ONLINE

Reteach to Build Understanding I

Provides scaffolded reteaching for the key lesson concepts.

Name ______

7-7 Reteach to Build Understanding

Factoring Special Cases

1. Label each item as *perfect-square trinomial* or *difference of two squares*.

$a^2 - b^2 = (a + b)(a - b)$ difference of two squares

$x^2 - 12x + 36 = (x - 6)^2$ perfect-square trinomial

Use this pattern when the first and last terms are perfect squares and the middle term is twice the product of the expressions being squared. perfect-square trinomial

$a^2 - 2ab + b^2 = (a - b)^2$ perfect-square trinomial

Use this pattern when a binomial can be written as the square of one number minus the square of another number. difference of two squares

$4x^2 - 49 = (2x - 7)(2x + 7)$ difference of two squares

$a^2 + 2ab + b^2 = (a + b)^2$ perfect-square trinomial

2. Complete the steps for factoring $2x^3 - 36x^2 + 162x$ by writing words, numbers, or expressions in the blanks.

$2x^3 - 36x^2 + 162x =$ 2x $(x^2 - 18x + 81)$ Factor out the GCF.

$=$ 2x $[x^2 - 2($ 9 $)x + ($ 9 $)^2]$ Rewrite the trinomial.

$=$ 2x $(x -$ 9 $)(x -$ 9 $)$ Use the perfect-square trinomial pattern.

$=$ 2x $(x -$ 9 $)^2$ Simplify.

3. Describe and correct the error Teddy made in factoring $x^2 - 49$.

$x^2 - 49 = (x - 7)^2$ Both terms in the binomial are perfect squares, so use the perfect-square trinomial pattern.

Teddy was incorrect, because the last term in the binomial is negative, and so the factored form should be the difference of two squares, $(x + 7)(x - 7)$.

enVision™ Algebra 1 • Teaching Resources

Additional Practice I O

Provides extra practice for each lesson.

Name ______

7-7 Additional Practice

Factoring Special Cases

Factor each trinomial completely.

1. $x^2 + 12x + 36$ $(x + 6)^2$
2. $x^2 - 24xy + 144y^2$ $(x - 12y)^2$
3. $4x^2 + 44x + 121$ $(2x + 11)^2$
4. $49x^2 - 14x + 1$ $(7x - 1)^2$
5. $32x^2 + 48xy + 18y^2$ $2(4x + 3y)^2$
6. $12x^2y^2 - 60xyz + 75z^2$ $3(2xy - 5z)^2$
7. $x^2 - 64$ $(x + 8)(x - 8)$
8. $x^2 - 289y^2$ $(x + 17y)(x - 17y)$
9. $4x^2 - 49$ $(2x + 7)(2x - 7)$
10. $27x^2 - 3$ $3(3x + 1)(3x - 1)$
11. $9x^2y^2 - 64z^2$ $(3xy + 8z)(3xy - 8z)$
12. $4x^4 - 36$ $4(x^2 + 3)(x^2 - 3)$

13. Under what conditions is a trinomial said to be completely factored?
Sample answer: A completely factored trinomial will show the GCF as a factor, and the remaining binomial factors will not be differences of perfect squares.

14. The area of a circle is $4\pi x^2 + 12\pi x + 9\pi$.
a. What is an expression for the radius of the circle?
$2x + 3$
b. What is the least possible integer value of x for the circle to exist? Explain.
-1; Sample answer: The radius must be positive. That is, $2x + 3 > 0$, or $x > -1.5$. Therefore, the least possible integer value of x is -1.

enVision™ Algebra 1 • Teaching Resources

Enrichment O A

Presents engaging problems and activities that extend the lesson concepts.

Name ______

7-7 Enrichment

Factoring Special Cases

A 25 × 25 square grid is used to make one large rectangle joined together as shown. All of the grid is used except for the shaded section of 11 × 11.

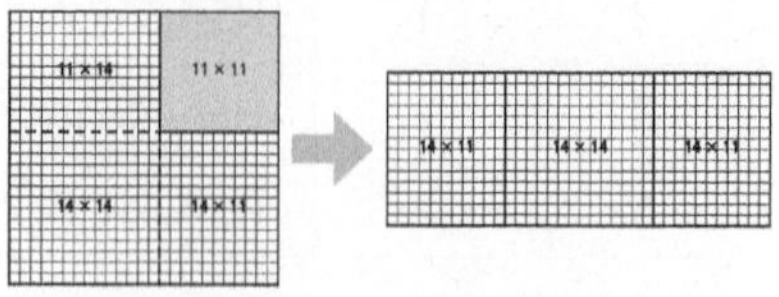
11 × 14
11 × 11
14 × 14
14 × 11
14 × 11
14 × 14
14 × 11

1. Write expressions for the length and width of the large rectangle in terms of 25 and 11.
Length = 25 + 11 units Width = 25 − 11 units
2. Use the formula for the area of a rectangle to write an equation for the area of the three combined rectangles in terms of 25 and 11.
Area = $(25 + 11)(25 - 11) = 25^2 + 275 - 275 - 11^2 = 504$ square units
3. Now, think about the original grid with 25 × 25 squares and the excluded shaded section measuring 11 × 11. Write an equation for the area of the grid by subtracting the area of the shaded section from the area of the original grid.
Area = $625 - 121 = 504$ square units
4. How does the equation in Exercise 3 relate to the equation in Exercise 2 for the area of the rectangle? These two equations give the same area.
5. Write $25^2 - 11^2$ as a product of a sum and a difference.
$25^2 - 11^2 = (25 + 11)(25 - 11)$
6. Consider a 36 × 36 grid that is used to make one large rectangle that is joined together. All of the grid is used except for the shaded section of 14 × 14. Use the formula for the area of a rectangle to write an equation for the area of the three combined rectangles as the product of the sum and the difference of 36 and 14.
$36^2 - 14^2 = (36 + 14)(36 - 14)$

enVision™ Algebra 1 • Teaching Resources

Mathematical Literacy and Vocabulary I O

Helps students develop and reinforce understanding of key terms and concepts.

Name ______

7-7 Mathematical Literacy and Vocabulary

Factoring Special Cases

Complete the vocabulary table by filling in the missing information.

Word or Word Phrase	Definition	Picture or Example
difference of two squares	A binomial in which a perfect square monomial is subtracted from another perfect square monomial	$x^2 - 16$
factoring a difference of two squares	1. For every real number a and b: $a^2 - b^2 = (a + b)(a - b)$	$x^2 - 25 = (x + 5)(x - 5)$
factoring perfect-square trinomials	For all real numbers a and b: $a^2 + 2ab + b^2 = (a + b)(a + b) = (a + b)^2$ or $a^2 - 2ab + b^2 = (a - b)(a - b) = (a - b)^2$.	2. Sample: $16x^2 + 24x + 9 = (4x + 3)^2$ $x^2 - 16x + 64 = (x - 8)^2$
perfect-square trinomial	3. A trinomial that results when a binomial is squared	$9x^2 + 24x + 16$

enVision™ Algebra 1 • Teaching Resources

Digital Resources and Video Tutorials I O A

The **Reteach to Build Understanding, Additional Practice,** and **Enrichment** activities are available as digital assignments powered by MathXL for School. These activities are automatically assigned when students complete the lesson quiz online and are automatically scored.

Students can access instructional tutorials using the **Virtual Nerd app.**

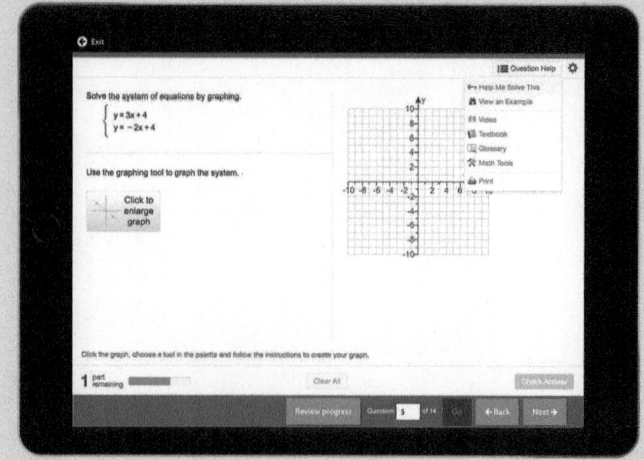
Solve the system of equations by graphing.
Use the graphing tool to graph the system.
Click to enlarge graph
Question Help
Review progress
Clear All
Check Answer

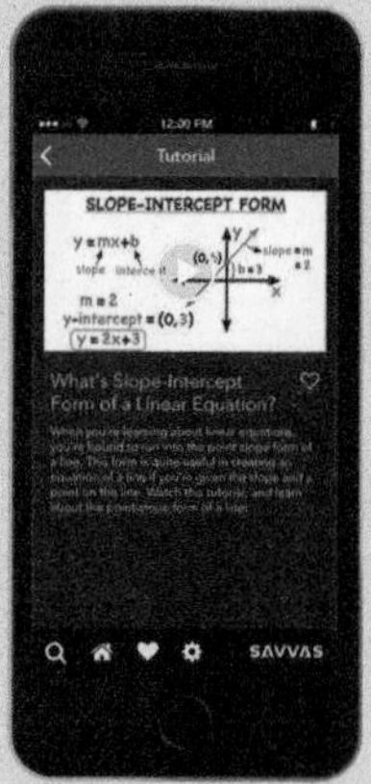
Tutorial
SLOPE-INTERCEPT FORM
What's Slope-Intercept Form of a Linear Equation?
SAVVAS

Students can also access Virtual Nerd videos using the **BouncePages app** to scan exercise pages marked with this icon. Students can download both apps for free in their mobile devices' app store.

TOPIC 7
Polynomials and Factoring

TOPIC REVIEW

TOPIC ESSENTIAL QUESTION

How do you work with polynomials to rewrite expressions and solve problems?

As students answer the Essential Question in writing, encourage them to include examples that support their answers. Look for the following points to come out while discussing students' answers.

- Polynomials form a system similar to the system of integers. Therefore, polynomials are closed under addition, subtraction, and multiplication.
- Polynomials are added or subtracted by combining like terms.
- Polynomials can be multiplied by applying the Distributive Property or by using a table.
- The greatest common factor of polynomials is the greatest common factor of the coefficients and the variables that are common factors of each term.
- When a trinomial is in the form $x^2 + bx + c$, the factors are found by identifying factor pairs of c that have a sum of b. The factors are then used to write binomial factors that have a product equal to the trinomial.
- A quadratic trinomial in the form $ax^2 + bx + c$ is factored by finding factor pairs of ac that have a sum of b. When ac and b are positive, the second terms in the binomial factors are also positive. When ac is negative, the second terms in the binomial factors have opposite signs.

Answers

2. Closure Property
3. perfect-square trinomial
4. monomial
5. difference of two squares
6. standard form of a polynomial
7. quadratic
8. constant
9. cubic
10. $7x - 4$
11. $-x^2 - 12x + 3$
12. $8b^4 + 8b^2 - 6$
13. $5x$; Answers may vary. Sample: In the sum, the coefficient of the x term is 8. So far, there is only $3x$ in the addends, so there is $5x$ missing.
14. $5x^2 + 19x + 51$

AVAILABLE **ONLINE**

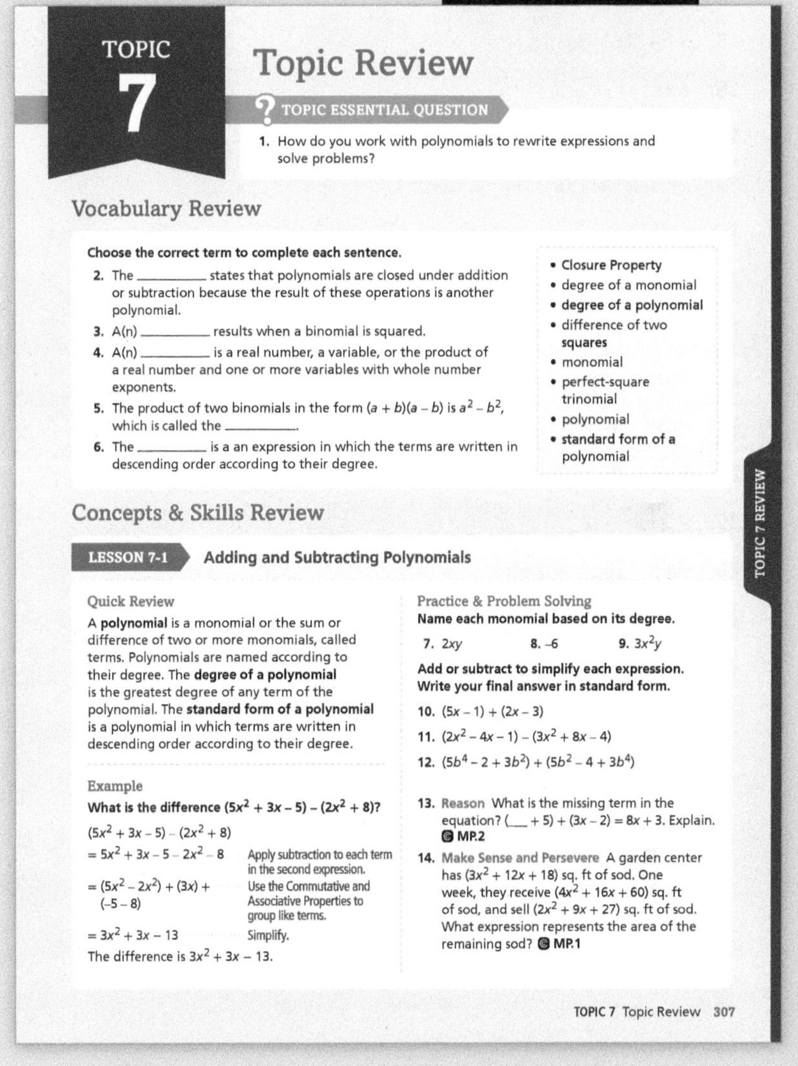

TOPIC 7

Topic Review

TOPIC ESSENTIAL QUESTION

1. How do you work with polynomials to rewrite expressions and solve problems?

Vocabulary Review

Choose the correct term to complete each sentence.

2. The ______ states that polynomials are closed under addition or subtraction because the result of these operations is another polynomial.
3. A(n) ______ results when a binomial is squared.
4. A(n) ______ is a real number, a variable, or the product of a real number and one or more variables with whole number exponents.
5. The product of two binomials in the form $(a + b)(a - b)$ is $a^2 - b^2$, which is called the ______.
6. The ______ is a an expression in which the terms are written in descending order according to their degree.

- Closure Property
- degree of a monomial
- degree of a polynomial
- difference of two squares
- monomial
- perfect-square trinomial
- polynomial
- standard form of a polynomial

Concepts & Skills Review

LESSON 7-1 Adding and Subtracting Polynomials

Quick Review

A **polynomial** is a monomial or the sum or difference of two or more monomials, called terms. Polynomials are named according to their degree. The **degree of a polynomial** is the greatest degree of any term of the polynomial. The **standard form of a polynomial** is a polynomial in which terms are written in descending order according to their degree.

Example

What is the difference $(5x^2 + 3x - 5) - (2x^2 + 8)$?

$(5x^2 + 3x - 5) - (2x^2 + 8)$

$= 5x^2 + 3x - 5 - 2x^2 - 8$ Apply subtraction to each term in the second expression.

$= (5x^2 - 2x^2) + (3x) + (-5 - 8)$ Use the Commutative and Associative Properties to group like terms.

$= 3x^2 + 3x - 13$ Simplify.

The difference is $3x^2 + 3x - 13$.

Practice & Problem Solving

Name each monomial based on its degree.

7. $2xy$ 8. -6 9. $3x^2y$

Add or subtract to simplify each expression. Write your final answer in standard form.

10. $(5x - 1) + (2x - 3)$
11. $(2x^2 - 4x - 1) - (3x^2 + 8x - 4)$
12. $(5b^4 - 2 + 3b^2) + (5b^2 - 4 + 3b^4)$
13. Reason What is the missing term in the equation? $(\_\_ + 5) + (3x - 2) = 8x + 3$. Explain. MP.2
14. Make Sense and Persevere A garden center has $(3x^2 + 12x + 18)$ sq. ft of sod. One week, they receive $(4x^2 + 16x + 60)$ sq. ft of sod, and sell $(2x^2 + 9x + 27)$ sq. ft of sod. What expression represents the area of the remaining sod? MP.1

TOPIC 7 REVIEW

TOPIC 7 Topic Review 307

AVAILABLE **ONLINE**

Go online at **SavvasRealize.com** for additional practice and mixed review.

Answers

15. $x^2 + 2x - 35$

16. $6x^2 - 13x - 5$

17. $20x^2 - 11xy - 3y^2$

18. $x^3 + x^2 - 13x - 4$

19. x; 8

20. $27x^3 - 27x^2 + 9x - 1$

21. $b^2 + 24b + 144$

22. $16x^2 + 8x + 1$

23. $36x^2 - 81$

24. $9x^2 - 16y^2$

25. $2.25x^2 - 4$

26. $9a^2 - 30ab + 25b^2$

27. 25

28. Surface area: $150x^2 - 120x + 24$ ft^2
Volume: $125x^3 - 150x^2 + 60x - 8$ ft^3

AVAILABLE **ONLINE**

LESSON 7-2 Multiplying Polynomials

Quick Review

Use the Distributive Property to multiply polynomials as you would when multiplying integers numbers. Distribute the first polynomial to each term in the second polynomial.

Example

How can you use the Distributive Property to rewrite $(3x - 5)(4x - 9)$ as a polynomial?

Distribute the first binomial to each term in the second binomial.

$(3x - 5)(4x - 9)$

$= 3x(4x - 9) - 5(4x - 9)$ — Distribute $3x$ and -5 to the second binomial.

$= 3x(4x) + 3x(-9) - 5(4x) - 5(-9)$ — Distribute $3x$ and -5 to each term in the second binomial.

$= 12x^2 - 27x - 20x + 45$ — Multiply.

$= 12x^2 - 47x + 45$ — Combine like terms.

The product is $12x^2 - 47x + 45$.

Practice & Problem Solving

Use the Distributive Property to find each product.

15. $(x + 7)(x - 5)$ **16.** $(2x - 5)(3x + 1)$

Use a table to find each product.

17. $(4x - 3y)(5x + y)$ **18.** $(x + 4)(x^2 - 3x - 1)$

19. Make Sense and Persevere Identify the missing terms in the quotient and divisor. MP.1

$(\_\_ + 3)(x + \_\_) = x^2 + 11x + 24$

20. Model With Mathematics The volume of a cube is calculated by multiplying the length, width and height. What is the volume of this cube in standard form? MP.4

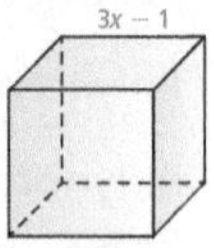
3x − 1

LESSON 7-3 Multiplying Special Cases

Quick Review

The square of a binomial always follows the same pattern, $a^2 + 2ab + b^2$. The product of two binomials in the form $(a + b)(a - b)$ is $a^2 - b^2$. This is called the **difference of two squares**.

Example

What is the product $(4x - 9)(4x + 9)$?

Use the pattern.

$(4x - 9)(4x + 9)$

$= (4x)^2 - (9)^2$ — Substitute $4x$ and 9 and for a and b in $a^2 - b^2$.

$= 16x^2 - 81$ — Simplify.

The product is $16x^2 - 81$.

Practice & Problem Solving

Write each product in standard form.

21. $(b + 12)(b + 12)$ **22.** $(4x + 1)(4x + 1)$

23. $(6x - 9)(6x + 9)$ **24.** $(3x - 4y)(3x + 4y)$

25. $(1.5x + 2)(1.5x - 2)$ **26.** $(3a - 5b)^2$

27. Look for Relationships Find a value for m to make a true statement. MP.7

$mx^2 - 64 = (5x + 8)(5x - 8)$

28. Modeling With Mathematics Write polynomials in standard form to represent the surface area and volume of the cube. MP.4

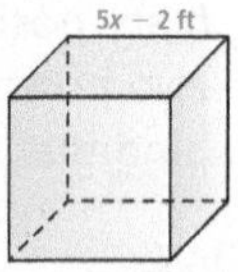
5x − 2 ft

308 TOPIC 7 Polynomials and Factoring

Go Online | PearsonRealize.com

TOPIC 7
Polynomials and Factoring

TOPIC REVIEW

Answers

29. $3x$

30. bc

31. $7xy^2$

32. 6

33. $3x(5x^2 - 14)$

34. $6y(y^4 - 7y^2 + 3)$

35. $6a(2a^2 + 3a - 6)$

36. $7ab(7a^4b^2 - 2ab + 5)$

37. Answers may vary. Sample: $9x^6 - 27x^3 + 6x$

38. $2x$; $2x(7x - 8)$

39. Sample answer:

Factors	Sum of Factors
–1 and 18	–17
1 and –18	17
–2 and 9	7

40. $(x + 8)(x + 4)$

41. $(x + 7)(x - 4)$

42. $(x + 3)(x - 16)$

43. $(x + 3y)(x + 15y)$

44. Both have the same factors of 7 and 3, but with different signs. The first expression has binomial factors $(x + 7)(x - 3)$ and the second expression has binomial factors $(x - 7)(x + 3)$.

AVAILABLE **ONLINE**

LESSON 7-4 Factoring Polynomials

Quick Review

To factor a common monomial factor out of a polynomial, first write the prime factorization of the coefficient for each term to determine if there is a greatest common factor other than 1. Then determine the greatest common factor for the variables of each term.

Example

What is the GCF of the terms of $16x^6 - 8x^4 + 4x^3$?

First, write the prime factorization of the coefficients for each term.

$16 = 2 \cdot 2 \cdot 2 \cdot 2$
$8 = 2 \cdot 2 \cdot 2$
$4 = 2 \cdot 2$

Each number has a common coefficient of 4, so the GCF of the coefficients is 4.

Next, determine the GCF of the variables for each term.

$x^6 = x \cdot x \cdot x \cdot x \cdot x \cdot x$
$x^4 = x \cdot x \cdot x \cdot x$
$x^3 = x \cdot x \cdot x$

Each term has the common factor of x^3, so the GCF of the variables is x^3.

The GCF of $16x^6 - 8x^4 + 4x^3$ is $4x^3$.

Practice & Problem Solving

Find the GCF of each group of monomials.

29. $6x^2$, $21x$ **30.** bc^2, b^3c

31. $14x^2y^2$, $84x^3y^5$, $21xy^3$ **32.** $24a^2$, 18

Factor out the GCF from each polynomial.

33. $15x^3 - 42x$

34. $6y^5 - 42y^3 + 18y$

35. $12a^3 + 18a^2 - 36a$

36. $49a^5b^3 - 14a^2b^2 + 35ab$

37. Look for Relationships Write a trinomial that has a GCF of $3x$. MP.7

38. Use Structure Determine the GCF and write the expression in factored form. MP.7

$(8x^2 - 12x) + (6x^2 - 4x)$

LESSON 7-5 Factoring $x^2 + bx + c$

Quick Review

To factor $x^2 + bx + c$, find the factor pair of c that has a sum of b. Then use those factors to write the binomial factors of the trinomial.

Example

What is the factored form of $x^2 - 9x + 14$?

Identify a factor pair of 14 that has a sum of –9.

Factors of 14	Sum of Factors
–1 and –14	–15
–2 and –7	–9

The factored form of $x^2 - 9x + 14$ is $(x - 2)(x - 7)$.

Practice & Problem Solving

Complete the table to factor the trinomial

39. $x^2 + 7x - 18$

Factors of c	Sum of Factors
▪	▪
▪	▪
▪	7

Write the factored form of each trinomial.

40. $x^2 + 12x + 32$ **41.** $x^2 + 3x - 28$

42. $x^2 - 13x - 48$ **43.** $x^2 + 18xy + 45y^2$

44. Look for Relationships How are the binomial factors of $x^2 + 4x - 21$ and $x^2 - 4x - 21$ similar? How are they different? MP.7

TOPIC 7 REVIEW

TOPIC REVIEW

Answers

45.

Factors	Sum of Factors
20 and 1	21
10 and 2	12
5 and 4	9

46.

Factors	Sum of Factors
−1 and 30	29
1 and −30	−29
−2 and 15	13
2 and −15	−13
−3 and 10	7
3 and −10	−7
−5 and 6	1
5 and −6	−1

47. $(3x + 4)(x + 2)$

48. $(4x + 5)(x - 2)$

49. $(5x - 3)(x + 2)$

50. $(3x + 2)(2x + 3)$

51. $(5x + 4)(2x - 1)$

52. $2(2x + 3)(3x + 1)$

53. 23, −23, 10, −10, 5, −5, 2, −2

54. $(2x - 1)$ m by $(x + 5)$ m. The new dimensions would be $(2x + 4)$ m by $(x + 9)$ m. The new area is $2x^2 + 22x + 36$ m^2.

AVAILABLE **ONLINE**

LESSON 7-6 Factoring $ax^2 + bx + c$

Quick Review

To factor a trinomial of the form $ax^2 + bx + c$, find the factor pair of ac that has a sum of b. Then use the factors you found to write the binomials that have a product equal to the trinomial.

Example

What is the factored form of $2x^2 + 9x - 5$?

For the trinomial $2x^2 + 9x - 5$, $a = 2$ and $c = -5$, so $ac = -10$. Find the factor pair of −10 that has a sum of 9.

Factors of −10	Sum of Factors
−2 and 5	3
2 and −5	−3
−1 and 10	9

Since −1 and 10 are the correct factor pair, rewrite $9x$ as $-1x$ and $10x$.

$2x^2 + 9x - 5$

$= 2x^2 + 10x - 1x - 5$ Rewrite.

$= (2x^2 + 10x) + (-1x - 5)$ Group as two binomials.

$= 2x(x + 5) - 1(x + 5)$ Factor out the GCFs.

$= (2x - 1)(x + 5)$ Distributive Property

The factored form of $2x^2 + 9x - 5$ is $(2x - 1)(x + 5)$.

Practice & Problem Solving

Identify all of the factor pairs of *ac* you could use to rewrite *b* in order to factor each trinomial by grouping.

45. $5x^2 + 9x + 4$

46. $2x^2 + x - 15$

Write the factored form of each trinomial.

47. $3x^2 + 10x + 8$

48. $4x^2 - 3x - 10$

49. $5x^2 + 7x - 6$

50. $6x^2 + 13x + 6$

51. $10x^2 + 3x - 4$

52. $12x^2 + 22x + 6$

53. Make Sense and Persevere What are all the possible values of b for which $3x^2 + bx - 8$ is factorable using only integer coefficients and constants? MP.1

54. Reason A parking lot has an area of $2x^2 + 9x - 5$ square meters. Use factoring to find possible dimensions of the parking lot. The parking lot is to be enlarged so that each dimension is 5 meters greater than it was originally. What are the new dimensions of the parking lot? What is the new area of the parking lot? MP.2

Go Online | PearsonRealize.com

TOPIC 7
Polynomials and Factoring

TOPIC REVIEW

Answers

55. 64

56. 98

57. $(x + 5)^2$

58. $(x + 11)(x - 11)$

59. $(x - 9)^2$

60. $(3x + 7y)(3x - 7y)$

61. $3(x + 3)^2$

62. $4(x - 7)^2$

63. No, 3 is not a perfect square so it is not a difference of two squares. Also, $3x^2$ and 49 share no common factor.

64. The playground is $(6x + 4y)$ ft long and $(6x - 4y)$ ft wide. The length is $8y$ ft longer than the width. You would need to subtract $4y$ from the length and add $4y$ to the width for the playground to be a square.

AVAILABLE **ONLINE**

LESSON 7-7 Factoring Special Cases

Quick Review

A **perfect-square trinomial** results when a binomial is squared.

Factor a perfect-square trinomial:

$a^2 + 2ab + b^2 = (a + b)^2$

$a^2 - 2ab + b^2 = (a - b)^2$

Use these patterns when the first and last terms are perfect squares and the middle term is twice the product of the numbers being squared.

Factor a difference of two squares:

$a^2 - b^2 = (a + b)(a - b)$

Use this pattern when a binomial can be written as a difference of two squares.

Example

What is the factored form of $9x^2 - 121$?

Write the first and last term as a perfect square.

$9x^2 - 121 = (3x)^2 - 11^2$

$= (3x - 11)(3x + 11)$

Practice & Problem Solving

Identify the value of c that would make each trinomial factorable using the perfect-square pattern.

55. $x^2 + 16x + c$ **56.** $2x^2 - 28x + c$

Write the factored form of each expression.

57. $x^2 + 10x + 25$ **58.** $x^2 - 121$

59. $x^2 - 18x + 81$ **60.** $9x^2 - 49y^2$

61. $3x^2 + 18x + 27$ **62.** $4x^2 - 56x + 196$

63. Reason Is the expression $3x^2 - 49$ factorable using only integer coefficients and constants? Explain why or why not. MP.2

64. Make Sense and Persevere The area of a playground is $36x^2 - 16y^2$ square feet. Without removing common factors, factor to find possible dimensions of the playground. How are the side lengths related? What value would you need to subtract from the longer side and add to the shorter side for the playground to be a square? MP.1

TOPIC 7 REVIEW

TOPIC 7 Topic Review 311

TOPIC ASSESSMENT Form A

AVAILABLE **ONLINE**

Name ______________________

enVision Algebra 1
PearsonRealize.com

7 Topic Assessment Form A

1. Which of the following expressions(s) are fourth-degree trinomials? Select all that apply.
   - Ⓐ $3x^2y + 5x^3y + 6y^4$
   - Ⓑ $6y^4 + 5x^3 + 1$
   - Ⓒ $5xy - 5x^2y^2 + 7$
   - Ⓓ $3y^3 + 3x^3y^3$

2. Write $8x^2 - 5 + 7x^4 - 9x - x^5$ in standard form.
   - Ⓐ $-9x + 8x^2 + 7x^4 - 5 - x^5$
   - Ⓑ $8x^2 - 5 + 7x^4 - 9x - x^5$
   - Ⓒ $-x^5 + 7x^4 + 8x^2 - 9x - 5$
   - Ⓓ $-5 - 9x + 8x^2 + 7x^4 - x^5$

3. Simplify: $(5x^3 + 7x - 8) + (2x^3 - 5x^2 - x + 3)$. Write your answer in standard form.
   $7x^3 - 5x^2 + 6x - 5$

4. Simplify: $(-7x + 5) - (2x^2 - 8x + 6)$. Write your answer in standard form.
   $-2x^2 + x - 1$

5. Find the product.
   $-8y^2(2y^2 + 7y - 5)$
   - Ⓐ $-16y^4 - 56y - 40$
   - Ⓑ $-16y^4 - 56y^3 + 40y^2$
   - Ⓒ $16y^4 + 56y^3 - 40y^2$
   - Ⓓ $-6y^4 - y^3 - 13y^2$

6. Find the product.
   $(6x^2 + 8)(3x^2 - 5x + 7)$
   $18x^4 - 30x^3 + 66x^2 - 40x + 56$

7. A portrait without its frame has a height 1.5 times its width w, in inches. Its frame is 2 in. wide all along its perimeter. What is an expression for the area of the framed portrait in terms of w? Simplify your expression and write it in standard form.
   $1.5w^2 + 10w + 16$

8. Find the product.
   $(6y - 2)^2$
   - Ⓐ $36y^2 - 24y + 4$
   - Ⓑ $36y^2 + 24y - 4$
   - Ⓒ $36y^2 + 4$
   - Ⓓ $12y^2 - 16y + 4$

9. Find the product.
   $(4x - 7)(4x + 7)$
   $16x^2 - 49$

10. A square picture has a 1-in. frame around it. If the area of the frame alone is 36 in.^{2}, what is the area of the picture?
    64 in.^{2}

11. What is the greatest common factor of the terms of the polynomial $-16y^4 + 12y^2 - 4y$?
    $-4y$

12. What is the prime factorization of 84?
    - Ⓐ $2 \cdot 3 \cdot 7$
    - Ⓑ $3 \cdot 4 \cdot 7$
    - Ⓒ $2 \cdot 2 \cdot 21$
    - Ⓓ $2 \cdot 2 \cdot 3 \cdot 7$

13. Factor out the greatest common factor from the terms of the polynomial $2x^3 - 5x^2 + 25$.
    - Ⓐ $x^2(2x - 5) + 25$
    - Ⓑ The expression is already fully factored.
    - Ⓒ $5x(x^2 - x + 5)$
    - Ⓓ $2x^3 - 5(x^2 - 5)$

14. What pair of factors of -42 has a sum of 1?
    7 and -6

15. What is the factored form of $x^2 - 10x + 21$?
    - Ⓐ $(x - 3)(x - 7)$
    - Ⓑ $(x - 3)(x + 7)$
    - Ⓒ The expression is already fully factored.
    - Ⓓ $x(x - 10) + 21$

16. What is the factored form of $x^2 + 3xy - 10y^2$?
    - Ⓐ $(x + 2y)(x - 5y)$
    - Ⓑ $(x - 2y)(x + 5y)$
    - Ⓒ $x(x + 3y) - y(3x - 10y)$
    - Ⓓ The expression is already fully factored.

17. Complete the following to factor the trinomial $6y^2 + 19y + 15$.
    $6y^2 + \underline{9}\,y + \underline{10}\,y + 15$
    $= \underline{3y}\,(2y + 3) + \underline{5}\,(2y + 3)$
    $= (\underline{3y} + \underline{5})(\underline{2y} + \underline{3})$

18. Factor $15y^2 + 10y - 40$.
    - Ⓐ $5(y + 4)(3y - 2)$
    - Ⓑ $(5y - 10)(3y + 4)$
    - Ⓒ $5(y - 2)(3y + 4)$
    - Ⓓ $5(y + 2)(3y - 4)$

19. If $9y^2 - 21y + 8$ is rewritten as $p^2 - 7p + 8$, what is p in terms of y?
    $p = 3y$

20. Factor the perfect square trinomial $x^2 - 12x + 36$.
    - Ⓐ $(x - 6)^2$
    - Ⓑ $(x - 6)(x + 6)$
    - Ⓒ $(x + 6)^2$
    - Ⓓ $(x - 12)^2$

21. Factor the perfect square trinomial $16y^2 - 24y + 9$.
    $(4y - 3)^2$

22. Factor the expression $25x^2 - 1$.
    $(5x + 1)(5x - 1)$

23. A cone with height h and radius r has volume $V = \frac{1}{3}\pi r^2 h$. If h is 9 in., and V is equal to $3\pi x^2 + 42\pi x + 147\pi$ in.^{3}, what is the cone's radius r in terms of x?
    $r = x + 7$

AVAILABLE **ONLINE**

Topic Assessment Assess students' understanding of topic concepts and skills using the Topic Assessment found at **SavvasRealize.com.** These auto-scored online assessments provide students with a breadth of technology-enhanced item types.

There are two versions of the Topic Assessment, Form A and Form B. These two versions, available in print and at **SavvasRealize.com,** are parallel tests that assess the same content item for item. The Item Analysis chart on the next page can be used for both versions.

SavvasRealize.com

Assess

TOPIC 7
Polynomials and Factoring

TOPIC ASSESSMENT Form B

AVAILABLE ONLINE

Name ______________ enVision Algebra 1 PearsonRealize.com

7 Topic Assessment Form B

1. Which of the following expression(s) are third-degree binomials? Select all that apply.
   - Ⓐ $2y - xy^3 + 7$
   - Ⓑ $3x^2y + 5xy$
   - Ⓒ $3y^3 + 3x^3y^4$
   - Ⓓ $3xy - 3xy^2$

2. Write $3x^3 - 5x + 7x^4 - 9 - x^2$ in standard form.
   - Ⓐ $-9 + 7x^4 - 5x + 3x^3 - x^2$
   - Ⓑ $3x^3 - 5x + 7x^4 - 9 - x^2$
   - Ⓒ $7x^4 + 3x^3 - x^2 - 5x - 9$
   - Ⓓ $-9 - 5x - x^2 + 3x^3 + 7x^4$

3. Simplify: $(3x^3 + 7x - 1) + (4x^3 - 9x^2 - 11x + 1)$. Write your answer in standard form.
   $7x^3 - 9x^2 - 4x$

4. Simplify: $(-5x + 7) - (x^2 - 3x + 2)$. Write your answer in standard form.
   $-x^2 - 2x + 5$

5. Find the product. $-7y^2(-2y^4 + y^2 - 1)$
   - Ⓐ $14y^8 - 7y^4 + 7y$
   - Ⓑ $14y^6 - 7y^4 + 7y^2$
   - Ⓒ $-14y^6 + 7y^4 - 7y^2$
   - Ⓓ $-9y^6 - 6y^4 - 8y^2$

6. Find the product. $(4x^2 + 6)(x^2 - 3x + 8)$
   $4x^4 - 12x^3 + 38x^2 - 18x + 48$

7. A portrait without its frame has a height 1.5 times its width w, in inches. Its frame is 4 in. wide all along its perimeter. What is an expression for the area of the framed portrait in terms of w? Simplify your expression and write it in standard form.
   $1.5w^2 + 20w + 64$

8. Find the product. $(2y - 6)^2$
   - Ⓐ $4y^2 - 24y + 36$
   - Ⓑ $4y^2 + 24y - 36$
   - Ⓒ $4y^2 + 36$
   - Ⓓ $4y^2 - 16y - 12$

9. Find the product. $(3x - 2)(3x + 2)$
   $9x^2 - 4$

10. A square picture has a 2-in. frame around it. If the area of the frame alone is 72 in.^{2}, what is the area of the picture?
    49 in.^{2}

11. What is the greatest common factor of the terms of the polynomial $-25y^3 + 15y^2 - 5y$?
    $-5y$

12. What is the prime factorization of 140?
    - Ⓐ $2 \cdot 5 \cdot 7$
    - Ⓑ $4 \cdot 5 \cdot 7$
    - Ⓒ $2 \cdot 2 \cdot 35$
    - Ⓓ $2 \cdot 2 \cdot 5 \cdot 7$

13. Factor out the greatest common factor from the terms of the polynomial $6x^3 - 12x^2 + 18x$.
    - Ⓐ $x^2(6x - 12) + 18$
    - Ⓑ $6x(x^2 - 2x + 3)$
    - Ⓒ The expression is already fully factored.
    - Ⓓ $6x^3 - 6x(2x - 3)$

14. What pair of factors of −45 has a sum of 4?
    9 and −5

15. What is the factored form of $x^2 - 3x - 10$?
    - Ⓐ $(x + 2)(x - 5)$
    - Ⓑ $(x - 2)(x + 5)$
    - Ⓒ $x(x - 3) - 10$
    - Ⓓ The expression is already fully factored.

16. What is the factored form of $x^2 - 2xy - 24y^2$?
    - Ⓐ $(x - 4y)(x + 6y)$
    - Ⓑ $(x + 4y)(x - 6y)$
    - Ⓒ $x(x - 2y) - y(2x + 24y)$
    - Ⓓ The expression is already fully factored.

17. Complete the following to factor the trinomial $8x^2 + 26x + 15$.
    $8x^2 + \underline{6}\,x + \underline{20}\,x + 15$
    $= \underline{2x}\,(4x + 3) + \underline{5}\,(4x + 3)$
    $= (\underline{2x} + \underline{5})(\underline{4x} + \underline{3})$

18. Factor $12y^2 - 6y - 90$.
    - Ⓐ $6y(2y - 1) - 15$
    - Ⓑ $(6y - 18)(2y - 5)$
    - Ⓒ $6(2y - 5)(y + 3)$
    - Ⓓ $6(y - 3)(2y + 5)$

19. If $9x^2 - 6x + 5$ is rewritten as $p^2 - 2p + 5$, what is p in terms of x?
    $p = 3x$

20. Factor the perfect square trinomial $x^2 - 18x + 81$.
    - Ⓐ $(x - 9)^2$
    - Ⓑ $(x - 9)(x + 9)$
    - Ⓒ $(x + 9)^2$
    - Ⓓ $(x - 18)^2$

21. Factor the perfect square trinomial $y^2 - 14y + 49$.
    $(y - 7)^2$

22. Factor the expression $36y^2 - 1$.
    $(6y + 1)(6y - 1)$

23. A cone with height h and radius r has volume $V = \frac{1}{3}\pi r^2 h$. If h is 9 in., and V is equal to $3\pi y^2 + 30\pi y + 75\pi$ in.^{3}, what is the cone's radius r in terms of y?
    $r = y + 5$

Item Analysis

Item	DOK	Standard	Item	DOK	Standard	Item	DOK	Standard
1	1	HSA.SSE.A.1.A	9	1	HSA.APR.A.1	17	2	HSA.SSE.A.1.A
2	1	HSA.SSE.A.1.A	10	2	HSA.APR.A.1	18	2	HSA.SSE.A.1.A
3	2	HSA.APR.A.1	11	1	HSA.APR.A.1	19	1	HSA.SSE.A.1.A
4	2	HSA.APR.A.1	12	1	HSA.SSE.A.1.A	20	1	HSA.SSE.A.1
5	1	HSA.APR.A.1	13	2	HSA.APR.A.1	21	2	HSA.SSE.A.1
6	2	HSA.APR.A.1	14	1	HSA.SSE.A.1.A	22	1	HSA.SSE.A.2
7, 8	2	HSA.APR.A.1	15, 16	2	HSA.SSE.A.1.A	23	3	HSA.SSE.A.2

AVAILABLE **ONLINE**

Name ______________________

enVision Algebra 1
PearsonRealize.com

7 Performance Assessment Form A

An architect is designing a new library. As shown, the library's floor plan is a rectangle divided into a bookshelf space with bookshelves, and a reading space with a rug and chairs. Each bookshelf is x ft wide and $x + 3$ ft long. The bookshelves are 3 ft from each other. The walkway between the two rows of bookshelves is 2 ft wide.

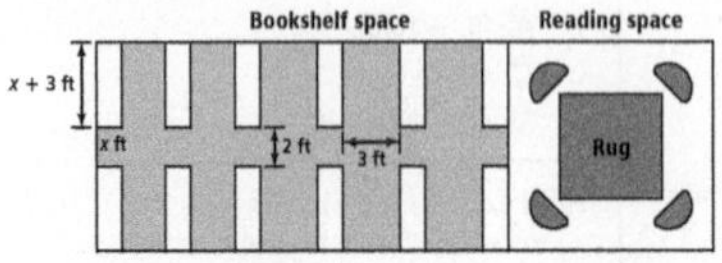

Bookshelf space
Reading space
x + 3 ft
x ft
2 ft
3 ft
Rug

1. What are the dimensions of the bookshelf space? What is the area of the bookshelf space? Write the dimensions and the area as polynomials in standard form. Explain.
   length: $6x + 15$ ft; width: $2x + 8$ ft; area: $12x^2 + 78x + 120$ ft^2; Sample answer: length $= 6x + 5(3)$ ft $= 6x + 15$ ft; width $= 2(x + 3) + 2$ ft $= 2x + 8$ ft; area $= (6x + 15)(2x + 8)$ ft^2 $= 12x^2 + 78x + 120$ ft^2

2. The reading space is a square. Write the area of the reading space as a polynomial in standard form. Explain.
   $4x^2 + 32x + 64$ ft^2; Sample answer: The length of one side of the reading space is $2x + 8$ ft. So area $= (2x + 8)^2$ ft^2.

3. **Part A**

   Use addition and your results from Items 1 and 2 to write a polynomial in standard form that represents the area of the entire library. Write an expression for the length of the entire library. Explain why the length and width of the library are factors of the area polynomial.

   Area of library = (area of bookshelf space) + (area of reading space)
   $= (12x^2 + 78x + 120) + (4x^2 + 32x + 64)$
   $= 16x^2 + 110x + 184$
   The width of the library is $2x + 8$ ft, and the length is $(6x + 15) + (2x + 8)$ ft $= 8x + 23$ ft.
   area = length × width
   $16x^2 + 110x + 184 = (8x + 23)(2x + 8)$

   Part B

   Identify all the factors of the polynomial that represents the area of the entire library. Explain.
   2, $(x + 4)$, and $(8x + 23)$; $16x^2 + 110x + 184 = (2x + 8)(8x + 23)$
   $= 2(x + 4)(8x + 23)$

4. The bookcases at the library can be moved out of the way to provide an additional seating area for special events, as shown. What is the area of the additional seating area? Explain.

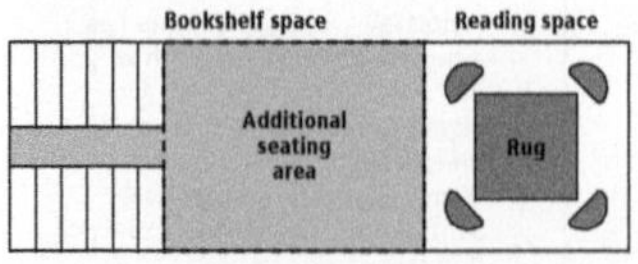

Bookshelf space
Reading space
Additional seating area
Rug

   Sample answer: The area of the portion of bookshelf space not used for additional seating area is the combined widths of the bookshelves multiplied by the width of the library.
   $6x(2x + 8)$ ft^2 $= 12x^2 + 48x$ ft^2
   So, the additional seating area = (total shelving area) − (area not used)
   $= (12x^2 + 78x + 120)$ ft^2 $- (12x^2 + 48x)$ ft^2
   $= 30x + 120$ ft^2.

5. The rug in the reading space is a square with area one fourth the area of the reading space. What is the area of the rug, and what is its side length? Explain.
   area: $x^2 + 8x + 16$ ft^2; side length: $x + 4$ ft;
   area $= 0.25(4x^2 + 32x + 64)$
   $= x^2 + 8x + 16$
   $x^2 + 8x + 16$ is a perfect square trinomial, so $x^2 + 8x + 16 = (x + 4)^2$, and the side length is $x + 4$ ft.

enVision™ **Algebra 1** • Assessment Resources

enVision™ **Algebra 1** • Assessment Resources

AVAILABLE **ONLINE**

Topic Performance Assessment Assess students' ability to apply the topic concepts and skills using the Topic Performance Assessments found at **SavvasRealize.com.** These online assessments include a breadth of technology-enhanced item types.

Item Analysis and Scoring Guide

Item	DOK	2-Point Responses	1-Point Responses	Standards
1	2	Correct answer and explanation	Correct answer only	HSA.APR.A.1, HSA.SSE.A.1
2	2	Correct answer and explanation	Correct answer only	HSA.APR.A.1, HSA.SSE.A.1
3A	2	Correct answer and explanation	Correct answer only	HSA.APR.A.1, HSA.SSE.A.1
3B	2	Correct answer and explanation	Correct answer only	HSA.APR.A.1, HSA.SSE.A.1, HSA.SSE.A.2
4	2	Correct answer and explanation	Correct answer only	HSA.APR.A.1, HSA.SSE.A.1
5	2	Correct answer and explanation	Correct answer only	HSA.APR.A.1, HSA.SSE.A.2

TOPIC 7

Polynomials and Factoring

TOPIC PERFORMANCE ASSESSMENT Form B

AVAILABLE ONLINE

Name ______________________ enVision Algebra 1 PearsonRealize.com

7 Performance Assessment Form B

Helena finds the area of irregular figures by using figures that she is familiar with.

1. Helena wants to change the figure shown into two or more figures so she can more easily find the area. Draw a line or lines to show what she could do. Then write an expression for the area of each smaller figure. Write an expression for the total area of the figure. Explain.

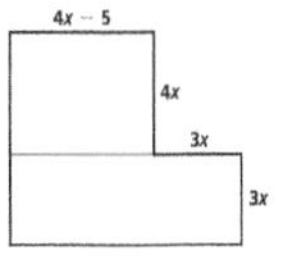
4x – 5
4x
3x
3x

$37x^2 - 35x$. Drawings may vary. Sample answer: For the top rectangle, the area is $(4x - 5)(4x) = 16x^2 - 20x$ square units. For the lower rectangle, the area is $(4x - 5 + 3x)(3x) = 21x^2 - 15x$ square units. The total area of the figure is the sum of the two smaller areas: $37x^2 - 35x$ square units.

2. Helena sketches a circular backyard skating pond that fits into a square section of her yard. In her sketch, what is the area of the shaded region? Factor out the GCF. Explain.

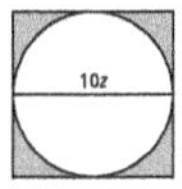
10z

$25z^2(4 - \pi)$; Sample answer: The area of the square is $(10z)^2 = 100z^2$. The radius of the circle is $5z$, so the area $= \pi(5z)^2$, or $25\pi z^2$. Area of shaded region: $100z^2 - 25\pi z^2$. Since the GCF is $25z^2$, $100z^2 - 25\pi z^2 = 25z^2(4 - \pi)$.

enVision™ Algebra 1 • Assessment Resources

3. Helena wants to build a plant stand like the one shown, and she wants to find its volume. Draw line(s) to show how she might divide the stand into two or more sections to make finding the volume easier. Find the volume of each section you identified. Then find the total volume of the stand. Explain.

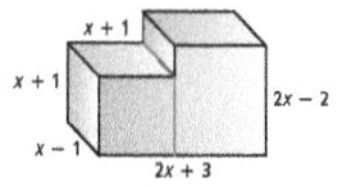
x + 1
x + 1
2x – 2
x – 1
2x + 3

Answers may vary. Sample drawing shown.

Sample answer: For the small prism on the left, $V = (x + 1)(x + 1)(x - 1) = (x^2 + 2x + 1)(x - 1) = x^3 + x^2 - x - 1$.

For the larger prism on the right, $V = (x + 2)(x - 1)(2x - 2) = (x^2 + x - 2)(2x - 2) = 2x^3 - 6x + 4$.

Total volume of the plant stand is $V = (x^3 + x^2 - x - 1) + (2x^3 - 6x + 4) = 3x^3 + x^2 - 7x + 3$.

4. Helena finds two pieces of a toy construction set that, when joined together, make a rectangular prism. She takes one piece away and is left with the piece shown in the diagram.

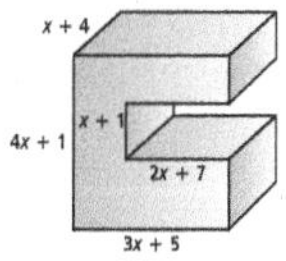
x + 4
x + 1
4x + 1
2x + 7
3x + 5

Part A

When joined together, the original two pieces form a rectangular prism with side lengths represented by the expressions $x + 4$, $4x + 1$, and $3x + 5$. What is the volume of that prism? Explain.

$12x^3 + 71x^2 + 97x + 20$;

Sample answer: $V = (x + 4)(4x + 1)(3x + 5)$
$= (4x^2 + 17x + 4)(3x + 5)$
$= 12x^3 + 71x^2 + 97x + 20$

Part B

Find the volume of the construction piece shown in the diagram. Explain.

$10x^3 + 54x^2 + 54x - 8$; Sample answer: The volume of the section removed is $(x + 4)(x + 1)(2x + 7)$, or $2x^3 + 17x^2 + 43x + 28$. The volume of the construction piece is
$12x^3 + 71x^2 + 97x + 20 - (2x^3 + 17x^2 + 43x + 28)$
$= 10x^3 + 54x^2 + 54x - 8$.

enVision™ Algebra 1 • Assessment Resources

AVAILABLE ONLINE

Topic Performance Assessment Assess students' ability to apply the topic concepts and skills using the Topic Performance Assessments found at **SavvasRealize.com.** These online assessments include a breadth of technology-enhanced item types.

Item Analysis and Scoring Guide

Item	DOK	2-Point Responses	1-Point Responses	Standards
1	3	Correct answer and explanation	Correct answer only	HSA.APR.A.1
2	2	Correct answer and explanation	Correct answer only	HSA.APR.A.1, HSA.SSE.A.2, HSA.SSE.A.1.A
3	3	Correct answer and explanation	Correct answer only	HSA.APR.A.1, HSA.SSE.A.2
4A	2	Correct answer and explanation	Correct answer only	HSA.APR.A.1
4B	3	Correct answer and explanation	Correct answer only	HSA.APR.A.1, HSA.SSE.A.2

MATH BACKGROUND FOCUS

Topic 8 focuses on extending students' previous understanding of functions to include quadratic functions: graphing them, using them to model real-world situations, and comparing them to linear and exponential functions.

Graphing Quadratic Functions

Key Features of a Quadratic Function The simplest quadratic function is of the form $y = x^2$, the parent function. Students should recognize that every quadratic function is a transformation of this function. In Lesson 8-1, students identify the vertex and axis of symmetry of the graph of a quadratic function and then look at the effect of changing the values of the leading coefficient *a* on the graph.

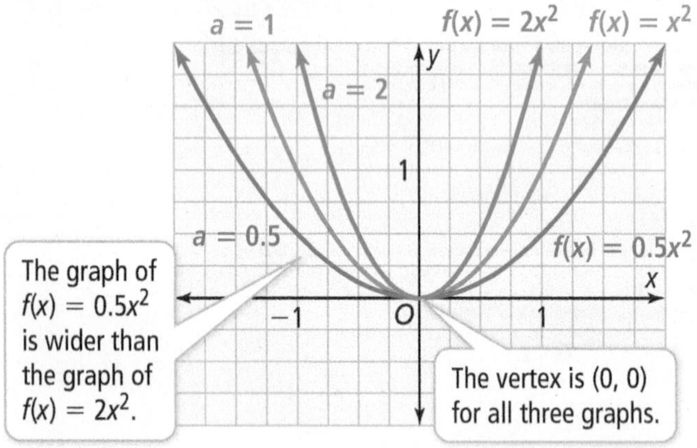

a = 1
f(x) = 2x²
f(x) = x²
a = 2
a = 0.5
f(x) = 0.5x²
The graph of f(x) = 0.5x² is wider than the graph of f(x) = 2x².
The vertex is (0, 0) for all three graphs.

Different Forms of Quadratic Functions In Lesson 8-2, students study vertical and horizontal translations of the graph of the quadratic parent function. In studying the vertical and horizontal translations of graphs, students understand the vertex form of a quadratic function and its usefulness in identifying key features of a graph of a quadratic function, specifically, the vertex and axis of symmetry.

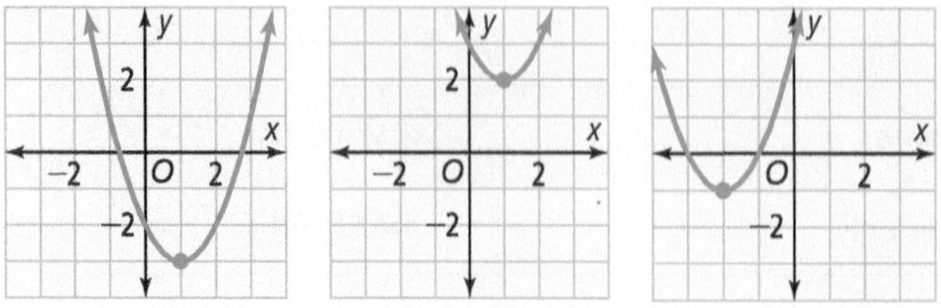

In Lesson 8-3, students study the standard form of a quadratic function and its usefulness in identifying key features of a graph of a quadratic function, specifically the *y*-intercept and axis of symmetry, which is also the *x*-coordinate of the vertex. Students compare the standard and vertex forms of the quadratic function to determine which form is more useful when solving real-world problems.

Quadratic Functions as Models

Modeling with Quadratic Functions In Lesson 8-4, students use quadratic functions to model real-world problem situations. Students explore area and vertical motion problems.

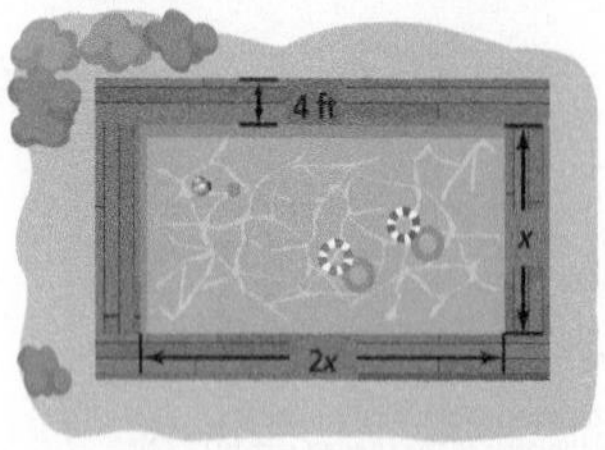

4 ft
x
2x

30 ft.

Students also use residuals to evaluate the fit of the model to the data. Quadratic regression is also used to find a good model that best fits a data set.

Comparing Linear, Exponential, and Quadratic Functions
In Lesson 8-5, students determine the type of function to best fit a set of data by looking for patterns in the values, such as whether first or second differences are constant or whether ratios of consecutive *y*-values are the same, and by looking at the shape of the graph of the data. Then they find a function that models the data using the regression function on a graphing calculator.

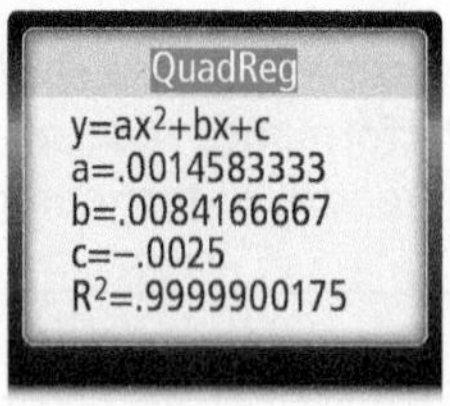

QuadReg
y=ax²+bx+c
a=.0014583333
b=.0084166667
c=-.0025
R²=.9999900175

TOPIC 8
Quadratic Functions

MATH BACKGROUND COHERENCE

Students learn best when concepts are connected through the curriculum. This coherence is achieved within topics, across topics, across domains, and across grade levels.

MAKING MATHEMATICAL CONNECTIONS

Looking Back

How does Topic 8 connect to what students learned earlier?

GRADE 8

- **Analyzing Graphs of Functions** Students compared linear and nonlinear functions, learned about increasing and decreasing intervals, and sketched functions from a verbal description. Students explored key features of linear functions including slope and rate of change. Students build on this understanding when they compare quadratic functions, identify key features of quadratic functions, and sketch a graph.

TOPIC 3

- **Use Functions to Model Relationships** Students modeled real-world situations with functions, tables, and graphs. Students will expand on their understanding of modeling problems with functions by using quadratic models.

TOPIC 6

- **Transformations of Graphs** Students graphed exponential functions and explored key features. Students transformed exponential functions through vertical and horizontal translations and reflections. Students will expand on their understanding of transformations of exponential functions to explore the graphs of quadratic functions using translations and reflections.

IN THIS TOPIC

How is content connected within Topic 8?

- **Quadratic Functions** In Lesson 8-1, students analyze the effect of changing the value of a in the function $f(x) = ax^2$ on the graph of f. Students extend this understanding in Lesson 8-2 when they explore quadratic functions written in vertex form $f(x) = a(x - h)^2 + k$ and use the structure of the function to predict the location and shape of the graph of f. In Lesson 8-3, students build on their understanding of the characteristics of a parabola by determining key features of the graph of a quadratic function written in standard form.

x	y
−2	0
−1	3.5
0	6
1	7.5
2	8

Vertex Form: $y = -0.5(x - 2)^2 + 8$
Standard Form: $y = -0.5x^2 + 2x + 6$

- **Modeling with Quadratic Functions** In Lesson 8-4, students extend their knowledge of the key features of the graphs of quadratic functions by applying quadratic functions to model area and vertical motion problems. They use quadratic regression to find the best model for a set of quadratic data. Students build on this understanding in Lesson 8-5 to analyze data and determine whether the data are best modeled by a linear, quadratic, or exponential function.

MAKING MATHEMATICAL CONNECTIONS

Looking Ahead

How does Topic 8 connect to what students will learn later?

ALGEBRA 1

- **Solving Quadratic Equations** Students will apply the key features of the graphs of quadratic functions when they solve quadratic equations graphically, algebraically, and numerically in tables.

ALGEBRA 2

- **Key Features of Functions** Students will extend their understanding of quadratic functions by exploring the domain and range of quadratic functions, studying quadratic functions in factored form, and applying the Zero Product Property to find the zeros.

- **Transformation of Graphs** Students will extend their knowledge of transformations of the graphs of quadratic functions to include reflections, dilations, stretches, and compressions.

- **Different Forms of Quadratic Functions** Students will analyze quadratic functions written in other forms, such as factored form, and identify key features, such as the x-intercepts. Student will also learn about key features of completing the square and the quadratic formula in order to solve a quadratic equation.

- **Linear-Quadratic Systems** Students will apply what they learned about the characteristics of the graphs of quadratic functions to predict and estimate the solution(s) to systems of linear and quadratic functions.

A rigorous curriculum emphasizes conceptual understanding, procedural skill and fluency, and applications.

Conceptual Understanding

- **Relating Graphs and Equations** Students will realize that the different forms of the quadratic function reveal different information about a real-world problem. Students understand the relationship between algebraic and graphical representations of quadratic equations. Students use the structure of algebraic expressions in quadratic equations to find the axis of symmetry, the vertex, and the *x*- and *y*-intercepts. Students also use the features of graphs of quadratic functions to write equations as models that help them solve problems.

- **Understanding Quadratic Functions as Models** Students extend their understanding of quadratic functions to solve real-world problems involving area and vertical motion. Students use regression models to solve and make predictions about other real-world problems. Students understand that the calculated average rates of change can be used to identify whether the data follows a linear, exponential, or quadratic pattern. Students analyze real-world problems by comparing average rates of change.

- **Graphing Quadratic Functions** Students use their understanding of transformations to see how the coefficients *a*, *b*, and *c* in $f(x) = ax^2 + bx + c$ affect the graph of the parent function, $f(x) = x^2$.

Procedural Skill and Fluency

- **Writing Different Forms of Quadratic Functions** Students write the equation of a quadratic function in either standard or vertex form to help identify the key features of the function.

- **Analyzing Models** Students use residuals to analyze the fit of the model.

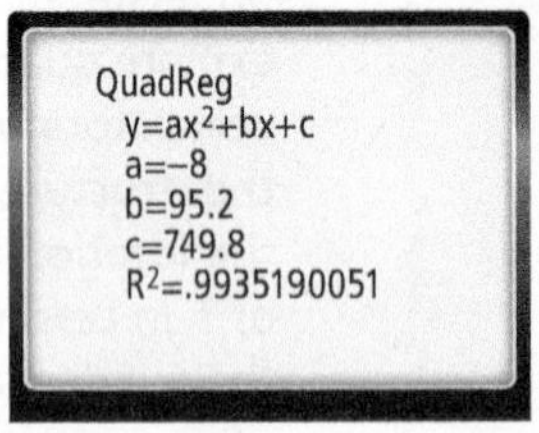
QuadReg
y=ax²+bx+c
a=−8
b=95.2
c=749.8
R²=.9935190051

	f(x)		
x	Actual Sales ($)	Predicted Sales ($)	Residual
0	745	749.8	−4.8
1	846	837	+9
2	910	908.2	+1.8
3	952	963.4	−11.4
4	1,008	1,002.6	+5.4

Applications

- **Modeling With Quadratic Equations** Throughout Topic 8, students use quadratic functions to model real-world situations, such as area problems and vertical motion problems. Students predict the path of objects in vertical motion and determine the time it takes a falling object to reach the ground.

30 ft.

TOPIC 8

Quadratic Functions

MATH PRACTICES & PROCESSES

Math Practices Within Topic 8 Lessons

The math practices describe the behaviors and habits of mind that mathematically proficient students demonstrate when actively engaged in mathematics work. Opportunities to develop expertise with these important behaviors and thinking habits exist throughout the topic and program. Here we focus on *mathematical modeling* and *using structure*.

As students solve quadratic equations, look for the following behaviors to assess and identify students who demonstrate proficiency with these math practices.

Highlighted Math Practices Within Topic 8 Lessons

Model With Mathematics **MP.4**	Look For and Make Use of Structure **MP.7**
Mathematically proficient students:	Mathematically proficient students:
• Use quadratic functions to model the trajectory of projectiles.	• See the standard form of a quadratic function as being composed of several objects, including values of *a*, *b*, and *c* that they can use to graph the Intercepts, the axis of symmetry, and the vertex of the parabola that represents the function $ax^2 + bx + c$.
• Solve a vertical motion problem by writing a quadratic function to represent the height *h* of a diver at time *t*.	• Analyze the effect of changes to the values of *h* and *k* in the vertex form of a quadratic function on the graph of the quadratic function.
	• Apply what they have learned about the overall structure of linear and absolute value functions to the structure of quadratic functions.
	• Look at the overall structure of the vertical motion model and relate it to the standard form of a quadratic equation.

Help students become more proficient with mathematical reasoning and explanation.

If students do not understand how to graph a quadratic function and use a quadratic function as a model, then use these questioning strategies to help them develop their proficiency with mathematical modeling and using structure as they solve problems throughout the topic.

Q: What kind of problems can be modeled by a quadratic function?

Q: How can you determine which model is a better fit for the data?

Q: When given a set of data in a table, how can you choose the type of function that will best fit the data?

Q: What is a residual and what does it mean?

Q: How can technology help you find a model that is a good fit to the data?

Q: How does the coefficient *a* in the function $f(x) = ax^2$ affect the parent function $f(x) = x^2$? Why?

Q: How does *k* in the function $f(x) = x^2 + k$ affect the parent function $f(x) = x^2$?

Q: How does *h* in the function $f(x) = (x - h)^2$ affect the parent function $f(x) = x^2$?

Q: How might the standard form of a quadratic function be beneficial?

Q: How can you change a quadratic function from vertex form to standard form?

Q: Why might you want to use the vertex form of a quadratic function?

TOPIC PLANNER

Lesson	New Vocabulary	Objective	Essential Understanding	Standards
8-1 2 DAYS Key Features of a Quadratic Function	• parabola • quadratic parent function	• Identify key features of the graph of a quadratic function using graphs, tables, and equations. • Explain the effect of the value of *a* on the quadratic parent function.	A quadratic function is a polynomial function in one or more variables in which the highest degree term is of the second degree. The graph of a quadratic function $f(x) = ax^2$ is a parabola. The value of the leading coefficient *a* determines both the width of the parabola and the direction the parabola opens (upward or downward).	HSA.CED.A.2, HSF.IF.B.6, HSF.BF.B.3 **Mathematical Practices** MP.2, MP.3, MP.7
8-2 2 DAYS Quadratic Functions in Vertex Form	• vertex form of a quadratic function	• Identify key features of the graph of quadratic functions written in vertex form. • Graph quadratic functions in vertex form.	The structure of a quadratic function in vertex form reveals the vertex and axis of a symmetry of the graph it represents.	HSF.IF.C.7, HSF.BF.B.3 **Mathematical Practices** MP.4, MP.6, MP.7
8-3 2 DAYS Quadratic Functions in Standard Form	• standard form of a quadratic function	• Graph quadratic functions in standard form and show intercepts, maxima, and minima. • Determine how the values of *a*, *b*, and *c* affect the graph of $f(x) = ax^2 + bx + c$. • Identify key features of parabolas. • Compare properties of quadratic functions presented in different forms (algebraically, in a table, graphically).	The standard form of a quadratic function is $f(x) = ax^2 + bx + c$, where *c* is the *y*-coordinate of the *y*-intercept and the axis of symmetry is the line $x = -\frac{b}{(2a)}$.	HSF.IF.B.4, HSF.IF.C.7.A, HSF.IF.C.8, HSF.IF.C.9 **Mathematical Practices** MP.1, MP.3, MP.7

Lesson Resources

Digital
Print

Student Edition

Student Companion

Assessment Resource Book
- Lesson Quiz

Digital

Digital Lesson Courseware
- Examples with Embedded Interactives
- Additional Examples
- Online Practice powered by MathXL for School
- Virtual Nerd Tutorials
- English/Spanish Glossary
- Digital Math Tools
- Mathematical Modeling in 3 Acts

Teaching Resources
- Reteach to Build Understanding
- Mathematical Literacy and Vocabulary
- Additional Practice
- Enrichment

Lesson Support for Teachers
- Professional Development Video
- Lesson Plans

The suggested pacing for each lesson is shown for a 45-minute class.
In addition, allow 1 day for the Topic Review and 1 day for the Topic Assessment.

TOPIC PLANNER

Lesson	New Vocabulary	Objective	Essential Understanding	Standards
8-4 2 DAYS Modeling With Quadratic Functions	• quadratic regression • vertical motion model	• Use quadratic functions fitted to data to model real-world situations. • Use the vertical motion model to write an equation. • Compare a model to a data set by analyzing and evaluating residuals.	A quadratic function can be used to model area and vertical motion problems. These models can be written in the same form as the quadratic function $f(x) = ax^2 + bx + c$ using key features to interpret and understand the situation.	HSF.IF.A.2, HSF.BF.A.1, HSS.ID.B.6.A, HSS.ID.B.6.B **Mathematical Practices** MP.4, MP.5, MP.8
Mathematical Modeling in 3 Acts: The Long Shot 2 DAYS	none	• Use mathematical modeling to represent a problem situation and to propose a solution. • Test and verify the appropriateness of their math models. • Explain why the results from their mathematical models might not align exactly with the problem situation.	Many real-world problem situations can be represented with a mathematical model, but that model might not represent the real-world situation exactly.	HSA.REI.D.10, HSF.IF.B.4 **Mathematical Practices** MP.4
8-5 2 DAYS Linear, Exponential, and Quadratic Models	none	• Determine which model—linear, exponential, or quadratic—best fits a set of data. • Use fitted functions to solve problems in the context of data.	Linear, quadratic, and exponential functions are differentiated by their average rates of change over different intervals. A linear function models a relationship between x and y in which the differences between successive y-values are constant. A quadratic function models a relationship in which the second differences, or the difference between the first differences, are constant. An exponential function models a relationship where the ratios of consecutive y-values are constant.	HSF.LE.A.3, HSS.ID.B.6.A **Mathematical Practices** MP.1, MP.2, MP.7

Topic Resources

Digital
Print

Student Edition
- enVision STEM
- Mathematical Modeling in 3 Acts
- Topic Review

Digital Lesson Courseware
- Topic Readiness Assessment
- Topic Assessment
- Topic Performance Assessment

Digital

Teaching Resources
- enVision STEM
- Graphing Technology Activities

Topic Support for Teachers
- Mathematical Modeling in 3 Acts
- ExamView
- Answers and Solutions

AVAILABLE **ONLINE**

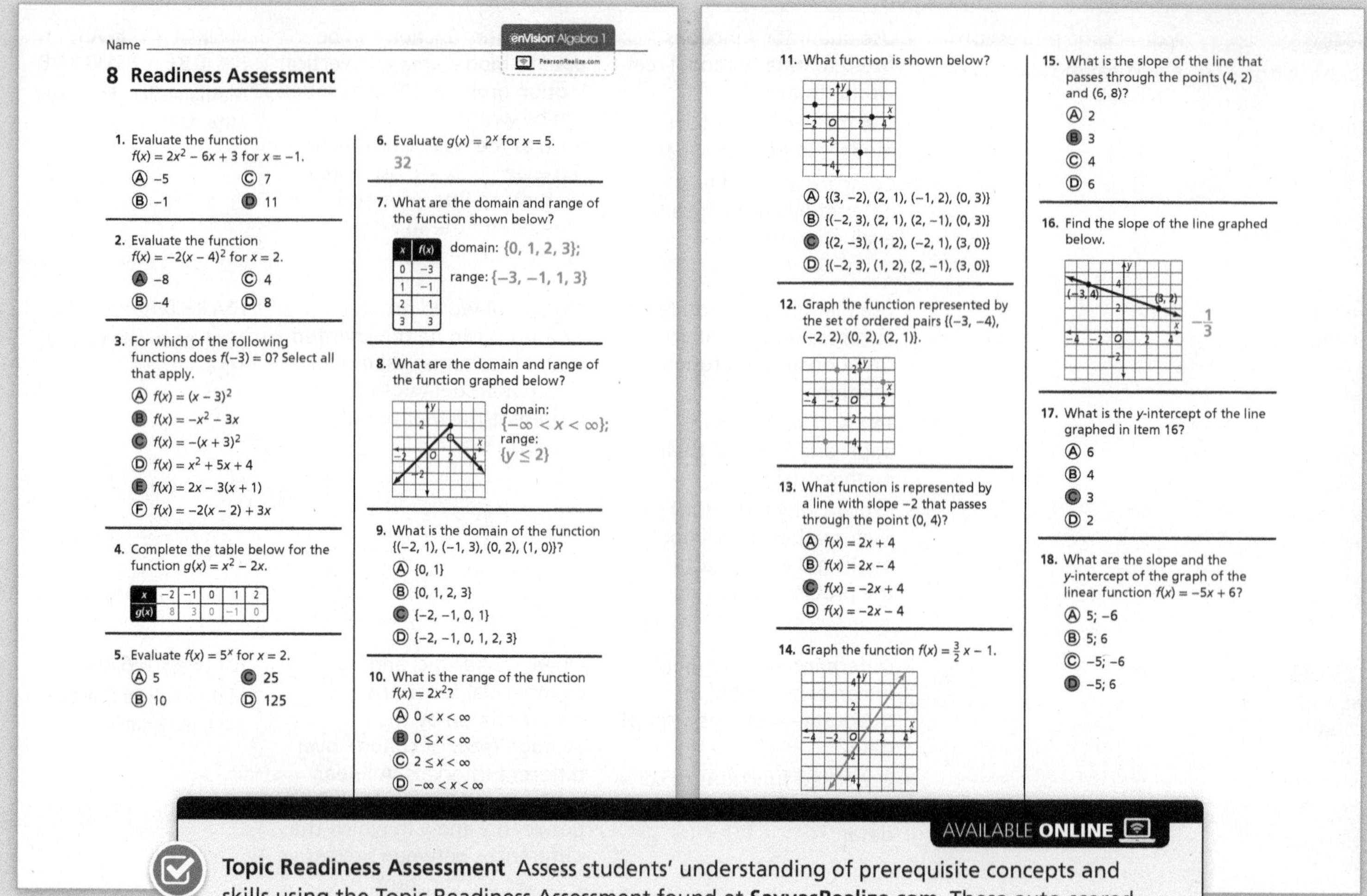

Name

enVision Algebra 1

PearsonRealize.com

8 Readiness Assessment

1. Evaluate the function $f(x) = 2x^2 - 6x + 3$ for $x = -1$.

Ⓐ −5 Ⓒ 7
Ⓑ −1 Ⓓ 11

2. Evaluate the function $f(x) = -2(x - 4)^2$ for $x = 2$.

Ⓐ −8 Ⓒ 4
Ⓑ −4 Ⓓ 8

3. For which of the following functions does $f(-3) = 0$? Select all that apply.

Ⓐ $f(x) = (x - 3)^2$
Ⓑ $f(x) = -x^2 - 3x$
Ⓒ $f(x) = -(x + 3)^2$
Ⓓ $f(x) = x^2 + 5x + 4$
Ⓔ $f(x) = 2x - 3(x + 1)$
Ⓕ $f(x) = -2(x - 2) + 3x$

4. Complete the table below for the function $g(x) = x^2 - 2x$.

x	−2	−1	0	1	2
g(x)	8	3	0	−1	0

5. Evaluate $f(x) = 5^x$ for $x = 2$.

Ⓐ 5 Ⓒ 25
Ⓑ 10 Ⓓ 125

6. Evaluate $g(x) = 2^x$ for $x = 5$.

32

7. What are the domain and range of the function shown below?

x	f(x)
0	−3
1	−1
2	1
3	3

domain: {0, 1, 2, 3};
range: {−3, −1, 1, 3}

8. What are the domain and range of the function graphed below?

domain: $\{-\infty < x < \infty\}$;
range: $\{y \le 2\}$

9. What is the domain of the function {(−2, 1), (−1, 3), (0, 2), (1, 0)}?

Ⓐ {0, 1}
Ⓑ {0, 1, 2, 3}
Ⓒ {−2, −1, 0, 1}
Ⓓ {−2, −1, 0, 1, 2, 3}

10. What is the range of the function $f(x) = 2x^2$?

Ⓐ $0 < x < \infty$
Ⓑ $0 \le x < \infty$
Ⓒ $2 \le x < \infty$
Ⓓ $-\infty < x < \infty$

11. What function is shown below?

Ⓐ {(3, −2), (2, 1), (−1, 2), (0, 3)}
Ⓑ {(−2, 3), (2, 1), (2, −1), (0, 3)}
Ⓒ {(2, −3), (1, 2), (−2, 1), (3, 0)}
Ⓓ {(−2, 3), (1, 2), (2, −1), (3, 0)}

12. Graph the function represented by the set of ordered pairs {(−3, −4), (−2, 2), (0, 2), (2, 1)}.

13. What function is represented by a line with slope −2 that passes through the point (0, 4)?

Ⓐ $f(x) = 2x + 4$
Ⓑ $f(x) = 2x - 4$
Ⓒ $f(x) = -2x + 4$
Ⓓ $f(x) = -2x - 4$

14. Graph the function $f(x) = \frac{3}{2}x - 1$.

15. What is the slope of the line that passes through the points (4, 2) and (6, 8)?

Ⓐ 2
Ⓑ 3
Ⓒ 4
Ⓓ 6

16. Find the slope of the line graphed below.

(−3, 4) (3, 2)

$-\frac{1}{3}$

17. What is the y-intercept of the line graphed in Item 16?

Ⓐ 6
Ⓑ 4
Ⓒ 3
Ⓓ 2

18. What are the slope and the y-intercept of the graph of the linear function $f(x) = -5x + 6$?

Ⓐ 5; −6
Ⓑ 5; 6
Ⓒ −5; −6
Ⓓ −5; 6

AVAILABLE **ONLINE**

Topic Readiness Assessment Assess students' understanding of prerequisite concepts and skills using the Topic Readiness Assessment found at **SavvasRealize.com.** These auto-scored online assessments provide students with a breadth of technology-enhanced item types.

Individualized Study Plan Based on their performance, students will be assigned a study plan tailored to their specific learning needs.

RtI Item Analysis for Diagnosis and Intervention

Item	DOK	Standard	Item	DOK	Standard
1	1	6.EE.A.2	10	1	HSF.IF.A.1
2	1	6.EE.A.2	11	1	HSF.IF.A.1
3	1	HSF.IF.A.2	12	1	HSF.IF.A.1
4	1	HSF.IF.A.2	13	2	HSA.CED.A.2
5	1	HSF.IF.A.2	14	2	HSA.CED.A.2
6	1	HSF.IF.A.2	15	2	HSA.CED.A.2
7	1	HSF.IF.A.1	16	2	HSA.CED.A.2
8	1	HSF.IF.A.1	17	2	HSF.LE.A.2
9	1	HSF.IF.A.1	18	2	HSF.LE.A.2

Quadratic Functions

TOPIC OPENER

AVAILABLE ONLINE

TOPIC 8

Quadratic Functions

TOPIC ESSENTIAL QUESTION

How can you use sketches and equations of quadratic functions to model situations and make predictions?

Topic Overview

Topic Vocabulary

- parabola
- quadratic parent function
- quadratic regression
- standard form of a quadratic function
- vertex form of a quadratic function
- vertical motion model

Digital Experience

INTERACTIVE STUDENT EDITION Access online or offline.

ACTIVITIES Complete ***Explore & Reason, Model & Discuss***, and ***Critique & Explain*** activities. Interact with Examples and Try Its.

ANIMATION View and interact with real-world applications.

PRACTICE Practice what you've learned.

Go online | PearsonRealize.com

MATHEMATICAL MODELING IN 3 ACTS

The Long Shot

Have you ever been to a basketball game where they hold contests at halftime? A popular contest is one where the contestant needs to make a basket from half court to win a prize. Contestants often shoot the ball in different ways. They might take a regular basketball shot, a hook shot, or an underhand toss.

What's the best way to shoot the basketball and make a basket? In the Mathematical Modeling in 3 Acts lesson, you decide!

TOPIC 8

VIDEOS Watch clips to support ***Mathematical Modeling in 3 Acts Lessons*** and **enVision™ *STEM Projects***.

CONCEPT SUMMARY Review key lesson content through multiple representations.

ASSESSMENT Show what you've learned.

GLOSSARY Read and listen to English and Spanish definitions.

TUTORIALS Get help from ***Virtual Nerd***, right when you need it.

MATH TOOLS Explore math with digital tools and manipulatives.

Topic Essential Question

How can you use sketches and equations of quadratic functions to model situations and make predictions?

Revisit the Topic Essential Question throughout the topic. See page 351 (Topic Review) for notes about answering the Topic Essential Question.

Mathematical Modeling in 3 Acts

Generate excitement about the upcoming Mathematical Modeling in 3 Acts lesson by having students read about the math modeling problem for this topic.

See page 343 for notes about how to use the lesson video in your classroom.

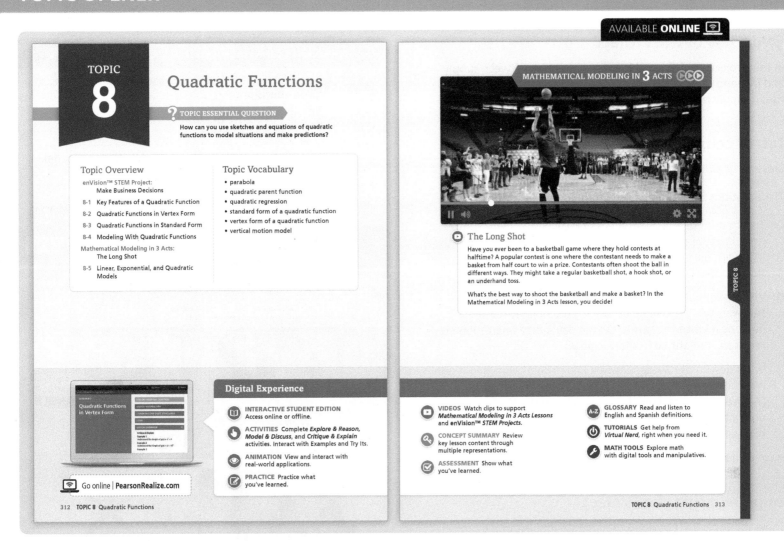

enVision™ STEM Project

Overview of the Project

In this project, students will learn the interplay between supply and demand. If supply is too low, there is a shortage and prices rise; if supply is too high, there is a surplus and prices fall.

Introducing the Project

Present the situation by discussing supply and demand.

The questions below can be used to guide the discussion.

Q: The amount people want an item is called the *demand* for the item. What are some examples that might be in high demand?
[Answers will vary. Samples: a new toy, the coolest smartphone]

Q: When might an item be in *short supply*?
[Answers will vary. Samples: During the holiday season, a new toy might be sold out. On the day a new smartphone is released, it might be in short supply.]

Q: What do you think happens to a low-priced item when it is in *high demand*?
[Answers will vary. Look for and probe students who understand that a price is likely to rise when an item is in high demand.]

Have students read the task they will be asked to complete.

Implementing the Project

Show the Topic 8 STEM video to generate interest in the project.

You can download blackline masters for use with the project from the Teacher Resource Center.

Finishing the Project

You may wish to plan a day when students share their completed business plans. Encourage students to explain their process as well as their results.

MAKING MATHEMATICAL CONNECTIONS	
In Topic 7 ...	... you used polynomials to model business decisions.
In this Topic ...	... you use quadratic functions to estimate business profits.
In Topic 9 ...	... you will use quadratic functions to model paths of launched objects.

AVAILABLE **ONLINE**

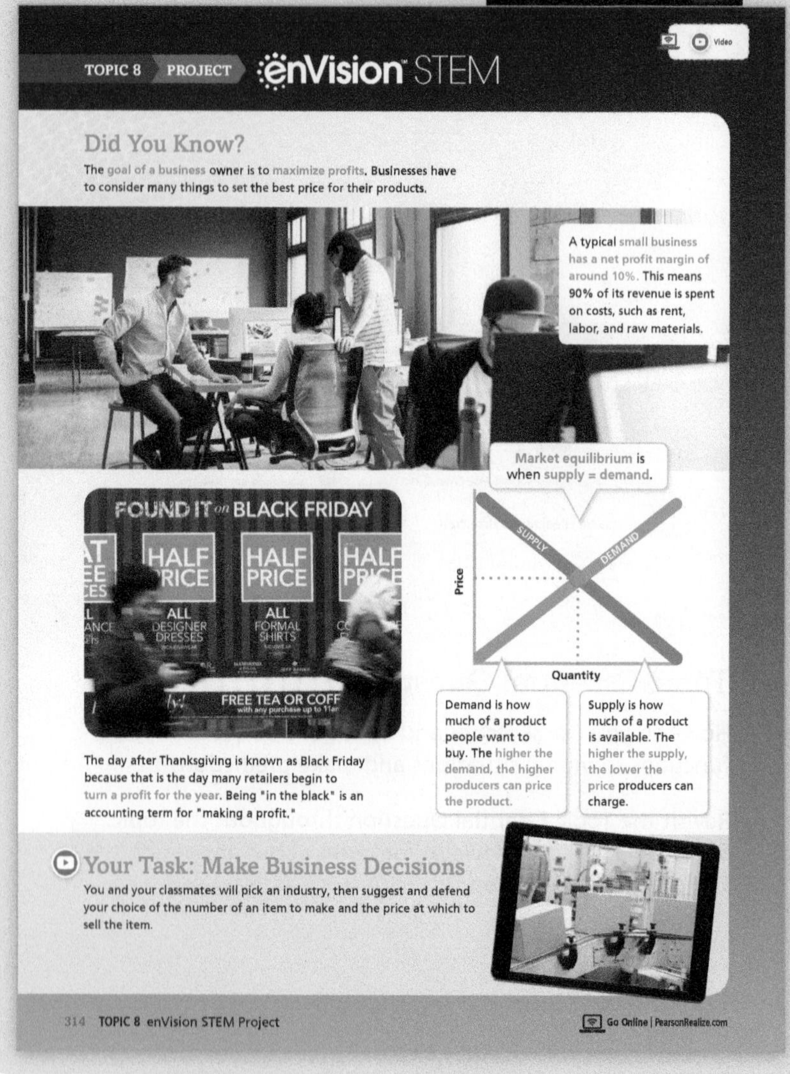

Video
TOPIC 8 PROJECT enVision STEM
Did You Know?
The goal of a business owner is to maximize profits. Businesses have to consider many things to set the best price for their products.
A typical small business has a net profit margin of around 10%. This means 90% of its revenue is spent on costs, such as rent, labor, and raw materials.
Market equilibrium is when supply = demand.
FOUND IT on BLACK FRIDAY
HALF PRICE
ALL DESIGNER DRESSES
ALL FORMAL SHIRTS
FREE TEA OR COFF
SUPPLY
DEMAND
Price
Quantity
Demand is how much of a product people want to buy. The higher the demand, the higher producers can price the product.
Supply is how much of a product is available. The higher the supply, the lower the price producers can charge.
The day after Thanksgiving is known as Black Friday because that is the day many retailers begin to turn a profit for the year. Being "in the black" is an accounting term for "making a profit."
Your Task: Make Business Decisions
You and your classmates will pick an industry, then suggest and defend your choice of the number of an item to make and the price at which to sell the item.
314 TOPIC 8 enVision STEM Project
Go Online | PearsonRealize.com

Common Core Standards HSA.APR.A.1, HSA.SSE.B.3, HSA.CED.A.2, HSF.IF.B.4, HSF.BF.A.1

Mathematical Practices MP.1, MP.4, MP.7

A-Z Glossary

LESSON 8-1

Key Features of a Quadratic Function

Lesson Overview

FOCUS

Objective

Students will be able to:

✔ Identify key features of the graph of a quadratic function using graphs, tables, and equations.

✔ Explain the effect of the value of *a* on the quadratic parent function.

Essential Understanding

A quadratic function is a polynomial function in one or more variables in which the highest degree term is of the second degree. The graph of a quadratic function $f(x) = ax^2$ is a parabola. The value of the leading coefficient *a* determines both the width of the parabola and the direction the parabola opens (upward or downward).

COHERENCE

Previously in this course, students:

- Interpreted and identified the key features of linear and exponential functions and used them to graph the functions.

In this lesson, students:

- Use graphs and tables to determine the key features of quadratic functions in the form $f(x) = ax^2$.

Later in this topic students will:

- Graph quadratic functions by identifying the key features of a quadratic equation written in vertex and standard forms.

RIGOR

This lesson emphasizes a blend of *conceptual understanding* and *application.*

- Students describe the effects of the leading coefficient *a* on the quadratic parent function.
- Students apply their understanding of the features of a quadratic function in the form $f(x) = ax^2$ to graph and interpret functions in real-world situations.

Vocabulary Builder

REVIEW VOCABULARY — **English** | *Spanish*

- **axis of symmetry** | *eje de simetria*
- **quadratic function** | *función cuadrática*
- **vertex** | *vértice*

NEW VOCABULARY

- **parabola** | *parábola*
- **quadratic parent function** | *función cuadrática madre*

VOCABULARY ACTIVITY

Review the vocabulary term *vertex* by drawing a parabola without a coordinate grid. Discuss that the vertex can be the maximum or the minimum point on the graph. Relate the *vertex of a parabola* to *vertex of an angle* and *vertex of a polygon*. As needed, have students complete these sentences.

1. The point where two rays interesect to form an angle is the ________. **[vertex of the angle]**
2. The point where two sides of a polygon intersect is a ________. **[vertex of the polygon]**
3. The maximum or minimum point of a parabola is the ________. **[vertex of the parabola]**

Student Companion

Students can do their in-class work for the lesson on pages 167–170 of their *Student Companion* or in Savvas Realize.

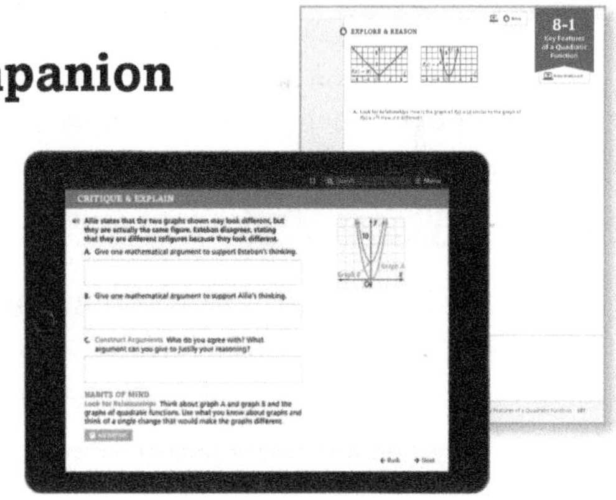

Mathematics Overview — COMMON CORE STANDARDS

Content Standards

In this lesson, students focus on these standards:

HSA.CED.A.2 Create equations in two or more variables to represent relationships between quantities; graph equations on coordinate axes with labels and scales.

HSF.IF.B.6 Calculate and interpret average rates of change of a function (presented symbolically or as a table) over a specified interval. Estimate the rate of change from a graph.

They also work with concepts related to this standard: **HSF.BF.B.3**

Mathematical Practice Standards

These standards are highlighted in this lesson:

MP.7 Look For and Make Use of Structure

Students apply what they have learned about the overall structure of linear and absolute value functions to the structure of quadratic functions.

MP.8 Look For and Express Regularity in Repeated Reasoning

Students make generalizations about the effect of the value of the leading coefficient *a* on the graphs of quadratic functions of the form $f(x) = ax^2$.

Activity

EXPLORE & REASON

INSTRUCTIONAL FOCUS Students use their knowledge of the features of the graph of the absolute value parent function to explore the graph of the quadratic parent function.

STUDENT COMPANION Students can complete the *Explore & Reason* activity on page 167 of their *Student Companion*.

Before WHOLE CLASS

Implement Tasks That Promote Reasoning and Problem Solving ETP

Q: What do you notice about the function and graph on the left?
[Answers may vary. Sample: The absolute value function has a minimum, reflection symmetry across the *y*-axis, and a non-negative range. The rate of change is negative to the left of the *y*-axis and positive to the right of the *y*-axis.]

During SMALL GROUP

Support Productive Struggle in Learning Mathematics ETP

Q: What features of the graph of the absolute value function could you look at to compare and contrast the two graphs?
[the vertex, the axis of symmetry, the shape, the direction of the graph]

For Early Finishers

Q: How does the graph on the right compare or contrast to the graph of a linear function? Of an exponential function?
[A linear function and an exponential function do not have an axis of symmetry or a maximum/minimum value.]

After WHOLE CLASS

Facilitate Meaningful Mathematical Discourse ETP

Facilitate a discussion about the similarities and differences of the graphs of absolute value and quadratic functions.

Q: What similarities do you notice between the two graphs? What differences?
[both have a vertex, both have an axis of symmetry; the graph on the left has straight line segments, the graph on the right has curves]

Q: When does the graph of an absolute value function open downward?
[when there is a negative sign outside of the absolute value symbol]

HABITS OF MIND

Use with **EXPLORE & REASON**

Construct Arguments Why is the graph of $y = x^2$ always positive? MP.3
[The *y*-values of $y = x^2$ are always positive (or zero) because when any real value of *x* is squared, the result is a positive number (or zero).]

AVAILABLE **ONLINE**

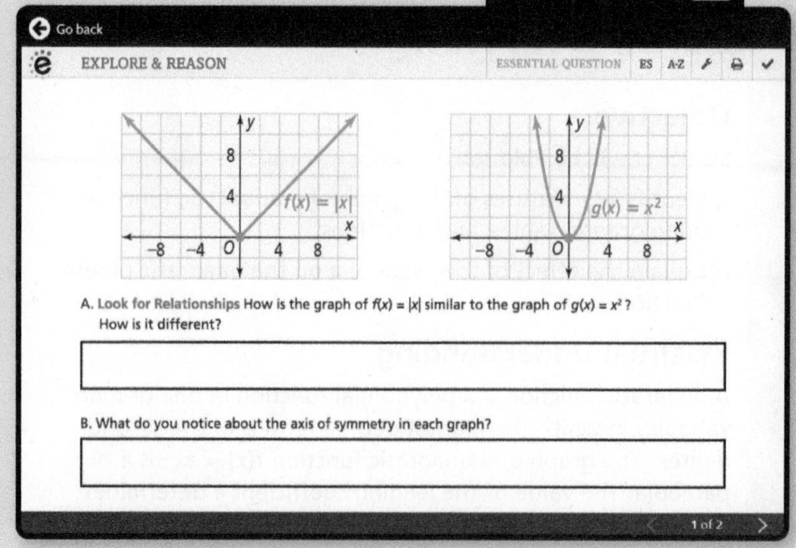

Go back
EXPLORE & REASON
ESSENTIAL QUESTION ES A-Z
y
8
4
f(x) = |x|
x
−8 −4 O 4 8
y
8
4
g(x) = x²
x
−8 −4 O 4 8
A. Look for Relationships How is the graph of f(x) = |x| similar to the graph of g(x) = x²? How is it different?
B. What do you notice about the axis of symmetry in each graph?
1 of 2

STUDENT EDITION, PAGE 315

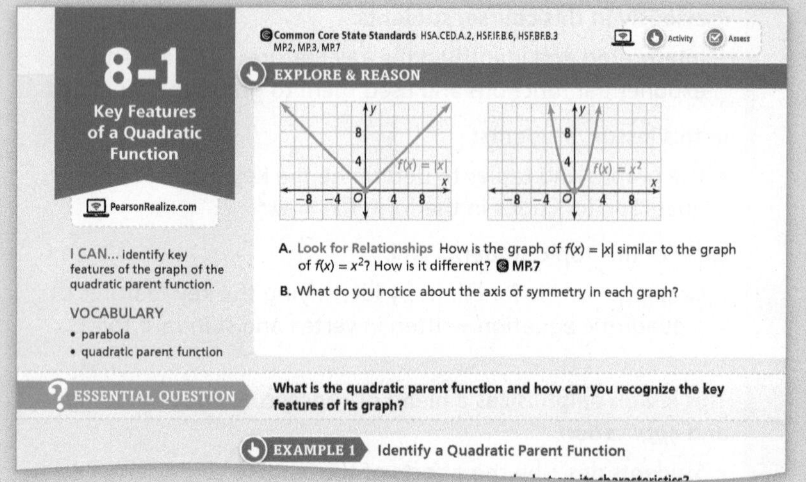
8-1 Key Features of a Quadratic Function

PearsonRealize.com

I CAN… identify key features of the graph of the quadratic parent function.

VOCABULARY
- parabola
- quadratic parent function

Common Core State Standards HSA.CED.A.2, HSF.IF.B.6, HSF.BF.B.3 MP.2, MP.3, MP.7

Activity Assess

EXPLORE & REASON

A. Look for Relationships How is the graph of $f(x) = |x|$ similar to the graph of $f(x) = x^2$? How is it different? MP.7

B. What do you notice about the axis of symmetry in each graph?

ESSENTIAL QUESTION What is the quadratic parent function and how can you recognize the key features of its graph?

EXAMPLE 1 Identify a Quadratic Parent Function

SAMPLE STUDENT WORK

A. Both graphs open upward, have turning points, and have symmetry about the y-axis. The graph of $f(x) = |x|$ is linear pieces while the graph of $g(x) = x^2$ is curved.

B. The axis of symmetry is $x = 0$ for both graphs.

INTRODUCE THE ESSENTIAL QUESTION

Establish Mathematics Goals to Focus Learning ETP

Introduce to students quadratic functions as functions in which the highest degree term is of the second degree. Remind them that, as with other functions, graphs and tables can help them identify the key features of quadratic functions. Explain that they will first study the quadratic parent function.

AVAILABLE ONLINE

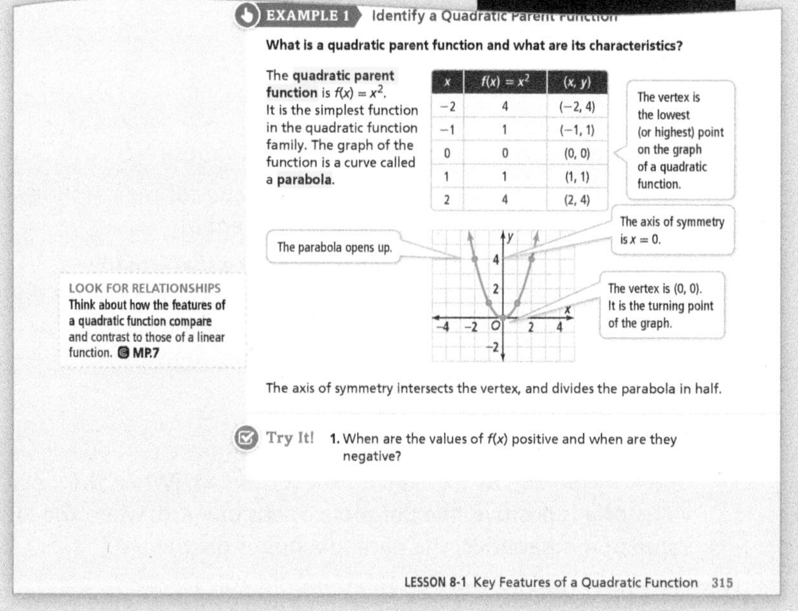

EXAMPLE 1 Identify a Quadratic Parent Function

What is a quadratic parent function and what are its characteristics?

The **quadratic parent function** is $f(x) = x^2$. It is the simplest function in the quadratic function family. The graph of the function is a curve called a **parabola**.

x	$f(x) = x^2$	(x, y)
−2	4	(−2, 4)
−1	1	(−1, 1)
0	0	(0, 0)
1	1	(1, 1)
2	4	(2, 4)

The vertex is the lowest (or highest) point on the graph of a quadratic function.

The parabola opens up.

The axis of symmetry is $x = 0$.

The vertex is (0, 0). It is the turning point of the graph.

LOOK FOR RELATIONSHIPS
Think about how the features of a quadratic function compare and contrast to those of a linear function. **MP.7**

The axis of symmetry intersects the vertex, and divides the parabola in half.

Try It! 1. When are the values of $f(x)$ positive and when are they negative?

LESSON 8-1 Key Features of a Quadratic Function 315

EXAMPLE 1 Identify a Quadratic Parent Function

Use and Connect Mathematical Representations ETP

Q: What features can you use to describe the graph of the quadratic parent function?
[its shape, the direction it opens, and the location of the vertex, symmetry across the y-axis]

Q: How are the representations of the vertex in the table and on the graph similar?
[The vertex represents the lowest value for $f(x)$ in the table and is also the lowest point on the graph.]

Try It! Answers

1. The values of $f(x)$ are always positive, except at the vertex where the value of $f(x)$ is 0.

AVAILABLE ONLINE

ADDITIONAL EXAMPLES

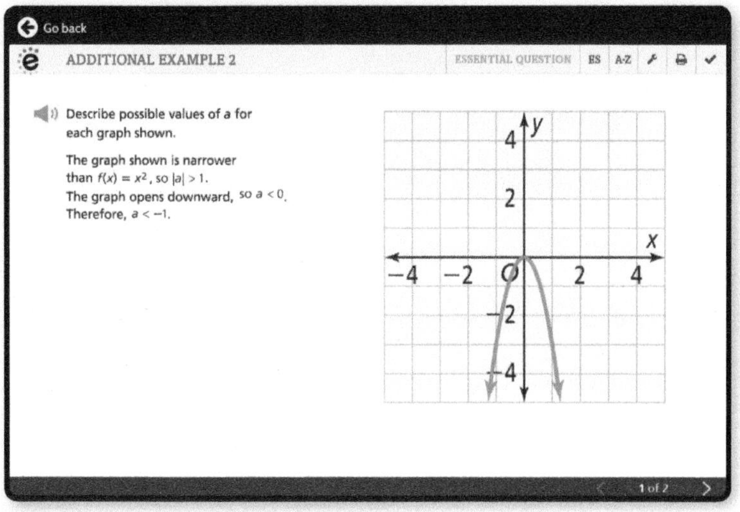

Go back

ADDITIONAL EXAMPLE 2 ESSENTIAL QUESTION ES A-Z

Describe possible values of a for each graph shown.

The graph shown is narrower than $f(x) = x^2$, so $|a| > 1$.
The graph opens downward, so $a < 0$.
Therefore, $a < -1$.

y
4
2
x
−4
−2
O
2
4
−2
−4

1 of 2

Example 2 Help students connect the shape of a parabola with the value of a in $f(x) = ax^2$.

Q: How can you use the graphs of the functions to determine the possible values for a?
[Look at whether the parabola opens upward or downward. If it opens upward, $a > 0$. If it opens downward, $a < 0$. Then look at the shape of the parabola compared to the parent function. If it is wider, then $0 < |a| < 1$. If it is narrower, then $|a| > 1$.]

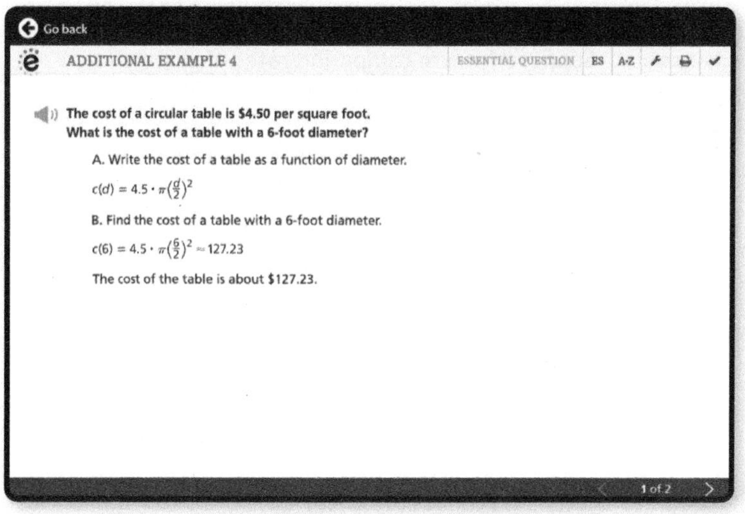

Go back

ADDITIONAL EXAMPLE 4 ESSENTIAL QUESTION ES A-Z

The cost of a circular table is $4.50 per square foot. What is the cost of a table with a 6-foot diameter?

A. Write the cost of a table as a function of diameter.

$c(d) = 4.5 \cdot \pi\left(\frac{d}{2}\right)^2$

B. Find the cost of a table with a 6-foot diameter.

$c(6) = 4.5 \cdot \pi\left(\frac{6}{2}\right)^2 \approx 127.23$

The cost of the table is about $127.23.

1 of 2

Example 4 Help students write a cost function based on the diameter of a circular table.

Q: What is a reasonable domain for this function?
[$x > 0$; The diameter must be a positive number.]

EXAMPLE 2 Understand the Graph of $y = ax^2$

Pose Purposeful Questions ETP

PART A

Q: What do you notice about the position of each parabola? [The vertex is at the origin, but the width varies.]

Q: What accounts for the variation in the shapes of the parabolas shown? [the value of the leading coefficient a]

Q: What generalization can you make about the shape of the parabola by looking at the leading coefficient a? [The greater the value of the leading coefficient a, the narrower the parabola. As the value of a decreases to 0, the wider the parabola.]

PART B

Q: What generalization can you make about how a parabola opens by looking at the leading coefficient a? [When the value of a is positive, the parabola opens upward; when the value of a is negative, the parabola opens downward.]

Q: How does the coefficient a relate to the minimum or maximum value of a quadratic function? [When the value of a is positive, the parabola opens upward, so the y-coordinate of the vertex is the minimum value of the function. When the value of a is negative, the parabola opens downward, so the y-coordinate of the vertex is the maximum value of the function.]

Try It! Answers

2. The sign of a does not affect the domain. When a is positive, the range is all real numbers greater than or equal to zero; when a is negative, the range is all real numbers less than or equal to zero.

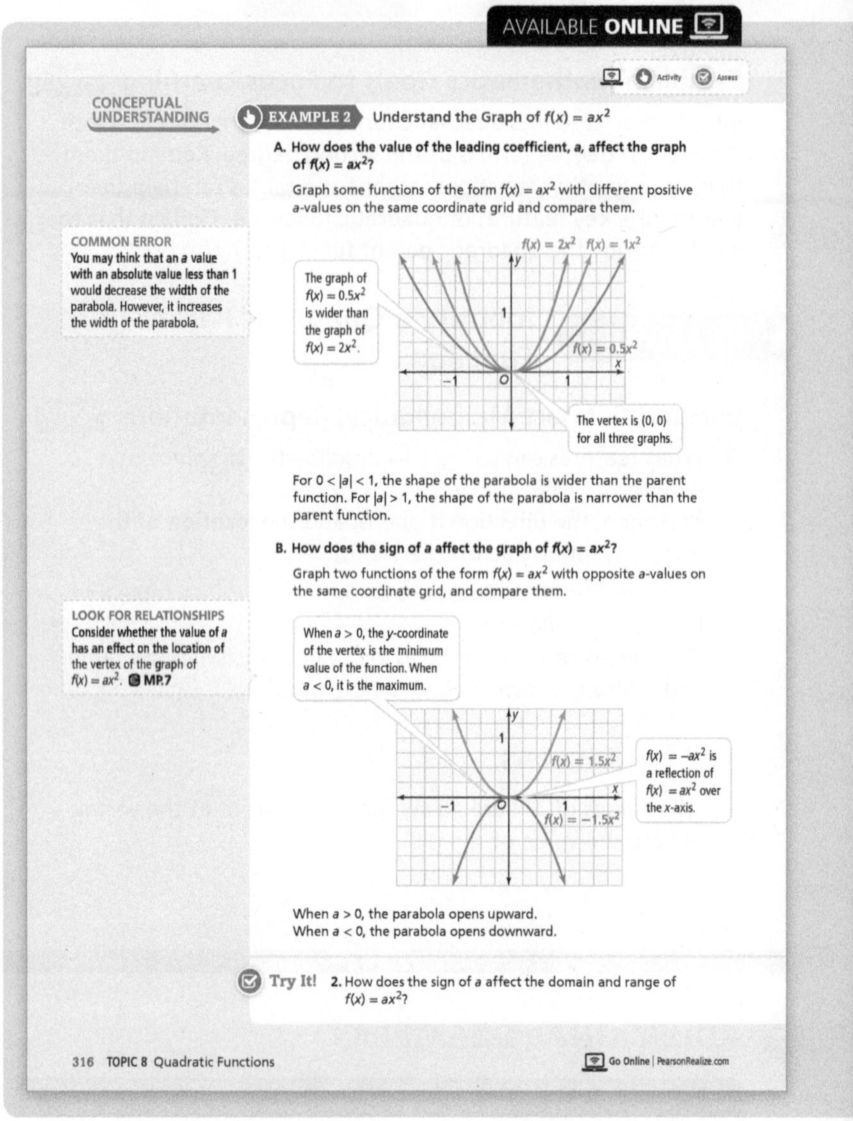
AVAILABLE **ONLINE**

Activity Assess

CONCEPTUAL UNDERSTANDING

EXAMPLE 2 Understand the Graph of $f(x) = ax^2$

A. How does the value of the leading coefficient, a, affect the graph of $f(x) = ax^2$?

Graph some functions of the form $f(x) = ax^2$ with different positive a-values on the same coordinate grid and compare them.

COMMON ERROR
You may think that an a value with an absolute value less than 1 would decrease the width of the parabola. However, it increases the width of the parabola.

$f(x) = 2x^2$
$f(x) = 1x^2$
The graph of $f(x) = 0.5x^2$ is wider than the graph of $f(x) = 2x^2$.
$f(x) = 0.5x^2$
y
x
1
−1
O
1
The vertex is (0, 0) for all three graphs.

For $0 < |a| < 1$, the shape of the parabola is wider than the parent function. For $|a| > 1$, the shape of the parabola is narrower than the parent function.

B. How does the sign of a affect the graph of $f(x) = ax^2$?

Graph two functions of the form $f(x) = ax^2$ with opposite a-values on the same coordinate grid, and compare them.

LOOK FOR RELATIONSHIPS
Consider whether the value of a has an effect on the location of the vertex of the graph of $f(x) = ax^2$. MP.7

When $a > 0$, the y-coordinate of the vertex is the minimum value of the function. When $a < 0$, it is the maximum.
y
1
$f(x) = 1.5x^2$
x
−1
O
1
$f(x) = -1.5x^2$
$f(x) = -ax^2$ is a reflection of $f(x) = ax^2$ over the x-axis.

When $a > 0$, the parabola opens upward.
When $a < 0$, the parabola opens downward.

Try It! 2. How does the sign of a affect the domain and range of $f(x) = ax^2$?

316 TOPIC 8 Quadratic Functions   Go Online | PearsonRealize.com

HABITS OF MIND

Use with **EXAMPLES 1, 2, & 3**

Reasoning Suppose you are comparing rates of change for two quadratic functions of the form $f(x) = ax^2$ over the interval $2 < x < 5$. One function has a positive rate of change and the other function has a negative rate of change over this interval. What can you conclude about the value of a in each function? Which function has a maximum value and which has a minimum value? Explain. **MP.2**

[The function with a negative rate of change over the interval $2 < x < 5$ has a negative a value and a maximum value. The function with a positive rate of change has a positive a value and a minimum value.]

RtI Struggling Students

USE WITH EXAMPLE 2 In the example and Try It, some students may have difficulty determining how the value of a is related to the information given. Have students sketch two parabolas with vertex at the origin, one that opens upward and one that opens downward. Ask them to label where each parabola is increasing and where it is decreasing.

Q: In which interval is a quadratic function increasing if the function has a maximum? A minimum?
[If the function has a maximum, it is increasing when $x < 0$. If the function has a minimum, it is increasing when $x > 0$.]

EXAMPLE 3 Interpret Quadratic Functions from Tables

Pose Purposeful Questions ETP

Q: What do you notice about the x- and $f(x)$-values in the table when the function is decreasing?
[The x-values, which are less than 0, are increasing, while the $f(x)$-values, which are greater than 0, are decreasing.]

Q: What do you notice about the x- and $f(x)$-values in the table when the function is increasing?
[Both the x-values and $f(x)$-values are greater than 0 and both are increasing.]

Try It! Answers

3. Answers may vary. Sample: –2; The graph is opening downward, so the value of a must be negative.

Elicit and use Evidence of Student Thinking ETP

Q: State two ways to read the inequality $x < 0$.
[x is less than 0; x is negative.]

EXAMPLE 4 Apply Quadratic Functions

Use and Connect Mathematical Representations ETP

Q: How would a change in the cost of the flooring affect the graph of this function?
[An increase in cost would make the parabola narrower, and a decrease would make it wider.]

Q: How would a change in the side lengths of the a square room affect the cost of the new floor?
[An increase in side length will result in a cost increase, and a decrease would lower the cost.]

Try It! Answers

4. The cost of the larger floor is \$2,528.75, so the cost increases by \$560.

AVAILABLE ONLINE

Activity Assess

EXAMPLE 3 Interpret Quadratic Functions from Tables

Over what interval is $f(x) = 4x^2$ increasing? Over what interval is it decreasing?

Use the function to make a table of values.

x	$f(x) = 4x^2$	(x, y)
−2	16	(−2, 16)
−1	4	(−1, 4)
0	0	(0, 0)
1	4	(1, 4)
2	16	(2, 16)

The function values are decreasing.

The vertex (0, 0) is the turning point of the function, where it changes from decreasing to increasing.

The function values are increasing.

STUDY TIP
Remember that since the function has a minimum value, the parabola opens upward. If the function has a maximum value, the parabola opens downward.

The function is decreasing over the interval $x < 0$ and increasing over the interval $x > 0$.

Try It! 3. A function of the form $g(x) = ax^2$ increases over the interval $x < 0$ and decreases over the interval $x > 0$. What is a possible value for a? Explain.

APPLICATION **EXAMPLE 4** Apply Quadratic Functions

The owner of a new dance studio is installing wooden floors in all of the dance rooms. How much should the owner expect to spend on flooring for a square room with 15-ft side lengths?

15 ft
15 ft
FLOORING SALE!
$8.75 per square foot

Write a function that can be used to determine the cost of the flooring.

$c(x)$ = price per ft² of flooring • area of dance floor in ft²
$c(x) = 8.75 \cdot x^2$

Find the value of the function when $x = 15$.

$c(x) = 8.75x^2$
$c(15) = 8.75(15)^2$ Substitute 15 for x.
$c(15) = 1{,}968.75$ Simplify.

The cost for a new floor for a square dance floor with sides of 15 ft is \$1,968.75.

Try It! 4. By how much will the cost increase if the side length of the dance floor is increased by 2 ft?

LESSON 8-1 Key Features of a Quadratic Function 317

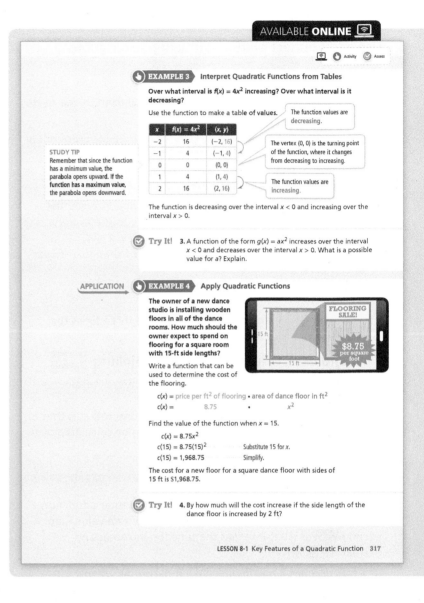

ELL English Language Learners (Use with EXAMPLE 4)

LISTENING BEGINNING Give students two note cards with $A = l \times w$ and $A = s^2$ written on them. Have them hold up a card to answer these questions.

Q: Which formula shows the area of a rectangle equals the length times the width? [$A = l \times w$]

Q: Which formula shows the area of a square is the length of one side squared? [$A = s^2$]

Ask additional questions about area, length, width, and squares.

WRITING INTERMEDIATE Have students write additional values of the function as complete sentences.

Q: When x is 10, the value of the function $c(x)$ is \$875. How do you interpret this value of the function?
[The cost for a new floor for a square dance floor with sides of 10 feet is \$875.]

Verify students wrote a complete sentence to answer the Try It.

SPEAKING ADVANCED Show these formulas.

$A = l \times w \quad A = s^2 \quad A = \frac{1}{2}bh$

Have students tell when they would use each formula and explain what each variable represents.

Q: Does the A stand for the same word in all of these formulas?
[Yes, the A represents area.]

Q: Which formula applies to this Example?
[$A = s^2$ because the dance floor is square.]

EXAMPLE 5 Compare the Rate of Change

Use and Connect Mathematical Representations ETP

Q: How do you find the average rate of change for linear functions?
[Find the slope. The rate of change is equal to the slope of the line.]

Q: Why must you find an *average* rate of change for exponential and quadratic functions?
[The rate of change is not constant; you can only find the average over an identified interval.]

Q: What is the average rate of change for function f over the interval $0 \le x \le 2$? How does that compare to the average rate of change for function f over the interval $2 \le x \le 4$?
[1.5; It is much less than the average rate of change of f over the interval $2 \le x \le 4$.]

Try It! Answers

5. The average rate of change for g, 10.5, is three times the average rate of change for f, 3.5.

Elicit and use Evidence of Student Thinking ETP

Q: How is the rate of change of a parabola different from the rate of change of a line?
[The rate of change of a parabola is not constant, as is that of a line, so only average rates of change can be calculated over given intervals.]

HABITS OF MIND

Use with **EXAMPLES 4 & 5**

Look for Relationships How does knowing whether a function of the form $f(x) = ax^2$ has a maximum or minimum value help you know over what intervals the function increases and decreases? MP.7

[If a function has a maximum value, it decreases when $x < 0$ and increases when $x > 0$. If a function has a minimum value, it increases when $x < 0$ and decreases when $x > 0$.]

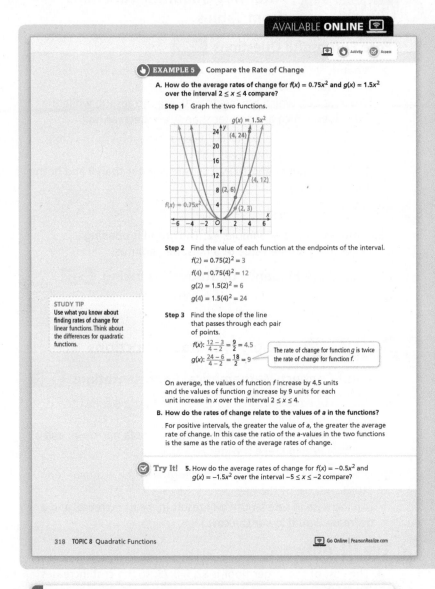

AVAILABLE **ONLINE**

Activity Assess

EXAMPLE 5 Compare the Rate of Change

A. How do the average rates of change for $f(x) = 0.75x^2$ and $g(x) = 1.5x^2$ over the interval $2 \le x \le 4$ compare?

Step 1 Graph the two functions.

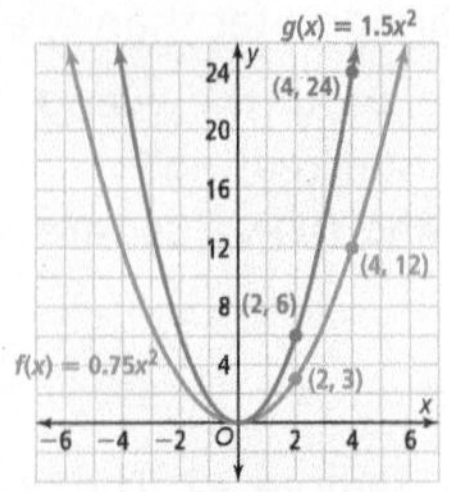

g(x) = 1.5x²
(4, 24)
(4, 12)
(2, 6)
(2, 3)
f(x) = 0.75x²
y
x
24
20
16
12
8
4
O
−6 −4 −2 2 4 6

Step 2 Find the value of each function at the endpoints of the interval.

$f(2) = 0.75(2)^2 = 3$

$f(4) = 0.75(4)^2 = 12$

$g(2) = 1.5(2)^2 = 6$

$g(4) = 1.5(4)^2 = 24$

STUDY TIP
Use what you know about finding rates of change for linear functions. Think about the differences for quadratic functions.

Step 3 Find the slope of the line that passes through each pair of points.

$f(x)$: $\frac{12 - 3}{4 - 2} = \frac{9}{2} = 4.5$

$g(x)$: $\frac{24 - 6}{4 - 2} = \frac{18}{2} = 9$

The rate of change for function g is twice the rate of change for function f.

On average, the values of function f increase by 4.5 units and the values of function g increase by 9 units for each unit increase in x over the interval $2 \le x \le 4$.

B. How do the rates of change relate to the values of a in the functions?

For positive intervals, the greater the value of a, the greater the average rate of change. In this case the ratio of the a-values in the two functions is the same as the ratio of the average rates of change.

Try It! 5. How do the average rates of change for $f(x) = -0.5x^2$ and $g(x) = -1.5x^2$ over the interval $-5 \le x \le -2$ compare?

Common Error

Try It 5 When comparing the rate of change for each function, some students may find the value of each function at the endpoints of the interval and just compare these values. Remind students that they need to find the slope of the line that passes through each pair of points.

ADV Advanced Students

USE WITH EXAMPLE 5 Have students expand their understanding of average rates of change over an interval for the quadratic function $f(x) = 3x^2$.

- Find the average rate of change of f over the given intervals.

1. $-2 \le x \le 2$
2. $-5 \le x \le 5$
3. $-10 \le x \le 10$

Q: What feature of the graph of $f(x)$ indicates why the average rate of change is the same for each interval given? Explain. [The axis of symmetry passes through the midpoint of each interval, so the negative and positive rates of change sum to 0.]

CONCEPT SUMMARY Features of the Quadratic Function $f(x) = ax^2$

Q: What characteristics of a quadratic function does the value of the leading coefficient *a* affect?
[the direction that the parabola opens and the width of the parabola]

Do You UNDERSTAND? | Do You KNOW HOW?

Common Error

Exercise 7 Students may think that since $5 > 1$, the graph of $f(x)$ would be wider than the parent function. Remind students that when $|a| > 1$, the graph is vertically stretched, and therefore is narrower than the parent function.

Answers

1. $f(x) = x^2$; a parabola that opens upward, with axis of symmetry $x = 0$, minimum, vertex, and *x*- and *y*-intercepts at (0, 0). The function decreases over the interval $x < 0$ and increases over the interval $x > 0$.
2. The graphs of both functions have axis of symmetry $x = 0$ and vertex and *x*- and *y*-intercepts at (0, 0). The graph of $f(x) = ax^2$ becomes narrower as $|a|$ becomes greater, and for $a < 0$, the graph opens downward.
3. The word "parent" is included because all other quadratic functions are related to the parent function.
4. The sign of the *y*-value is incorrect. The point should be (–2, –52).
5. The graph is narrower than the graph of the parent function.
6. The graph is wider than the graph of the parent function.
7. The graph is narrower than the graph of the parent function and opens downward.
8. The graph is wider than the graph of the parent function and opens downward.
9. 10; the graph of the function opens upward since it is increasing to the right of the axis of symmetry.

AVAILABLE ONLINE

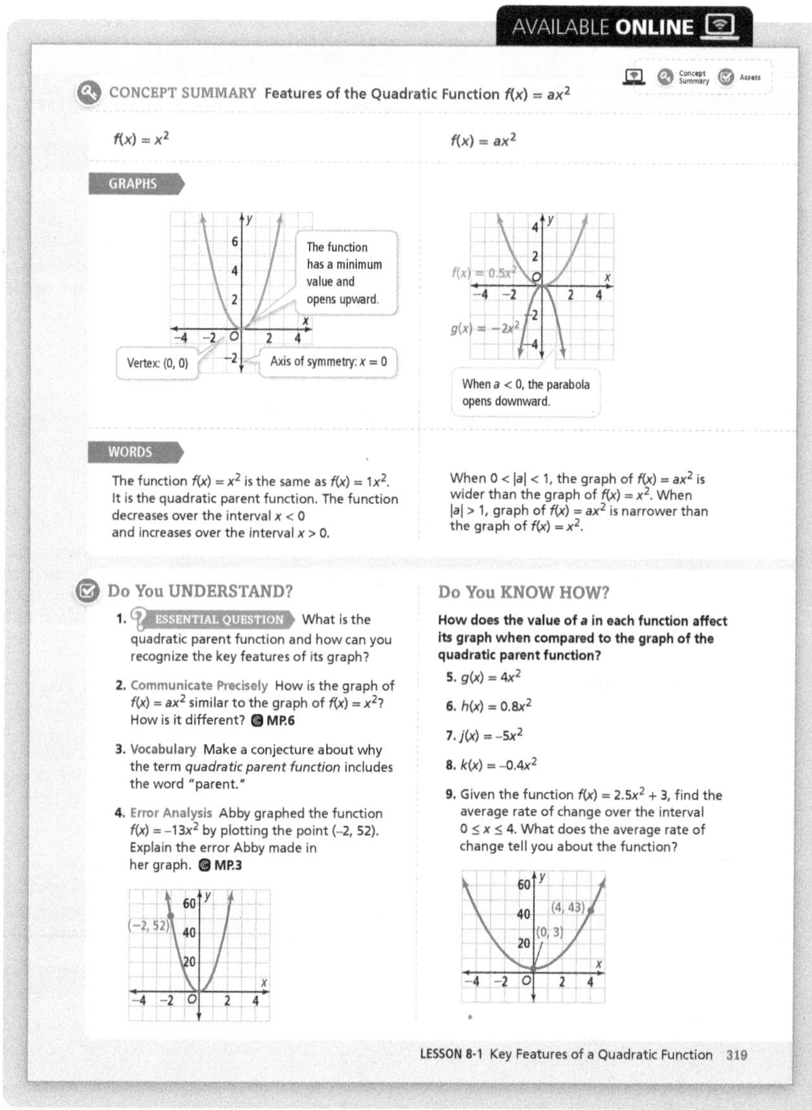

CONCEPT SUMMARY Features of the Quadratic Function $f(x) = ax^2$

	$f(x) = x^2$	$f(x) = ax^2$
GRAPHS	The function has a minimum value and opens upward. Vertex: (0, 0). Axis of symmetry: $x = 0$	$f(x) = 0.5x^2$; $g(x) = -2x^2$. When $a < 0$, the parabola opens downward.
WORDS	The function $f(x) = x^2$ is the same as $f(x) = 1x^2$. It is the quadratic parent function. The function decreases over the interval $x < 0$ and increases over the interval $x > 0$.	When $0 < \lvert a\rvert < 1$, the graph of $f(x) = ax^2$ is wider than the graph of $f(x) = x^2$. When $\lvert a\rvert > 1$, graph of $f(x) = ax^2$ is narrower than the graph of $f(x) = x^2$.

Do You UNDERSTAND?

1. ESSENTIAL QUESTION What is the quadratic parent function and how can you recognize the key features of its graph?
2. Communicate Precisely How is the graph of $f(x) = ax^2$ similar to the graph of $f(x) = x^2$? How is it different? MP.6
3. Vocabulary Make a conjecture about why the term *quadratic parent function* includes the word "parent."
4. Error Analysis Abby graphed the function $f(x) = -13x^2$ by plotting the point (–2, 52). Explain the error Abby made in her graph. MP.3

Do You KNOW HOW?

How does the value of *a* in each function affect its graph when compared to the graph of the quadratic parent function?

5. $g(x) = 4x^2$
6. $h(x) = 0.8x^2$
7. $j(x) = -5x^2$
8. $k(x) = -0.4x^2$
9. Given the function $f(x) = 2.5x^2 + 3$, find the average rate of change over the interval $0 \le x \le 4$. What does the average rate of change tell you about the function?

(–2, 52)
(4, 43)
(0, 3)

LESSON 8-1 Key Features of a Quadratic Function 319

PRACTICE & PROBLEM SOLVING

AVAILABLE ONLINE

Lesson Practice You may opt to have students complete the automatically scored Practice and Problem Solving items online powered by MathXL for School.

Choose from: ☑ **Lesson Practice**

Adaptive Practice

You may also take advantage of the bank of exercises for assigning additional practice.

Assignment Guide

Basic	Advanced
10–21, 23, 25–31	10–13, 16–31

Item Analysis

Example	Items	DOK
1	14–19	1
2	10, 14–19, 30	1
	13	3
3	20, 21	1
	11	3
4	12, 22, 23	1
5	24, 25	2
	26–29	3
	31	4

AVAILABLE ONLINE

PRACTICE & PROBLEM SOLVING

Scan for Multimedia

Practice Tutorial

Additional Exercises Available Online

UNDERSTAND

10. **Generalize** The graph of the parent quadratic function $f(x) = x^2$ and that of a second function of the form $g(x) = ax^2$ are shown. What conclusion can you make about the value of a in the equation of the second function? MP.8

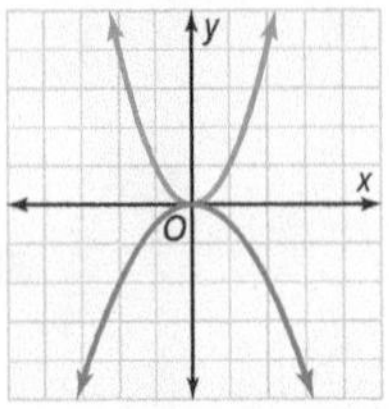
y
x
O

11. **Error Analysis** Describe and correct the error a student made in finding the average rate of change for $f(x) = 0.5x^2$ over the interval $-4 \leq x \leq -2$. MP.3

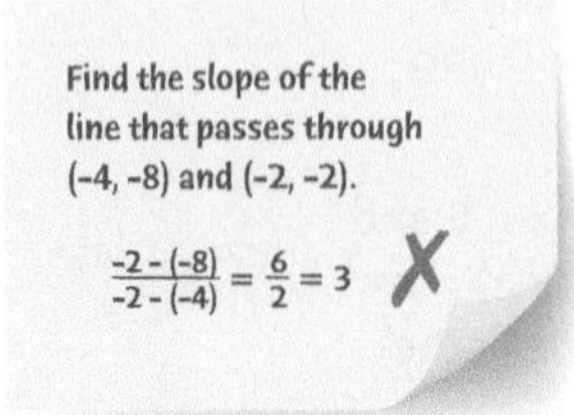
Find the slope of the line that passes through (-4, -8) and (-2, -2).
$\frac{-2-(-8)}{-2-(-4)} = \frac{6}{2} = 3$ X

12. **Use Structure** Use the table shown below to describe the intervals over which $f(x) = 15x^2$ is increasing and decreasing. MP.7

x	$f(x) = 15x^2$	(x, y)
−2	60	(−2, 60)
−1	15	(−1, 15)
0	0	(0, 0)
1	15	(1, 15)
2	60	(2, 60)

13. **Higher Order Thinking** Tell whether each statement about a function of the form $f(x) = ax^2$ is *always true, sometimes true,* or *never true.*
    a. The graph is a parabola that opens upward.
    b. The vertex of the graph is (0, 0).
    c. The axis of symmetry of the graph is $x = 0$.

PRACTICE

How does the value of a in each function affect its graph when compared to the graph of the quadratic parent function? SEE EXAMPLES 1 AND 2

14. $g(x) = 6x^2$
15. $f(x) = 0.6x^2$
16. $f(x) = -7x^2$
17. $h(x) = -0.15x^2$
18. $C(x) = 0.04x^2$
19. $g(x) = 4.5x^2$

Over what interval is each function increasing and over what interval is each function decreasing? SEE EXAMPLE 3

20.

x	$f(x) = -0.3x^2$	(x, y)
−2	−1.2	(−2, −1.2)
−1	−0.3	(−1, −0.3)
0	0	(0, 0)
1	−0.3	(1, −0.3)
2	−1.2	(2, −1.2)

21.

x	$f(x) = 13x^2$	(x, y)
−2	52	(−2, 52)
−1	13	(−1, 13)
0	0	(0, 0)
1	13	(1, 13)
2	52	(2, 52)

Write a quadratic function for the area of each figure. Then find the area for the given value of x. SEE EXAMPLE 4

22. $x = 13$

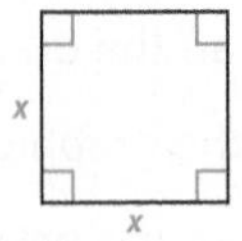
x
x

23. $x = 2.5$

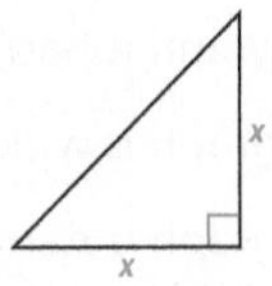
x
x

How do the average rates of change for each pair of functions compare over the given interval? SEE EXAMPLE 5

24. $f(x) = 0.1x^2$
    $g(x) = 0.3x^2$
    $1 \leq x \leq 4$

25. $f(x) = -2x^2$
    $g(x) = -4x^2$
    $-4 \leq x \leq -2$

Answers

10. $-1 < a < 0$
11. The coordinates used to calculate the slope are incorrect. Use (–4, 8) and (–2, 2). The average rate of change is –3.
12. increasing: $x > 0$; decreasing: $x < 0$
13. a. sometimes true
    b. always true
    c. always true
14. The graph is narrower.
15. The graph is wider.
16. The graph is narrower and opens downward.
17. The graph is wider and opens downward.
18. The graph is wider.
19. The graph is narrower.
20. decreasing: $x > 0$; increasing: $x < 0$
21. decreasing: $x < 0$; increasing $x > 0$
22. $A(x) = x^2$; 169 units^2
23. $A(x) = 0.5x^2$; 3.125 units^2
24. The average rate of change of g, 1.5, is 3 times greater than the average rate of change of f, 0.5.
25. The average rate of change of g, 24, is 2 times greater than the average rate of change of f, 12.

Answers

26. $f(x) = 9x^2$; $x \geq 0$; 144 carrots

27. a. 24.36; 34.8

b. Between diameters of 6 and 8 inches, the number of calories in a tortilla increased by an average of 24.36 calories per inch of diameter. Between diameters of 9 and 11 inches, the number of calories in a tortilla increased by an average of 34.8 calories per inch of diameter.

c. As the diameter of a tortilla increases, the number of calories in the tortilla increases more and more rapidly.

28. (–7, 2); The ramp is a parabola symmetric about the *y*-axis. So, if (7, 2) is on the skateboard ramp design, then (–7, 2) is also on the parabola.

29. B, C

30. A

31. Part A Design A: $f(x) = 0.03x^2$; Design B: $g(x) = 0.024x^2$; in each function, the value of *a* is the product of the cost per square inch and 6, because x^2 models the area of a square with side length *x*, and a cube has 6 square sides.

Part B The average rate of change is 0.42 for Design A and 0.336 for Design B. This means that for every increase of 1 inch in side length between 6 and 8 inches, the cost of the box increases an average of \$0.42 using Design A and an average of \$0.336 using Design B. The average rate of change for Design A is 1.25 times as great as the average rate of change for Design B.

Part C Answers may vary. Sample: Regardless of the side length, the packaging cost for Design A is 1.25 times as great as the packaging cost for Design B.

AVAILABLE **ONLINE**

PRACTICE & PROBLEM SOLVING

Practice Tutorial
Mixed Review Available Online

APPLY

26. Reason Some students can plant 9 carrots per square foot in the community garden shown. Write a function *f* that can be used to determine the number of carrots the students can plant. Give a reasonable domain for the function. How many carrots can the students plant in a garden that is square with 4-ft side lengths? **MP.2**

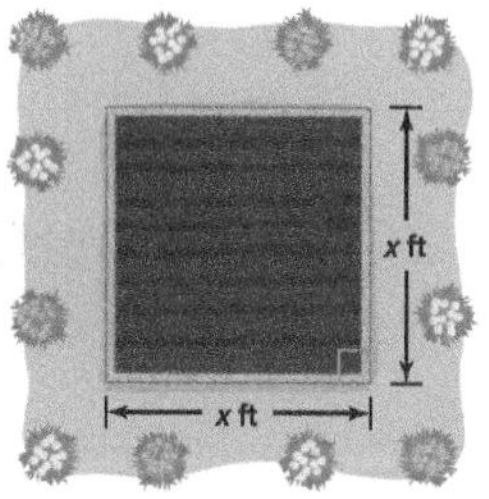
x ft
x ft

27. Make Sense and Persevere A burrito company uses the function $C(x) = 1.74x^2$ to calculate the number of calories in a tortilla with a diameter of *x* inches.

a. Find the average rates of change for the function over the intervals $6 < x < 8$ and $9 < x < 11$.

b. Interpret the average rates of change.

c. What does the difference in the average rates of change mean in terms of the situation? **MP.1**

28. Reason An architect uses a computer program to design a skateboard ramp. The function $f(x) = ax^2$ represents the shape of the ramp's cross section. A portion of the design is shown. The scale of each axis is 1 unit per grid line. On the ramp, a person can skateboard from point *A* through point *B* and over to a point *C*. If point *C* is the same distance above the *x*-axis as point *B*, what are its coordinates? Explain. **MP.2**

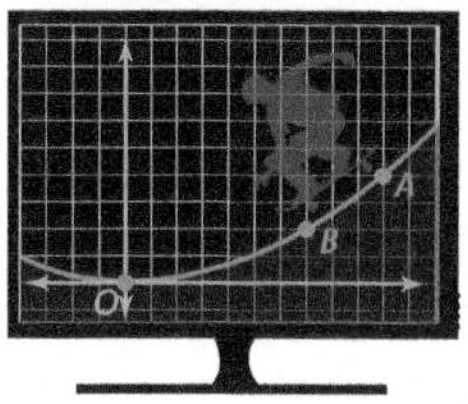
A
B
O

ASSESSMENT PRACTICE

29. The total cost, in dollars, of a square carpet can be determined by using $f(x) = 15x^2$, where *x* is the side length in yards. Which of the following are true? Select all that apply.

Ⓐ The cost of a carpet increases and then decreases as the side length increases.

Ⓑ The cost of the carpet is \$15 per square yard.

Ⓒ The cost of a carpet with a side length of 3 yd is \$135.

Ⓓ The cost of a carpet with 6-yd sides is twice the cost of a carpet with 3-yd sides.

Ⓔ The cost of a carpet increases at a constant rate as the side length increases.

30. SAT/ACT The graph of $f(x) = ax^2$ opens downward and is narrower than the graph of the quadratic parent function. Which of the following could be the value of *a*?

Ⓐ –2 Ⓑ –0.5 Ⓒ 0.5 Ⓓ 1 Ⓔ 2

31. Performance Task A manufacturer has two options for making cube-shaped boxes. The cost is calculated by multiplying the surface area of the box by the cost per square inch of the cardboard.

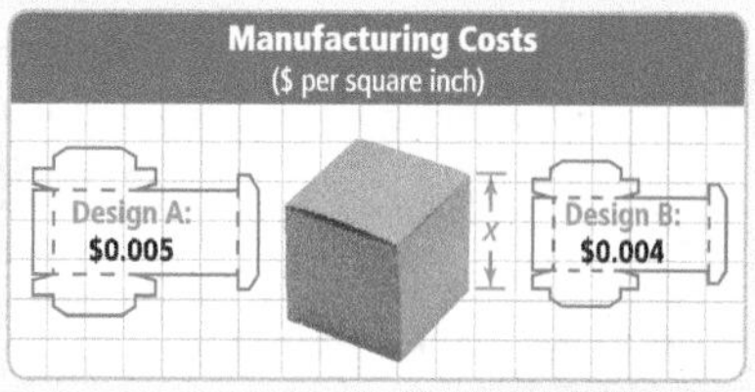
Manufacturing Costs
($ per square inch)
Design A:
$0.005
x
Design B:
$0.004

Part A Write a quadratic function of the form $f(x) = ax^2$ for each design that can be used to determine the total cardboard cost for cubes with any side length. Interpret the value of *a* in each function.

Part B How do the average rates of change for the designs compare for cubes with side lengths greater than 6 in., but less than 8 in.?

Part C Make a conjecture about the packaging costs for each design when the side length of the cube is greater than 36 in. Explain your conjecture.

LESSON QUIZ

Use the Lesson Quiz to assess students' understanding of the mathematics in the lesson.

Students can take the Lesson Quiz online or you can download a printable copy from **SavvasRealize.com**. The Lesson Quiz is also available in the *Assessment Resources* book.

Item Analysis

Item	DOK	Standards
1	1	HSF.IF.B.4
2	1	HSF.IF.B.3, HSF.IF.C.7
3	2	HSF.IF.B.6
4	1	HSF.IF.B.6
5	2	HSA.CED.A.2, HSF.IF.A.2

RtI Use the student scores on the Lesson Quiz to prescribe differentiated assignments.

If students take the Lesson Quiz online, it will be automatically scored and appropriate differentiated practice will be assigned based on student performance.

I Intervention	0–3 points	• Reteach to Build Understanding • Mathematical Literacy and Vocabulary • Additional Practice
O On-Level	4 points	• Mathematical Literacy and Vocabulary • Additional Practice • Enrichment
A Advanced	5 points	• Enrichment

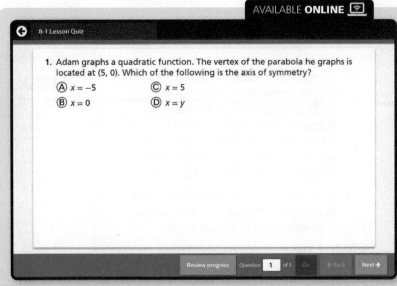

AVAILABLE **ONLINE**

8-1 Lesson Quiz

1. Adam graphs a quadratic function. The vertex of the parabola he graphs is located at (5, 0). Which of the following is the axis of symmetry?

Ⓐ $x = -5$ Ⓒ $x = 5$
Ⓑ $x = 0$ Ⓓ $x = y$

Review progress Question 1 of 5 Go ← Back Next →

ASSESSMENT RESOURCES

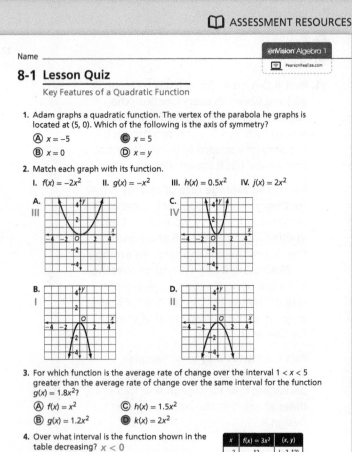

Name ______________________ enVision Algebra 1 PearsonRealize.com

8-1 Lesson Quiz

Key Features of a Quadratic Function

1. Adam graphs a quadratic function. The vertex of the parabola he graphs is located at (5, 0). Which of the following is the axis of symmetry?

Ⓐ $x = -5$ Ⓒ $x = 5$
Ⓑ $x = 0$ Ⓓ $x = y$

2. Match each graph with its function.

I. $f(x) = -2x^2$ II. $g(x) = -x^2$ III. $h(x) = 0.5x^2$ IV. $j(x) = 2x^2$

A. III
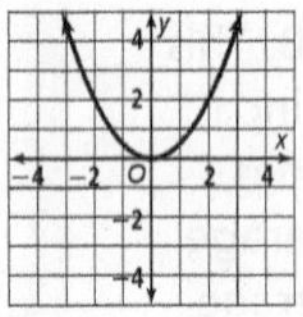

C. IV
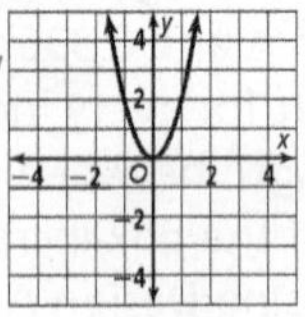

B. I
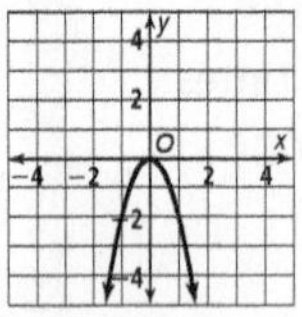

D. II
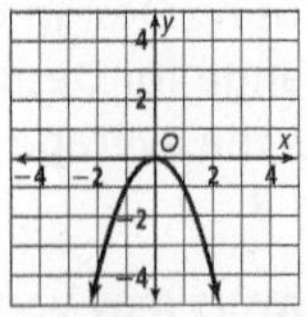

3. For which function is the average rate of change over the interval $1 < x < 5$ greater than the average rate of change over the same interval for the function $g(x) = 1.8x^2$?

Ⓐ $f(x) = x^2$ Ⓒ $h(x) = 1.5x^2$
Ⓑ $g(x) = 1.2x^2$ Ⓓ $k(x) = 2x^2$

4. Over what interval is the function shown in the table decreasing? $x < 0$

x	$f(x) = 3x^2$	(x, y)
−2	12	(−2, 12)
−1	3	(−1, 3)
0	0	(0, 0)
1	3	(1, 3)
2	12	(2, 12)

5. Cindy's square garden has a side length of x ft. She will plant 5 tulip bulbs per square foot. Write a function g to model the number of bulbs she will plant. How many bulbs will she plant if the garden has a side length of 8 feet? $g(x) = 5x^2$; 320 bulbs

enVision™ **Algebra 1** • Assessment Resources

STEP 4 | Assess & Differentiate

SavvasRealize.com

Assess | Tutorials | Worksheets

DIFFERENTIATED RESOURCES

I = Intervention O = On-Level A = Advanced

= This activity is available as a digital assignment powered by MathXL® for School.

AVAILABLE **ONLINE**

Reteach to Build Understanding I

Provides scaffolded reteaching for the key lesson concepts.

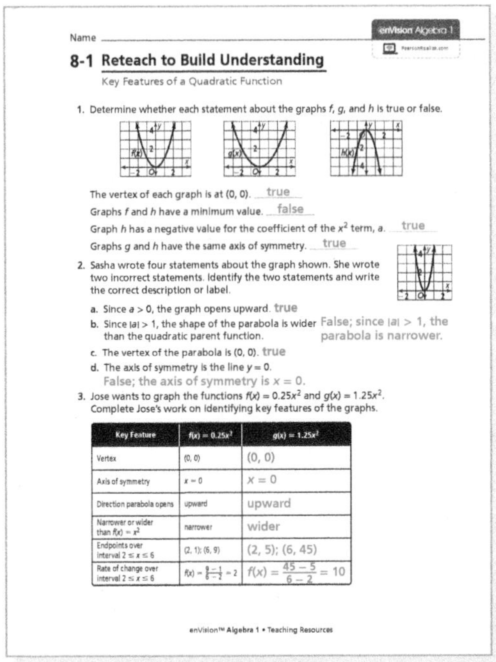

Name

8-1 Reteach to Build Understanding

Key Features of a Quadratic Function

1. Determine whether each statement about the graphs f, g, and h is true or false.

The vertex of each graph is at (0, 0). true

Graphs f and h have a minimum value. false

Graph h has a negative value for the coefficient of the x^2 term, a. true

Graphs g and h have the same axis of symmetry. true

2. Sasha wrote four statements about the graph shown. She wrote two incorrect statements. Identify the two statements and write the correct description or label.

a. Since $a > 0$, the graph opens upward. true

b. Since $|a| > 1$, the shape of the parabola is wider than the quadratic parent function. False; since $|a| > 1$, the parabola is narrower.

c. The vertex of the parabola is (0, 0). true

d. The axis of symmetry is the line $y = 0$. False; the axis of symmetry is $x = 0$.

3. Jose wants to graph the functions $f(x) = 0.25x^2$ and $g(x) = 1.25x^2$. Complete Jose's work on identifying key features of the graphs.

Key Feature	$f(x) = 0.25x^2$	$g(x) = 1.25x^2$
Vertex	(0, 0)	(0, 0)
Axis of symmetry	$x = 0$	$x = 0$
Direction parabola opens	upward	upward
Narrower or wider than $f(x) = x^2$	narrower	wider
Endpoints over interval $2 \le x \le 6$	(2, 1); (6, 9)	(2, 5); (6, 45)
Rate of change over interval $2 \le x \le 6$	$f(x) = \frac{9-1}{6-2} = 2$	$f(x) = \frac{45-5}{6-2} = 10$

enVision™ Algebra 1 • Teaching Resources

Additional Practice I O

Provides extra practice for each lesson.

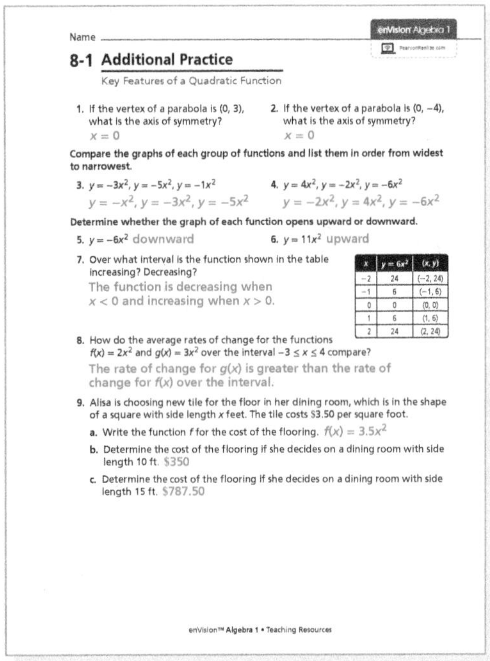

Name

8-1 Additional Practice

Key Features of a Quadratic Function

1. If the vertex of a parabola is (0, 3), what is the axis of symmetry? $x = 0$

2. If the vertex of a parabola is (0, −4), what is the axis of symmetry? $x = 0$

Compare the graphs of each group of functions and list them in order from widest to narrowest.

3. $y = -3x^2, y = -5x^2, y = -1x^2$
$y = -x^2, y = -3x^2, y = -5x^2$

4. $y = 4x^2, y = -2x^2, y = -6x^2$
$y = -2x^2, y = 4x^2, y = -6x^2$

Determine whether the graph of each function opens upward or downward.

5. $y = -6x^2$ downward

6. $y = 11x^2$ upward

7. Over what interval is the function shown in the table increasing? Decreasing?
The function is decreasing when $x < 0$ and increasing when $x > 0$.

x	$y = 6x^2$	(x, y)
−2	24	(−2, 24)
−1	6	(−1, 6)
0	0	(0, 0)
1	6	(1, 6)
2	24	(2, 24)

8. How do the average rates of change for the functions $f(x) = 2x^2$ and $g(x) = 3x^2$ over the interval $-3 \le x \le 4$ compare?
The rate of change for $g(x)$ is greater than the rate of change for $f(x)$ over the interval.

9. Alisa is choosing new tile for the floor in her dining room, which is in the shape of a square with side length x feet. The tile costs $3.50 per square foot.

a. Write the function f for the cost of the flooring. $f(x) = 3.5x^2$

b. Determine the cost of the flooring if she decides on a dining room with side length 10 ft. $350

c. Determine the cost of the flooring if she decides on a dining room with side length 15 ft. $787.50

enVision™ Algebra 1 • Teaching Resources

Enrichment O A

Presents engaging problems and activities that extend the lesson concepts.

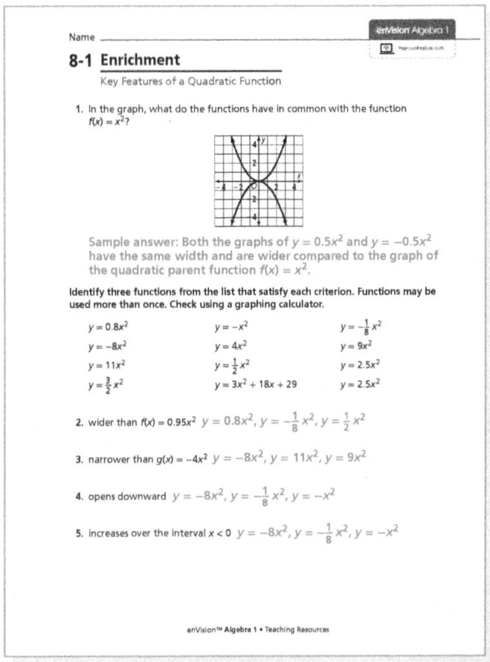

Name

8-1 Enrichment

Key Features of a Quadratic Function

1. In the graph, what do the functions have in common with the function $f(x) = x^2$?

Sample answer: Both the graphs of $y = 0.5x^2$ and $y = -0.5x^2$ have the same width and are wider compared to the graph of the quadratic parent function $f(x) = x^2$.

Identify three functions from the list that satisfy each criterion. Functions may be used more than once. Check using a graphing calculator.

$y = 0.8x^2$ | $y = -x^2$ | $y = -\frac{1}{8}x^2$
$y = -8x^2$ | $y = 4x^2$ | $y = 9x^2$
$y = 11x^2$ | $y = \frac{1}{2}x^2$ | $y = 2.5x^2$
$y = \frac{3}{2}x^2$ | $y = 3x^2 + 18x + 29$ | $y = 2.5x^2$

2. wider than $f(x) = 0.95x^2$ $y = 0.8x^2, y = -\frac{1}{8}x^2, y = \frac{1}{2}x^2$

3. narrower than $g(x) = -4x^2$ $y = -8x^2, y = 11x^2, y = 9x^2$

4. opens downward $y = -8x^2, y = -\frac{1}{8}x^2, y = -x^2$

5. increases over the interval $x < 0$ $y = -8x^2, y = -\frac{1}{8}x^2, y = -x^2$

enVision™ Algebra 1 • Teaching Resources

Mathematical Literacy and Vocabulary I O

Helps students develop and reinforce understanding of key terms and concepts.

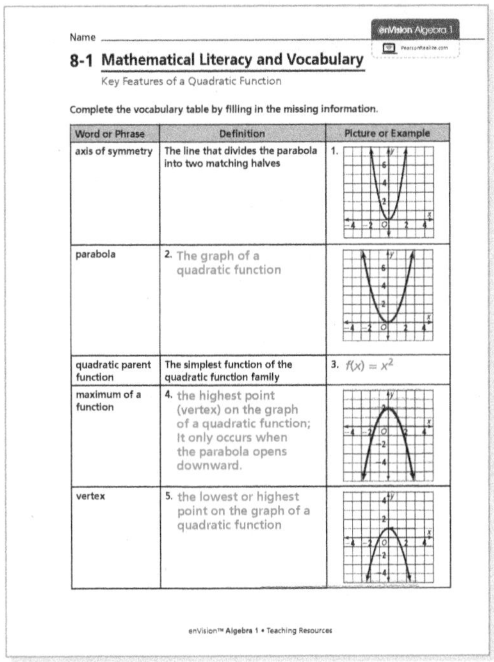

Name

8-1 Mathematical Literacy and Vocabulary

Key Features of a Quadratic Function

Complete the vocabulary table by filling in the missing information.

Word or Phrase	Definition	Picture or Example
axis of symmetry	The line that divides the parabola into two matching halves	1.
parabola	2. The graph of a quadratic function	
quadratic parent function	The simplest function of the quadratic function family	3. $f(x) = x^2$
maximum of a function	4. the highest point (vertex) on the graph of a quadratic function; It only occurs when the parabola opens downward.	
vertex	5. the lowest or highest point on the graph of a quadratic function	

enVision™ Algebra 1 • Teaching Resources

Digital Resources and Video Tutorials I O A

The **Reteach to Build Understanding**, **Additional Practice**, and **Enrichment** activities are available as digital assignments powered by MathXL for School. These activities are automatically assigned when students complete the lesson quiz online and are automatically scored.

Students can access instructional tutorials using the **Virtual Nerd app**.

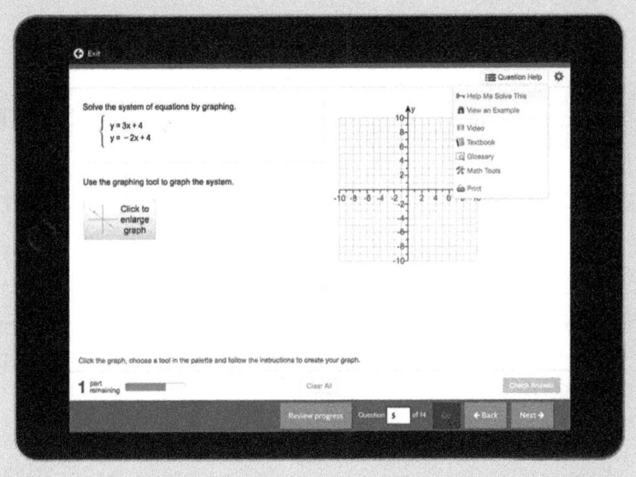
Solve the system of equations by graphing.
y = 3x + 4
y = −2x + 4
Use the graphing tool to graph the system.
Click to enlarge graph
Question Help
Help Me Solve This
View an Example
Video
Textbook
Glossary
Math Tools
Print
Review progress
Back
Next

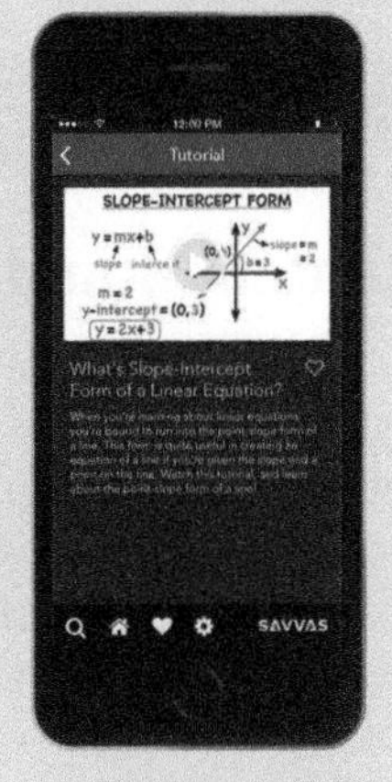
Tutorial
SLOPE-INTERCEPT FORM
What's Slope-Intercept Form of a Linear Equation?
SAVVAS

Students can also access Virtual Nerd videos using the **BouncePages app** to scan exercise pages marked with this icon. Students can download both apps for free in their mobile devices' app store.

Lesson Overview

FOCUS

Objective

Students will be able to:

✔ Identify key features of the graph of quadratic functions written in vertex form.

✔ Graph quadratic functions in vertex form.

Essential Understanding

The structure of a quadratic function in vertex form reveals the vertex and axis of a symmetry of the graph it represents.

COHERENCE

Previously in this topic, students:

- Determined how the value of *a* affects the graph of $f(x) = ax^2$.

In this lesson, students:

- Identify the effect on the graph of $f(x) = ax^2$ when replacing $f(x)$ with $f(x) + k$, $f(x + k)$, for specific values of *k*, both positive and negative.
- Identify the key features of the graph of a quadratic equation written in vertex form.

Later in this topic, students will:

- Identify key features of the graph of a quadratic function written in standard form.

RIGOR

This lesson emphasizes a blend of *conceptual understanding* and *application*.

- Students understand that they can easily identify the vertex of a graph from the vertex form of a quadratic function $f(x) = a(x - h)^2 + k$.
- Students apply their understanding of the vertex form to find the vertex in projectile motion problems.

Vocabulary Builder

REVIEW VOCABULARY — **English** | *Spanish*

- **axis of symmetry** | *eje de simetría*
- **parabola** | *parábola*
- **vertex** | *vértice*

NEW VOCABULARY

- **vertex form of a quadratic function** | *forma vértice de una función cuadrática*

VOCABULARY ACTIVITY

Introduce the new term. Discuss how the vertex form of a quadratic function connects to the terms listed in the review vocabulary. As needed, have students complete these sentences.

1. The function $f(x) = a(x - h)^2 + k$ is written in the ________. **[vertex form of a quadratic function]**
2. The graph of $f(x) = a(x - h)^2 + k$ is called a ________. **[parabola]**
3. The ________ **[axis of symmetry]** of a parabola is a line that divides a parabola into two congruent halves and intersects the parabola at its ________. **[vertex]**

Student Companion

Students can do their in-class work for the lesson on pages 171–174 of their *Student Companion* or in Savvas Realize.

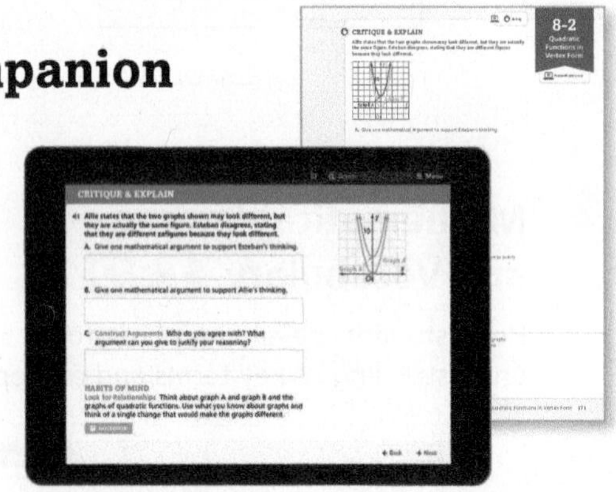

Mathematics Overview — COMMON CORE STANDARDS

Content Standards

In this lesson, students focus on these standards:

HSF.IF.C.7 Graph functions expressed symbolically and show key features of the graph, by hand in simple cases and using technology for more complicated cases.

HSF.BF.B.3 Identify the effect on the graph of replacing $f(x)$ by $f(x) + k$, $k\,f(x)$, $f(kx)$, and $f(x + k)$ for specific values of *k* (both positive and negative); find the value of *k* given the graphs. Experiment with cases and illustrate an explanation of the effects on the graph using technology.

Mathematical Practice Standards

These standards are highlighted in this lesson:

MP.4 Model With Mathematics

Students use quadratic functions to model the trajectory of projectiles.

MP.7 Look For and Make Use of Structure

Students analyze the effect of changes to the values of *h* and *k* in the vertex form of a quadratic function on the graph of the quadratic function.

CRITIQUE & EXPLAIN

INSTRUCTIONAL FOCUS Students construct mathematical arguments that convey their understanding of translations of graphs of quadratic functions.

STUDENT COMPANION Students can complete the *Critique & Explain* activity on page 171 of their *Student Companion*.

Before WHOLE CLASS

Implement Tasks that Promote Reasoning and Problem Solving ETP

Q: What does it mean to be the same figure?
[Answers may vary. Sample: to have the same shape]

During SMALL GROUP

Support Productive Struggle in Learning Mathematics ETP

Q: Is position important when determining whether two figures are the same?
[No; two figures can have the same shape, but different positions.]

Q: How can you compare the widths of the parabolas?
[From the vertex of each, count 1 unit up and then determine how far apart the points on the parabola are from the axis of symmetry.]

For Early Finishers

Q: Draw another parabola on the grid that has at least one thing in common with the graphs shown, but differs in some way. What similarities and differences do you notice between the graphs?
[Answers may vary. Sample: The axis of symmetry is different, but the width is the same.]

After WHOLE CLASS

Facilitate Meaningful Mathematical Discourse ETP

Facilitate a discussion about the students' answers from Part C.

Q: What strategies did you use to determine who is correct?
[Answers may vary. Sample: Because Graph A is a vertical translation of Graph B, the figures have the same shape; since the graphs are in different places on the coordinate plane, the points on the graphs with the same *x*-coordinates have different *y*-coordinates, but the difference in the corresponding *y*-coordinates is constant.]

Introduce students to the importance of position and shape of a quadratic function.

HABITS OF MIND *Use with* **CRITIQUE & EXPLAIN**

Look for Relationships Think about Graph A and Graph B and the graphs of quadratic functions. Use what you know about graphs and think of a single change that would make the graphs different. MP.7
[Answers may vary. Sample: Stretch one graph vertically, so it does not have the same shape.]

AVAILABLE **ONLINE**

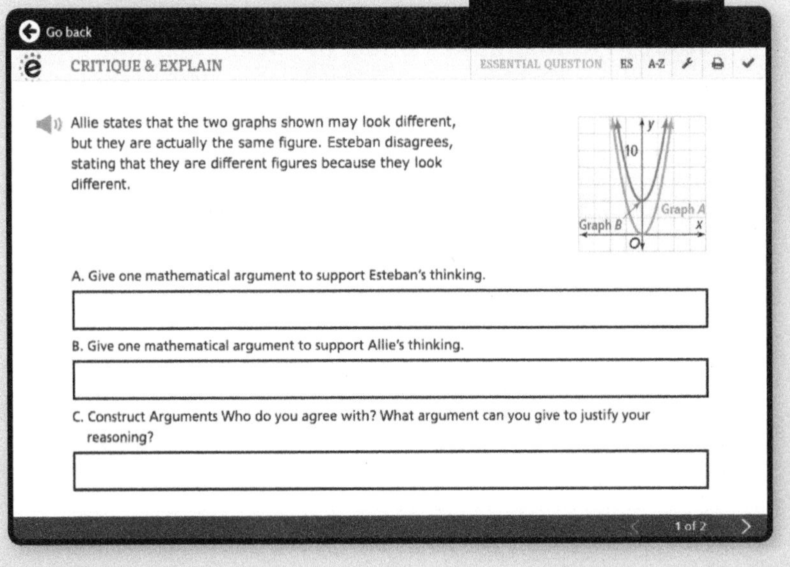
Go back
CRITIQUE & EXPLAIN
ESSENTIAL QUESTION ES A-Z

Allie states that the two graphs shown may look different, but they are actually the same figure. Esteban disagrees, stating that they are different figures because they look different.

y
10
Graph A
Graph B
x
O

A. Give one mathematical argument to support Esteban's thinking.

B. Give one mathematical argument to support Allie's thinking.

C. Construct Arguments Who do you agree with? What argument can you give to justify your reasoning?

1 of 2

STUDENT EDITION, PAGE 322

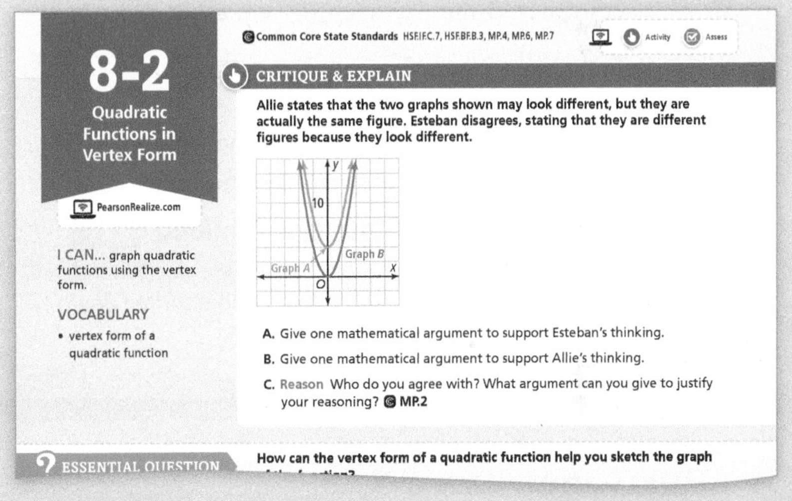
8-2
Quadratic Functions in Vertex Form

PearsonRealize.com

I CAN… graph quadratic functions using the vertex form.

VOCABULARY
• vertex form of a quadratic function

Common Core State Standards HSF.IF.C.7, HSF.BF.B.3, MP.4, MP.6, MP.7

Activity Assess

CRITIQUE & EXPLAIN

Allie states that the two graphs shown may look different, but they are actually the same figure. Esteban disagrees, stating that they are different figures because they look different.

y
10
Graph A
Graph B
x
O

A. Give one mathematical argument to support Esteban's thinking.
B. Give one mathematical argument to support Allie's thinking.
C. Reason Who do you agree with? What argument can you give to justify your reasoning? MP.2

ESSENTIAL QUESTION How can the vertex form of a quadratic function help you sketch the graph of the function?

SAMPLE STUDENT WORK

A. When $y = 2$, the width of Graph A is 0 but the width of Graph B is 2. You can see that the width of Graph A is always less than the width of Graph B, so these are different figures.

B. The points at $x = -1$, 0, and 1 in Graph A are each 2 units above the corresponding point in Graph B. So the graphs appear to have the same shape.

C. Allie; because the point at each value of x in Graph A is 2 units above the corresponding point in Graph B. If you translate Graph B down 2 units, they would be the same.

INTRODUCE THE ESSENTIAL QUESTION

Establish Mathematics Goals to Focus Learning ETP

Have students focus on the location and shape of the graphs of the quadratic functions throughout the lesson.

EXAMPLE 1 Understand the Graph of $g(x) = x^2 + k$

Use and Connect Mathematical Representations ETP

Q: If the graph of g was not given, how could you compare f and g? [Make a table of values for each function.]

Q: Make a table of values for f and g using the integers between -3 and 3 for the x values. How do the y-values of the functions compare? [For each value of x, the y-value of g is 4 less than the y-value of f.]

Common Error

Try It! 1 Students often use the incorrect sign for the value of k. Have them write the expression $x^2 - k$ as a sum, $x^2 + (-k)$.

AVAILABLE ONLINE

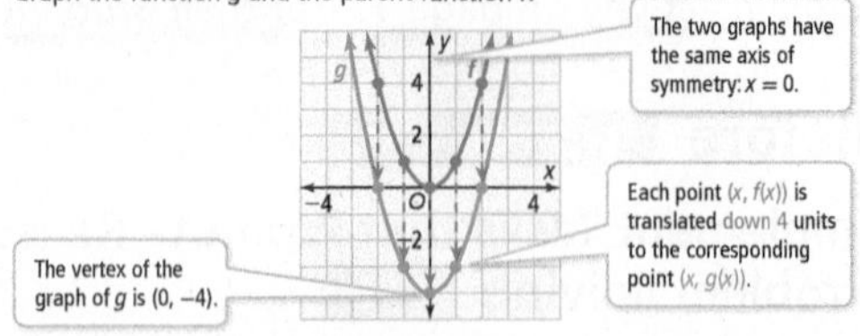

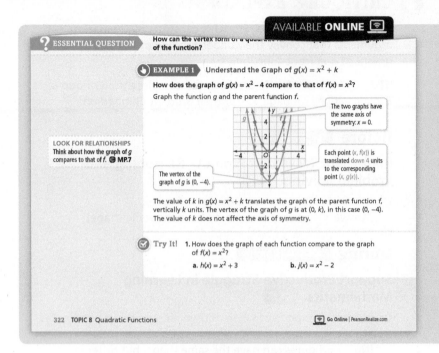

ESSENTIAL QUESTION How can the vertex form of a quadratic function help you sketch the graph of the function?

EXAMPLE 1 Understand the Graph of $g(x) = x^2 + k$

How does the graph of $g(x) = x^2 - 4$ compare to that of $f(x) = x^2$?

Graph the function g and the parent function f.

The two graphs have the same axis of symmetry: x = 0.
Each point (x, f(x)) is translated down 4 units to the corresponding point (x, g(x)).
The vertex of the graph of g is (0, −4).

LOOK FOR RELATIONSHIPS Think about how the graph of g compares to that of f. MP.7

The value of k in $g(x) = x^2 + k$ translates the graph of the parent function f, vertically k units. The vertex of the graph of g is at $(0, k)$, in this case $(0, -4)$. The value of k does not affect the axis of symmetry.

Try It! 1. How does the graph of each function compare to the graph of $f(x) = x^2$?

a. $h(x) = x^2 + 3$

b. $j(x) = x^2 - 2$

322 TOPIC 8 Quadratic Functions — Go Online | PearsonRealize.com

Try It! Answers

1. a. vertex up 3 units; axis of symmetry is the same
   b. vertex down 2 units; axis of symmetry is the same

Elicit and Use Evidence of Student Thinking ETP

Q: Summarize how k affects the graph of $f(x) = x^2 + k$. [When $k > 0$, the graph is shifted up. When $k < 0$, the graph is shifted down.]

AVAILABLE ONLINE

ADDITIONAL EXAMPLES

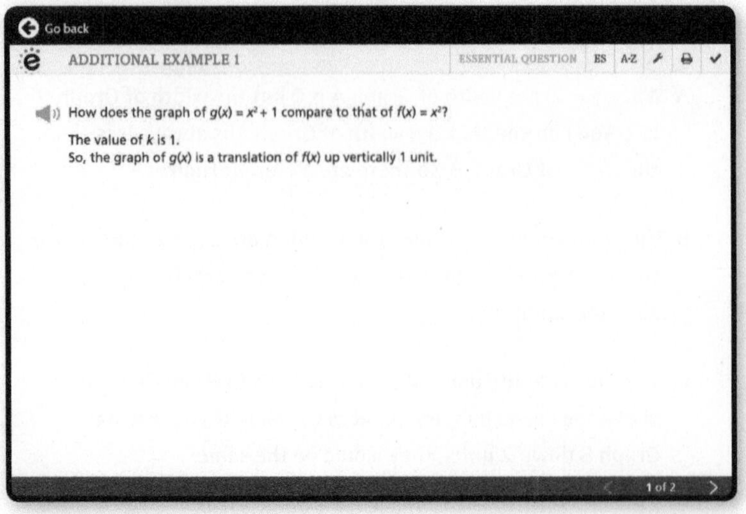

Go back
ADDITIONAL EXAMPLE 1
ESSENTIAL QUESTION ES A-Z
How does the graph of g(x) = x² + 1 compare to that of f(x) = x²?
The value of k is 1.
So, the graph of g(x) is a translation of f(x) up vertically 1 unit.
1 of 2

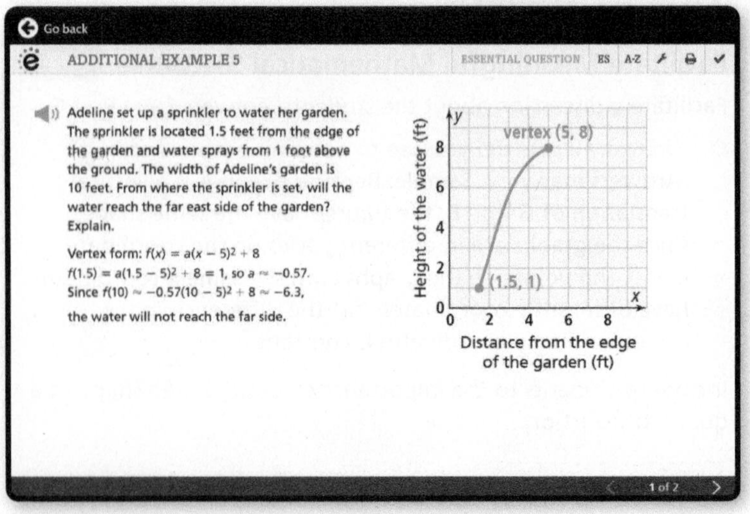

Go back
ADDITIONAL EXAMPLE 5
ESSENTIAL QUESTION ES A-Z
Adeline set up a sprinkler to water her garden. The sprinkler is located 1.5 feet from the edge of the garden and water sprays from 1 foot above the ground. The width of Adeline's garden is 10 feet. From where the sprinkler is set, will the water reach the far east side of the garden? Explain.
Vertex form: f(x) = a(x − 5)² + 8
f(1.5) = a(1.5 − 5)² + 8 = 1, so a ≈ −0.57.
Since f(10) ≈ −0.57(10 − 5)² + 8 ≈ −6.3,
the water will not reach the far side.
vertex (5, 8)
(1.5, 1)
Height of the water (ft)
Distance from the edge of the garden (ft)
1 of 2

Example 1 Help students understand the relationship between the equations and the graphs.

Q: What does the value of k tell you about how to translate the graph? [the direction and the number of units to move the vertex vertically]

Example 5 Help students use the structure of the vertex form of a quadratic function to model a new situation.

Q: What is the equation of the function in vertex form? [$f(x) = -\frac{4}{7}(x - 5)^2 + 8$]

EXAMPLE 2 Understand the Graph of $g(x) = (x - h)^2$

Use and Connect Mathematical Representations ETP

Q: What value of x would make $g(x)$ zero?
[3; because $3 - 3 = 0$ and the point (3, 0) is on the graph]

Try It! Answers

2. a. The vertex and axis of symmetry are shifted 1 unit left.
   b. The vertex and axis of symmetry are shifted 5 units right.

HABITS OF MIND

Use with **EXAMPLES 1 & 2**

Make Sense and Persevere What are the values of h and k for a quadratic function with vertex (1, 2)? **MP.1**
[$h = 1$; $k = 2$]

EXAMPLE 3 Understand the Graph of $f(x) = a(x - h)^2 + k$

Implement Tasks that Promote Reasoning and Problem Solving ETP

PART A

Q: Which function has a different axis of symmetry than $f(x) = x^2$: $g(x) = x^2 - 4$ or $h(x) = (x - 3)^2$? Explain.
[h; The graph is translated 3 units right, so the axis of symmetry is $x = 3$.]

PART B

Q: Why does the graph of a parabola look narrower when $|a| > 1$ and flatter when $0 < |a| < 1$?
[When $|a| > 1$, the graph is vertically stretched and when $0 < |a| < 1$, the graph is vertically compressed.]

Try It! Answers

3. The graph of f is translated up 7 units and right 5 units. It is narrower than the parent function and opens downward.

AVAILABLE ONLINE

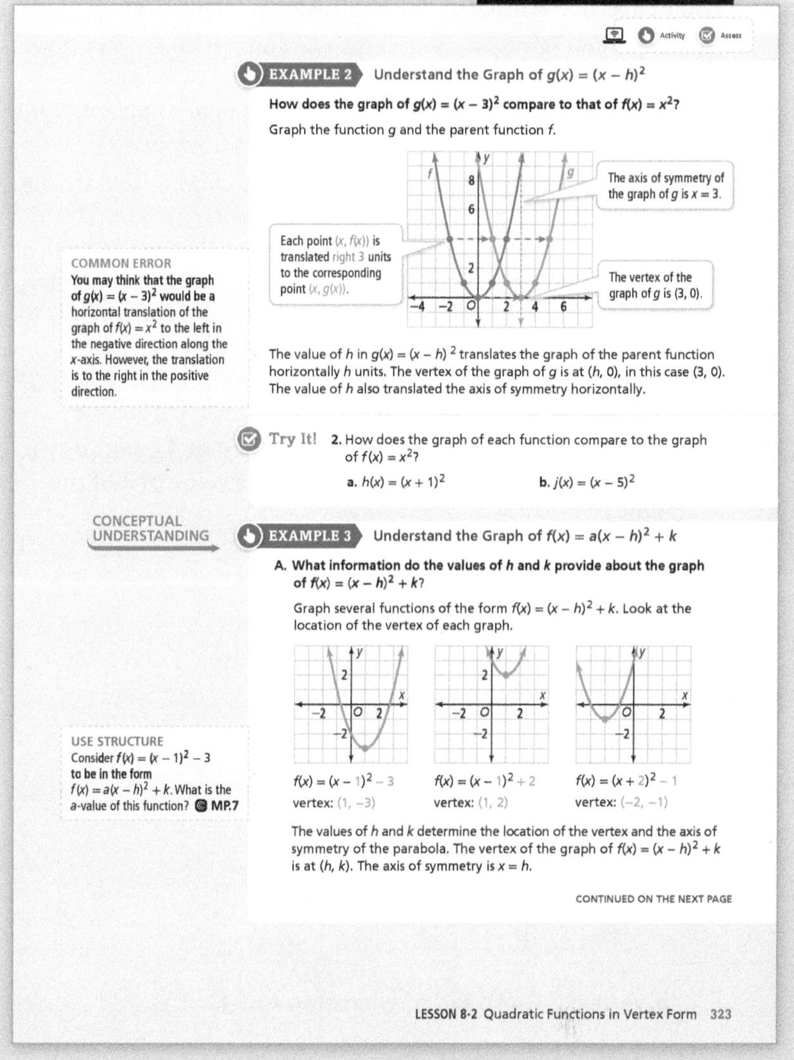

Activity Assess

EXAMPLE 2 Understand the Graph of $g(x) = (x - h)^2$

How does the graph of $g(x) = (x - 3)^2$ compare to that of $f(x) = x^2$?

Graph the function g and the parent function f.

Each point $(x, f(x))$ is translated right 3 units to the corresponding point $(x, g(x))$.
The axis of symmetry of the graph of g is $x = 3$.
The vertex of the graph of g is (3, 0).

COMMON ERROR
You may think that the graph of $g(x) = (x - 3)^2$ would be a horizontal translation of the graph of $f(x) = x^2$ to the left in the negative direction along the x-axis. However, the translation is to the right in the positive direction.

The value of h in $g(x) = (x - h)^2$ translates the graph of the parent function horizontally h units. The vertex of the graph of g is at $(h, 0)$, in this case (3, 0). The value of h also translated the axis of symmetry horizontally.

Try It! 2. How does the graph of each function compare to the graph of $f(x) = x^2$?
a. $h(x) = (x + 1)^2$ b. $j(x) = (x - 5)^2$

CONCEPTUAL UNDERSTANDING

EXAMPLE 3 Understand the Graph of $f(x) = a(x - h)^2 + k$

A. What information do the values of h and k provide about the graph of $f(x) = (x - h)^2 + k$?

Graph several functions of the form $f(x) = (x - h)^2 + k$. Look at the location of the vertex of each graph.

$f(x) = (x - 1)^2 - 3$ vertex: (1, −3)
$f(x) = (x - 1)^2 + 2$ vertex: (1, 2)
$f(x) = (x + 2)^2 - 1$ vertex: (−2, −1)

USE STRUCTURE
Consider $f(x) = (x - 1)^2 - 3$ to be in the form $f(x) = a(x - h)^2 + k$. What is the a-value of this function? **MP.7**

The values of h and k determine the location of the vertex and the axis of symmetry of the parabola. The vertex of the graph of $f(x) = (x - h)^2 + k$ is at (h, k). The axis of symmetry is $x = h$.

CONTINUED ON THE NEXT PAGE

LESSON 8-2 Quadratic Functions in Vertex Form 323

Struggling Students

USE WITH EXAMPLE 2 Help students understand the direction of the horizontal translation and the change in the axis of symmetry for functions of the form $f(x) = (x - h)^2$.

- Give students these functions.

1. $f(x) = (x - 2)^2$ **2.** $g(x) = (x + 3)^2$ **3.** $h(x) = (x - 4)^2$

Q: For $y = x^2$, the axis of symmetry is $x = 0$. What is the equation for the axis of symmetry for each of these graphs?
[**1.** $x = 2$ **2.** $x = -3$ **3.** $x = 4$]

Q: Generalize your findings about the axis of symmetry for functions of the form $f(x) = (x - h)^2$.
[The axis of symmetry is $x = h$.]

ADV Advanced Students

USE WITH EXAMPLE 3 Have students practice rewriting functions in order to easily identify the vertex.

- Give students these functions.

1. $f(x) = -2x^2 - 12x - 23$
2. $g(x) = \frac{1}{2}x^2 - 2x + 6$
3. $h(x) = 3x^2 - 6x + 1$

Q: What do you think the first step of rewriting the function so it is in vertex form would be?
[factoring out the leading coefficient from the variable terms]

Q: What are the vertices of the three functions?
[**1.** (−3, −5) **2.** (2, 4) **3.** (1, −2)]

Activity Assess

EXAMPLE 4 Graph Using Vertex Form

Facilitate Meaningful Mathematical Discourse ETP

Q: Before you plot any points, how can you tell which way the parabola opens?
[If the value of a is positive, the parabola opens upward. If the value of a is negative, the parabola opens downward.]

Q: How do you determine which x values you should evaluate the function for in order to find two other points?
[Answers may vary. Sample: It is common to choose the x values that are 1 unit and 2 units to the right of the axis of symmetry. However, if a is a fraction, choose x values more strategically to ensure your points have integer coordinates.]

Q: How is knowing the axis of symmetry helpful when sketching the graph of a quadratic function?
[Using the axis of symmetry allows you to plot 4 points other than the vertex while only calculating the value of 2 of the points.]

Try It! Answers

4. a. vertex: (2, 1); axis of symmetry: $x = 2$

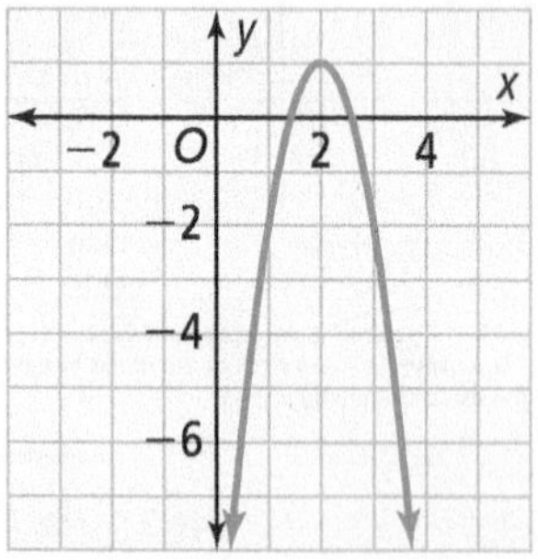

y
x
−2
O
2
4
−2
−4
−6

b. vertex: (−1, −4); axis of symmetry: $x = -1$

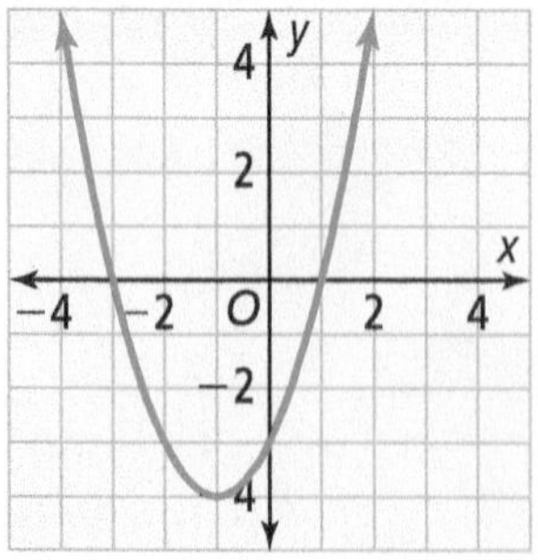

4
y
2
x
−4
−2
O
2
4
−2
4

Elicit and use Evidence of Student Thinking ETP

Q: How could you use the value of a to locate a second point on the graph of a quadratic function without evaluating the function for another x value?
[Considering that you locate the second point on the graph of parent function by moving right 1 unit and up 1 unit from the vertex, you can locate the second point on the graph of any quadratic function by moving right 1 unit from the vertex and up a units if a is positive or down $|a|$ units if a is negative.]

AVAILABLE ONLINE

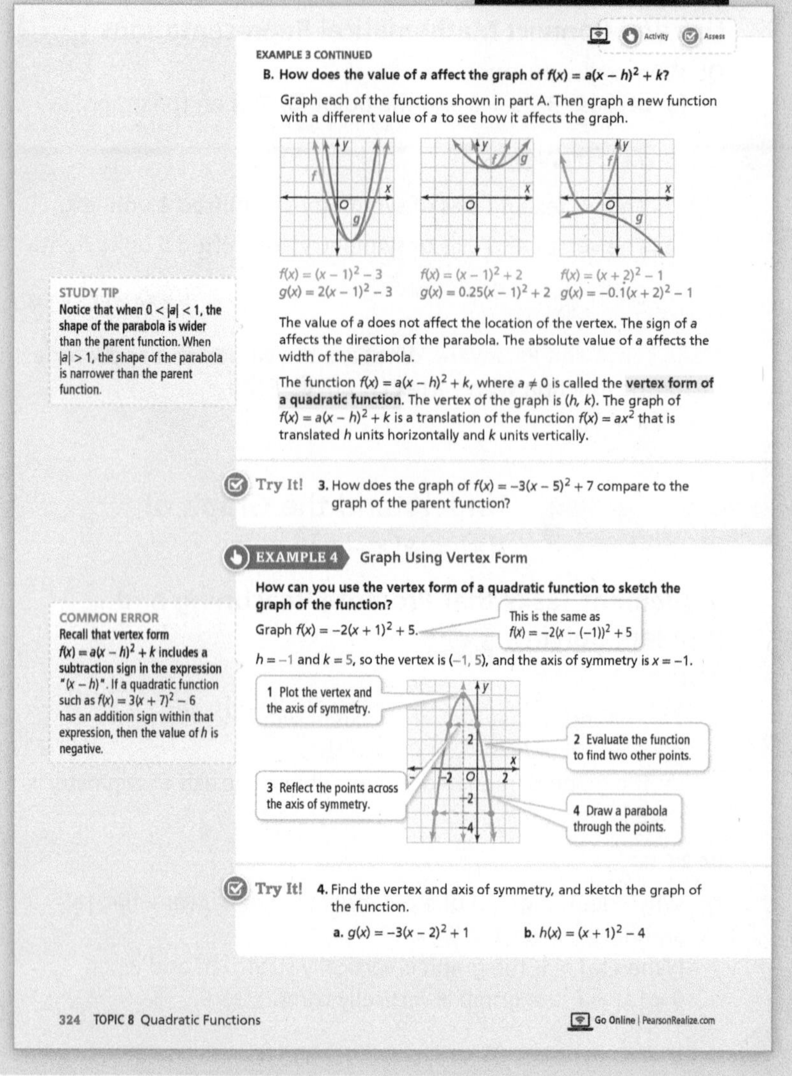

Activity Assess

EXAMPLE 3 CONTINUED

B. How does the value of a affect the graph of $f(x) = a(x - h)^2 + k$?

Graph each of the functions shown in part A. Then graph a new function with a different value of a to see how it affects the graph.

$f(x) = (x - 1)^2 - 3$ $g(x) = 2(x - 1)^2 - 3$

$f(x) = (x - 1)^2 + 2$ $g(x) = 0.25(x - 1)^2 + 2$

$f(x) = (x + 2)^2 - 1$ $g(x) = -0.1(x + 2)^2 - 1$

STUDY TIP
Notice that when $0 < |a| < 1$, the shape of the parabola is wider than the parent function. When $|a| > 1$, the shape of the parabola is narrower than the parent function.

The value of a does not affect the location of the vertex. The sign of a affects the direction of the parabola. The absolute value of a affects the width of the parabola.

The function $f(x) = a(x - h)^2 + k$, where $a \neq 0$ is called the **vertex form of a quadratic function**. The vertex of the graph is (h, k). The graph of $f(x) = a(x - h)^2 + k$ is a translation of the function $f(x) = ax^2$ that is translated h units horizontally and k units vertically.

Try It! 3. How does the graph of $f(x) = -3(x - 5)^2 + 7$ compare to the graph of the parent function?

EXAMPLE 4 Graph Using Vertex Form

How can you use the vertex form of a quadratic function to sketch the graph of the function?

Graph $f(x) = -2(x + 1)^2 + 5$.

This is the same as $f(x) = -2(x - (-1))^2 + 5$

$h = -1$ and $k = 5$, so the vertex is $(-1, 5)$, and the axis of symmetry is $x = -1$.

1 Plot the vertex and the axis of symmetry.

2 Evaluate the function to find two other points.

3 Reflect the points across the axis of symmetry.

4 Draw a parabola through the points.

COMMON ERROR
Recall that vertex form $f(x) = a(x - h)^2 + k$ includes a subtraction sign in the expression "$(x - h)$". If a quadratic function such as $f(x) = 3(x + 7)^2 - 6$ has an addition sign within that expression, then the value of h is negative.

Try It! 4. Find the vertex and axis of symmetry, and sketch the graph of the function.

a. $g(x) = -3(x - 2)^2 + 1$ b. $h(x) = (x + 1)^2 - 4$

324 TOPIC 8 Quadratic Functions Go Online | PearsonRealize.com

HABITS OF MIND

Use with **EXAMPLES 3 & 4**

Construct Arguments The vertex of a parabola is in the second quadrant, and the parabola intersects the x-axis. A student says that $f(x) = -3(x + 1)^2 - 5$ could be an equation for the parabola. Another student says that $f(x) = 3(x + 1)^2 + 5$ could be the equation. Which student is correct? Explain. MP.3

[The second student is correct. The vertex is (−1, 5), which is in the second quadrant. The first function has a vertex at (−1, −5), which is in the third quadrant.]

EXAMPLE 5 Use Vertex Form to Solve Problems

Support Productive Struggle in Learning Mathematics

Q: What information does the graphic tell you about the path of the ball?
[the point where Chris's foot makes contact with the ball; the maximum height that the ball reaches]

Q: Is it possible to solve the problem without writing a function?
[Yes; you could find the points that are reflections across the axis of symmetry for the points shown and use those to show the arc of the ball as it descends.]

Try It! Answers

5. Yes; the ball will go in the goal because at $x = 25$ the ball will be 6.95 ft above the ground and the goal is 8 ft high.

Elicit and Use Evidence of Student Thinking ETP

Q: Write a word problem that can be solved using the vertex form of a quadratic function. Exchange with a partner and solve.
[Check students' work.]

HABITS OF MIND

Use with **EXAMPLE 5**

Reasoning Can you always write a function in vertex form for a parabola given the coordinates of the vertex and the coordinates of another point on the parabola? Explain. MP.2

[Yes, the coordinates of the vertex can be substituted for *h* and *k*. The coordinates of the other point can be substituted for *x* and *y* in order to solve for *a*.]

AVAILABLE ONLINE

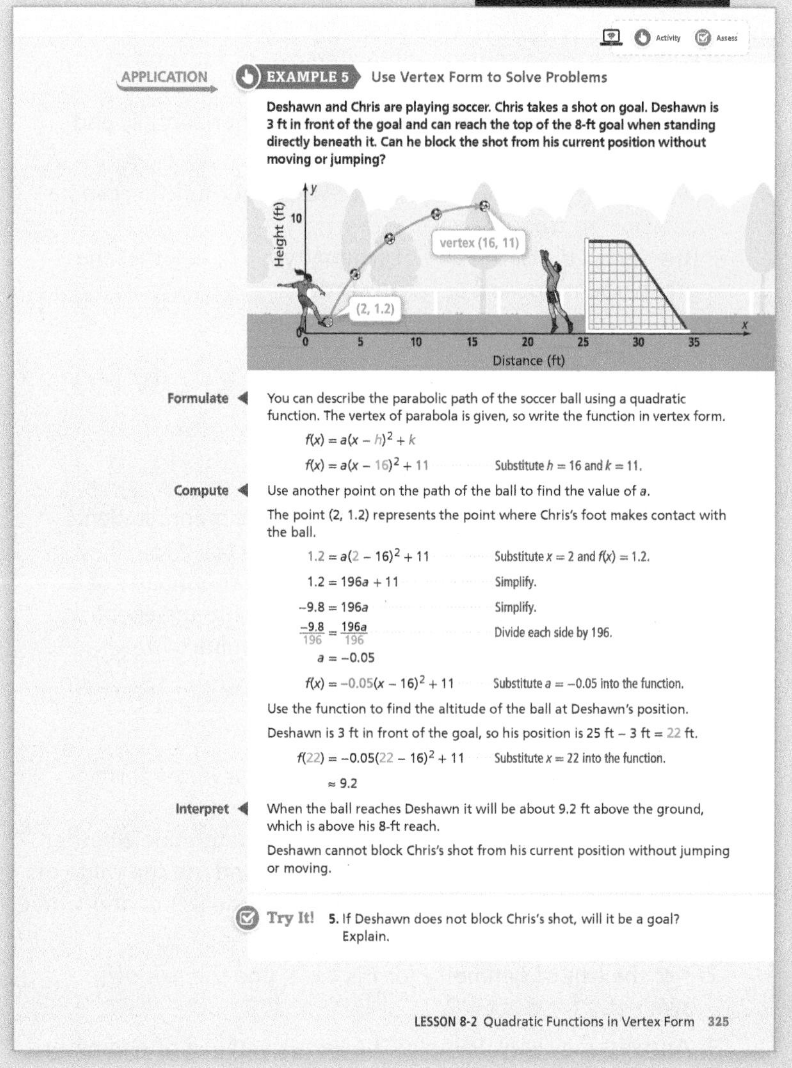

Activity Assess

APPLICATION EXAMPLE 5 Use Vertex Form to Solve Problems

Deshawn and Chris are playing soccer. Chris takes a shot on goal. Deshawn is 3 ft in front of the goal and can reach the top of the 8-ft goal when standing directly beneath it. Can he block the shot from his current position without moving or jumping?

y
10
Height (ft)
vertex (16, 11)
(2, 1.2)
0
5
10
15
20
25
30
35
x
Distance (ft)

Formulate ◀ You can describe the parabolic path of the soccer ball using a quadratic function. The vertex of parabola is given, so write the function in vertex form.

$f(x) = a(x - h)^2 + k$

$f(x) = a(x - 16)^2 + 11$ Substitute $h = 16$ and $k = 11$.

Compute ◀ Use another point on the path of the ball to find the value of *a*.

The point (2, 1.2) represents the point where Chris's foot makes contact with the ball.

$1.2 = a(2 - 16)^2 + 11$ Substitute $x = 2$ and $f(x) = 1.2$.

$1.2 = 196a + 11$ Simplify.

$-9.8 = 196a$ Simplify.

$\frac{-9.8}{196} = \frac{196a}{196}$ Divide each side by 196.

$a = -0.05$

$f(x) = -0.05(x - 16)^2 + 11$ Substitute $a = -0.05$ into the function.

Use the function to find the altitude of the ball at Deshawn's position.

Deshawn is 3 ft in front of the goal, so his position is 25 ft − 3 ft = 22 ft.

$f(22) = -0.05(22 - 16)^2 + 11$ Substitute $x = 22$ into the function.

≈ 9.2

Interpret ◀ When the ball reaches Deshawn it will be about 9.2 ft above the ground, which is above his 8-ft reach.

Deshawn cannot block Chris's shot from his current position without jumping or moving.

Try It! 5. If Deshawn does not block Chris's shot, will it be a goal? Explain.

LESSON 8-2 Quadratic Functions in Vertex Form 325

ELL English Language Learners *(Use with* **EXAMPLE 4**)

LISTENING BEGINNING Explain that as a noun, *graph* means a diagram that represents a relationship between two or more variables. As a verb, *graph* means to plot points or draw a curve to represent a function. Read the words and phrases below. Ask students to stand if graph is used as a noun and to sit if graph is used as a verb.

Q: The company's profits are shown on a graph.
[noun]

Q: Please graph the line $y = x$.
[verb]

Q: How many homework problems have graphs?
[noun]

WRITING INTERMEDIATE Consider the words *value* and *evaluate*. Spend 3–5 minutes discussing how the words are similar and how they are different. Then, ask students to answer the questions in their journals.

Q: Is *value* a noun or a verb?
[It can be either a noun or a verb.]

Q: Is *evaluate* a noun or a verb?
[verb]

Q: Explain how the two words are related.
[Evaluate is the process used to find the value of an expression.]

SPEAKING ADVANCED Place students in groups of 2–3. Give them index cards and have them write each step from the example. Have them shuffle the cards and take turns drawing cards and putting them in order.

Q: Which step comes first?
[Plot the vertex and axis of symmetry.]

Q: Which step comes second?
[Evaluate the function to find two other points.]

Q: Which step comes last?
[Draw a parabola through the points.]

CONCEPT SUMMARY

Vertex Form of a Quadratic Function

Q: In the vertex form of a quadratic function $f(x) = a(x - h)^2 + k$, what do h and k tell about how the parent function is translated?
[The parent function is translated h units horizontally and k units vertically.]

Q: What key features of the graph of a quadratic function can be determined from the vertex form?
[the vertex (h, k), the axis of symmetry $x = h$, whether the graph opens upward or downward]

Do You UNDERSTAND? | Do You KNOW HOW?

Common Error

Exercise 8 After locating the vertex on the graph, students may incorrectly write the function as $f(x) = (x + 1)^2 - 3$. Point out that they need to substitute the coordinates of a point on the graph other than the vertex into the equation $f(x) = a(x + 1)^2 - 3$ and solve to find the value of a.

AVAILABLE ONLINE

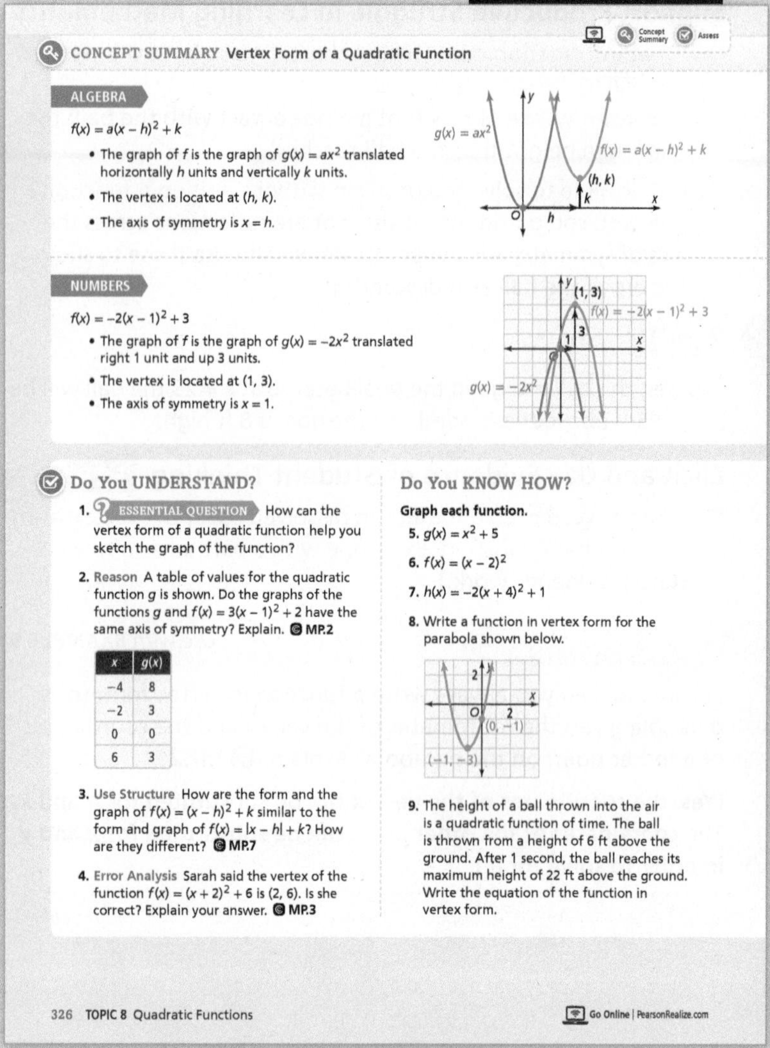
CONCEPT SUMMARY Vertex Form of a Quadratic Function

ALGEBRA

$f(x) = a(x - h)^2 + k$

- The graph of f is the graph of $g(x) = ax^2$ translated horizontally h units and vertically k units.
- The vertex is located at (h, k).
- The axis of symmetry is $x = h$.

$g(x) = ax^2$
$f(x) = a(x - h)^2 + k$
(h, k)

NUMBERS

$f(x) = -2(x - 1)^2 + 3$

- The graph of f is the graph of $g(x) = -2x^2$ translated right 1 unit and up 3 units.
- The vertex is located at (1, 3).
- The axis of symmetry is $x = 1$.

(1, 3)
$f(x) = -2(x - 1)^2 + 3$
$g(x) = -2x^2$

Do You UNDERSTAND?

1. ESSENTIAL QUESTION How can the vertex form of a quadratic function help you sketch the graph of the function?
2. Reason A table of values for the quadratic function g is shown. Do the graphs of the functions g and $f(x) = 3(x - 1)^2 + 2$ have the same axis of symmetry? Explain. MP.2

x	$g(x)$
−4	8
−2	3
0	0
6	3

3. Use Structure How are the form and the graph of $f(x) = (x - h)^2 + k$ similar to the form and graph of $f(x) = |x - h| + k$? How are they different? MP.7
4. Error Analysis Sarah said the vertex of the function $f(x) = (x + 2)^2 + 6$ is (2, 6). Is she correct? Explain your answer. MP.3

Do You KNOW HOW?

Graph each function.

5. $g(x) = x^2 + 5$
6. $f(x) = (x - 2)^2$
7. $h(x) = -2(x + 4)^2 + 1$
8. Write a function in vertex form for the parabola shown below.

(0, −1)
(−1, −3)

9. The height of a ball thrown into the air is a quadratic function of time. The ball is thrown from a height of 6 ft above the ground. After 1 second, the ball reaches its maximum height of 22 ft above the ground. Write the equation of the function in vertex form.

326 TOPIC 8 Quadratic Functions   Go Online | PearsonRealize.com

Answers

1. You can use the values of h and k from the vertex form to determine the locations of the vertex and the axis of symmetry. You can use the value of a to determine whether the graph opens upward or downward, and use the value of a to locate points on the graph 1 unit to the left of and 1 unit to right of the vertex.
2. No; the axis of symmetry for f is $x = 1$, and the axis of symmetry for g is $x = 2$.
3. Answers may vary. Sample: The vertex and line of symmetry are the same for both functions. The quadratic function is curved while the absolute value function is not.
4. No; the vertex of a function in vertex form is (h, k), so the vertex is (−2, 6).
5.

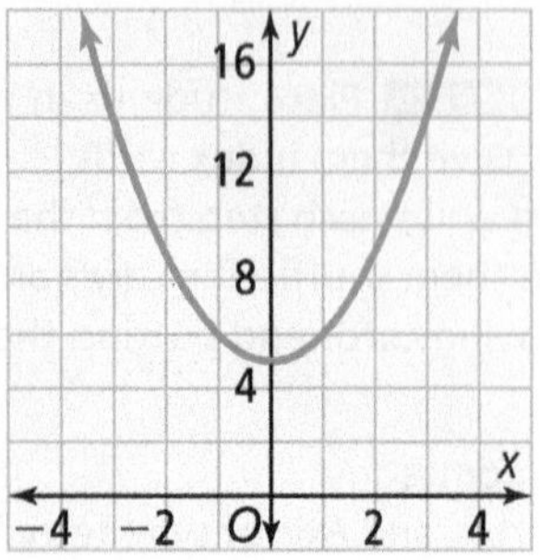

6.

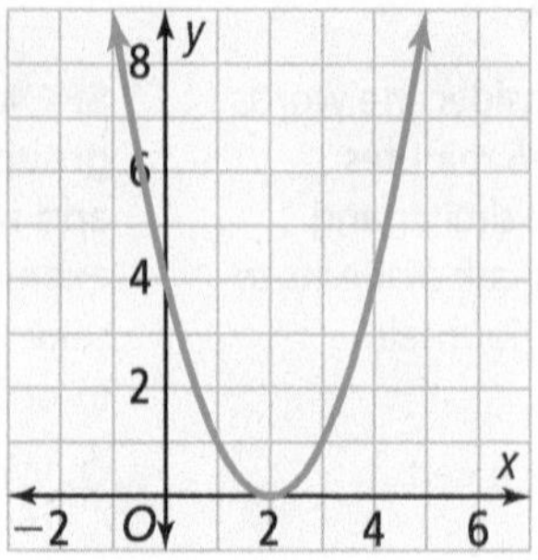

7.

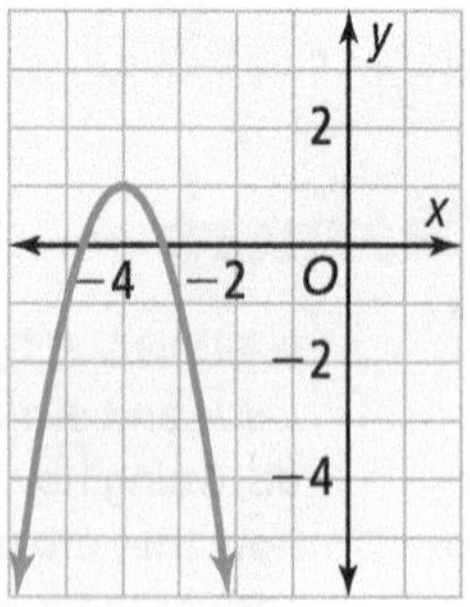

8. $f(x) = 2(x + 1)^2 - 3$
9. $f(x) = -16(x - 1)^2 + 22$

PRACTICE & PROBLEM SOLVING

AVAILABLE **ONLINE**

Lesson Practice You may opt to have students complete the automatically scored Practice and Problem Solving items online powered by MathXL for School.

Choose from: **Lesson Practice**

Adaptive Practice

You may also take advantage of the bank of exercises for assigning additional practice.

Assignment Guide

Basic	Advanced
10–24, 27–31, 35–44	10–14, 19–26, 28–44

Item Analysis

Example	Items	DOK
1	15–21	1
2	22–26	1
3	13, 27, 28, 43	1
	29–32, 37, 38	2
	10, 11, 14	3
4	33–36, 42	2
	12	3
5	39	2
	40, 41, 44	3

Answers

10. The coordinates of the vertex are (h, k). From the graph, $h = 3$ and $k = -2$; $f(x) = (x - 3)^2 - 2$
11. No; because $|a| > 1$, the graph of this parabola is narrower than the graph of the parent function $f(x) = x^2$.
12. The vertex should be plotted at (1, 6), not (–1, 6).
13. $f(x) = 2(x - 1)^2 - 3$
14. a. The graph of h is a translation 3 units left and 3 units up of the graph of $f(x) = x^2$.
    b. $h(x) = (x + 3)^2 + 3$

AVAILABLE **ONLINE**

PRACTICE & PROBLEM SOLVING

Scan for Multimedia

Practice Tutorial

Additional Exercises Available Online

UNDERSTAND

10. Make Sense and Persevere How can you determine the values of h and k from the graph shown? Write the function for the parabola. MP.1

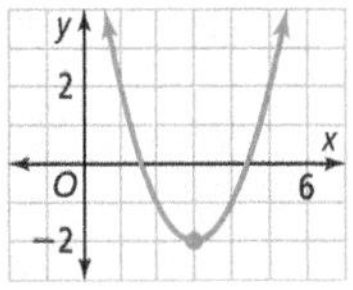

11. Reason To graph the function $f(x) = (x - 5)^2 - 8$, a student translates the graph of the quadratic parent function 5 units right and 8 units down. Can a student produce the graph of $f(x) = 2(x + 3)^2 - 5$ by simply translating the quadratic parent function? Explain. MP.2

12. Error Analysis A student used the steps shown to graph $f(x) = (x - 1)^2 + 6$. Describe and correct the student's error. MP.3

1. Plot the vertex at (-1, 6).
2. Graph points at (-2, 15) and (-3, 22).
3. Reflect the points across the axis of symmetry $x = -1$.
4. Connect the points with a parabola.

13. Mathematical Connections The graph shown is a translation of the graph of $f(x) = 2x^2$. Write the function for the graph in vertex form.

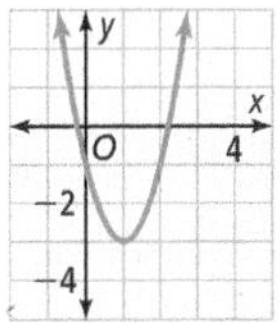

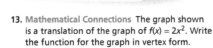

14. Higher Order Thinking The graph of h is the graph of $g(x) = (x - 2)^2 + 6$ translated 5 units left and 3 units down.
    a. Describe the graph of h as a translation of the graph of $f(x) = x^2$.
    b. Write the function h in vertex form.

PRACTICE

Identify the vertex and the axis of symmetry for each function. SEE EXAMPLES 1 AND 2

15. $f(x) = x^2 + 2$ (0, 2); $x = 0$
16. $f(x) = x^2 - 5$ (0, –5); $x = 0$
17. $g(x) = x^2 - 1$ (0, –1); $x = 0$
18. $h(x) = x^2 + 0.5$ (0, 0.5); $x = 0$
19. $f(x) = x^2 - 2.25$ (0, –2.25); $x = 0$
20. $f(x) = x^2 + 50$ (0, 50); $x = 0$
21. $h(x) = x^2 + 7$ (0, 7); $x = 0$
22. $g(x) = (x - 1)^2$ (1, 0); $x = 1$
23. $g(x) = (x + 2)^2$ (–2, 0); $x = -2$
24. $f(x) = (x - 6)^2$ (6, 0); $x = 6$
25. $f(x) = (x - 0.5)^2$ (0.5, 0); $x = 0.5$
26. $g(x) = (x - 4)^2$ (4, 0); $x = 4$

Each graph shown is a translation of the graph of $f(x) = x^2$. Write each function in vertex form. SEE EXAMPLE 3

27. 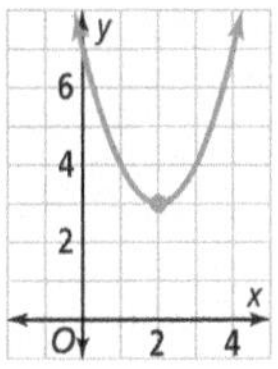

$f(x) = (x - 2)^2 + 3$

28. 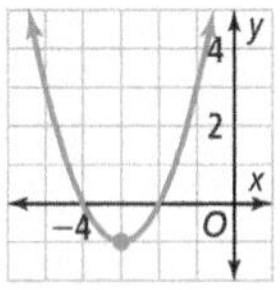

$f(x) = (x + 3)^2 - 1$

Identify the vertex, axis of symmetry, and direction of the graph of each function. Compare the width of the graph to the width of the graph of $f(x) = x^2$. SEE EXAMPLE 3

29. $f(x) = 2(x + 1)^2 + 4$
30. $g(x) = (x - 3)^2 - 3$
31. $g(x) = -0.75(x - 5)^2 + 6$
32. $h(x) = -3(x + 2)^2 - 5$

Sketch the graph of each function. SEE EXAMPLE 4

33. $f(x) = 2(x - 1)^2 + 4$
34. $g(x) = -2(x - 0.5)^2 + 1$
35. $f(x) = 0.5(x + 2)^2 + 2$
36. $h(x) = -2(x - 2)^2 - 2$

Each graph represents a quadratic function. Write each function in vertex form. SEE EXAMPLE 5

37. 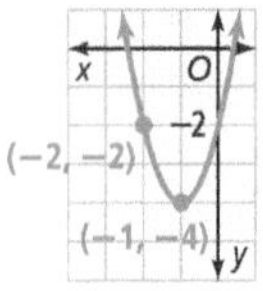
(−2, −2)
(−1, −4)

38. 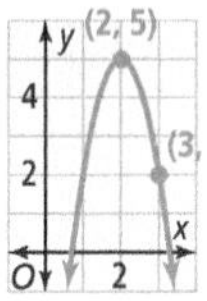
(2, 5)
(3, 2)

29. (–1, 4); $x = -1$; opens upward; narrower than the width of the graph of $f(x) = x^2$
30. (3, –3); $x = 3$; opens upward; same width as the width of the graph of $f(x) = x^2$
31. (5, 6); $x = 5$; opens downward; wider than the width of the graph of $f(x) = x^2$
32. (–2, –5); $x = -2$; opens downward; narrower than the width of the graph of $f(x) = x^2$

See next page for Exercises 33–38.

Answers

33.

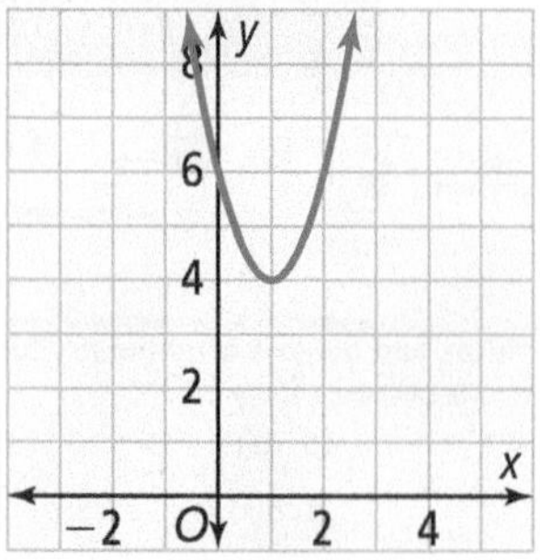

34.

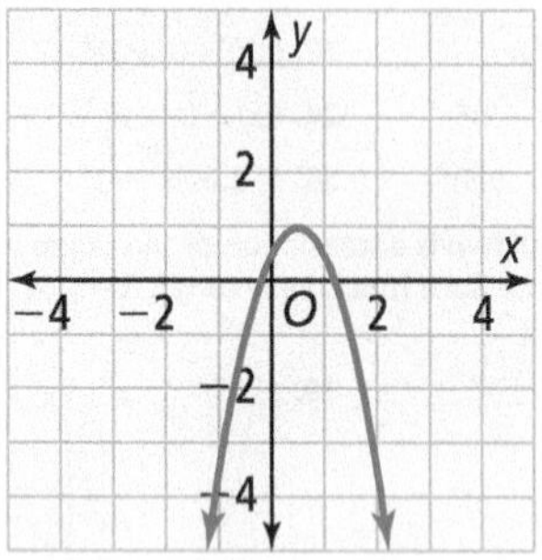

35.

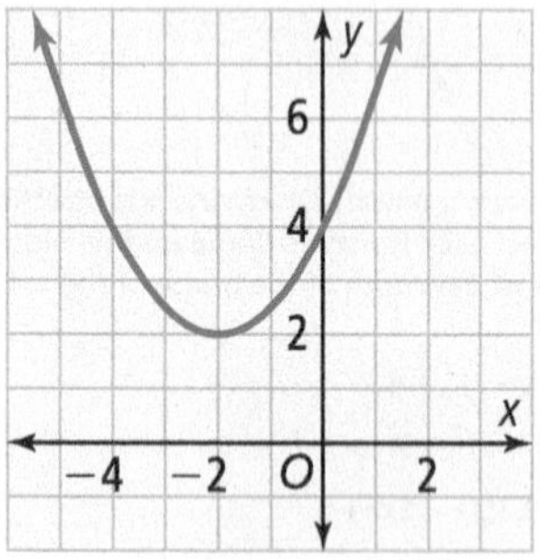

36.

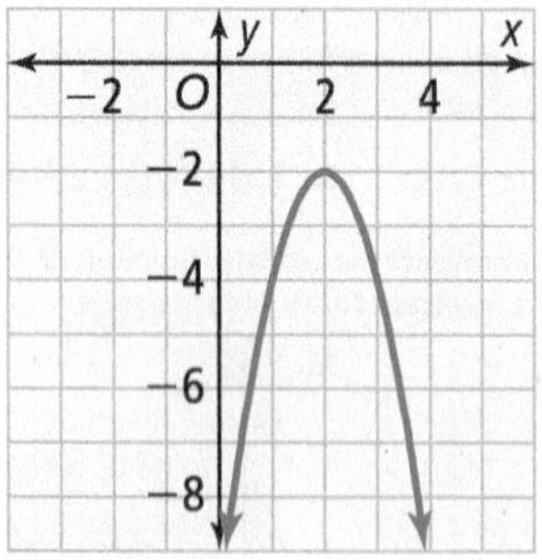

37. $f(x) = 2(x + 1)^2 - 4$

38. $f(x) = -3(x - 2)^2 + 5$

39. (–1, 42)

40. a. $b(x) = a(x - 28.5)^2 + k$;
The x-coordinate of the vertex can be determined, but the y-coordinate of the vertex and the value of a cannot be determined because only the x-intercepts are given.

b. Answers may vary. Sample: $k = 10$, so $a \approx -0.01231$; The value of k represents the maximum height of the ball, the x-intercepts represent when the ball is on the ground, and the value of a shows that the arc of the ball opens downward.

AVAILABLE **ONLINE**

PRACTICE & PROBLEM SOLVING

Practice Tutorial

Mixed Review Available Online

APPLY

39. Make Sense and Persevere A computer game designer uses the function $f(x) = 4(x - 2)^2 + 6$ to model the path of the fish. The horizontal path of the squid intersects the path of the fish. At what other point does the squid's path intersect the path of the fish? **MP.1**

y
(5, 42)
x
O

40. Model With Mathematics Suppose a goalie kicks a soccer ball. The ball travels in a parabolic path from point (0, 0) to (57, 0). **MP.4**

a. Consider a quadratic function in vertex form for the path of the ball. Which values can you determine? What values are you unable to determine? Explain.

b. Technology Use a graphing calculator to explore the undetermined values. Find a set of values that generates a realistic graph. Explain how the key features of the graph correspond to the situation.

41. Construct Arguments The function $f(x) = -(x - 1)^2 + 8$ models the path of a volleyball. The height of the net is 7 ft 4 in.

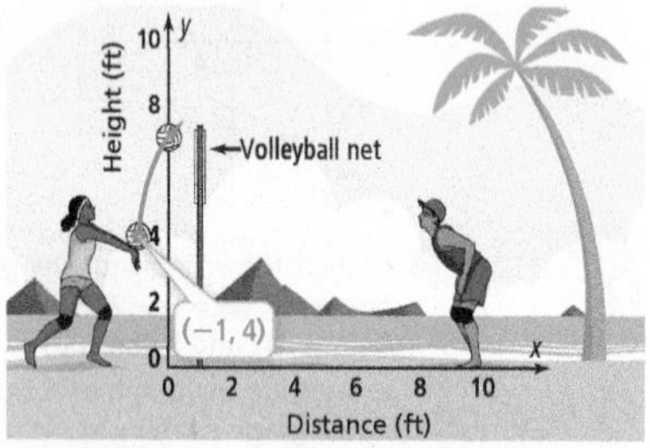

10 y
8
Height (ft)
Volleyball net
4
2
0
(−1, 4)
0 2 4 6 8 10
x
Distance (ft)

Will the ball go over if the player is 2 ft from the net? 4 ft, from the net? Explain. **MP.3**

ASSESSMENT PRACTICE

42. The function $f(x) = 2(x - 3)^2 + 9$ is graphed in the coordinate plane. Which of the following are true? Select all that apply.

Ⓐ The graph is a parabola that opens downward.
Ⓑ The vertex of the graph is (–3, 9).
Ⓒ The axis of symmetry of the graph is $x = 3$.
Ⓓ The y-intercept of the graph is 9.
Ⓔ The minimum of the function is 9.

43. SAT/ACT The graph of $g(x) = x^2$ is translated right 2 units and down 10 units. Which of the following is the function of the new graph?

Ⓐ $f(x) = (x + 2)^2 - 10$
Ⓑ $f(x) = (x - 2)^2 - 10$
Ⓒ $f(x) = 2x^2 - 10$
Ⓓ $f(x) = -2x^2 - 10$
Ⓔ $f(x) = -2(x - 10)^2$

44. Performance Task An engineer is designing a suspension bridge with a center cable. The cable is shaped like a parabola and is attached to stability towers on both ends at the same height. For simplicity she assumes a quadratic function, and uses $f(x) = 0.0006(x - 300)^2 + 6$ to model the cable between the towers.

60 m
y
?
x

Part A How high above the road surface is the lowest point of the cable?

Part B How far apart are the two towers? Explain.

41. If the player is 2 ft away from the net, the net is located at $x = 1$, and the height of the ball is $f(1) = 8$, or 8 ft so the ball will go over the net. If the player hits the ball from 4 ft away, then they are 2 ft further away, and so the parabola is translated 2 ft to the left. The function $g(x) = -(x + 1)^2 + 8$ models the path of the volleyball. The net is still at $x = 1$, and $g(1) = 4$, so the ball will not go over the net.

44. Part A 6 m

Part B 600 m; The height of the cable is 60 m at both of the towers, and $x = 0$ and $x = 600$ when $f(x) = 60$, so the towers are 600 m apart.

SavvasRealize.com

Assess | Tutorials | Worksheets

LESSON QUIZ

Use the Lesson Quiz to assess students' understanding of the mathematics in the lesson.

Students can take the Lesson Quiz online or you can download a printable copy from **SavvasRealize.com**. The Lesson Quiz is also available in the *Assessment Resources* book.

Item Analysis

Item	DOK	Standards
1	1	HSF.BF.B.3
2	1	HSF.BF.B.3
3	2	HSF.BF.B.3
4	1	HSF.IF.C.7
5	2	HSF.IF.C.7

RtI Use the student scores on the Lesson Quiz to prescribe differentiated assignments.

If students take the Lesson Quiz online, it will be automatically scored and appropriate differentiated practice will be assigned based on student performance.

I Intervention	0–3 points	• Reteach to Build Understanding • Mathematical Literacy and Vocabulary • Additional Practice
O On-Level	4 points	• Mathematical Literacy and Vocabulary • Additional Practice • Enrichment
A Advanced	5 points	• Enrichment

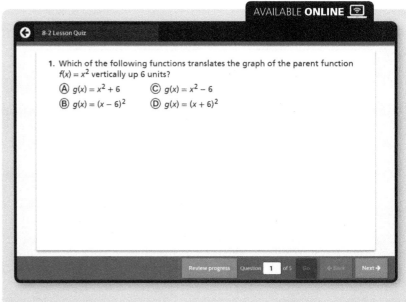

AVAILABLE **ONLINE**

8-2 Lesson Quiz

1. Which of the following functions translates the graph of the parent function $f(x) = x^2$ vertically up 6 units?

Ⓐ $g(x) = x^2 + 6$ Ⓒ $g(x) = x^2 - 6$

Ⓑ $g(x) = (x - 6)^2$ Ⓓ $g(x) = (x + 6)^2$

Review progress Question 1 of 5 Go Back Next

ASSESSMENT RESOURCES

Name ______

enVision Algebra 1

PearsonRealize.com

8-2 Lesson Quiz

Quadratic Functions in Vertex Form

1. Which of the following functions translates the graph of the parent function $f(x) = x^2$ vertically up 6 units?

Ⓐ $g(x) = x^2 + 6$ Ⓒ $g(x) = x^2 - 6$

Ⓑ $g(x) = (x - 6)^2$ Ⓓ $g(x) = (x + 6)^2$

2. Which of the following functions translates the graph of the parent function $f(x) = x^2$ horizontally left 8 units?

Ⓐ $h(x) = x^2 + 8$ Ⓒ $h(x) = x^2 - 8$

Ⓑ $h(x) = (x - 8)^2$ Ⓓ $h(x) = (x + 8)^2$

3. Which of the following functions has a graph with the vertex and the axis of symmetry to the left of the vertex and the axis of symmetry of the graph of $f(x) = (x - 1)^2 + 1$? Select all that apply.

Ⓐ $g(x) = 2(x - 1)^2 - 1$

Ⓑ $g(x) = -(x + 1)^2 - 2$

Ⓒ $g(x) = 2(x - 1)^2 + 2$

Ⓓ $g(x) = -(x - 2)^2 + 1$

Ⓔ $g(x) = -(x + 2)^2 + 2$

Ⓕ $g(x) = 2(x + 1)^2 + 2$

4. Graph the function $f(x) = -(x + 1)^2 + 2$. Identify the vertex and the axis of symmetry.

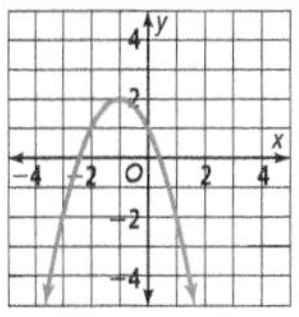

y
4
2
x
−4
−2
O
2
4
−2
−4

$x = -1$; $(-1, 2)$

5. The graph of function g is a parabola with the vertex located at (5, 9). The parabola also passes through the point (3, 1). Write an equation in vertex form for the function. $g(x) = -2(x - 5)^2 + 9$

enVision™ **Algebra 1** • Assessment Resources

DIFFERENTIATED RESOURCES

I = Intervention **O** = On-Level **A** = Advanced

= This activity is available as a digital assignment powered by MathXL® for School.

AVAILABLE **ONLINE**

Reteach to Build Understanding I

Provides scaffolded reteaching for the key lesson concepts.

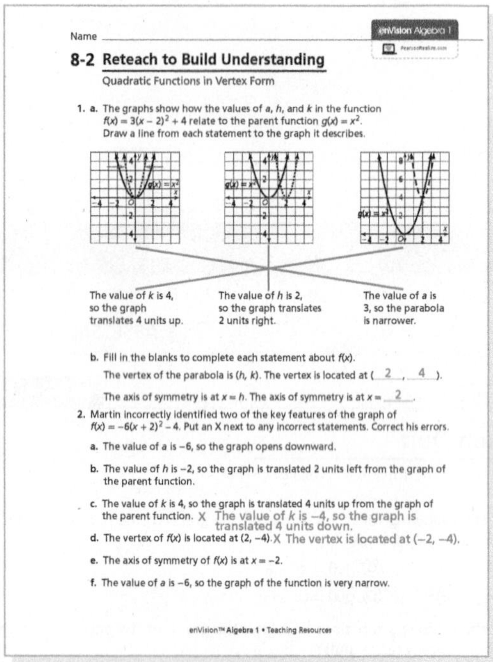

Name

8-2 Reteach to Build Understanding

Quadratic Functions in Vertex Form

1. a. The graphs show how the values of a, h, and k in the function $f(x) = 3(x - 2)^2 + 4$ relate to the parent function $g(x) = x^2$. Draw a line from each statement to the graph it describes.

The value of k is 4, so the graph translates 4 units up. The value of h is 2, so the graph translates 2 units right. The value of a is 3, so the parabola is narrower.

b. Fill in the blanks to complete each statement about $f(x)$.

The vertex of the parabola is (h, k). The vertex is located at (2 , 4).

The axis of symmetry is at $x = h$. The axis of symmetry is at $x =$ 2 .

2. Martin incorrectly identified two of the key features of the graph of $f(x) = -6(x + 2)^2 - 4$. Put an X next to any incorrect statements. Correct his errors.

a. The value of a is -6, so the graph opens downward.

b. The value of h is -2, so the graph is translated 2 units left from the graph of the parent function.

c. The value of k is 4, so the graph is translated 4 units up from the graph of the parent function. X The value of k is -4, so the graph is translated 4 units down.

d. The vertex of $f(x)$ is located at $(2, -4)$. X The vertex is located at $(-2, -4)$.

e. The axis of symmetry of $f(x)$ is at $x = -2$.

f. The value of a is -6, so the graph of the function is very narrow.

enVision™ Algebra 1 • Teaching Resources

Additional Practice I O

Provides extra practice for each lesson.

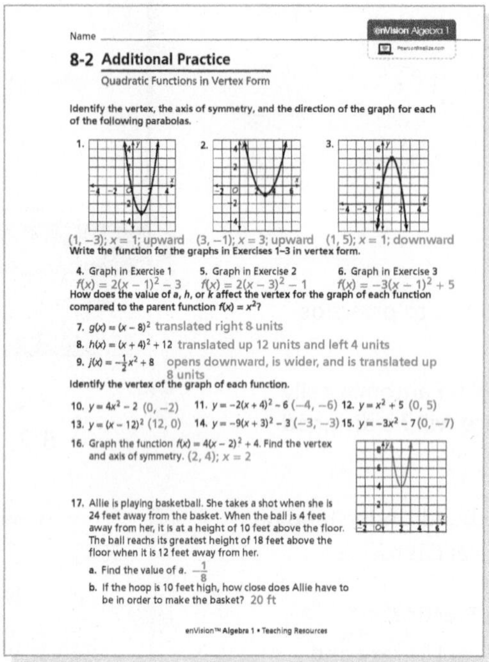

Name

8-2 Additional Practice

Quadratic Functions in Vertex Form

Identify the vertex, the axis of symmetry, and the direction of the graph for each of the following parabolas.

1. $(1, -3)$; $x = 1$; upward 2. $(3, -1)$; $x = 3$; upward 3. $(1, 5)$; $x = 1$; downward

Write the function for the graphs in Exercises 1–3 in vertex form.

4. Graph in Exercise 1 $f(x) = 2(x - 1)^2 - 3$ 5. Graph in Exercise 2 $f(x) = 2(x - 3)^2 - 1$ 6. Graph in Exercise 3 $f(x) = -3(x - 1)^2 + 5$

How does the value of a, h, or k affect the vertex for the graph of each function compared to the parent function $f(x) = x^2$?

7. $g(x) = (x - 8)^2$ translated right 8 units

8. $h(x) = (x + 4)^2 + 12$ translated up 12 units and left 4 units

9. $j(x) = -\frac{1}{2}x^2 + 8$ opens downward, is wider, and is translated up 8 units

Identify the vertex of the graph of each function.

10. $y = 4x^2 - 2$ $(0, -2)$ 11. $y = -2(x + 4)^2 - 6$ $(-4, -6)$ 12. $y = x^2 + 5$ $(0, 5)$

13. $y = (x - 12)^2$ $(12, 0)$ 14. $y = -9(x + 3)^2 - 3$ $(-3, -3)$ 15. $y = -3x^2 - 7$ $(0, -7)$

16. Graph the function $f(x) = 4(x - 2)^2 + 4$. Find the vertex and axis of symmetry. $(2, 4)$; $x = 2$

17. Allie is playing basketball. She takes a shot when she is 24 feet away from the basket. When the ball is 4 feet away from her, it is at a height of 10 feet above the floor. The ball reachs its greatest height of 18 feet above the floor when it is 12 feet away from her.

a. Find the value of a. $-\frac{1}{8}$

b. If the hoop is 10 feet high, how close does Allie have to be in order to make the basket? 20 ft

enVision™ Algebra 1 • Teaching Resources

Enrichment O A

Presents engaging problems and activities that extend the lesson concepts.

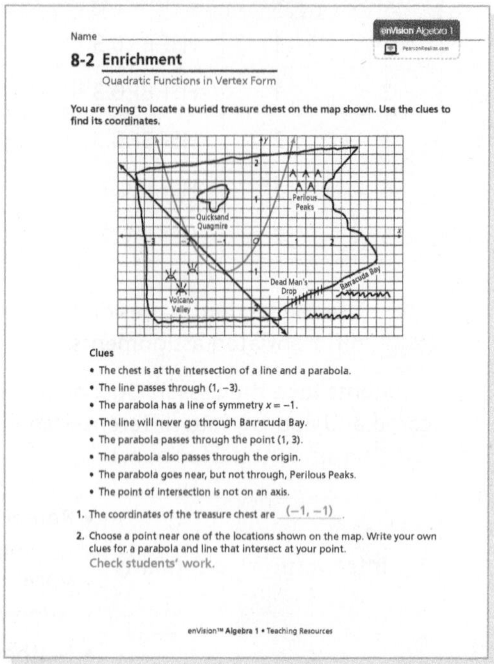

Name

8-2 Enrichment

Quadratic Functions in Vertex Form

You are trying to locate a buried treasure chest on the map shown. Use the clues to find its coordinates.

Quicksand Quagmire
Perilous Peaks
Dead Man's Drop
Barracuda Bay
Volcano Valley

Clues

- The chest is at the intersection of a line and a parabola.
- The line passes through $(1, -3)$.
- The parabola has a line of symmetry $x = -1$.
- The line will never go through Barracuda Bay.
- The parabola passes through the point $(1, 3)$.
- The parabola also passes through the origin.
- The parabola goes near, but not through, Perilous Peaks.
- The point of intersection is not on an axis.

1. The coordinates of the treasure chest are $(-1, -1)$

2. Choose a point near one of the locations shown on the map. Write your own clues for a parabola and line that intersect at your point. Check students' work.

enVision™ Algebra 1 • Teaching Resources

Mathematical Literacy and Vocabulary I O

Helps students develop and reinforce understanding of key terms and concepts.

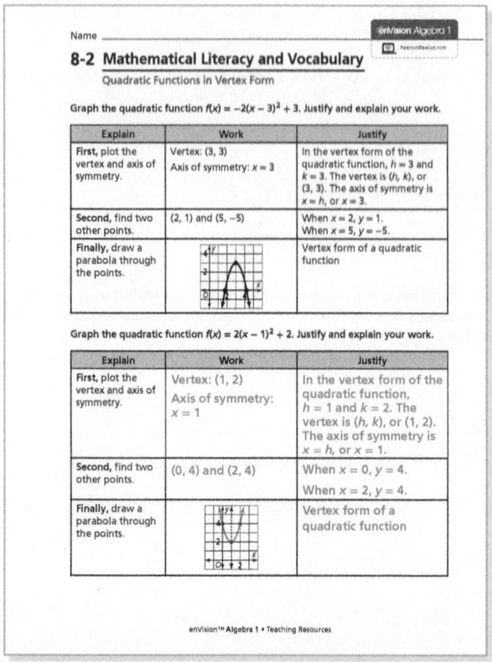

Name

8-2 Mathematical Literacy and Vocabulary

Quadratic Functions in Vertex Form

Graph the quadratic function $f(x) = -2(x - 3)^2 + 3$. Justify and explain your work.

Explain	Work	Justify
First, plot the vertex and axis of symmetry.	Vertex: (3, 3) Axis of symmetry: $x = 3$	In the vertex form of the quadratic function, $h = 3$ and $k = 3$. The vertex is (h, k), or (3, 3). The axis of symmetry is $x = h$, or $x = 3$.
Second, find two other points.	(2, 1) and (5, −5)	When $x = 2$, $y = 1$. When $x = 5$, $y = -5$.
Finally, draw a parabola through the points.		Vertex form of a quadratic function

Graph the quadratic function $f(x) = 2(x - 1)^2 + 2$. Justify and explain your work.

Explain	Work	Justify
First, plot the vertex and axis of symmetry.	Vertex: (1, 2) Axis of symmetry: $x = 1$	In the vertex form of the quadratic function, $h = 1$ and $k = 2$. The vertex is (h, k), or (1, 2). The axis of symmetry is $x = h$, or $x = 1$.
Second, find two other points.	(0, 4) and (2, 4)	When $x = 0$, $y = 4$. When $x = 2$, $y = 4$.
Finally, draw a parabola through the points.		Vertex form of a quadratic function

enVision™ Algebra 1 • Teaching Resources

Digital Resources and Video Tutorials I O A

The **Reteach to Build Understanding, Additional Practice,** and **Enrichment** activities are available as digital assignments powered by MathXL for School. These activities are automatically assigned when students complete the lesson quiz online and are automatically scored.

Students can access instructional tutorials using the **Virtual Nerd app.**

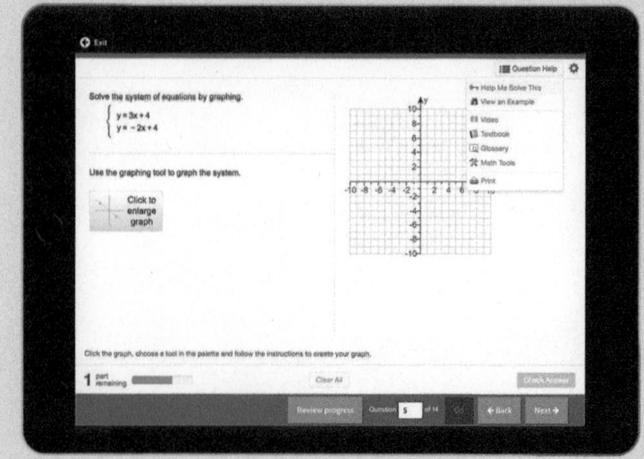

Solve the system of equations by graphing.
Use the graphing tool to graph the system.
Click to enlarge graph
Question Help
Review progress
Back
Next

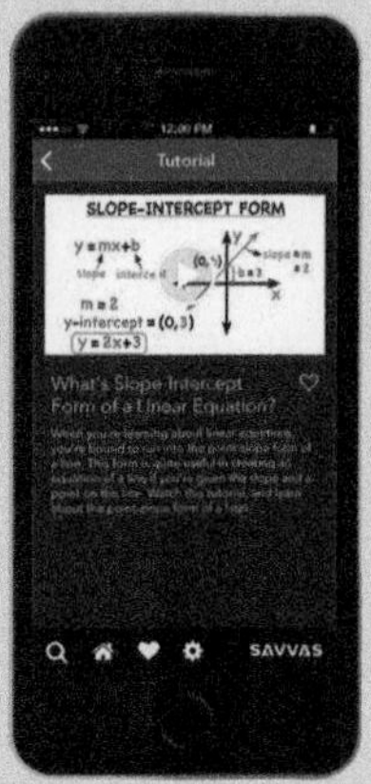

Tutorial
SLOPE-INTERCEPT FORM
SAVVAS

Students can also access Virtual Nerd videos using the **BouncePages app** to scan exercise pages marked with this icon. Students can download both apps for free in their mobile devices' app store.

A-Z Glossary

LESSON 8-3
Quadratic Functions in Standard Form

Lesson Overview

FOCUS

Objective

Students will be able to:

✔ Graph quadratic functions in standard and show intercepts, maxima, and minima.

✔ Determine how the values of a, b, and c affect the graph of $f(x) = ax^2 + bx + c$.

✔ Identify key features of parabolas.

✔ Compare properties of quadratic functions, presented in different forms (algebraically, in a table, graphically).

Essential Understanding

The standard form of a quadratic function is $f(x) = ax^2 + bx + c$. The value of c is the y-coordinate of the y-intercept and the axis of symmetry is the line $x = -\frac{b}{2a}$.

COHERENCE

Previously in this topic, students:

- Identified key features and graphed quadratic functions in vertex form.

In this lesson, students:

- Identify key features and graph quadratic functions in standard form.
- Compare properties of quadratic functions.

Later in this topic, students will:

- Compare properties and use key features of quadratic functions to model area and vertical motion problems.

RIGOR

This lesson emphasizes a blend of *conceptual understanding* and *procedural skill and fluency.*

- Students understand that the form of a quadratic function reveals key information about features of the graph of the function.
- Students use the values of a, b, and c of many functions in standard form and the values of h and k of functions in vertex form to sketch graphs of parabolas that represent those functions.

A-Z Vocabulary Builder

REVIEW VOCABULARY — **English** | *Spanish*

- **axis of symmetry** | *eje de simetría*
- **quadratic function** | *función cuadrática*
- **vertex** | *vértice*

NEW VOCABULARY

- **standard form of a quadratic function** | *forma de una función cuadrática*

VOCABULARY ACTIVITY

Discuss how to recognize a quadratic function written in *standard form*. As needed, have students choose the best answer to the following statements.

1. A(n) ________ can be used to model the path of a soccer ball kicked to a goal.

A. quadratic functon

B. linear function

C. axis of symmetry

2. The vertex of a parabola shows the ________.

A. highest point of the function

B. lowest point of the function

C. highest or lowest point of the function

Student Companion

Students can do their in-class work for the lesson on pages 175–178 of their *Student Companion* or in Savvas Realize.

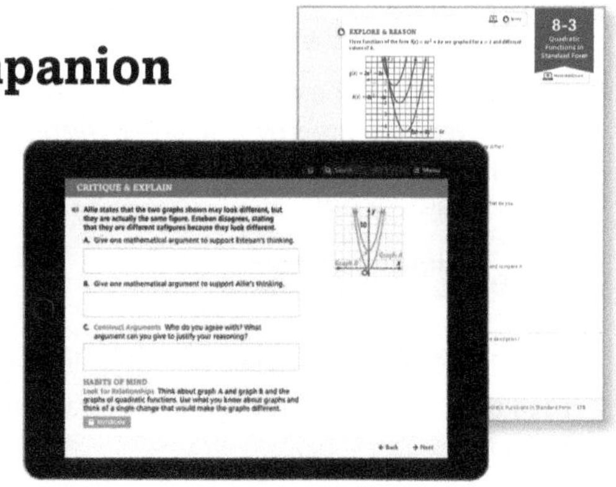

Mathematics Overview — COMMON CORE STANDARDS

Content Standards

In this lesson, students focus on this standard:

HSF.IF.B.4 For a function that models a relationship between two quantities, interpret key features of graphs and tables in terms of the quantities, and sketch graphs showing key features given a verbal description of the relationship.

They also work with concepts related to these standards:

HSF.IF.C.7.A, HSF.IF.C.8, HSF.IF.C.9

Mathematical Practice Standards

MP.3 Construct Viable Arguments

Students analyze the forms of a quadratic function to construct an argument as to whether standard form or vertex form is more useful for identifying the y-intercept.

MP.7 Look For and Make Use of Structure

Students see the standard form of a quadratic function as being composed of several objects, including values of a, b, and c, that they can use to graph the intercepts, the axis of symmetry, and the vertex of the parabola that represents the function $ax^2 + bx + c$.

EXPLORE & REASON

INSTRUCTIONAL FOCUS Students discover that the value of *b* in the equation of a quadratic function affects its vertex and axis of symmetry.

STUDENT COMPANION Students can complete the *Explore & Reason* activity on page 175 of their *Student Companion*.

Before — WHOLE CLASS

Implement Tasks that Promote Reasoning and Problem Solving ETP

Q: How can you use the equations to identify the values of *b* for *g*, *h*, and *j*.
[Rewrite the functions as $g(x) = 2x^2 + (-2)x$, $h(x) = 2x^2 + (-4)x$, and $j(x) = 2x^2 + (-6)x$, showing that the *b* values are –2, –4, and –6, respectively.]

During — SMALL GROUP

Support Productive Struggle in Learning Mathematics ETP

Q: What features of each graph could you look at to compare them?
[Answers may vary. Samples: the shape, the vertex, the line of symmetry, the *x*- and *y*-intercepts]

For Early Finishers

Q: What would the graphs look like if the *b* values of –2, –4, and –6 were replaced by 2, 4, and 6 (respectively)?
[The current graphs would be reflected across the *y*-axis.]

After — WHOLE CLASS

Facilitate Meaningful Mathematical Discourse ETP

Facilitate a discussion about the characteristics of parabolas of the form $f(x) = 2x^2 + bx$.

Q: How might the function $k(x) = 2x^2 - 8x$ compare to the other 3 graphs?
[The vertex would be lower and to the right of *j*. The right *x*-intercept of *k* would be 1 unit to the right of the right *x*-intercept of *j*.]

Q: What do you notice about the axes of symmetry for each graph?
[The distance between the axes of symmetry for the graphs of *g* and *h* and for the graphs of *h* and *j* is 0.5.]

HABITS OF MIND

Use with **EXPLORE & REASON**

Construct Arguments Can more than one parabola have the same description? Explain. **MP.3**

[No; two different parabolas can have some similarities in their descriptions, but if they have the same description then both are the same parabola.]

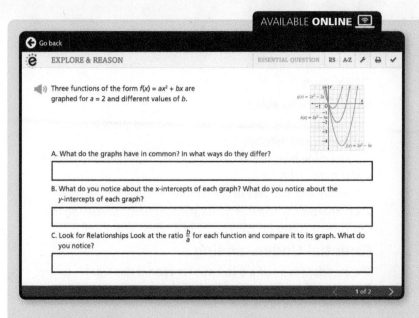

AVAILABLE **ONLINE**

Go back

EXPLORE & REASON — ESSENTIAL QUESTION | ES | A-Z

Three functions of the form $f(x) = ax^2 + bx$ are graphed for $a = 2$ and different values of *b*.

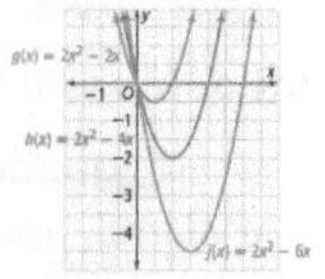

A. What do the graphs have in common? In what ways do they differ?

B. What do you notice about the x-intercepts of each graph? What do you notice about the *y*-intercepts of each graph?

C. Look for Relationships Look at the ratio $\frac{b}{a}$ for each function and compare it to its graph. What do you notice?

1 of 2

STUDENT EDITION, PAGE 329

8-3
Quadratic Functions in Standard Form

PearsonRealize.com

I CAN… graph quadratic functions using standard form.

VOCABULARY
- standard form of a quadratic function

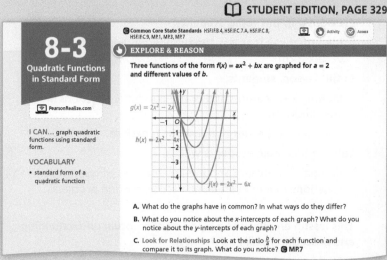

Common Core State Standards HSF.IF.B.4, HSF.IF.C.7.A, HSF.IF.C.8, HSF.IF.C.9, MP.1, MP.3, MP.7

Activity | Assess

EXPLORE & REASON

Three functions of the form $f(x) = ax^2 + bx$ are graphed for $a = 2$ and different values of *b*.

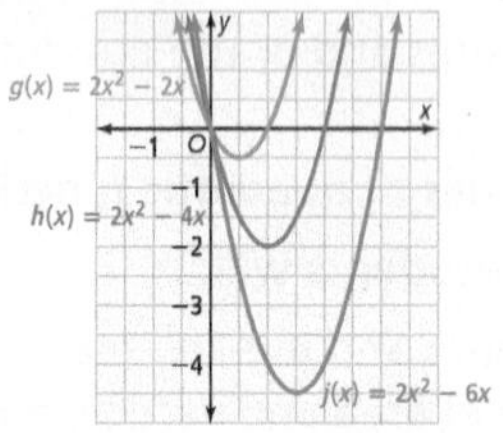

$g(x) = 2x^2 - 2x$
$h(x) = 2x^2 - 4x$
$j(x) = 2x^2 - 6x$
y
x
O
–1
–2
–3
–4

A. What do the graphs have in common? In what ways do they differ?

B. What do you notice about the *x*-intercepts of each graph? What do you notice about the *y*-intercepts of each graph?

C. Look for Relationships Look at the ratio $\frac{b}{a}$ for each function and compare it to its graph. What do you notice? **MP.7**

SAMPLE STUDENT WORK

A. All 3 graphs are parabolas opening upward. *g* has vertex (0.5, –0.5), *h* has vertex (1, –2), and *j* has vertex (1.5, –4.5).

B. All three functions have one x-intercept at (0, 0). g(x) has another x-intercept at (1, 0), h(x) has another x-intercept at (2, 0), and j(x) has another x-intercept at (3, 0). All the functions have a y-intercept at (0, 0).

C. For g(x), = –1, for h(x), = –2, and for j(x), = –3. Each of the values of is the negative of one of the x-intercepts of the function's graph. For instance, g(x) has x-intercepts at x = 0 and x = 1, and its ratio is –1.

SavvasRealize.com
Activity Assess

INTRODUCE THE ESSENTIAL QUESTION

Establish Mathematics Goals to Focus Learning ETP

Introduce to students the standard form of a quadratic function. They will use this form to help them sketch the graph of the function. Explain that you can write the equation of a quadratic function in standard form or in vertex form. Writing the equation in different forms can tell you different information about the function.

EXAMPLE 1 Relate c to the Graph of $f(x) = ax^2 + bx + c$

Use and Connect Representations ETP

Q: What connection do you notice about the value of c for each function and the graphs? [The value of c is the y-coordinate of the y-intercept on the graphs.]

Q: How would the graphs change if the value of c was the same for all of the functions?
[Each graph would have the same y-intercept.]

Try It! Answers

1. $f(0) = c$; From Example 1, this means the y-intercept is $(0, c)$.

Elicit and Use Evidence of Student Thinking ETP

Q: If the value of a was positive, would it change the value of the y-intercept? Explain. [No; whether a is positive or negative, multiplying it by an x-value of 0 results in 0. Only the sign of c affects the value of the y-intercept.]

AVAILABLE ONLINE

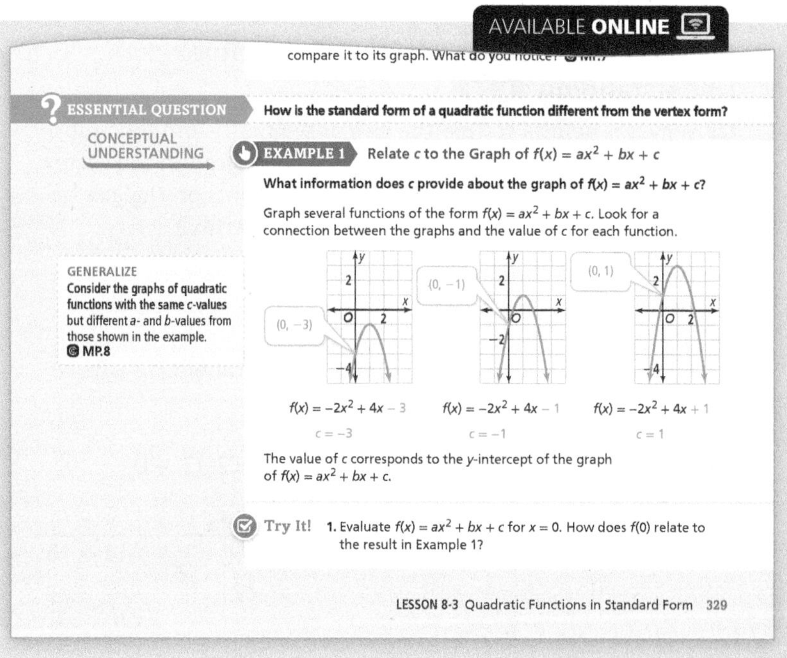
compare it to its graph. What do you notice? MP.7

ESSENTIAL QUESTION How is the standard form of a quadratic function different from the vertex form?

CONCEPTUAL UNDERSTANDING

EXAMPLE 1 Relate c to the Graph of $f(x) = ax^2 + bx + c$

What information does c provide about the graph of $f(x) = ax^2 + bx + c$?

Graph several functions of the form $f(x) = ax^2 + bx + c$. Look for a connection between the graphs and the value of c for each function.

(0, −3)
(0, −1)
(0, 1)
$f(x) = -2x^2 + 4x - 3$
$c = -3$
$f(x) = -2x^2 + 4x - 1$
$c = -1$
$f(x) = -2x^2 + 4x + 1$
$c = 1$

GENERALIZE
Consider the graphs of quadratic functions with the same c-values but different a- and b-values from those shown in the example. MP.8

The value of c corresponds to the y-intercept of the graph of $f(x) = ax^2 + bx + c$.

Try It! 1. Evaluate $f(x) = ax^2 + bx + c$ for $x = 0$. How does $f(0)$ relate to the result in Example 1?

LESSON 8-3 Quadratic Functions in Standard Form 329

AVAILABLE ONLINE

ADDITIONAL EXAMPLES

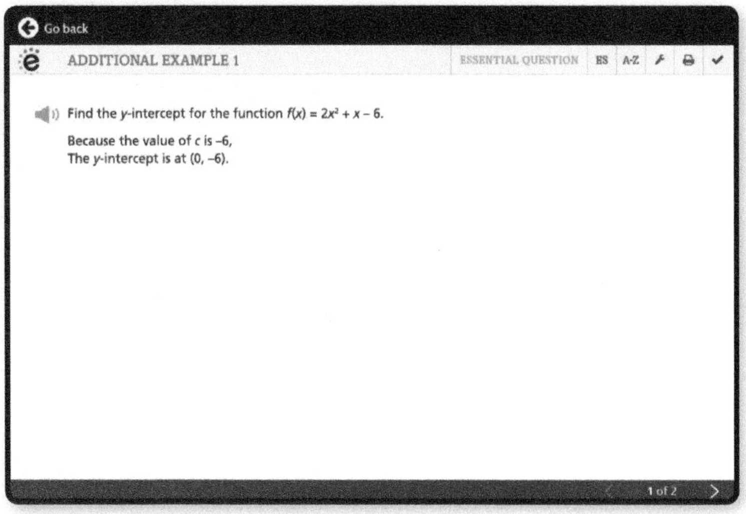
Go back
ADDITIONAL EXAMPLE 1

Find the y-intercept for the function $f(x) = 2x^2 + x - 6$.

Because the value of c is −6,
The y-intercept is at (0, −6).

1 of 2

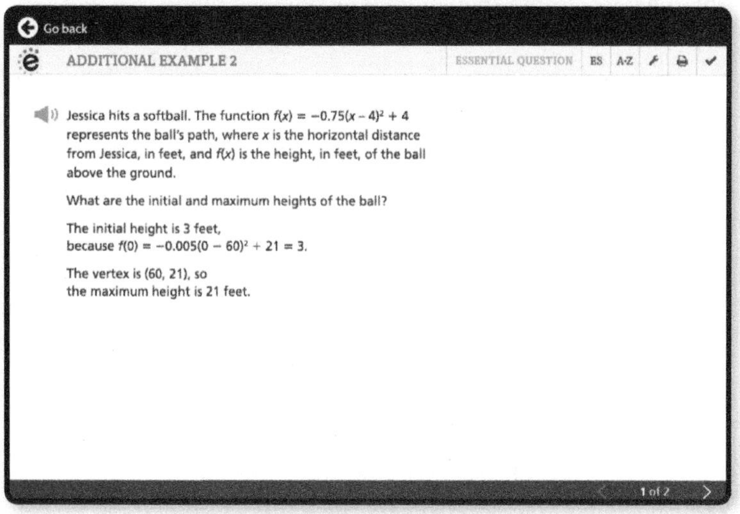
Go back
ADDITIONAL EXAMPLE 2

Jessica hits a softball. The function $f(x) = -0.75(x - 4)^2 + 4$ represents the ball's path, where x is the horizontal distance from Jessica, in feet, and $f(x)$ is the height, in feet, of the ball above the ground.

What are the initial and maximum heights of the ball?

The initial height is 3 feet,
because $f(0) = -0.005(0 - 60)^2 + 21 = 3$.

The vertex is (60, 21), so
the maximum height is 21 feet.

1 of 2

Example 1 Help students transition to identifying the y-intercept of a function from its equation.

Q: How is the y-intercept related to the equation?
[In the equation, the value of c corresponds with the y-intercept.]

Example 2 Help students distinguish between the key features of the vertex form of a quadratic function and the standard form with this additional example.

Q: Which answer could you find using the form of the function given? [maximum height]

Q: What could you do to find the other answer?
[convert the equation to standard form]

EXAMPLE 2 Graph a Quadratic Function in Standard Form

Build Procedural Fluency from Conceptual Understanding ETP

Q: Why is it helpful to find the axis of symmetry and then plot the vertex? [The axis of symmetry passes through the vertex of the function, so the *x*-coordinate of points on the axis of symmetry is also the *x*-coordinate of the vertex.]

Q: Why is useful to find the reflection of the *y*-intercept and another point? [A parabola is symmetrical about its axis of symmetry. You can reflect any point across the axis of symmetry to find another point on the parabola.]

Try It! Answers

2. a. 4; $x = -1$; $(-1, 3)$ **b.** -4; $x = 2$; $(2, -1)$

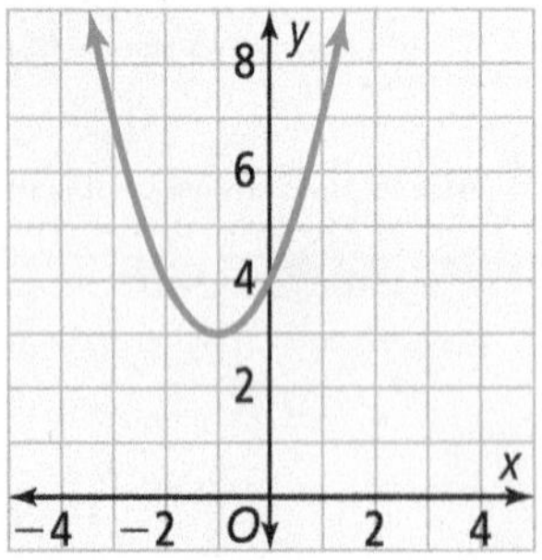

y
8
6
4
2
x
−4
−2
O
2
4

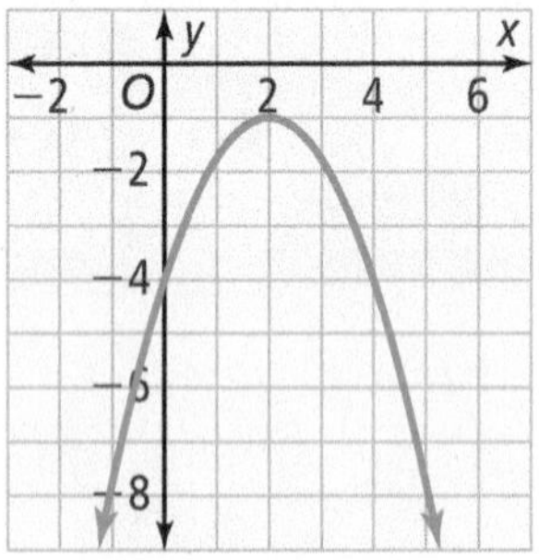

y
x
−2
O
2
4
6
−2
−4
−6
−8

HABITS OF MIND

Use with **EXAMPLES 1 & 2**

Use Appropriate Tools Suppose you want to graph a quadratic function in standard form on a graphing calculator. How could finding the vertex, axis of symmetry, and *y*-intercept of the function help you choose a viewing window for the graph? **MP.5**

[The axis of symmetry can help to determine the domain that will show the parabola centered in the viewing window. The vertex and the *y*-intercept can help to determine the range that will show the key features of the parabola.]

AVAILABLE **ONLINE**

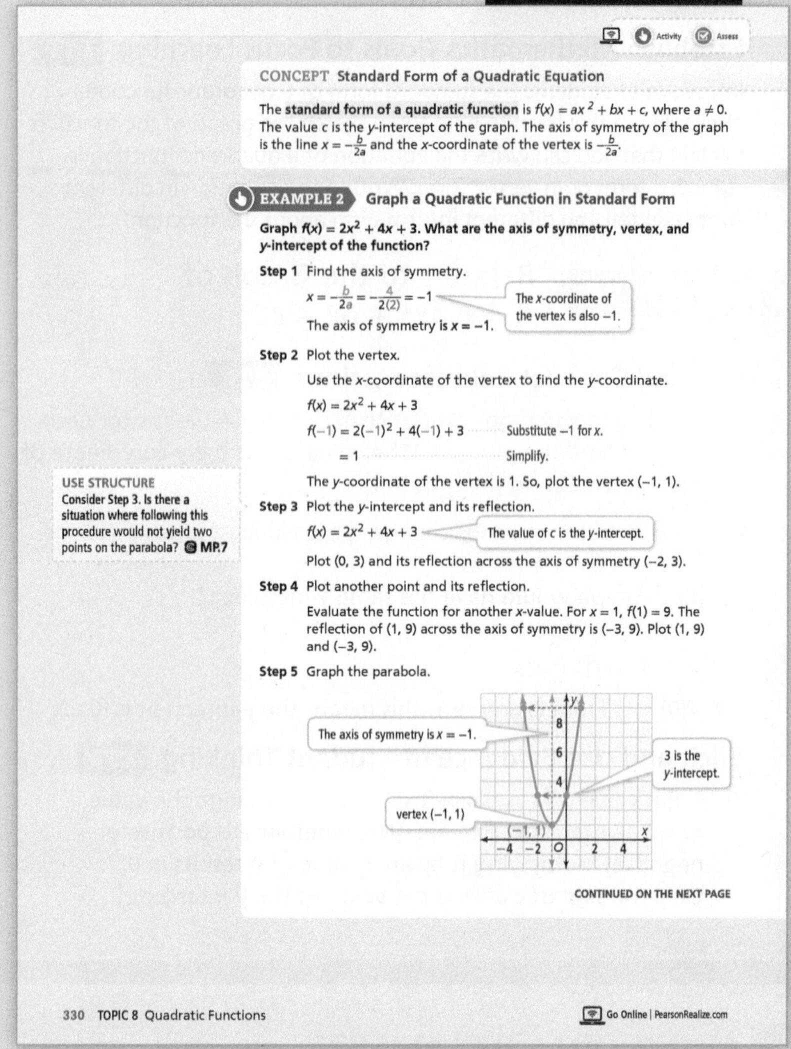

Activity Assess

CONCEPT **Standard Form of a Quadratic Equation**

The **standard form of a quadratic function** is $f(x) = ax^2 + bx + c$, where $a \neq 0$. The value c is the *y*-intercept of the graph. The axis of symmetry of the graph is the line $x = -\frac{b}{2a}$ and the *x*-coordinate of the vertex is $-\frac{b}{2a}$.

EXAMPLE 2 **Graph a Quadratic Function in Standard Form**

Graph $f(x) = 2x^2 + 4x + 3$. What are the axis of symmetry, vertex, and *y*-intercept of the function?

Step 1 Find the axis of symmetry.

$x = -\frac{b}{2a} = -\frac{4}{2(2)} = -1$ — The *x*-coordinate of the vertex is also −1.

The axis of symmetry is $x = -1$.

Step 2 Plot the vertex.

Use the *x*-coordinate of the vertex to find the *y*-coordinate.

$f(x) = 2x^2 + 4x + 3$

$f(-1) = 2(-1)^2 + 4(-1) + 3$ Substitute −1 for *x*.

$= 1$ Simplify.

The *y*-coordinate of the vertex is 1. So, plot the vertex (−1, 1).

USE STRUCTURE
Consider Step 3. Is there a situation where following this procedure would not yield two points on the parabola? MP.7

Step 3 Plot the *y*-intercept and its reflection.

$f(x) = 2x^2 + 4x + 3$ — The value of *c* is the *y*-intercept.

Plot (0, 3) and its reflection across the axis of symmetry (−2, 3).

Step 4 Plot another point and its reflection.

Evaluate the function for another *x*-value. For $x = 1$, $f(1) = 9$. The reflection of (1, 9) across the axis of symmetry is (−3, 9). Plot (1, 9) and (−3, 9).

Step 5 Graph the parabola.

The axis of symmetry is x = −1.
3 is the y-intercept.
vertex (−1, 1)
(−1, 1)
y
x
8
6
4
−4
−2
O
2
4

CONTINUED ON THE NEXT PAGE

330 TOPIC 8 Quadratic Functions

Go Online | PearsonRealize.com

Common Error

Try It! Students may try to graph a quadratic function using only one or two points. Emphasize that the more points students plot, the more accurate the shape of their parabola will be.

ADV Advanced Students

USE WITH EXAMPLE 2 Have students practice graphing quadratic functions in standard form in order to solve systems of quadratic equations.

- Give students these pairs of functions.
- Challenge them to approximate the solutions graphically.

1. $f(x) = 0.5x^2 - 3x + 2$; $g(x) = -2x^2 + x + 7$

2. $h(x) = -0.25x^2 + 2x + 9$; $p(x) = 3x^2 - 3x - 6$

Q: What is one way to solve the systems of quadratic equations? [Graph the functions and estimate their points of intersection.]

Q: What are the approximate solutions of each system? [(−0.8, 4.8) and (2.4, −2.3); (−1.5, 5.4) and (3.1, 12.8)]

EXAMPLE 3 Compare Properties of Quadratic Functions

Pose Purposeful Questions ETP

Q: For both of the fountains, how do you know that the vertex represents the maximum height?
[The trajectories of the water from both of the fountains open downward. Therefore, their vertices are the maximum values.]

Q: How do you know (−4, 10) is the highest point for Fountain B?
[The points (−5, 8) and (−3, 8) are reflections across the line $x = -4$, so the vertex is located at the point with an x-value of −4.]

Try It! Answers

3. f: 0.1, g: 0; f has the greater maximum value.

Elicit and Use Evidence of Student Thinking ETP

Q: Describe two methods you could use to answer the Try It.
[Find the vertex of f algebraically and compare it to the graph of g. Graph f on a graphing calculator and compare its maximum to the maximum of g.]

HABITS OF MIND

Use with **EXAMPLE 3**

Reasoning How can you tell from the equation of function f that the function has a maximum? How can you tell from the table of function g that function g has a maximum? **MP.2**

[Function f has a maximum because the coefficient of the x^2 term is negative. You know that function g has a maximum because as x-values increase, the y-values increase and then decrease.]

AVAILABLE **ONLINE**

Activity Assess

EXAMPLE 2 CONTINUED

Try It! **2.** Graph each function. What are the y-intercept, the axis of symmetry, and the vertex of each function?

a. $f(x) = x^2 + 2x + 4$ **b.** $g(x) = -0.75x^2 + 3x - 4$

APPLICATION

EXAMPLE 3 Compare Properties of Quadratic Functions

The trajectory of the water from Fountain A is represented by a function in standard form while the trajectory of the water from Fountain B is represented by a table of values. Compare the vertex of each function. Which trajectory reaches a greater height in feet?

Fountain A:
$f(x) = -x^2 + 2x + 8$

A
B

Fountain B:

x	y
−6	5
−5	8
−4	10
−3	8
−2	5

COMMON ERROR
You may incorrectly state that the x-coordinate of the vertex is −1. Remember that the formula is $-\frac{b}{2a}$. Make sure to include the negative in your calculations.

Find the vertex of each function.

Fountain A

Find the x-coordinate.

$-\frac{b}{2a} = -\frac{2}{2(-1)} = 1$

Find the y-coordinate.

$f(1) = -(1)^2 + 2(1) + 8 = 9$

The vertex is (1, 9).

Fountain A reaches a height of 9 ft.

Fountain B

Find the vertex.

x	y
−6	5
−5	8
−4	10
−3	8
−2	5

The vertex is (−4, 10).

Fountain **B** reaches a height of 10 ft.

The water from Fountain B reaches a greater height.

CONTINUED ON THE NEXT PAGE

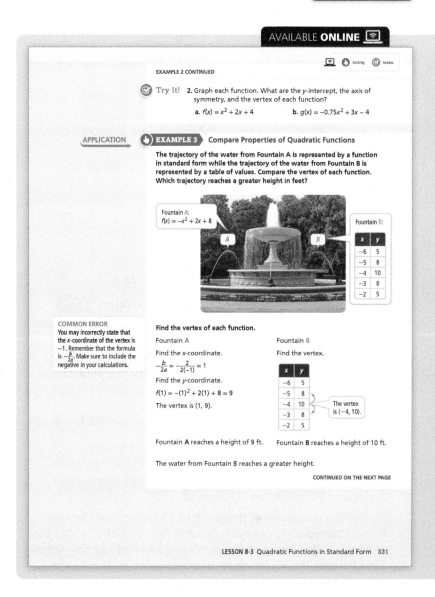

ELL English Language Learners *(Use with* **EXAMPLE 3***)*

LISTENING BEGINNING Define trajectory as a path, a course, a line, or a route. Demonstrate trajectory by showing students the path of water from a drinking fountain and tracing its path in the air.

Q: How can you describe the path of the water?
[Answers may vary. Sample: The water starts by going up, reaches a high point, and then goes down lower than the height at which it started.]

SPEAKING INTERMEDIATE In groups, have students rephrase the problem statement to each other. Have each group present a sentence explaining how they determined which fountain's water reached a greater height.

Q: How are the trajectories of the water from the two fountains represented?
[The water from fountain A is represented by an equation. The water from fountain B is represented by a table.]

WRITING ADVANCED Ask students to make a diagram that shows how the phrases *greatest height*, *maximum height*, and *vertex* are related to each other. Then have students write about how to find the maximum height and the greatest height, knowing the vertex of a quadratic function.

Q: Which phrases mean the same thing?
[greatest height and maximum height]

Activity Assess

EXAMPLE 4 Analyze the Structure of Different Forms

Use and Connect Mathematical Representations ETP

Q: How does the situation shown in the diagram relate to the vertex form of the equation?
[The vertex form of the equation shows the values of h and k which relate to the vertex of the graph of the function shown in the diagram.]

Q: How does the situation shown in the diagram relate to the standard form of the equation?
[The standard form of the equation shows the value of c which relates to the y-intercept of the graph of the function shown in the diagram.]

Try It! Answers

4. initial height = 6 ft; maximum height = 6.25 ft

Elicit and Use Evidence of Student Thinking ETP

Q: Is one form of the equation of a function always better than another form?
[No; each form makes it easy to identify specific information about a function. The best form depends on the information you are looking for.]

HABITS OF MIND

Use with **EXAMPLE 4**

Use Structure Consider the different forms of a quadratic function. Which form would you use to find the y-intercept of its graph? Which form would you use to find the maximum or minimum of the function? Explain. MP.7

[To find the y-intercept of the graph of a function, use standard form because the y-intercept is equal to the value of c. To find the minimum or maximum of the graph of a function, use the vertex form because the minimum or maximum value is equal to the value of k.]

AVAILABLE ONLINE

Activity Assess

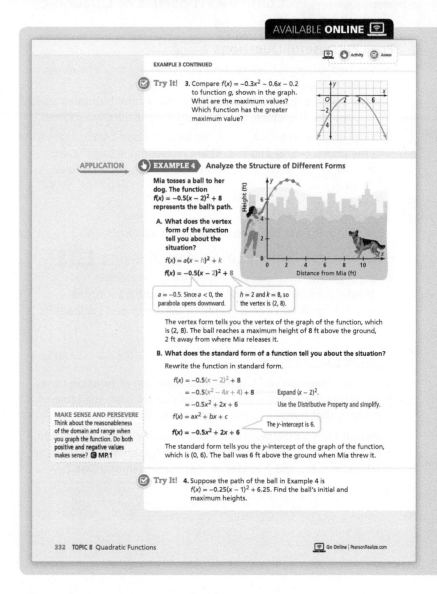

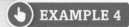

EXAMPLE 3 CONTINUED

Try It! 3. Compare $f(x) = -0.3x^2 - 0.6x - 0.2$ to function g, shown in the graph. What are the maximum values? Which function has the greater maximum value?

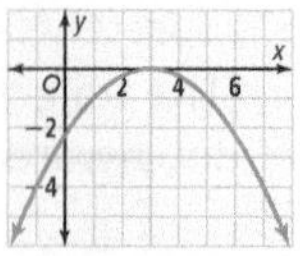

y
x
O
2
4
6
−2
−4

APPLICATION

EXAMPLE 4 Analyze the Structure of Different Forms

Mia tosses a ball to her dog. The function $f(x) = -0.5(x - 2)^2 + 8$ represents the ball's path.

A. What does the vertex form of the function tell you about the situation?

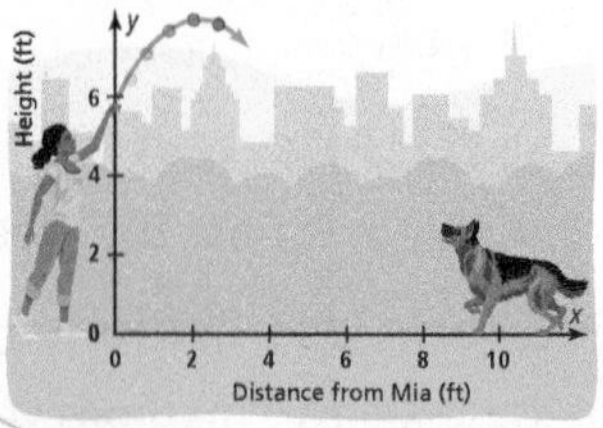

y
Height (ft)
6
4
2
0
0
2
4
6
8
10
x
Distance from Mia (ft)

$f(x) = a(x - h)^2 + k$

$f(x) = -0.5(x - 2)^2 + 8$

$a = -0.5$. Since $a < 0$, the parabola opens downward.

$h = 2$ and $k = 8$, so the vertex is (2, 8).

The vertex form tells you the vertex of the graph of the function, which is (2, 8). The ball reaches a maximum height of 8 ft above the ground, 2 ft away from where Mia releases it.

B. What does the standard form of a function tell you about the situation?

Rewrite the function in standard form.

$f(x) = -0.5(x - 2)^2 + 8$

$= -0.5(x^2 - 4x + 4) + 8$ Expand $(x - 2)^2$.

$= -0.5x^2 + 2x + 6$ Use the Distributive Property and simplify.

$f(x) = ax^2 + bx + c$

$f(x) = -0.5x^2 + 2x + 6$ The y-intercept is 6.

The standard form tells you the y-intercept of the graph of the function, which is (0, 6). The ball was 6 ft above the ground when Mia threw it.

MAKE SENSE AND PERSEVERE Think about the reasonableness of the domain and range when you graph the function. Do both positive and negative values makes sense? MP.1

Try It! 4. Suppose the path of the ball in Example 4 is $f(x) = -0.25(x - 1)^2 + 6.25$. Find the ball's initial and maximum heights.

332 TOPIC 8 Quadratic Functions Go Online | PearsonRealize.com

Struggling Students

USE WITH EXAMPLE 4 Some students have difficulty squaring a binomial and then distributing a coefficient. Have students practice converting a quadratic function in vertex form to standard form.

Q: $y = 2(x - 3)^2 + 4$
[$y = 2x^2 - 12x + 22$]

Q: $y = 2(x + 3)^2 - 22$
[$y = 2x^2 + 12x - 4$]

Q: $y = 3(x + 1)^2 + 6$
[$y = 3x^2 + 6x + 9$]

Q: What are the necessary steps to write the vertex form of a function in standard form?
[Use the order of operations to simplify the expression. Square the binomial, distribute the coefficient, and combine like terms.]

Q: What is the y-intercept of the graph of each function?
[(0, 22), (0, −4), (0, 9)]

CONCEPT SUMMARY Standard Form of a Quadratic Function

Facilitate Meaningful Mathematical Discourse ETP

Q: What are the key features of a quadratic function that can be identified from the standard form of the equation?
[the axis of symmetry, the vertex, the *y*-intercept]

Do You UNDERSTAND? | Do You KNOW HOW?

Common Error

Exercise 9 Students may misinterpret 9 as the initial height rather than the maximum height. Remind students that the function is already in vertex form. They can find the vertex, which is the maximum, without rewriting the equation in standard form.

AVAILABLE ONLINE

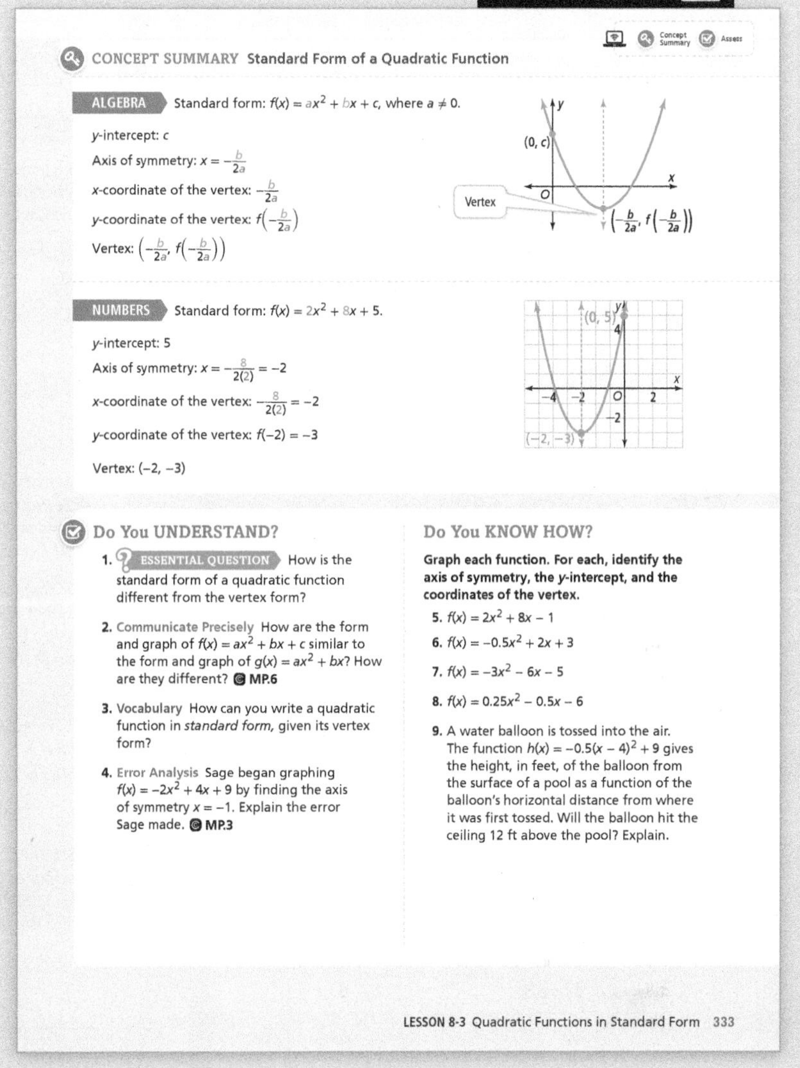

CONCEPT SUMMARY Standard Form of a Quadratic Function

ALGEBRA Standard form: $f(x) = ax^2 + bx + c$, where $a \neq 0$.

y-intercept: c

Axis of symmetry: $x = -\frac{b}{2a}$

x-coordinate of the vertex: $-\frac{b}{2a}$

y-coordinate of the vertex: $f\left(-\frac{b}{2a}\right)$

Vertex: $\left(-\frac{b}{2a}, f\left(-\frac{b}{2a}\right)\right)$

(0, c)
Vertex
$\left(-\frac{b}{2a}, f\left(-\frac{b}{2a}\right)\right)$

NUMBERS Standard form: $f(x) = 2x^2 + 8x + 5$.

y-intercept: 5

Axis of symmetry: $x = -\frac{8}{2(2)} = -2$

x-coordinate of the vertex: $-\frac{8}{2(2)} = -2$

y-coordinate of the vertex: $f(-2) = -3$

Vertex: $(-2, -3)$

(0, 5)
(−2, −3)

Do You UNDERSTAND?

1. ESSENTIAL QUESTION How is the standard form of a quadratic function different from the vertex form?

2. Communicate Precisely How are the form and graph of $f(x) = ax^2 + bx + c$ similar to the form and graph of $g(x) = ax^2 + bx$? How are they different? MP.6

3. Vocabulary How can you write a quadratic function in *standard form*, given its vertex form?

4. Error Analysis Sage began graphing $f(x) = -2x^2 + 4x + 9$ by finding the axis of symmetry $x = -1$. Explain the error Sage made. MP.3

Do You KNOW HOW?

Graph each function. For each, identify the axis of symmetry, the *y*-intercept, and the coordinates of the vertex.

5. $f(x) = 2x^2 + 8x - 1$

6. $f(x) = -0.5x^2 + 2x + 3$

7. $f(x) = -3x^2 - 6x - 5$

8. $f(x) = 0.25x^2 - 0.5x - 6$

9. A water balloon is tossed into the air. The function $h(x) = -0.5(x - 4)^2 + 9$ gives the height, in feet, of the balloon from the surface of a pool as a function of the balloon's horizontal distance from where it was first tossed. Will the balloon hit the ceiling 12 ft above the pool? Explain.

LESSON 8-3 Quadratic Functions in Standard Form 333

Answers

1. The standard form of a function is the expansion of the vertex form.

2. Both functions are in standard form and have graphs that are parabolas. Each parabola has an axis of symmetry of $x = -\frac{b}{2a}$. The function f has *y*-intercept of c, while the function g has *y*-intercept 0.

3. Square the binomial in the vertex form, multiply using the Distributive Property, and simplify.

4. The sign is incorrect. The axis of symmetry is $x = 1$. Sage may have forgotten to include the negative sign in $x = -\frac{b}{2a}$.

5. 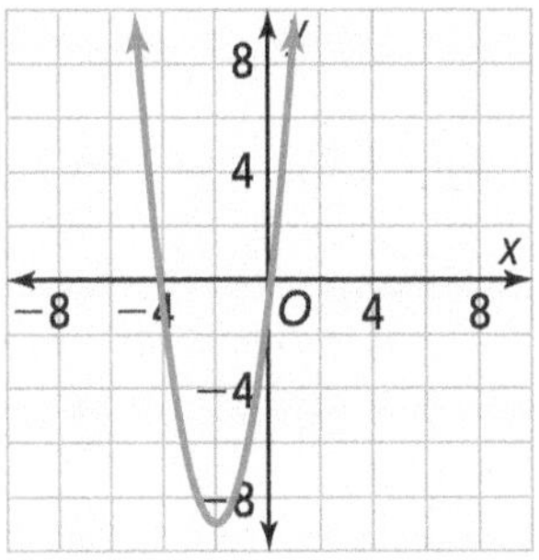

axis of symmetry: $x = -2$; *y*-intercept: -1; vertex: $(-2, -9)$

6. 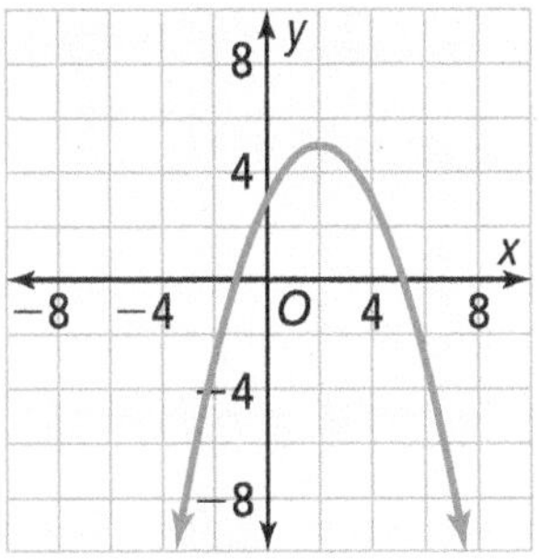

axis of symmetry: $x = 2$; *y*-intercept: 3; vertex: $(2, 5)$

7. 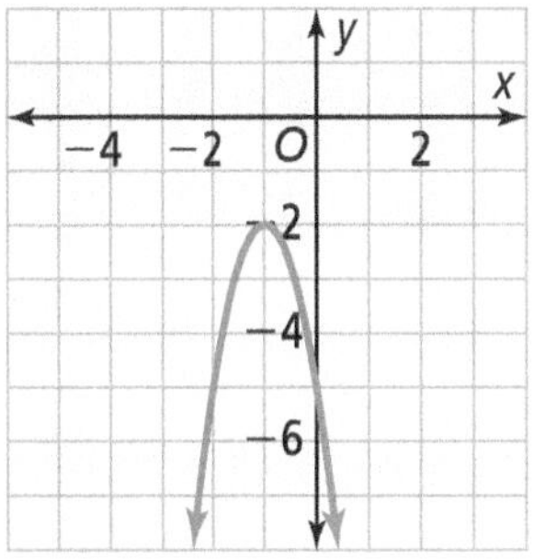

axis of symmetry: $x = -1$; *y*-intercept: -5; vertex: $(-1, -2)$

8. 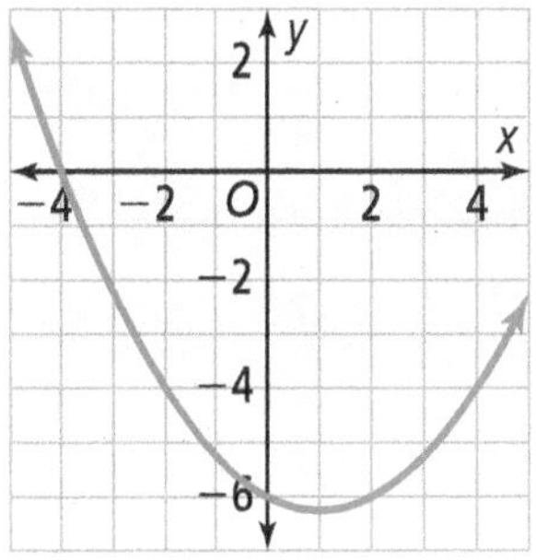

axis of symmetry: $x = 1$; *y*-intercept: -6; vertex: $(1, -6.25)$

9. No; the maximum height of the balloon is 9 ft.

Practice | Tutorials | Math Tools

PRACTICE & PROBLEM SOLVING

AVAILABLE ONLINE

Lesson Practice You may opt to have students complete the automatically scored Practice and Problem Solving items online powered by MathXL for School.

Choose from: **Lesson Practice**

Adaptive Practice

You may also take advantage of the bank of exercises for assigning additional practice.

Assignment Guide

Basic	Advanced
10–26, 29–34, 37–42	10–14, 17–20, 23–42

Item Analysis

Example	Items	DOK
1	15–20, 41	2
2	10, 21–28	1
	13	2
	14	3
3	29, 30, 40	2
	37–39	3
	42	4
4	33–36	1
	31, 32	2
	11, 12	3

AVAILABLE ONLINE

PRACTICE & PROBLEM SOLVING

Scan for Multimedia | Practice | Tutorial | Additional Exercises Available Online

UNDERSTAND

10. Make Sense and Persevere The graph of the function $f(x) = 2x^2 - bx - 6$ is shown. What is the value of b? Explain. MP.1

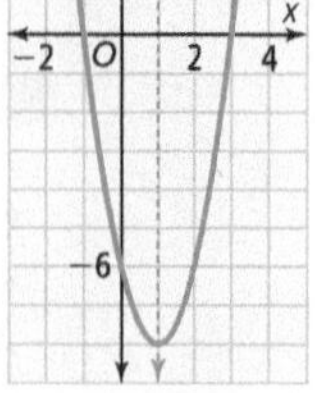

11. Construct Arguments To identify the y-intercept of a quadratic function, would you choose to use vertex form or standard form? Explain. MP.3

12. Error Analysis Describe and correct the error a student made when writing the quadratic function $f(x) = 2(x + 3)^2 - 4$ in standard form. MP.3

$f(x) = 2(x + 3)^2 - 4$
$f(x) = 2x^2 + 6x + 9 - 4$
$f(x) = 2x^2 + 6x + 5$ ✗

13. Communicate Precisely Estimate the coordinates of the vertex of the graph of $f(x) = 1.25x^2 - 2x - 1$ below. Then explain how to find the exact coordinates. MP.6

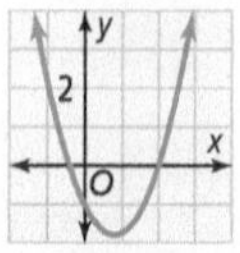

14. Higher Order Thinking Points (2, −1), (−2, 7), (1, −2), (0, −1), and (4, 7) lie on the graph of a quadratic function.

a. What is the axis of symmetry of the graph?

b. What is the vertex?

c. What is the y-intercept?

d. Over what interval does the function increase?

PRACTICE

What is the y-intercept of each function? SEE EXAMPLE 1

15. $f(x) = 2x^2 - 4x - 6$ −6
16. $f(x) = 0.3x^2 + 0.6x - 0.7$ −0.7
17. $f(x) = -2x^2 - 8x - 7$ −7
18. $f(x) = 3x^2 + 6x + 5$ 5
19. $f(x) = -x^2 - 2x + 3$ 3
20. $f(x) = -0.5x^2 + x + 2$ 2

Find the y-intercept, the axis of symmetry, and the vertex of the graph of each function. SEE EXAMPLE 2

21. $f(x) = 2x^2 + 8x + 2$
22. $f(x) = -2x^2 + 4x - 3$
23. $f(x) = 0.4x^2 + 1.6x$
24. $f(x) = -x^2 - 2x - 5$
25. $f(x) = 5x^2 + 5x + 12$
26. $f(x) = 4x^2 + 12x + 5$
27. $f(x) = x^2 - 6x + 12$
28. $f(x) = -2x^2 + 16x + 40$

Compare each function to function f, shown in the table. Which function has a lesser minimum value? Explain. SEE EXAMPLE 3

x	$(x, f(x))$
1	(1, 0)
2	(2, −3)
3	(3, −4)
4	(4, −3)
5	(5, 0)

29. $g(x) = 2x^2 + 8x + 3$
30. $h(x) = x^2 + x - 3.5$

Compare each function to function f, shown in the graph below. Which function has a greater maximum value? SEE EXAMPLE 3

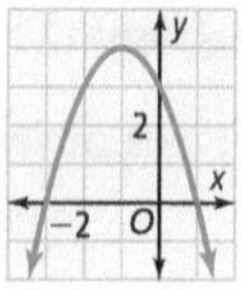

31. $g(x) = -2x^2 - 4x + 3$
32. $h(x) = -1.5x^2 - 4.5x + 1$

Write each function in standard form. SEE EXAMPLE 4

33. $f(x) = 4(x + 1)^2 - 3$ $f(x) = 4x^2 + 8x + 1$
34. $f(x) = 0.1(x - 2)^2 - 0.1$ $f(x) = 0.1x^2 - 0.4x + 0.3$
35. $f(x) = -2(x - 9)^2 + 15$ $f(x) = -2x^2 + 36x - 147$
36. $f(x) = -(x + 3)^2 + 8$ $f(x) = -x^2 - 6x - 1$

334 TOPIC 8 Quadratic Functions | Go Online | PearsonRealize.com

Answers

10. $b = 4$; $-\frac{-b}{2a} = 1$; $a = 2$, so solve $\frac{b}{2(2)} = 1$ for b.

11. standard form; c is the y-intercept.

12. The student did not correctly use the Distributive Property to multiply $2 \cdot (x^2 + 6x + 9)$.

13. (1, −2); The exact axis of symmetry can be found to be $x = -\frac{-2}{2(1.25)} = 0.8$; Then, substitute 0.8 into $f(x) = 1.25x^2 - 2x - 1$; $f(0.8) = 1.25(0.8)^2 - 2(0.8) - 1 = -1.8$; (0.8, −1.8)

14. a. $x = 1$ b. (1, −2) c. −1 d. $x > 1$

21. 2; $x = -2$; (−2, −6)

22. −3; $x = 1$; (1, −1)

23. 0; $x = -2$; (−2, −1.6)

24. −5; $x = -1$; (−1, −4)

25. 12; $x = -0.5$; (−0.5, 10.75)

26. 5; $x = -1.5$; (−1.5, −4)

27. 12; $x = 3$; (3, 3)

28. 40; $x = 4$; (4, 72)

29. g; minimum of g is −5; minimum of f is −4.

30. f; minimum of f is −4; minimum of h is −3.75.

31. g; maximum of g is 5; maximum of f is 4.

32. h: maximum of h is 4.375; maximum of f is 4.

Answers

37. Ball B; 1 m; Answers may vary. Sample: The maximum height is the y-coordinate of the vertex. Use $\frac{-b}{2a}$ for function f: $\frac{-b}{2a} = \frac{-14.7}{2(-4.9)} = 1.5$, so 1.5 is the x-coordinate of the vertex, and $f(1.5) = 12$, so the maximum height for Ball A is 12 m. The table shows that function g has symmetry about $x = 1.5$, so (1.5, 13) is the vertex and the maximum height for Ball B is 13 m.

38. 1 ft; (10, 12)

39. 8.5 ft; Sample answer: The lowest point above the ground is the y-coordinate of the vertex. Find the x-coordinate: $\frac{-b}{2a} = \frac{1}{2(0.25)} = \frac{1}{0.5} = 2$. Then find the y-coordinate: $f(2) = 8.5$.

42. Part A Model A: \$5; Model B: \$6; Answers may vary. Sample: Maximum revenues are at the vertex. The x-coordinate of the vertex gives the number of \$1 price increases needed to maximize revenue. The price to maximize revenue would be \$1 times x-coordinate of the vertex plus \$2.

Part B \$11; The points are symmetric about $x = 9$, so (9, 605) is the vertex, and \$9 + \$2 = \$11.

AVAILABLE **ONLINE**

PRACTICE & PROBLEM SOLVING

Practice Tutorial
Mixed Review Available Online

APPLY

37. Use Structure Two balls are tossed up into the air. The function $f(x) = -4.9x^2 + 14.7x + 0.975$ models the path of Ball A. The path of Ball B over time is shown in the table. Which ball reaches a greater height? How much greater? Explain how you can answer without graphing either function. MP.7

Time (s) x	Height (m) $g(x)$
0	1.975
1	11.775
1.5	13
2	11.775
2.5	1.975

38. Use Structure The position of a ball after it is kicked can be determined by using the function $f(x) = -0.11x^2 + 2.2x + 1$, where y is the height, in feet, above the ground and x is the horizontal distance, in feet, of the ball from the point at which it was kicked. What is the height of the ball when it is kicked? What is the highest point of the ball in the air? MP.7

39. Reason A banner is hung for a party. The distance from a point on the bottom edge of the banner to the floor can be determined by using the function $f(x) = 0.25x^2 - x + 9.5$, where x is the distance, in feet, of the point from the left end of the banner. How high above the floor is the lowest point on the bottom edge of the banner? Explain. MP.2

y
FIESTA
0
x

ASSESSMENT PRACTICE

40. An object is launched at 64 ft per second from an elevated platform. The function $f(x) = -16x^2 + 64x + 6$, models its trajectory over time, x. Which of the following are true? Select all that apply.

Ⓐ The height of the platform is 6 ft.
Ⓑ The object reaches its maximum height after 2 seconds.
Ⓒ The maximum height of the object is 70 ft.
Ⓓ The object will be lower than 40 feet at 1 second.
Ⓔ The height of the object increases and then decreases.

41. SAT/ACT What is the maximum value of $f(x) = -4x^2 + 16x + 12$?

Ⓐ 12 Ⓑ 16 Ⓒ 24 Ⓓ 28 Ⓔ 64

42. Performance Task Two models are used to predict monthly revenue for a new sports drink. In each model, x is the number of \$1-price increases from the original \$2 per bottle price.

Model A $f(x) = -12.5x^2 + 75x + 200$

Model B

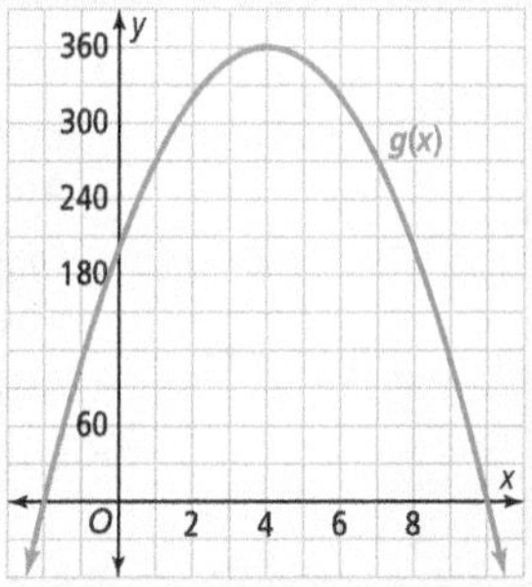
y
360
300
240
180
60
O
2
4
6
8
x
g(x)

Part A Identify the price you would set for each model to maximize monthly revenue. Explain.

Part B A third model includes the points (9, 605), (8, 600), (10, 600), (7, 585), and (11, 585). What price maximizes revenue according to this model? Explain.

LESSON QUIZ

Use the Lesson Quiz to assess students' understanding of the mathematics in the lesson.

Students can take the Lesson Quiz online or you can download a printable copy from **SavvasRealize.com**. The Lesson Quiz is also available in the *Assessment Resources* book.

Item Analysis

Item	DOK	Standards
1	1	HSF.IF.B.4
2	2	HSF.IF.C.8, HSF.IF.B.4
3	1	HSF.IF.C.7
4	2	HSF.IF.C.7.A
5	1	HSF.IF.B.4

RtI Use the student scores on the Lesson Quiz to prescribe differentiated assignments.

If students take the Lesson Quiz online, it will be automatically scored and appropriate differentiated practice will be assigned based on student performance.

I Intervention	0–3 points	• Reteach to Build Understanding • Mathematical Literacy and Vocabulary • Additional Practice
O On-Level	4 points	• Mathematical Literacy and Vocabulary • Additional Practice • Enrichment
A Advanced	5 points	• Enrichment

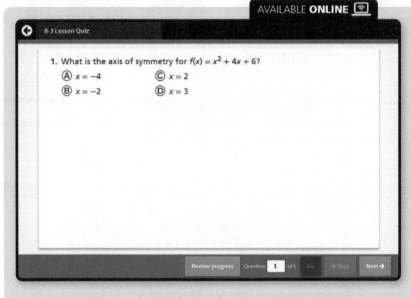

AVAILABLE **ONLINE**

8-3 Lesson Quiz

1. What is the axis of symmetry for $f(x) = x^2 + 4x + 6$?

Ⓐ $x = -4$ Ⓒ $x = 2$
Ⓑ $x = -2$ Ⓓ $x = 3$

Review progress Question 1 of 5 Go Back Next

ASSESSMENT RESOURCES

Name ____________

enVision Algebra 1 PearsonRealize.com

8-3 Lesson Quiz

Quadratic Functions in Standard Form

1. What is the axis of symmetry for $f(x) = x^2 + 4x + 6$?

Ⓐ $x = -4$ Ⓒ $x = 2$
Ⓑ $x = -2$ Ⓓ $x = 3$

2. A ball is thrown into the air. The height h, in feet, of the ball after x seconds is given by the function $h = -16(x - 2)^2 + 72$. What is the equation in standard form, and what is the maximum height of the ball?

Ⓐ $h(x) = -16x^2 + 32x + 72$; 72 ft
Ⓑ $h(x) = -16x^2 - 32x + 72$; 32 ft
Ⓒ $h(x) = -16x^2 - 64x + 32$; 32 ft
Ⓓ $h(x) = -16x^2 + 64x + 8$; 72 ft

3. Graph the function $f(x) = 0.5x^2 - 2x - 2$. Find the axis of symmetry, the vertex, and the y-intercept.

Axis of symmetry: $x = 2$
Vertex: $(2, -4)$
y-intercept: -2

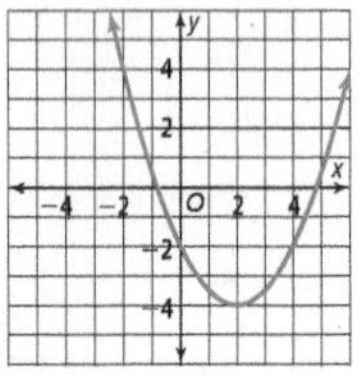

y
4
2
x
−4
−2
O
2
4
−2
−4

4. Which statements about functions $g(x) = x^2 - 4x + 3$ and $f(x) = x^2 - 4x$ are true? Select all that apply.

Ⓐ The vertex of the graph of function g is above the vertex of the graph of function f.
Ⓑ The graphs have the same axis of symmetry.
Ⓒ Function f has a maximum value and function g has a minimum value.

5. The graph of the function $y = 2x^2 + bx + 8$ is shown. What is the value of b?

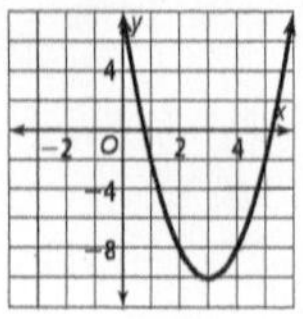

y
4
x
−2
O
2
4
−4
−8

$b = -12$

enVision™ Algebra 1 • Assessment Resources

DIFFERENTIATED RESOURCES

I = Intervention O = On-Level A = Advanced

= This activity is available as a digital assignment powered by MathXL® for School.

AVAILABLE ONLINE

Reteach to Build Understanding I

Provides scaffolded reteaching for the key lesson concepts.

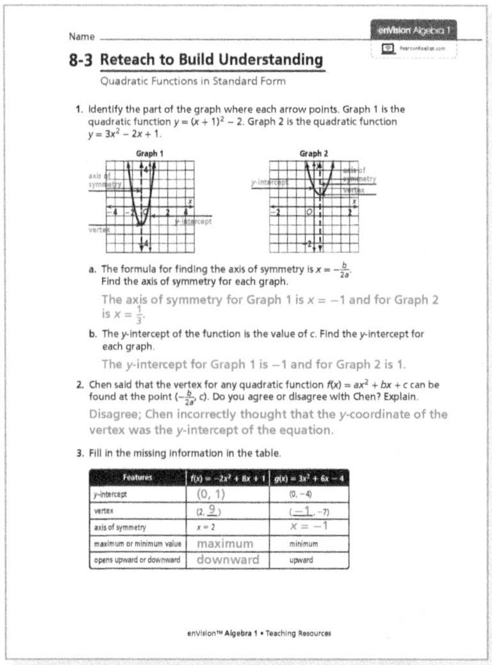

Name
8-3 Reteach to Build Understanding
Quadratic Functions in Standard Form

1. Identify the part of the graph where each arrow points. Graph 1 is the quadratic function $y = (x + 1)^2 - 2$. Graph 2 is the quadratic function $y = 3x^2 - 2x + 1$.

a. The formula for finding the axis of symmetry is $x = -\frac{b}{2a}$. Find the axis of symmetry for each graph.
The axis of symmetry for Graph 1 is $x = -1$ and for Graph 2 is $x = \frac{1}{3}$.

b. The y-intercept of the function is the value of c. Find the y-intercept for each graph.
The y-intercept for Graph 1 is −1 and for Graph 2 is 1.

2. Chen said that the vertex for any quadratic function $f(x) = ax^2 + bx + c$ can be found at the point $(-\frac{b}{2a}, c)$. Do you agree or disagree with Chen? Explain.
Disagree; Chen incorrectly thought that the y-coordinate of the vertex was the y-intercept of the equation.

3. Fill in the missing information in the table.

Features	$f(x) = -2x^2 + 8x + 1$	$g(x) = 3x^2 + 6x - 4$
y-intercept	(0, 1)	(0, −4)
vertex	(2, 9)	(−1, −7)
axis of symmetry	x = 2	x = −1
maximum or minimum value	maximum	minimum
opens upward or downward	downward	upward

enVision™ Algebra 1 • Teaching Resources

Additional Practice I O

Provides extra practice for each lesson.

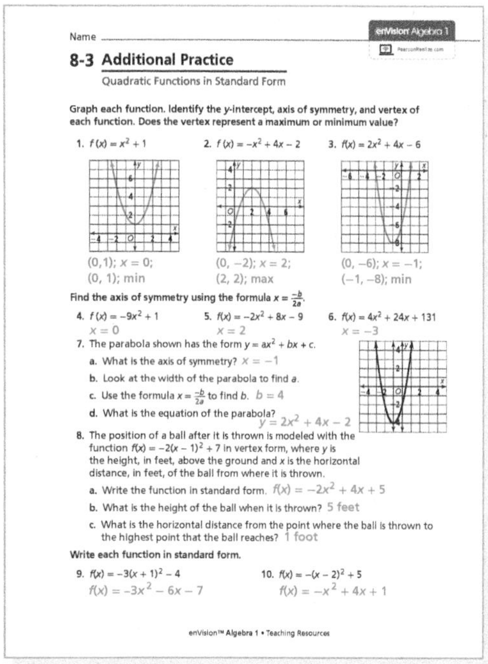

Name
8-3 Additional Practice
Quadratic Functions in Standard Form

Graph each function. Identify the y-intercept, axis of symmetry, and vertex of each function. Does the vertex represent a maximum or minimum value?

1. $f(x) = x^2 + 1$ (0, 1); x = 0; (0, 1); min
2. $f(x) = -x^2 + 4x - 2$ (0, −2); x = 2; (2, 2); max
3. $f(x) = 2x^2 + 4x - 6$ (0, −6); x = −1; (−1, −8); min

Find the axis of symmetry using the formula $x = \frac{-b}{2a}$.

4. $f(x) = -9x^2 + 1$ x = 0
5. $f(x) = -2x^2 + 8x - 9$ x = 2
6. $f(x) = 4x^2 + 24x + 131$ x = −3

7. The parabola shown has the form $y = ax^2 + bx + c$.
a. What is the axis of symmetry? x = −1
b. Look at the width of the parabola to find a.
c. Use the formula $x = \frac{-b}{2a}$ to find b. b = 4
d. What is the equation of the parabola? $y = 2x^2 + 4x - 2$

8. The position of a ball after it is thrown is modeled with the function $f(x) = -2(x - 1)^2 + 7$ in vertex form, where y is the height, in feet, above the ground and x is the horizontal distance, in feet, of the ball from where it is thrown.
a. Write the function in standard form. $f(x) = -2x^2 + 4x + 5$
b. What is the height of the ball when it is thrown? 5 feet
c. What is the horizontal distance from the point where the ball is thrown to the highest point that the ball reaches? 1 foot

Write each function in standard form.

9. $f(x) = -3(x + 1)^2 - 4$ $f(x) = -3x^2 - 6x - 7$
10. $f(x) = -(x - 2)^2 + 5$ $f(x) = -x^2 + 4x + 1$

enVision™ Algebra 1 • Teaching Resources

Enrichment O A

Presents engaging problems and activities that extend the lesson concepts.

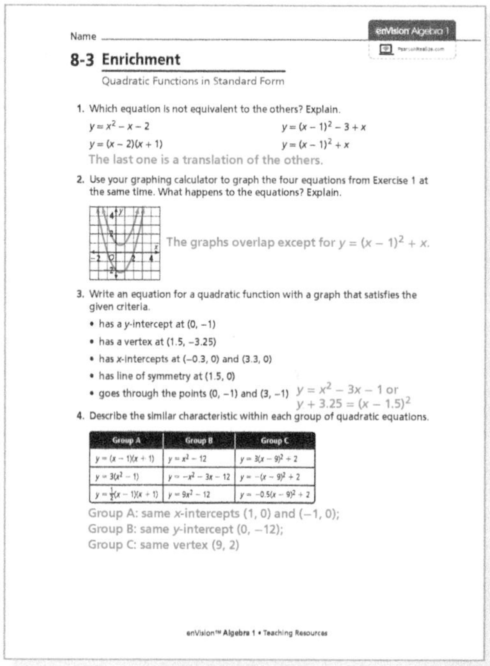

Name
8-3 Enrichment
Quadratic Functions in Standard Form

1. Which equation is not equivalent to the others? Explain.
$y = x^2 - x - 2$ $y = (x - 1)^2 - 3 + x$
$y = (x - 2)(x + 1)$ $y = (x - 1)^2 + x$
The last one is a translation of the others.

2. Use your graphing calculator to graph the four equations from Exercise 1 at the same time. What happens to the equations? Explain.
The graphs overlap except for $y = (x - 1)^2 + x$.

3. Write an equation for a quadratic function with a graph that satisfies the given criteria.
• has a y-intercept at (0, −1)
• has a vertex at (1.5, −3.25)
• has x-intercepts at (−0.3, 0) and (3.3, 0)
• has line of symmetry at (1.5, 0)
• goes through the points (0, −1) and (3, −1)
$y = x^2 - 3x - 1$ or $y + 3.25 = (x - 1.5)^2$

4. Describe the similar characteristic within each group of quadratic equations.

Group A	Group B	Group C
$y = (x - 1)(x + 1)$	$y = x^2 - 12$	$y = 3(x - 9)^2 + 2$
$y = 3(x^2 - 1)$	$y = -x^2 - 3x - 12$	$y = -(x - 9)^2 + 2$
$y = \frac{1}{2}(x - 1)(x + 1)$	$y = 9x^2 - 12$	$y = -0.5(x - 9)^2 + 2$

Group A: same x-intercepts (1, 0) and (−1, 0);
Group B: same y-intercept (0, −12);
Group C: same vertex (9, 2)

enVision™ Algebra 1 • Teaching Resources

Mathematical Literacy and Vocabulary I O

Helps students develop and reinforce understanding of key terms and concepts.

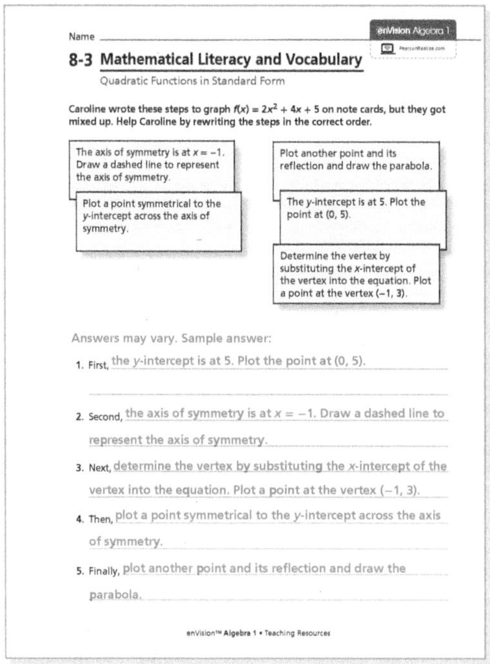

Name
8-3 Mathematical Literacy and Vocabulary
Quadratic Functions in Standard Form

Caroline wrote these steps to graph $f(x) = 2x^2 + 4x + 5$ on note cards, but they got mixed up. Help Caroline by rewriting the steps in the correct order.

The axis of symmetry is at x = −1. Draw a dashed line to represent the axis of symmetry.
Plot another point and its reflection and draw the parabola.
Plot a point symmetrical to the y-intercept across the axis of symmetry.
The y-intercept is at 5. Plot the point at (0, 5).
Determine the vertex by substituting the x-intercept of the vertex into the equation. Plot a point at the vertex (−1, 3).

Answers may vary. Sample answer:
1. First, the y-intercept is at 5. Plot the point at (0, 5).
2. Second, the axis of symmetry is at x = −1. Draw a dashed line to represent the axis of symmetry.
3. Next, determine the vertex by substituting the x-intercept of the vertex into the equation. Plot a point at the vertex (−1, 3).
4. Then, plot a point symmetrical to the y-intercept across the axis of symmetry.
5. Finally, plot another point and its reflection and draw the parabola.

enVision™ Algebra 1 • Teaching Resources

Digital Resources and Video Tutorials I O A

The **Reteach to Build Understanding, Additional Practice,** and **Enrichment** activities are available as digital assignments powered by MathXL for School. These activities are automatically assigned when students complete the lesson quiz online and are automatically scored.

Students can access instructional tutorials using the **Virtual Nerd app**.

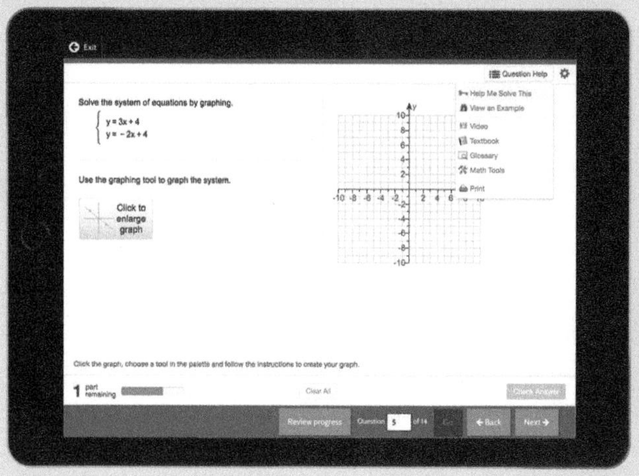
Solve the system of equations by graphing.
Use the graphing tool to graph the system.
Question Help
Review progress
Next

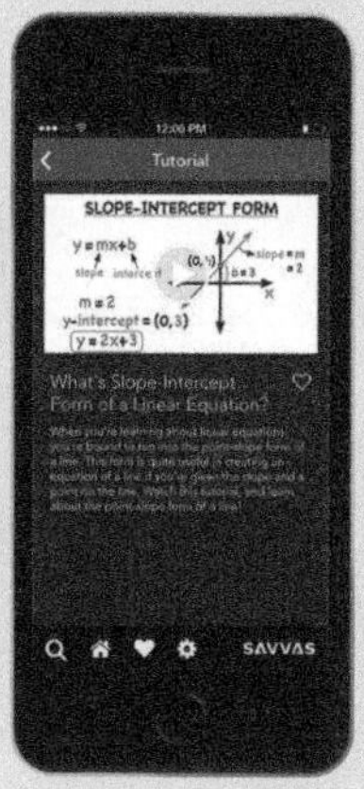
Tutorial
SLOPE-INTERCEPT FORM
SAVVAS

Students can also access Virtual Nerd videos using the **BouncePages app** to scan exercise pages marked with this icon. Students can download both apps for free in their mobile devices' app store.

Lesson Overview

FOCUS

Objective

Students will be able to:

✔ Use quadratic functions fitted to data to model real-world situations.

✔ Use the vertical motion model to write an equation.

✔ Compare a model to a data set by analyzing and evaluating residuals.

Essential Understanding

A quadratic function can be used to model area and vertical motion problems. These models can be written in the same form as the quadratic function $f(x) = ax^2 + bx + c$ using key features to interpret and understand the situation.

COHERENCE

Previously in this topic, students:

- Used key features to interpret and graph quadratic functions written in vertex form and standard form.

In this lesson, students:

- Extend their understanding of quadratic functions and solve problems involving area and vertical motion.
- Apply their knowledge of quadratic functions to analyze residuals and make predictions using the quadratic regression model.

Later in this topic, students will:

- Determine which type of function—linear, exponential or quadratic—to use when analyzing data and solving problems.

RIGOR

This lesson emphasizes a blend of *conceptual understanding* and *application*.

- Students understand that real-world situations like area and vertical motion problems can be modeled by quadratic functions.
- Students apply their understanding of quadratic functions to fit a quadratic function to data using quadratic regression.

A-Z Vocabulary Builder

REVIEW VOCABULARY — **English** | *Spanish*

- **quadratic function** | *function cuadrática*
- **residual** | *residuo*

NEW VOCABULARY

- **quadratic regression** | *regression cuadrática*
- **vertical motion model** | *modelo de movimiento vertical*

VOCABULARY ACTIVITY

Throw a ball into the air several times, varying the height from which you throw and the force with which you throw. Repeat the activity by dropping the ball from different heights.

Q: What variables affect the height of the ball? [height from which it is thrown/dropped, how hard it is thrown, time in the air]

As students respond, provide the correct vocabulary for their descriptions. Then explain that the *vertical motion model* is a *quadratic function* that relates the height of an object above the ground to time.

Student Companion

Students can do their in-class work for the lesson on pages 179–182 of their *Student Companion* or in Savvas Realize.

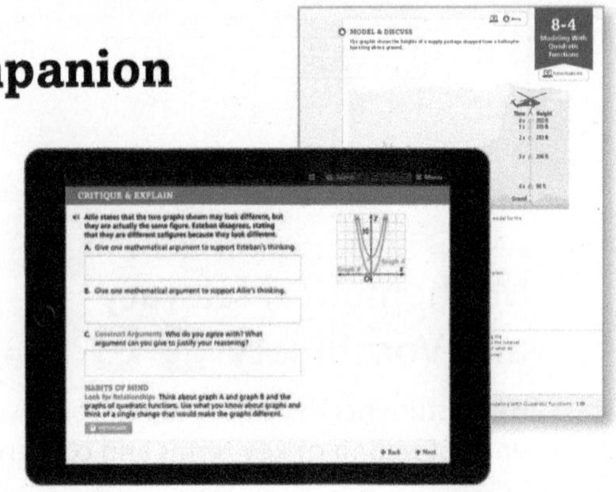

© Mathematics Overview — COMMON CORE STANDARDS

Content Standards

In this lesson students focus on these standards:

HSF.IF.A.2 Use function notation, evaluate functions for inputs in their domains, and interpret statements that use function notation in terms of a context.

HSS.ID.B.6.A Fit a function to the data; use functions fitted to data to solve problems in the context of the data.

They also work with concepts related to these standards:
HSF.BF.A.1, HSS.ID.B.6.B

Mathematical Practice Standards

These standards are highlighted in this lesson:

MP.4 Model With Mathematics

Students solve a vertical motion problem by writing a quadratic function to represent the height h of a diver at time t.

MP.7 Look For and Make Use of Structure

Students look at the overall structure of the vertical motion model and relate it to the standard form of a quadratic equation.

Activity

MODEL & DISCUSS

INSTRUCTIONAL FOCUS Students explore how to model a real-world situation given data. Students decide whether a linear or quadratic function best models the situation. This prepares students to model area and vertical motion problems using quadratic functions.

STUDENT COMPANION Students can complete the *Model & Discuss* activity on page 179 of their *Student Companion*.

Before WHOLE CLASS

Implement Tasks That Promote Reasoning and Problem Solving ETP

Q: What information do you see in the graphic?
[The graphic shows the height of the package at different times.]

Q: What are different ways you could model height and time?
[graphs, tables, equations, words]

During SMALL GROUP

Support Productive Struggle in Learning Mathematics ETP

Q: How can you tell if a function is a good model for data?
[The data points will be on or close to the graph of the function.]

For Early Finishers

Q: What data related to this scenario could be modeled by a linear function?
[Answers may vary. Sample: the number of miles the helicopter has flown and the number of gallons of fuel remaining]

After WHOLE CLASS

Facilitate Meaningful Mathematical Discourse ETP

Facilitate a discussion about which model students feel is a good choice. Some students may have chosen a linear function or a quadratic function as their model. Discuss the reasons behind their choice.

Q: How do you decide whether a linear or a quadratic model would be a better fit for a given set of data?
[Answers will vary. Sample: Look at the shape of the data on a graph. If the shape appears to be a straight line, use a linear model. If it curves like a parabola, use a quadratic model.]

HABITS OF MIND

Use with **MODEL & DISCUSS**

Reasoning Compare the rate of change for the function representing the supply package heights for the interval from 0 to 1 second and for the interval from 3 to 4 seconds. What do these rates of change represent, and what do they reveal about how quickly the supply package is falling over time? MP.2

[−15; −110; The rates represent the distance the package falls in different one-second intervals. They show that the package falls faster as more time passes.]

AVAILABLE **ONLINE**

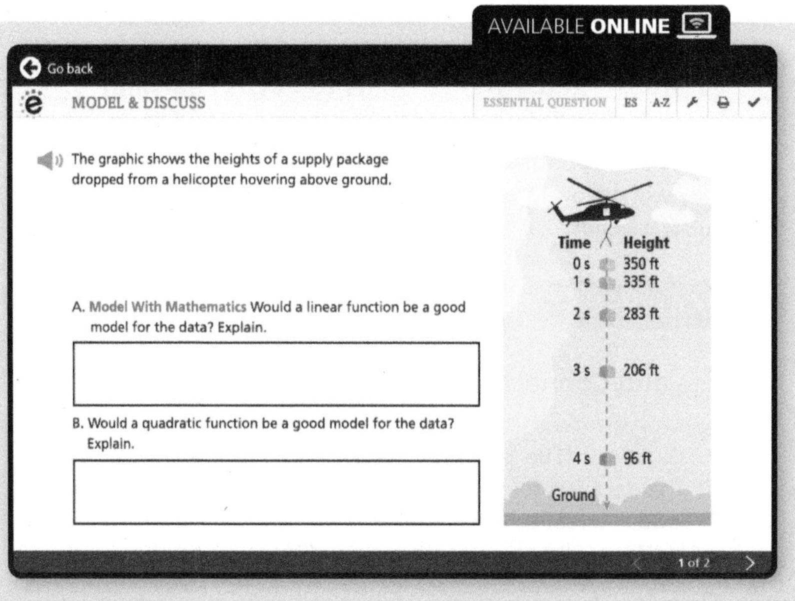
Go back
MODEL & DISCUSS
ESSENTIAL QUESTION ES A-Z
The graphic shows the heights of a supply package dropped from a helicopter hovering above ground.
A. Model With Mathematics Would a linear function be a good model for the data? Explain.
B. Would a quadratic function be a good model for the data? Explain.

Time
Height
0 s
350 ft
1 s
335 ft
2 s
283 ft
3 s
206 ft
4 s
96 ft
Ground
1 of 2

STUDENT EDITION, PAGE 336

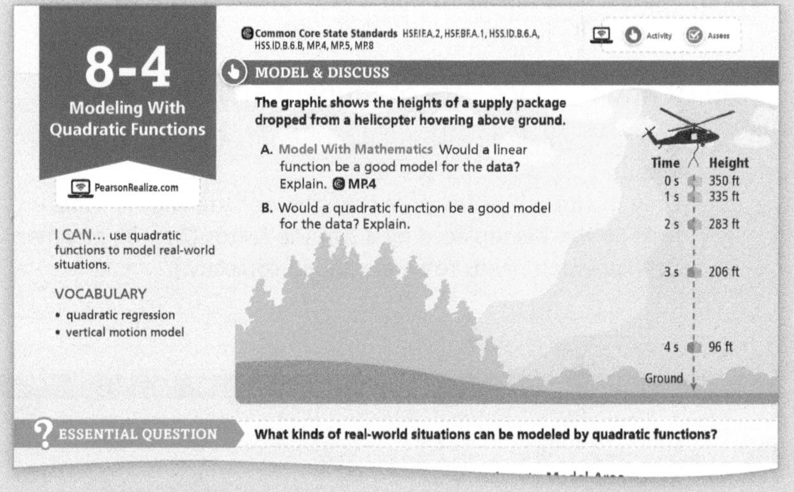
8-4 Modeling With Quadratic Functions
PearsonRealize.com
I CAN… use quadratic functions to model real-world situations.
VOCABULARY
• quadratic regression
• vertical motion model
Common Core State Standards HSF.IF.A.2, HSF.BF.A.1, HSS.ID.B.6.A, HSS.ID.B.6.B, MP.4, MP.5, MP.8
MODEL & DISCUSS
The graphic shows the heights of a supply package dropped from a helicopter hovering above ground.
A. Model With Mathematics Would a linear function be a good model for the data? Explain. MP.4
B. Would a quadratic function be a good model for the data? Explain.

Activity
Assess
Time
Height
0 s
350 ft
1 s
335 ft
2 s
283 ft
3 s
206 ft
4 s
96 ft
Ground

ESSENTIAL QUESTION What kinds of real-world situations can be modeled by quadratic functions?

SAMPLE STUDENT WORK

A. No, a linear function would not be a good model for the data. If you plot the given data, the points do not appear to stay close to a line. The path of the data appears to be more curved than linear.

B. Yes, a quadratic function would be a better model for the data. When you graph the data, the points appear to follow a curved, parabolic path.

INTRODUCE THE ESSENTIAL QUESTION

Establish Mathematics Goals to Focus Learning ETP

Introduce to students that a model can help them analyze information about a real-world situation. Remind them that they will discover how to identify and use the information in a quadratic model as they work through the examples in the lesson.

EXAMPLE 1 Use Quadratic Functions to Model Area

Use and Connect Mathematical Represenations ETP

Q: Explain how the function $f(x) = (2x + 8)(x + 8)$ models the situation. [The length of the pool is $2x$, and the width is x. The deck is 4 feet wide and extends on all sides of the pool, so it adds 8 feet to the length and to the width. So the function for area = length × width is $f(x) = (2x + 8)(x + 8)$.]

Try It! Answers

1. The 2 is replaced by a 3: $f(x) = (3x + 8)(x + 8)$. The expanded form of the function is $f(x) = 3x^2 + 32x + 64$.

Elicit and Use Evidence of Student Thinking ETP

Q: Why can't you just replace the coefficent of x^2 with a 3 in the equation $f(x) = 2x^2 + 24x + 64$?
[Only the length of the pool changes, not the width of the deck. So the 2 is replaced by a 3 in the factor $(2x + 8)$, but then the expression needs to be expanded correctly.]

AVAILABLE **ONLINE**

APPLICATION

EXAMPLE 1 Use Quadratic Functions to Model Area

A company offers rectangular pool sizes with dimensions as shown. Each pool includes a deck around it. If Carolina wants a 15-ft wide pool with a deck, how many square feet will she need to have available in her yard?

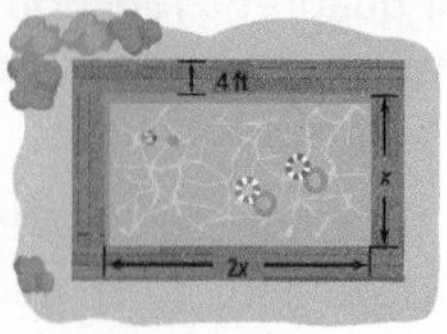
4 ft
x
2x

A. Write a quadratic function to represent the area of the pool and deck.

Let x be the width of the pool.

$$f(x) = (2x + 8)(x + 8)$$ Area = Length × Width

$$= 2x^2 + 24x + 64$$

The quadratic function $f(x) = 2x^2 + 24x + 64$ can be used to find the area of the rectangular pool and the deck.

B. Find the area of the pool and the deck.

$$f(15) = 2(15)^2 + 24(15) + 64$$ Substitute 15 for x.

$$= 874$$

Carolina needs 874 ft^2 to build a 15-ft wide pool with deck.

LOOK FOR RELATIONSHIPS To write the function, think about how the length of the pool is related to its width. Then write expressions for the length and width of the rectangular area that contains both the pool and the deck. MP.7

Try It! 1. Suppose the length of the pool in Example 1 is 3 times the width. How does the function that represents the combined area of the pool and the deck change? Explain.

336 TOPIC 8 Quadratic Functions

Go Online | PearsonRealize.com

Common Error

Try It! 1 When calculating the combined area of the pool and the deck, students may rely on the values shown in the diagram and only add 4 to the length and width to account for the deck. Remind them that that there are an extra 4 feet of deck on all four sides of the pool.

ADDITIONAL EXAMPLES

AVAILABLE **ONLINE**

Go back

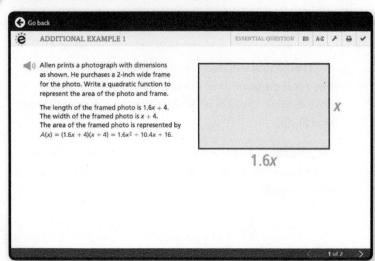

ADDITIONAL EXAMPLE 1 ESSENTIAL QUESTION ES A-Z

Allen prints a photograph with dimensions as shown. He purchases a 2-inch wide frame for the photo. Write a quadratic function to represent the area of the photo and frame.

The length of the framed photo is $1.6x + 4$.
The width of the framed photo is $x + 4$.
The area of the framed photo is represented by $A(x) = (1.6x + 4)(x + 4) = 1.6x^2 + 10.4x + 16$.

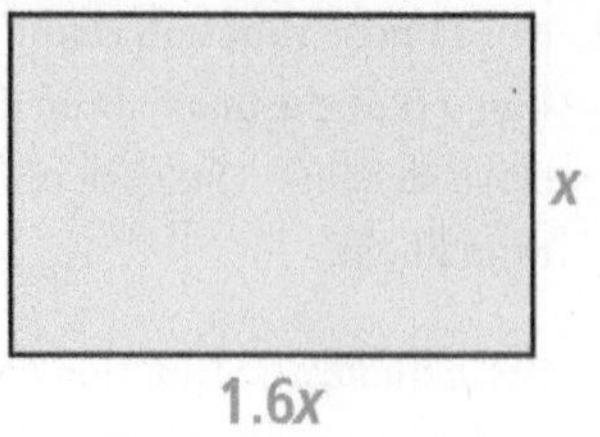
x
1.6x

1 of 2

Example 1 Show students they can also model the area of a photo and a frame with a quadratic function with this additional example.

Q: How can you write a quadratic equation for this situation?
[First, write expressions for the length and the width with frame included. Then multiply the expressions to find the model of the area.]

Go back

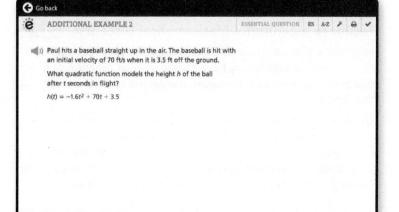

ADDITIONAL EXAMPLE 2 ESSENTIAL QUESTION ES A-Z

Paul hits a baseball straight up in the air. The baseball is hit with an initial velocity of 70 ft/s when it is 3.5 ft off the ground.

What quadratic function models the height h of the ball after t seconds in flight?

$h(t) = -1.6t^2 + 70t + 3.5$

1 of 2

Example 2 Help students apply what they have learned about writing quadratic functions to model the path of a baseball hit into the air with this additional example.

Q: Why would you use a quadratic equation as a model?
[This is a vertical motion problem, and the equation is quadratic.]

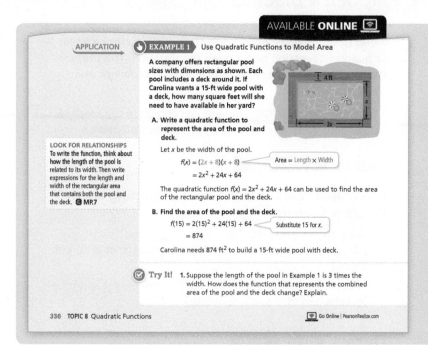

SavvasRealize.com

Activity Assess

EXAMPLE 2 Model Vertical Motion

Facilitate Meaningful Mathematical Discourse ETP

PART A

Q: Why can this situation be represented by a quadratic function?
[The vertical motion of the diver can be modeled by a quadratic function.]

Q: How does the vertical motion model relate to the standard form of a quadratic function?
[It is the same, where *a* is a the constant −16, *b* specifically represents the intial velocity, and *c* specifically represents the initial height.]

PART B

Q: Which do you think has a greater effect on the maximum height, the initial velocity or the initial height?
[initial height; because the increase in height from initial velocity is much less than the height of the platform]

Try It! Answers

2. 21 feet

Elicit and Use Evidence of Student Thinking ETP

Q: What is different about this situation that will impact writing the quadratic function?
[The platform is 10 ft lower, so the initial height h_0 would be 20 in the quadratic function.]

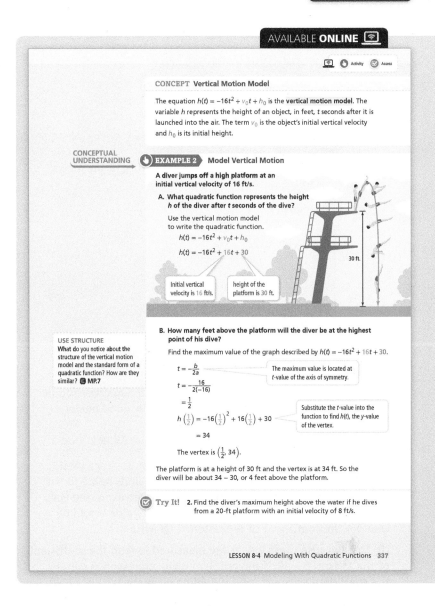

AVAILABLE ONLINE

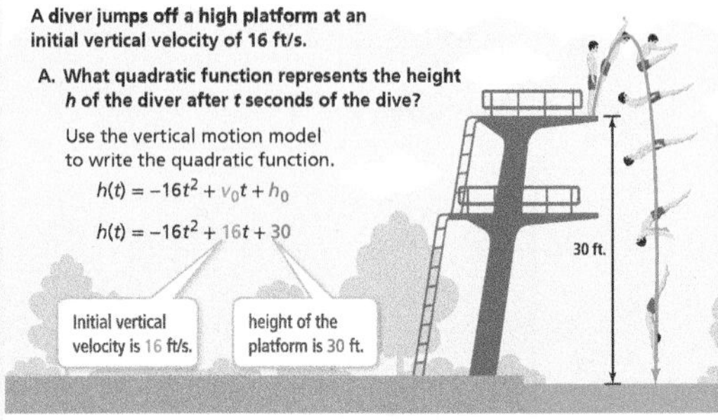

Activity Assess

CONCEPT Vertical Motion Model

The equation $h(t) = -16t^2 + v_0t + h_0$ is the **vertical motion model**. The variable *h* represents the height of an object, in feet, *t* seconds after it is launched into the air. The term v_0 is the object's initial vertical velocity and h_0 is its initial height.

CONCEPTUAL UNDERSTANDING

EXAMPLE 2 Model Vertical Motion

A diver jumps off a high platform at an initial vertical velocity of 16 ft/s.

A. What quadratic function represents the height *h* of the diver after *t* seconds of the dive?

Use the vertical motion model to write the quadratic function.

$h(t) = -16t^2 + v_0t + h_0$

$h(t) = -16t^2 + 16t + 30$

Initial vertical velocity is 16 ft/s.
height of the platform is 30 ft.
30 ft.

B. How many feet above the platform will the diver be at the highest point of his dive?

Find the maximum value of the graph described by $h(t) = -16t^2 + 16t + 30$.

$t = -\frac{b}{2a}$ — The maximum value is located at *t*-value of the axis of symmetry.

$t = -\frac{16}{2(-16)}$

$= \frac{1}{2}$

$h\left(\frac{1}{2}\right) = -16\left(\frac{1}{2}\right)^2 + 16\left(\frac{1}{2}\right) + 30$ — Substitute the *t*-value into the function to find *h*(*t*), the *y*-value of the vertex.

$= 34$

The vertex is $\left(\frac{1}{2}, 34\right)$.

The platform is at a height of 30 ft and the vertex is at 34 ft. So the diver will be about 34 − 30, or 4 feet above the platform.

USE STRUCTURE What do you notice about the structure of the vertical motion model and the standard form of a quadratic function? How are they similar? MP.7

Try It! **2.** Find the diver's maximum height above the water if he dives from a 20-ft platform with an initial velocity of 8 ft/s.

LESSON 8-4 Modeling With Quadratic Functions 337

ELL English Language Learners *(Use with* EXAMPLE 2)

LISTENING BEGINNING Read the example aloud. Explain that initial means to happen in the beginning and that velocity means the speed of an object. When the two words are combined, a new concept is created.

Q: How can you put the two terms together to form your own definition of initial velocity?
[the starting speed of an object]

Q: What is the initial velocity of a golf ball sitting on a golf tee? [0]

WRITING INTERMEDIATE Distribute two sticky notes to each student. On one, have them write words that describe *initial height* and on the other, have them write words that describe *maximum height*. Direct small groups of students to stand near a wall. Have one student from each group throw a small object into the air. Using the wall for reference, have another student mark the initial height of the object with a sticky note and a third student mark the maximum height of the object with a sticky note.

Q: How are the terms *initial velocity* and *maximum velocity* the same? How are they different?
[Both describe velocity. One is the beginning velocity and the other is the fastest.]

SPEAKING ADVANCED Study the illustration of the platform diver. Imagine there are two divers; one is 5 feet tall and one is 6 feet tall. In small groups, discuss the initial height of each diver.

Q: Do you think the divers' initial heights will be the same or different?
[The same; the initial height is based on the height of the platform, not on the height of the diver.]

Q: What other situations might involve an initial height that is not 0?
[Answers may vary. Sample: jumping from a plane, dismounting from a balance beam, knocking a glass off a table]

Activity Assess

EXAMPLE 3 Assess the Fit of a Function by Analyzing Residuals

Pose Purposeful Questions ETP

Q: What do you notice about the relationship between the scatterplot of data and the graph of the function?
[They appear to be a good fit.]

Q: Why is it important to calculate the residuals when finding a good model to fit the data?
[Residuals can help determine how good of a fit the model actually is to the data.]

Try It! Answers

3.

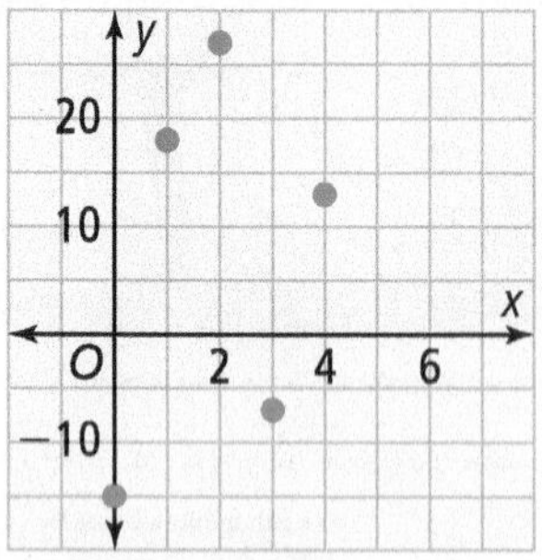

y
20
10
x
O
2
4
6
−10

The residual plot shows both positive and negative residuals. This indicates that function f is a generally good model.

HABITS OF MIND

Use with **EXAMPLES 1, 2, & 3**

Communicate Precisely In Examples 1–3, what units are used for the initial height and velocity? How do these units relate to the coefficient of the t^2-term? Suppose the problem expressed the initial height and velocity using meters. What value would be used for the coefficient of the t^2-term? MP.6

[ft; ft/s; Because these values are measured in feet, the coefficient of the t^2 term is −16. If the problem were expressed in meters, the coefficient of the t^2 term would be different.]

AVAILABLE **ONLINE**

Activity Assess

APPLICATION

EXAMPLE 3 Assess the Fit of a Function by Analyzing Residuals

Each year, for the past five years, ticket prices for a school play have increased by $1. The director used the function $f(x) = -7x^2 + 90x + 750$ to represent the relationship between the number of price increases and the average predicted revenue per show, shown in the table. How well does the function represent the actual revenue data?

Step 1 Use the function to find the predicted values for each price increase. Subtract the predicted from the actual revenues to find the residuals.

Ticket Price ($)	Price Increase x	Actual Revenue ($)	Predicted Revenue $f(x)$	Residual
5	0	745	750	−5
6	1	846	833	+13
7	2	910	902	+8
8	3	952	957	−5
9	4	1008	988	+10

Step 2 Make a scatterplot of the data and graph the function on the same coordinate grid.

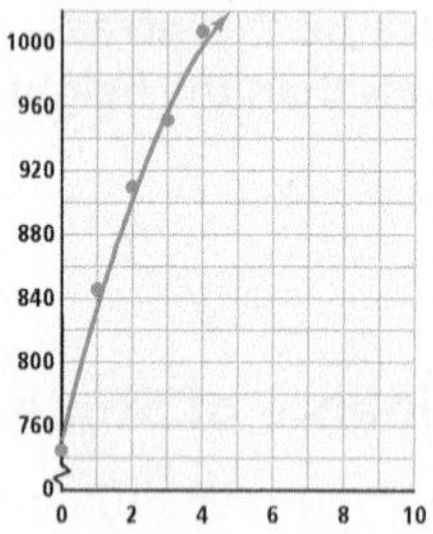

1000
960
920
880
840
800
760
0
0
2
4
6
8
10

Step 3 Make a residual plot to show the fit of the function to the data.

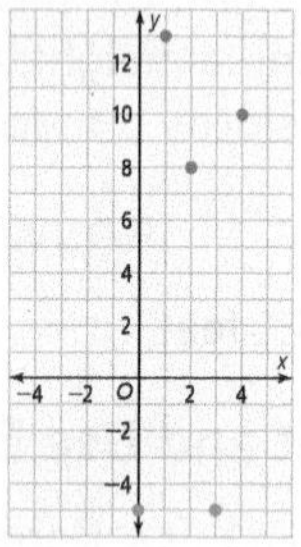

y
12
10
8
6
4
2
x
−4
−2
O
2
4
−2
−4

STUDY TIP
Recall from your work with trend lines, that a good model would have roughly equal numbers of positive and negative residuals.

Step 4 Assess the fit of the function using the residual plot.

The residual plot shows both positive and negative residuals, which indicates a generally good model.

Try It! **3.** Make a scatterplot of the data and graph the function $f(x) = -8x^2 + 95x + 745$. Make a residual plot and describe how well the function fits the data.

Price Increase ($)	0	1	2	3	4
Sales ($)	730	850	930	951	1010

338 TOPIC 8 Quadratic Functions

Go Online | PearsonRealize.com

ADV Advanced Students

USE WITH EXAMPLE 3 Have students compare residuals of a linear model to determine which model is the better fit.

The assistant director thought the function $g(x) = 63x + 766$ would represent the relationship just as well.

Q: Make a residual plot to show the fit of the data.
[Check students' work.]

Q: Which model do you think is a better fit for the data, the director's or the assistant director's? Explain.
[Answers may vary. Sample: director's model; For the assistant director's model, there are two residuals above the x-axis and three residuals below. But most of the residual values are farther away from the x-axis than on the director's model.]

EXAMPLE 4 Fit a Quadratic Function to Data

Establish Mathematics Goals to Focus Learning ETP

Q: What is the difference between linear regression and quadratic regression?
[Linear regression fits a line to data and quadratic regression fits a parabola to data.]

Q: How can you use what you know about linear regression to help you understand quadratic regression?
[The process is similar, but the resulting form of the equation is different.]

Try It! Answers

4. \$1,033; \$1,024.20; The revenue has started to decrease.

Elicit and Use Evidence of Student Thinking ETP

Q: In terms of the context of this situation, explain why a quadratic model makes more sense than a linear model.
[When prices increase a little, people are still likely to buy tickets, so revenue will increase. But if prices increase too much, people will not be able to afford the tickets, so overall revenue will begin to decrease. A quadratic model is a good representation because it increases and then decreases at different rates of change. A linear model would not represent this situation because it would either constantly increase or constantly decrease.]

HABITS OF MIND

Use with **EXAMPLE 4**

Construct Arguments A student thinks that the first list on the graphing calculator screen shown in Step 1 of Example 4 should show the admission prices in dollars: 5, 6, 7, 8, and 9. Explain why these prices are not used for this list. **MP.3**

[Using the number of increases instead of the actual cost of the ticket allows you to start at zero.]

AVAILABLE **ONLINE**

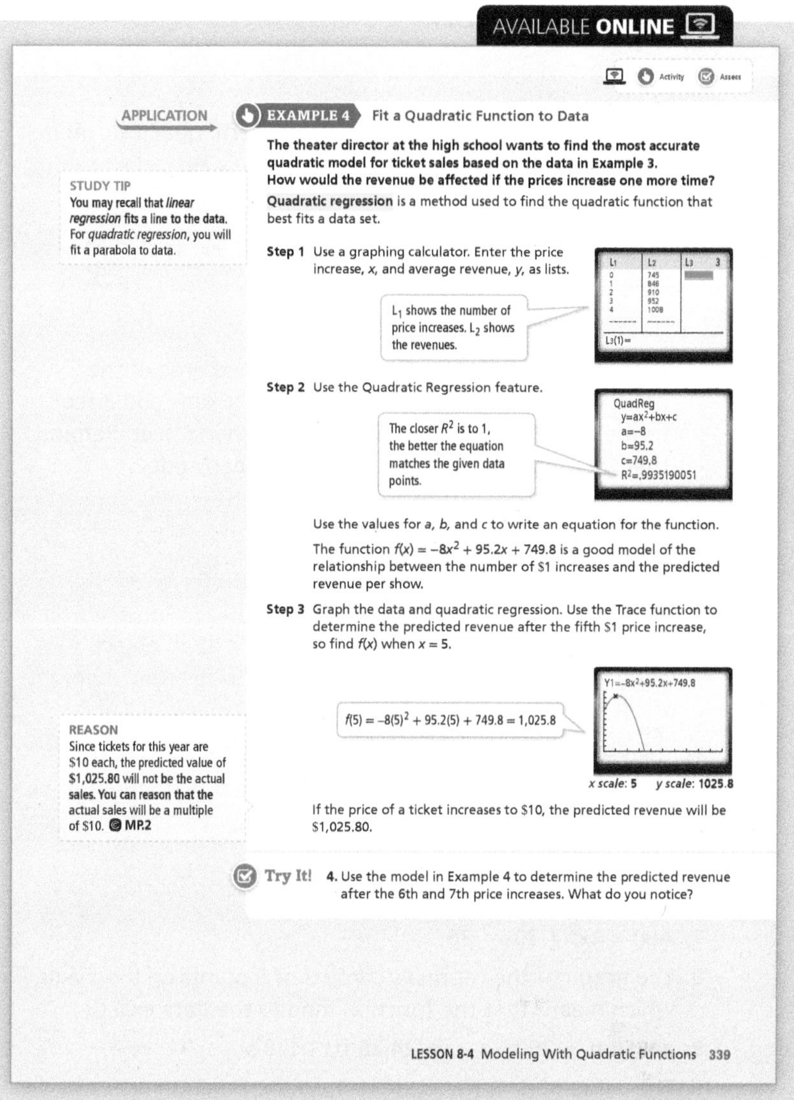
Activity Assess

APPLICATION

EXAMPLE 4 Fit a Quadratic Function to Data

The theater director at the high school wants to find the most accurate quadratic model for ticket sales based on the data in Example 3.
How would the revenue be affected if the prices increase one more time?

Quadratic regression is a method used to find the quadratic function that best fits a data set.

STUDY TIP
You may recall that *linear regression* fits a line to the data. For *quadratic regression*, you will fit a parabola to data.

Step 1 Use a graphing calculator. Enter the price increase, x, and average revenue, y, as lists.

L_1	L_2	L_3 3
0	745	
1	846	
2	910	
3	952	
4	1008	

L3(1) =

L_1 shows the number of price increases. L_2 shows the revenues.

Step 2 Use the Quadratic Regression feature.

QuadReg
y=ax²+bx+c
a=−8
b=95.2
c=749.8
R²=.9935190051

The closer R^2 is to 1, the better the equation matches the given data points.

Use the values for a, b, and c to write an equation for the function.

The function $f(x) = -8x^2 + 95.2x + 749.8$ is a good model of the relationship between the number of \$1 increases and the predicted revenue per show.

Step 3 Graph the data and quadratic regression. Use the Trace function to determine the predicted revenue after the fifth \$1 price increase, so find $f(x)$ when $x = 5$.

Y1=−8x²+95.2x+749.8

$f(5) = -8(5)^2 + 95.2(5) + 749.8 = 1{,}025.8$

x scale: **5** *y scale*: **1025.8**

REASON
Since tickets for this year are \$10 each, the predicted value of \$1,025.80 will not be the actual sales. You can reason that the actual sales will be a multiple of \$10. **MP.2**

If the price of a ticket increases to \$10, the predicted revenue will be \$1,025.80.

Try It! **4.** Use the model in Example 4 to determine the predicted revenue after the 6th and 7th price increases. What do you notice?

LESSON 8-4 Modeling With Quadratic Functions 339

Struggling Students

USE WITH EXAMPLE 4 Students may have difficulty using the quadratic regression and trace features of a graphing calculator.

- Have students practice fitting a quadratic function to data by finding a good model for the data given in Try It! 3.

Q: What data should you enter into the calculator for L_1? for L_2?
[For L_1, enter the price increases. For L_2, enter the sales.]

Q: What equation models the data?
[$y = -12.9x^2 + 117.8x + 736.1$]

Q: How can you tell the equation is a good fit for the data?
[The R^2 value is about 0.983, which is very close to 1.]

Q: Graph the model and use the Trace function to determine the predicted sales after the seventh \$1 price increase.
[about \$927]

CONCEPT SUMMARY Modeling With Quadratic Functions

Q: Why might you want to use a quadratic function to model a real-world situation?
[When the data follows a parabolic pattern, quadratic models can help you analyze and make predictions.]

Do You UNDERSTAND? | Do You KNOW HOW?

Common Error

Exercise 7 When calculating the combined area of the patio with the brick border, students may only add 3 feet to the length and to the width, rather than 6 feet. Remind that that the border must be added to each side.

Answers

1. area and vertical motion problems
2. The equation models the height at time t of an object launched at an initial vertical velocity of b ft/s from a height of c ft.
3. The object is dropped.
4. Chen switched the values of b and c. The function should be $h(t) = -16t^2 + 16t + 6$.
5. $h(t) = -16t^2 + 32t + 20$; 36 ft; 1 s
6. $h(t) = -16t^2 + 120t + 50$; 275 ft; 3.75 s
7. $A(x) = 4x^2 + 30x + 36$
8. The graph of the residuals consists of 5 points on the x-axis, which means that the function models the data exactly.
9. a. 650 ft; 6.25 s b. 24.25 ft; 1.125 s
10. The value of R^2 is not close to 1, so the function does not model the data closely. The data may not be quadratic.
11. In a graph of a vertical motion model, the x-axis represents time, not horizontal distance.
12. The initial velocity is the value of b in the standard form of the quadratic function being graphed, and $\frac{-b}{2a}$ is the t-coordinate of the vertex, which represents the amount of time to reach the maximum height.
13. a. length: $x + 5$, width: $x - 2$
    b. Answers may vary. Sample: Since the width, $x - 2$, must be positive, a reasonable domain is $x > 2$, and a reasonable range is $f(x) > 0$.

AVAILABLE **ONLINE**

Concept Summary Assess

CONCEPT SUMMARY Modeling With Quadratic Functions

AREA

When the length and width of rectangle are each variable expressions, a quadratic function can be used to model the rectangle's area.

$A = (3x + 4)(x - 2)$
$= 3x^2 - 2x - 8$

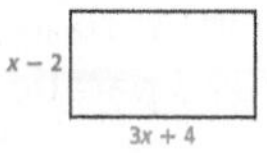
x − 2
3x + 4

VERTICAL MOTION

The vertical motion model gives the height h, in feet, of an object t seconds after launch.

$h(t) = -16t^2 + v_0t + h_0$

v_0 is the initial velocity

h_0 is the initial height

DATA

Quadratic regression finds the best model for a set of quadratic data.

For any model, analyzing the residuals determines how well the model fits the data.

Residual = Data value − Predicted value

Do You UNDERSTAND?

1. ESSENTIAL QUESTION What kinds of real-world situations can be modeled by quadratic functions?
2. **Look for Relationships** How is the function $h(t) = -16t^2 + bt + c$ related to vertical motion? **MP.7**
3. **Vocabulary** What does it mean in a real-world situation when the *initial velocity* is 0?
4. **Error Analysis** Chen uses $h(t) = -16t^2 + 6t + 16$ to determine the height of a ball t seconds after it is thrown at an initial velocity of 16 ft/s from an initial height of 6 ft. Describe the error Chen made. **MP.3**

Do You KNOW HOW?

Write a vertical motion model in the form $h(t) = -16t^2 + v_0t + h_0$ for each situation presented. For each situation, determine how long, in seconds, it takes the thrown object to reach maximum height.

5. Initial velocity: 32 ft/s; initial height: 20 ft
6. Initial velocity: 120 ft/s; initial height: 50 ft
7. A rectangular patio has a length four times its width. It also has a 3-ft wide brick border around it. Write a quadratic function to determine the area of the patio and border.
8. The data are modeled by $f(x) = -2x^2 + 16.3x + 40.7$. What does the graph of the residuals tell you about the fit of the model?

x	y
1	55.0
2	65.3
3	71.6
4	73.9
5	72.2

340 TOPIC 8 Quadratic Functions   Go Online | PearsonRealize.com

14. $f(x) = 2x^2 + 10x + 12$

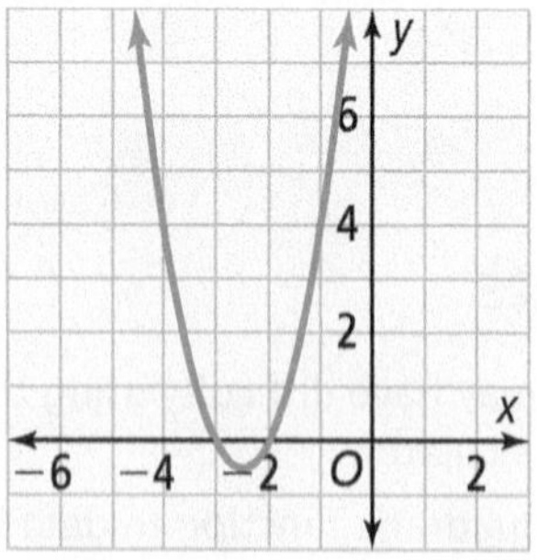
y
6
4
2
x
−6
−4
−2
O
2

$f(8) = 220$

15. $f(x) = 3x^2 - 3x - 18$

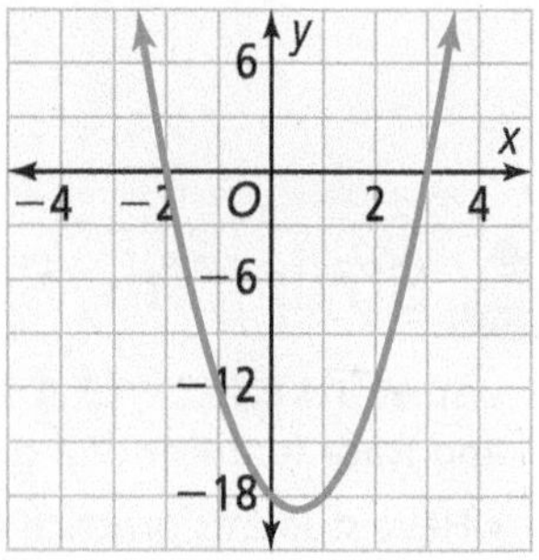
y
6
x
−4
−2
O
2
4
−6
−12
−18

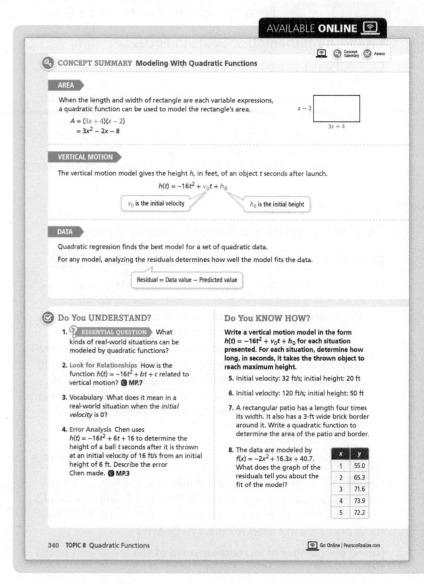

$f(8) = 150$

PRACTICE & PROBLEM SOLVING

AVAILABLE ONLINE

Lesson Practice You may opt to have students complete the automatically scored Practice and Problem Solving items online powered by MathXL for School.

Choose from: **Lesson Practice**
Adaptive Practice

You may also take advantage of the bank of exercises for assigning additional practice.

Assignment Guide

Basic	Advanced
9–20, 23–29	9–14, 18–29

Item Analysis

Example	Items	DOK
1	20, 21	2
	13, 26	3
2	28	1
	9, 11, 16–19, 27	2
	12, 14, 15, 24, 29	3
3	22, 23	2
	10	3
4	25	3

Answers

9–15. See previous page.

20.

x	y	f(x)	Residual
−2	13	11	+2
−1	8	4	+4
0	6	1	+5
1	9	2	+7
2	12	7	+5

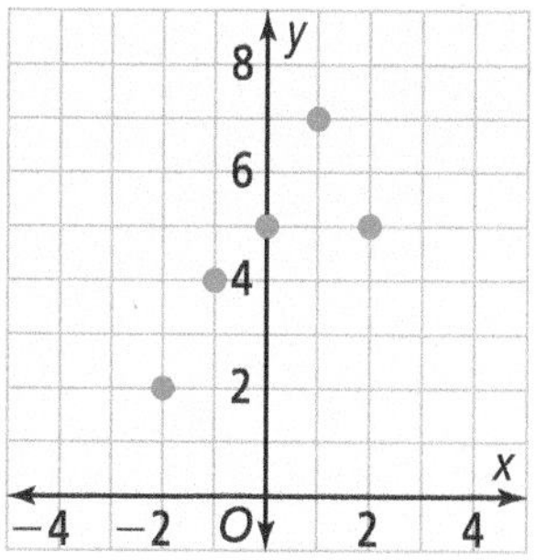
y
8
6
4
2
x
−4
−2
O
2
4

All the residuals are positive, which indicates the function may not be a good fit.

21.

x	y	f(x)	Residual
−2	−6	−8	+2
−1	−1	−2	+1
0	3	2	+1
1	4	4	0
2	3	4	−1

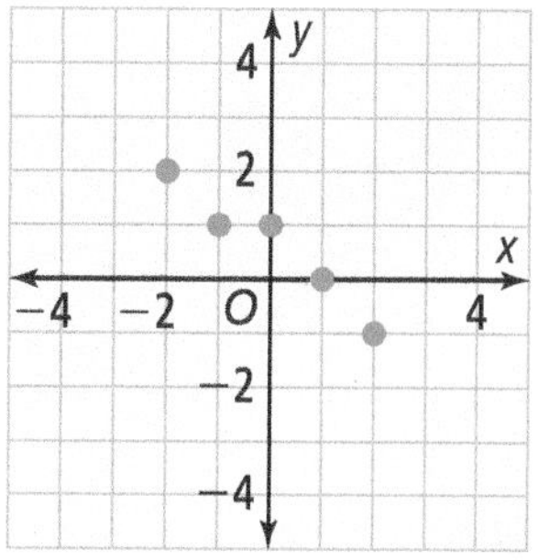
y
4
2
x
−4
−2
O
4
−2
−4

The residuals are on or close to the x-axis, which indicates the function may be a good fit.

AVAILABLE ONLINE

PRACTICE & PROBLEM SOLVING

Scan for Multimedia | Practice | Tutorial | Additional Exercises Available Online

UNDERSTAND

9. Make Sense and Persevere For each vertical motion model, identify the maximum height reached by the object and the amount of time for the object to reach the maximum height. MP.1
a. $h(t) = -16t^2 + 200t + 25$
b. $h(t) = -16t^2 + 36t + 4$

10. Reason When a student uses quadratic regression on a graphing calculator to model data, the value of R^2 is 0.2. Make a conjecture about the fit of the model. MP.2

11. Error Analysis Describe and correct the error a student made when interpreting the graph of the vertical motion model $h(t) = -at^2 + bt + c$. MP.3

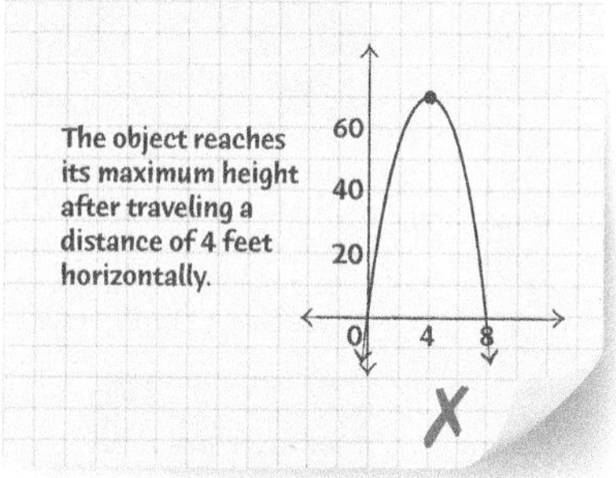
The object reaches its maximum height after traveling a distance of 4 feet horizontally.
60
40
20
0
4
8
X

12. Look for Relationships In the graph of a vertical motion model shown, how is the initial velocity related to the vertex of the parabola? MP.7

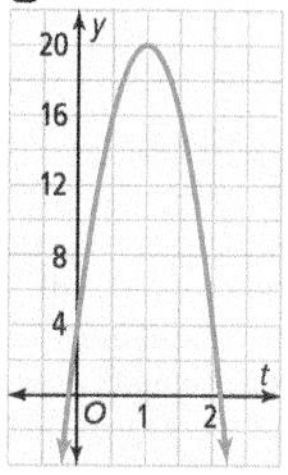
y
20
16
12
8
4
O
1
2
t

13. Higher Order Thinking The function $f(x) = x^2 + 3x - 10$ models the area of a rectangle.
a. Describe the length and width of the rectangle in terms of x.
b. What is a reasonable domain and range for the situation? Explain.

PRACTICE

Use a quadratic function to model the area of each rectangle. Graph the function. Evaluate each function for $x = 8$. SEE EXAMPLE 1

14.

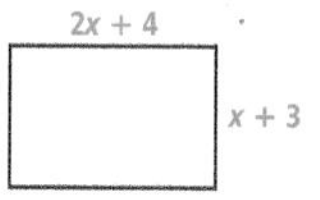
2x + 4
x + 3

15.

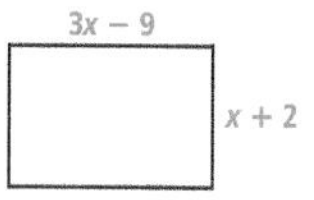
3x − 9
x + 2

Write a function h to model the vertical motion for each situation, given $h(t) = -16t^2 + v_0t + h_0$. Find the maximum height. SEE EXAMPLE 2

16. initial vertical velocity: 32 ft/s initial height: 75 ft
$h(t) = -16t^2 + 32t + 75$; 91 ft

17. initial vertical velocity: 200 ft/s initial height: 0 ft
$h(t) = -16t^2 + 200t$; 625 ft

18. initial vertical velocity: 50 ft/s initial height: 5 ft
$h(t) = -16t^2 + 50t + 5$; 44.0625 ft

19. initial vertical velocity: 48 ft/s initial height: 6 ft
$h(t) = -16t^2 + 48t + 6$; 42 ft

Make a scatterplot of the data and graph the function on the same coordinate grid. Calculate the residuals and make a residual plot. Describe the fit of the function to the data. SEE EXAMPLE 3

20. $f(x) = 2x^2 - x + 1$

x	y
−2	13
−1	8
0	6
1	9
2	12

21. $f(x) = -x^2 + 3x + 2$

x	y
−2	−6
−1	−1
0	3
1	4
2	3

Use a graphing calculator to find a quadratic regression for each data set. Round values to the nearest ten-thousandth. SEE EXAMPLE 4

22.

x	y
0	15.50
1	11.21
2	8.43
3	5.67
4	3.43

$y = 0.2943x^2 - 4.1451x + 15.3726$

23.

x	y
100	567.3
500	443.2
900	362.3
1,300	312.2
1,700	307.3

$y = .0.0001x^2 - 0.3791x + 603.8225$

Answers

24. $h(t) = -16t^2 + 200$; 56 ft

25. Answers may vary. Sample: No; a price of \$15 is too high. Using quadratic regression on a graphing calculator gives the model $f(x) = -2.57x^2 + 67.57x - 182.8$. The price generating the highest profit is the x-value of the vertex, which is $\frac{-b}{2a}$, which is about 13.15. So, the price that will maximize profits should be about \$13.

26. $f(x) = -1.25x^2 + 75x + 60$; \$1,060.00

29. Part A $h(t) = -16t^2 + 35t + 6$

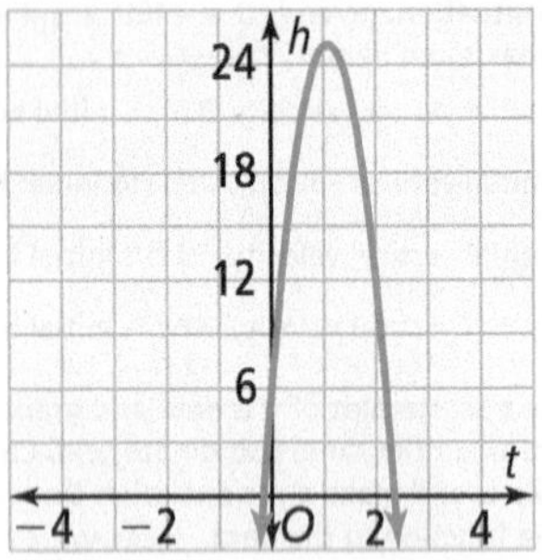

h
24
18
12
6
t
−4
−2
O
2
4

Part B Yes; The maximum height of the ball is about 25 ft, so it will land on the upper deck.

AVAILABLE ONLINE

Practice Tutorial
Mixed Review Available Online

PRACTICE & PROBLEM SOLVING

APPLY

24. Model With Mathematics A student drops a rock over the edge of the well and hears it splash into water after 3 seconds. Write a function in the form $h(t) = -16t^2 + v_0t + h_0$ to determine the height of the rock above the bottom of the well t seconds after the student drops the rock. What is the distance from the surface of the water to the bottom of the well? MP.4

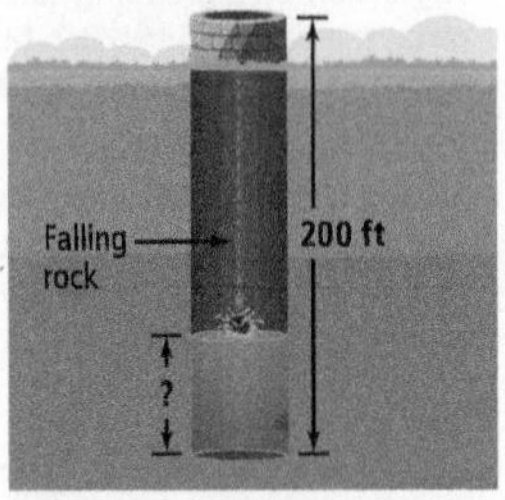

Falling rock
200 ft
?

25. Construct Arguments The table below shows profits for a new model of headphones as a function of price x. The manufacturer says the price should be set at \$15 to maximize profits. Do you agree? Justify your answers. MP.3

Price (\$)	Profit (\$ thousands)
16	240
17	223
18	200
19	173
20	140

26. Mathematical Connections Dakota bought 120 ft of wire fencing at \$0.50/ft to enclose a rectangular playground. The playground surface will be covered with mulch at a cost of \$1.25/ft². Write a quadratic function that can be used to determine the total cost of fencing and mulch for a playground with side length x. What is the cost if one side is 20 ft?

ASSESSMENT PRACTICE

27. The function $h(t) = -16t^2 + 96t + 10$ models the path of a projectile.

By inspecting the function you can tell that the initial height of the projectile is 10 ft, and the initial velocity is 96 ft/s.

The projectile reaches a maximum height of 154 ft at time 3 s.

28. SAT/ACT A basketball is thrown straight up into the air from a height of 2.1 ft with an initial velocity of 7 ft/s. Which function models the height of the ball after t seconds?

Ⓐ $h(t) = -16t^2 + 2.1t + 7$
Ⓑ $h(t) = -16t^2 - 2.1t + 7$
Ⓒ $h(t) = -16t^2 + 2.1t - 7$
Ⓓ $h(t) = -16t^2 + 7t + 2.1$
Ⓔ $h(t) = -16t^2 - 7t + 2.1$

29. Performance Task A baseball player is standing 1.5 ft away from the edge of the upper deck that is 20 ft above the baseball field. He throws a ball into the air for the fans sitting in the upper deck.

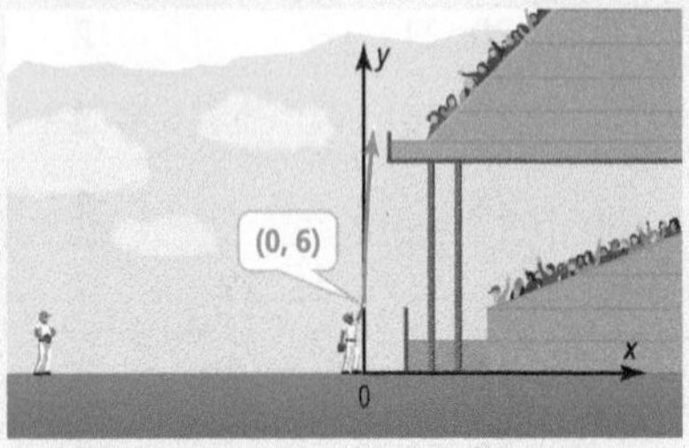

y
(0, 6)
x
0

Part A Write a quadratic function that can be used to determine the height of the ball if it is thrown at an initial velocity of 35 ft/s from a height of 6 ft. Graph the function.

Part B The seats for the upper deck start 2 ft from the edge. Will the ball travel high enough to land on the upper deck?

SavvasRealize.com

Assess Tutorials Worksheets

LESSON QUIZ

Use the Lesson Quiz to assess students' understanding of the mathematics in the lesson.

Students can take the Lesson Quiz online or you can download a printable copy from **SavvasRealize.com**. The Lesson Quiz is also available in the *Assessment Resources* book.

Item Analysis

Item	DOK	Standards
1	2	HSF.BF.A.1, HSF.IF.A.2
2	1	HSF.IF.A.2
3	2	HSF.BF.A.1
4	2	HSS.ID.B.6.B
5	1	HSS.ID.B.6.A

RtI Use the student scores on the Lesson Quiz to prescribe differentiated assignments.

If students take the Lesson Quiz online, it will be automatically scored and appropriate differentiated practice will be assigned based on student performance.

I Intervention	0–3 points	• Reteach to Build Understanding • Mathematical Literacy and Vocabulary • Additional Practice
O On-Level	4 points	• Mathematical Literacy and Vocabulary • Additional Practice • Enrichment
A Advanced	5 points	• Enrichment

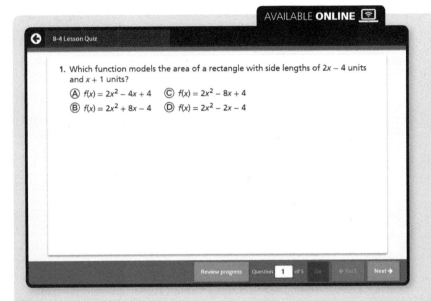

AVAILABLE **ONLINE**

8-4 Lesson Quiz

1. Which function models the area of a rectangle with side lengths of $2x - 4$ units and $x + 1$ units?

Ⓐ $f(x) = 2x^2 - 4x + 4$ Ⓒ $f(x) = 2x^2 - 8x + 4$
Ⓑ $f(x) = 2x^2 + 8x - 4$ Ⓓ $f(x) = 2x^2 - 2x - 4$

Review progress Question 1 of 5 Go ← Back Next →

ASSESSMENT RESOURCES

Name ____________

enVision Algebra 1
PearsonRealize.com

8-4 Lesson Quiz

Modeling with Quadratic Functions

1. Which function models the area of a rectangle with side lengths of $2x - 4$ units and $x + 1$ units?

Ⓐ $f(x) = 2x^2 - 4x + 4$ Ⓒ $f(x) = 2x^2 - 8x + 4$
Ⓑ $f(x) = 2x^2 + 8x - 4$ Ⓓ $f(x) = 2x^2 - 2x - 4$

2. The function $h(t) = -16t^2 + 32t + 24$ models the height h, in feet, of a ball t seconds after it is thrown straight up into the air. What are the initial velocity and the initial height of the ball?

Ⓐ 16 ft/s; 32 ft Ⓒ 32 ft/s; 24 ft
Ⓑ 24 ft/s; 32 ft Ⓓ 48 ft/s; 24 ft

3. One edge of a painting is 6 in. longer than the other edge. The picture has a 2-inch-wide frame. Write a quadratic function f in standard form to represent the total area of the picture and frame. Then find the total area of the picture and the frame if its shorter edge is 8 inches long.

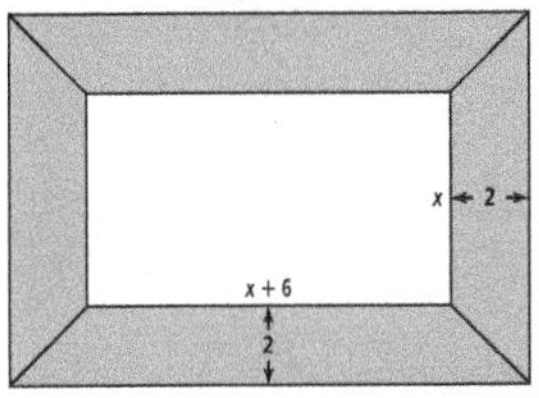
x
2
x + 6
2

function: $f(x) = x^2 + 14x + 40$

area: 216 in.^{2}

4. Avery collects data about the value of a collectible baseball card over time. The table shows the card's value y, in dollars, after x years. The quadratic function $f(x) = 3x^2 - 7x + 10$ models the relationship of the data. Calculate the residuals for the data.

x	y	Residual
0	9	−1
1	7	1
2	10	2
3	12	−4

5. Charles uses a graphing calculator to find a quadratic regression model f for a given set of data. When he compares model f to an earlier regression model g for the same data, he determines that g more accurately models the data. Which of the following statements are true? Select all that apply.

Ⓐ Function f likely had fewer residuals near the x-axis than function g.
Ⓑ Function f likely had more residuals equal to 0 than function g.
Ⓒ Function g had more residuals near the y-axis than function f.

enVision™ Algebra 1 • Assessment Resources

DIFFERENTIATED RESOURCES

I = Intervention **O** = On-Level **A** = Advanced

= This activity is available as a digital assignment powered by MathXL® for School.

AVAILABLE **ONLINE**

Reteach to Build Understanding I

Provides scaffolded reteaching for the key lesson concepts.

Name ____________ enVision Algebra 1 PearsonRealize.com

8-4 Reteach to Build Understanding

Modeling with Quadratic Functions

1. Match the phrase with the correct type of quadratic model.

Input the table of values into a graphing calculator.

x	1	2	3	4
y	0	4	16	27

Use the quadratic regression feature to find a quadratic model for the data, $y = 1.75x^2 + 0.55x - 2.75$.

The side lengths of a square can be represented by the expression $x - 2$. The formula for area of a square is $A = s^2$, where s is the side length. The quadratic model for the area of the square is $A = (x - 2)^2$.

A ball is dropped from the top of 10-foot-tall bleachers at an initial upward velocity of 2 ft/s. The quadratic model for the height h of the ball t seconds after it falls is $h(t) = -16t^2 + 2t + 10$.

area model | vertical motion model | data model

2. Kiyo and his friend are designing a rectangular garden with a 2-foot-wide path around it. They want the length of the garden to be 3 times as long as the width. Kiyo and his friend both write quadratic functions to find the area of the garden and path. Which one has the correct model? Explain.

Kiyo's Work
$f(x) = (x + 4)(3x + 4)$
$f(x) = 3x^2 + 16x + 16$

Kiyo's Friend's Work
$f(x) = (x + 2)(3x + 2)$
$f(x) = 3x^2 + 8x + 4$

Kiyo; Kiyo's friend only included the width of the path around half of the garden.

3. Fill in the missing information to find the area of the quadratic model for a rectangle. Then find the area for $x = 4$ inches.

$f(x) = (3x + 1)(\underline{x} + \underline{2})$
$f(x) = \underline{3x^2} + 6x + x + \underline{2}$
$f(x) = \underline{3x^2} + 7x + \underline{2}$
area = 78 square inches

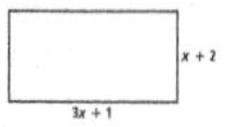
x + 2
3x + 1

enVision™ Algebra 1 • Teaching Resources

Additional Practice I O

Provides extra practice for each lesson.

Name ____________ enVision Algebra 1 PearsonRealize.com

8-4 Additional Practice

Modeling with Quadratic Functions

1. An acrobat is on a platform that is 25 feet in the air. She jumps with an initial upward vertical velocity of 4 ft/s. Write a quadratic function to represent the height h of the acrobat t seconds after the jump. If a safety net is placed 5 feet above the ground, how long will it take for her to land safely on the net? $-16t^2 + 4t + 25$; 5 s
2. A disc is thrown into the air with an upward velocity of 20 ft/s. Its height h in feet after t seconds is given by the function $h = -16t^2 + 20t + 6$. What is the maximum height the disc reaches? How long does it take for the disc to reach the maximum height? How long does it take for the disc to descend to 3 feet above the ground? 12.25 ft; 0.625 s; 1.385 s
3. During a physics experiment, a class drops a golf ball off a bridge toward pavement below. The bridge is 75 ft high. The function $h = -16t^2 + 75$ gives the golf ball's height h in feet above the pavement after t seconds. Use the graph of the function at the right. After how many seconds does the golf ball hit the pavement? about 2.2 s

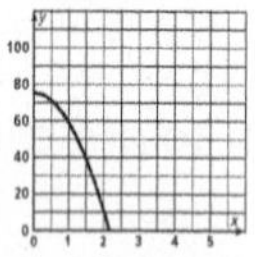
y
100
80
60
40
20
0
1
2
3
4
5
x

4. The length of a rectangular park is twice its width. The park is surrounded by a 3-foot-wide path. Write a quadratic function to represent the total area of the park and the path. $f(x) = (x + 6)(2x + 6) = 2x^2 + 18x + 36$
5. For the vertical motion model $h(t) = -16t^2 + 54t + 3$, identify the maximum height reached by an object and the amount of time the object is in the air to reach the maximum height. Round to the nearest tenth. 48.6 ft; 1.7 s
6. Compare the models $f(x) = -0.5x^2 + 0.5x + 10$ and $g(x) = -0.5x^2 + 0.45x + 10.25$ by evaluating the residuals in the tables shown. Analyze how the points are distributed about the line $y = 0$. Which function better represents the actual data?

f(x)					
x	1	2	3	4	5
residual	10	9	8	4	0

g(x)					
x	1	2	3	4	5
residual	10.2	9.15	7.1	4.05	0

The function $f(x)$ best represents the actual data.

7. An object is thrown off a platform that is 15 ft high with an initial upward velocity of 8.5 ft/s. What function models the height h of the object after t seconds?
$h(t) = -16t^2 + 8.5t + 15$

enVision™ Algebra 1 • Teaching Resources

Enrichment O A

Presents engaging problems and activities that extend the lesson concepts.

Name ____________ enVision Algebra 1 PearsonRealize.com

8-4 Enrichment

Modeling with Quadratic Functions

The St. Louis Gateway Arch in St. Louis, Missouri was built as a monument to the vision of Thomas Jefferson and of St. Louis's role in the westward expansion of the United States. The shape of the arch can be approximated by a parabola.

1. Let y be the height of the arch, in feet, and let x be the distance from the left base of the arch, in feet. Suppose a quadratic equation that models the shape of the Gateway Arch is $y = -0.00635x^2 + 4x$. Graph the function. What do you notice about the graph? How would you interpret the graph in terms of the shape of the arch?
The distance between the x-intercepts is about 630 units and the maximum height is about 630 units. That means the distance between the legs of the Gateway Arch is 630 feet and the height is also 630 feet.
2. The foundation for each leg of the Gateway Arch is about 60 feet deep. Sketch a graph of the Gateway Arch, indicating the foundations on the graph.

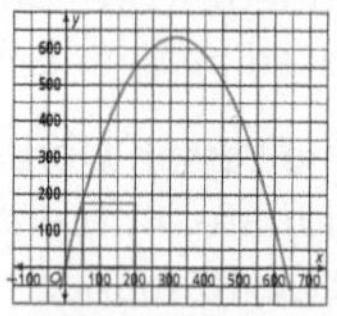
y
600
500
400
300
200
100
-100
O
100
200
300
400
500
600
700
x

3. If you had to fit a rectangular scaffolding structure inside the left side of the Gateway Arch for repairs 175 feet above the ground, at what height would the platform be? What is the closest distance from the scaffolding structure to the base of the arch? Draw a diagram of the scaffolding structure on the graph in Item 2. 175 feet, 47 feet
4. The exterior of the Gateway Arch is made of 142 4-foot stainless steel sections. Building the Gateway Arch cost $13,420,168. If that amount were divided evenly among all the sections, what would each one cost?
$94,508.23

enVision™ Algebra 1 • Teaching Resources

Mathematical Literacy and Vocabulary I O

Helps students develop and reinforce understanding of key terms and concepts.

Name ____________ enVision Algebra 1 PearsonRealize.com

8-4 Mathematical Literacy and Vocabulary

Modeling with Quadratic Functions

Concept List

vertical motion model	residual
v_0	initial height
quadratic function	quadratic regression
scatterplot	residual plot

Choose the word or phrase from the Concept List that best represents the contents of each box.

1. Initial velocity v_0	2. The difference between an actual value and a predicted value residual
3. A method used to write a quadratic model for data that may show a quadratic pattern quadratic regression	4. $h(t) = -16t^2 + v_0t + h_0$ vertical motion model
5. h_0 initial height	6. A graph of plotted points that show the relationship between two data sets scatterplot
7. A graph of plotted points that represent the relationship between the x-value and the difference of the predicted value and the actual value residual plot	8. $y = ax^2 + bx + c$ quadratic function

enVision™ Algebra 1 • Teaching Resources

Digital Resources and Video Tutorials I O A

The **Reteach to Build Understanding, Additional Practice,** and **Enrichment** activities are available as digital assignments powered by MathXL for School. These activities are automatically assigned when students complete the lesson quiz online and are automatically scored.

Students can access instructional tutorials using the **Virtual Nerd app.**

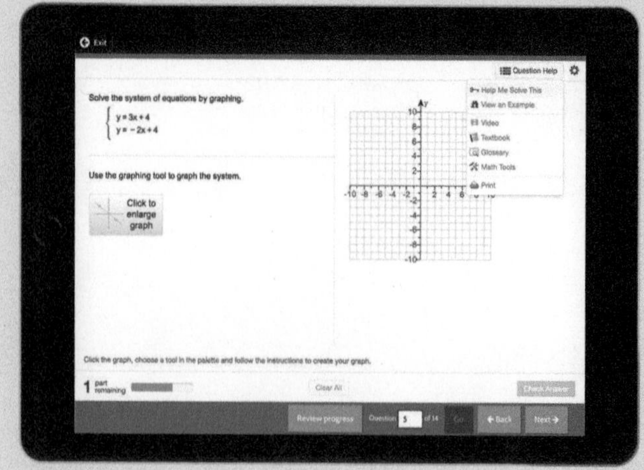
Exit
Question Help
Solve the system of equations by graphing.
Use the graphing tool to graph the system.
Click to enlarge graph
Help Me Solve This
View an Example
Video
Textbook
Glossary
Math Tools
Print
Clear All
Check Answer
Review progress
Back
Next

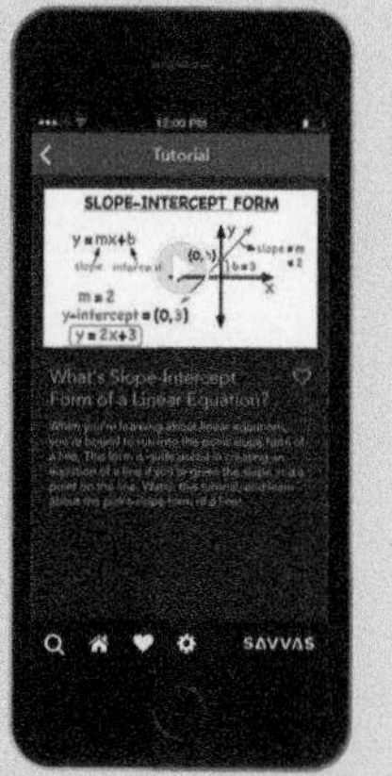
Tutorial
SLOPE-INTERCEPT FORM
y = mx + b
What's Slope-Intercept Form of a Linear Equation?
SAVVAS

Students can also access Virtual Nerd videos using the **BouncePages app** to scan exercise pages marked with this icon. Students can download both apps for free in their mobile devices' app store.

Video

TOPIC 8
Mathematical Modeling in 3 Acts: The Long Shot

Lesson Overview

FOCUS

Objective

Students will be able to:

✔ Use mathematical modeling to represent a problem situation and to propose a solution.

✔ Test and verify the appropriateness of their math models.

✔ Explain why the results from their mathematical models might not align exactly with the problem situation.

Essential Understanding

Many real-world problem situations can be represented with a mathematical model, but that model might not represent the real-world situation exactly.

COHERENCE

Earlier in this topic, students:

- Explored different forms of quadratic functions and models.

In this lesson, students:

- Develop a mathematical model to represent and propose a solution to a problem situation involving quadratic functions.

Later in this topic, students will:

- Refine their mathematical modeling skills by comparing linear, exponential, and quadratic models.

RIGOR

This mathematical modeling lesson focuses on application of both math content and math practices and processes.

- Students draw on their understanding of concepts related to quadratic functions to develop a representative model.
- Students apply their mathematical model to test and validate its applicability to similar problem situations.

MATHEMATICAL MODELING IN 3 ACTS

PearsonRealize.com

Common Core State Standards HSA.REI.D.10, HSF.IF.B.4, MP.4

Video

The Long Shot

Have you ever been to a basketball game where they hold contests at halftime? A popular contest is one where the contestant needs to make a basket from half court to win a prize. Contestants often shoot the ball in different ways. They might take a regular basketball shot, a hook shot, or an underhand toss.

What is the best way to shoot the basketball to make a basket? Think about this during this Mathematical Modeling in 3 Acts lesson.

Scan for Multimedia

ACT 1 Identify the Problem

1. What is the first question that comes to mind after watching the video?
2. Write down the Main Question you will answer.
3. Make an initial conjecture that answers this Main Question.
4. Explain how you arrived at your conjecture.

ACT 2 Develop a Model

5. Use the math that you have learned in the topic to refine your conjecture.

ACT 3 Interpret the Results

6. Did your refined conjecture match the actual answer exactly? If not, what might explain the difference?

TOPIC 8 Mathematical Modeling in 3 Acts 343

Student Companion

Students can do their work for the task on pages 183–184 of their *Student Companion* or on **SavvasRealize.com**.

Mathematics Overview COMMON CORE STANDARDS

Content Standards

In this lesson, students apply concepts and skills related to Common Core Standards **HSA.REI.D.10** and **HSF.IF.B.4**.

HSA.REI.D.10 Understand that the graph of an equation in two variables is the set of all its solutions plotted in the coordinate plane.

HSF.IF.B.4 For a function that models a relationship between two quantities, interpret key features of graphs, and sketch graphs showing key features.

Mathematical Practice Standards

MP.4 Model With Mathematics

To solve the problem presented, students identify variables and the relationship among them, develop a model that represents the situation, and use the model to propose a solution. Students interpret their solutions and propose explanations for why their answer may not match the real-world answer.

Students also engage in sense-making **(MP.1)**, abstract and quantitative reasoning **(MP.2)**, and strategic tool use **(MP.5)**. In testing their models, students look for patterns in the structure of their models **(MP.7, MP.8)**.

Video

The Long Shot

In this mathematical modeling task, students analyze partial views of basketball shots to determine whether the attempts are successful. They need to determine whether the ball's path will pass through an additional point—the basket. To do so, they apply concepts they study in Topic 8.

ACT 1 The Hook

Play the video. The video shows an athlete taking basketball shots, each of which traces out a half-parabola. The video does not show the result of any of the attempts.

After the question brainstorming, present to students the Main Question they will be tasked with answering. Remind students to write down their questions and conjectures.

MAIN QUESTION

Which of the player's shots go in?

Shot 1

ACT 2 Modeling With Math

Think about the task. Ask students to speculate how they can determine which shots go in. Then have them think about what information they need.

Reveal the information. Use the tool, which includes a coordinate grid for each shot, to give students specific information about the paths.

What's the connection? Give students time to struggle as they think about how to connect their ideas to what they learned in this topic about quadratic functions. Challenge them to use related vocabulary, such as *line of symmetry, parabola*, and *vertex*.

Before showing the answers, find out where there is disagreement. Allow students to argue their cases and update their conjectures.

INTERESTING MOMENTS WITH STUDENTS

Students may conclude you need to reflect only one point to find out if the ball goes in. You can reflect the basketball hoop across the line of symmetry and see if it reflects onto a ball on the other side of the line. Invite any student who uses this method to explain it during Act 3. This may lead to a conversation about how Shot 5 is a counterexample to this conjecture.

Necessary Information

Shot types

- Shots 1–3: free throw
- Shots 4–6: three-point shot

The highest point of each shot is shown.
No wind affects the path of the ball.

Shot 1
y
O

Video

ACT 3 The Solution

Play the video. The final video shows the entirety of the six shots. The outcome of each shot is revealed. After each shot, ask students for a show of hands of whose initial conjecture was accurate and give them some praise.

Shot 1

MAIN QUESTION ANSWER

Shot 1: The ball goes in – a swish.

Shot 2: The ball goes in – off the backboard.

Shot 3: The ball misses – short.

Shot 4: The ball goes in.

Shot 5: The ball looks like it's going in, but then it hits the left side of the rim and bounces away.

Shot 6: The ball misses. It hits the back of the rim.

Do the "post-game" analysis. Help students understand why a shot's result may not match what the parabola predicts. Students should focus on how the paths are not perfect parabolas. Students may suggest reasons the paths are not quite symmetric, such as gravity and air resistance. Look for creative ideas students offer to improve the method for predicting whether a shot goes in.

ONE POSSIBLE SOLUTION

For each shot, draw the line of symmetry. Then reflect the points shown across the line to see whether or not the shot goes in.

Using this method, Shots 1, 4, and 5 will go in, Shots 2 and 6 will be too long, and Shot 3 will be too short.

INTERESTING MOMENTS WITH STUDENTS

Shots 2 and 5 are designed to start a discussion. Students can discuss how the backboard influences the path of the ball for Shot 2. Meanwhile, Shot 5 may look like it will go in, but basketball shots do not necessarily travel in the plane shown in the video.

SEQUEL

As students finish, tell them that the athlete makes another shot, this time from half court. Ask them to describe a shot that goes in and a shot that misses. [Answers will vary. Students' descriptions should include the line of symmetry and enough points to determine whether the shot goes in.]

A-Z Glossary

LESSON 8-5

Linear, Exponential, and Quadratic Models

Lesson Overview

FOCUS

Objective

Students will be able to:

✔ Determine which model—linear, exponential, or quadratic—best fits a set of data.

✔ Use fitted functions to solve problems in the context of data.

Essential Understanding

Linear, quadratic, and exponential functions are differentiated by their average rates of change over different intervals. A linear function models a relationship between x and y in which the differences between successive y-values are constant. A quadratic function models a relationship in which the second differences, or the difference between the first differences, are constant. An exponential function models a relationship where the ratios of consecutive y-values are constant.

COHERENCE

Previously in this topic, students:

- Used quadratic functions to analyze data and solve problems.

In this lesson, students:

- Compare the use of quadratic models of data with linear models and exponential models.

Later in Statistics, students will:

- Explore other functions, including cubic functions, to anaylze data.

RIGOR

This lesson emphasizes a blend of *conceptual understanding* and *application*.

- Students understand how the rates of change shown in data tables can be used to identify linear, exponential, and quadratic functions.
- Students apply their understanding of functions to analyze packing expenses and population models.

Vocabulary Builder

REVIEW VOCABULARY — **English** | *Spanish*

- **exponential function** | *función exponencial*
- **linear function** | *función lineal*
- **quadratic function** | *función cuadrática*
- **regression** | *regression*

VOCABULARY ACTIVITY

Discuss the essential features of *linear*, *exponential*, and *quadratic functions*. As needed complete this matching activity to help students visually differentiate among the graphs of the three functions.

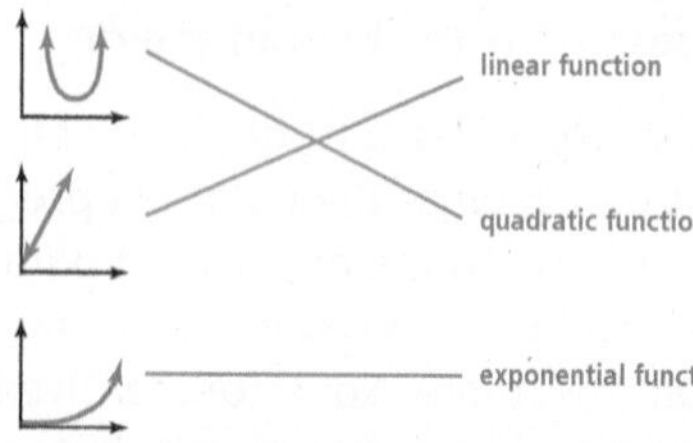
linear function
quadratic function
exponential function

Student Companion

Students can do their in-class work for the lesson on pages 185–188 of their *Student Companion* or in Savvas Realize.

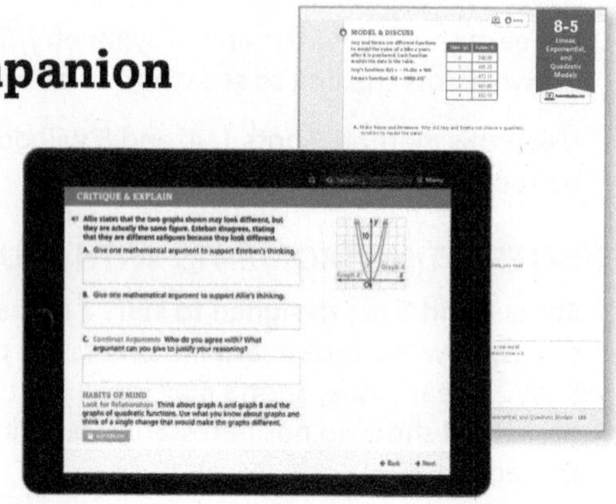

Mathematics Overview

COMMON CORE STANDARDS

Content Standards

In this lesson, students focus on these standards:

HSF.LE.A.3 Observe using graphs and tables that a quantity increasing exponentially eventually exceeds a quantity increasing linearly, quadratically, or (more generally) as a polynomial function.

HSS.ID.B.6.A Fit a function to the data; use functions fitted to data to solve problems in the context of the data. Use given functions or choose a function suggested by the context. Emphasize linear, quadratic, and exponential models.

Mathematical Practice Standards

These standards are highlighted in this lesson:

MP.1 Make Sense and Persevere

Students evaluate the characteristics of different algebraic models for linear, exponential, and quadratic functions. They refine their models to solve problems.

MP.7 Use Structure

Students examine the structure of linear, exponential, and quadratic graphs and relate their findings to the structure of corresponding tables.

STEP 1 | Explore

MODEL & DISCUSS

INSTRUCTIONAL FOCUS Students use their knowledge of functions to determine whether a linear, exponential, or quadratic function bests models a set of data.

STUDENT COMPANION Students can complete the *Model & Discuss* activity on page 185 of their *Student Companion.*

Before WHOLE CLASS

Implement Tasks that Promote Reasoning and Problem Solving ETP

Q: What do you notice about the data in the table in relation to the two functions?
[Answers may vary. Sample: As the number of years increases, the value decreases.]

During SMALL GROUP

Support Productive Struggle in Learning Mathematics ETP

Q: How are the two functions similar? How are they different?
[Answers may vary. Sample: They both include the value 500; Jacy's function is linear and Emma's function is exponential.]

Q: What clues from the data should you consider when determining whether a linear, quadratic, or exponential function would better model the data?
[Look at where the data are increasing and decreasing.]

For Early Finishers

Q: How might you adjust the model to better fit the data?
[Answers may vary. Sample: Change the slope so that the values of the model are closer to the data after four years. Use $f(x) = -11.9x + 500$. Initially, the model is a little farther off, but it better matches the trend starting at year 3.]

After WHOLE CLASS

Facilitate Meaningful Mathematical Discourse ETP

Ask students to share how they evaluated the models using the data in the table.

Q: How can you tell that a function is a good model for a situation? [The predicted values from the model and the actual values from the data are close.]

Q: What strategies did you use to determine which function is a better fit for the model? [Answers may vary. Sample: Since the changes in value were not constant, the relationship did not seem to be linear, so I chose the exponential model.]

HABITS OF MIND *Use with* **MODEL & DISCUSS**

Communicate Precisely How is finding the best model for data in a real-world situation similar to finding the best model in a mathematical situation? How is it different? **MP.6**

[They both involve using information that you have to inform the model. Real-world situations can be more complex to model because they are affected by many factors.]

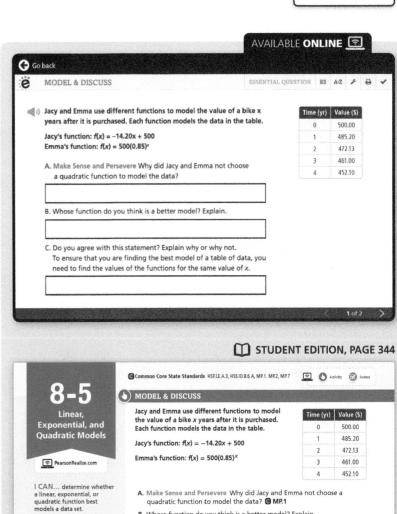

AVAILABLE **ONLINE**

Go back

MODEL & DISCUSS — ESSENTIAL QUESTION | ES | A-Z

Jacy and Emma use different functions to model the value of a bike *x* years after it is purchased. Each function models the data in the table.

Jacy's function: $f(x) = -14.20x + 500$
Emma's function: $f(x) = 500(0.85)^x$

Time (yr)	Value ($)
0	500.00
1	485.20
2	472.13
3	461.00
4	452.10

A. Make Sense and Persevere Why did Jacy and Emma not choose a quadratic function to model the data?

B. Whose function do you think is a better model? Explain.

C. Do you agree with this statement? Explain why or why not.
To ensure that you are finding the best model of a table of data, you need to find the values of the functions for the same value of *x*.

1 of 2

STUDENT EDITION, PAGE 344

8-5
Linear, Exponential, and Quadratic Models

PearsonRealize.com

I CAN… determine whether a linear, exponential, or quadratic function best models a data set.

Common Core State Standards HSF.LE.A.3, HSS.ID.B.6.A, MP.1, MP.2, MP.7 — Activity — Assess

MODEL & DISCUSS

Jacy and Emma use different functions to model the value of a bike *x* years after it is purchased. Each function models the data in the table.

Jacy's function: $f(x) = -14.20x + 500$

Emma's function: $f(x) = 500(0.85)^x$

Time (yr)	Value ($)
0	500.00
1	485.20
2	472.13
3	461.00
4	452.10

A. Make Sense and Persevere Why did Jacy and Emma not choose a quadratic function to model the data? MP.1

B. Whose function do you think is a better model? Explain.

C. Do you agree with this statement? Explain why or why not.
To ensure that you are finding the best model for a table of data, you need to find the values of the functions for the same values of *x*.

ESSENTIAL QUESTION How can you determine whether a linear, exponential, or quadratic function …

SAMPLE STUDENT WORK

A. A quadratic function wouldn't make sense because the bike's value is always decreasing.

B. Jacy's function is a better model because it stays closer to the data points.

C. When you are comparing multiple models for a set of data, it is helpful to find the values of the functions to compare and determine which is the best model.

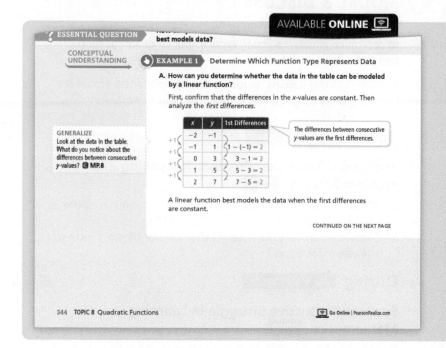

INTRODUCE THE ESSENTIAL QUESTION

Establish Mathematics Goals to Focus Learning ETP

Point out to students that they will examine data for characteristics of linear, exponential, and quadratic functions, which they will then use to determine which model best fits the data.

EXAMPLE 1 Determine Which Function Type Represents Data

Pose Purposeful Questions ETP

Q: Why is it important to use the consecutive *x*-values when calculating the differences or ratios?
[If the differences between the *x*-values are not constant, then the differences or ratios between the *y*-values will not be accurate to determine the best model that represents the data.]

Q: How is it helpful to recognize whether 1st differences, 2nd differences, or ratios between consecutive *y*-values are equal?
[It helps determine which type of function to use to represent the data.]

AVAILABLE **ONLINE**

ESSENTIAL QUESTION best models data?

CONCEPTUAL UNDERSTANDING

EXAMPLE 1 Determine Which Function Type Represents Data

A. How can you determine whether the data in the table can be modeled by a linear function?

First, confirm that the differences in the *x*-values are constant. Then analyze the *first differences.*

GENERALIZE
Look at the data in the table. What do you notice about the differences between consecutive *y*-values? MP.8

x	*y*	1st Differences
−2	−1	
−1	1	1 − (−1) = 2
0	3	3 − 1 = 2
1	5	5 − 3 = 2
2	7	7 − 5 = 2

(+1 between consecutive *x*-values)

The differences between consecutive *y*-values are the first differences.

A linear function best models the data when the first differences are constant.

CONTINUED ON THE NEXT PAGE

ADDITIONAL EXAMPLES

AVAILABLE **ONLINE**

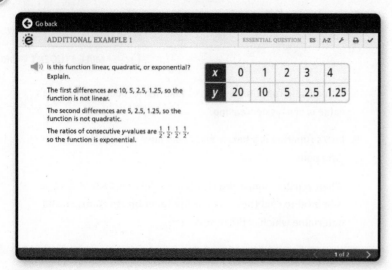

Go back

ADDITIONAL EXAMPLE 1 ESSENTIAL QUESTION ES A-Z

Is this function linear, quadratic, or exponential? Explain.

x	0	1	2	3	4
y	20	10	5	2.5	1.25

The first differences are 10, 5, 2.5, 1.25, so the function is not linear.

The second differences are 5, 2.5, 1.25, so the function is not quadratic.

The ratios of consecutive *y*-values are $\frac{1}{2}, \frac{1}{2}, \frac{1}{2}, \frac{1}{2}$, so the function is exponential.

1 of 2

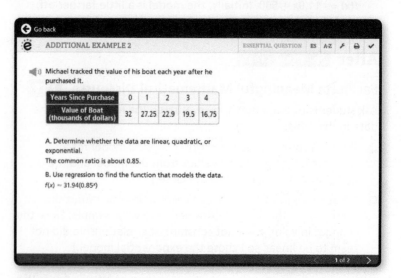

Go back

ADDITIONAL EXAMPLE 2 ESSENTIAL QUESTION ES A-Z

Michael tracked the value of his boat each year after he purchased it.

Years Since Purchase	0	1	2	3	4
Value of Boat (thousands of dollars)	32	27.25	22.9	19.5	16.75

A. Determine whether the data are linear, quadratic, or exponential.
The common ratio is about 0.85.

B. Use regression to find the function that models the data.
$f(x) \approx 31.94(0.85^x)$

1 of 2

Example 1 Give students more practice choosing the most appropriate function to model data with this additional example.

Q: What patterns do you see in the table?
[As *x* increases, *y* decreases.]

Q: How can you tell what kind of function is shown?
[Since the ratios between consecutive *y*-values equal the same value, the function is exponential.]

Example 2 Help students practice using the regression features of a graphing calculator to find a function to model the data with this additional example.

Q: How can you use R^2 to analyze the quality of your function as a model for the data?
[R^2 values that are very close to 1 indicate a good model for the data.]

STEP 2 Understand & Apply

Try It! Answers

1. a. Quadratic; 2nd differences are the same.
   b. Exponential; ratios of consecutive y-values are the same.

Elicit and Use Evidence of Student Thinking ETP

Q: Does analyzing where the data are increasing or decreasing help to determine which type of function will be a better model? [You may look for data that are decreasing and then increasing to support that a quadratic model is best. However, in part (a), the data are continually decreasing, so it may be harder to tell only by looking at the data that a quadratic model is best.]

Common Error

Try It! 1 In part (a), students may say that the difference between −2 and −5 is 3 rather than −3. This will cause them to find second differences that are not equal. Remind them that the order in which they subtract is important and should be $y_2 - y_1$. Then, the first difference is −5 − (−2), or −3.

AVAILABLE **ONLINE**

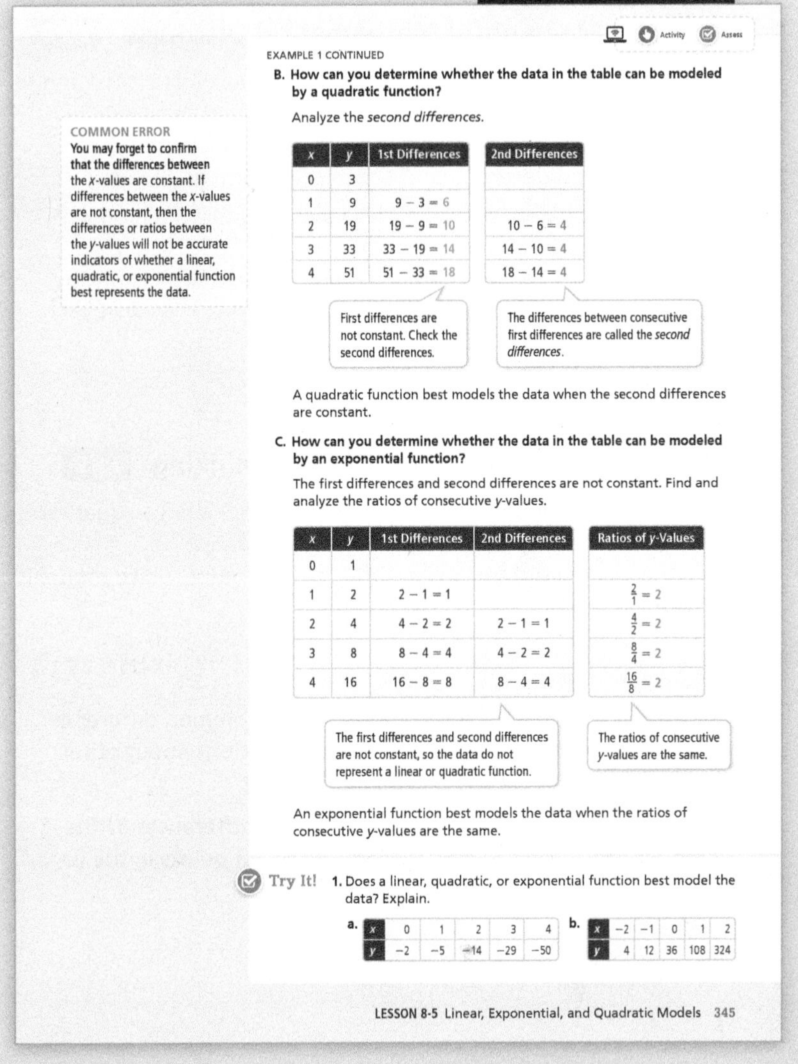

Activity Assess

EXAMPLE 1 CONTINUED

B. How can you determine whether the data in the table can be modeled by a quadratic function?

Analyze the *second differences*.

COMMON ERROR
You may forget to confirm that the differences between the x-values are constant. If differences between the x-values are not constant, then the differences or ratios between the y-values will not be accurate indicators of whether a linear, quadratic, or exponential function best represents the data.

x	y	1st Differences	2nd Differences
0	3		
1	9	9 − 3 = 6	
2	19	19 − 9 = 10	10 − 6 = 4
3	33	33 − 19 = 14	14 − 10 = 4
4	51	51 − 33 = 18	18 − 14 = 4

First differences are not constant. Check the second differences.

The differences between consecutive first differences are called the *second differences*.

A quadratic function best models the data when the second differences are constant.

C. How can you determine whether the data in the table can be modeled by an exponential function?

The first differences and second differences are not constant. Find and analyze the ratios of consecutive y-values.

x	y	1st Differences	2nd Differences	Ratios of y-Values
0	1			
1	2	2 − 1 = 1		$\frac{2}{1} = 2$
2	4	4 − 2 = 2	2 − 1 = 1	$\frac{4}{2} = 2$
3	8	8 − 4 = 4	4 − 2 = 2	$\frac{8}{4} = 2$
4	16	16 − 8 = 8	8 − 4 = 4	$\frac{16}{8} = 2$

The first differences and second differences are not constant, so the data do not represent a linear or quadratic function.

The ratios of consecutive y-values are the same.

An exponential function best models the data when the ratios of consecutive y-values are the same.

Try It! 1. Does a linear, quadratic, or exponential function best model the data? Explain.

a.

x	0	1	2	3	4
y	−2	−5	−14	−29	−50

b.

x	−2	−1	0	1	2
y	4	12	36	108	324

LESSON 8-5 Linear, Exponential, and Quadratic Models 345

ADV Advanced Students

USE WITH EXAMPLE 1 Have students explore different types of functions by examining the data in the tables shown.

1.

x	0	1	2	3	4
y	3.5	0.25	−3	−6.25	−9.5

2.

x	0	0.1	0.2	0.3	0.4
y	0.4	0.8	1.6	3.2	6.4

Q: What type of function would you use to model the data in each table? [linear; exponential]

Q: Create a table of values that could either be modeled by a linear, an exponential, or a quadratic function. Exchange with a classmate and ask them to identify which type of function should be used to model the data. [Check students work.]

Activity Assess

EXAMPLE 2 Choose a Function Type for Real-World Data

Facilitate Meaningful Mathematical Discourse ETP

Q: What information do you need about a real-world situation to determine a function type?
[You need to know how the data change, when the data increase and decrease, and the average rate of change.]

Q: How do you determine when to use regression to model real-world data?
[You use regression when you need to make predictions or estimate data values that are not given.]

Try It! Answers

2. linear; $y = -10.55x + 100.02$

Elicit and Use Evidence of Student Thinking ETP

Q: What step is helpful in determining whether a linear, quadratic, or exponential model best fits the given data?
[Analyze the differences or ratios to determine which model is the best fit.]

HABITS OF MIND

Use with **EXAMPLES 1 & 2**

Reasoning If a table of data does not have common differences or a common ratio, can you still make predictions about other data points in the data set? Explain. MP.2

[Yes, even if you do not know the common differences or the common ratio, you can still analyze the given points in the data set to try to determine other data points.]

AVAILABLE ONLINE

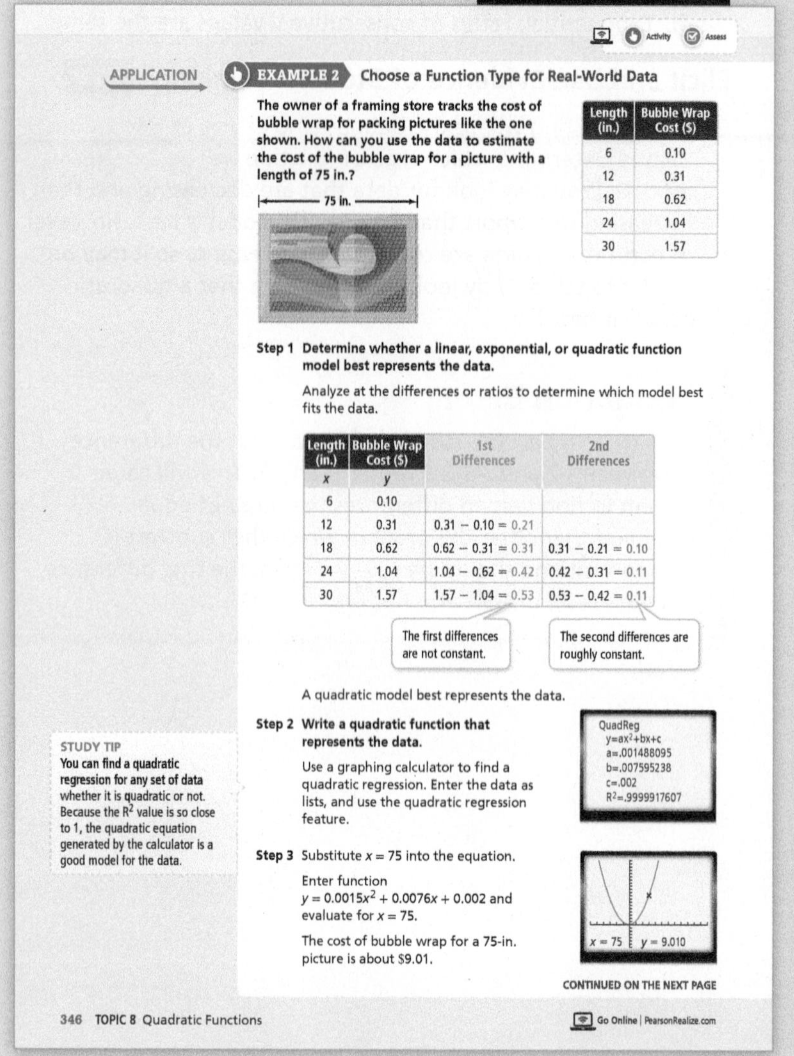

Activity Assess

APPLICATION

EXAMPLE 2 Choose a Function Type for Real-World Data

The owner of a framing store tracks the cost of bubble wrap for packing pictures like the one shown. How can you use the data to estimate the cost of the bubble wrap for a picture with a length of 75 in.?

75 in.

Length (in.)	Bubble Wrap Cost ($)
6	0.10
12	0.31
18	0.62
24	1.04
30	1.57

Step 1 Determine whether a linear, exponential, or quadratic function model best represents the data.

Analyze at the differences or ratios to determine which model best fits the data.

Length (in.)	Bubble Wrap Cost ($)	1st Differences	2nd Differences
x	y		
6	0.10		
12	0.31	$0.31 - 0.10 = 0.21$	
18	0.62	$0.62 - 0.31 = 0.31$	$0.31 - 0.21 = 0.10$
24	1.04	$1.04 - 0.62 = 0.42$	$0.42 - 0.31 = 0.11$
30	1.57	$1.57 - 1.04 = 0.53$	$0.53 - 0.42 = 0.11$

The first differences are not constant.

The second differences are roughly constant.

A quadratic model best represents the data.

Step 2 Write a quadratic function that represents the data.

Use a graphing calculator to find a quadratic regression. Enter the data as lists, and use the quadratic regression feature.

QuadReg
y=ax²+bx+c
a=.001488095
b=.007595238
c=.002
R²=.9999917607

STUDY TIP
You can find a quadratic regression for any set of data whether it is quadratic or not. Because the R^2 value is so close to 1, the quadratic equation generated by the calculator is a good model for the data.

Step 3 Substitute $x = 75$ into the equation.

Enter function $y = 0.0015x^2 + 0.0076x + 0.002$ and evaluate for $x = 75$.

The cost of bubble wrap for a 75-in. picture is about $9.01.

$x = 75$ $y = 9.010$

CONTINUED ON THE NEXT PAGE

346 TOPIC 8 Quadratic Functions

Go Online | PearsonRealize.com

Struggling Students

USE WITH EXAMPLE 2 When the values of y are decreasing, some students may struggle to find the differences.

- Have students practice finding differences that are negative numbers.

x	0	1	2	3	4
y	7	2	−1	−2	−1

Q: Find the first differences.
[−5, −3, −1, 1]

Q: Find the second differences.
[2, 2, 2]

Q: What type of function can you use to model the data?
[quadratic function]

EXAMPLE 3 Compare Linear, Exponential, and Quadratic Growth

Facilitate Meaningful Mathematical Discourse ETP

Q: What do you know about the growth of the cities based on the graph?
[Answers may vary. Sample: In the first five years, City A is growing fastest and City C is growing slowest.]

Q: Why is it important to look at the rate of change for multiple intervals?
[to see how the growth rate is changing]

Q: How would you expect the growth rate to change over the same interval for a linear, quadratic, and exponential function?
[The growth rate should be constant for a linear function. It should gradually increase or decrease for a quadratic function. It should increase or decrease more quickly for an exponential function.]

Try It! Answers

3. Initially, $g(0) > f(0) > h(0)$, but eventually, $h(x)$ will be greater than $f(x)$ and $g(x)$ for larger values of x. For example, if $x = 15$, $f(15) = 47$, $g(15) = 453$, $h(15) = 32{,}768$, so $h(x)$ will eventually exceed $f(x)$ and $g(x)$.

Elicit and Use Evidence of Student Thinking ETP

Q: How do you know that $h(x)$ will eventually exceed $f(x)$ and $g(x)$?
[$h(x)$ is increasing exponentially and $f(x)$ and $g(x)$ are increasing at slower rates of change.]

HABITS OF MIND

Use with **EXAMPLE 3**

Generalize How can the rate of change help determine the type of function that best fits the data? MP.8

[If the rate of change is constant, then the function is linear. If the differences between the different rates of change are constant, then the function is quadratic.]

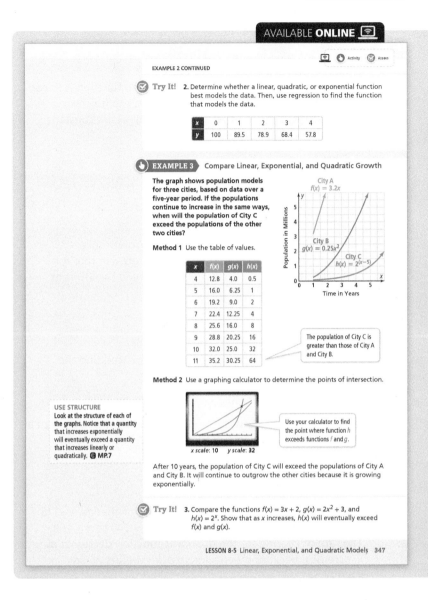

AVAILABLE **ONLINE**

Activity Assess

EXAMPLE 2 CONTINUED

Try It! **2.** Determine whether a linear, quadratic, or exponential function best models the data. Then, use regression to find the function that models the data.

x	0	1	2	3	4
y	100	89.5	78.9	68.4	57.8

EXAMPLE 3 Compare Linear, Exponential, and Quadratic Growth

The graph shows population models for three cities, based on data over a five-year period. If the populations continue to increase in the same ways, when will the population of City C exceed the populations of the other two cities?

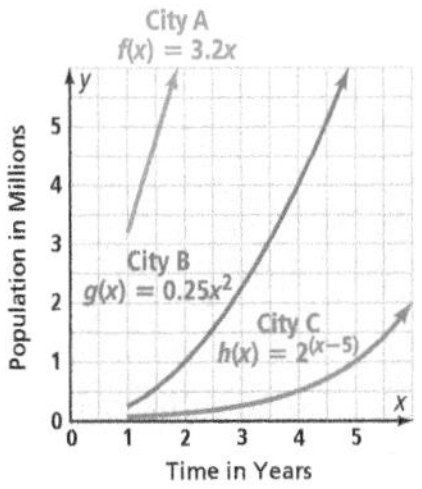
City A
$f(x) = 3.2x$
City B
$g(x) = 0.25x^2$
City C
$h(x) = 2^{(x-5)}$
Population in Millions
Time in Years
y
x
0
1
2
3
4
5

Method 1 Use the table of values.

x	$f(x)$	$g(x)$	$h(x)$
4	12.8	4.0	0.5
5	16.0	6.25	1
6	19.2	9.0	2
7	22.4	12.25	4
8	25.6	16.0	8
9	28.8	20.25	16
10	32.0	25.0	32
11	35.2	30.25	64

The population of City C is greater than those of City A and City B.

Method 2 Use a graphing calculator to determine the points of intersection.

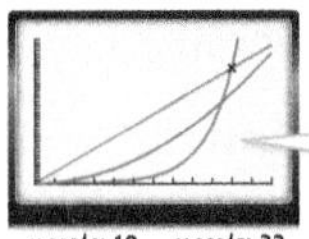

x scale: 10 *y scale*: 32

Use your calculator to find the point where function h exceeds functions f and g.

USE STRUCTURE
Look at the structure of each of the graphs. Notice that a quantity that increases exponentially will eventually exceed a quantity that increases linearly or quadratically. MP.7

After 10 years, the population of City C will exceed the populations of City A and City B. It will continue to outgrow the other cities because it is growing exponentially.

Try It! **3.** Compare the functions $f(x) = 3x + 2$, $g(x) = 2x^2 + 3$, and $h(x) = 2^x$. Show that as x increases, $h(x)$ will eventually exceed $f(x)$ and $g(x)$.

LESSON 8-5 Linear, Exponential, and Quadratic Models 347

ELL English Language Learners (*Use with* EXAMPLE 3)

READING BEGINNING Write the words *line* and *linear* on the board and ask students to read them silently. Ask students to think of how the words are similar and how they are different. Notice how adding a suffix to *line* turns the word into an adjective.

Q: What word do you hear in *exponential* when the suffix -ial is removed? [exponent]

Q: How is *exponential* used as an adjective to describe an equation?
[It describes an equation in which the exponent is a variable.]

SPEAKING INTERMEDIATE *Population* refers to the number of people that live in a geographical area. *Model* refers to a representation used for comparison. Group students in pairs to discuss a definition for the term *population model*.

Q: What might population models be used for?
[Answers will vary. Sample: to determine the number of homes, the size of schools, and the number of doctors a community will need in the future]

WRITING ADVANCED Some meanings for the term *model* include a standard for comparison, an image made from clay or wax that represents what a final product will look like, a person who poses for an artist to draw, or a person who is pictured wearing clothing that is for sale.

Q: Make a graphic organizer around the word *model*. Include as many meanings as you can. [Check students work.]

Q: Write a paragraph explaining the meaning of the term *model* in this example. [Check students work.]

CONCEPT SUMMARY Linear, Quadratic, and Exponential Functions

Q: How can the data in a table show the characteristics of linear, quadratic, and exponential functions?
[If the first differences are constant then the function is linear. If the second differences are constant then the function is quadratic. If the ratios of consecutive y-values are constant then the function is exponential.]

Do You UNDERSTAND? | Do You KNOW HOW?

Common Error

Exercise 6 Students may think that the growth rate does not change. Remind them that the growth rate for quadratic functions is not constant, so it will be different over different intervals.

Answers

1. Look at the first differences, second differences, and the ratios of consecutive terms.
2. quadratic or exponential
3. Data with constant first differences should be modeled with a linear function, not a quadratic function.
4. quadratic
5. linear
6. The profit is decreasing. The average rate of change is –175 from $x = 120$ to $x = 140$ and –375 from $x = 140$ to $x = 160$. The rate of change for the quadratic function decreases as x increases, because the maximum profit occurs when $x = 112.5$.

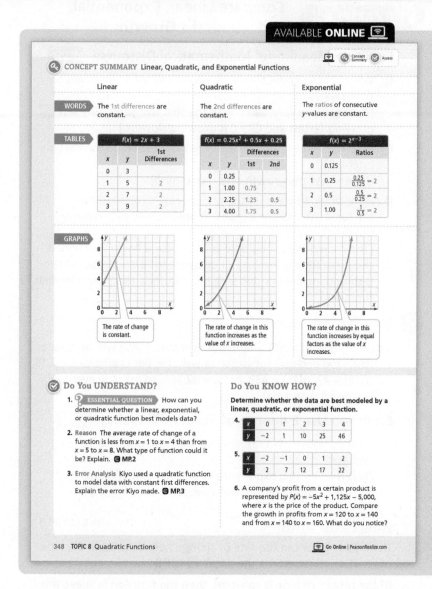

AVAILABLE ONLINE

Concept Summary Assess

CONCEPT SUMMARY Linear, Quadratic, and Exponential Functions

	Linear	Quadratic	Exponential
WORDS	The 1st differences are constant.	The 2nd differences are constant.	The ratios of consecutive y-values are constant.

TABLES

$f(x) = 2x + 3$

x	y	1st Differences
0	3	
1	5	2
2	7	2
3	9	2

$f(x) = 0.25x^2 + 0.5x + 0.25$

x	y	Differences 1st	Differences 2nd
0	0.25		
1	1.00	0.75	
2	2.25	1.25	0.5
3	4.00	1.75	0.5

$f(x) = 2^{x-3}$

x	y	Ratios
0	0.125	
1	0.25	$\frac{0.25}{0.125} = 2$
2	0.5	$\frac{0.5}{0.25} = 2$
3	1.00	$\frac{1}{0.5} = 2$

GRAPHS

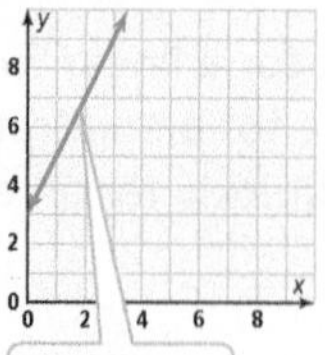
y
8
6
4
2
0
0 2 4 6 8
x

The rate of change is constant.

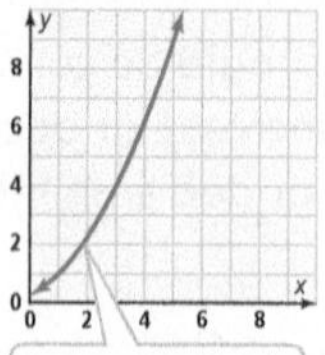
y
8
6
4
2
0
0 2 4 6 8
x

The rate of change in this function increases as the value of x increases.

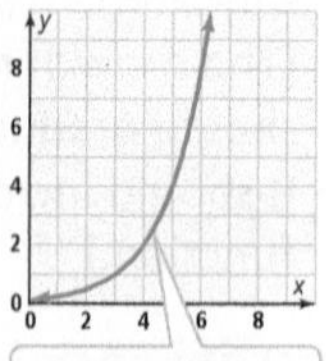
y
8
6
4
2
0
0 2 4 6 8
x

The rate of change in this function increases by equal factors as the value of x increases.

Do You UNDERSTAND?

1. ESSENTIAL QUESTION How can you determine whether a linear, exponential, or quadratic function best models data?
2. **Reason** The average rate of change of a function is less from $x = 1$ to $x = 4$ than from $x = 5$ to $x = 8$. What type of function could it be? Explain. **MP.2**
3. **Error Analysis** Kiyo used a quadratic function to model data with constant first differences. Explain the error Kiyo made. **MP.3**

Do You KNOW HOW?

Determine whether the data are best modeled by a linear, quadratic, or exponential function.

4.

x	0	1	2	3	4
y	−2	1	10	25	46

5.

x	−2	−1	0	1	2
y	2	7	12	17	22

6. A company's profit from a certain product is represented by $P(x) = -5x^2 + 1{,}125x - 5{,}000$, where x is the price of the product. Compare the growth in profits from $x = 120$ to $x = 140$ and from $x = 140$ to $x = 160$. What do you notice?

PRACTICE & PROBLEM SOLVING

AVAILABLE ONLINE

Lesson Practice You may opt to have students complete the automatically scored Practice and Problem Solving items online powered by MathXL for School.

Choose from: **Lesson Practice**
Adaptive Practice

You may also take advantage of the bank of exercises for assigning additional practice.

Assignment Guide

Basic	Advanced
7–15, 17–23	7–10, 12–23

Item Analysis

Example	Items	DOK
1	7, 11–14, 21	1
	9	3
2	8, 15, 16	2
3	22	2
	10, 17–20	3
	23	4

AVAILABLE ONLINE

PRACTICE & PROBLEM SOLVING

Scan for Multimedia

Practice Tutorial
Additional Exercises Available Online

UNDERSTAND

7. **Communicate Precisely** Create a flow chart to show the process to determine whether a given data set represents a function that is linear, quadratic, exponential, or none of these. MP.6

8. **Generalize** Calculate the 2nd differences for data in each table. Use a graphing calculator to find the quadratic regression for each data set. Make a conjecture about the relationship between the a values in the quadratic models and the 2nd differences of the data. MP.8

x	y
0	0
1	3
2	12
3	27
4	48

x	y
1	0.5
2	2
3	4.5
4	8
5	12.5

x	y
0	4
1	16
2	36
3	64
4	100

x	y
3	58.5
5	162.5
7	318.5
9	526.5
11	786.5

9. **Error Analysis** What is the error in the student's reasoning below? Describe how to correct the statement. MP.3

The data can be modeled with a linear function because the first differences are constant.

x	y
-3	-8
-1	-2
0	4
1	10
3	16

✗

10. **Higher Order Thinking** A savings account has a balance of \$1. Savings Plan A will add \$1,000 to an account each month, and Plan B will double the amount each month.

a. Which plan is better in the short run? For how long? Explain.

b. Which plan is better in the long run? Explain.

PRACTICE

Determine whether a linear, quadratic, or exponential function is the best model for the data in each table. SEE EXAMPLE 1

11.

x	y
0	1
1	3
2	9
3	27
4	81

12.

x	y
0	1
1	2
2	7
3	16
4	29

13.

x	y
0	56
1	57
2	50
3	35
4	12

14.

x	y
0	−6
1	−3
2	0
3	3
4	6

Do the data suggest a linear, quadratic, or an exponential function? Use regression to find a model for each data set. SEE EXAMPLE 2

15.

x	0	1	2	3	4
y	−20	−17.5	−15.1	−12.5	−10

16.

x	6	7	8	9	10
y	−19	−12	−7	−4	−3

17. **Use the functions shown.** SEE EXAMPLE 3

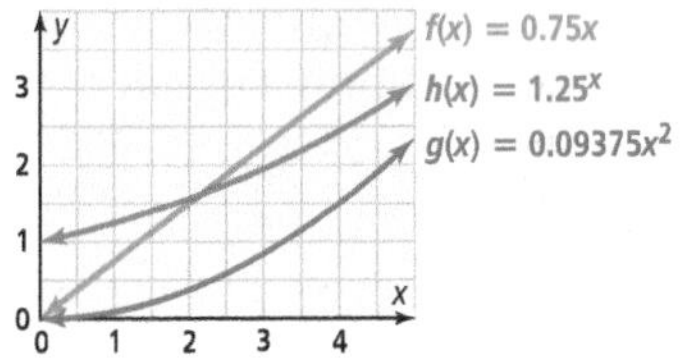
y
x
0
1
2
3
4
1
2
3
$f(x) = 0.75x$
$h(x) = 1.25^x$
$g(x) = 0.09375x^2$

a. Evaluate each function for $x = 6$, $x = 8$ and $x = 12$.

b. When will function h exceed function f and function g?

LESSON 8-5 Linear, Exponential, and Quadratic Models 349

Answers

7. A flow chart should show the following reasoning.
IF the first differences are constant, then the function is linear;
ELSE IF the second differences are constant, then the function is quadratic;
ELSE IF the common ratios are constant, then the function is exponential;
ELSE the function is not linear, quadratic, or exponential.

8. For the first three tables, the second difference is twice the value of the leading coefficient. For the last table, the second difference is eight times the value of the leading coefficient, but observe that the difference in consecutive x-values is 2, not 1 like in the other tables.

9. For analysis of first differences to give good information, the differences of the related x-values must also be constant. If the student only considers the data for $x = -3, -1, 1$, and 3, then a linear, quadratic, or exponential function would not model the data.

10. a. Plan A is better for the first 14 months, and then Plan B is better.
b. Plan B is better in the long run, because Plan B increases at a far greater rate.

11. exponential

12. quadratic

13. quadratic

14. linear

15. linear; $f(x) = 2.5x - 20.02$

16. quadratic; $f(x) = -x^2 + 20x - 103$

17. a. $f(6) = 4.5$, $f(8) = 6$, $f(12) = 9$; $g(6) = 3.375$, $g(8) = 6$, $g(12) = 13.5$; $h(6) \approx 3.815$, $h(8) \approx 5.960$, $h(12) \approx 14.552$
b. Starting at about $x = 10.3$, function h exceeds functions f and function g.

Answers

18. No; a linear regression model for this data predicts that after 10 years, the population will be about 885,400 people, so the city will not need a new water plant.

19. The budget will not be sufficient. Using quadratic regression, the function $f(x) = 2.65x^2 + 3.1x - 40$ models the data with correlation coefficient $r = 0.999$. Based on the model, the cost of the 150-meter-wide parking lot is \$60,050.

20. Carmen should use Plan B. Plan A is modeled by $f(x) = 10{,}000(0.9)^x$ and Plan B is modeled by $g(x) = -500x + 10{,}000$. After 20 years, he will pay off the loan with Plan B, while he will still owe \$1,215.77 with Plan A.

23. Part A App A: $f(x) = 3^x$;
App B: $g(x) = 998x + 50$;
App C: $h(x) = 100x^2 + 75x + 2{,}500$;
App A is exponential because ratios of consecutive y-values are constant, App B is linear because first differences are constant, and App C is quadratic because second differences are constant.

Part B App A will take the greatest amount of time as the number of data items to be analyzed increases; Answers will vary. Sample: The conjecture could be supported using a graph of the three functions.

AVAILABLE **ONLINE**

PRACTICE & PROBLEM SOLVING

Practice Tutorial
Mixed Review Available Online

APPLY

18. Model With Mathematics The data in the table show the population of a city for the past five years. A new water plant will be built when the population exceeds 1 million. Will the city need a new water plant in the next ten years? Use a function model to justify your answer. MP.4

Year	2016	2017	2018	2019	2020
Population	794,000	803,000	814,000	822,000	830,000

19. Construct Arguments The graphic shows costs for rectangular lots of different widths. Each lot is twice as long as it is wide.

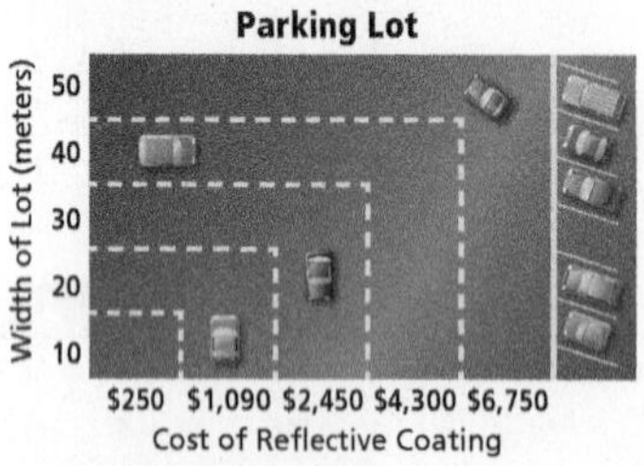
Parking Lot
Width of Lot (meters)
50
40
30
20
10
$250 $1,090 $2,450 $4,300 $6,750
Cost of Reflective Coating

To coat a parking lot 300 m long and 150 m wide, a developer budgeted \$20,220, or three times the cost of a lot 50 m wide. Will the budget be sufficient? Justify your answers using a function model. MP.3

20. Construct Arguments Carmen is considering two plans to pay off a \$10,000 loan. The tables show the amount remaining on the loan after x years.

Plan A	
Year	Amount Remaining
0	10,000
1	9,000
2	8,100
3	7,290
4	6,561

Plan B	
Year	Amount Remaining
0	10,000
1	9,500
2	9,000
3	8,500
4	8,000

Which plan should Carmen use to pay off the loan as soon as possible? Justify your answer using a function model. MP.3

ASSESSMENT PRACTICE

21. Function f has constant second differences. Which of the following are true? Select all that apply.

Ⓐ The graph of f is a parabola.
Ⓑ The graph of f is a straight line.
Ⓒ The ratios of the y-values increase as x increases.
Ⓓ The function f is an exponential function.
Ⓔ The function f has constant first differences.

22. SAT/ACT At what point will $f(x) = 3^x$ exceed $g(x) = 2x + 5$ and $h(x) = x^2 + 4$?

Ⓐ (1, 7)
Ⓑ (1.8, 7.3)
Ⓒ (2, 9)
Ⓓ (2.4, 9.8)

23. Performance Task Ella wrote three different computer apps to analyze some data. The tables show the time in milliseconds y for each app to analyze data as a function of the number of data items x.

App A		App B		App C	
x	y	x	y	x	y
4	81	4	4,042	4	4,400
5	243	5	5,040	5	5,375
6	729	6	6,038	6	6,550
7	2,187	7	7,036	7	7,925
8	6,561	8	8,034	8	9,500

Part A Use regression on a graphing calculator to find a function that models each data set. Explain your choice of model.

Part B Make a conjecture about which app will require the most time as the number of data items gets very large. How could you support your conjecture?

SavvasRealize.com

Assess Tutorials Worksheets

LESSON QUIZ

Use the Lesson Quiz to assess students' understanding of the mathematics in the lesson.

Students can take the Lesson Quiz online or you can download a printable copy from **SavvasRealize.com**. The Lesson Quiz is also available in the *Assessment Resources* book.

Item Analysis

Item	DOK	Standards
1	1	HSF.LE.A.1
2	2	HSS.ID.B.6.A
3	1	HSF.LE.A.3
4	1	HSS.ID.B.6.A
5	2	HSF.LE.A.3

RtI Use the student scores on the Lesson Quiz to prescribe differentiated assignments.

If students take the Lesson Quiz online, it will be automatically scored and appropriate differentiated practice will be assigned based on student performance.

I Intervention	0–3 points	• Reteach to Build Understanding • Mathematical Literacy and Vocabulary • Additional Practice
O On-Level	4 points	• Mathematical Literacy and Vocabulary • Additional Practice • Enrichment
A Advanced	5 points	• Enrichment

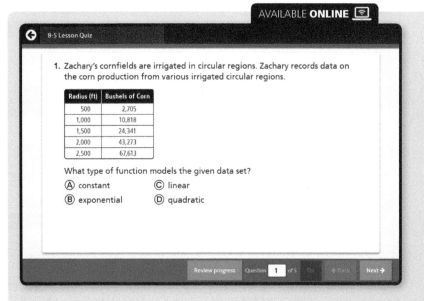

AVAILABLE **ONLINE**

8-5 Lesson Quiz

1. Zachary's cornfields are irrigated in circular regions. Zachary records data on the corn production from various irrigated circular regions.

Radius (ft)	Bushels of Corn
500	2,705
1,000	10,818
1,500	24,341
2,000	43,273
2,500	67,613

What type of function models the given data set?

Ⓐ constant Ⓒ linear

Ⓑ exponential Ⓓ quadratic

Review progress Question 1 of 5 Go ← Back Next →

ASSESSMENT RESOURCES

Name ______

enVision Algebra 1

PearsonRealize.com

8-5 Lesson Quiz

Linear, Exponential, and Quadratic Models

1. Zachary's cornfields are irrigated in circular regions. Zachary records data on the corn production from various irrigated circular regions.

Radius (ft)	Bushels of Corn
500	2,705
1,000	10,818
1,500	24,341
2,000	43,273
2,500	67,613

What type of function models the given data set?

Ⓐ constant Ⓒ linear

Ⓑ exponential Ⓓ quadratic

2. Function f has constant first differences. Which of the following must be true?

Ⓐ The graph of f is a parabola.

Ⓑ The function f has constant values.

Ⓒ The second differences for f are all zero.

Ⓓ The growth rate for f increases as x increases.

3. The average rate of change for a function is greater from $x = 1$ to $x = 2$ than from $x = 2$ to $x = 3$. What type of function could it be? Select all that apply.

Ⓐ linear

Ⓑ quadratic

Ⓒ exponential

4. Does a linear, quadratic, or exponential function best model the data?

x	0	1	2	3	4
y	6	8	14	24	38

quadratic

5. A quadratic function f models the predicted population growth in Town F after x years. An exponential function g models the predicted population growth in Town G after x years. Use the table to compare the average rate of change for each function from $x = 1$ to $x = 3$. Which function has a greater average rate of change over that interval?

x	f(x)	g(x)
0	0	1
1	5	5
2	20	25
3	45	125

function g

enVision™ **Algebra 1** • Assessment Resources

DIFFERENTIATED RESOURCES

I = Intervention O = On-Level A = Advanced

= This activity is available as a digital assignment powered by MathXL® for School.

AVAILABLE ONLINE

Reteach to Build Understanding I

Provides scaffolded reteaching for the key lesson concepts.

Name

8-5 Reteach to Build Understanding

Linear, Exponential, and Quadratic Models

1. Complete each table with the missing numbers for each column. Then circle the word that tells what is the same in each function.

x	y	Differences 1st	2nd
−2	−5		
−1	−6	−6 − (−5) = −1	
0	−3	−3 − (−6) = 3	3 − (−1) = 4
1	4	7	4

a. What are the same in a quadratic function?
1st differences
2nd differences (circled)
ratios of consecutive y-values

x	y	Differences 1st
−2	−11	
−1	−6	−6 − (−11) = 5
0	−1	−1 − (−6) = 5
1	4	5

b. What are the same in a linear function?
1st differences (circled)
2nd differences
ratios of consecutive y-values

x	y	Differences 1st	2nd	Ratios
0	1			
1	4	4 − 1 = 3		$\frac{4}{1} = 4$
2	16	16 − 4 = 12	12 − 3 = 9	$\frac{16}{4} = 4$
3	64	48	36	$\frac{64}{16} = 4$

c. What are the same in an exponential function?
1st differences
2nd differences
ratios of consecutive y-values (circled)

2. Emma calculated the 1st differences for a function as 1, 1, −3, and −5. Then Emma calculated the 2nd differences as −2 for all of them. She determined that the function was linear. What was her error?
Emma thought that a common 2nd difference indicated a linear equation. Common 2nd differences indicate a quadratic equation.

3. Complete the table to determine whether the function is linear, quadratic, or exponential.

This function is linear.

x	y	Differences 1st	2nd	Ratios
0	−3			
1	−1	2		$\frac{1}{3}$
2	1	2	0	−1
3	3	2	0	3

enVision™ Algebra 1 • Teaching Resources

Additional Practice I O

Provides extra practice for each lesson.

Name

8-5 Additional Practice

Linear, Exponential, and Quadratic Models

Determine whether each function is linear, quadratic, or exponential. Then use regression to find the function that models the data.

1.

x	y	Differences 1st	2nd	Ratio
0	7			
1	28	21		
2	49	21		
3	70	21		
4	91	21		

linear, $f(x) = 21x + 7$

2.

x	y	Differences 1st	2nd	Ratio
0	5			
1	5	0		
2	11	6	6	
3	23	12	6	
4	41	18	6	

quadratic; $f(x) = 3x^2 - 3x + 5$

3.

x	y	Differences 1st	2nd	Ratio
0	1			
1	0.25	−0.75		0.25
2	0.0625	−0.1875	−0.5625	0.25
3	0.0156	−0.0469	−0.1406	0.25
4	0.0039	−0.0117	−0.0352	0.25

exponential; $f(x) = 0.25^x$

4. The data in the table represent the population of a town for the past five years. When the population reaches 100,000, the town can be reclassified as a city. Does this situation suggest a linear, exponential, or quadratic function model? Will the town be reclassified as a city in the next 8 years? quadratic; yes

x	y
1	85,000
2	85,000
3	86,000
4	88,000
5	91,000

5. Consider linear, quadratic, and exponential functions.
a. What type of function would best model the area of a figure? quadratic
b. What type of function would best model the perimeter of a figure? linear

6. Compare the average rates of change for $f(x) = 2x + 4$, $g(x) = 2x^2 + 4$, and $h(x) = 2^x$ over the interval $x = 3$ to $x = 5$. Which function has the greatest average rate of change?
Function g has the greatest average rate of change over the interval.

enVision™ Algebra 1 • Teaching Resources

Enrichment O A

Presents engaging problems and activities that extend the lesson concepts.

Name

8-5 Enrichment

Linear, Exponential, and Quadratic Models

Videos of music performances are posted on a website by competing bands. The bands are getting new viewers each day, but in different patterns.

- Rock-o-Rama's video: Every day, the original viewer tells three more new people to watch the video.
- Pop Wave's video: Every day, the total number of viewers is given by $v = 2d^2 + 4d + 3$, where v represents the number of viewers, and d represents the number of days.
- Country Beat's video: Every day, the total number of viewers doubles in size.

1. Fill in the tables to determine how many new viewers each band has added per day.

Rock-o-Rama's Video

Days	Total Viewers
0	1
1	4
2	7
3	10
4	13
5	16

Pop Wave's Video

Days	Total Viewers
0	3
1	9
2	19
3	33
4	51
5	73

Country Beat's Video

Days	Total Viewers
0	1
1	2
2	4
3	8
4	16
5	32

2. There is going to be a Battle of the Bands competition. Each band can only enter the competition if its music video gets at least 1,000 views on the 10th day. Can any of the three bands enter the Battle of the Bands competition?
Yes, Country Beat will have 1,024 views. Rock-o-Rama will only have 31 views and Pop Wave will only have 243 views.

3. Why are the values of each table misleading when considering the long-term success of each band?
Sample answer: Although Pop Wave has the most viewers in the first few days, Country Beat will eventually have more viewers, because its viewer growth model is an exponential function.

enVision™ Algebra 1 • Teaching Resources

Mathematical Literacy and Vocabulary I O

Helps students develop and reinforce understanding of key terms and concepts.

Name

8-5 Mathematical Literacy and Vocabulary

Linear, Exponential, and Quadratic Models

Complete the table by filling in the missing information about when to use a linear, exponential, or quadratic function to model data.

Models	When to Use
1. linear	constant first differences
quadratic or exponential, but not linear	2. no constant first differences
quadratic	3. constant second differences
4. exponential	constant ratios of consecutive y-values

enVision™ Algebra 1 • Teaching Resources

Digital Resources and Video Tutorials I O A

The **Reteach to Build Understanding**, **Additional Practice**, and **Enrichment** activities are available as digital assignments powered by MathXL for School. These activities are automatically assigned when students complete the lesson quiz online and are automatically scored.

Students can access instructional tutorials using the **Virtual Nerd app**.

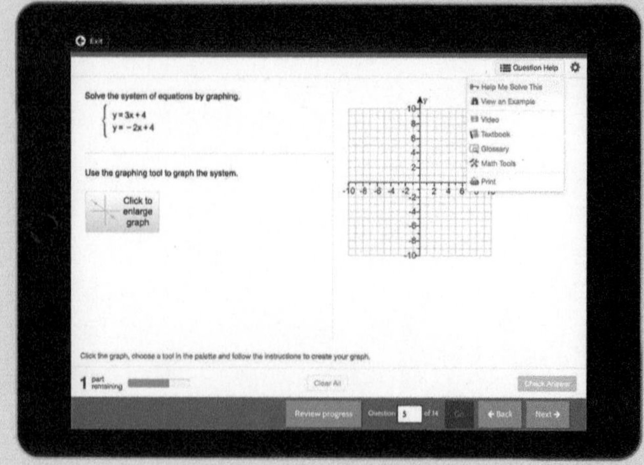

Question Help
Help Me Solve This
View an Example
Video
Textbook
Glossary
Math Tools
Print
Solve the system of equations by graphing.
y = 3x + 4
y = −2x + 4
Use the graphing tool to graph the system.
Click to enlarge graph
Click the graph, choose a tool in the palette and follow the instructions to create your graph.
Review progress
Back
Next

Tutorial
SLOPE-INTERCEPT FORM
What's Slope-Intercept Form of a Linear Equation?
SAVVAS

Students can also access Virtual Nerd videos using the **BouncePages app** to scan exercise pages marked with this icon. Students can download both apps for free in their mobile devices' app store.

TOPIC 8
Quadratic Functions

TOPIC REVIEW

TOPIC ESSENTIAL QUESTION

How can you use sketches and equations of quadratic functions to model situations and make predictions?

As students answer the Essential Question in writing, encourage them to include examples that support their answers. Look for the following points to come out while discussing students' answers.

- The form of a quadratic function can be helpful to determine features of the graph of the function. For example, vertex form can be used to quickly determine the maximum or minimum value of a quadratic equation, while standard form can be used to identify the initial value and the axis of symmetry.
- You can use first and second differences and the ratios between consecutive terms to determine whether a set of data can be modeled with a linear, quadratic, or exponential function.

Answers

2. parabola
3. quadratic parent function
4. vertical motion model
5. standard form of a quadratic function
6. quadratic regression
7. The graph of $g(x) = 1.5x^2$ is narrower.
8. The graph of $h(x) = -9x^2$ is narrower and opens downward.
9. When a > 0, the function has a minimum value. When a < 0, the function has a maximum value. The maximum or minimum value is always (0, 0).
10. artificial turf: $A(x) = 15x^2$; sod: $s(x) = 0.15x^2$; The graph of A is narrower than the graph of s since the cost per square foot of artificial turf is greater than the cost per square foot of sod.

AVAILABLE **ONLINE**

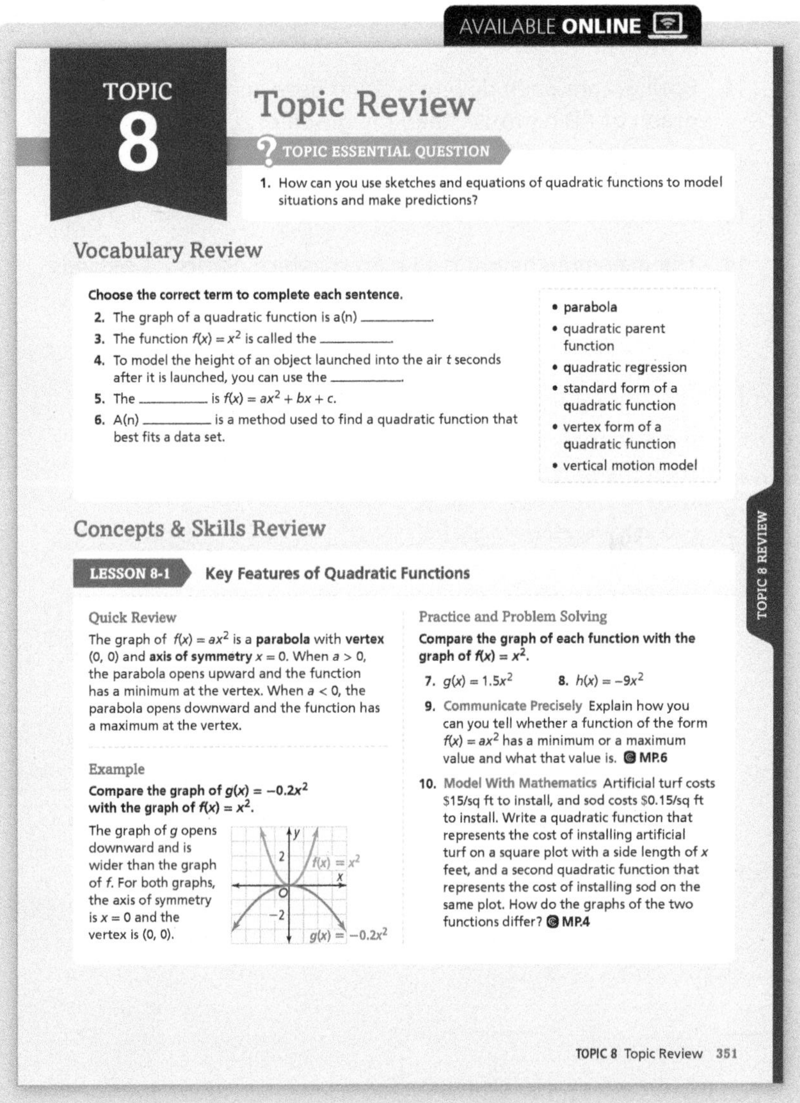
TOPIC 8

Topic Review

TOPIC ESSENTIAL QUESTION

1. How can you use sketches and equations of quadratic functions to model situations and make predictions?

Vocabulary Review

Choose the correct term to complete each sentence.

2. The graph of a quadratic function is a(n) ______.
3. The function $f(x) = x^2$ is called the ______.
4. To model the height of an object launched into the air t seconds after it is launched, you can use the ______.
5. The ______ is $f(x) = ax^2 + bx + c$.
6. A(n) ______ is a method used to find a quadratic function that best fits a data set.

- parabola
- quadratic parent function
- quadratic regression
- standard form of a quadratic function
- vertex form of a quadratic function
- vertical motion model

Concepts & Skills Review

LESSON 8-1 **Key Features of Quadratic Functions**

Quick Review

The graph of $f(x) = ax^2$ is a **parabola** with **vertex** (0, 0) and **axis of symmetry** $x = 0$. When $a > 0$, the parabola opens upward and the function has a minimum at the vertex. When $a < 0$, the parabola opens downward and the function has a maximum at the vertex.

Example

Compare the graph of $g(x) = -0.2x^2$ with the graph of $f(x) = x^2$.

The graph of g opens downward and is wider than the graph of f. For both graphs, the axis of symmetry is $x = 0$ and the vertex is (0, 0).

y
2
f(x) = x²
x
O
−2
g(x) = −0.2x²

Practice and Problem Solving

Compare the graph of each function with the graph of $f(x) = x^2$.

7. $g(x) = 1.5x^2$
8. $h(x) = -9x^2$
9. Communicate Precisely Explain how you can you tell whether a function of the form $f(x) = ax^2$ has a minimum or a maximum value and what that value is. MP.6
10. Model With Mathematics Artificial turf costs \$15/sq ft to install, and sod costs \$0.15/sq ft to install. Write a quadratic function that represents the cost of installing artificial turf on a square plot with a side length of x feet, and a second quadratic function that represents the cost of installing sod on the same plot. How do the graphs of the two functions differ? MP.4

TOPIC 8 REVIEW

TOPIC 8 Topic Review 351

AVAILABLE **ONLINE**

Go online at **SavvasRealize.com** for additional practice and mixed review.

TOPIC 8
Quadratic Functions

TOPIC REVIEW

Answers

11. Both graphs open downward and have vertex (3, 2). The graph of f is narrower than the graph of g.
12. $(-8, 1)$; $x = -8$
13. $(5, -2)$; $x = 5$
14. The maximum height is 15 meters, which occurs 2.5 seconds after the rock is thrown.
15. 5; $x = 2$; $(2, 9)$
16. 1; $x = \frac{7}{6}$; $\left(\frac{7}{6}, \frac{61}{12}\right)$
17. If $a > 0$, then the parabola has a minimum value. If $a < 0$, then the parabola has a maximum value.
18. 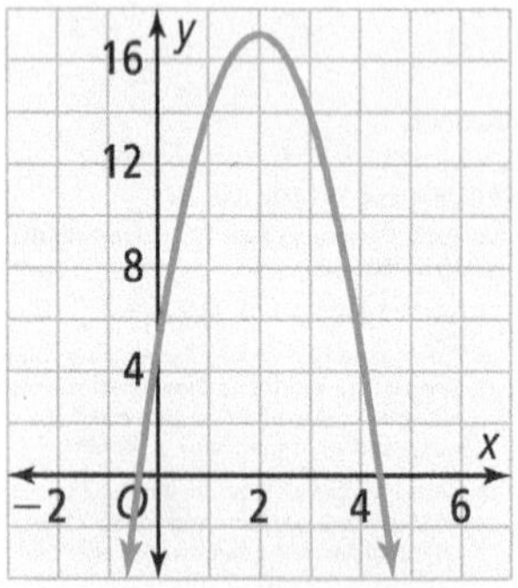

y
16
12
8
4
x
−2
O
2
4
6

19. The ball was tossed at 5 ft.

AVAILABLE ONLINE

LESSON 8-2 Quadratic Functions in Vertex Form

Quick Review

The **vertex form of a quadratic function** is $f(x) = a(x - h)^2 + k$. The vertex of the graph is at (h, k) and the axis of symmetry is $x = h$.

Example

Graph the function $f(x) = (x + 1)^2 - 1$.

The vertex is $(-1, -1)$ and the axis of symmetry is $x = -1$.

Use the points (0, 0) and (1, 3) to find two other points. Reflect each point across the axis of symmetry.

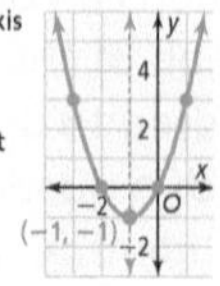

y
4
2
x
−2
O
(−1, −1)
−2

Practice and Problem Solving

11. Look for Relationships Graph the functions below. How are the graphs alike? How are the graphs different from each other? MP.7

$$f(x) = -5(x - 3)^2 + 2$$
$$g(x) = -2(x - 3)^2 + 2$$

Identify the vertex and axis of symmetry of the graph of each function.

12. $g(x) = (x + 8)^2 + 1$
13. $h(x) = (x - 5)^2 - 2$
14. An astronaut on the moon throws a moon rock into the air. The rock's height, in meters, above the moon's surface x seconds after it is thrown can be determined by the function $h(x) = -1.6(x - 2.5)^2 + 15$. What is the maximum height of the rock above the moon's surface? How many seconds after being thrown does the rock reach this height?

LESSON 8-3 Quadratic Functions in Standard Form

Quick Review

The standard form of a quadratic function is $f(x) = ax^2 + bx + c$, where $a \neq 0$. The y-intercept is c and the axis of symmetry, which is also the x-coordinate of the vertex, is $x = -\frac{b}{2a}$.

Example

Graph the function $f(x) = 3x^2 - 6x + 2$.

The y-intercept is 2.

Find the axis of symmetry.

$$x = -\frac{b}{2a} = -\frac{-6}{2(3)} = 1$$

Find the y-coordinate of the vertex.

$$f(1) = 3(1)^2 - 6(1) + 2 = -1$$

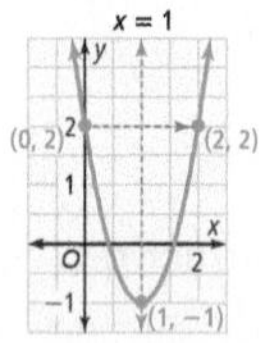

x = 1
y
(0, 2)
2
(2, 2)
1
x
O
2
−1
(1, −1)

Plot the vertex $(1, -1)$ and identify the axis of symmetry.

Plot the y-intercept (0, 2). Reflect that point across the axis of symmetry.

Practice and Problem Solving

Identify the y-intercept, axis of symmetry, and vertex of the graph of each function.

15. $g(x) = -x^2 + 4x + 5$
16. $h(x) = -3x^2 + 7x + 1$
17. When given a function in standard form, how can you determine if the parabola has a minimum or maximum value?
18. Graph the function $f(x) = -3x^2 + 12x + 5$.
19. Reason A ball is tossed into the air. The function $f(x) = -16x^2 + 4x + 5$ represents the height in feet of the ball x seconds after it is thrown. At what height was the ball tossed into the air? MP.2

352 TOPIC 8 Quadratic Functions Go Online | PearsonRealize.com

TOPIC 8
Quadratic Functions

TOPIC REVIEW

Answers

20. $h(x) = -16x^2 + 54x + 7$; 52.6 ft

21. $h(x) = -16x^2 + 18x + 9$; 14.1 ft

22. $f(x) = 2x^2 + 9x - 5$

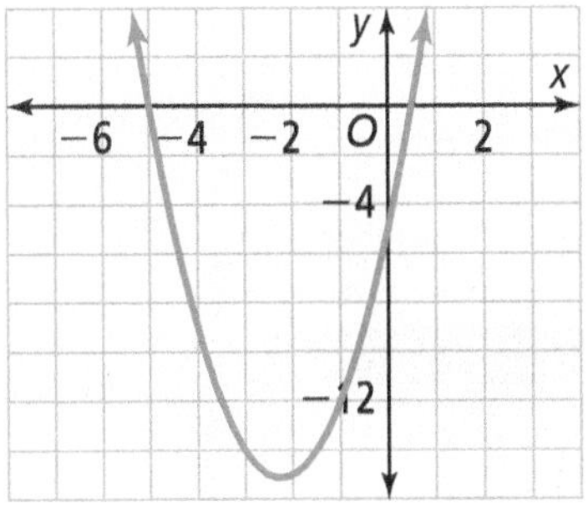
y
x
−6
−4
−2
O
2
−4
−12

The vertex is (–2.25, –15.125), which represents the minimum area of the rectangle when $x = -2.25$ if the value of $x = -2.25$ is possible for the rectangle, for which it is not. The x-intercepts represent when the area of the rectangle is 0.

x-intercepts: (–5, 0), (0.5, 0); y-intercept: (0, –3)

domain: $x > 0.5$; range: $y > 0$

23. $f(x) = 2x^2 - x - 3$

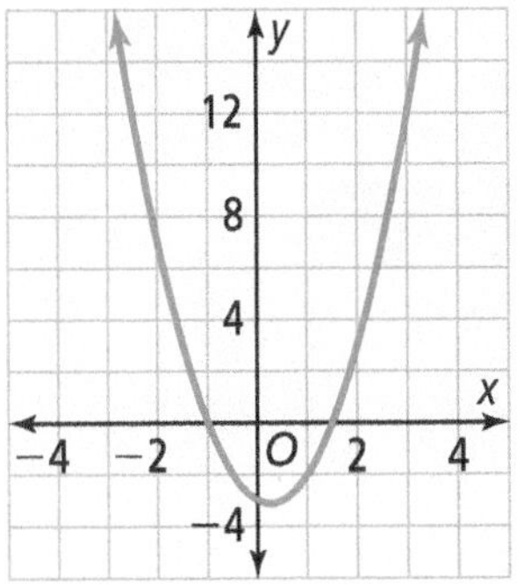
y
12
8
4
x
−4
−2
O
2
4
−4

The vertex (0.25, –3.125) represents the minimum area of the rectangle when $x = 0.25$ if the value of $x = 0.25$ is possible for the rectangle, for which it is not. The x-intercepts, –1 and 1.5, represent when the area of the rectangle is 0.

domain: $x > 1.5$; range: $y > 0$

24. Find the t-intercepts by graphing the function.

25. Determine if the differences in the x-values are constant.

26. quadratic

27. linear

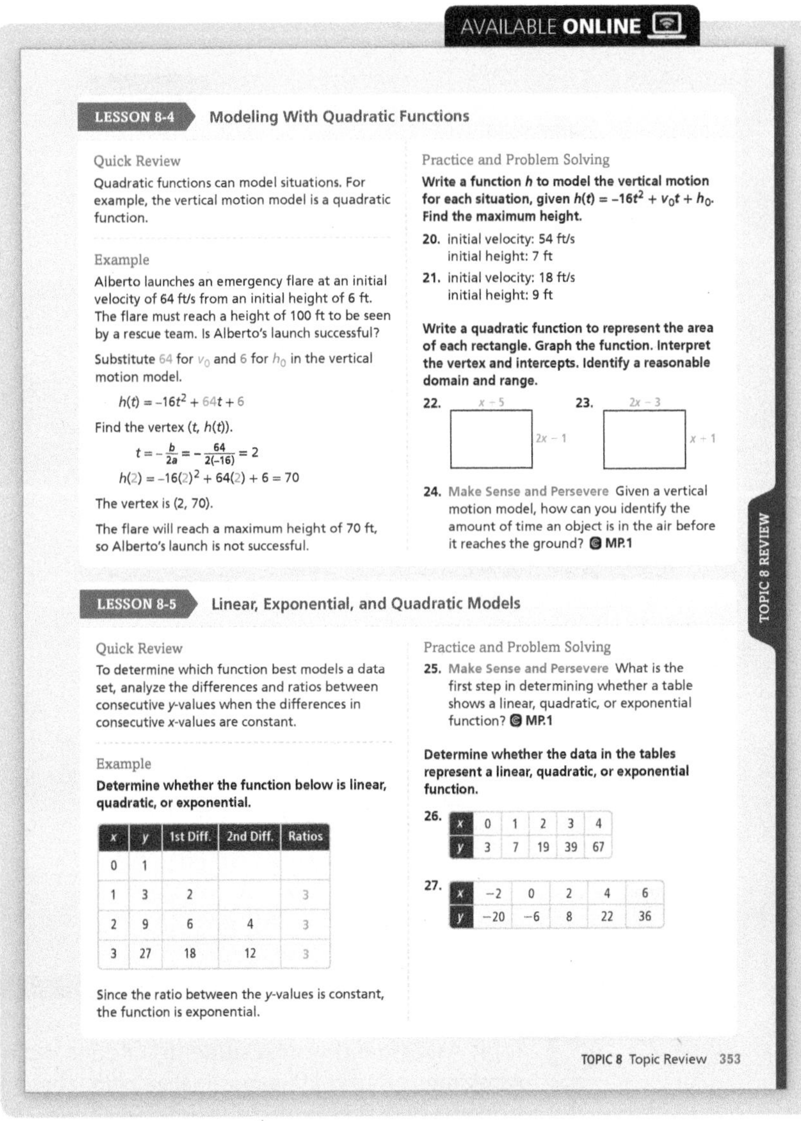

AVAILABLE **ONLINE**

LESSON 8-4 Modeling With Quadratic Functions

Quick Review

Quadratic functions can model situations. For example, the vertical motion model is a quadratic function.

Example

Alberto launches an emergency flare at an initial velocity of 64 ft/s from an initial height of 6 ft. The flare must reach a height of 100 ft to be seen by a rescue team. Is Alberto's launch successful?

Substitute 64 for v_0 and 6 for h_0 in the vertical motion model.

$$h(t) = -16t^2 + 64t + 6$$

Find the vertex $(t, h(t))$.

$$t = -\frac{b}{2a} = -\frac{64}{2(-16)} = 2$$

$$h(2) = -16(2)^2 + 64(2) + 6 = 70$$

The vertex is (2, 70).

The flare will reach a maximum height of 70 ft, so Alberto's launch is not successful.

Practice and Problem Solving

Write a function h to model the vertical motion for each situation, given $h(t) = -16t^2 + v_0t + h_0$. Find the maximum height.

20. initial velocity: 54 ft/s
initial height: 7 ft

21. initial velocity: 18 ft/s
initial height: 9 ft

Write a quadratic function to represent the area of each rectangle. Graph the function. Interpret the vertex and intercepts. Identify a reasonable domain and range.

22. $x + 5$; $2x - 1$

23. $2x - 3$; $x + 1$

24. Make Sense and Persevere Given a vertical motion model, how can you identify the amount of time an object is in the air before it reaches the ground? MP.1

LESSON 8-5 Linear, Exponential, and Quadratic Models

Quick Review

To determine which function best models a data set, analyze the differences and ratios between consecutive y-values when the differences in consecutive x-values are constant.

Example

Determine whether the function below is linear, quadratic, or exponential.

x	y	1st Diff.	2nd Diff.	Ratios
0	1			
1	3	2		3
2	9	6	4	3
3	27	18	12	3

Since the ratio between the y-values is constant, the function is exponential.

Practice and Problem Solving

25. Make Sense and Persevere What is the first step in determining whether a table shows a linear, quadratic, or exponential function? MP.1

Determine whether the data in the tables represent a linear, quadratic, or exponential function.

26.

x	0	1	2	3	4
y	3	7	19	39	67

27.

x	−2	0	2	4	6
y	−20	−6	8	22	36

TOPIC 8 REVIEW

TOPIC 8 Topic Review 353

TOPIC ASSESSMENT Form A

AVAILABLE **ONLINE**

Name ______________________

enVision Algebra 1
PearsonRealize.com

8 Topic Assessment Form A

1. The graph of $g(x) = ax^2$ opens downward and is narrower than the graph of $f(x) = x^2$. Which of the following could be the value of a?

(A) -3 (B) -0.6 (C) 0.5 (D) 2

2. What is the average rate of change of the function $f(x) = 2x^2 + x + 5$ over the interval $-2 \leq x \leq 2$?

(A) -4 (B) -1 (C) 1 (D) 4

3. Which statements about the graphs of functions $g(x) = -\frac{1}{4}x^2$ and $f(x) = x^2$ are true? Select all that apply.

(A) g is wider than f.

(B) f and g open in the same direction.

(C) f and g have the same vertex.

(D) f and g have the same axis of symmetry.

4. Over what interval is the function increasing?

x	$y = -\frac{1}{2}x^2$	(x, y)
-4	-8	$(-4, -8)$
-2	-2	$(-2, -2)$
0	0	$(0, 0)$
2	-2	$(2, -2)$
4	-8	$(4, -8)$

$x < 0$

5. What is the vertex of the graph of function $f(x) = 2(x - 2)^2 + 3$?

$(2, 3)$

6. What is the axis of symmetry for the function $y = -(x - 3)^2 + 5$?

(A) $x = -5$ (C) $x = 3$

(B) $x = -3$ (D) $x = 5$

7. Which of the following functions has a graph with a vertex that is a translation 5 units horizontally to the right of the vertex of the graph of $g(x) = (x + 2)^2 + 2$?

(A) $g(x) = -(x - 3)^2 + 2$

(B) $g(x) = (x + 7)^2 + 2$

(C) $g(x) = (x + 5)^2 + 2$

(D) $g(x) = -(x + 2)^2 + 5$

8. Identify the vertex and y-intercept of the graph of the function $y = (x + 2)^2 - 3$.

vertex: $(-2, -3)$

y-intercept: 1

9. The graph of h is a translation 4 units right and 1 unit down of the graph of $f(x) = x^2$. Write function h in vertex form.

$h(x) = (x - 4)^2 - 1$

10. What is the axis of symmetry of the graph of the function $f(x) = 2x^2 + 8x - 5$?

(A) $x = -5$ (C) $x = -2$

(B) $x = -4$ (D) $x = 2$

11. The function $h(t) = -16t^2 + 24t$ models the height, in feet, of a kangaroo t seconds after it jumps. What is the maximum height of the jump?

(A) 9 ft (C) 27 ft

(B) 18 ft (D) 36 ft

12. The function $f(x) = -x^2 + bx + 1$ is shown in the graph. What is the value of b?

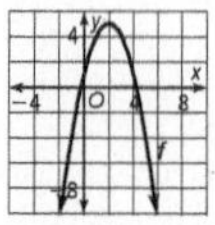

y
4
x
−4
O
4
8
f
−8

$b = 4$

13. Nicky wants to surround a painting 5 inches by 11 inches with a frame that is w inches wide. Write a quadratic function A in standard form to represent the combined area A of the picture and the frame.

$A(w) = 4w^2 + 32w + 55$

14. Suppose that in Item 13, the frame must be at at least 1 inch and no more than 3 inches wide. What are the domain and the range of the function?

domain: $1 \leq w \leq 3$

range: $91 < A(w) < 187$

15. The rate of change of function f is the same from $x = -2$ to $x = 1$ as it is from $x = 1$ to $x = 4$. Is function f linear, quadratic, or exponential?

linear

16. Which function best models the data?

Time, t (s)	0	0.5	1.0	1.5	2.0
Height, h (m)	3.0	6.7	8.2	7.0	3.3

(A) $h(t) = -15.9t^2 + 2.99t + 10.22$

(B) $h(t) = -16.1t^2 + 10.22t + 2.99$

(C) $h(t) = -5.03t^2 + 10.22t + 2.99$

(D) $h(t) = -5.03t^2 + 2.99t + 10.22$

17. The function $f(x) = -4x^2 + 18x + 16$ models the predicted sales of a hat after x price increases. Use the table showing actual and predicted sales to find the residuals for the model.

x	Actual Sales ($)	Predicted Sales ($)	Residual
0	17	16	1
1	29	30	−1
2	34	34	0
3	33	34	−1
4	22	24	−2

18. Function g also models the data in Item 17. For function g, the average distance of the residuals from the line $y = 0$ is 1.3. Is f or g a better model for the data? f

19. Over what interval does $f(x) = 3^x$ increase faster than $g(x) = 9x$?

(A) $0 < x < 3$ (C) $0 < x < 2$

(B) $x > 3$ (D) $2 < x < 3$

20. Do the data suggest a linear, quadratic, or exponential model?

x	0	1	2	3	4
y	2.5	5	10	20	40

exponential

AVAILABLE **ONLINE**

Topic Assessment Assess students' understanding of topic concepts and skills using the Topic Assessment found at **SavvasRealize.com**. These auto-scored online assessments provide students with a breadth of technology-enhanced item types.

There are two versions of the Topic Assessment, Form A and Form B. These two versions, available in print and at **SavvasRealize.com**, are parallel tests that assess the same content item for item. The Item Analysis chart on the next page can be used for both versions.

TOPIC 8

Quadratic Functions

TOPIC ASSESSMENT Form B

AVAILABLE ONLINE

Name ______________________

enVision Algebra 1

PearsonRealize.com

8 Topic Assessment Form B

1. The graph of $f(x) = ax^2$ opens downward and is wider than the graph of $f(x) = x^2$. Which of the following could be the value of a?

   (A) −10 **(B) −0.1** (C) 0.1 (D) 10

2. What is the average rate of change of $f(x) = 2x^2 - x - 4$ over the interval $-4 \le x \le 2$?

   (A) −8 **(B) −5** (C) 1 (D) 5

3. Which statements about the graphs of $g(x) = -5x^2$ and $f(x) = x^2$ are true? Select all that apply.

   (A) g is wider than f.
   (B) f and g open in the same direction.
   (C) f and g have the same vertex.
   (D) f and g have the same axis of symmetry..

4. Over what interval is the function increasing?

x	$y = \frac{3}{4}x^2$	(x, y)
−4	12	(−4, 12)
−2	3	(−2, 3)
0	0	(0, 0)
2	3	(2, 3)
4	12	(4, 12)

$x > 0$

5. What is the vertex of the graph of function $f(x) = 2(x - 4)^2 - 1$?

   (4, −1)

6. What is the axis of symmetry of the function $y = -3(x - 2)^2 + 1$?

   (A) $x = -3$ (B) $x = -2$ (C) $x = 1$ **(D) $x = 2$**

7. Which of the following functions has a graph with a vertex that is translated 3 units horizontally to the left of the vertex of the graph of $f(x) = (x + 1)^2 - 4$?

   (A) $g(x) = (x + 1)^2 + 4$
   (B) $g(x) = -(x + 3)^2 + 3$
   (C) $g(x) = 2(x + 4)^2 - 4$
   (D) $g(x) = (x - 2)^2 - 4$

8. Identify the vertex and the y-intercept of the graph of $f(x) = (x - 1)^2 - 4$.

   vertex: (1, −4)

   y-intercept: −3

9. The graph of h is the graph of $f(x) = x^2$ translated 4 units left and 7 units down. Write the function h in vertex form. $h(x) = (x + 4)^2 - 7$

10. What is the axis of symmetry of the graph of the function $f(x) = -x^2 - 6x + 8$?

   (A) $x = -6$ **(B) $x = -3$** (C) $x = 3$ (D) $x = 8$

11. The function $h(t) = -16t^2 + 18t$ models the height, in feet, of a jaguar t seconds after it jumps. What is the maximum height of the jump?

   (A) 5 ft (B) 6 ft (C) 7 ft (D) 8 ft

12. The function $f(x) = 2x^2 + bx + 74$ is shown in the graph. What is the value of b?

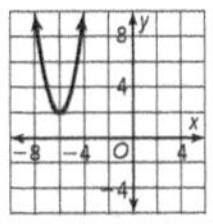

   $b = 24$

13. Joshua wants to surround a painting 16 inches by 20 inches with a frame that is x inches wide. Write a quadratic function A in standard form to represent the combined area of the painting and frame.

   $A(x) = 4x^2 + 72x + 320$

14. Suppose that in Item 13, the frame must be at at least 1 inch and no more than 3 inches wide. What are the domain and the range of the function?

   domain: $1 \le x \le 3$

   range: $396 < A(x) < 572$

15. The rate of change of function g from $x = -3$ to $x = -1$ is same as it is from $x = -1$ to $x = 1$. Is function g linear, quadratic, or exponential?

   linear

16. Which function best models the data?

Time, t (s)	0	0.5	1.0	1.5	2.0
Height, h (m)	1.5	2.11	2.3	2.02	1.38

   (A) $h(t) = -2.9t^2 + 7.99t + 4.32$
   (B) $h(t) = 0.85t^2 + 1.63t + 1.51$
   (C) $h(t) = 2.9t^2 + 7.99t + 4.32$
   (D) $h(t) = -0.85t^2 + 1.63t + 1.51$

17. The function $f(x) = -5x^2 + 17x + 21$ models the predicted sales of a pen after x price increases. Use the table showing actual and predicted sales to find the residuals for the model.

x	Actual Sales ($)	Predicted Sales ($)	Residual
0	22	21	1
1	33	33	0
2	36	35	1
3	28	27	−1

18. Function g also models the data in Item 17. For function g, the average distance of the residuals from the line $y = 0$ is 1.1. Is f or g a better model for the data? f

19. Over which interval does $f(x) = 2^x$ increase faster than $g(x) = \frac{8}{3}x$?

   (A) $1 < x < 3$ **(B) $x > 3$** (C) $2 < x < 3$ (D) $1 > x > 2$

20. Do the data suggest a linear, quadratic, or exponential model?

x	−2	−1	0	1	2
y	−36	−6	16	30	36

   quadratic

Item Analysis

Item	DOK	Standard	Item	DOK	Standard	Item	DOK	Standard
1	2	HSF.IF.C.7	8	2	HSF.BF.B.3	15	2	HSF.IF.B.5
2	1	HSF.IF.B.6	9	2	HSF.IF.C.7.A	16	1	HSF.LE.A.1
3	2	HSF.IF.C.7	10	2	HSA.CED.A.2, HSF.BF.B.3	17	1	HSS.ID.B.6.A
4	1	HSF.IF.B.4	11	1	HSF.IF.C.7	18	1	HSS.ID.B.6.B
5	2	HSF.IF.A.2	12	2	HSF.IF.B.4	19	1	HSS.ID.B.6.B
6	1	HSF.BF.B.3	13	2	HSF.IF.C.7	20	2	HSF.LE.A.3
7	2	HSF.IF.C.7	14	2	HSF.IF.C.8, HSF.BF.A.1			

TOPIC PERFORMANCE ASSESSMENT Form A

AVAILABLE **ONLINE**

Name ____________________

enVision Algebra 1
PearsonRealize.com

8 Performance Assessment Form A

A high school drama club is selling tickets for a fundraiser event. Based on data from past events, the number of tickets sold can be modeled by the linear function $Q(x) = -40x + 640$, where x is the price, in dollars, of each ticket.

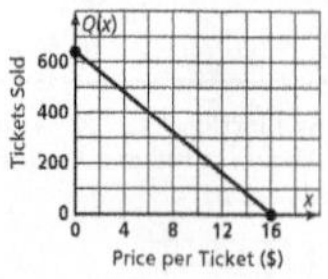

Q(x)
600
400
200
0
Tickets Sold
0 4 8 12 16
x
Price per Ticket ($)

1. What are a reasonable domain and a reasonable range for function Q? Explain.

   Domain: $0 \le x \le 16$; range: $0 \le Q(x) \le 640$; prices and the numbers of tickets sold need to be positive numbers.

2. The revenue R can be modeled by multiplying the ticket price x by the number of tickets sold. Write a quadratic function R that correctly represents that model. Justify your answer.

   $R(x) = x(-40x + 640) = -40x^2 + 640x$

3. Graph function R below. Label the vertex. What does the vertex represent in this context? Explain.

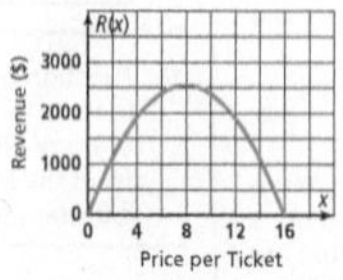

R(x)
3000
2000
1000
0
Revenue ($)
0 4 8 12 16
x
Price per Ticket

   The vertex is (8, 2,560). The vertex represents a maximum for the function, so the greatest revenue is earned when the price is \$8 per ticket. The maximum revenue that can be generated is \$2,560.

enVision™ Algebra 1 • Assessment Resources

4. The table on the right shows ticket prices and actual revenues from past events.

Price	Actual Revenue (\$)	Predicted Revenue (\$)	Residual
4	2,012	1,920	92
5	2,275	2,220	75
6	2,352	2,400	−48
7	2,506	2,520	−14
8	2,616	2,560	56
9	2,529	2,520	9
10	2,330	2,400	−70
11	2,079	2,200	−121
12	1,824	1,920	−96

Part A

Plot the given data (price, actual revenue) on the graph below. Then use the model you wrote in Item 2 to fill in the predicted revenue column in the table. Finally, fill in the residual column.

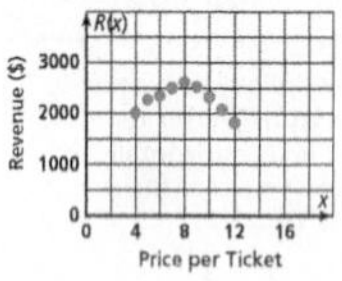

R(x)
3000
2000
1000
0
Revenue ($)
0 4 8 12 16
x
Price per Ticket

Part B

The drama club president tries a different model for the data, $P(x) = -41x^2 + 630x$, where P is the predicted revenue given a ticket price of x dollars. Compare that model and the model you found in Item 2 by graphing the residuals. Which model is a better fit for the data? Justify your answer.

Check students' graphs. Sample answer: Function R is a better model than function P. When the residuals for both models are plotted on a coordinate graph, the average distance of function R's residuals from the line $y = 0$ is 64.6, and the average distance of function P's residuals is 69.7.

Part C

Use a graphing calculator to find a quadratic regression model A for the actual revenue amounts shown in the table in Part A. Make a conjecture about the fit of your model.

$A(x) = -41x^2 + 626x + 136$; the equation models the data well, because the R^2 value is close to 1.

enVision™ Algebra 1 • Assessment Resources

AVAILABLE **ONLINE**

Topic Performance Assessment Assess students' ability to apply the topic concepts and skills using the Topic Performance Assessments found at **SavvasRealize.com.** These online assessments include a breadth of technology-enhanced item types.

Item Analysis and Scoring Guide

Item	DOK	2-Point Responses	1-Point Responses	Standards
1	2	Correct domain and explanation	Incomplete explanation	HSF.IF.B.5
2	2	Correct model and explanation	Incomplete explanation	HSF.BF.A.1, HSF.IF.C.8
3	2	Correct graph and explanation	Incomplete explanation	HSF.IF.C.7, HSF.IF.C.7.A, HSF.IF.B.4, HSA.CED.A.2
4A	3	Correct graph and table	Incomplete graph or table	HSS.ID.B.6.B
4B	3	Correct identification of R	Incorrect identification of P	HSS.ID.B.6.B
4C	2	Correct regression model and conjecture	Incomplete conjecture	HSS.ID.B.6.A

TOPIC 8
Quadratic Functions

TOPIC PERFORMANCE ASSESSMENT Form B

AVAILABLE ONLINE

Name ______________________ enVision Algebra 1 PearsonRealize.com

8 Performance Assessment Form B

Tavon makes gift boxes of various sizes by removing a square from each corner of a rectangular piece of cardboard and then folding up the sides, as shown in the figure. He wants to know how much cardboard he uses for each box and the volume of each box.

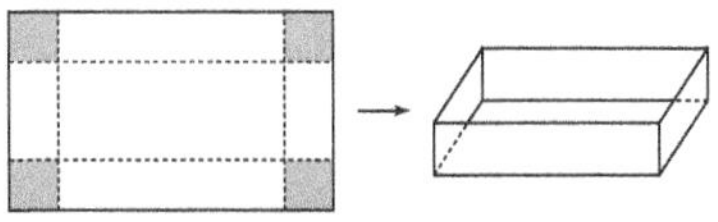

1. To make a box 3 inches deep, Tavon removes a 3-inch by 3-inch square from each corner of an x-inch by x-inch square of cardboard. Write a quadratic function A in standard form to model the area of the remaining cardboard after the corners are removed. Justify your answer.

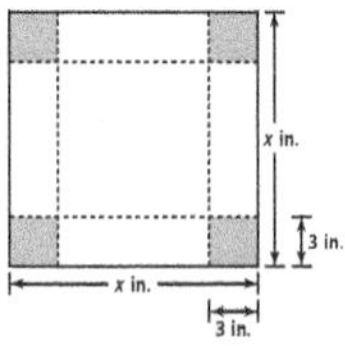
x in.
3 in.
x in.
3 in.

   $A(x) = (x^2 - 36)$ in.^{2}; $4 \bullet 3^2$ in.$^2 = 36$ in.^{2} of cardboard are removed. Total area = area of cardboard − area of cardboard removed. So $A(x) = (x^2 - 36)$ in.^{2}.

2. Write a quadratic function V in standard form to model the volume of the box after the sides have been folded up. Justify your answer.

   $V(x) = (3x^2 - 36x + 108)$ in.^{3}; the square base has side lengths $(x - 6)$ in. and area $(x - 6)^2$ in.$^2 = (x^2 - 12x + 36)$ in.^{2}. volume = base • height, so $V(x) = 3(x^2 - 12x + 36)$ in.^{3} $= (3x^2 - 36x + 108)$ in.^{3}

3. Graph functions A and V on a graphing calculator. Describe a reasonable domain for each function.

   Check students' graphs. $x > 6$ is a reasonable domain given that 3-in. corners must be cut out. There may be an upper limit for the domain given the size of cardboard available.

4. Tavon makes another box with height h inches from a piece of cardboard that measures 12 inches by 12 inches. To make the box, he removes an h-inch square from each corner and folds up the sides.

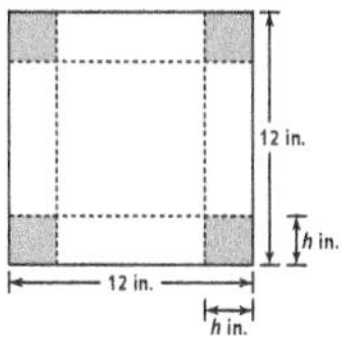
12 in.
h in.
12 in.
h in.

Part A

Write a quadratic function B in standard form to model the area of the base of the new box. Describe a reasonable domain and range for the function. Justify your answer.

$B(h) = (4h^2 - 48h + 144)$ in.^{2}; $B(h) = (12 - 2h)^2$ in.^{2} = $(4h^2 - 48h + 144)$ in.^{2}. The box height must be greater than 0 and less than half the side length of the 12-in. square, so a reasonable domain is $0 < h < 6$ and a reasonable range is $0 < B < 144$.

Part B

Tavon uses cardboard squares 12 inches by 12 inches to make boxes of different heights. Complete the table to find the base area and the volume of each box. Describe any patterns you see.

Box height, h (in.)	Base area, B	Volume
1	100	100
2	64	128
3	36	108
4	16	64
5	4	20

Sample answer: As the height increases, the base area B decreases. The volume increases and then decreases.

Part C

Write a function V for the volume of a box like those described in Part B. Is your function a quadratic function? Explain why or why not.

$V(h) = (h^3 - 48h^2 + 144h)$ in.^{3}; no; one term is of degree 3.

AVAILABLE ONLINE

Topic Performance Assessment Assess students' ability to apply the topic concepts and skills using the Topic Performance Assessments found at **SavvasRealize.com.** These online assessments include a breadth of technology-enhanced item types.

Item Analysis and Scoring Guide

Item	DOK	2-Point Responses	1-Point Responses	Standards
1	2	Correct model and explanation	Incomplete explanation	HSF.IF.A.1, HSF.IF.A.2, HSF.BF.B.3
2	3	Correct model and explanation	Incomplete explanation	HSF.IF.C.8, HSF.BF.A.1, HSA.CED.A.2
3	2	Correct graph and explanation	Incomplete explanation	HSF.IF.C.7, HSF.IF.B.5
4A	2	Correct model and explanation	Incomplete explanation	HSF.IF.A.2, HSF.BF.A.1, HSF.IF.B.5
4B	3	Correct table and description	No observation of patterns	HSF.IF.B.5
4C	2	Correct function and determination	Incorrect determination	HSF.IF.A.1

MATH BACKGROUND FOCUS

Topic 9 focuses on extending knowledge of quadratic functions. Students learn to solve quadratic equations using tables, graphs, and factoring. Students also solve quadratic equations using square roots, completing the square, and the quadratic formula. Students learn different methods, such as graphing, elimination, and substitution, for solving linear-quadratic systems.

Solving Quadratic Equations

Using Tables, Graphs, and Factoring In Lesson 9-1, students learn that in a quadratic equation written in standard form, where $a \neq 0$, the x-intercepts are the solutions. Students learn that a table can be used find solutions of a quadratic equation and the solutions are the x-values when the y-values are 0. There can be 0, 1, or 2 solutions. In Lesson 9-2, students rewrite quadratic equations in factored form and use the Zero-Product Property to find solutions of a quadratic equation.

Using Square Roots In Lesson 9-4, students learn to solve a quadratic equation by isolating the variable and taking the square roots of each side of the equation. Students learn to rewrite the equations so they are in a form that can be solved by taking square roots.

Using Completing the Square In Lesson 9-5, students solve quadratic equations by completing the square. Students learn that to complete the square, they need to add the square of half of the coefficient of x to each side. Students use completing the square to write quadratic equations in vertex form.

Using the Quadratic Formula In Lesson 9-6, students learn to derive the quadratic formula and use it to solve quadratic equations. Students learn about the discriminant and use it to determine the number of solutions of a quadratic equation.

$$x^2 - 4x + 5 = 0$$
$$(-4)^2 - 4(1)(5) = -4$$

The discriminant is < 0, so there are no real roots.

Solving Linear-Quadratic Systems

Solving Systems of Equations by Graphing In Lesson 9-7, students understand that a linear-quadratic system of equations includes a linear equation and a quadratic equation. Students learn to solve a linear-quadratic system of equations by graphing. Students set each side of the equation equal to y and graph each equation on the same coordinate plane. The solutions of the system are the points where the two graphs intersect.

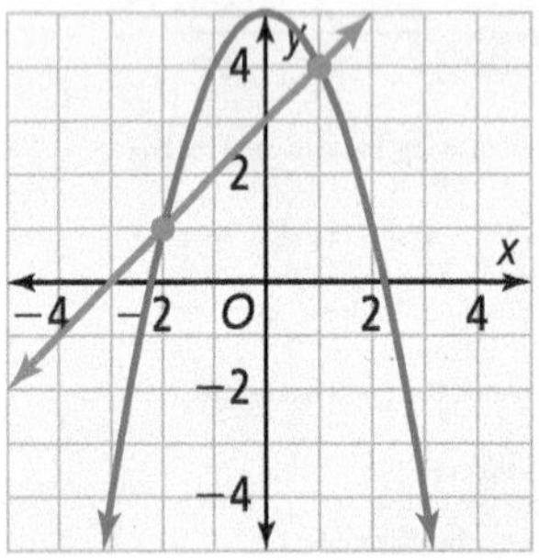

y
4
2
x
−4
−2
O
2
4
−2
−4

Solving Systems of Equations by Elimination In Lesson 9-7, students solve a linear-quadratic system of equations by elimination. Students learn to subtract one equation from another to eliminate one variable and solve for the remaining variable. Then they substitute the resulting value(s) into the original equation to find the value(s) of the other variable.

Solving Systems of Equations Using Substitution In Lesson 9-7, students solve a linear-quadratic system of equations by substitution. Students solve one equation for one of the variables and then substitute that solution for that variable in the other equation. This results in one equation with one variable. Students solve the equation and use the solution(s) to find the value(s) of the other variable.

TOPIC 9

Solving Quadratic Equations

MATH BACKGROUND COHERENCE

Students learn best when concepts are connected through the curriculum. This coherence is achieved within topics, across topics, across domains, and across grade levels.

MAKING MATHEMATICAL CONNECTIONS

Looking Back

How does Topic 9 connect to what students learned earlier?

TOPIC 1

- **Solving Linear Equations** Students learned methods for solving linear equations. In **Topic 9, students use their** knowledge of solving linear equations, along with the Zero-Product Property, to solve the linear equations that result from factoring a quadratic equation.

TOPIC 4

- **Solving Systems of Linear Equations** Students learned to solve systems of linear equations by graphing, substitution, and elimination. In Topic 9, students apply these same methods to solve linear-quadratic systems of equations.

TOPIC 8

- **Graphing Quadratic Functions** Students learned to graph quadratic functions. In Topic 9, students continue to graph quadratic functions and use the *x*-intercepts of the graphs to identify the solutions of the related quadratic equations. Students also solve linear-quadratic systems of equations by graphing.

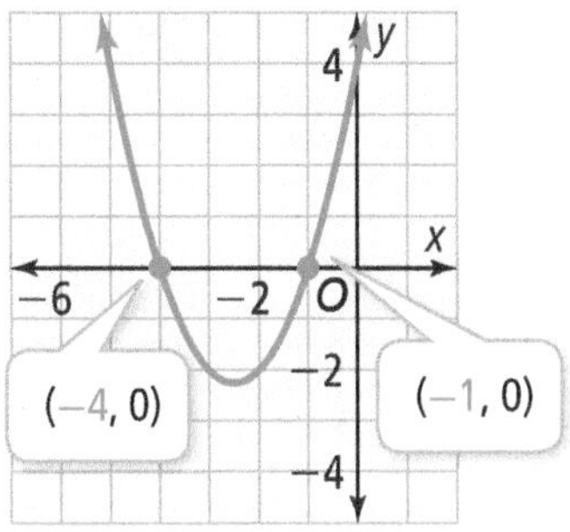

4
y
x
−6
−2
O
−2
−4
(−4, 0)
(−1, 0)

IN THIS TOPIC

How is content connected within Topic 9?

- **Solving Quadratic Equations** Throughout Topic 9, students employ different methods to solve quadratic equations. In Lesson 9-1, students solve quadratic equations using tables and graphs. In Lesson 9-2, students solve quadratic equations by factoring. In Lesson 9-3, students learn to rewrite radical expressions, a skill students then apply in Lessons 9-4 and 9-5 when they solve quadratic equations by taking square roots and by completing the square. In Lesson 9-6, students learn that they can solve any quadratic equation using the quadratic formula.

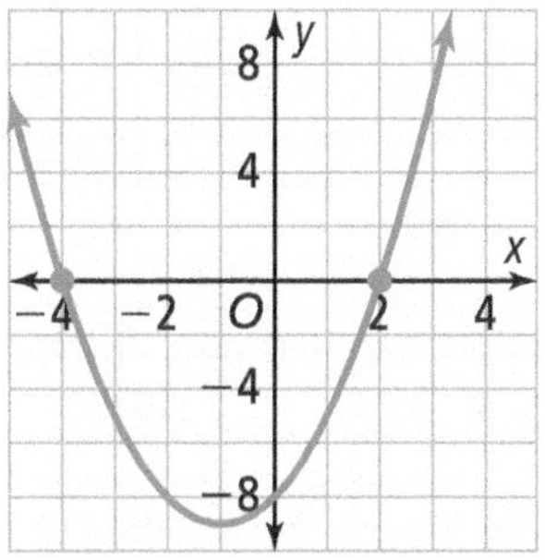

8
y
4
x
−4
−2
O
2
4
−4
−8

- **Solving Linear-Quadratic Systems of Equations** In Lesson 9-7, students solve linear-quadratic systems of equations. Students solve these systems by graphing, substitution, and elimination.

MAKING MATHEMATICAL CONNECTIONS

Looking Ahead

How does Topic 9 connect to what students will learn later?

ALGEBRA 2

- **Solving Quadratic Equations with Complex Roots** In Lesson 9-6, students learn to find the real solutions of quadratic equations using the quadratic formula. In Algebra 2, students will learn to use the quadratic formula to solve quadratic equations with complex solutions.

- **Zeros of Polynomial Functions** In Topic 9, students solve quadratic equations using different methods, including factoring and the quadratic formula. In Algebra 2, students will continue to use these methods to find the zeros of polynomial equations.

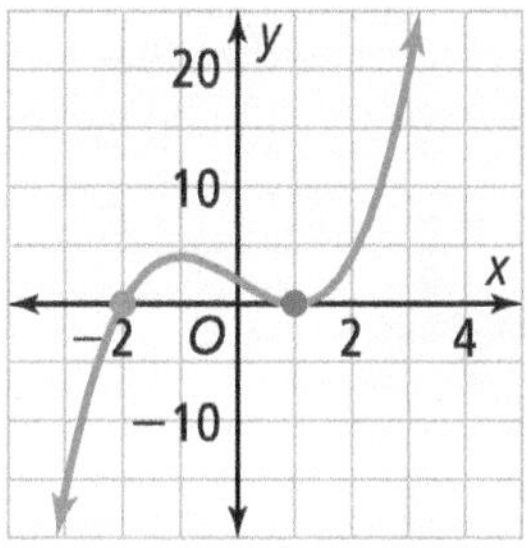

20
y
10
x
−2
O
2
4
−10

MATH BACKGROUND **RIGOR**

A rigorous curriculum emphasizes conceptual understanding, procedural skill and fluency, and applications.

Conceptual Understanding

- **Solutions of Quadratic Equations Using Graphs** Students understand that the *x*-coordinates of the *x*-intercepts of a quadratic equation represent the solutions to the quadratic equation. Understanding this allows students to interpret the graph of a quadratic function by identifying the *x*-intercepts as the solutions of the related quadratic equation.

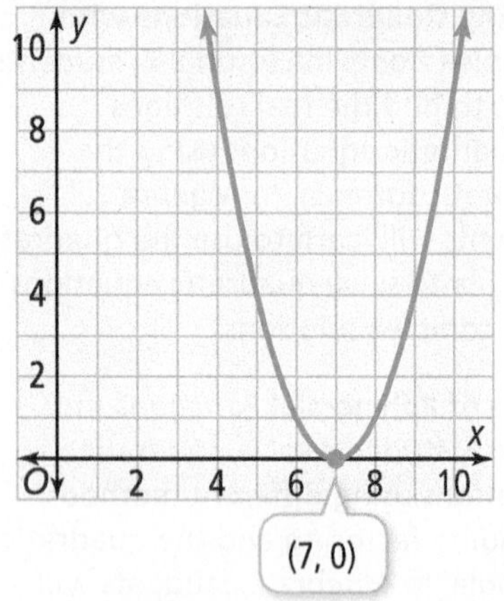

y
10
8
6
4
2
O
2
4
6
8
10
x
(7, 0)

- **Completing the Square** Students understand that a perfect square trinomial creates a square when modeled with algebra tiles. Students recognize that they can use completing the square to write a quadratic function in vertex form.

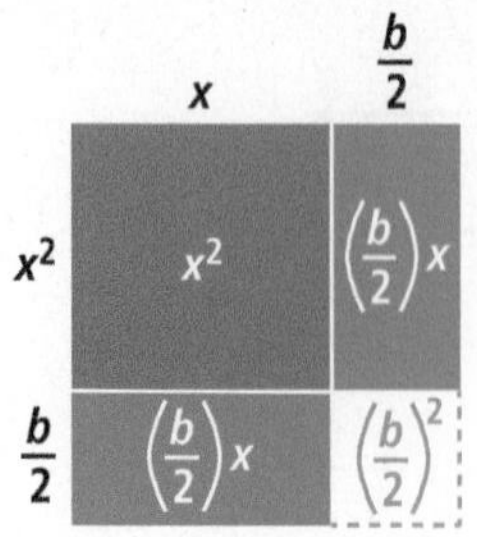

x
b/2
x²
x²
(b/2)x
b/2
(b/2)x
(b/2)²

Procedural Skill and Fluency

- **Rewriting Radical Expressions** Students identify the perfect square factors of a radical and use properties of exponents to write a radical expression as a product of square roots.
- **Solving Quadratic Equations Using Square Roots** Students solve quadratic equations by isolating the variable and taking the square root of each side of the equation.
- **Using the Discriminant to Determine the Number of Solutions** Students use the discriminant to determine how many real solutions a quadratic equation has without solving it.

Applications

- **Using Graphs of Quadratic Equations** Students use the graph of a quadratic equation to approximate the solutions to real-world problems, such as finding the amount of time that a golf ball is in the air.

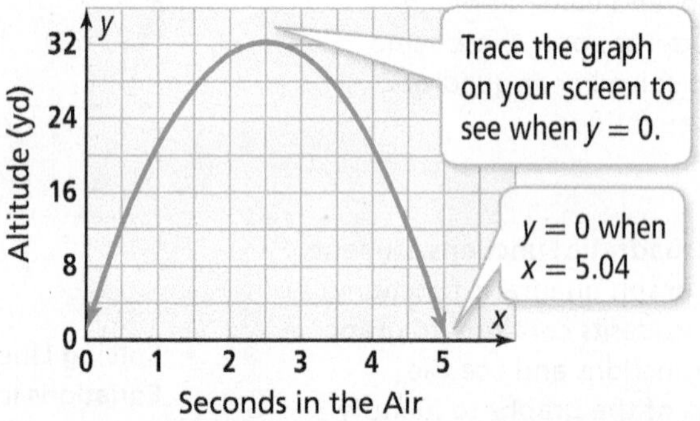

y
32
24
16
8
0
Altitude (yd)
0
1
2
3
4
5
x
Seconds in the Air
Trace the graph on your screen to see when y = 0.
y = 0 when x = 5.04

- **Using Radical Expressions** Students write radical expressions to represent real-world problems, such as finding the slant height of a cone with a given radius.

TOPIC 9

Solving Quadratic Equations

MATH PRACTICES & PROCESSES

Math Practices Within Topic 9 Lessons

The math practices describe the behaviors and habits of mind that mathematically proficient students demonstrate when actively engaged in mathematics work. Opportunities to develop expertise with these important behaviors and thinking habits exist throughout the topic and program. Here we focus on *making sense of problems* and *reasoning*.

As students solve quadratic equations, look for the following behaviors to assess and identify students who demonstrate proficiency with these math practices.

Highlighted Math Practices Within Topic 9 Lessons

Make Sense of Problems and Persevere in Solving Them **MP.1**	Reason Abstractly and Quantitatively **MP.2**
Mathematically proficient students:	Mathematically proficient students:
• Analyze given information to make sense of problems, such as recognizing the quadratic relationship between the term number and the number of objects used to create a triangle.	• Make sense of quantities and their relationships when they verify given solutions of a quadratic equation by substituting solutions into the original equation or by finding zeros after factoring.
• Persevere when they plan, perform, and describe the steps of solving a linear-quadratic system of equations by the methods of graphing, elimination, and substitution.	• Apply properties of equality and properties of exponents when finding solutions to quadratic equations.
• See relationships between various representations when they use equations to find the locations where a parabola and line, both shown graphically, would intersect.	• Consider the possible values for *c* in the standard form of a quadratic equation by thinking about whether *c* can have a negative value in a perfect square trinomial.
• Ask themselves if their solution makes sense in the context of a real-world problem, such as determining that length can only be represented by the positive solution, and that, therefore, a negative solution to a quadratic equation does not apply.	• Contextualize the solutions of quadratic equations when they interpret whether the solutions can be positive, negative, or both, based on the real-world situation.

Help students become more proficient with making sense of problems and reasoning.

If students do not understand how to identify and use appropriate strategies for understanding and solving problems involving quadratic equations, then use these questioning strategies to help them develop their proficiency with making sense of problems and reasoning as they solve problems throughout the topic.

Q: What steps should you use to solve a quadratic equation by factoring?

Q: What do you notice about the quadratic formula?

Q: Describe how to write an expression of the product of two radicals without perfect square factors in the radicand.

Q: Describe the relationship between the solutions of a quadratic equation and the graph of its related quadratic function.

Q: How did you decide which method to use when solving a quadratic equation?

Q: What do the values *a*, *b*, and *c* in the quadratic formula represent?

Q: How is the quadratic formula related to completing the square?

Q: What properties might you use when solving a quadratic equation by factoring?

TOPIC PLANNER

Lesson	New Vocabulary	Objective	Essential Understanding	Standards
9-1 2 DAYS Solving Quadratic Equations Using Graphs and Tables	• quadratic equation, zeros of a function	• Use a graph to identify the *x*-intercepts as solutions of a quadratic equation. • Use a graphing calculator to make a table of values to approximate or solve a quadratic equation.	A quadratic equation is an equation of the second degree. It can have 0, 1, or 2 solutions. The *x*-intercepts of a graph and the zeros in a table can be used to identify the real solutions.	HSA.CED.A.2, HSA.REI.D.11, HSA.CED.A.1, HSA.REI.B.4.B **Mathematical Practices** MP.3, MP.5, MP.7
9-2 2 DAYS Solving Quadratic Equations by Factoring	• standard form of a quadratic equation, Zero-Product Property	• Use the Zero-Product Property and factoring to find the solutions of a quadratic equation. • Apply factoring to solve real-world problems. • Use the zeros of a quadratic equation to sketch a graph. • Write the factored form of a quadratic function from a graph.	In the standard form of a quadratic equation $ax^2 + bx + c = 0$, where $a \neq 0$, the factors of the equation determine the solutions. The Zero-Product Property states that for all real numbers *a* and *b*, if $ab = 0$, then either $a = 0$ or $b = 0$.	HSA.SSE.B.3.A, HSA.APR.B.3, HSA.REI.B.4.B, HSF.IF.C.8.A **Mathematical Practices** MP.2, MP.3, MP.7
9-3 2 DAYS Rewriting Radical Expressions	• Product Property of Square Roots	• Use properties of exponents to rewrite radical expressions. • Multiply radical expressions. • Write a radical expression to model or represent a real-world problem.	Properties of exponents are used to rewrite radical expressions in different forms. A radical expression is written in the simplest form when there are no perfect square factors other than 1 in the radicand.	HSN.RN.A.2 **Mathematical Practices** MP.2, MP.3, MP.7
9-4 2 DAYS Solving Quadratic Equations Using Square Roots	none	• Solve quadratic equations by finding square roots. • Determine reasonable solutions for real-world problems.	When a quadratic equation is in the form $ax^2 + b = c$, it can be solved by isolating the ax^2 term, simplifying to remove the coefficients, and then taking the square root of each side of the equation.	HSA.SSE.A.2, HSA.REI.B.4.B, HSA.CED.A.1 **Mathematical Practices** MP.1, MP.2, MP.7

Lesson Resources

Digital

Print

Student Edition

Student Companion

Assessment Resource Book
- Lesson Quiz

Digital

Digital Lesson Courseware
- Examples with Embedded Interactives
- Additional Examples
- Online Practice powered by MathXL for School
- Virtual Nerd Tutorials
- English/Spanish Glossary
- Digital Math Tools
- Mathematical Modeling in 3 Acts

Teaching Resources
- Reteach to Build Understanding
- Mathematical Literacy and Vocabulary
- Additional Practice
- Enrichment

Lesson Support for Teachers
- Professional Development Video
- Lesson Plans

Digital

The suggested pacing for each lesson is shown for a 45-minute class.
In addition allow 1 day for the Topic Review and 1 day for the Topic Assessment.

TOPIC PLANNER

Lesson	New Vocabulary	Objective	Essential Understanding	Standards
9-5 2 DAYS Completing the Square	• completing the square	• Solve a quadratic trinomial by completing the square to transform a quadratic equation into a perfect square trinomial. • Use completing the square to write a quadratic equation in vertex form.	To complete the square, add the square of half of the coefficient of x to each side of the equation. Completing the square is useful when solving quadratic equations that are not factorable.	HSA.REI.B.4.A, HSA.SSE.B.3.B, HSF.IF.C.8.A **Mathematical Practices** MP.1, MP.2, MP.7
9-6 2 DAYS The Quadratic Formula and the Discriminant	• discriminant, quadratic formula, root	• Derive the quadratic formula by completing the square. • Solve quadratic equations in one variable by using the quadratic formula. • Use the discriminant to determine the number and type of solutions to a quadratic equation.	The quadratic formula can be used to solve every quadratic equation and is particularly useful for those that cannot be easily factored. The discriminant of the quadratic formula indicates the number of solutions of the equation.	HSA.REI.B.4.A, HSA.REI.B.4.B, HSA.SSE.B.3, HSA.CED.A.1 **Mathematical Practices** MP.3, MP.6, MP.7
Mathematical Modeling in 3 Acts: Unwrapping Change 1 DAY	none	• Use mathematical modeling to represent a problem situation. • Test and verify the appropriateness of their math models. • Explain why the results might not exactly match the problem situation.	Many real-world problem situations can be represented with a mathematical model, but that model might not represent the real-world situation exactly.	HSA.CED.A.1, HSA.CED.A.3, HSA.REI.B.4 **Mathematical Practices** MP.4
9-7 2 DAYS Solving Systems of Linear and Quadratic Equations	• linear-quadratic system	• Describe a linear-quadratic system of equations. • Solve a linear-quadratic system of equations by graphing, elimination, or substitution.	For any system of two equations in two variables, the solution consists of the ordered pairs that satisfy both equations.	HSA.REI.C.7, HSA.REI.D.11 **Mathematical Practices** MP.1, MP.5, MP.7

Topic Resources

Digital
Print

Student Edition
- enVision STEM
- Mathematical Modeling in 3 Acts
- Topic Review

Digital Lesson Courseware
- Topic Readiness Assessment
- Topic Assessment
- Topic Performance Assessment

Digital

Teaching Resources
- enVision STEM
- Graphing Technology Activities

Topic Support for Teachers
- Mathematical Modeling in 3 Acts
- ExamView
- Answers and Solutions

TOPIC READINESS ASSESSMENT

AVAILABLE ONLINE

Name ______

enVision Algebra 1

PearsonRealize.com

9 Readiness Assessment

1. Solve $5x - 4 - x = 0$.
   1

2. What is the solution of $\frac{1}{2}(x-6) - \frac{5}{6}(x + 4.8) = 0$?
   Ⓐ $x = -\frac{7}{3}$
   Ⓑ $x = -\frac{11}{3}$
   Ⓒ $x = -21$
   Ⓓ $x = -33$

3. For the formula $F = \frac{9}{5}K - 455.67$, what is the value of K when $F = 0$?
   Ⓐ −455.67
   Ⓑ 253.15
   Ⓒ 455.67
   Ⓓ 820.206

4. What is the x-intercept of the graph of $y = 4x - 12$?
   Ⓐ −12
   Ⓑ $\frac{1}{3}$
   Ⓒ 3
   Ⓓ 4

5. Solve $y = -\frac{2}{3}(x + 9) + 4$ for x when $y = 0$.
   −3

6. What is the x-intercept of the graphed function?

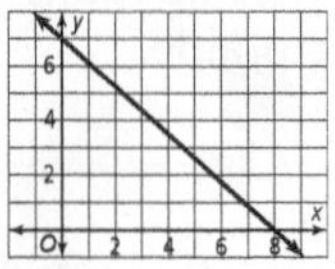

   Ⓐ $-\frac{7}{8}$
   Ⓑ 7
   Ⓒ $-\frac{8}{7}$
   Ⓓ 8

7. Simplify: $-\sqrt{49}$
   −7

8. Which value is equivalent to $\sqrt{3^6}$?
   Ⓐ 9
   Ⓑ 18
   Ⓒ 27
   Ⓓ 729

9. Which value(s) are solutions of $x^2 = 16$? Select all that apply.
   Ⓐ −8
   Ⓑ −4
   Ⓒ 4
   Ⓓ 8

10. Which pair(s) of numbers have a product of 36? Select all that apply.
   Ⓐ 3, 12
   Ⓑ 4, 9
   Ⓒ 6, 6
   Ⓓ 18, 18

11. Which of the following are factors of −30 that have a difference of 13?
   Ⓐ −15 and −2
   Ⓑ −10 and −3
   Ⓒ 15 and −2
   Ⓓ 10 and −3

12. Which of the following are factors of 60 that have a sum of 17?
   Ⓐ 3, 20
   Ⓑ 5, 12
   Ⓒ −5, −12
   Ⓓ −3, 20

13. Rewrite the equation $y = 2(x - 7)$ in standard form. Then identify the x- and y-intercepts of the graph of the equation.
   Equation: $2x - y = 14$
   x-intercept: 7 y-intercept: −14

14. Which function(s) are equivalent to $y - 2 = \frac{3}{4}(x - 12)$? Select all that apply.
   Ⓐ $y = \frac{3}{4}x - 11$
   Ⓑ $3x - 4y = 28$

15. Which of the following equations is in slope-intercept form and is equivalent to the equation $2x - 6y = 18$?
   Ⓐ $y = 3x - 3$
   Ⓑ $x = 3y + 9$
   Ⓒ $x - 3y = 9$
   Ⓓ $y = \frac{1}{3}x - 3$

16. Which is the solution of the graphed system of equations?

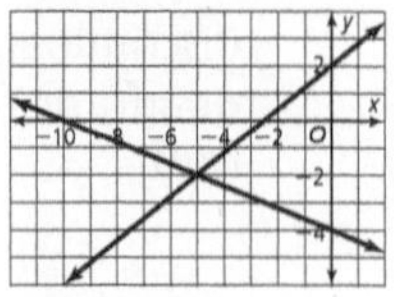

   Ⓐ (−10, 0)
   Ⓑ (−5, −2)
   Ⓒ (−4, 0)
   Ⓓ (2, 0)

17. What is the x-coordinate of the ordered pair for the solution of the system of equations $\begin{cases} y = -x + 10 \\ 2x + 6y = 8 \end{cases}$?
   13

18. What is the solution of the system of equations?
   $\begin{cases} 2x - 7y = -15 \\ 4x - 14y = 30 \end{cases}$
   Ⓐ No Solution
   Ⓑ Infinitely Many Solutions
   Ⓒ $\left(0, -\frac{15}{7}\right)$

AVAILABLE ONLINE

Topic Readiness Assessment Assess students' understanding of prerequisite concepts and skills using the Topic Readiness Assessment found at **SavvasRealize.com.** These auto-scored online assessments provide students with a breadth of technology-enhanced item types.

Individualized Study Plan Based on their performance, students will be assigned a study plan tailored to their specific learning needs.

RtI

Item Analysis for Diagnosis and Intervention

Item	DOK	Standard	Item	DOK	Standard
1	1	HSA.REI.B.3	10	1	HSA.SSE.A.2
2	2	HSA.REI.B.3	11	2	HSA.SSE.A.1
3	2	HSA.REI.B.3	12	2	HSA.SSE.A.1
4	2	HSF.IF.B.4	13	2	HSF.IF.C.8
5	2	HSF.IF.B.4	14	2	HSF.IF.C.8
6	1	HSF.IF.B.4	15	2	HSF.IF.C.8
7	1	8.EE.A.1	16	1	HSA.REI.C.6
8	2	8.EE.A.1	17	2	HSA.REI.C.6
9	2	8.EE.A.2	18	2	HSA.REI.C.6

Solving Quadratic Equations

TOPIC OPENER

AVAILABLE ONLINE

TOPIC 9

Solving Quadratic Equations

TOPIC ESSENTIAL QUESTION

How do you use quadratic equations to model situations and solve problems?

Topic Overview

Topic Vocabulary

- completing the square
- discriminant
- linear-quadratic system
- Product Property of Square Roots
- quadratic equation
- quadratic formula
- root
- standard form of a quadratic equation
- Zero-Product Property
- zeros of a function

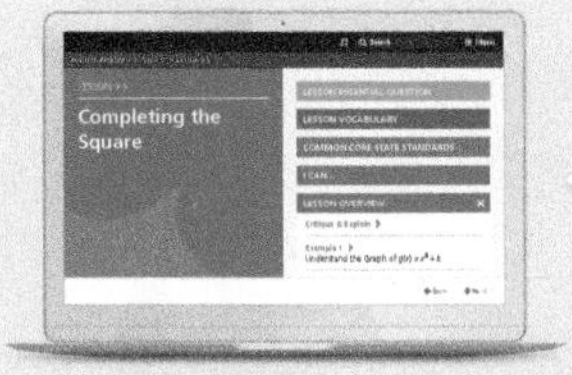

Go online | PearsonRealize.com

Digital Experience

INTERACTIVE STUDENT EDITION Access online or offline.

ACTIVITIES Complete ***Explore & Reason, Model & Discuss,*** and ***Critique & Explain*** activities. Interact with Examples and Try Its.

ANIMATION View and interact with real-world applications.

PRACTICE Practice what you've learned.

MATHEMATICAL MODELING IN 3 ACTS

QUARTERS 10$
2 NICKELS 2$
25 DIMES 5$

Unwrapping Change

When you arrange a group of objects in different ways, it seems like the space they take up has changed. But, the number of objects didn't change!

We use coin wrappers to store coins in an efficient way. How much more efficient is it than the alternative? Think about this during the Mathematical Modeling in 3 Acts lesson.

VIDEOS Watch clips to support ***Mathematical Modeling in 3 Acts Lessons*** and **enVision™ *STEM Projects.***

CONCEPT SUMMARY Review key lesson content through multiple representations.

ASSESSMENT Show what you've learned.

GLOSSARY Read and listen to English and Spanish definitions.

TUTORIALS Get help from ***Virtual Nerd***, right when you need it.

MATH TOOLS Explore math with digital tools and manipulatives.

354 TOPIC 9 Solving Quadratic Equations

TOPIC 9 Solving Quadratic Equations 355

Topic Essential Question

How do you use quadratic equations to model situations and solve problems?

Revisit the Topic Essential Question throughout the topic. See page 403 (Topic Review) for notes about answering the Topic Essential Question.

Mathematical Modeling in 3 Acts

Generate excitement about the upcoming Mathematical Modeling in 3 Acts lesson by having students read about the math modeling problem for this topic.

See pages 396–396B for notes about how to use the lesson video in your classroom.

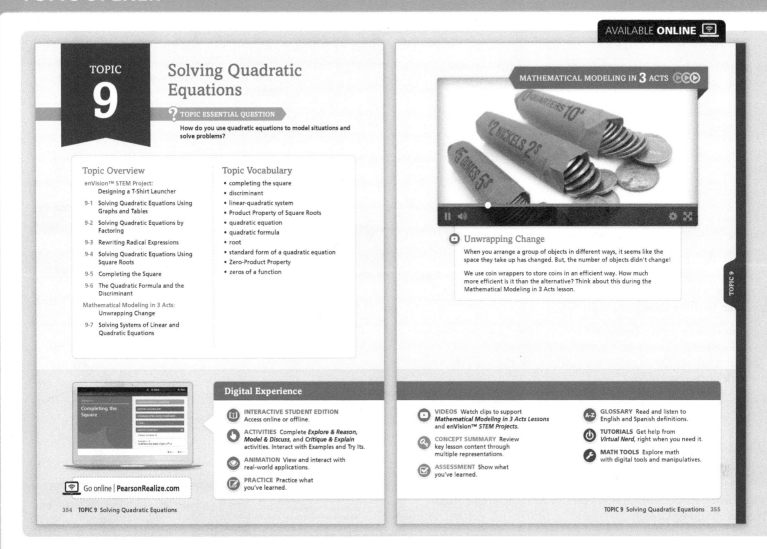

Overview of the Project

In this project, students will learn how to combine the horizontal and vertical velocities of a projectile to determine its path.

Introducing the Project

Present the situation by discussing souvenir T-shirts and sports arenas.

The questions below can be used to guide the discussion.

Q: If I tossed a T-shirt into the class, where would it land?
[Sample: It depends on where you aim and how strong your throw is.]

Q: Has anyone ever seen a T-shirt launcher in operation?
[If no one in the class has seen a T-shirt launcher in action, be prepared to show some images.]

Q: Suppose I used a T-shirt launcher to toss a T-shirt into the class. How would that change where the T-shirt landed?
[The extra power would make it possible to throw the T-shirt to the back of the classroom.]

Have students read the task they will be asked to complete.

Implementing the Project

Show the Topic 9 STEM video to generate interest in the project.

You can download blackline masters for use with the project from the Teacher Resource Center.

Encourage students to use technology to show their planned trajectories.

For students who are interested in physics, mention that the launcher physics should take wind resistance into account.

Finishing the Project

You may wish to plan a day when students share their completed projects. Encourage students to explain their process as well as their results.

MAKING MATHEMATICAL CONNECTIONS	
In Topic 5 ...	... you analyzed piecewise functions to model insect populations.
In this topic ...	... you use quadratic functions to model paths of launched objects.
In Topic 10 ...	... you will use square roots to determine square footage in a building.

AVAILABLE **ONLINE**

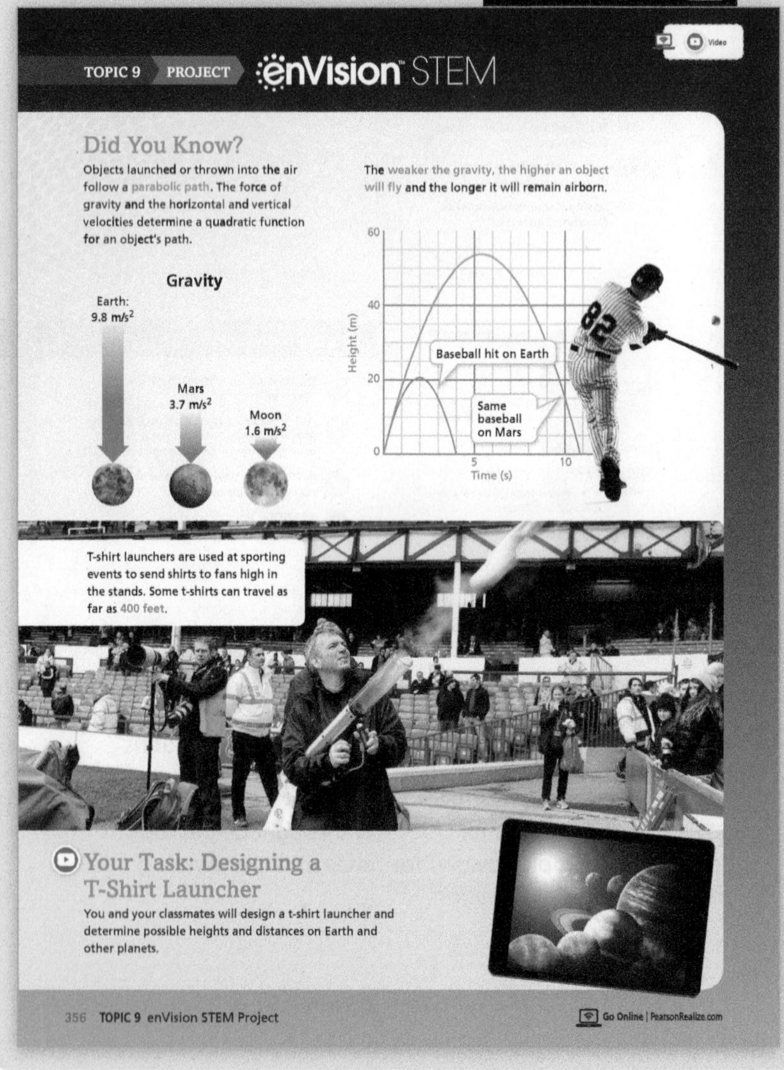
TOPIC 9 PROJECT ënVision STEM
Video
Did You Know?
Objects launched or thrown into the air follow a parabolic path. The force of gravity and the horizontal and vertical velocities determine a quadratic function for an object's path.
Gravity
Earth: 9.8 m/s2
Mars 3.7 m/s2
Moon 1.6 m/s2
The weaker the gravity, the higher an object will fly and the longer it will remain airborn.
Height (m)
Time (s)
Baseball hit on Earth
Same baseball on Mars
T-shirt launchers are used at sporting events to send shirts to fans high in the stands. Some t-shirts can travel as far as 400 feet.
Your Task: Designing a T-Shirt Launcher
You and your classmates will design a t-shirt launcher and determine possible heights and distances on Earth and other planets.
356 TOPIC 9 enVision STEM Project
Go Online | PearsonRealize.com

Common Core Standards HSA.CED.A.1, HSA.CED.A.2, HSA.SSE.A.1, HSA.REI.B.4

Mathematical Practices MP.4, MP.5, MP.7

A-Z Glossary

LESSON 9-1

Solving Quadratic Equations Using Graphs and Tables

Lesson Overview

FOCUS

Objective

Students will be able to:

✔ Use a graph to identify the x-intercepts as solutions of a quadratic equation.

✔ Use a graphing calculator to make a table of values to approximate or solve a quadratic equation.

Essential Understanding

A quadratic equation is an equation of the second degree. It can have 0, 1, or 2 solutions. The x-intercepts of a graph and the zeros in a table can be used to identify the real solutions.

COHERENCE

Previously in this course, students:

- Graphed and analyzed the key features of a quadratic function, including the intercepts.

In this lesson, students:

- Solve quadratic equations by graphing the equation and identifying the x-intercepts as solutions.
- Approximate or solve quadratic equations by using a graphing calculator or technology to make a table of values.

Later in this topic, students will:

- Solve quadratic equations by factoring, using the quadratic formula, and completing the square.

RIGOR

This lesson emphasizes a blend of *conceptual understanding* and *application.*

- Students understand that the x-intercepts of a quadratic equation are the zeros of the function and represent the solutions of the equation.
- Students use a graph to approximate the solutions to real-world problems, such as finding the amount of time that a golf ball is in the air.

A-Z Vocabulary Builder

REVIEW VOCABULARY **English** | *Spanish*

- **degree** | *grado*
- **intercept** | *intercepto*
- **solution** | *solución*

NEW VOCABULARY

- **quadratic equation** | *ecuación cuadrática*
- **zeros of a function** | *cero de una función*

VOCABULARY ACTIVITY

Review the term *degree* with students by having them identify the degree of each of the equations shown below.

$x^2 + 4 = 8$ **[2nd]** $x^4 + 3x^3 + 2x^2 + 5 = 25$ **[4th]** $x - 2 = 3$ **[1st]**

Then explain that a *quadratic equation* is an equation of the second degree. Have students identify which of the equations below are quadratic equations.

$x^2 + x + 1 = 18$ **[yes]** $x^3 + 2 = 10$ **[no]**

$x^2 + 2x - 8 = 24$ **[yes]** $x + 2x = 9$ **[no]**

Student Companion

Students can do their in-class work for the lesson on pages 189–192 of their *Student Companion* or in Savvas Realize.

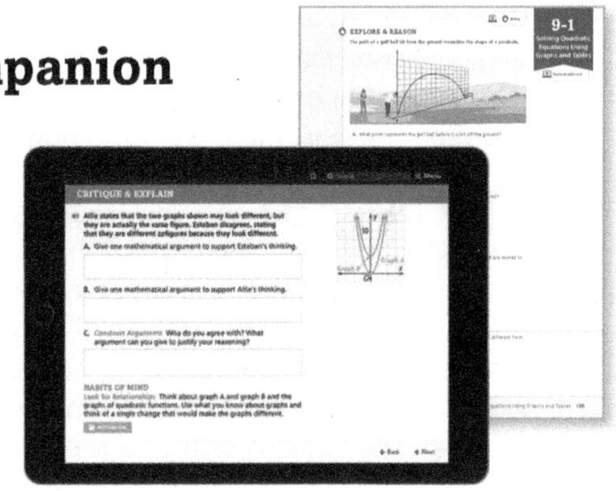

Mathematics Overview COMMON CORE STANDARDS

Content Standards

In this lesson, students focus on this standard:

HSA.REI.D.11 Explain why the x-coordinates of the points where the graphs of the equations $y = f(x)$ and $y = g(x)$ intersect are the solutions of the equation $f(x) = g(x)$; find the solutions approximately—e.g., using technology to graph the functions, make tables of values, or find successive approximations.

They also work with concepts related to these standards: **HSA.CED.A.1**, **HSA.CED.A.2**, and **HSA.REI.B.4.B**

Mathematical Practice Standards

This standard is highlighted in this lesson:

MP.3 Construct Viable Arguments

Students analyze problems and use stated mathematical assumptions about the connection between the graph of the function and the solutions of the quadratic equation to construct an argument proving that the x-intercept of the graph is the solution of the quadratic equation.

Activity

EXPLORE & REASON

INSTRUCTIONAL FOCUS Students examine the path of a golf ball, relating the position of the golf ball in its trajectory to the variables of height and distance. This exploration helps students understand the connection between the graphs of quadratic functions and the solutions of quadratic equations.

STUDENT COMPANION Students can complete the *Explore & Reason* activity on page 189 of their *Student Companion.*

Before WHOLE CLASS

Implement Tasks that Promote Reasoning and Problem Solving ETP

Q: What do you notice about the path of the golf ball?
[The starting and ending heights are the same, and the path is symmetrical on either side of the maximum height.]

During SMALL GROUP

Support Productive Struggle in Learning Mathematics ETP

Q: What is the relationship between height and distance when the height is zero?
[The distance is both the farthest away (200 yd) and the closest (0 yd), at the starting point, when the height is zero.]

Q: How do height and distance relate to each other when the height is at its maximum?
[The maximum height coincides with the halfway point between the starting and ending points.]

For Early Finishers

Q: Sketch the graph of the path of the ball if it travelled twice as high and half as far. Describe how this graph differs from the original path.
[The starting point would be the same, but ending point would coincide with the maximum height of the original path. The maximum height of the new path would fall at a distance halfway between the starting and ending points.]

After WHOLE CLASS

Facilitate Meaningful Mathematical Discourse ETP

Q: How does the path of the ball relate to key features of a parabola?
[The maximum height is the vertex of the parabola that models the path and defines the line of symmetry of the path. The starting and landing points are the *x*-intercepts.]

Q: How could the shape of the parabola that models the path of the ball change?
[Changing the height that the ball reaches, or the distance it travels, would change the shape of the parabola.]

AVAILABLE **ONLINE**

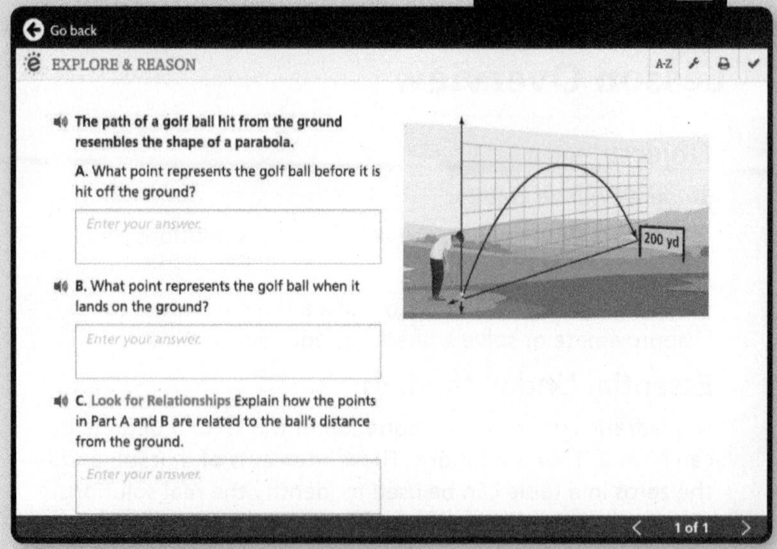
Go back
EXPLORE & REASON
The path of a golf ball hit from the ground resembles the shape of a parabola.
A. What point represents the golf ball before it is hit off the ground?
Enter your answer.
B. What point represents the golf ball when it lands on the ground?
Enter your answer.
C. Look for Relationships Explain how the points in Part A and B are related to the ball's distance from the ground.
Enter your answer.
200 yd
1 of 1

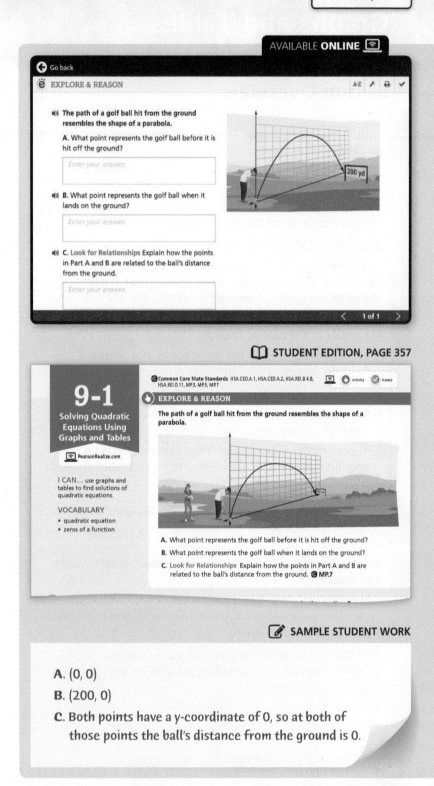

STUDENT EDITION, PAGE 357

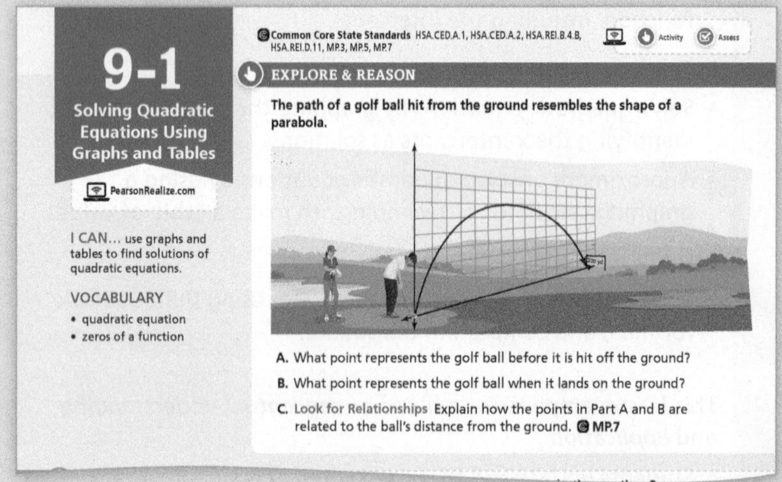
9-1
Solving Quadratic Equations Using Graphs and Tables
PearsonRealize.com
I CAN… use graphs and tables to find solutions of quadratic equations.
VOCABULARY
- quadratic equation
- zeros of a function

Common Core State Standards HSA.CED.A.1, HSA.CED.A.2, HSA.REI.B.4.B, HSA.REI.D.11, MP.3, MP.5, MP.7
EXPLORE & REASON
The path of a golf ball hit from the ground resembles the shape of a parabola.
A. What point represents the golf ball before it is hit off the ground?
B. What point represents the golf ball when it lands on the ground?
C. Look for Relationships Explain how the points in Part A and B are related to the ball's distance from the ground. MP.7
Activity
Assess

SAMPLE STUDENT WORK

A. (0, 0)
B. (200, 0)
C. Both points have a y-coordinate of 0, so at both of those points the ball's distance from the ground is 0.

HABITS OF MIND *Use with* **EXPLORE & REASON**

Communicate Precisely Generally, in a table, how are independent variables different from dependent variables? Explain. **MP.6**

[In a table, the independent variable is listed in the first column and the dependent variable is listed in the second column.]

SavvasRealize.com

Activity Assess

INTRODUCE THE ESSENTIAL QUESTION

Establish Mathematics Goals to Focus Learning ETP

Students learn to recognize the solutions of a quadratic equation by graphing the related function and identifying the x-intercepts. Students also learn to use tables to solve quadratic equations.

EXAMPLE 1 Recognize Solutions of Quadratic Equations

Pose Purposeful Questions ETP

Q: In Part A, how does the graph provide information about the solutions of the equation?
[The solutions are the x-intercepts of the graph.]

Q: How does knowing that the quadratic equation is a second-degree equation help determine the number of real solutions of the equation?
[The maximum number of real solutions of the equation is determined by the degree of the equation.]

Common Error

Try It 2 Students may look at the graph where $x = 0$ to find the solution of the equation. Have students look at where the graph crosses the x-axis to help them realize that the x-intercepts are where the y-coordinate is 0.

AVAILABLE ONLINE

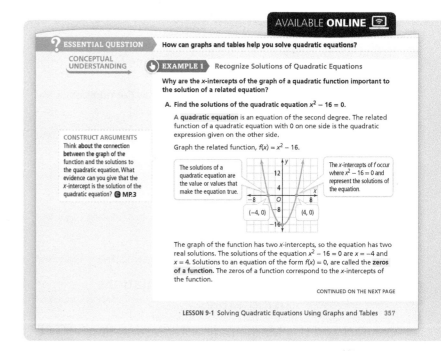

ESSENTIAL QUESTION How can graphs and tables help you solve quadratic equations?

CONCEPTUAL UNDERSTANDING

EXAMPLE 1 Recognize Solutions of Quadratic Equations

Why are the x-intercepts of the graph of a quadratic function important to the solution of a related equation?

A. Find the solutions of the quadratic equation $x^2 - 16 = 0$.

A **quadratic equation** is an equation of the second degree. The related function of a quadratic equation with 0 on one side is the quadratic expression given on the other side.

Graph the related function, $f(x) = x^2 - 16$.

CONSTRUCT ARGUMENTS Think about the connection between the graph of the function and the solutions to the quadratic equation. What evidence can you give that the x-intercept is the solution of the quadratic equation? MP.3

The solutions of a quadratic equation are the value or values that make the equation true.

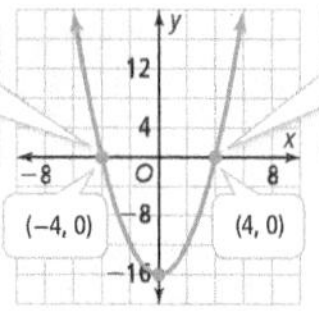

y
12
4
x
−8
O
8
−8
−16
(−4, 0)
(4, 0)

The x-intercepts of f occur where $x^2 - 16 = 0$ and represent the solutions of the equation.

The graph of the function has two x-intercepts, so the equation has two real solutions. The solutions of the equation $x^2 - 16 = 0$ are $x = -4$ and $x = 4$. Solutions to an equation of the form $f(x) = 0$, are called the **zeros of a function**. The zeros of a function correspond to the x-intercepts of the function.

CONTINUED ON THE NEXT PAGE

LESSON 9-1 Solving Quadratic Equations Using Graphs and Tables 357

ADDITIONAL EXAMPLES

AVAILABLE ONLINE

Go back

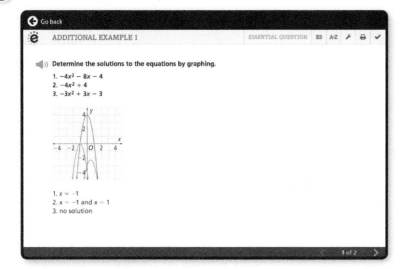

ADDITIONAL EXAMPLE 1 ESSENTIAL QUESTION ES A-Z

Determine the solutions to the equations by graphing.

1. $-4x^2 - 8x - 4$
2. $-4x^2 + 4$
3. $-3x^2 + 3x - 3$

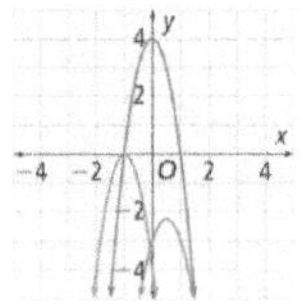

y
4
2
x
−4
−2
O
2
4
−2
−4

1. $x = -1$
2. $x = -1$ and $x = 1$
3. no solution

1 of 2

Example 1 Students find solutions of a quadratic equation written in standard form $ax^2 + bx + c = 0$ by graphing an equation where the value of a is negative.

Q: If a is negative, when does the quadratic equation have no real solutions?
[when the y-coordinate of the vertex is negative]

Go back

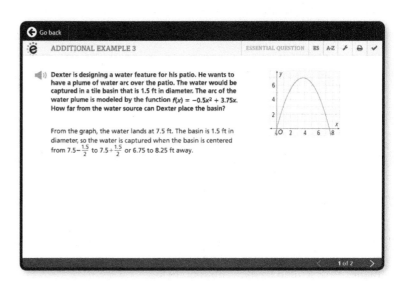

ADDITIONAL EXAMPLE 3 ESSENTIAL QUESTION ES A-Z

Dexter is designing a water feature for his patio. He wants to have a plume of water arc over the patio. The water would be captured in a tile basin that is 1.5 ft in diameter. The arc of the water plume is modeled by the function $f(x) = -0.5x^2 + 3.75x$. How far from the water source can Dexter place the basin?

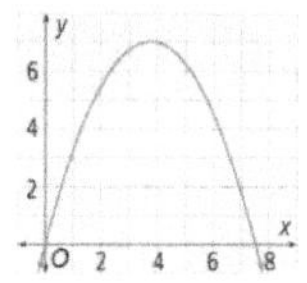

y
6
4
2
x
O
2
4
6
8

From the graph, the water lands at 7.5 ft. The basin is 1.5 ft in diameter, so the water is captured when the basin is centered from $7.5 - \frac{1.5}{2}$ to $7.5 + \frac{1.5}{2}$ or 6.75 to 8.25 ft away.

1 of 2

Example 3 Students apply solutions of a quadratic equation to a real-world problem.

Q: Explain how far from the water fountain the basin needs to be placed to catch the water if the basin is 1.75 ft in diameter.
[Since the basin is 1.75 ft in diameter, it can be centered between 6.625 ft and 8.375 ft away and still catch the water.]

Activity Assess

EXAMPLE 1 CONTINUED

Pose Purposeful Questions ETP

Q: In Part B, how does the number of real solutions of the quadratic equation relate to the graph of the function described by the equation?
[The number of real solutions is the same as the number of points on the graph that intercept the *x*-axis.]

Q: In Part C, how can you determine that there are no real solutions to the quadratic equation from the graph?
[The graph does not intersect the *x*-axis, so there are no *x*-intercepts.]

Try It! Answers

1. a. −6, 6

b. −3

EXAMPLE 2 Solve Quadratic Equations Using Tables

Connect and Use Mathematical Representations ETP

Q: In Part A, why are the solutions of the quadratic equation the values in the table for *x* when $y = 0$?
[The *x*-intercepts are the points on the graph of a quadratic function where $y = 0$.]

HABITS OF MIND

Use with **EXAMPLES 1 & 2**

Communicate Precisely When is it easier to solve a quadratic equation by graphing? When is it easier to solve a quadratic equation using a table? **MP.6**

[It is easier to solve by graphing when the scale of the graph allows for precise identification of the *x*-intercept(s). It is easier to solve using a table when the *x*-intercept is not an integer, or the scale of the graph makes it difficult to precisely identify the *x*-intercept(s).]

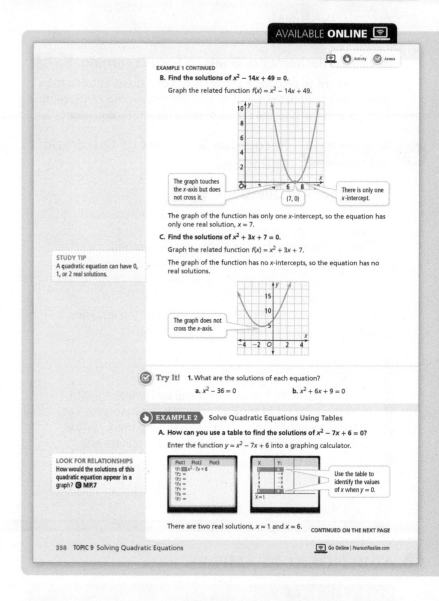

AVAILABLE **ONLINE**

Activity Assess

EXAMPLE 1 CONTINUED

B. Find the solutions of $x^2 - 14x + 49 = 0$.

Graph the related function $f(x) = x^2 - 14x + 49$.

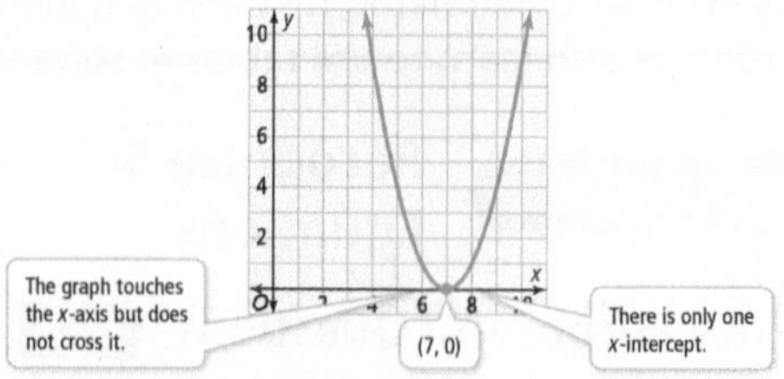

The graph touches the *x*-axis but does not cross it.
(7, 0)
There is only one *x*-intercept.

The graph of the function has only one *x*-intercept, so the equation has only one real solution, $x = 7$.

C. Find the solutions of $x^2 + 3x + 7 = 0$.

Graph the related function $f(x) = x^2 + 3x + 7$.

The graph of the function has no *x*-intercepts, so the equation has no real solutions.

STUDY TIP
A quadratic equation can have 0, 1, or 2 real solutions.

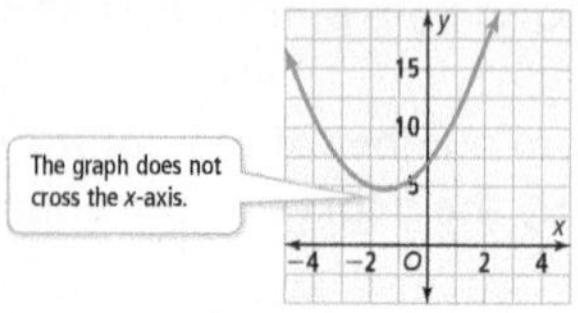

The graph does not cross the *x*-axis.

Try It! 1. What are the solutions of each equation?

a. $x^2 - 36 = 0$

b. $x^2 + 6x + 9 = 0$

EXAMPLE 2 Solve Quadratic Equations Using Tables

A. How can you use a table to find the solutions of $x^2 - 7x + 6 = 0$?

Enter the function $y = x^2 - 7x + 6$ into a graphing calculator.

LOOK FOR RELATIONSHIPS
How would the solutions of this quadratic equation appear in a graph? **MP.7**

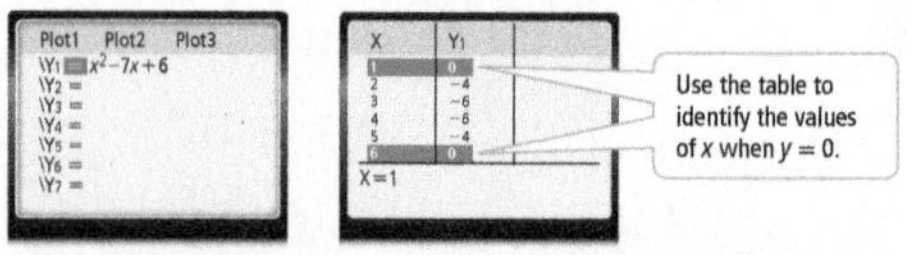

Plot1 Plot2 Plot3
\Y1 x²−7x+6
Use the table to identify the values of *x* when $y = 0$.

There are two real solutions, $x = 1$ and $x = 6$.

CONTINUED ON THE NEXT PAGE

358 TOPIC 9 Solving Quadratic Equations

Go Online | PearsonRealize.com

ELL English Language Learners *(Use with* **EXAMPLE 1***)*

WRITING BEGINNING First, have students write the definition of *quadratic*: "a polynomial equation of the second degree." Then have students write some examples of quadratic equations. Next, display the sentence: *If the graph of a quadratic function crosses or touches the x-axis* ________ *time(s), then there are* ________ *real solution(s).* Ask students to copy the sentence stem three times, filling in the blanks as described by each situation below.

Q: The graph does not cross the *x*-axis.
[zero; no]

Q: The graph touches the *x*-axis but does not cross it.
[one; one]

Q: The graph crosses the *x*-axis twice.
[two; two]

SPEAKING INTERMEDIATE Make sure students understand the use of the word *degree* in the example. Have students talk with a partner about the word *degree*.

Q: What is another common everyday use of the word *degree*?
[to describe the air or water temperature]

Q: What two ways can the word *degree* be used in math?
[a unit of measurement of an angle; the highest power of polynomial terms]

Q: What does it mean that a quadratic equation is an equation of the second *degree*?
[The highest power a variable is raised to in a quadratic equation is 2.]

LISTENING ADVANCED Read aloud the following sentence: *The x-intercepts of the graph of the function are called the zeros of the function*. Explain that *zeros* is the plural form of the noun *zero,* meaning "no quantities." *Zeroes*, with an e added, is a verb meaning "to bring within range of something." Ask students to listen to the following sentences. Students should stay seated if the sentence uses *zeros* and stand if the sentence uses *zeroes*.

Q: The hunter zeroes in on his target. **[stand]**

Q: There are many zeros in the number one trillion. **[sit]**

Q: The teacher was surprised by the number of students who got zeros on the quiz. **[sit]**

Q: Leilani zeroes in on the best deal. **[stand]**

Activity Assess

Connect and Use Mathematical Representations ETP

Q: In Part B, why is the solution estimated to be between 0.25 and 0.5?
[The solution is between $x = 0.25$ and $x = 0.5$ because the y-values transition from negative to positive, so the graph must have crossed the x-axis.]

Try It! Answer

2. −1.75, 1

Elicit and Use Evidence of Student Thinking ETP

Q: How would you refine the table settings to make an approximation to the nearest tenth?
[Change the table settings to show steps of 0.1 units.]

EXAMPLE 3 Use Approximate Solutions

Connect and Use Mathematical Representations ETP

Q: How do you know which solution to the equation represents the amount of time that the ball was in the air?
[One solution is when x equals 0, which does not make sense in the context of the problem.]

Q: What other strategy could you use to approximate a solution?
[Use a table of values.]

Try It! Answer

3. ≈ 1.05 s

HABITS OF MIND

Use with **EXAMPLE 3**

Look for Relationships How is the graph of an absolute value function related to the graph of a quadratic function? Explain. MP.7

[Both absolute value functions and quadratic functions have a vertex that is the maximum/minimum of the function, which divides the graph of the function into symmetric halves.]

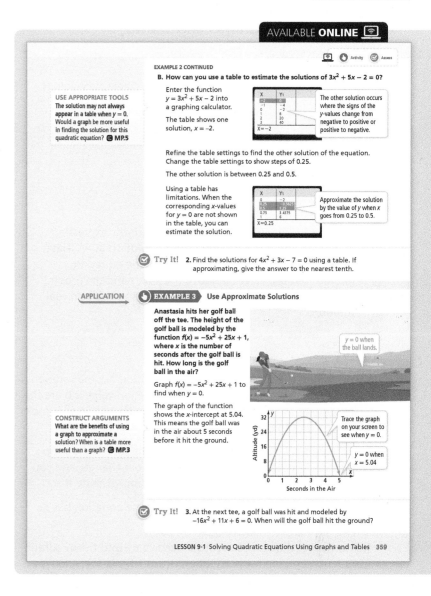

AVAILABLE **ONLINE**

Activity Assess

EXAMPLE 2 CONTINUED

B. How can you use a table to estimate the solutions of $3x^2 + 5x - 2 = 0$?

USE APPROPRIATE TOOLS
The solution may not always appear in a table when $y = 0$. Would a graph be more useful in finding the solution for this quadratic equation? MP.5

Enter the function $y = 3x^2 + 5x - 2$ into a graphing calculator.

The table shows one solution, $x = -2$.

X	Y1
−2	0
−1	−4
0	−2
1	6
2	20
3	40

X=−2

The other solution occurs where the signs of the y-values change from negative to positive or positive to negative.

Refine the table settings to find the other solution of the equation. Change the table settings to show steps of 0.25.

The other solution is between 0.25 and 0.5.

Using a table has limitations. When the corresponding x-values for $y = 0$ are not shown in the table, you can estimate the solution.

X	Y1
0	−2
0.25	−0.5625
0.5	1.25
0.75	3.4375
1	6

X=0.25

Approximate the solution by the value of y when x goes from 0.25 to 0.5.

Try It! **2.** Find the solutions for $4x^2 + 3x - 7 = 0$ using a table. If approximating, give the answer to the nearest tenth.

APPLICATION

EXAMPLE 3 Use Approximate Solutions

Anastasia hits her golf ball off the tee. The height of the golf ball is modeled by the function $f(x) = -5x^2 + 25x + 1$, where x is the number of seconds after the golf ball is hit. How long is the golf ball in the air?

y = 0 when the ball lands.

Graph $f(x) = -5x^2 + 25x + 1$ to find when $y = 0$.

The graph of the function shows the x-intercept at 5.04. This means the golf ball was in the air about 5 seconds before it hit the ground.

CONSTRUCT ARGUMENTS
What are the benefits of using a graph to approximate a solution? When is a table more useful than a graph? MP.3

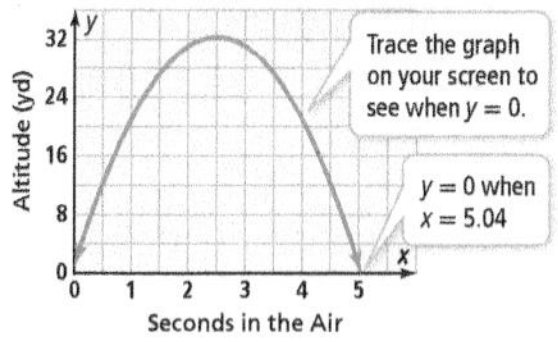

y
32
24
16
8
0
Altitude (yd)
0 1 2 3 4 5
x
Seconds in the Air
Trace the graph on your screen to see when y = 0.
y = 0 when x = 5.04

Try It! **3.** At the next tee, a golf ball was hit and modeled by $-16x^2 + 11x + 6 = 0$. When will the golf ball hit the ground?

LESSON 9-1 Solving Quadratic Equations Using Graphs and Tables 359

RtI Struggling Students

USE WITH EXAMPLE 2 Students may struggle with solving quadratic equations using tables. Have students practice analyzing a table of values to find solutions of a quadratic equation.

- Use the table to find solutions of the quadratic equation.

x	y
−2	1
−1	−1
0	−1
1	1
2	5

Q: By looking at the table, how do you know the quadratic equation has two solutions?
[The signs for the values of y change twice, so the graph must cross the x-axis twice.]

ADV Advanced Students

USE WITH EXAMPLE 3 Have students use solutions for a quadratic equation to determine the design of a roller coaster.

- The function $f(x) = -2x^2 + 15x + 10$ models the first elevation and drop of a roller coaster.

Q: How far from the starting point would the roller coaster car have to turn around to experience the maximum drop without hitting the ground?
[The roller coaster would reach the ground a little more than 8 ft away, so the car would have to turn just before.]

Q: How high does the roller coaster car climb before it begins to drop?
[a height of about 38 ft]

CONCEPT SUMMARY Solving Quadratic Equations Using Graphs and Tables

Q: How are the solutions of a quadratic equation identified in a table or graph?
[In a table, the solutions are the x-values when the y-values are zero. In a graph, the x-intercepts are the solutions to the equation.]

Do You UNDERSTAND? | Do You KNOW HOW?

Common Error

Exercise 8 Students may factor the quadratic expression as $(x + 1)^2$ and therefore identify the solution as -1. Have students check their work by graphing the equation, finding that the vertex is above the x-axis and the graph opens upward (since a is positive). Thus, there are no real solutions.

Answers

1. For graphs, the zeros of the related function are the solutions. For tables, the values of x when the function value is 0 are the solutions. If exact values don't give a function value of 0, look where sign changes occur and find approximations.
2. If the sign of the function value never changes, there is no solution. There is a solution if the sign does change, and you can use smaller and smaller intervals to approximate it.
3. Eli found the solutions of $x^2 - 100 = 0$. The equation has no solution.
4. The two x-intercepts; Substitute each value into the quadratic equation and see if the equation is true. If it is, the value is a solution.
5. 1
6. -3, 2
7. -1, 3
8. no solution
9. -4, 1
10. no solution
11. ≈ 2.2 and -0.2

AVAILABLE **ONLINE**

Concept Summary | Assess

CONCEPT SUMMARY Solving Quadratic Equations Using Graphs and Tables

WORDS A quadratic equation can be written in standard form $ax^2 + bx + c = 0$, where $a \neq 0$.

A quadratic equation can have 0, 1, or 2 real solutions.

Zeros of the function related to a quadratic equation are the solutions of the equation.

ALGEBRA $x^2 + 5x + 4 = 0$ The solutions are $x = -4$ and $x = -1$.

GRAPH $f(x) = x^2 + 5x + 4$

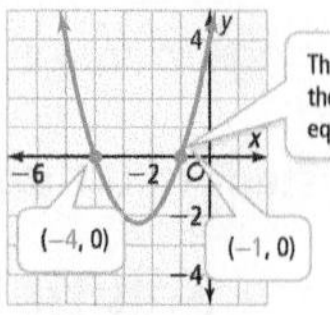
y
x
4
−6
−2
O
−2
−4
(−4, 0)
(−1, 0)

The x-intercepts are the solutions of the equation.

TABLE

x	y
−5	4
−4	0
−3	−2
−2	−2
−1	0

The solutions are the x-values when the y-values are 0.

Do You UNDERSTAND?

1. ESSENTIAL QUESTION How can graphs and tables help you solve quadratic equations?
2. **Reason** In a table that shows no exact solutions, how do you know if there are any solutions? How can you find an approximate solution? MP.2
3. **Error Analysis** Eli says that the solutions to $x^2 + 100 = 0$ are -10 and 10 because 10^2 is 100. What is the error that Eli made? Explain. MP.3
4. **Communicate Precisely** When you graph a quadratic function, the y-intercept appears to be 1, and the x-intercepts appear to be -4 and 2.5. Which values represent the solution(s) to the related quadratic equation of the function? How can you verify this? Explain. MP.6

Do You KNOW HOW?

Use each graph to find the solution of the equation.

5. $-x^2 + 2x - 1 = 0$

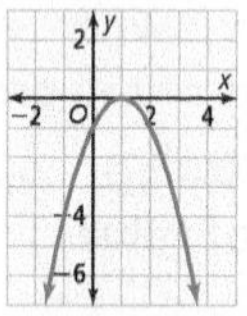
y
x
2
−2
O
2
4
−4
−6

6. $x^2 + x - 6 = 0$

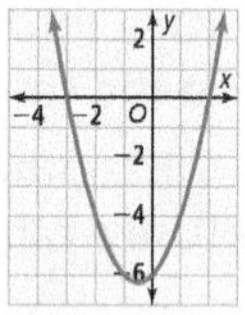
y
x
2
−4
−2
O
−2
−4
−6

Solve each quadratic equation by graphing the related function.

7. $x^2 - 2x - 3 = 0$
8. $x^2 + x + 1 = 0$

Find the solutions of each equation using a table. Round approximate solutions to the nearest tenth.

9. $x^2 + 3x - 4 = 0$
10. $3x^2 - 2x + 1 = 0$
11. What are the solutions of $-5x^2 + 10x + 2 = 0$? Round approximate solutions to the nearest tenth.

360 TOPIC 9 Solving Quadratic Equations

Go Online | PearsonRealize.com

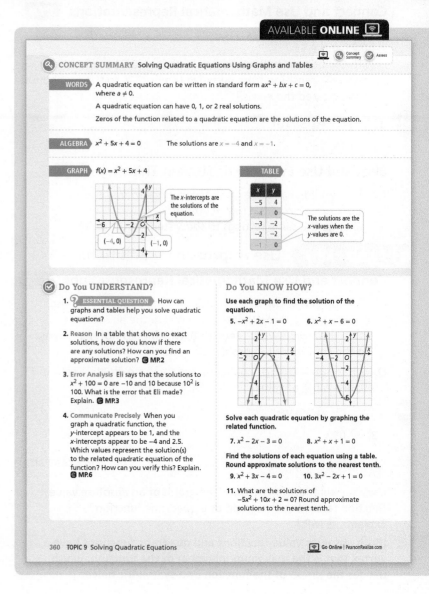

PRACTICE & PROBLEM SOLVING

AVAILABLE ONLINE

Lesson Practice You may opt to have students complete the automatically scored Practice and Problem Solving items online powered by MathXL for School.

Choose from: **Lesson Practice**

Adaptive Practice

You may also take advantage of the bank of exercises for assigning additional practice.

Assignment Guide

Basic	Advanced
12–27, 31–39	12–18, 22–39

Item Analysis

Example	Items	DOK
1	13, 14, 16, 18–29, 35, 36, 38	1
	15, 17	2
2	30–33, 37	1
	12	2
3	34	1
	39	2

Answers

12. a. Graph $f(x) = x^2 + 2x - 24$. The intercepts are the solutions.

b. The values of x for $y = x^2 + 2x - 24$ when $y = 0$ are the solutions.

14. A quadratic equation can have 1 solution. For example, $x^2 = 0$ has only 0 as a solution.

15. Answers may vary. Sample:

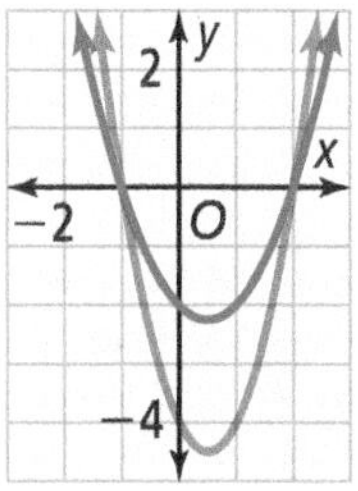

16. 2, because there is one zero between 1 and 2, and the left side of the curve goes to infinity, so there has to be another zero

17. 2; the vertex is above the x-axis, and the parabola opens downward.

AVAILABLE ONLINE

PRACTICE & PROBLEM SOLVING

Scan for Multimedia | Practice | Tutorial | Additional Exercises Available Online

UNDERSTAND

12. Communicate Precisely Consider the quadratic equation $x^2 + 2x - 24 = 0$. MP.6

a. How could you solve the equation using a graph? Explain.

b. How could you solve the equation using a table? Explain.

13. Generalize For an equation of the form $ax^2 + bx + c = 0$, where the graph crosses the y-axis once and does not intersect the x-axis. Describe the solution(s) of the equation. MP.8
There is no solution.

14. Error Analysis Describe and correct the error a student made in stating the number of solutions of a quadratic equation. Explain. MP.3

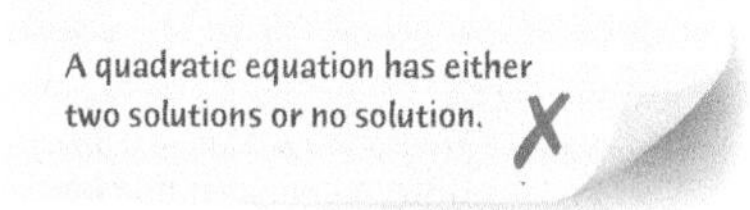
A quadratic equation has either two solutions or no solution.

15. Higher Order Thinking Infinitely many quadratic equations of the form $ax^2 + bx + c = 0$ can have the same two solutions. Sketch the graphs of two quadratic functions on the same grid to show how this could be true.

16. Communicate Precisely How many zeros does the function shown have? Explain. MP.6

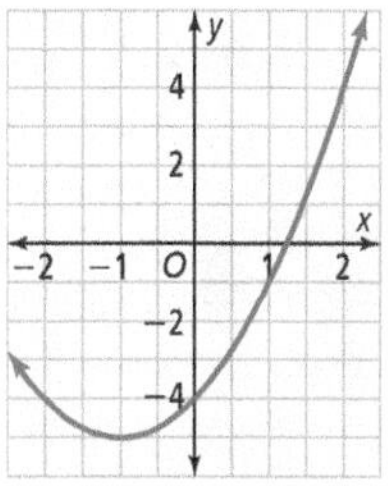

17. Mathematical Connections If a quadratic function has a maximum value that is greater than 0, how many zeros does the function have? Explain.

PRACTICE

Use each graph to find the solution of the related equation. SEE EXAMPLE 1

18. $x^2 - 2x + 2 = 0$ no solution

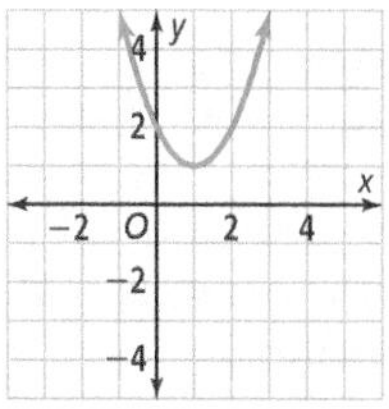

19. $-x^2 - x + 6 = 0$ −3, 2

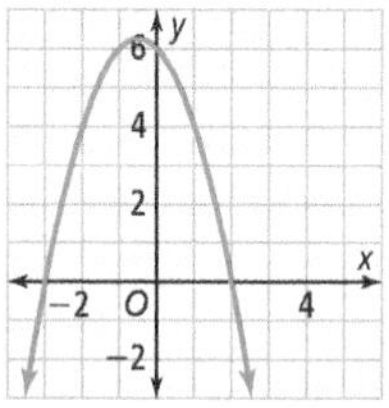

Solve each quadratic equation by graphing the related function. Round approximate solutions to the nearest tenth. SEE EXAMPLES 1 AND 3

20. $x^2 - 121 = 0$ −11, 11

21. $x^2 - 4x + 4 = 0$ 2

22. $x^2 + 3x + 7 = 0$ no solution

23. $x^2 - 5x = 0$ 0, 5

24. $-x^2 + 6x + 7 = 0$ −1, 7

25. $-x^2 + 8x - 7 = 0$ 1, 7

26. $x^2 - 2 = 0$ $\approx -1.4, \approx 1.4$

27. $2x^2 - 11x + 12 = 0$ 1.5, 4

28. $-3x^2 + 5x + 7 = 0$ $\approx -0.9, \approx 2.6$

29. $-16x^2 + 70 = 0$ $\approx -2.1, \approx 2.1$

Find the solutions for each equation using a table. Round approximate solutions to the nearest tenth. SEE EXAMPLE 2

30. $x^2 - 16 = 0$ −4, 4

31. $x^2 + 8x + 16 = 0$ −4

32. $x^2 + 3x + 1 = 0$ $\approx -2.6, \approx -0.4$

33. $x^2 + 4x + 6 = 0$ no solution

Answers

35. No, the solutions to the equation $0.5n^2 + 0.5n = 50$ are not integers, because the related quadratic equation $n^2 + n - 100 = 0$ is not factorable. A solution must be a positive integer for it to be a triangular number.

36. a. 0.97 s

b. 0.63 s

39. Part A $-16x^2 + 50x + 20 = 0$; $x \approx -0.36$, $x \approx 3.48$

Part B No; -0.36 is a solution of the equation, but not the problem, because time cannot be negative.

Part C 59 ft

AVAILABLE ONLINE

PRACTICE & PROBLEM SOLVING

Practice Tutorial
Mixed Review Available Online

APPLY

34. Model With Mathematics A small company shows the profits from their business with the function $P(x) = -0.01x^2 + 60x + 500$, where x is the number of units they sell and P is the profit in dollars. **MP.4**

a. How many units are sold by the company to earn the maximum profit? 3,000 units

b. How many units are sold when the company starts showing a loss? more than 6,008 units

35. Make Sense and Persevere A pattern of triangular numbers is shown. The first is 1, the second is 3, the third is 6, and so on.

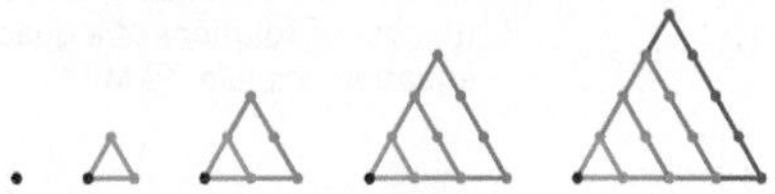
1
3
6
10
15

The formula $0.5n^2 + 0.5n$ can be used to find the nth triangular number. Is 50 a triangular number? Explain. **MP.1**

36. Make Sense and Persevere The equation $-16x^2 + 10x + 15 = 0$ represents the height, in feet, of a flotation device above the water after x seconds. The linear term represents the initial velocity. The constant term represents the initial height.

a. If the initial velocity is 0, when should the flotation device land in the water?

b. If the initial height is 0, when does the flotation device land in the water? **MP.1**

ASSESSMENT PRACTICE

37. Does each quadratic equation have two solutions? Select *Yes* or *No*.

	Yes	No
$0 = 2x^2 + 1$	☐	☑
$0 = 2x^2 + 5x + 1$	☑	☐
$0 = 2x^2 + 5x$	☑	☐
$0 = 4x^2 - 4x + 1$	☐	☑
$0 = 4x^2 - 4x - 1$	☑	☐

38. SAT/ACT What are the solutions of $x^2 + 2x - 15 = 0$ using the graph shown?

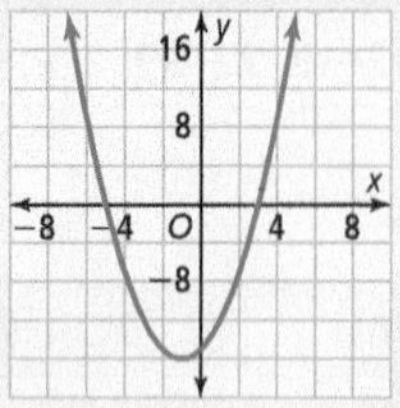
16
y
8
x
−8
−4
O
4
8
−8

Ⓐ −3, 3
Ⓑ −5, 3
Ⓒ −8, 5
Ⓓ −16, 0

39. Performance Task A human catapult is used to launch a person into a lake. The height, in feet, of the person is modeled as shown, where x is the time in seconds from the launch.

$f(x) = -16x^2 + 50x + 20$

Part A What equation can you use to find when the person touches the lake? Find the solution.

Part B Are your solutions the same for the equation and problem? Why or why not?

Part C What is the greatest height reached?

362 TOPIC 9 Solving Quadratic Equations

Go Online | PearsonRealize.com

SavvasRealize.com

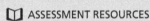

Assess | Tutorials | Worksheets

LESSON QUIZ

Use the Lesson Quiz to assess students' understanding of the mathematics in the lesson.

Students can take the Lesson Quiz online or you can download a printable copy from **SavvasRealize.com**. The Lesson Quiz is also available in the *Assessment Resources* book.

Item Analysis

Item	DOK	Standards
1	1	HSA.REI.D.11
2	2	HSA.REI.B.4.B
3	1	HSA.REI.B.4.B, HSA.CED.A.2
4	2	HSA.REI.B.4.B
5	2	HSA.CED.A.1

RtI Use the student scores on the Lesson Quiz to prescribe differentiated assignments.

If students take the Lesson Quiz online, it will be automatically scored and appropriate differentiated practice will be assigned based on student performance.

I Intervention	0–3 points	• Reteach to Build Understanding • Mathematical Literacy and Vocabulary • Additional Practice
O On-Level	4 points	• Mathematical Literacy and Vocabulary • Additional Practice • Enrichment
A Advanced	5 points	• Enrichment

AVAILABLE **ONLINE**

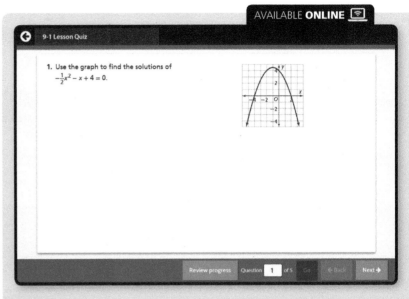

9-1 Lesson Quiz

1. Use the graph to find the solutions of $-\frac{1}{2}x^2 - x + 4 = 0$.

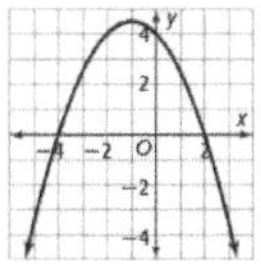

Review progress Question 1 of 5 Go ← Back Next →

ASSESSMENT RESOURCES

Name ______

enVision Algebra 1 PearsonRealize.com

9-1 Lesson Quiz

Solving Quadratic Equations Using Graphs and Tables

1. Use the graph to find the solutions of $-\frac{1}{2}x^2 - x + 4 = 0$.
   $x = -4, x = 2$

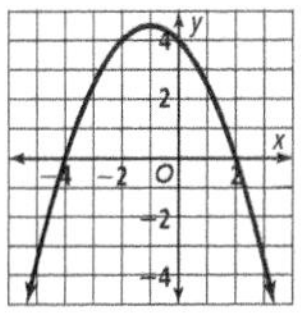

2. The equation $ax^2 + bx + c = 0$ has no real solutions. Which statement about the graph of $f(x) = ax^2 + bx + c$ could be true?
   Ⓐ It could pass through the origin.
   Ⓑ Its vertex could be at (–6, 0).
   Ⓒ It could have a maximum at (–3, 2).
   Ⓓ It could have a minimum at (0, 4).

3. Solve the equation $x^2 - 2x - 3 = 0$ by graphing.
   $x = -1, x = 3$

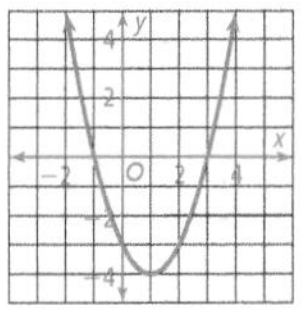

4. The table shows input and output values of the function $y = x^2 + 12x - 2$. What is an approximate solution of the equation $x^2 + 12x - 2 = 0$?

X	Y_1
−0.2	−4.36
−0.1	−3.19
0	−2
0.1	−0.79
0.2	0.44
0.3	1.69

   Ⓐ –2
   Ⓑ –0.2
   Ⓒ 0
   Ⓓ 0.13

5. The path of a volleyball thrown over a net is modeled with the function $A(x) = -0.02x^2 + 0.6x + 5$, where x is the horizontal distance, in feet, from the starting point, and A is the altitude of the ball in feet. Write an equation that can be solved to find out how far the ball travels horizontally before it hits the ground. Then find the distance.
   equation: $-0.02x^2 + 0.6x + 5 = 0$ distance: about 37 ft

enVision™ Algebra 1 • Assessment Resources

Assess | Tutorials | Worksheets

DIFFERENTIATED RESOURCES

I = Intervention   O = On-Level   A = Advanced

= This activity is available as a digital assignment powered by MathXL® for School.

AVAILABLE ONLINE

Reteach to Build Understanding I

Provides scaffolded reteaching for the key lesson concepts.

Name

9-1 Reteach to Build Understanding

Solving Quadratic Equations Using Graphs and Tables

1. The graph and table both show methods that can be used to solve the equation $x^2 - x - 2 = 0$. Circle the points in the graph and the numbers in the table that indicate the solutions of the equation. Then complete the statement about the solution by writing numbers in the blanks.

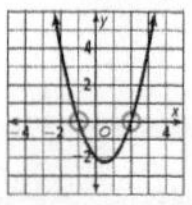

x	y
−2	4
−1	0
0	−2
1	−2
2	0

The solutions of the equation $x^2 - x - 2 = 0$ are −1 and 2.

2. Marcela incorrectly used graphing to find the solution of $x^2 - 2x + 5 = 0$. Find and correct her error.

Graph the related function $f(x) = x^2 - 2x + 5$.

The graph intercepts the y-axis at (0, 5).
The solution of the equation is 5. X

Marcela incorrectly identified the y-intercept as the solution of the equation. Because the graph of the related function has no x-intercepts, the equation has no real solutions.

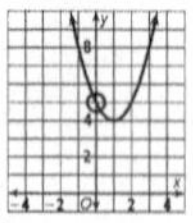

3. Find the solutions of the equation $x^2 + 3x + 2 = 0$.

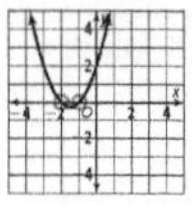

x	y
−3	2
−2	0
−1	0
0	2
1	6

The solutions of the equation $x^2 + 3x + 2 = 0$ are −2 and −1.

enVision™ Algebra 1 • Teaching Resources

Additional Practice I O

Provides extra practice for each lesson.

Name

9-1 Additional Practice

Solving Quadratic Equations Using Graphs and Tables

Solve each equation by graphing.

1. $x^2 + x - 12 = 0$
2. $x^2 + 4 = 4x$
3. $-x^2 + 6x - 10 = 0$

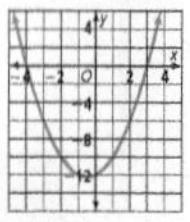

−4, 3

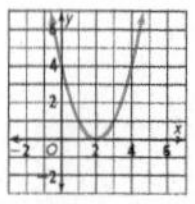

2

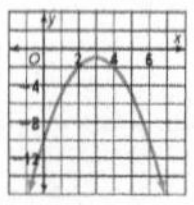

no solution

Use a table to find the solutions for each equation. You may use a calculator. For approximate solutions, use the average rounded to the nearest tenth of the two consecutive x-values for which the sign of the y-values changes.

4. $4x^2 - 36 = 0$ −3, 3
5. $x^2 + 4x = 5$ −5, 1
6. $x^2 + 2x - 6 = 0$ −3.5, 1.5
7. $2x^2 - 3x + 1 = 0$ 0.5, 1
8. $x^2 + 3x - 6 = 0$ −4.5, 1.5
9. $4x^2 + 20x + 25 = 0$ −2.5
10. Armando kicks a football into the air. The equation $f(x) = -6x^2 + 38x + 0.25$ models the height of the football from the ground, in feet, with respect to the time x, in seconds. Use a graph or table to estimate the time for the ball to return to the ground after being kicked.
6.3 s
11. When using a table to find the solutions to a quadratic equation, how can you be sure you have found all the solutions?
Sample answer: Make sure you have found the vertex of the function. Then you will be able to complete the table to find the correct number of places the graph intersects the x-axis or whether the graph does not intersect the x-axis.

enVision™ Algebra 1 • Teaching Resources

Enrichment O A

Presents engaging problems and activities that extend the lesson concepts.

Name

9-1 Enrichment

Solving Quadratic Equations Using Graphs and Tables

Match the sentence in Column A with the equation in Column B. Graph the equation if needed. Then write the number matching each letter in the empty puzzle grid. The sum of all the numbers in every column, row, and diagonal should be the same.

Column A	Column B
1. The graph of this equation is wider than $y = x^2$.	A. $y = x^2 - 3$
2. The graph of this equation has a minimum at (0, −4).	B. $y = 0.25x^2 + 1$
3. The graph of this equation has the range $y \geq -2$.	C. $y = x^2 - 4$
4. The graph of this equation has a vertex at (0, 3).	D. $y = x^2 + 3$
5. This is the quadratic parent function.	E. $y = x^2 - 2$
6. This equation is not in standard form.	F. $y = x^2$
7. This equation's graph is the same as $y = x^2$, translated down by 3.	G. $y = 2 - 3x^2$
8. The graph of this equation does not intersect the line $y = 2$.	H. $y = -2x^2 + 3$

A. 7	12	B. 1	14	34
C. 2	13	D. 8	11	34
16	E. 3	10	F. 5	34
9	G. 6	15	H. 4	34
34	34	34	34	34

What is the sum of every column, row, and diagonal? 34

enVision™ Algebra 1 • Teaching Resources

Mathematical Literacy and Vocabulary I O

Helps students develop and reinforce understanding of key terms and concepts.

Name

9-1 Mathematical Literacy and Vocabulary

Solving Quadratic Equations Using Graphs and Tables

Choose the word from the list that best matches each phrase.

quadratic equation | zeros of a function | related function | solutions

1. the value(s) that make an equation true solution
2. an equation in two variables that can be used to solve a different equation in one variable related function
3. an equation of the second degree quadratic equation
4. the x-intercepts of the graph of a function zeros of a function

Use the graph shown and a word from the concept list to complete each sentence.

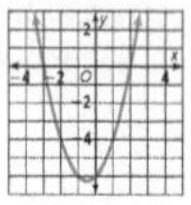

5. For the graph shown, the values −2 and 3 are the zeros of a function.
6. The equation $x^2 + x - 6 = 0$ is a quadratic equation.
7. The graph shown is a graph of the related function $f(x) = x^2 + x - 6$.
8. The values −2 and 3 are both solutions of the equation $x^2 + x - 6 = 0$.

enVision™ Algebra 1 • Teaching Resources

Digital Resources and Video Tutorials I O A

The **Reteach to Build Understanding, Additional Practice**, and **Enrichment** activities are available as digital assignments powered by MathXL for School. These activities are automatically assigned when students complete the lesson quiz online and are automatically scored.

Students can access instructional tutorials using the **Virtual Nerd app**.

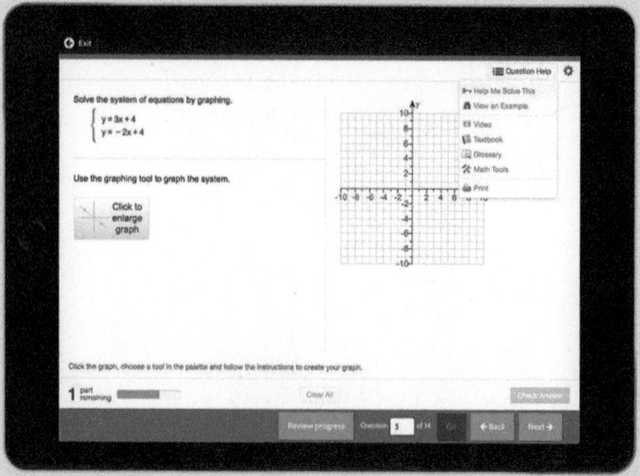
Exit
Question Help
Help Me Solve This
View an Example
Video
Textbook
Glossary
Math Tools
Print
Solve the system of equations by graphing.
y = 3x + 4
y = −2x + 4
Use the graphing tool to graph the system.
Click to enlarge graph
Click the graph, choose a tool in the palette and follow the instructions to create your graph.
1 part remaining
Clear All
Check Answer
Review progress
Question 5 of 14
Back
Next

Tutorial
SLOPE-INTERCEPT FORM
What's Slope-Intercept Form of a Linear Equation?
SAVVAS

Students can also access Virtual Nerd videos using the **BouncePages app** to scan exercise pages marked with this icon. Students can download both apps for free in their mobile devices' app store.

SavvasRealize.com

A-Z Glossary

LESSON 9-2

Solving Quadratic Equations by Factoring

Lesson Overview

FOCUS

Objective

Students will be able to:

✓ Use the Zero-Product Property and factoring to find the solutions of a quadratic equation.

✓ Apply factoring to solve real-world problems.

✓ Use the zeros of a quadratic equation to sketch a graph.

✓ Write the factored form of a quadratic function from a graph.

Essential Understanding

In the standard form of a quadratic equation $ax^2 + bx + c = 0$, where $a \neq 0$, the factors of the equation determine the solutions. The Zero-Product Property states that for all real numbers a and b, if $ab = 0$, then either $a = 0$ or $b = 0$.

COHERENCE

Previously in this course, students:

- Used graphs and tables to identify the solutions of a quadratic equation.
- Factored quadratic trinomials

In this lesson, students:

- Solve a quadratic equation in standard form by factoring and using the Zero-Product Property.

Later in this topic, students will:

- Solve quadratic equations by completing the square.

RIGOR

This lesson emphasizes a blend of *conceptual understanding* and *application.*

- Students understand that because a quadratic equation written in standard form is set equal to zero, once factored, the Zero-Product Property can be used to find the solutions.
- Students apply factoring to solve real-world problems, such as finding the width of the outer wall of a vault when given the area and dimensions of the vault written as binomial factors.

A-Z Vocabulary Builder

REVIEW VOCABULARY — **English** | *Spanish*

- **factored form** | *forma del factor*
- **parabola** | *parábola*
- **vertex** | *vértice*

NEW VOCABULARY

- **standard form of a quadratic equation** | *forma normal de una función cuadrática*
- **Zero-Product Property** | *Propiedad del Producto Cero*

VOCABULARY ACTIVITY

Review the term *factor,* reminding students that factors can be *expressions* and not just *integers* or *monomials.* Explain that the *standard form of a quadratic equation* is $ax^2 + bx + c = 0$, where $a \neq 0$. A quadratic equation can also be written in *factored form,* which can be used to find the x-intercepts or the solutions of the equation. Have students match each term to the correct form of the equation.

$x^2 + 3x - 18 = 0$ — **factored form**

$(x + 6)(x - 3) = 0$ — **standard form**

Student Companion

Students can do their in-class work for the lesson on pages 193–196 of their *Student Companion* or in Savvas Realize.

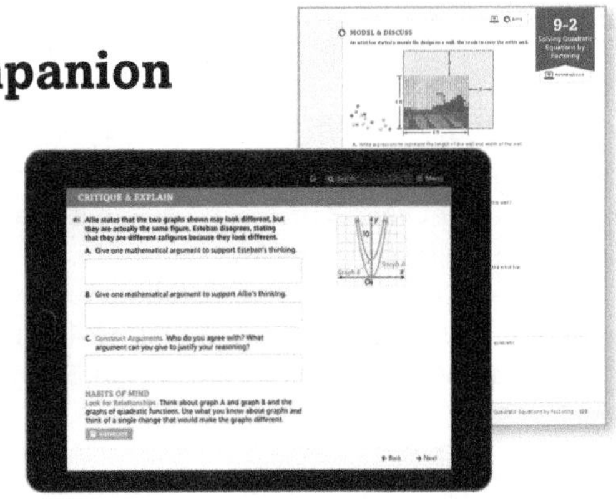

Mathematics Overview — COMMON CORE STANDARDS

Content Standards

In this lesson, students focus on these standards:

HSA.SSE.B.3.A Factor a quadratic expression to reveal the zeros of the function it defines.

HSA.APR.B.3 Identify zeros of polynomials when suitable factorizations are available, and use the zeros to construct a rough graph of the function defined by the polynomial.

They also work with concepts related to these standards: **HSA.REI.B.4.B** and **HSF.IF.C.8.A**

Mathematical Practice Standards

These standards are highlighted in this lesson:

MP.2 Reason Abstractly and Quantitatively

Students make sense of quantities and their relationships when they verify given solutions of a quadratic equation by substituting the solutions back into the original equation and check that the resulting equation is a true statement.

MP.7 Look For and Make Use of Structure

Students connect their understanding of solving quadratic equations by factoring and by graphing when they describe how their solutions found by factoring would appear in a graph.

Activity

MODEL & DISCUSS

INSTRUCTIONAL FOCUS Students write two expressions, one representing the length and one representing the width. They then use the Distributive Property to multiply the length by the width to write an expression that represents the entire area of the wall. By recognizing the two expressions as factors, students prepare to factor the standard form of a quadratic equation and use the factored form to solve the equation.

STUDENT COMPANION Students can complete the *Model & Discuss* activity on page 193 of their *Student Companion.*

AVAILABLE **ONLINE**

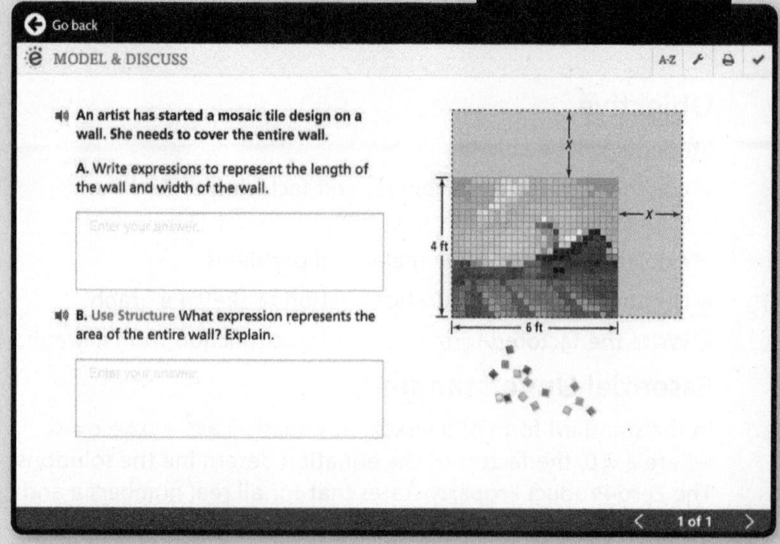

Go back
MODEL & DISCUSS
A-Z
An artist has started a mosaic tile design on a wall. She needs to cover the entire wall.
A. Write expressions to represent the length of the wall and width of the wall.
Enter your answer.
B. Use Structure What expression represents the area of the entire wall? Explain.
Enter your answer.
x
x
4 ft
6 ft
1 of 1

STUDENT EDITION, PAGE 363

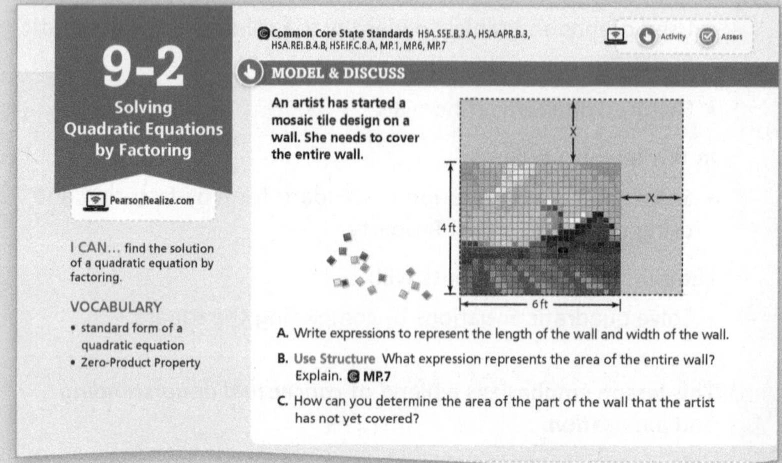

Common Core State Standards HSA.SSE.B.3.A, HSA.APR.B.3, HSA.REI.B.4.B, HSF.IF.C.8.A, MP.1, MP.6, MP.7
Activity
Assess
9-2
Solving Quadratic Equations by Factoring
PearsonRealize.com
I CAN… find the solution of a quadratic equation by factoring.
VOCABULARY
• standard form of a quadratic equation
• Zero-Product Property
MODEL & DISCUSS
An artist has started a mosaic tile design on a wall. She needs to cover the entire wall.
x
x
4 ft
6 ft
A. Write expressions to represent the length of the wall and width of the wall.
B. Use Structure What expression represents the area of the entire wall? Explain. MP.7
C. How can you determine the area of the part of the wall that the artist has not yet covered?

Before WHOLE CLASS

Implement Tasks that Promote Reasoning and Problem Solving ETP

Q: What do you know about the dimensions of the wall by looking at the image?
[Both dimensions are variable expressions, so the dimensions would change based on the value of x.]

During SMALL GROUP

Support Productive Struggle in Learning Mathematics ETP

Q: What is the relationship between the expressions that represent the dimensions of the wall and the area of the wall?
[The product of the dimensions is equal to the area.]

For Early Finishers

Q: Describe the graph that would show the area of the wall for different values of x. How would it change if the width of the wall were just 4?
[The graph would be a parabola with x-intercepts at -4 and -6. If the width were changed to 4, the graph would be a straight line with a y-intercept of 24 and a slope of 4.]

After WHOLE CLASS

Facilitate Meaningful Mathematical Discourse ETP

Q: How do you know what operation to use to find the area that needs to be finished?
[Since you have found the area of the entire wall and can easily find the area where the mosaic tile was started, you know to subtract to find the area of the wall that still needs to be completed.]

HABITS OF MIND *Use with* **MODEL & DISCUSS**

Make Sense and Persevere How might factoring help you solve a quadratic equation? Explain. **MP.1**

[The solutions are where the graph crosses the x-axis, or when $y = 0$. Factoring a quadratic equation can make it easier to determine what the x-values are when $y = 0$.]

SAMPLE STUDENT WORK

A. length $x + 6$ ft, width $x + 4$ ft

B. $(x + 6)(x + 4) = x^2 + 10x + 24$; Area is the product of the length and the width.

C. You can subtract the area of the wall that is already finished from the area of the entire wall. The area of the entire wall is $x^2 + 10x + 24$, and the area of the finished section is 24. When you subtract, you are left with $x^2 + 10x$.

INTRODUCE THE ESSENTIAL QUESTION

Establish Mathematics Goals to Focus Learning ETP

Students learn to solve quadratic equations using factoring and the Zero-Product Property. Students find the value(s) of x that make the equations true. Students understand that factoring is just one method for solving quadratic equations.

EXAMPLE 1 Use the Zero-Product Property

Pose Purposeful Questions ETP

Q: Why do you set each factor equal to zero and then solve?
[Because of the Zero-Product Property, if the product is zero, one of the factors must be zero. Solving finds the value of x that makes each factor zero.]

Q: What is another strategy you could use to find the solution of the equation?
[You could graph the related function. There would be two x-intercepts, one at 9 and one at $-\frac{2}{5}$, which would be the zeros of the function and the solutions of the equation.]

Try It! Answers

1. a. $\frac{1}{2}, -3$ b. $-\frac{3}{2}, \frac{1}{3}$

Elicit and Use Evidence of Student Thinking ETP

Q: Which factor of the equation must be set equal to zero to find the correct solution?
[Both, you must set each factor equal to 0 and solve to find the solutions. If you only set one factor equal to 0 and solve, you will only get part of the solution.]

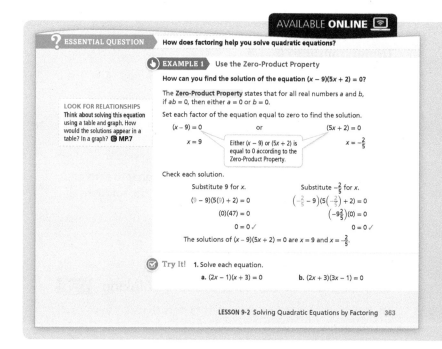

AVAILABLE ONLINE

ESSENTIAL QUESTION How does factoring help you solve quadratic equations?

EXAMPLE 1 Use the Zero-Product Property

How can you find the solution of the equation $(x-9)(5x+2)=0$?

The **Zero-Product Property** states that for all real numbers a and b, if $ab=0$, then either $a=0$ or $b=0$.

LOOK FOR RELATIONSHIPS
Think about solving this equation using a table and graph. How would the solutions appear in a table? In a graph? MP.7

Set each factor of the equation equal to zero to find the solution.

$(x-9)=0$ or $(5x+2)=0$

$x=9$ $x=-\frac{2}{5}$

Either $(x-9)$ or $(5x+2)$ is equal to 0 according to the Zero-Product Property.

Check each solution.

Substitute 9 for x.

$(9-9)(5(9)+2)=0$

$(0)(47)=0$

$0=0$ ✓

Substitute $-\frac{2}{5}$ for x.

$\left(-\frac{2}{5}-9\right)\left(5\left(-\frac{2}{5}\right)+2\right)=0$

$\left(-9\frac{2}{5}\right)(0)=0$

$0=0$ ✓

The solutions of $(x-9)(5x+2)=0$ are $x=9$ and $x=-\frac{2}{5}$.

Try It! 1. Solve each equation.

a. $(2x-1)(x+3)=0$ b. $(2x+3)(3x-1)=0$

LESSON 9-2 Solving Quadratic Equations by Factoring 363

ADDITIONAL EXAMPLES

AVAILABLE ONLINE

Go back

ADDITIONAL EXAMPLE 1 ESSENTIAL QUESTION ES A-Z

Solve the equation.

$(x-9)^2=0$

$(x-9)^2=0$ means $(x-9)(x-9)=0$. Use the Zero-Product Property. $(x-9)=0$ and $(x-9)=0$ So, $x=9$ and $x=9$. There is only one solution, $x=9$.

1 of 2

Example 1 Students extend their understanding of the Zero-Product Property to equations with only one solution.

Q: Why is there only one solution to this equation?
[Since the factor is squared, both factors are the same. Therefore, the solution when each factor is set equal to zero is the same.]

Go back

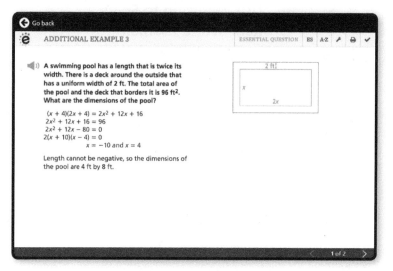

ADDITIONAL EXAMPLE 3 ESSENTIAL QUESTION ES A-Z

A swimming pool has a length that is twice its width. There is a deck around the outside that has a uniform width of 2 ft. The total area of the pool and the deck that borders it is 96 ft^2. What are the dimensions of the pool?

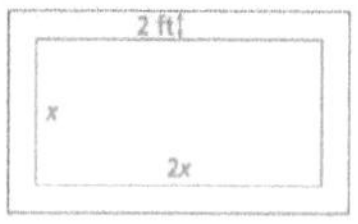
2 ft
x
2x

$(x+4)(2x+4)=2x^2+12x+16$
$2x^2+12x+16=96$
$2x^2+12x-80=0$
$2(x+10)(x-4)=0$
$x=-10$ and $x=4$

Length cannot be negative, so the dimensions of the pool are 4 ft by 8 ft.

1 of 2

Example 3 Students solve a real-world problem in which the dimensions are variable expressions.

Q: Is 4 the complete solution to the problem?
[No; the problem asks for both dimensions. Since each dimension is a variable expression, you need to substitute 4 for x in each dimension to find the answers.]

Activity Assess

EXAMPLE 2 Solve by Factoring

Build Procedural Fluency From Conceptual Understanding ETP

Q: Why must the equation be written in standard form first in order to solve the equation by factoring?
[You need the equation written in standard form to make it easier to factor. That way you are looking for factor pairs of *ac* that have a sum of *b*.]

Q: How does factoring the equation help you find the solution?
[After factoring, each factor can be set equal to zero and solved. The solutions of these factors are the solutions of the quadratic equation.]

Try It! Answers

2. a. –8 **b.** 16, –4

Elicit and Use Evidence of Student Thinking ETP

Q: Describe how to find the set of factors that can solve each equation.
[Part a: factors of 64 with a sum of 16. Part b: factors of –64 with a sum of –12.]

Common Error

Try It 2b Students may try to factor the left side of the equation, forgetting that they need to write the equation in standard form first. Have students write the general standard form of a quadratic equation and circle the 0 on the right side. Then have them check to make sure that their equation is in standard form by having them confirm that the number on the right side of their equation is also 0. Then have them compare the left side of their equation to the left side of the general standard form.

AVAILABLE ONLINE

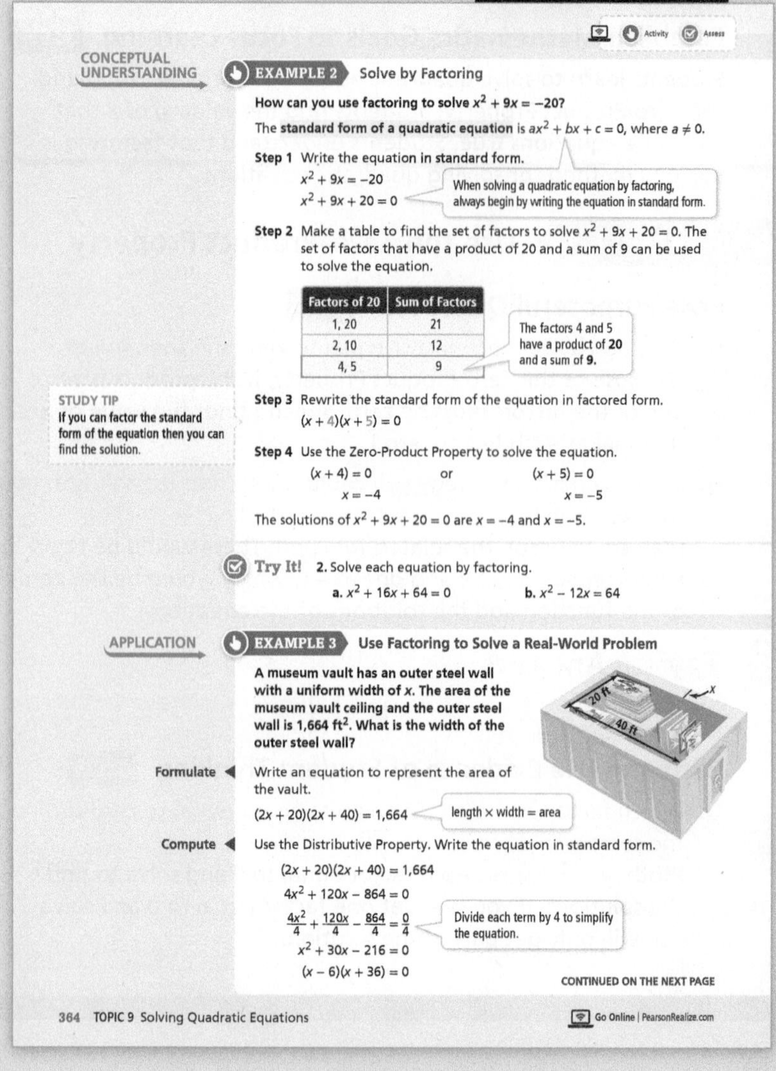

Activity Assess

CONCEPTUAL UNDERSTANDING

EXAMPLE 2 Solve by Factoring

How can you use factoring to solve $x^2 + 9x = -20$?

The **standard form of a quadratic equation** is $ax^2 + bx + c = 0$, where $a \neq 0$.

Step 1 Write the equation in standard form.

$x^2 + 9x = -20$

$x^2 + 9x + 20 = 0$

When solving a quadratic equation by factoring, always begin by writing the equation in standard form.

Step 2 Make a table to find the set of factors to solve $x^2 + 9x + 20 = 0$. The set of factors that have a product of 20 and a sum of 9 can be used to solve the equation.

Factors of 20	Sum of Factors
1, 20	21
2, 10	12
4, 5	9

The factors 4 and 5 have a product of **20** and a sum of **9.**

STUDY TIP
If you can factor the standard form of the equation then you can find the solution.

Step 3 Rewrite the standard form of the equation in factored form.

$(x + 4)(x + 5) = 0$

Step 4 Use the Zero-Product Property to solve the equation.

$(x + 4) = 0$ or $(x + 5) = 0$

$x = -4$ $x = -5$

The solutions of $x^2 + 9x + 20 = 0$ are $x = -4$ and $x = -5$.

Try It! **2.** Solve each equation by factoring.

a. $x^2 + 16x + 64 = 0$ **b.** $x^2 - 12x = 64$

APPLICATION

EXAMPLE 3 Use Factoring to Solve a Real-World Problem

A museum vault has an outer steel wall with a uniform width of *x*. The area of the museum vault ceiling and the outer steel wall is 1,664 ft^2. What is the width of the outer steel wall?

20 ft
40 ft
x

Formulate Write an equation to represent the area of the vault.

$(2x + 20)(2x + 40) = 1{,}664$ length × width = area

Compute Use the Distributive Property. Write the equation in standard form.

$(2x + 20)(2x + 40) = 1{,}664$

$4x^2 + 120x - 864 = 0$

$\frac{4x^2}{4} + \frac{120x}{4} - \frac{864}{4} = \frac{0}{4}$ Divide each term by 4 to simplify the equation.

$x^2 + 30x - 216 = 0$

$(x - 6)(x + 36) = 0$

CONTINUED ON THE NEXT PAGE

364 TOPIC 9 Solving Quadratic Equations Go Online | PearsonRealize.com

EXAMPLE 3 Use Factoring to Solve a Real-World Problem

Pose Purposeful Questions ETP

Q: Can you set the factors in the first equation equal to zero and then solve to find the solutions?
[No, the equation is not in standard form, so the Zero-Product Property would not apply.]

ADV Advanced Students

USE WITH EXAMPLE 2 Students may recall that not all expressions have a 1 for the coefficient *a* of the standard form of the quadratic equation $ax^2 + bx + c = 0$.

- Challenge students to solve equations with initial coefficient $a \neq 1$ by factoring.

1. $2x^2 - x - 6 = 0$ [$x = 2, x = -\frac{3}{2}$]

2. $4x^2 + 3x - 10 = 0$ [$x = -2, x = \frac{5}{4}$]

Q: How does the process of factoring change when solving an equation with an initial coefficient $a \neq 1$?
[It is no longer as simple as finding numbers that are factor pairs of *c* with a sum of *b*. You need to take the coefficient *a* into consideration as well.]

Q: How can you tell if the solutions are integers or fractions?
[For each factor, if the constant is divisible by the coefficient of *x*, then the solution is an integer. If the constant is not evenly divisible by the coefficient, then the solution is a fraction.]

Pose Purposeful Questions ETP

Q: Why is there only one solution to this problem?
[Because this is a real-world problem, the negative solution cannot be used. No measurement of length is negative.]

Try It! Answer

3. 2.5 cm

HABITS OF MIND

Use with **EXAMPLES 1–3**

Reason Why is there only one solution to a quadratic equation in the form $x^2 + 2ax + a^2 = 0$? **MP.2**

[There is only one solution because it is a perfect square trinomial that factors to be $(x + a)^2$. The only solution is $-a$.]

EXAMPLE 4 Use Factored Form to Graph a Quadratic Equation

Use and Connect Mathematical Representations ETP

Q: How are the solutions to the equation related to the graph?
[They are the x-intercepts.]

Q: How is the average of the x-intercepts related to the x-coordinate of the vertex?
[The average of the x-intercepts is the point halfway between the x-intercepts, so it is the x-coordinate of the vertex and the x-coordinate of every point on the axis of symmetry.]

Try It! Answer

4.

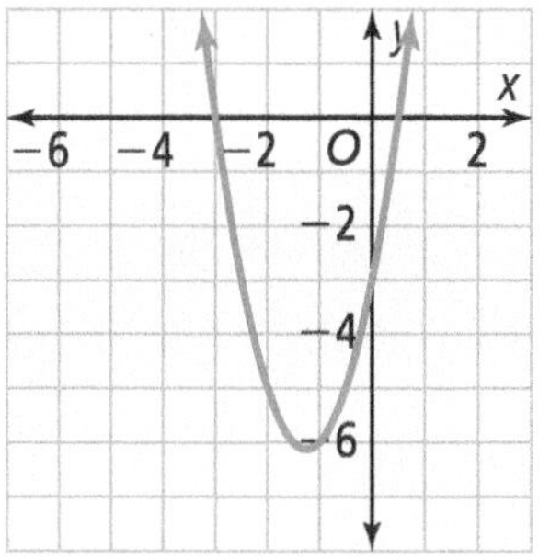
y
x
−6
−4
−2
O
2
−2
−4
−6

AVAILABLE ONLINE

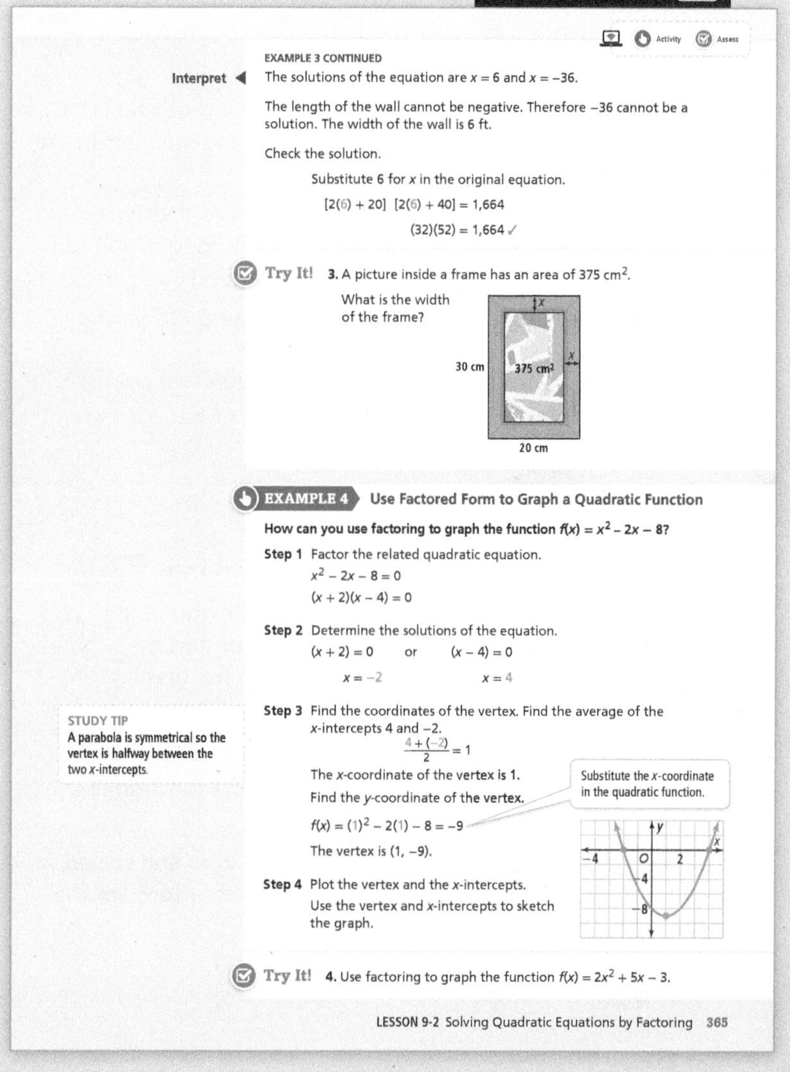

Activity Assess

EXAMPLE 3 CONTINUED

Interpret The solutions of the equation are $x = 6$ and $x = -36$.

The length of the wall cannot be negative. Therefore −36 cannot be a solution. The width of the wall is 6 ft.

Check the solution.

Substitute 6 for x in the original equation.

$$[2(6) + 20]\ [2(6) + 40] = 1{,}664$$
$$(32)(52) = 1{,}664 \checkmark$$

Try It! **3.** A picture inside a frame has an area of 375 cm^2. What is the width of the frame?

x
30 cm
375 cm²
x
20 cm

EXAMPLE 4 Use Factored Form to Graph a Quadratic Function

How can you use factoring to graph the function $f(x) = x^2 - 2x - 8$?

Step 1 Factor the related quadratic equation.
$x^2 - 2x - 8 = 0$
$(x + 2)(x - 4) = 0$

Step 2 Determine the solutions of the equation.
$(x + 2) = 0$ or $(x - 4) = 0$
$x = -2$ $x = 4$

STUDY TIP
A parabola is symmetrical so the vertex is halfway between the two x-intercepts.

Step 3 Find the coordinates of the vertex. Find the average of the x-intercepts 4 and −2.
$\frac{4 + (-2)}{2} = 1$
The x-coordinate of the vertex is 1.
Find the y-coordinate of the vertex.
$f(x) = (1)^2 - 2(1) - 8 = -9$
The vertex is (1, −9).

Substitute the x-coordinate in the quadratic function.

Step 4 Plot the vertex and the x-intercepts.
Use the vertex and x-intercepts to sketch the graph.

y
x
−4
O
2
−4
−8

Try It! **4.** Use factoring to graph the function $f(x) = 2x^2 + 5x - 3$.

LESSON 9-2 Solving Quadratic Equations by Factoring 365

ELL English Language Learners *(Use with* **EXAMPLE 3***)*

LISTENING BEGINNING Ask students to listen to the following sentences, the last of which comes from the example.

- Most of the money was stored in the bank *vault.*
- Her body was buried in the family *vault.*
- A museum *vault* has an outer steel wall with a uniform width of x around it.

Q: What do you think the word *vault* means?
[some sort of chamber or room for keeping valuables safe]

Q: What context clues helped you figure out the meaning?
[money, buried, outer steel wall]

READING INTERMEDIATE *Steel* is a homophone. It sounds the same as *steal,* but has a different meaning. Ask students to read the following sentences.

- The bridge was made of *steel.*
- The defense attempted to *steal* the ball from the offense.
- *Steel* pipes run under the city.
- Plagiarism is when you *steal* someone's writing.

Q: Do *steel* and *steal* mean the same thing?
[no]

Q: Read the first sentence of the example. What does *steel* mean?
[a strong metal]

SPEAKING ADVANCED Display an athletic *uniform* and ask students to identify what it is and what it represents. Then distribute a lump of clay to each student. Ask them to roll the clay like a snake and cut the pieces so that they are all the same length. Explain that when they cut the clay, all the pieces could be considered a *uniform* size.

Q: Discuss how this meaning of *uniform* is similar to the athletic *uniform.*
[Athletic uniforms for a particular team all look the same.]

Q: When in math might things be considered uniform?
[Units used in a problem are uniform.]

EXAMPLE 5 Write the Factored Form of a Quadratic Function

Use and Connect Mathematical Representations ETP

Q: Why is the factored form a good choice when using the graph of a parabola to write the equation of a quadratic function?
[The x-intercepts correspond directly with the numbers in the factored form of the equation.]

Q: How can you determine which point to use as the third point?
[Any point can be used as the third point as long as you can clearly see the coordinate values in the graph.]

Q: Why do you need three points to write the equation of a parabola?
[An infinite number of parabolas go through two points. You need a third point to determine the value of a.]

Try It! Answer

5. $(x - 3)(x - 9)$

Elicit and Use Evidence of Student Thinking ETP

Q: Which three points will you use to write the equation?
[(3, 0), (9, 0), and (6, –9); They are the vertex and the x-intercepts, which are easily identified on the graph.]

HABITS OF MIND

Use with **EXAMPLES 4 & 5**

Communicate Precisely How do the factors of a function relate to the graph of the function? Explain. **MP.6**

[The factors of a function can be set equal to zero and solved for because of the Zero-Product Property. These solutions are the zeros, or the x-intercepts of the graph.]

AVAILABLE **ONLINE**

Activity Assess

EXAMPLE 5 Write the Factored Form of a Quadratic Function

How can you write the factored form of the quadratic function related to a graph?

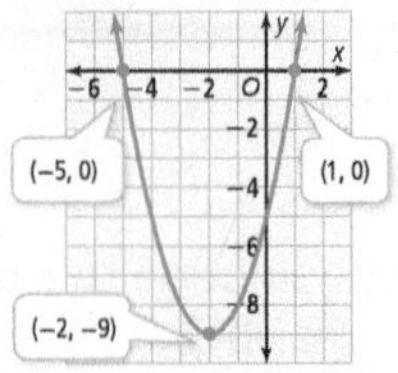

y
x
–6
–4
–2
O
2
–2
–4
–6
–8
(–5, 0)
(1, 0)
(–2, –9)

Step 1 Find the x-intercepts.
The x-intercepts are –5 and 1.

Step 2 Write a quadratic equation in factored form.
Use the x-intercepts, which are also the solutions of the quadratic equation, as the factors.

$a(x - p)(x - q) = 0$
$a[x - (-5)]\ [x - (1)] = 0$ — Substitute the x-intercepts for p and q.
$a(x + 5)(x - 1) = 0$

STUDY TIP
There are an infinite number of parabolas that pass through (–5, 0) and (1, 0). You will need to determine the value of a to find the one parabola that also passes through (–2, –9).

Step 3 Write the function in factored form.
Use a third point to solve for a.

$f(x) = a(x + 5)(x - 1)$
$-9 = a(-2 + 5)(-2 - 1)$ — Use the vertex. Substitute –2 for x and –9 for $f(x)$.
$a = 1$

The factored form of the quadratic function is $f(x) = 1(x + 5)(x - 1)$ or $f(x) = (x + 5)(x - 1)$.

Try It! 5. What is the factored form of the function?

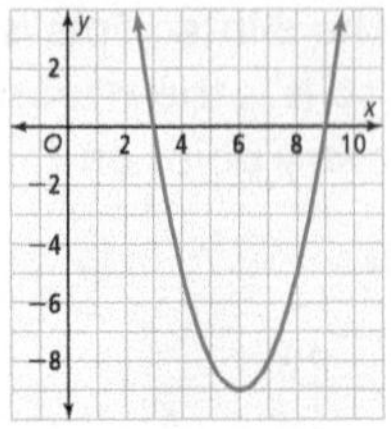

y
x
2
O
2
4
6
8
10
–2
–4
–6
–8

366 TOPIC 9 Solving Quadratic Equations

Go Online | PearsonRealize.com

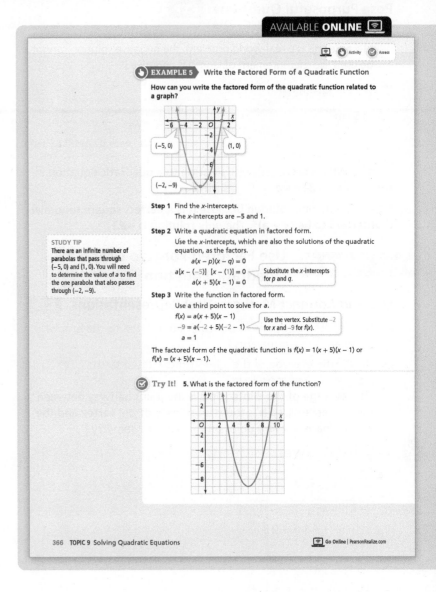

Struggling Students

USE WITH EXAMPLE 5 Some students may struggle with using the three points to write the equation of a parabola.

- Have them practice finding the equations of the parabolas through the sets of points described below.

1. (2, 0), (–4, 0) (–1, –27)
[$y = 3(x - 2)(x + 4)$]

2. (1, 0), (–2, 0), (–0.5, –1.125)
[$y = 0.5(x - 1)(x + 2)$]

Q: Explain how to use the x-intercepts to write the factored form of the equation for the parabola.
[Each x-intercept is subtracted from x in one of the factors.]

Q: Why is the third point necessary?
[The third point helps to identify a, the coefficient that gives the parabola its shape by identifying how wide or narrow it is.]

CONCEPT SUMMARY Solving Quadratic Equations by Factoring

Q: How can you use the factors of a quadratic function to determine the solutions of a quadratic equation?
[From the standard form of the equation, factor the equation, set each factor equal to zero, and solve. The resulting solutions are also the *x*-intercepts and zeros of the function.]

Do You UNDERSTAND? | Do You KNOW HOW?

Common Error

Exercise 13 Some students may use only two points to find the equation of the parabola. Have them plot those two points on a separate grid and draw as many parabolas as they can through the two points. This helps them recognize that a third point is needed to determine the value of *a*. When writing the equation of a parabola in factored form, encourage students to highlight the *a* so as not to omit it.

Answers

1. If a quadratic equation can be factored, you can use the Zero-Product Property. The two linear factors can be set to zero and solved to find the solution(s).
2. All terms of $4x^2 + 10x - 14 = 0$ are multiples of 2. When 2 is divided out, the equation is the same as $2x^2 + 5x - 7 = 0$. So the solutions of both equations are the same.
3. The Zero-Product Property says that for all real numbers a and *b*, if $ab = 0$, then either $a = 0$ or $b = 0$. If you can factor a quadratic equation that has 0 on one side, then each factor set equal to 0 is a solution.
4. 1, a perfect-square trinomial has 2 identical factors that each give the same solution when set equal to 0.
5. 10, –20
6. $-\frac{4}{3}$, 4
7. $(x + 16)(x + 2) = 0$; –16, –2
8. $(x + 3)(x - 7) = 0$; –3, 7
9. –1
10. –1, 9
11. $\frac{5}{2}$, –3
12. $\frac{9}{5}$, 2

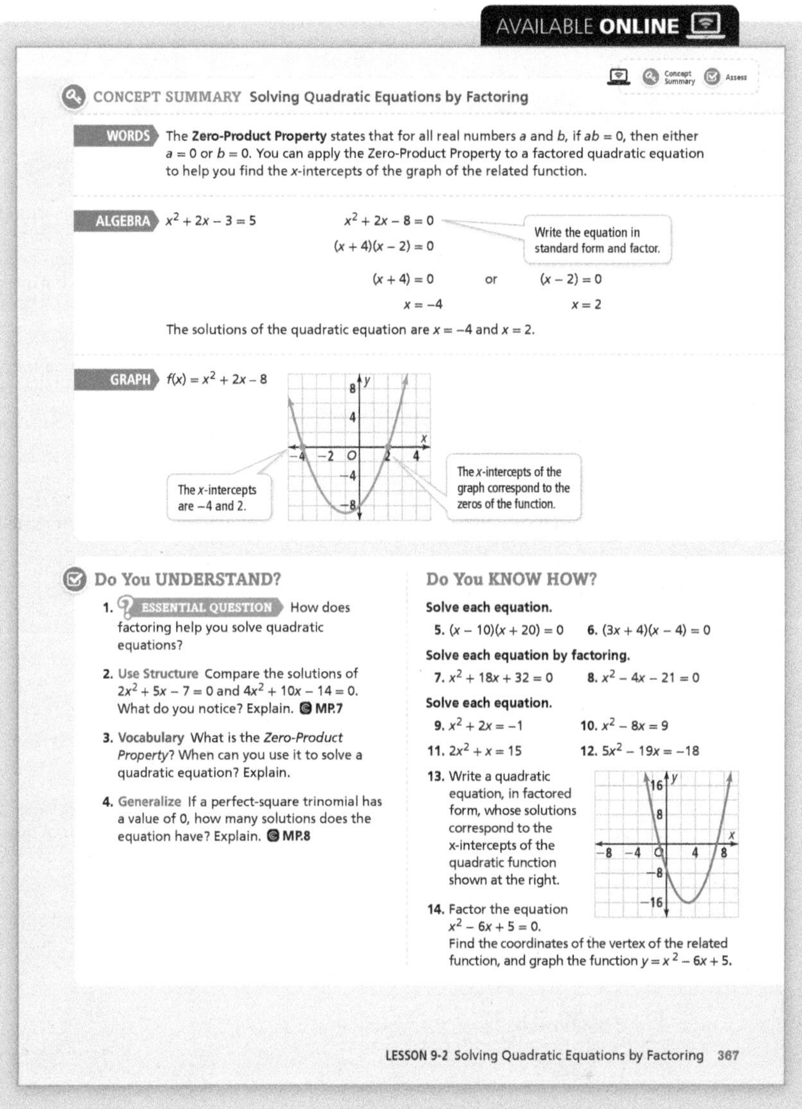
AVAILABLE ONLINE

Concept Summary Assess

CONCEPT SUMMARY Solving Quadratic Equations by Factoring

WORDS The **Zero-Product Property** states that for all real numbers *a* and *b*, if $ab = 0$, then either $a = 0$ or $b = 0$. You can apply the Zero-Product Property to a factored quadratic equation to help you find the *x*-intercepts of the graph of the related function.

ALGEBRA $x^2 + 2x - 3 = 5$

$x^2 + 2x - 8 = 0$

$(x + 4)(x - 2) = 0$

Write the equation in standard form and factor.

$(x + 4) = 0$ or $(x - 2) = 0$

$x = -4$ $x = 2$

The solutions of the quadratic equation are $x = -4$ and $x = 2$.

GRAPH $f(x) = x^2 + 2x - 8$

The x-intercepts are –4 and 2.
The x-intercepts of the graph correspond to the zeros of the function.

Do You UNDERSTAND?

1. ESSENTIAL QUESTION How does factoring help you solve quadratic equations?
2. Use Structure Compare the solutions of $2x^2 + 5x - 7 = 0$ and $4x^2 + 10x - 14 = 0$. What do you notice? Explain. MP.7
3. Vocabulary What is the *Zero-Product Property*? When can you use it to solve a quadratic equation? Explain.
4. Generalize If a perfect-square trinomial has a value of 0, how many solutions does the equation have? Explain. MP.8

Do You KNOW HOW?

Solve each equation.

5. $(x - 10)(x + 20) = 0$
6. $(3x + 4)(x - 4) = 0$

Solve each equation by factoring.

7. $x^2 + 18x + 32 = 0$
8. $x^2 - 4x - 21 = 0$

Solve each equation.

9. $x^2 + 2x = -1$
10. $x^2 - 8x = 9$
11. $2x^2 + x = 15$
12. $5x^2 - 19x = -18$
13. Write a quadratic equation, in factored form, whose solutions correspond to the *x*-intercepts of the quadratic function shown at the right.
14. Factor the equation $x^2 - 6x + 5 = 0$. Find the coordinates of the vertex of the related function, and graph the function $y = x^2 - 6x + 5$.

LESSON 9-2 Solving Quadratic Equations by Factoring 367

13. $(x + 1)(x - 7) = 0$
14. $(x - 5)(x - 1) = 0$; (3, –4)

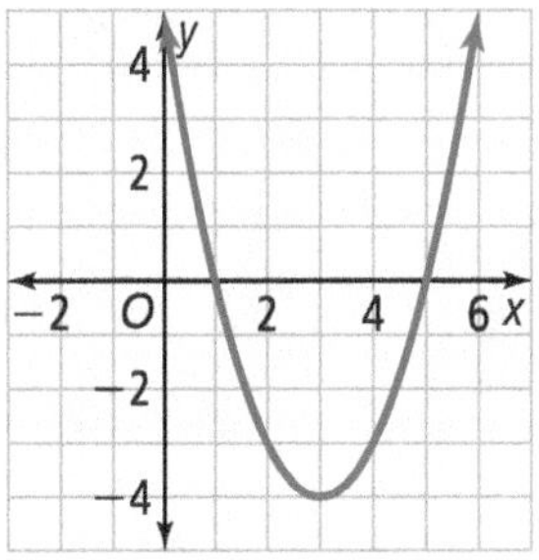

PRACTICE & PROBLEM SOLVING

AVAILABLE **ONLINE**

Lesson Practice You may opt to have students complete the automatically scored Practice and Problem Solving items online powered by MathXL for School.

Choose from: **Lesson Practice**

Adaptive Practice

You may also take advantage of the bank of exercises for assigning additional practice.

Assignment Guide

Basic	Advanced
15–27, 30–39	15–19, 22–39

Item Analysis

Example	Items	DOK
1	20–23	1
	15	3
2	24–29, 38	1
	18	2
	17	3
3	30, 31, 37	3
4	32, 33	1
5	34, 35	1
	16, 36	2
	19	3
	39	4

AVAILABLE **ONLINE**

PRACTICE & PROBLEM SOLVING

Scan for Multimedia

Practice Tutorial

Additional Exercises Available Online

UNDERSTAND

15. Reason One solution of a quadratic equation is 8. What do you know about the quadratic equation? What are two ways you would know if a quadratic equation could have this solution? **MP.2**

16. Communicate Precisely Write a quadratic equation for each condition below. Explain your reasoning. **MP.6**

a. The equation has solutions that are opposites.

b. The equation has one solution.

17. Error Analysis Describe and correct the error a student made in factoring. **MP.3**

$x^2 + 2x - 3 = 5$
$(x - 1)(x + 3) = 5$
$x - 1 = 5$ or $x + 3 = 5$ ✗
$x = 6$ or $x = 2$

18. Make Sense and Persevere Explain how you would factor $2x^2 + 8x + 6 = 0$. **MP.1**

19. Higher Order Thinking Both parabolas are graphs of quadratic functions.

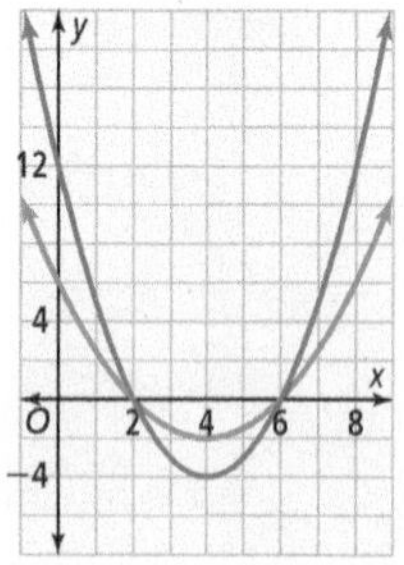

a. Write the factored form of the equation related to one of the functions. Which curve is related to your function?

b. Use a constant factor to find the equation related to the other function.

c. What relationship do you see between the two functions? How are these reflected in the constant?

PRACTICE

Solve each equation. SEE EXAMPLE 1

20. $(x - 5)(x + 2) = 0$ 5, −2

21. $(2x - 5)(7x + 2) = 0$

22. $3(x + 2)(x - 2) = 0$ −2, 2

23. $(3x - 8)^2 = 0$ $\frac{8}{3}$

Solve each equation by factoring. SEE EXAMPLES 2 AND 3

24. $x^2 + 2x + 1 = 0$ −1

25. $x^2 - 5x - 14 = 0$ −2, 7

26. $x^2 + 7x = 0$ 0, −7

27. $2x^2 - 5x + 2 = 0$

28. $2x^2 + 3x = 5$

29. $5x^2 + 16x = -3$

Write an equation to represent the shaded area. Then find the value of *x*. SEE EXAMPLE 3

30. Total area = 198 cm²

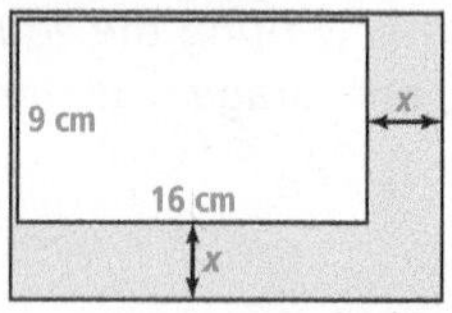

9 cm
16 cm
x
x

31.

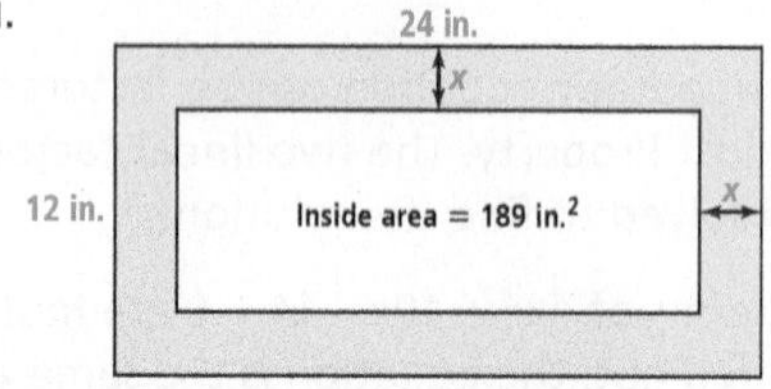

24 in.
12 in.
Inside area = 189 in.²
x
x

Factor, find the coordinates of the vertex of the related function, then graph. SEE EXAMPLE 4

32. $x^2 - 2x - 63 = 0$

33. $x^2 + 16x + 63 = 0$

Write the factored form for the quadratic function. SEE EXAMPLE 5

34.

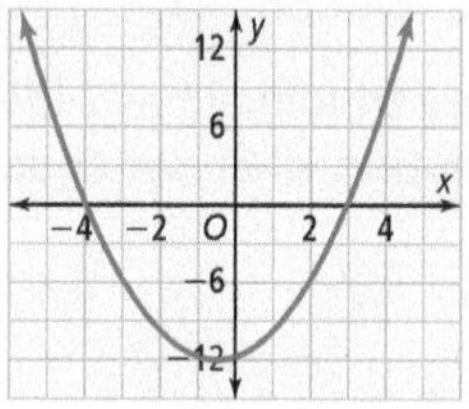

Go Online | PearsonRealize.com

Answers

15. $x - 8$ must be a factor; Substitute 8 into the quadratic equation and see if it checks, or factor the equation to see if $x - 8$ is a factor.

16. a. For the opposite roots, multiply $(x - r)$ and $(x + r)$. The equation will have a quadratic term and a constant term only.

b. For the double root, square $(x - r)$. The equation will be a trinomial square.

17. The student did not get 0 on one side of the equation.

$x^2 + 2x - 3 = 5$

$x^2 + 2x - 8 = 0$

$(x - 2)(x + 4) = 0$

$x - 2 = 0$ or $x + 4 = 0$

$x = 2$ or $x = -4$

18. First factor out a common factor of 2 to get $2(x^2 + 4x + 3)$. Then factor the trinomial to get $2(x + 3)(x + 1)$.

19. a. $(x - 2)(x - 6) = 0$; the blue curve, with vertex of (4, –4)

b. $\frac{1}{2}(x - 2)(x - 6) = 0$

c. The graph of the second equation is compressed by a factor of $\frac{1}{2}$, which is the constant factor.

21. $\frac{5}{2}, -\frac{2}{7}$

27. $\frac{1}{2}, 2$

28. $-\frac{5}{2}, 1$

29. $-3, -\frac{1}{5}$

30. $(x + 9)(x + 16) = 198$; 2 cm

See answers for 31–34 on next page.

Answers

31. $(24 - 2x)(12 - 2x) = 189$; 1.5 in.

32. $(x + 7)(x - 9) = 0$; $(1, -64)$

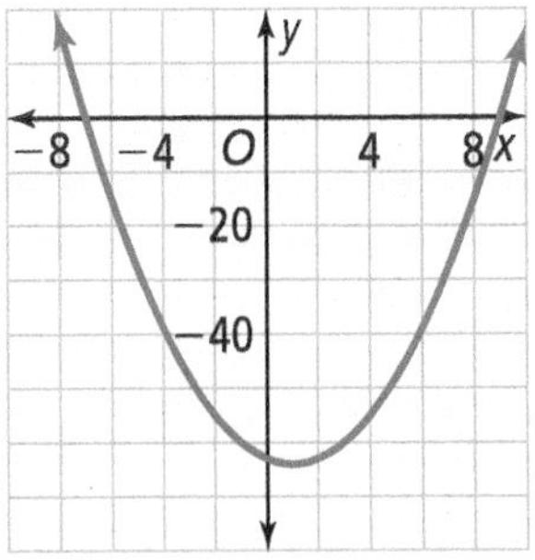
y
x
−8
−4
O
4
8
−20
−40

33. $(x + 7)(x + 9) = 0$; $(-8, -1)$

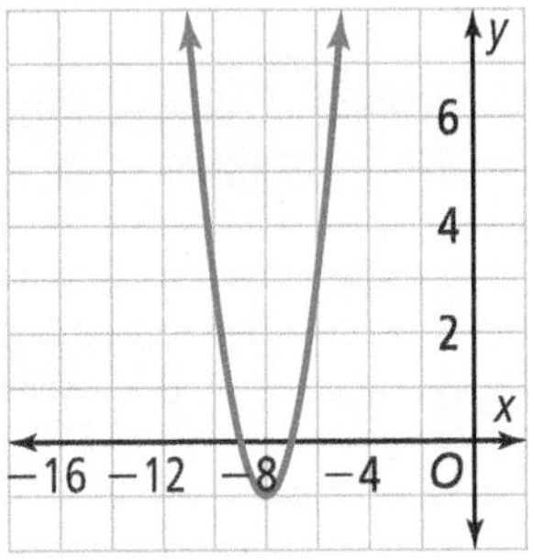
y
x
6
4
2
−16
−12
−8
−4
O

34. $(x + 4)(x - 3) = 0$

35. **a.** $-(x - 3)(x - 8) = 0$

b. $(5.5, 6.25)$

c. Multiply by 16; $-16(x - 3)(x - 8) = 0$. The equation has the same roots, but the vertex is $(5.5, 16 \cdot 6.25)$, or $(5.5, 100)$.

36. **a.** the Pythagorean Theorem

b. $x^2 + (x - 3)^2 = 15^2$

$x^2 + x^2 - 6x + 9 = 225$

$2x^2 - 6x - 216 = 0$

$x^2 - 3x - 108 = 0$

$(x - 12)(x + 9) = 0$

$x = 12$ or $x = -9$

A negative value does not make sense, so the pole is 12 ft high.

c. 12 ft

AVAILABLE **ONLINE**

PRACTICE & PROBLEM SOLVING

Practice Tutorial

Mixed Review Available Online

APPLY

35. Mathematical Connections A streamer is launched 3 s after a fuse is lit and lands 8 s after it is lit.

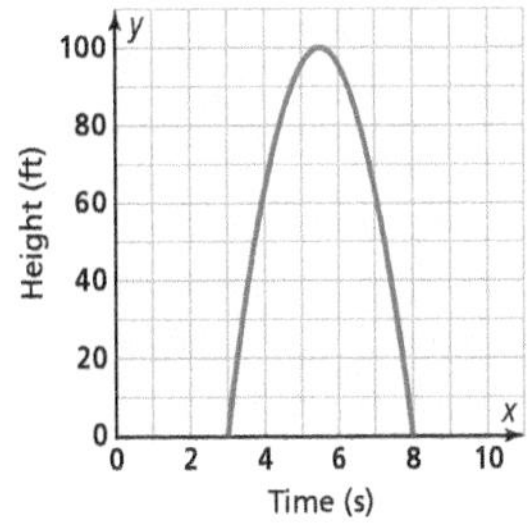
y
100
80
60
40
20
0
Height (ft)
x
0
2
4
6
8
10
Time (s)

a. What is a quadratic equation in factored form that models the situation?

b. What is the vertex of the function related to your equation? How does this compare with the vertex of the graph?

c. What can you multiply your factored form by to get the function for the graph? Explain your answer.

36. Use Structure A 15 ft long cable is connected from a hook to the top of a pole that has an unknown height. The distance from the hook to the base of the pole is 3 ft shorter than the height of the pole. MP.7

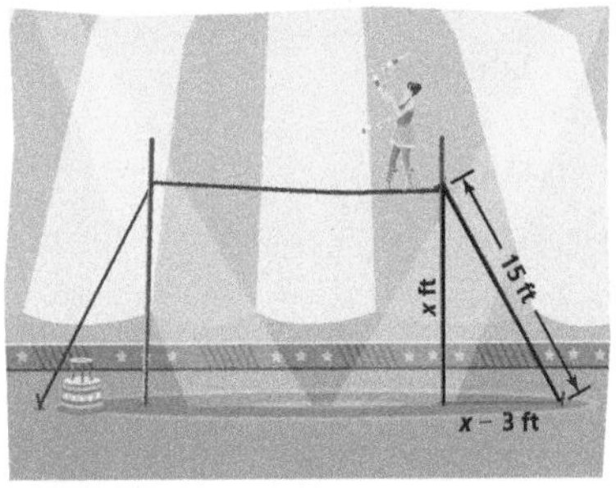
15 ft
x ft
x − 3 ft

a. What can you use to find the height of the pole?

b. Write and solve a quadratic equation to find the height of the pole.

c. How far is the hook from the base of the pole?

ASSESSMENT PRACTICE

37. Match each equation with one or more factors of its standard form.

I.	$x^2 + 6x = -8$	A. $2x - 3$
II.	$2x^2 + x = 6$	B. $x + 4$
III.	$x^2 + 2x = 8$	C. $x - 4$
IV.	$2x^2 + 5x = 12$	D. $x + 2$
V.	$2x^2 - 11x = -12$	E. $x - 2$

38. SAT/ACT A quadratic equation of the form $x^2 + bx + c = 0$ has a solution of -2. Its related function has a vertex at $(2.5, -20.25)$. What is the other solution to the equation?

Ⓐ −11
Ⓑ −4.5
Ⓒ 0.5
Ⓓ 7
Ⓔ 9

39. Performance Task An engineer is designing a water fountain that starts 1 ft off of the edge of a 10 ft wide pool. The water from the fountain needs to project into the center of the pool. The path of the water from the fountain is in the shape of a parabola.

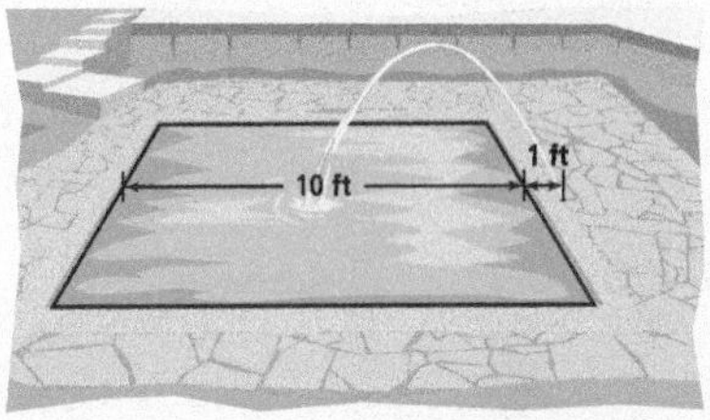
10 ft
1 ft

Part A Let the the point (1, 0) be the location of the starting point of the water. Write a quadratic equation to model the path of the water.

Part B What is the maximum height of the water? Use your equation from Part A.

Part C What is the equation for the path of the water if the maximum height of the water must be 4 ft?

LESSON 9-2 Solving Quadratic Equations by Factoring 369

37. I. B, D
II. A, D
III. B, E
IV. A, B
V. A, C

39. **Part A** Check students' equations. The starting point of the water is at (1, 0) so the ending point is (6, 0). Both points must satisfy students' equations, and the leading coefficient must be negative.

Part B The height of the water is the y-value from the vertex based on the equation from Part A. The distance from the edge of the pool to where the water hits the center is 5 ft, or half the width of the pool.

Part C Check students' work.

LESSON QUIZ

Use the Lesson Quiz to assess students' understanding of the mathematics in the lesson.

Students can take the Lesson Quiz online or you can download a printable copy from **SavvasRealize.com**. The Lesson Quiz is also available in the *Assessment Resources* book.

Item Analysis

Item	DOK	Standards
1	1	HSA.APR.B.3
2	1	HSA.REI.B.4.B, HSA.SSE.B.3.A
3	1	HSA.REI.B.4.B, HSA.SSE.B.3.A
4	2	HSA.APR.B.3, HSA.SSE.B.3.A
5	2	HSA.REI.B.4.B, HSF.IF.C.8.A

RtI Use the student scores on the Lesson Quiz to prescribe differentiated assignments.

If students take the Lesson Quiz online, it will be automatically scored and appropriate differentiated practice will be assigned based on student performance.

I Intervention	0–3 points	• Reteach to Build Understanding • Mathematical Literacy and Vocabulary • Additional Practice
O On-Level	4 points	• Mathematical Literacy and Vocabulary • Additional Practice • Enrichment
A Advanced	5 points	• Enrichment

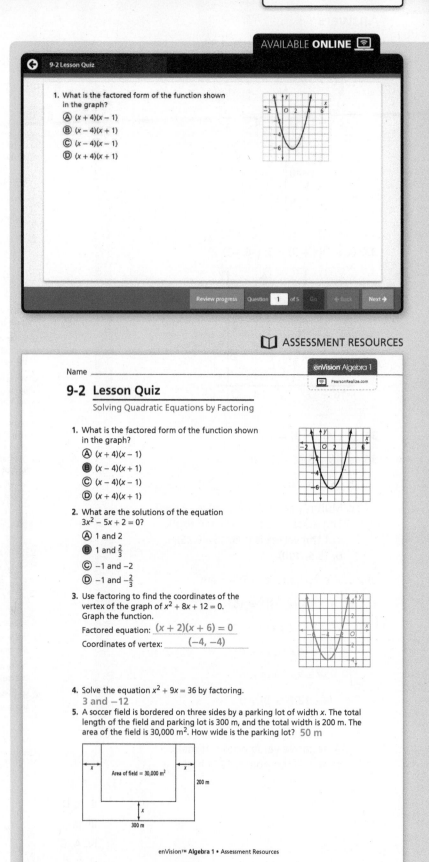

AVAILABLE **ONLINE**

9-2 Lesson Quiz

1. What is the factored form of the function shown in the graph?

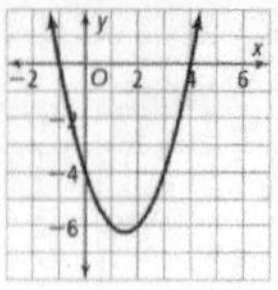

Ⓐ $(x + 4)(x - 1)$
Ⓑ $(x - 4)(x + 1)$
Ⓒ $(x - 4)(x - 1)$
Ⓓ $(x + 4)(x + 1)$

Review progress Question 1 of 5 Go ← Back Next →

ASSESSMENT RESOURCES

Name ______

enVision Algebra 1

PearsonRealize.com

9-2 Lesson Quiz

Solving Quadratic Equations by Factoring

1. What is the factored form of the function shown in the graph?

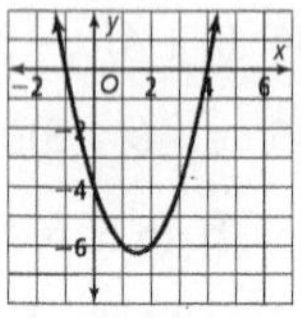

Ⓐ $(x + 4)(x - 1)$
Ⓑ $(x - 4)(x + 1)$
Ⓒ $(x - 4)(x - 1)$
Ⓓ $(x + 4)(x + 1)$

2. What are the solutions of the equation $3x^2 - 5x + 2 = 0$?

Ⓐ 1 and 2
Ⓑ 1 and $\frac{2}{3}$
Ⓒ −1 and −2
Ⓓ −1 and $-\frac{2}{3}$

3. Use factoring to find the coordinates of the vertex of the graph of $x^2 + 8x + 12 = 0$. Graph the function.

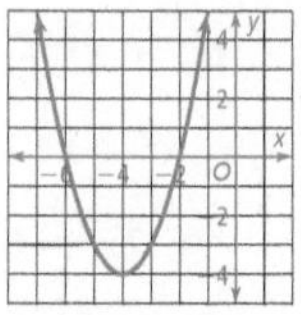

Factored equation: $(x + 2)(x + 6) = 0$

Coordinates of vertex: $(-4, -4)$

4. Solve the equation $x^2 + 9x = 36$ by factoring.

3 and −12

5. A soccer field is bordered on three sides by a parking lot of width x. The total length of the field and parking lot is 300 m, and the total width is 200 m. The area of the field is 30,000 m². How wide is the parking lot? 50 m

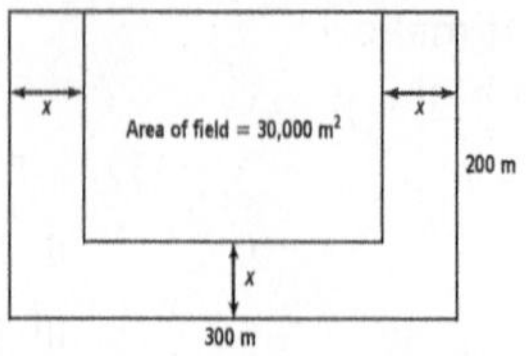
Area of field = 30,000 m²
x
x
x
200 m
300 m

enVision™ **Algebra 1** • Assessment Resources

Assess | Tutorials | Worksheets

STEP 4 | Assess & Differentiate

DIFFERENTIATED RESOURCES

I = Intervention **O** = On-Level **A** = Advanced

⚙ = This activity is available as a digital assignment powered by MathXL® for School.

AVAILABLE **ONLINE**

Reteach to Build Understanding I ⚙

Provides scaffolded reteaching for the key lesson concepts.

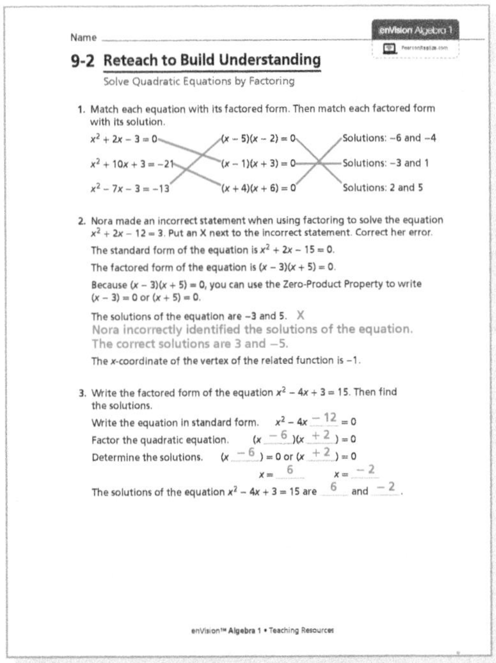

Name

enVision Algebra 1

9-2 Reteach to Build Understanding

Solve Quadratic Equations by Factoring

1. Match each equation with its factored form. Then match each factored form with its solution.

$x^2 + 2x - 3 = 0$ $(x - 5)(x - 2) = 0$ Solutions: −6 and −4

$x^2 + 10x + 3 = -21$ $(x - 1)(x + 3) = 0$ Solutions: −3 and 1

$x^2 - 7x - 3 = -13$ $(x + 4)(x + 6) = 0$ Solutions: 2 and 5

2. Nora made an incorrect statement when using factoring to solve the equation $x^2 + 2x - 12 = 3$. Put an X next to the incorrect statement. Correct her error.

The standard form of the equation is $x^2 + 2x - 15 = 0$.

The factored form of the equation is $(x - 3)(x + 5) = 0$.

Because $(x - 3)(x + 5) = 0$, you can use the Zero-Product Property to write $(x - 3) = 0$ or $(x + 5) = 0$.

The solutions of the equation are −3 and 5. X

Nora incorrectly identified the solutions of the equation. The correct solutions are 3 and −5.

The x-coordinate of the vertex of the related function is −1.

3. Write the factored form of the equation $x^2 - 4x + 3 = 15$. Then find the solutions.

Write the equation in standard form. $x^2 - 4x - 12 = 0$

Factor the quadratic equation. $(x - 6)(x + 2) = 0$

Determine the solutions. $(x - 6) = 0$ or $(x + 2) = 0$

$x = 6$ $x = -2$

The solutions of the equation $x^2 - 4x + 3 = 15$ are 6 and −2.

enVision™ Algebra 1 • Teaching Resources

Additional Practice I O ⚙

Provides extra practice for each lesson.

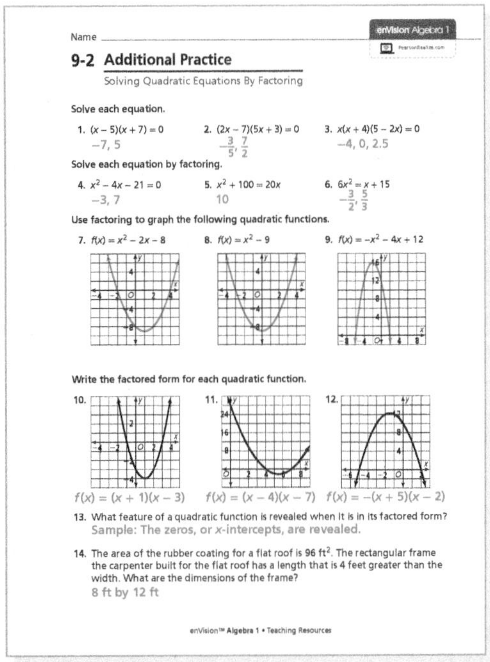

Name

enVision Algebra 1

9-2 Additional Practice

Solving Quadratic Equations By Factoring

Solve each equation.

1. $(x - 5)(x + 7) = 0$ −7, 5
2. $(2x - 7)(5x + 3) = 0$ $-\frac{3}{5}, \frac{7}{2}$
3. $x(x + 4)(5 - 2x) = 0$ −4, 0, 2.5

Solve each equation by factoring.

4. $x^2 - 4x - 21 = 0$ −3, 7
5. $x^2 + 100 = 20x$ 10
6. $6x^2 = x + 15$ $-\frac{3}{2}, \frac{5}{3}$

Use factoring to graph the following quadratic functions.

7. $f(x) = x^2 - 2x - 8$
8. $f(x) = x^2 - 9$
9. $f(x) = -x^2 - 4x + 12$

Write the factored form for each quadratic function.

10. $f(x) = (x + 1)(x - 3)$
11. $f(x) = (x - 4)(x - 7)$
12. $f(x) = -(x + 5)(x - 2)$

13. What feature of a quadratic function is revealed when it is in its factored form? Sample: The zeros, or x-intercepts, are revealed.

14. The area of the rubber coating for a flat roof is 96 ft². The rectangular frame the carpenter built for the flat roof has a length that is 4 feet greater than the width. What are the dimensions of the frame? 8 ft by 12 ft

enVision™ Algebra 1 • Teaching Resources

Enrichment O A ⚙

Presents engaging problems and activities that extend the lesson concepts.

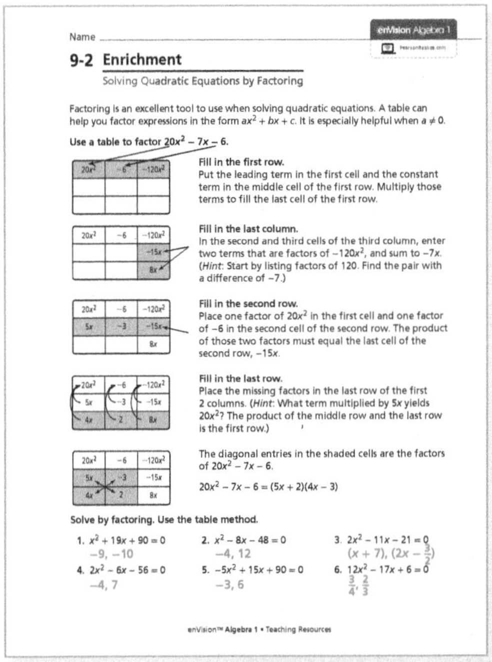

Name

enVision Algebra 1

9-2 Enrichment

Solving Quadratic Equations by Factoring

Factoring is an excellent tool to use when solving quadratic equations. A table can help you factor expressions in the form $ax^2 + bx + c$. It is especially helpful when $a \neq 0$.

Use a table to factor $20x^2 - 7x - 6$.

Fill in the first row. Put the leading term in the first cell and the constant term in the middle cell of the first row. Multiply those terms to fill the last cell of the first row.

Fill in the last column. In the second and third cells of the third column, enter two terms that are factors of $-120x^2$, and sum to $-7x$. (*Hint:* Start by listing factors of 120. Find the pair with a difference of −7.)

Fill in the second row. Place one factor of $20x^2$ in the first cell and one factor of −6 in the second cell of the second row. The product of those two factors must equal the last cell of the second row, $-15x$.

Fill in the last row. Place the missing factors in the last row of the first 2 columns. (*Hint:* What term multiplied by 5x yields $20x^2$? The product of the middle row and the last row is the first row.)

$20x^2$	−6	$-120x^2$
5x	−3	−15x
4x	2	8x

The diagonal entries in the shaded cells are the factors of $20x^2 - 7x - 6$.

$20x^2 - 7x - 6 = (5x + 2)(4x - 3)$

Solve by factoring. Use the table method.

1. $x^2 + 19x + 90 = 0$ −9, −10
2. $x^2 - 8x - 48 = 0$ −4, 12
3. $2x^2 - 11x - 21 = 0$ $(x + 7), (2x - \frac{3}{2})$
4. $2x^2 - 6x - 56 = 0$ −4, 7
5. $-5x^2 + 15x + 90 = 0$ −3, 6
6. $12x^2 - 17x + 6 = 0$ $\frac{3}{4}, \frac{2}{3}$

enVision™ Algebra 1 • Teaching Resources

Mathematical Literacy and Vocabulary I O

Helps students develop and reinforce understanding of key terms and concepts.

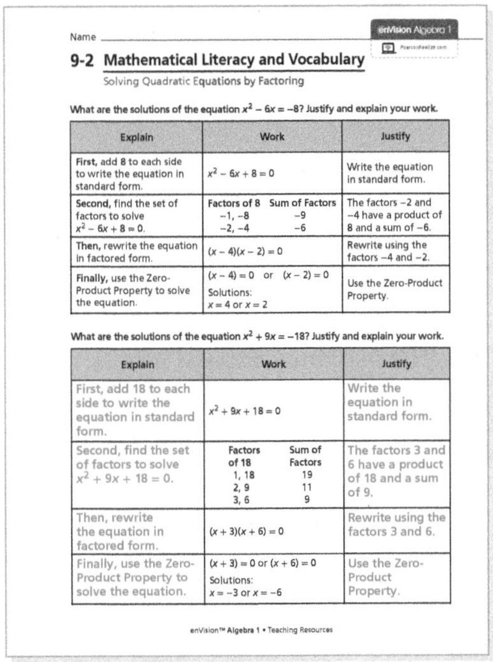

Name

enVision Algebra 1

9-2 Mathematical Literacy and Vocabulary

Solving Quadratic Equations by Factoring

What are the solutions of the equation $x^2 - 6x = -8$? Justify and explain your work.

Explain	Work	Justify
First, add 8 to each side to write the equation in standard form.	$x^2 - 6x + 8 = 0$	Write the equation in standard form.
Second, find the set of factors to solve $x^2 - 6x + 8 = 0$.	Factors of 8: −1, −8; −2, −4. Sum of Factors: −9; −6	The factors −2 and −4 have a product of 8 and a sum of −6.
Then, rewrite the equation in factored form.	$(x - 4)(x - 2) = 0$	Rewrite using the factors −4 and −2.
Finally, use the Zero-Product Property to solve the equation.	$(x - 4) = 0$ or $(x - 2) = 0$; Solutions: $x = 4$ or $x = 2$	Use the Zero-Product Property.

What are the solutions of the equation $x^2 + 9x = -18$? Justify and explain your work.

Explain	Work	Justify
First, add 18 to each side to write the equation in standard form.	$x^2 + 9x + 18 = 0$	Write the equation in standard form.
Second, find the set of factors to solve $x^2 + 9x + 18 = 0$.	Factors of 18: 1, 18; 2, 9; 3, 6. Sum of Factors: 19; 11; 9	The factors 3 and 6 have a product of 18 and a sum of 9.
Then, rewrite the equation in factored form.	$(x + 3)(x + 6) = 0$	Rewrite using the factors 3 and 6.
Finally, use the Zero-Product Property to solve the equation.	$(x + 3) = 0$ or $(x + 6) = 0$; Solutions: $x = -3$ or $x = -6$	Use the Zero-Product Property.

enVision™ Algebra 1 • Teaching Resources

Digital Resources and Video Tutorials I O A ⚙

The **Reteach to Build Understanding, Additional Practice,** and **Enrichment** activities are available as digital assignments powered by MathXL for School. These activities are automatically assigned when students complete the lesson quiz online and are automatically scored.

Students can access instructional tutorials using the **Virtual Nerd app.**

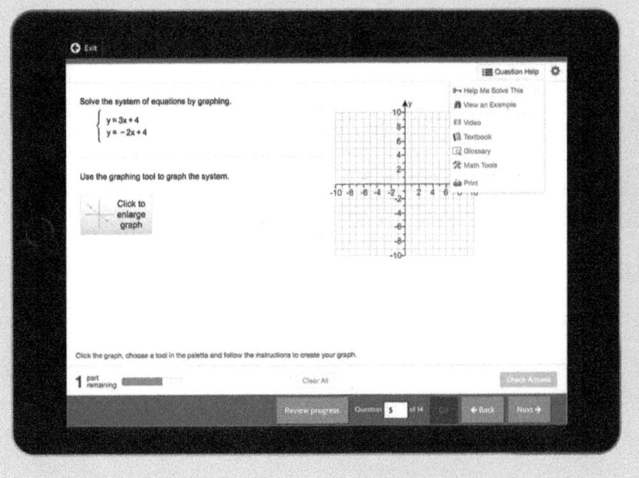
Solve the system of equations by graphing.
y = 3x + 4
y = −2x + 4
Use the graphing tool to graph the system.
Click to enlarge graph
Question Help
Help Me Solve This
View an Example
Video
Textbook
Glossary
Math Tools
Print
Click the graph, choose a tool in the palette and follow the instructions to create your graph.
Clear All
Check Answer
Review progress
Back
Next

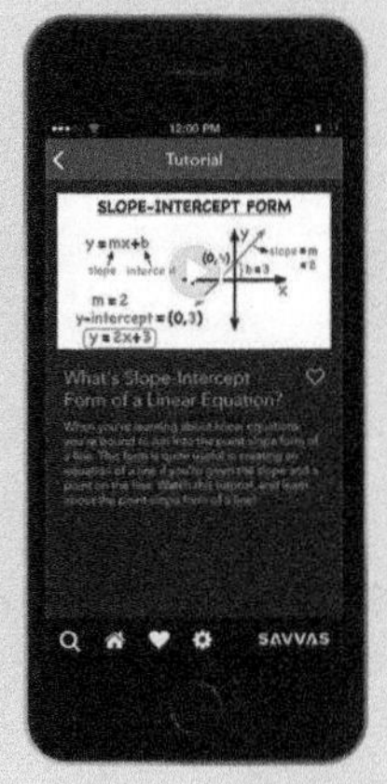
Tutorial
SLOPE-INTERCEPT FORM
What's Slope-Intercept Form of a Linear Equation?
SAVVAS

Students can also access Virtual Nerd videos using the **BouncePages app** to scan exercise pages marked with this icon. Students can download both apps for free in their mobile devices' app store.

Lesson Overview

FOCUS

Objective

Students will be able to:

✔ Use properties of exponents to rewrite radical expressions.

✔ Multiply radical expressions.

✔ Write a radical expression to model or represent a real-world problem.

Essential Understanding

Properties of exponents are used to rewrite radical expressions in different forms. A radical expression is written in the simplest form when there are no perfect square factors other than 1 in the radicand.

COHERENCE

Previously in this course, students:

- Used properties of exponents to solve exponential equations.

In this lesson, students:

- Rewrite radical expressions using properties of exponents.

Later in this topic, students will:

- Solve quadratic equations by using the properties of equality and taking square roots.

RIGOR

This lesson emphasizes a blend of *procedural skill and fluency* and *application.*

- Students use properties of exponents to identify the perfect square factors in a radical and then rewrite a radical expression as a product of square roots.
- Students write a radical expression to represent a real-world problem, such as finding the slant height of a cone with a given radius.

A-Z Vocabulary Builder

REVIEW VOCABULARY

English | *Spanish*

- **perfect square factor** | *factor del cuadrado perfecto*
- **radical** | *radical*
- **radical expression** | *ecuación radica*
- **radicand** | *radicandol*

NEW VOCABULARY

- **Product Property of Square Roots** | *propiedad de producto de raíces cuadradas*

VOCABULARY ACTIVITY

Review the terms *radical, radicand,* and *radical expression.* These terms are very similar, and students may confuse them. Have students complete the fill-in-the-blank activity.

The symbol $\sqrt{\ }$ with an expression under it is a ______. [radical]

The expression under the radical sign is the ______. [radicand]

An expression that contains a radical is a ______. [radical expression]

Student Companion

Students can do their in-class work for the lesson on pages 197–200 of their *Student Companion* or in Savvas Realize.

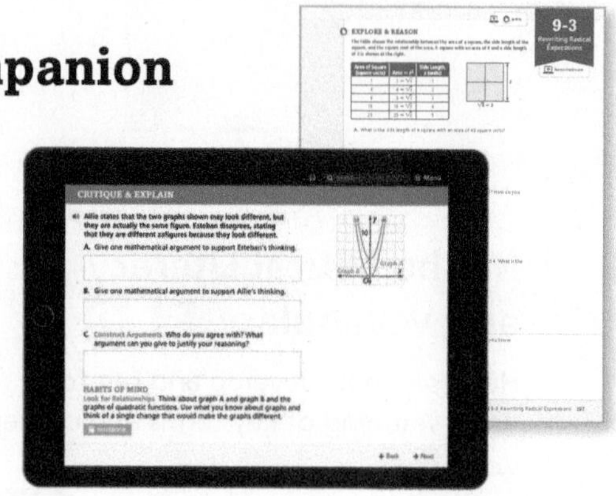
9-3
CRITIQUE & EXPLAIN

Mathematics Overview

COMMON CORE STANDARDS

Content Standards

In this lesson, students focus on this standard:

HSN.RN.A.2 Rewrite expressions involving radicals and rational exponents using the properties of exponents.

Mathematical Practice Standards

These standards are highlighted in this lesson:

MP.3 Construct Viable Arguments

Students use properties of radicals to construct arguments about whether or not a given radical is in simplest form.

MP.7 Look For and Make Use of Structure

Students look for the overall structure of variables with exponents that are perfect squares and connect how the exponent of a variable determines when a perfect square exists.

SavvasRealize.com

Activity

EXPLORE & REASON

INSTRUCTIONAL FOCUS Students explore how the side length of a square compares to the square root of its area. Students build on their understanding of how to find the square root of an integer to rewrite radical expressions and write equivalent radical expressions.

STUDENT COMPANION Students can complete the *Explore & Reason* activity on page 197 of their *Student Companion*.

Before WHOLE CLASS

Implement Tasks that Promote Reasoning and Problem Solving ETP

Q: What does the table represent?
[The relationship between the area of a square, the square root of the area, and the side length.]

Q: Why use the area of a square to discuss square roots?
[Since the sides of a square are of equal length, and the area of a square is $A = s^2$, you can find the length of a side by taking the square root of the area.]

During SMALL GROUP

Support Productive Struggle in Learning Mathematics ETP

Q: How do you know when the number under the square root sign is not a perfect square?
[If you cannot multiply a number by itself to get the number under the radical sign, then the number is not a perfect square.]

For Early Finishers

Q: What are the areas of three possible squares, each with a side length between $6x$ and $7x$?
[$38x^2$, $41x^2$, $47x^2$; Answers may vary. Sample: You square the side length to find the area; $(6x)^2 = 36x^2$ and $(7x)^2 = 49x^2$. Therefore, any area x^2 with coefficients between 36 and 49 can represent the area of a square with side length between $6x$ and $7x$.]

Q: What are the side lengths of squares with the following areas: $16x^2$, $64x^2$, and $144x^2$?
[$4x$, $8x$, $12x$]

After WHOLE CLASS

Facilitate Meaningful Mathematical Discourse ETP

Q: How does finding the integers that a radicand falls between compare to finding the areas of squares with side lengths between integers?
[When there is a radical sign, you need to find the square root of the radicand. When you need to find the area of a square, you square the side length.]

AVAILABLE **ONLINE**

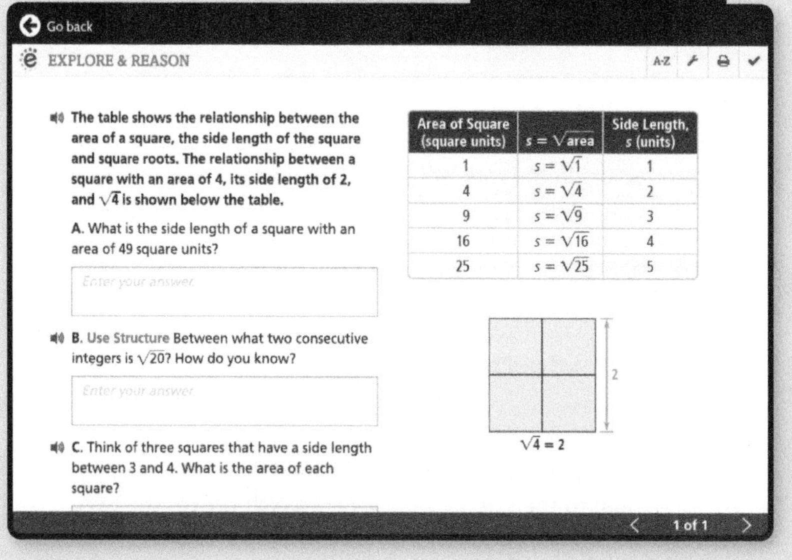

Go back

EXPLORE & REASON

The table shows the relationship between the area of a square, the side length of the square and square roots. The relationship between a square with an area of 4, its side length of 2, and $\sqrt{4}$ is shown below the table.

A. What is the side length of a square with an area of 49 square units?

Enter your answer

B. Use Structure Between what two consecutive integers is $\sqrt{20}$? How do you know?

Enter your answer

C. Think of three squares that have a side length between 3 and 4. What is the area of each square?

Area of Square (square units)	$s = \sqrt{area}$	Side Length, s (units)
1	$s = \sqrt{1}$	1
4	$s = \sqrt{4}$	2
9	$s = \sqrt{9}$	3
16	$s = \sqrt{16}$	4
25	$s = \sqrt{25}$	5

2
$\sqrt{4} = 2$

1 of 1

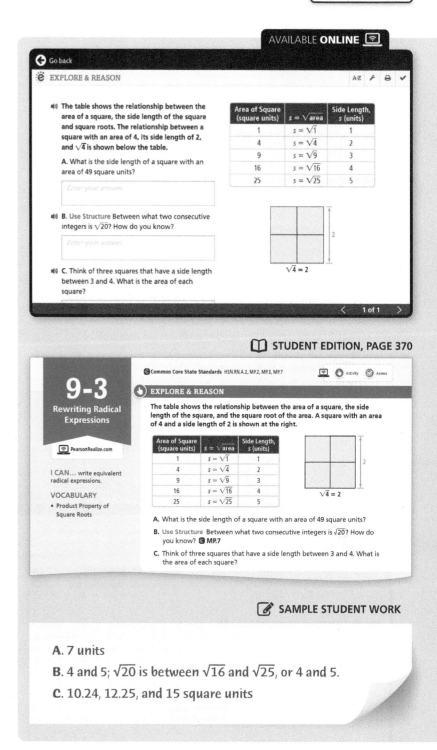

STUDENT EDITION, PAGE 370

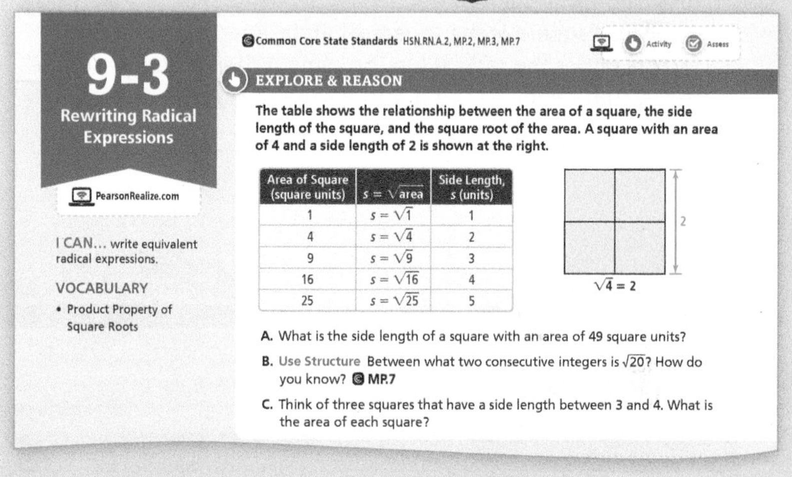

9-3 Rewriting Radical Expressions

PearsonRealize.com

I CAN… write equivalent radical expressions.

VOCABULARY
- Product Property of Square Roots

Common Core State Standards HSN.RN.A.2, MP.2, MP.3, MP.7

Activity Assess

EXPLORE & REASON

The table shows the relationship between the area of a square, the side length of the square, and the square root of the area. A square with an area of 4 and a side length of 2 is shown at the right.

Area of Square (square units)	$s = \sqrt{area}$	Side Length, s (units)
1	$s = \sqrt{1}$	1
4	$s = \sqrt{4}$	2
9	$s = \sqrt{9}$	3
16	$s = \sqrt{16}$	4
25	$s = \sqrt{25}$	5

2
$\sqrt{4} = 2$

A. What is the side length of a square with an area of 49 square units?

B. Use Structure Between what two consecutive integers is $\sqrt{20}$? How do you know? MP.7

C. Think of three squares that have a side length between 3 and 4. What is the area of each square?

SAMPLE STUDENT WORK

A. 7 units

B. 4 and 5; $\sqrt{20}$ is between $\sqrt{16}$ and $\sqrt{25}$, or 4 and 5.

C. 10.24, 12.25, and 15 square units

HABITS OF MIND

Use with **EXPLORE & REASON**

Communicate Precisely Explain why the expression $\sqrt{-x}$ does not represent a real number. **MP.6**

[For positive values of x, $-x$ is a negative number. In order to multiply 2 numbers to get a negative result, the numbers must have opposite signs, so there is no number that can be multiplied by itself to get a negative number. Therefore, $\sqrt{-x}$ is not a real number for positive values of x.]

INTRODUCE THE ESSENTIAL QUESTION

Establish Mathematics Goals to Focus Learning ETP

Students learn to use the Product Property of Square Roots to rewrite radical expressions. Students learn to write equivalent radical expressions with and without variables by finding perfect square factors in the radicand, which allows the expressions to be written in simplest form.

EXAMPLE 1 Use Properties to Rewrite Radical Expressions

Pose Purposeful Questions ETP

Q: In Part A, how does drawing squares help you understand the expressions?
[The squares show that the 2 combined side lengths of $\sqrt{4}$ are equal to the side length of $\sqrt{16}$, which proves the two expressions are equivalent to each other.]

Q: In Part B, why does a perfect square factor need to be removed from the radicand?
[A perfect square is the square of an integer, meaning two factors under the radical are the same. When a perfect square exists, that factor is placed outside the radical.]

AVAILABLE **ONLINE**

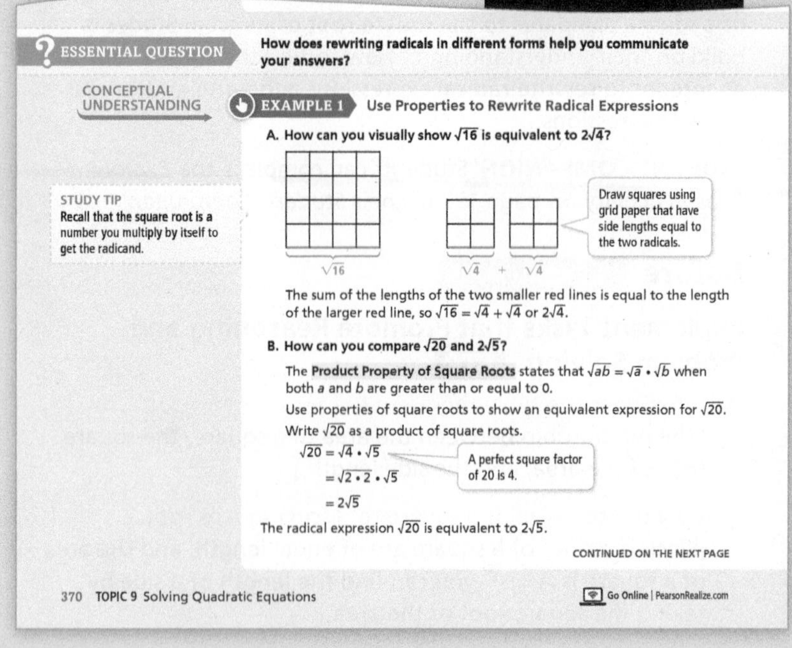
ESSENTIAL QUESTION How does rewriting radicals in different forms help you communicate your answers?

CONCEPTUAL UNDERSTANDING

EXAMPLE 1 Use Properties to Rewrite Radical Expressions

STUDY TIP
Recall that the square root is a number you multiply by itself to get the radicand.

A. How can you visually show $\sqrt{16}$ is equivalent to $2\sqrt{4}$?

$\sqrt{16}$
$\sqrt{4}$ + $\sqrt{4}$
Draw squares using grid paper that have side lengths equal to the two radicals.

The sum of the lengths of the two smaller red lines is equal to the length of the larger red line, so $\sqrt{16} = \sqrt{4} + \sqrt{4}$ or $2\sqrt{4}$.

B. How can you compare $\sqrt{20}$ and $2\sqrt{5}$?

The **Product Property of Square Roots** states that $\sqrt{ab} = \sqrt{a} \cdot \sqrt{b}$ when both a and b are greater than or equal to 0.

Use properties of square roots to show an equivalent expression for $\sqrt{20}$.

Write $\sqrt{20}$ as a product of square roots.

$$\sqrt{20} = \sqrt{4} \cdot \sqrt{5}$$
$$= \sqrt{2 \cdot 2} \cdot \sqrt{5}$$
$$= 2\sqrt{5}$$

A perfect square factor of 20 is 4.

The radical expression $\sqrt{20}$ is equivalent to $2\sqrt{5}$.

CONTINUED ON THE NEXT PAGE

370 TOPIC 9 Solving Quadratic Equations Go Online | PearsonRealize.com

Try It! Answers

1. a. $\sqrt{36} = 6$; $3\sqrt{6}$ cannot be simplified and is equal to $\sqrt{54}$.
   b. $6\sqrt{2} = \sqrt{72}$; $\sqrt{72} = \sqrt{6 \cdot 6 \cdot 2} = 6\sqrt{2}$

AVAILABLE **ONLINE**

ADDITIONAL EXAMPLES

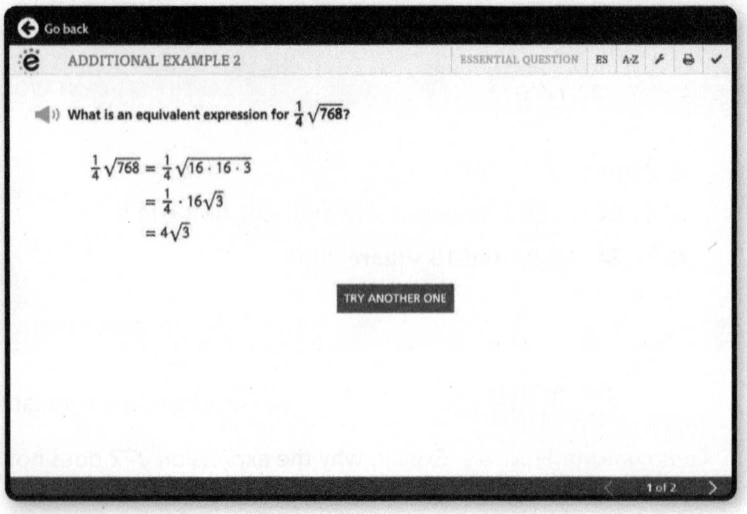

Go back
ADDITIONAL EXAMPLE 2
ESSENTIAL QUESTION ES A-Z
What is an equivalent expression for $\frac{1}{4}\sqrt{768}$?
$\frac{1}{4}\sqrt{768} = \frac{1}{4}\sqrt{16 \cdot 16 \cdot 3}$
$= \frac{1}{4} \cdot 16\sqrt{3}$
$= 4\sqrt{3}$
TRY ANOTHER ONE
1 of 2

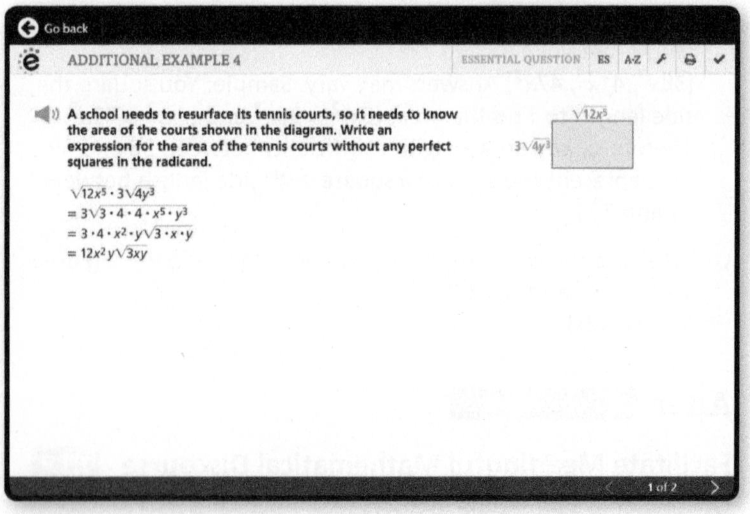

Go back
ADDITIONAL EXAMPLE 4
ESSENTIAL QUESTION ES A-Z
A school needs to resurface its tennis courts, so it needs to know the area of the courts shown in the diagram. Write an expression for the area of the tennis courts without any perfect squares in the radicand.
$\sqrt{12x^5}$
$3\sqrt{4y^3}$
$\sqrt{12x^5} \cdot 3\sqrt{4y^3}$
$= 3\sqrt{3 \cdot 4 \cdot 4 \cdot x^5 \cdot y^3}$
$= 3 \cdot 4 \cdot x^2 \cdot y\sqrt{3 \cdot x \cdot y}$
$= 12x^2y\sqrt{3xy}$
1 of 2

Example 2 Students transition to comparing radical expressions with fractions outside the radical.

Q: What is another mistake you or your classmates may make when finding equivalent radical expressions?
[They may recognize the radicand as a perfect square in the first expression but rewrite the radicand outside the radical without taking the square root.]

Example 4 Students practice finding the areas of rectangles with different variables representing the side lengths of the rectangles.

Q: Would you be able to write an equivalent expression for the area of the tennis courts if you did not multiply the two side lengths first?
[Yes, in this case, you could find the factors of each expression representing the side lengths before combining the two expressions.]

EXAMPLE 2 Write Equivalent Radical Expressions

Pose Purposeful Questions ETP

Q: How do you decide how to factor radical expressions?
[First, find all of the perfect squares in the radical expression. Finding the square root of the perfect squares removes them from the radicand. If the additional factors are not perfect squares, they remain under the radical sign.]

Try It! Answers

2. a. $2\sqrt{11}$

b. $9\sqrt{3}$

EXAMPLE 3 Write Equivalent Radical Expressions With Variables

Use and Connect Mathematical Representations ETP

Q: How do you recognize that a radical expression is written in simplest form?
[No perfect squares other than 1 are in the radicand.]

Q: How do you recognize when variables with exponents are perfect squares?
[Since a perfect square is a number multiplied by itself, a variable with an exponent multiplied by itself is also a perfect square. When two exponents with the same variable are multiplied, the exponents are added, so for the factors to be the same, the exponents should be the same. For example, $x^2 \cdot x^2 = x^4$.]

Q: How does an even exponent compare to an odd exponent in the radicand?
[For an even exponent, the equivalent expression does not contain a variable in the radicand since all variables with even exponents are perfect squares. For an odd exponent, the equivalent expression contains a variable in the radicand because a variable with an odd exponent is not a perfect square.]

Try It! Answers

3. a. $5x\sqrt{x}$

b. $10x^8\sqrt{x}$

AVAILABLE ONLINE

Activity Assess

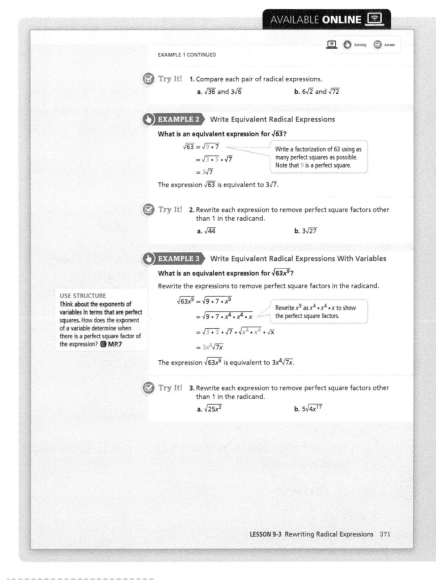

EXAMPLE 1 CONTINUED

Try It! 1. Compare each pair of radical expressions.

a. $\sqrt{36}$ and $3\sqrt{6}$ b. $6\sqrt{2}$ and $\sqrt{72}$

EXAMPLE 2 Write Equivalent Radical Expressions

What is an equivalent expression for $\sqrt{63}$?

$$\sqrt{63} = \sqrt{9 \cdot 7}$$
$$= \sqrt{3 \cdot 3} \cdot \sqrt{7}$$
$$= 3\sqrt{7}$$

Write a factorization of 63 using as many perfect squares as possible. Note that 9 is a perfect square.

The expression $\sqrt{63}$ is equivalent to $3\sqrt{7}$.

Try It! 2. Rewrite each expression to remove perfect square factors other than 1 in the radicand.

a. $\sqrt{44}$ b. $3\sqrt{27}$

EXAMPLE 3 Write Equivalent Radical Expressions With Variables

What is an equivalent expression for $\sqrt{63x^9}$?

Rewrite the expressions to remove perfect square factors in the radicand.

$$\sqrt{63x^9} = \sqrt{9 \cdot 7 \cdot x^9}$$
$$= \sqrt{9 \cdot 7 \cdot x^4 \cdot x^4 \cdot x}$$
$$= \sqrt{3 \cdot 3} \cdot \sqrt{7} \cdot \sqrt{x^4 \cdot x^4} \cdot \sqrt{x}$$
$$= 3x^4\sqrt{7x}$$

Rewrite x^9 as $x^4 \cdot x^4 \cdot x$ to show the perfect square factors.

USE STRUCTURE
Think about the exponents of variables in terms that are perfect squares. How does the exponent of a variable determine when there is a perfect square factor of the expression? MP.7

The expression $\sqrt{63x^9}$ is equivalent to $3x^4\sqrt{7x}$.

Try It! 3. Rewrite each expression to remove perfect square factors other than 1 in the radicand.

a. $\sqrt{25x^3}$ b. $5\sqrt{4x^{17}}$

LESSON 9-3 Rewriting Radical Expressions 371

HABITS OF MIND

Use with **EXAMPLES 1–3**

Generalize How does the exponent of a variable help you to determine if the term is a perfect square? MP.8

[If the exponent of a variable is even, the variable is a perfect square. If the exponent of a variable is odd, the variable is not a perfect square.]

RtI Struggling Students

USE WITH EXAMPLE 2 Have students practice finding perfect squares of the radicand and comparing similar expressions.

Q: What are the perfect squares in the radicand $\sqrt{126}$?
[9]

Q: What is the equivalent expression to $\sqrt{126}$?
[$3\sqrt{14}$]

Q: How does the equivalent expression of $\sqrt{126}$ compare to the equivalent expression of $2\sqrt{126}$?
[The integer before the radical is doubled to equal $6\sqrt{14}$.]

ADV Advanced Students

USE WITH EXAMPLE 3 Students explore writing equivalent radical expressions by rewriting each expression with perfect squares in the radicand.

Q: Write two equivalent expressions *with* perfect squares in the radicand for each of the given radical expressions.

1. $24x^3\sqrt{13}$
[$12\sqrt{52x^6}$ or $2\sqrt{1872x^6}$]

2. $6x^5\sqrt{19x}$
[$3\sqrt{76x^{11}}$ or $2\sqrt{171x^{11}}$]

EXAMPLE 4 Multiply Radical Expressions

Pose Purposeful Questions ETP

Q: How is the Product Property of Square Roots helpful when multiplying radical expressions?
[Since $\sqrt{ab} = \sqrt{a} \cdot \sqrt{b}$, the Product Property of Square Roots helps to pair factors and variable expressions with the same exponents.]

Try It! Answers

4. a. $14x^2\sqrt{3x}$ **b.** $12x^7\sqrt{6}$

Common Error

Try It! 4 When finding the product of the radical expressions, students may multiply the exponents (x^3 and x^2) under the radical sign instead of adding them. Encourage students to compare the Power of a Power Property for $(x^3)^2$ and the Product of Powers Property for $x^3 \cdot x^2$ to help them choose the correct operation.

EXAMPLE 5 Write a Radical Expression

Pose Purposeful Questions ETP

Q: Why do you need to substitute values into the slant height expression?
[All the variables need to be in terms of the radius, so the height is 7 times the radius, $7r$.]

Try It! Answer

5. $2r\sqrt{6}$

Use with **EXAMPLES 4 & 5**

HABITS OF MIND

Reason When is a radical expression in simplest form? Justify your answer. **MP.2**

[A radical expression is in simplest form when there are no perfect square factors remaining in the radicand.]

AVAILABLE **ONLINE**

Activity Assess

EXAMPLE 4 Multiply Radical Expressions

How can you write an expression for the product of $3\sqrt{5x} \cdot 2\sqrt{15x^3}$ without any perfect square factors in the radicand?

Find the product.

$$3\sqrt{5x} \cdot 2\sqrt{15x^3}$$
$$= 3 \cdot 2\sqrt{5x \cdot 15x^3}$$
$$= 6\sqrt{5 \cdot 3 \cdot 5 \cdot x^4}$$
$$= 6 \cdot \sqrt{5 \cdot 5} \cdot \sqrt{3} \cdot \sqrt{x^2 \cdot x^2}$$
$$= 6 \cdot 5 \cdot x^2 \cdot \sqrt{3}$$
$$= 30x^2\sqrt{3}$$

Use the Product Property of Square Roots to multiply the radicands.

Rewrite to show the perfect-square factors.

STUDY TIP
When rewriting the product under the radicand, it is easier to find perfect squares by replacing each number with its factors. Instead of writing $5 \cdot 15$ as 75, write the factors, $5 \cdot 3 \cdot 5$.

The expression $3\sqrt{5x} \cdot 2\sqrt{15x^3}$ is equivalent to $30x^2\sqrt{3}$.

Try It! **4.** Write an expression for each product without perfect square factors in the radicand.

a. $\frac{1}{2}\sqrt{21x^3} \cdot 4\sqrt{7x^2}$ **b.** $2\sqrt{12x^9} \cdot \sqrt{18x^5}$

APPLICATION

EXAMPLE 5 Write a Radical Expression

A light fixture in an ice cream shop is in the shape of an ice cream cone and the cone has a height that is 7 times the radius. The expression for the slant height is $\sqrt{r^2 + h^2}$, where r is the radius and h is the height of the cone. The slant height should be no longer than 24 in. to fit on the wall. What is the slant height of the cone with the radius shown?

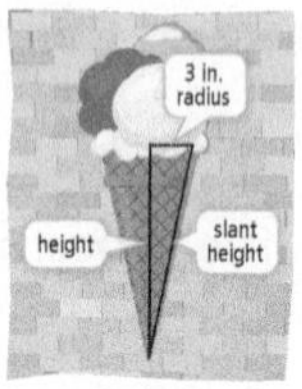
3 in.
radius
height
slant
height

Formulate Let r = radius and $7r$ = height.

$$\sqrt{r^2 + h^2} = \sqrt{r^2 + (7r)^2}$$

Compute
$$= \sqrt{r^2 + 49r^2}$$
$$= \sqrt{50r^2}$$
$$= \sqrt{5 \cdot 5 \cdot 2 \cdot r^2}$$
$$= 5r\sqrt{2}$$

Substitute the values into the slant height expression

Interpret To determine the slant height of the cone, evaluate the expression for $r = 3$.

$$5 \cdot 3\sqrt{2} \approx 21.2$$

The slant height is about 21 in. so it will fit on the wall.

Try It! **5.** Another cone has a slant height s that is 5 times the radius. What is the simplified expression for the height in terms of the radius?

ELL English Language Learners *(Use with* **EXAMPLE 5***)*

WRITING INTERMEDIATE Display the following sentences on the board. Ask students to copy the sentences into their journals and fill in the blanks to correctly complete the sentences. If necessary, provide a word list of possible answer choices.

Q: The _______ is the distance from the center to any point on a circle. [radius]

Q: Height is the shortest distance between two points and is always _______ to the base. [perpendicular]

Q: Slant height is the distance from the _______ of a right circular cone to any point on the circumference of the base. [vertex]

LISTENING BEGINNING Remind students that a *cone* is a three-dimensional figure with a single circular base that tapers to a point. Provide each student with a copy of the net of a cone, using two templates that have the same radius but different heights. Instruct students to cut out their nets and to measure the radius and height. Then instruct them to close and tape their nets to form a cone and measure the slant height.

Q: Find someone in the room whose cone is a different height than yours. How do the slant heights of your cones compare?
[The cone with the greater height also has a greater slant height.]

READING BEGINNING Have students read the first sentence of the example, pointing to the word *fixture* as they read. Then have them read the following definitions: *fix*—to repair or mend; *affix*—to fasten, join, or attach.

Q: Which word, *fix* or *affix,* seems to be more closely related to *fixture*?
[*affix*; The light is probably attached to a wall or sign. It does not look like it is in need of repair.]

Q: What do you think *fixture* means?
[something securely, and usually permanently, attached, as to a building]

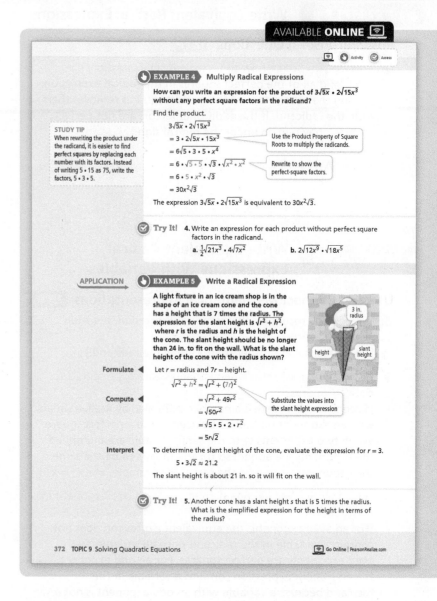

CONCEPT SUMMARY Rewriting Radical Expressions

Q: How do you rewrite a radical expression that has variables in the radicand?
[Find the factors of the integers and variables under the radical. Remove the perfect squares from the radicand. Leave the remaining values under the radical sign.]

Do You UNDERSTAND? | Do You KNOW HOW?

Common Error

Exercise 14 Students may forget to multiply the perfect squares that were removed from the radicand, $4x^3$, by the coefficients and variables already outside the radicand, $2x^2$. Encourage students to look at the original expression and highlight the numbers and variables not under the radical. This reminds them to multiply the highlighted numbers and variables by the perfect squares they have removed from the radicand.

Answers

1. Simplifying radicals creates consistency in your mathematical answers. When answers have a constant form, people can easily see and compare their results.
2. For two positive numbers, the square root of the product equals the product of the square roots.
3. Write the prime factorization:
   $\sqrt{2 \cdot 2 \cdot 2 \cdot 2 \cdot 2}$
   Remove each pair of 2s inside the radicand and write one factor of 2 outside the radicand for each pair.
   $= 2 \cdot 2\sqrt{\cancel{2 \cdot 2} \cdot \cancel{2 \cdot 2} \cdot 2}$
   $= 4\sqrt{2}$
4. Rikki simplified $\sqrt{3}$ to equal 3, but $\sqrt{3}$ cannot be factored out. The product $\sqrt{3x^3} \cdot \sqrt{x}$ is $\sqrt{3 \cdot x \cdot x \cdot x \cdot x}$, which is $x^2\sqrt{3}$.
5. No; Since 9 is a factor of 45 and 9 is a perfect square, the radical can be rewritten as $3\sqrt{5}$.
6. Write the prime factorization of the radicand. Remove any pairs of factors inside the radicand, writing one factor outside of the radicand for each pair. Once all pairs have been removed from the radicand, multiply the factors outside the radicand to find the coefficient. Then multiply the factors remaining in the radicand to find the final, simplified rational expression.
7. $4\sqrt{5}$
8. $x^3\sqrt{x}$
9. $2x^2\sqrt{10}$
10. $x^2\sqrt{11x}$
11. $10\sqrt{2}$
12. $16\sqrt{2}$

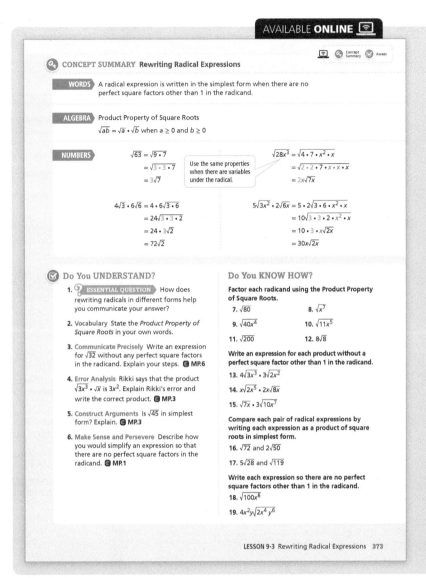

AVAILABLE ONLINE

Concept Summary Assess

CONCEPT SUMMARY Rewriting Radical Expressions

WORDS A radical expression is written in the simplest form when there are no perfect square factors other than 1 in the radicand.

ALGEBRA Product Property of Square Roots
$\sqrt{ab} = \sqrt{a} \cdot \sqrt{b}$ when $a \geq 0$ and $b \geq 0$

NUMBERS

$\sqrt{63} = \sqrt{9 \cdot 7}$
$= \sqrt{3 \cdot 3 \cdot 7}$
$= 3\sqrt{7}$

Use the same properties when there are variables under the radical.

$\sqrt{28x^3} = \sqrt{4 \cdot 7 \cdot x^2 \cdot x}$
$= \sqrt{2 \cdot 2 \cdot 7 \cdot x \cdot x \cdot x}$
$= 2x\sqrt{7x}$

$4\sqrt{3} \cdot 6\sqrt{6} = 4 \cdot 6\sqrt{3 \cdot 6}$
$= 24\sqrt{3 \cdot 3 \cdot 2}$
$= 24 \cdot 3\sqrt{2}$
$= 72\sqrt{2}$

$5\sqrt{3x^2} \cdot 2\sqrt{6x} = 5 \cdot 2\sqrt{3 \cdot 6 \cdot x^2 \cdot x}$
$= 10\sqrt{3 \cdot 3 \cdot 2 \cdot x^2 \cdot x}$
$= 10 \cdot 3 \cdot x\sqrt{2x}$
$= 30x\sqrt{2x}$

Do You UNDERSTAND?

1. ESSENTIAL QUESTION How does rewriting radicals in different forms help you communicate your answer?
2. **Vocabulary** State the *Product Property of Square Roots* in your own words.
3. **Communicate Precisely** Write an expression for $\sqrt{32}$ without any perfect square factors in the radicand. Explain your steps. **MP.6**
4. **Error Analysis** Rikki says that the product $\sqrt{3x^3} \cdot \sqrt{x}$ is $3x^2$. Explain Rikki's error and write the correct product. **MP.3**
5. **Construct Arguments** Is $\sqrt{45}$ in simplest form? Explain. **MP.3**
6. **Make Sense and Persevere** Describe how you would simplify an expression so that there are no perfect square factors in the radicand. **MP.1**

Do You KNOW HOW?

Factor each radicand using the Product Property of Square Roots.

7. $\sqrt{80}$
8. $\sqrt{x^7}$
9. $\sqrt{40x^4}$
10. $\sqrt{11x^5}$
11. $\sqrt{200}$
12. $8\sqrt{8}$

Write an expression for each product without a perfect square factor other than 1 in the radicand.

13. $4\sqrt{3x^3} \cdot 3\sqrt{2x^2}$
14. $x\sqrt{2x^5} \cdot 2x\sqrt{8x}$
15. $\sqrt{7x} \cdot 3\sqrt{10x^7}$

Compare each pair of radical expressions by writing each expression as a product of square roots in simplest form.

16. $\sqrt{72}$ and $2\sqrt{50}$
17. $5\sqrt{28}$ and $\sqrt{119}$

Write each expression so there are no perfect square factors other than 1 in the radicand.

18. $\sqrt{100x^8}$
19. $4x^2y\sqrt{2x^4y^6}$

LESSON 9-3 Rewriting Radical Expressions 373

13. $12x^2\sqrt{6x}$
14. $8x^5$
15. $3x^4\sqrt{70}$
16. The expressions are not equivalent; $\sqrt{72} = 6\sqrt{2}$ and $2\sqrt{50} = 10\sqrt{2}$
17. The expressions are not equivalent; $5\sqrt{28} = 10\sqrt{7}$ and $\sqrt{119} = \sqrt{17 \cdot 7}$
18. $10x^4$
19. $4x^4y^4\sqrt{2}$

PRACTICE & PROBLEM SOLVING

AVAILABLE **ONLINE**

Lesson Practice You may opt to have students complete the automatically scored Practice and Problem Solving items online powered by MathXL for School.

Choose from: **Lesson Practice**

Adaptive Practice

You may also take advantage of the bank of exercises for assigning additional practice.

Assignment Guide

Basic	Advanced
20–37, 42–53	20–25, 30–53

Item Analysis

Example	Items	DOK
1	26–31	1
2	32–35	1
3	36–39, 51	1
	20, 23, 24	2
	25	3
4	40–45	1
	21, 22	2
5	46, 47	1
	48–50, 52	2
	53	3

AVAILABLE **ONLINE**

PRACTICE & PROBLEM SOLVING

Scan for Multimedia | Practice | Tutorial | Additional Exercises Available Online

UNDERSTAND

20. **Use Structure** For $\sqrt{x^n}$, consider rewriting this expression without a perfect square factor in the radicand for even and odd values of n, where n is a positive integer. **MP.7**

a. What is the expression when n is even?

b. What is the expression when n is odd?

21. **Error Analysis** Describe and correct the error a student made in multiplying $2\sqrt{7x^2}$ by $2\sqrt{14x^3}$. **MP.3**

$2\sqrt{7x^2} \cdot 2\sqrt{14x^3}$
$= 2 \cdot 2\sqrt{7x^2 \cdot 14x^3}$
$= 4\sqrt{7 \cdot 2 \cdot 7 \cdot x \cdot x \cdot x \cdot x \cdot x}$
$= 8 \cdot 7\sqrt{x^2 \cdot x^2 \cdot x}$
$= 56x^2\sqrt{x}$ ✗

22. **Use Structure** Find $\sqrt{591x^{15}y^3} \cdot \sqrt{591x^{15}y^3}$ without calculating or simplifying. **MP.7**

23. **Communicate Precisely** Why do the multiplication properties of exponents apply to radicals? Explain. **MP.6**

24. **Make Sense and Persevere** How many perfect squares are under each radical? **MP.1**

Radical	Perfect squares
$\sqrt{8}$	
$\sqrt{18}$	
$\sqrt{32x^6}$	
$\sqrt{50x}$	
$\sqrt{72}$	

25. **Higher Order Thinking** Can you use the Product Property of Square Roots to find equivalent expressions for each radical? Explain.

a. $\sqrt[3]{24x^8}$

b. $\sqrt[4]{3^9x^{13}}$

PRACTICE

Compare each pair of radical expressions. SEE EXAMPLE 1

26. $6\sqrt{3}$ and $\sqrt{108}$

27. $2\sqrt{21}$ and $4\sqrt{5}$

28. $40\sqrt{42}$ and $42\sqrt{40}$

29. $\frac{1}{2}\sqrt{120}$ and $\sqrt{30}$ $\frac{1}{2}\sqrt{120} = \sqrt{30}$

30. $\sqrt{68}$ and $2\sqrt{18}$ $2\sqrt{17}$; $6\sqrt{2}$

31. $\sqrt{96}$ and $3\sqrt{15}$ $4\sqrt{6}$; $3\sqrt{15}$ cannot be simplified.

Write each expression so the radicand has no perfect squares other than 1. SEE EXAMPLES 2 AND 3

32. $\sqrt{210}$ $\sqrt{210}$

33. $\sqrt{250}$ $5\sqrt{10}$

34. $\sqrt{108}$ $6\sqrt{3}$

35. $2\sqrt{21}$ $2\sqrt{21}$

36. $\sqrt{98x^8}$ $7x^4\sqrt{2}$

37. $\sqrt{200x^3}$ $10x\sqrt{2x}$

38. $\sqrt{32x^4y^3}$ $4x^2y\sqrt{2y}$

39. $4x\sqrt{\frac{1}{4}x^6}$ $2x^4$

Write each expression so the radicand has no perfect squares other than 1. SEE EXAMPLE 4

40. $\sqrt{12x} \cdot \sqrt{3x}$ $6x$

41. $\sqrt{2x^9} \cdot \sqrt{26x^6}$ $2x^7\sqrt{13x}$

42. $\sqrt{27m} \cdot \sqrt{6m^{20}}$ $9m^{10}\sqrt{2m}$

43. $\sqrt{2x^3} \cdot \sqrt{25x^2y}$ $5x^2\sqrt{2xy}$

44. $\sqrt{9x^9} \cdot \sqrt{18x^3}$ $9x^6\sqrt{2}$

45. $\sqrt{32x} \cdot \sqrt{72x^{18}}$ $48x^9\sqrt{x}$

Write an expression in simplest form for the missing side length. Then find the side lengths of each triangle to the nearest tenth when $x = 15$. SEE EXAMPLE 5

46.

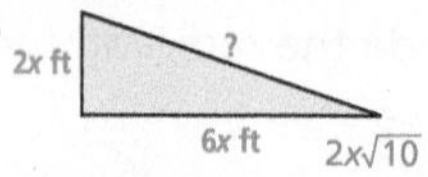

2x ft
?
6x ft

$2x\sqrt{10}$ ft; 30 ft, 90 ft, ≈94.9 ft

47.

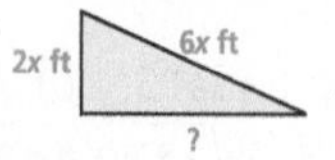

2x ft
6x ft
?

$4x\sqrt{2}$ ft; 30 ft, ≈84.9 ft, 90 ft

Answers

20. a. The square root simplifies completely, and the simplified answer is x with an exponent of $\frac{n}{2}$.

b. The square root does not simplify completely. The radicand is $\sqrt{x}$.

21. In the next-to-last step, 2 was removed from the square root.

$4\sqrt{7 \cdot 2 \cdot 7 \cdot x \cdot x \cdot x \cdot x \cdot x}$
$= 4 \cdot 7\sqrt{2 \cdot x^2 \cdot x^2 \cdot x}$
$= 28x^2\sqrt{2x}$

22. $591x^{15}y^3$

23. Radicals are equivalent to exponents: $\sqrt{x} = x^{\frac{1}{2}}$. So multiplying radical expressions is the same as multiplying exponential expressions.

24. 1; 1; 2; 1; 1

25. a. $2x^2\sqrt[3]{3x^2}$;

Factor $\sqrt[3]{24x^8}$.

$= \sqrt[3]{2^3 \cdot 3 \cdot (x^2 \cdot x^2 \cdot x^2) \cdot x^2}$

$= 2x^2\sqrt[3]{3x^2}$

b. $9x^3\sqrt[4]{3x}$;

Factor $\sqrt[4]{3^9x^{13}}$.

$= \sqrt[4]{(3^2 \cdot 3^2 \cdot 3^2 \cdot 3^2) \cdot 3 \cdot (x^3 \cdot x^3 \cdot x^3 \cdot x^3) \cdot x}$

$= 9x^3\sqrt[4]{3x}$

26. $\sqrt{108} = 6\sqrt{3}$

27. Neither expression can be simplified.

28. $40\sqrt{42}$ cannot be simplified; $42\sqrt{40} = 84\sqrt{10}$

SavvasRealize.com

Practice Tutorials Math Tools

Answers

48. **a.** $d\sqrt{d}$

b. 29.28 years; $\sqrt{d^3} = \sqrt{857.375} \approx 29.28$
$d\sqrt{d} = 9.5\sqrt{9.5} \approx 9.5 \cdot 3.08 \approx 29.28$

49. **a.** $90\sqrt{2}$ ft; 127.3 ft

b. 6.3 ft; The distance to 2nd base is $127.3 - 60.5 = 66.8$ ft; $66.8 - 60.5 = 6.3$ ft

50. **a.** $2h\ h^2 + (1.732h)^2$,
so $h = \sqrt{h^2 + (1.732h)^2} \approx \sqrt{h^2 + 3h^2} \approx \sqrt{4h^2} \approx 2h$

b. $5.464h$

51.

	$\sqrt{48}$	$5x\sqrt{6x^3}$
$\sqrt{12}$	24	$30x^2\sqrt{2x}$
$2x\sqrt{6x}$	$24x\sqrt{2x}$	$60x^4$
$4x^2\sqrt{2x^5}$	$16x^4\sqrt{6x}$	$40x^7\sqrt{3}$

53. Part A

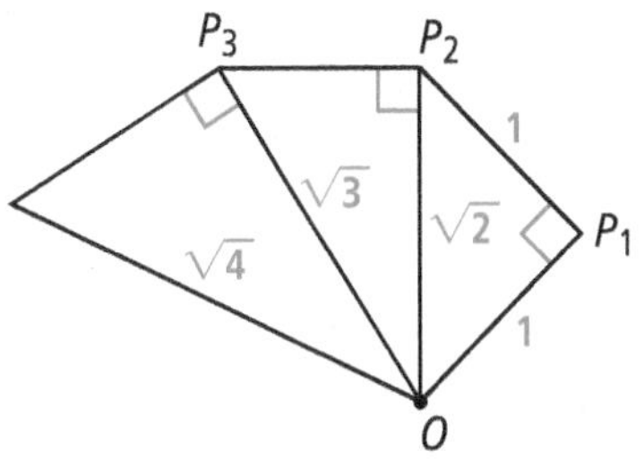

P_3
P_2
P_1
1
$\sqrt{3}$
$\sqrt{2}$
$\sqrt{4}$
1
O

Part B

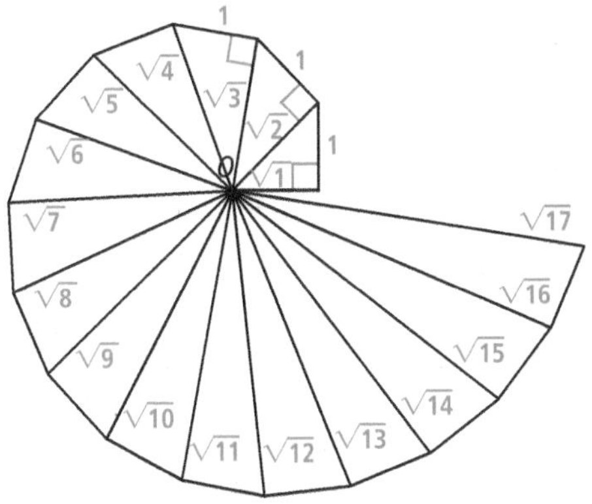

1
1
1
$\sqrt{4}$
$\sqrt{3}$
$\sqrt{2}$
$\sqrt{5}$
$\sqrt{6}$
$\sqrt{1}$
$\sqrt{7}$
$\sqrt{17}$
$\sqrt{8}$
$\sqrt{16}$
$\sqrt{9}$
$\sqrt{15}$
$\sqrt{14}$
$\sqrt{10}$
$\sqrt{11}$
$\sqrt{12}$
$\sqrt{13}$

Part C Unsimplified; The radicands each increase by 1, but this is not apparent with simplified square roots.

AVAILABLE **ONLINE**

PRACTICE & PROBLEM SOLVING

Practice Tutorial

Mixed Review Available Online

APPLY

48. Use Structure The time it takes a planet to revolve around the sun in Earth years can be modeled by $t = \sqrt{d^3}$, where d is the average distance from the sun in astronomical units (AU). MP.7

9.5 AU

a. Write an equivalent equation for the function.

b. How long does it take Saturn, pictured above, to orbit the sun? Show that both expressions give the same value.

49. Model With Mathematics A baseball "diamond" is a square that measures 90 ft on each side. MP.4

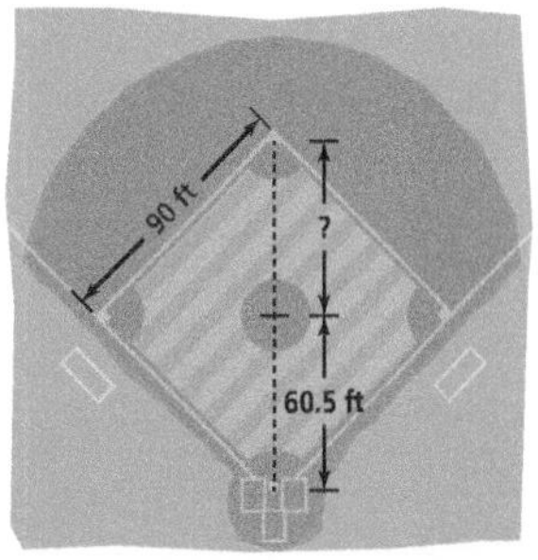

90 ft
?
60.5 ft

a. Write an expression for the distance from 2nd base to home plate in feet. What is this distance to the nearest tenth?

b. The pitcher standing on the pitcher's mound is about to throw to home plate but turns around and throws to 2nd base. How much farther is the throw? Explain.

50. Model With Mathematics A framed television has a ratio of width to height of about 1.732 : 1. MP.4

a. For a television with a height of h inches, what is an equivalent expression for the length of the diagonal? Justify your answer.

b. Write an expression for the perimeter.

ASSESSMENT PRACTICE

51. Copy and complete the table. Find the product of each row and column without a perfect square factor in the radicand and enter it in the appropriate cell.

	$\sqrt{48}$	$5x\sqrt{6x^3}$
$\sqrt{12}$	■	■
$2x\sqrt{6x}$	■	■
$4x^2\sqrt{2x^5}$	■	■

52. SAT/ACT A car skidded s ft when traveling on a damp paved road. The expression $r = \sqrt{18s}$ is an estimate of the car's rate of speed in ft/s.

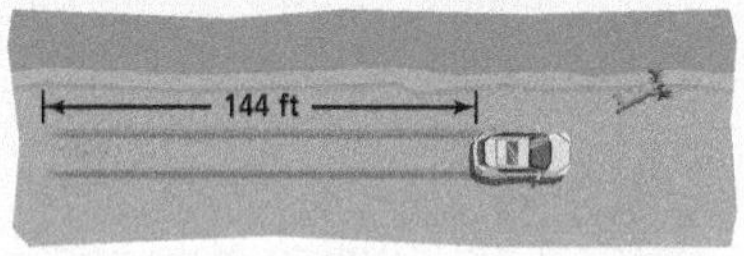

144 ft

Which expression represents the speed of the car in feet per second?

Ⓐ $24\sqrt{6}$
Ⓑ $12\sqrt{6}$
Ⓒ $36\sqrt{2}$
Ⓓ $24\sqrt{3}$
Ⓔ $48\sqrt{2}$

53. Performance Task Copy the figure. Center it on a large piece of paper so you can expand it.

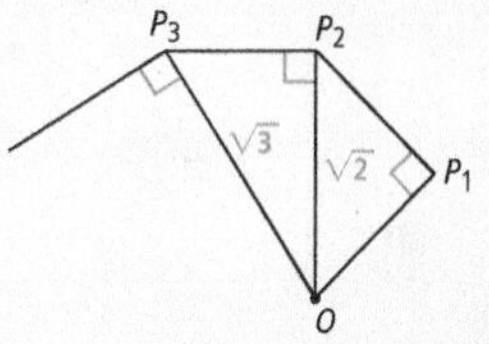

P_3
P_2
$\sqrt{3}$
$\sqrt{2}$
P_1
O

Part A Use the pattern to complete the triangle on the left. Label the side lengths.

Part B Continue using the pattern to add triangles while labeling side lengths.

Part C Are equivalent expressions of the square roots appropriate? Explain your reasoning.

LESSON 9-3 Rewriting Radical Expressions 375

LESSON QUIZ

Use the Lesson Quiz to assess students' understanding of the mathematics in the lesson.

Students can take the Lesson Quiz online or you can download a printable copy from **SavvasRealize.com**. The Lesson Quiz is also available in the *Assessment Resources* book.

Item Analysis

Item	DOK	Standards
1	1	HSN.RN.A.2
2	1	HSN.RN.A.2
3	1	HSN.RN.A.2
4	2	HSN.RN.A.2
5	2	HSN.RN.A.2

RtI Use the student scores on the Lesson Quiz to prescribe differentiated assignments.

If students take the Lesson Quiz online, it will be automatically scored and appropriate differentiated practice will be assigned based on student performance.

I Intervention	0–3 points	• Reteach to Build Understanding • Mathematical Literacy and Vocabulary • Additional Practice
O On-Level	4 points	• Mathematical Literacy and Vocabulary • Additional Practice • Enrichment
A Advanced	5 points	• Enrichment

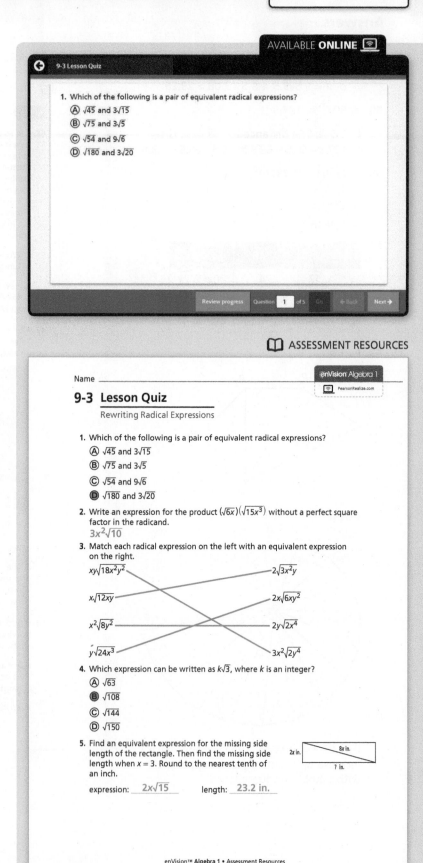

AVAILABLE **ONLINE**

9-3 Lesson Quiz

1. Which of the following is a pair of equivalent radical expressions?
   - Ⓐ $\sqrt{45}$ and $3\sqrt{15}$
   - Ⓑ $\sqrt{75}$ and $3\sqrt{5}$
   - Ⓒ $\sqrt{54}$ and $9\sqrt{6}$
   - Ⓓ $\sqrt{180}$ and $3\sqrt{20}$

Review progress Question 1 of 5 Go ← Back Next →

ASSESSMENT RESOURCES

Name ______________ enVision Algebra 1 PearsonRealize.com

9-3 Lesson Quiz

Rewriting Radical Expressions

1. Which of the following is a pair of equivalent radical expressions?
   - Ⓐ $\sqrt{45}$ and $3\sqrt{15}$
   - Ⓑ $\sqrt{75}$ and $3\sqrt{5}$
   - Ⓒ $\sqrt{54}$ and $9\sqrt{6}$
   - Ⓓ $\sqrt{180}$ and $3\sqrt{20}$
2. Write an expression for the product $(\sqrt{6x})(\sqrt{15x^3})$ without a perfect square factor in the radicand.
   $3x^2\sqrt{10}$
3. Match each radical expression on the left with an equivalent expression on the right.

$xy\sqrt{18x^2y^2}$	$2\sqrt{3x^2y}$
$x\sqrt{12xy}$	$2x\sqrt{6xy^2}$
$x^2\sqrt{8y^2}$	$2y\sqrt{2x^4}$
$y\sqrt{24x^3}$	$3x^2\sqrt{2y^4}$

4. Which expression can be written as $k\sqrt{3}$, where k is an integer?
   - Ⓐ $\sqrt{63}$
   - Ⓑ $\sqrt{108}$
   - Ⓒ $\sqrt{144}$
   - Ⓓ $\sqrt{150}$
5. Find an equivalent expression for the missing side length of the rectangle. Then find the missing side length when $x = 3$. Round to the nearest tenth of an inch.

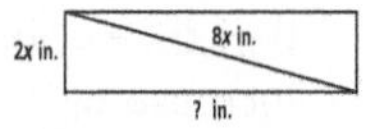

8x in.
2x in.
? in.

expression: $2x\sqrt{15}$ length: 23.2 in.

enVision™ **Algebra 1** • Assessment Resources

SavvasRealize.com

Assess Tutorials Worksheets

DIFFERENTIATED RESOURCES

I = Intervention O = On-Level A = Advanced

⚙ = This activity is available as a digital assignment powered by MathXL® for School.

AVAILABLE ONLINE

Reteach to Build Understanding I ⚙

Provides scaffolded reteaching for the key lesson concepts.

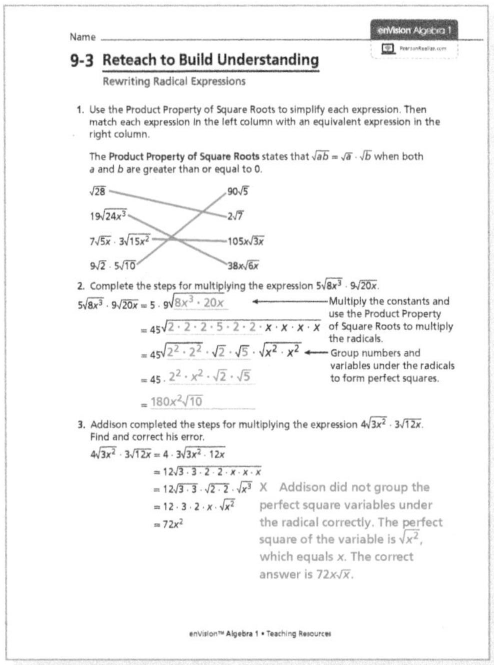

Name

9-3 Reteach to Build Understanding

Rewriting Radical Expressions

1. Use the Product Property of Square Roots to simplify each expression. Then match each expression in the left column with an equivalent expression in the right column.

The Product Property of Square Roots states that $\sqrt{ab} = \sqrt{a} \cdot \sqrt{b}$ when both a and b are greater than or equal to 0.

$\sqrt{28}$ — $90\sqrt{5}$

$19\sqrt{24x^3}$ — $2\sqrt{7}$

$7\sqrt{5x} \cdot 3\sqrt{15x^2}$ — $105x\sqrt{3x}$

$9\sqrt{2} \cdot 5\sqrt{10}$ — $38x\sqrt{6x}$

2. Complete the steps for multiplying the expression $5\sqrt{8x^3} \cdot 9\sqrt{20x}$.

$5\sqrt{8x^3} \cdot 9\sqrt{20x} = 5 \cdot 9\sqrt{8x^3 \cdot 20x}$ ← Multiply the constants and use the Product Property of Square Roots to multiply the radicals.

$= 45\sqrt{2 \cdot 2 \cdot 2 \cdot 5 \cdot 2 \cdot 2 \cdot x \cdot x \cdot x \cdot x}$

$= 45\sqrt{2^2 \cdot 2^2} \cdot \sqrt{2} \cdot \sqrt{5} \cdot \sqrt{x^2 \cdot x^2}$ ← Group numbers and variables under the radicals to form perfect squares.

$= 45 \cdot 2^2 \cdot x^2 \cdot \sqrt{2} \cdot \sqrt{5}$

$= 180x^2\sqrt{10}$

3. Addison completed the steps for multiplying the expression $4\sqrt{3x^2} \cdot 3\sqrt{12x}$. Find and correct his error.

$4\sqrt{3x^2} \cdot 3\sqrt{12x} = 4 \cdot 3\sqrt{3x^2 \cdot 12x}$

$= 12\sqrt{3 \cdot 3 \cdot 2 \cdot 2 \cdot x \cdot x \cdot x}$

$= 12\sqrt{3 \cdot 3} \cdot \sqrt{2 \cdot 2} \cdot \sqrt{x^3}$ X

$= 12 \cdot 3 \cdot 2 \cdot x \cdot \sqrt{x^2}$

$= 72x^2$

Addison did not group the perfect square variables under the radical correctly. The perfect square of the variable is $\sqrt{x^2}$, which equals x. The correct answer is $72x\sqrt{x}$.

enVision™ Algebra 1 • Teaching Resources

Additional Practice I O ⚙

Provides extra practice for each lesson.

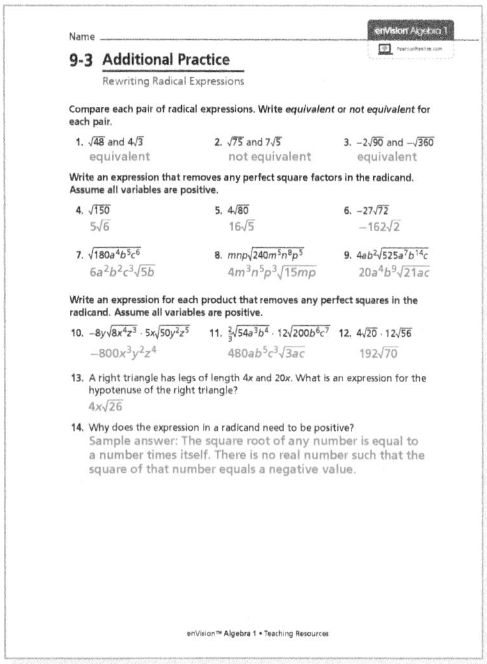

Name

9-3 Additional Practice

Rewriting Radical Expressions

Compare each pair of radical expressions. Write *equivalent* or *not equivalent* for each pair.

1. $\sqrt{48}$ and $4\sqrt{3}$ — equivalent
2. $\sqrt{75}$ and $7\sqrt{5}$ — not equivalent
3. $-2\sqrt{90}$ and $-\sqrt{360}$ — equivalent

Write an expression that removes any perfect square factors in the radicand. Assume all variables are positive.

4. $\sqrt{150}$ — $5\sqrt{6}$
5. $4\sqrt{80}$ — $16\sqrt{5}$
6. $-27\sqrt{72}$ — $-162\sqrt{2}$
7. $\sqrt{180a^4b^5c^6}$ — $6a^2b^2c^3\sqrt{5b}$
8. $mnp\sqrt{240m^5n^8p^5}$ — $4m^3n^5p^3\sqrt{15mp}$
9. $4ab^2\sqrt{525a^7b^{14}c}$ — $20a^4b^9\sqrt{21ac}$

Write an expression for each product that removes any perfect squares in the radicand. Assume all variables are positive.

10. $-8y\sqrt{8x^4z^3} \cdot 5x\sqrt{50y^2z^5}$ — $-800x^3y^2z^4$
11. $\frac{1}{3}\sqrt{54a^3b^4} \cdot 12\sqrt{200b^6c^7}$ — $480ab^5c^3\sqrt{3ac}$
12. $4\sqrt{20} \cdot 12\sqrt{56}$ — $192\sqrt{70}$

13. A right triangle has legs of length $4x$ and $20x$. What is an expression for the hypotenuse of the right triangle? $4x\sqrt{26}$

14. Why does the expression in a radicand need to be positive? Sample answer: The square root of any number is equal to a number times itself. There is no real number such that the square of that number equals a negative value.

enVision™ Algebra 1 • Teaching Resources

Enrichment O A ⚙

Presents engaging problems and activities that extend the lesson concepts.

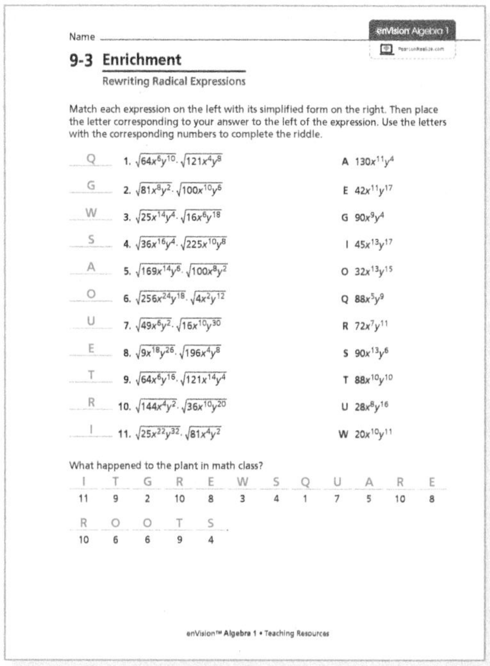

Name

9-3 Enrichment

Rewriting Radical Expressions

Match each expression on the left with its simplified form on the right. Then place the letter corresponding to your answer to the left of the expression. Use the letters with the corresponding numbers to complete the riddle.

Q	1. $\sqrt{64x^6y^{10}} \cdot \sqrt{121x^4y^8}$	A $130x^{11}y^4$
G	2. $\sqrt{81x^8y^2} \cdot \sqrt{100x^{10}y^6}$	E $42x^{11}y^{17}$
W	3. $\sqrt{25x^{14}y^4} \cdot \sqrt{16x^6y^{18}}$	G $90x^9y^4$
S	4. $\sqrt{36x^{16}y^4} \cdot \sqrt{225x^{10}y^8}$	I $45x^{13}y^{17}$
A	5. $\sqrt{169x^{14}y^6} \cdot \sqrt{100x^8y^2}$	O $32x^{13}y^{15}$
O	6. $\sqrt{256x^{24}y^{18}} \cdot \sqrt{4x^2y^{12}}$	Q $88x^5y^9$
U	7. $\sqrt{49x^6y^2} \cdot \sqrt{16x^{10}y^{30}}$	R $72x^7y^{11}$
E	8. $\sqrt{9x^{18}y^{26}} \cdot \sqrt{196x^4y^8}$	S $90x^{13}y^6$
T	9. $\sqrt{64x^6y^{16}} \cdot \sqrt{121x^{14}y^4}$	T $88x^{10}y^{10}$
R	10. $\sqrt{144x^4y^2} \cdot \sqrt{36x^{10}y^{20}}$	U $28x^8y^{16}$
I	11. $\sqrt{25x^{22}y^{32}} \cdot \sqrt{81x^4y^2}$	W $20x^{10}y^{11}$

What happened to the plant in math class?

I T G R E W S Q U A R E
11 9 2 10 8 3 4 1 7 5 10 8

R O O T S
10 6 6 9 4

enVision™ Algebra 1 • Teaching Resources

Mathematical Literacy and Vocabulary I O

Helps students develop and reinforce understanding of key terms and concepts.

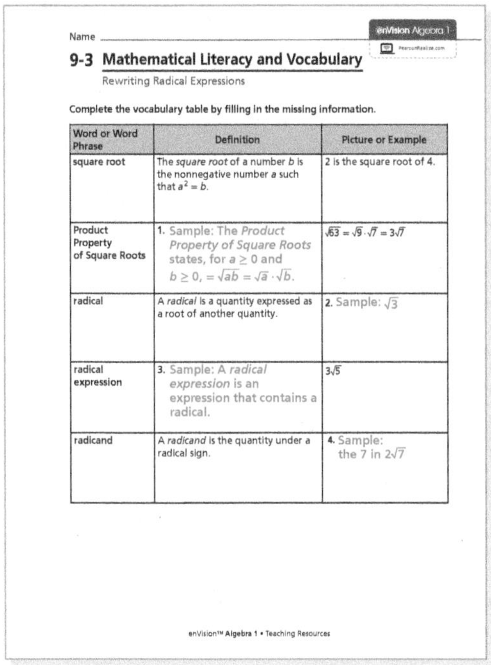

Name

9-3 Mathematical Literacy and Vocabulary

Rewriting Radical Expressions

Complete the vocabulary table by filling in the missing information.

Word or Word Phrase	Definition	Picture or Example
square root	The *square root* of a number b is the nonnegative number a such that $a^2 = b$.	2 is the square root of 4.
Product Property of Square Roots	1. Sample: The *Product Property of Square Roots* states, for $a \geq 0$ and $b \geq 0$, $\sqrt{ab} = \sqrt{a} \cdot \sqrt{b}$.	$\sqrt{63} = \sqrt{9} \cdot \sqrt{7} = 3\sqrt{7}$
radical	A *radical* is a quantity expressed as a root of another quantity.	2. Sample: $\sqrt{3}$
radical expression	3. Sample: A *radical expression* is an expression that contains a radical.	$3\sqrt{5}$
radicand	A *radicand* is the quantity under a radical sign.	4. Sample: the 7 in $2\sqrt{7}$

enVision™ Algebra 1 • Teaching Resources

Digital Resources and Video Tutorials I O A ⚙

The **Reteach to Build Understanding, Additional Practice,** and **Enrichment** activities are available as digital assignments powered by MathXL for School. These activities are automatically assigned when students complete the lesson quiz online and are automatically scored.

Students can access instructional tutorials using the **Virtual Nerd app.**

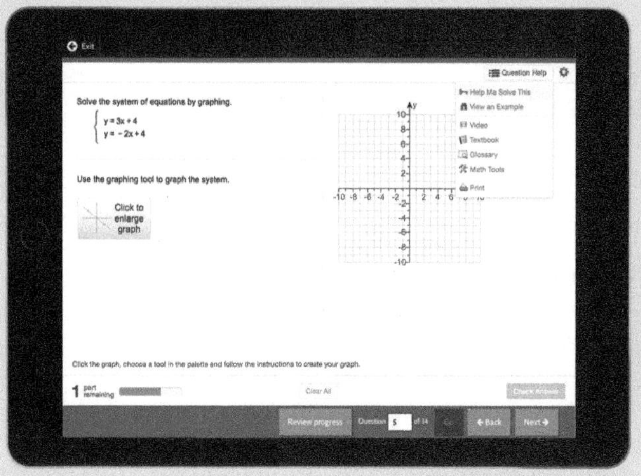

Students can also access Virtual Nerd videos using the **BouncePages app** to scan exercise pages marked with this icon. Students can download both apps for free in their mobile devices' app store.

LESSON 9-4

Solving Quadratic Equations Using Square Roots

A-Z Glossary

Lesson Overview

FOCUS

Objective

Students will be able to:

✔ Solve quadratic equations by finding square roots.

✔ Determine reasonable solutions for real-world problems.

Essential Understanding

When a quadratic equation is in the form $ax^2 + b = c$, it can be solved by isolating the ax^2 term, simplifying to remove the coefficients, and then taking the square root of each side of the equation.

COHERENCE

Previously in this topic, students:

- Solved quadratic equations using graphs, tables, or factoring.
- Used the Product Property of Square Roots to rewrite radical expressions.

In this lesson, students:

- Solve quadratic equations of the form $ax^2 + bx = c$ using square roots.

Later in this topic, students will:

- Solve quadratic equations by completing the square.

RIGOR

This lesson emphasizes a blend of *procedural skill and fluency* and *application.*

- Students solve quadratic equations of the form $ax^2 + b = c$ by isolating the variable and then taking the square root of each side of the equation.
- Students apply the process of solving quadratic equations using square roots to determine reasonable solutions to problems, such as finding the height of a cell phone tower.

A-Z Vocabulary Builder

REVIEW VOCABULARY — **English** | *Spanish*

- **isolate** | *aislar*
- **linear equation** | *ecuación lineal*
- **properties of equality** | *propiedades de la igualdad*
- **quadratic equation** | *ecuación cuadrática*

VOCABULARY ACTIVITY

Review the definitions and give examples of *linear equations* and *quadratic equations.* Have students think about how they use the terms *isolate* and *properties of equality* when solving equations. Have students complete the sentences using these terms.

To solve the equation $x + 8 = 20$, ________ [isolate] the variable by subtracting 8 from each side of the equation.

The ________ [properties of equality] allow you to balance quadratic equations by doing the same operation to each side of the equation.

An example of a ________ [linear equation] is $3x + 7 = 13$, and an example of a ________ [quadratic equation] is $x^2 - 4 = 20$.

Student Companion

Students can do their in-class work for the lesson on pages 201–204 of their *Student Companion* or in Savvas Realize.

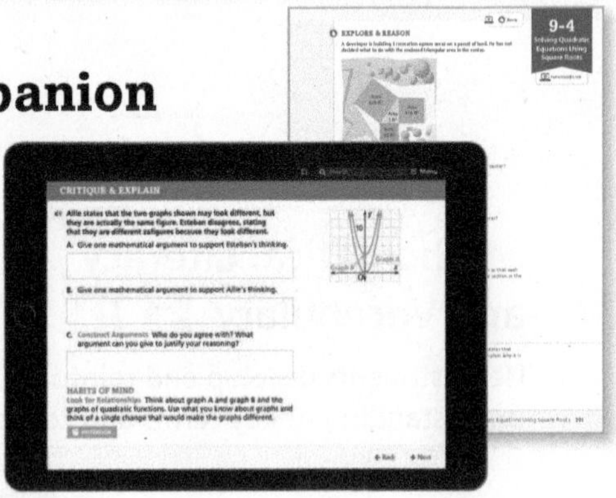

Mathematics Overview — COMMON CORE STANDARDS

Content Standards

In this lesson, students focus on these standards:

HSA.SSE.A.2 Use the structure of an expression to identify ways to rewrite it.

HSA.REI.B.4.B Solve quadratic equations by inspection (e.g., for $x^2 = 49$), taking square roots, completing the square, using the quadratic formula, and factoring, as appropriate to the initial form of the equation. Recognize when the quadratic formula gives complex solutions and write them as $a \pm bi$ for real numbers a and b.

They also work with concepts related to this standard:
HSA.CED.A.1

Mathematical Practice Standards

These standards are highlighted in this lesson:

MP.2 Reason Abstractly and Quantitatively

Students contextualize the solutions of quadratic equations when they use the context of a real-world situation to determine when it's appropriate to use the symbol $\pm$, and when only a positive or a negative value applies.

MP.7 Look For and Make Use of Structure

Students compare the steps used to solve a quadratic equation to those they used when solving a linear equation.

Activity

EXPLORE & REASON

INSTRUCTIONAL FOCUS Students explore using square roots to find the side lengths of squares. This prepares them to understand how to solve quadratic equations using square roots.

STUDENT COMPANION Students can complete the *Explore & Reason* activity on page 201 of their *Student Companion.*

Before WHOLE CLASS

Implement Tasks that Promote Reasoning and Problem Solving ETP

Q: What do you notice about the picture?
[There are three squares with different areas. One side of each square is a side of the enclosed triangle. The triangle appears to be a right triangle.]

During SMALL GROUP

Support Productive Struggle in Learning Mathematics ETP

Q: What do you know about the side lengths of each square in relation to the area of each square?
[You find the length of a side of the square by taking the square root of the area of the square.]

For Early Finishers

Q: Consider the square with an area of 576 ft^2. Multiply the side lengths of the square by 2, 4, $\frac{1}{2}$, and $\frac{1}{3}$, and then calculate the areas of the new squares. What do you notice about the new areas?
[New areas: 2,304 ft^2; 9,216 ft^2; 144 ft^2; and 64 ft^2; The area of the new square is equal to the original area times the square of each of the multiples.]

After WHOLE CLASS

Facilitate Meaningful Mathematical Discourse ETP

Q: If you were given the side lengths of the triangle, could you determine the area of each square?
[Yes; each side length of the triangle is a side length of one of the squares. The area of each square is equal to its corresponding side length squared.]

Q: The enclosed triangle appears to be a right triangle. Is it possible to determine if the triangle is a right triangle?
[Yes; you can determine the lengths of each side of the triangle and then use the Pythagorean Theorem to see if the side lengths form a right triangle.]

HABITS OF MIND

Use with **EXPLORE & REASON**

Make Sense and Persevere The Product Property of Square Roots states that $\sqrt{ab} = \sqrt{a} \cdot \sqrt{b}$ when both a and b are greater than or equal to 0. Explain why it is essential that a and b are greater than or equal to 0. MP.1

[It is essential that *a* and *b* are greater than or equal to 0 because the square roots of negative numbers are not real numbers.]

AVAILABLE **ONLINE**

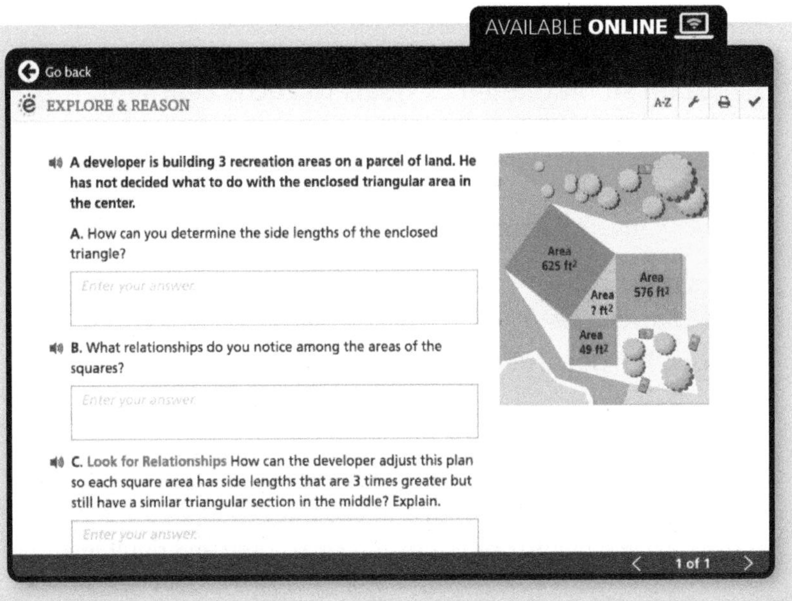
Go back
EXPLORE & REASON
A developer is building 3 recreation areas on a parcel of land. He has not decided what to do with the enclosed triangular area in the center.
A. How can you determine the side lengths of the enclosed triangle?
Enter your answer
B. What relationships do you notice among the areas of the squares?
Enter your answer
C. Look for Relationships How can the developer adjust this plan so each square area has side lengths that are 3 times greater but still have a similar triangular section in the middle? Explain.
Enter your answer
1 of 1

Area
625 ft²
Area
576 ft²
Area
? ft²
Area
49 ft²

STUDENT EDITION, PAGE 376

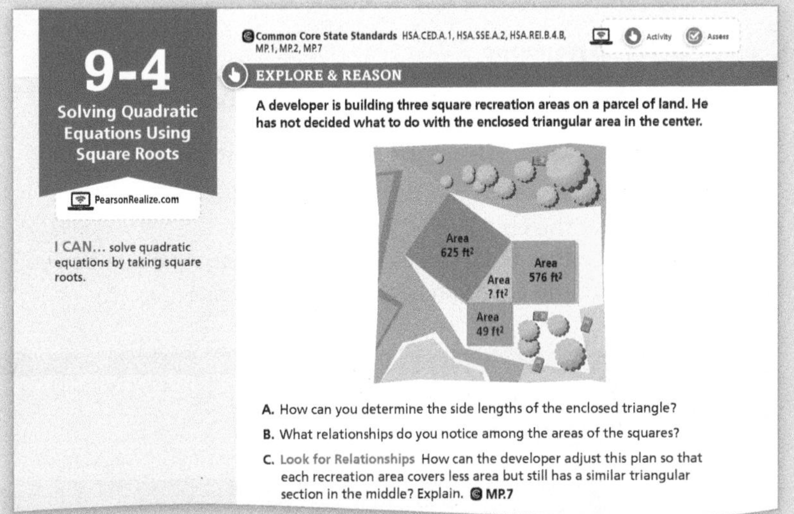
9-4 Solving Quadratic Equations Using Square Roots
PearsonRealize.com
I CAN… solve quadratic equations by taking square roots.
Common Core State Standards HSA.CED.A.1, HSA.SSE.A.2, HSA.REI.B.4.B, MP.1, MP.2, MP.7
Activity Assess
EXPLORE & REASON
A developer is building three square recreation areas on a parcel of land. He has not decided what to do with the enclosed triangular area in the center.

Area
625 ft²
Area
576 ft²
Area
? ft²
Area
49 ft²

A. How can you determine the side lengths of the enclosed triangle?
B. What relationships do you notice among the areas of the squares?
C. Look for Relationships How can the developer adjust this plan so that each recreation area covers less area but still has a similar triangular section in the middle? Explain. MP.7

SAMPLE STUDENT WORK

A. Take the square root of each square area. This is equal to the square's side length; one side of each square is one of the sides of the triangle.

B. The sum of the areas of the two smaller squares is equal to the area of the largest square.

C. Triangles are similar as long as their angles are congruent and their corresponding sides are in proportion, so multiplying each side by $\frac{1}{3}$ would create a triangle that is similar and cover less area than the original triangle.

Activity Assess

INTRODUCE THE ESSENTIAL QUESTION

Establish Mathematics Goals to Focus Learning ETP

Students learn to solve quadratic equations using square roots. Students learn that certain forms of quadratic equations can be rewritten so they can be solved by isolating the variable and taking square roots of each side of the equation.

EXAMPLE 1 Solve Equations of the Form $x^2 = a$

Pose Purposeful Questions ETP

Q: Why are the solutions to an equation of the form $x^2 = a$ both the positive and negative square roots?
[When each square root is multiplied by itself, the result is a.]

Q. Why does a negative radicand indicate no solution?
[No real number can be multiplied by itself and result in a negative product.]

Q: Does the equation $x^2 = 0$ have a solution?
[Yes; the solution is $x = 0$, because $0 \cdot 0 = 0$.]

Try It! Answers

1. a. ± 13 b. no real solution

Elicit and Use Evidence of Student Thinking ETP

Q: What can you tell about the solutions of the equation by looking at the equation?
[If you see that the value equal to x^2 is a negative number, you know that the equation has no real solutions.]

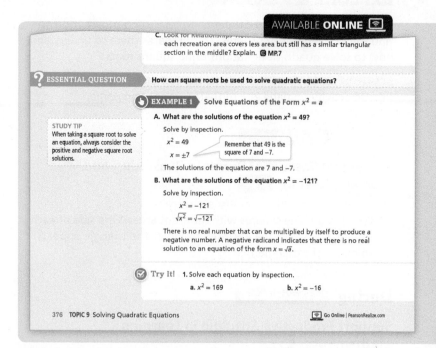

AVAILABLE ONLINE

C. Look for Relationships ... each recreation area covers less area but still has a similar triangular section in the middle? Explain. MP.7

ESSENTIAL QUESTION How can square roots be used to solve quadratic equations?

EXAMPLE 1 Solve Equations of the Form $x^2 = a$

A. What are the solutions of the equation $x^2 = 49$?

Solve by inspection.

$x^2 = 49$

$x = \pm 7$

Remember that 49 is the square of 7 and −7.

The solutions of the equation are 7 and −7.

STUDY TIP
When taking a square root to solve an equation, always consider the positive and negative square root solutions.

B. What are the solutions of the equation $x^2 = -121$?

Solve by inspection.

$x^2 = -121$

$\sqrt{x^2} = \sqrt{-121}$

There is no real number that can be multiplied by itself to produce a negative number. A negative radicand indicates that there is no real solution to an equation of the form $x = \sqrt{a}$.

Try It! 1. Solve each equation by inspection.

a. $x^2 = 169$ b. $x^2 = -16$

376 TOPIC 9 Solving Quadratic Equations Go Online | PearsonRealize.com

Common Error

Try It! 1b Students may say that $x = -4$ is the solution to this equation. Show students that there is no real number that when multiplied by itself results in a negative number. A negative radicand indicates that there is no real solution.

ADDITIONAL EXAMPLES

AVAILABLE ONLINE

Go back

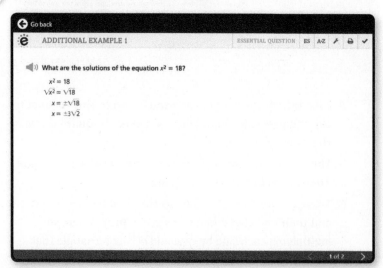

ADDITIONAL EXAMPLE 1 ESSENTIAL QUESTION ES A-Z

What are the solutions of the equation $x^2 = 18$?

$x^2 = 18$

$\sqrt{x^2} = \sqrt{18}$

$x = \pm\sqrt{18}$

$x = \pm 3\sqrt{2}$

1 of 2

Example 1 Students transition to solving quadratic equations with square roots when the solutions contain radicals.

Q: What other way can you represent the solution of the equation when there is a radical in the solution?
[You can use a calculator to estimate the value of the radical.]

Go back

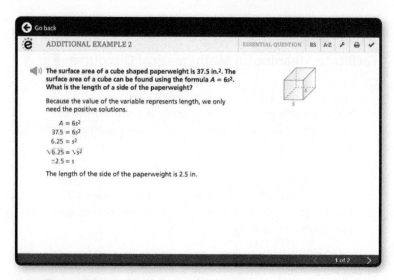

ADDITIONAL EXAMPLE 2 ESSENTIAL QUESTION ES A-Z

The surface area of a cube shaped paperweight is 37.5 in.^{2}. The surface area of a cube can be found using the formula $A = 6s^2$. What is the length of a side of the paperweight?

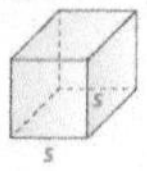

s
s

Because the value of the variable represents length, we only need the positive solutions.

$A = 6s^2$

$37.5 = 6s^2$

$6.25 = s^2$

$\sqrt{6.25} = \sqrt{s^2}$

$\pm 2.5 = s$

The length of the side of the paperweight is 2.5 in.

1 of 2

Example 2 Students transition to solving real-world quadratic equations with square roots.

Q: Suppose the surface area of another paperweight cube was 4 times larger than the original paperweight. How does the side length of this paperweight compare to the original?
[The side length of the new paperweight is twice as long as the original paperweight.]

STEP 2 | Understand & Apply

EXAMPLE 2 Solve Equations of the Form $ax^2 = c$

Pose Purposeful Questions ETP

Q: What is another strategy you could use to solve equations of the form $ax^2 = c$?
[You could graph the related function $f(x) = ax^2 - c$. When a and c are both positive or negative, the graph of f has x-intercepts. When either a or c is negative, the graph of the function does not have x-intercepts.]

Q. Why are the properties of equalities helpful when solving equations of the form $ax^2 = c$?
[You use the properties of equality to isolate the variable and make the equation easier to solve.]

Try It! Answers

2. a. ± 5

   b. $\pm 6\sqrt{2}$; between 8 and 9 or −9 and −8

Elicit and Use Evidence of Student Thinking ETP

Q: Why should you divide both sides by the coefficient of the variable term before taking the square root of each side?
[If you take the square root first, you may end up with numbers that contain radicals, which would make isolating the variable more complicated.]

Use with **EXAMPLES 1 & 2**

HABITS OF MIND

Construct Arguments What is an advantage of solving a quadratic equation using square roots? What is a disadvantage? Explain your reasoning. **MP.3**

[Solving a quadratic equation using square roots allows you to quickly find or approximate the x-intercept(s). However, it does not provide an integer solution when the radicand is not a perfect square.]

AVAILABLE **ONLINE**

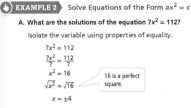

Activity Assess

EXAMPLE 2 Solve Equations of the Form $ax^2 = c$

A. What are the solutions of the equation $7x^2 = 112$?

Isolate the variable using properties of equality.

$$7x^2 = 112$$
$$\frac{7x^2}{7} = \frac{112}{7}$$
$$x^2 = 16$$
$$\sqrt{x^2} = \sqrt{16}$$
$$x = \pm 4$$

16 is a perfect square.

B. What are the solutions of the equation $-3x^2 = -24$?

Isolate the variable using properties of equality.

$$-3x^2 = -24$$
$$\frac{-3x^2}{-3} = \frac{-24}{-3}$$
$$x^2 = 8$$
$$x = \pm\sqrt{8}$$

Take the square root of both sides to solve for x.

REASON
You could rewrite $\pm\sqrt{8}$ as $\pm 2\sqrt{2}$. What is the advantage of using $\pm\sqrt{8}$? What would be the advantage of using $\pm 2\sqrt{2}$? MP.2

Try It! **2.** What are the solutions for each equation? If the solution is not a perfect square, state what two integers the solution is between.

a. $5x^2 = 125$ **b.** $-\frac{1}{2}x^2 = -36$

CONCEPTUAL UNDERSTANDING

EXAMPLE 3 Solve Equations of the Form $ax^2 + b = c$

How can you solve the quadratic equation $3x^2 - 5 = 22$?

Rewrite the equation in the form $x^2 = a$.

$$3x^2 - 5 = 22$$
$$3x^2 = 27$$
$$x^2 = 9 \quad \text{Write in the form } x^2 = a\text{, where } a \text{ is a real number.}$$
$$\sqrt{x^2} = \sqrt{9} \quad \text{Take the square root of each side of the equation.}$$
$$x = \pm 3$$

LOOK FOR RELATIONSHIPS
Compare the steps to solve a quadratic equation to those of solving a linear equation. How are the steps similar? How are they different? MP.7

You can use the properties of equality to write the equation $3x^2 - 5 = 22$ in the form $x^2 = a$. Since a is a perfect square there are two integer answers. The solutions of this quadratic equation are −3 and 3.

Try It! **3.** Solve the quadratic equations.

a. $-5x^2 - 19 = 144$ **b.** $3x^2 + 17 = 209$

LESSON 9-4 Solving Quadratic Equations Using Square Roots 377

EXAMPLE 3 Solve Equations of the Form $ax^2 + b = c$

Pose Purposeful Questions ETP

Q: Why do you want to rewrite the equation in the form $x^2 = a$?
[If you rewrite the equation in the form $x^2 = a$, you can solve the equation by taking the square root of each side of the equation.]

Try It! Answers

3. a. no real solution

   b. ± 8

RtI Struggling Students

USE WITH EXAMPLE 2 Some students may struggle with rewriting radicals in the simplest form when solving the quadratic equation.

Have students write each radical in the simplest form. Show students the following example.

$$\sqrt{54} = \sqrt{9 \cdot 6}$$
$$= \sqrt{9} \cdot \sqrt{6}$$
$$= 3\sqrt{6}$$

1. $\sqrt{72}$ $[6\sqrt{2}]$ **2.** $\sqrt{75}$ $[5\sqrt{3}]$ **3.** $\sqrt{90}$ $[3\sqrt{10}]$

ADV Advanced Students

USE WITH EXAMPLE 3 Have students solve quadratic equations that result in a fraction under the radical.

Solve.

1. $4x^2 - 7 = 93$ $[\pm 5]$
2. $16x^2 + 20 = 344$ $\left[\pm\frac{9}{2}\right]$
3. $4x^2 - 25 = 56$ $\left[\pm\frac{9}{2}\right]$
4. $25x^2 - 23 = 41$ $\left[\pm\frac{8}{5}\right]$

EXAMPLE 4 Determine a Reasonable Solution

Pose Purposeful Questions ETP

Q: What do you know about the height of the tower from looking at the diagram?
[You know that the height of the tower is less than 200 ft, because the triangle is a right triangle and the hypotenuse is the longest side of a right triangle.]

Q: Why is it helpful to factor the radicand when solving the problem?
[Rewriting the radicand in factored form makes it easier to identify any perfect square factors. This helps when simplifying the radical expression.]

Try It! Answer

4. 100 ft

Elicit and Use Evidence of Student Thinking ETP

Q: What method did you use to solve this problem?
[Use the side length of the larger triangle you found in Example 4. This is the hypotenuse of the new triangle. Use half of the length of the guy wire for one leg and x for the other. Solve using the Pythagorean Theorem.]

Use with **EXAMPLES 3 & 4**

HABITS OF MIND

Communicate Precisely When is the negative square root not a reasonable solution? Explain and give an example. **MP.6**

[Negative square roots are not a reasonable solution for any real-world scenario that cannot have a negative value. For example, the negative square root in Example 4 is not reasonable because height cannot be negative.]

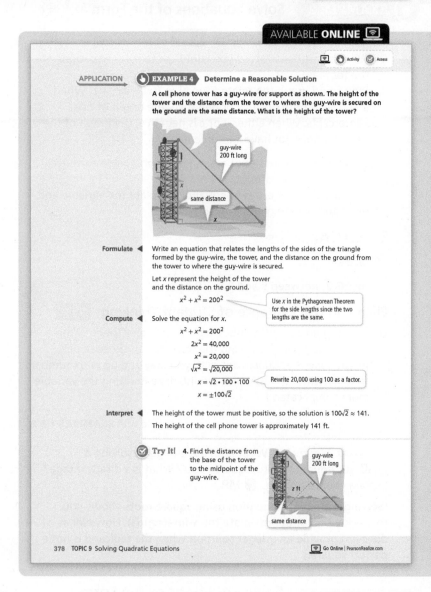

AVAILABLE **ONLINE**

Activity Assess

APPLICATION

EXAMPLE 4 Determine a Reasonable Solution

A cell phone tower has a guy-wire for support as shown. The height of the tower and the distance from the tower to where the guy-wire is secured on the ground are the same distance. What is the height of the tower?

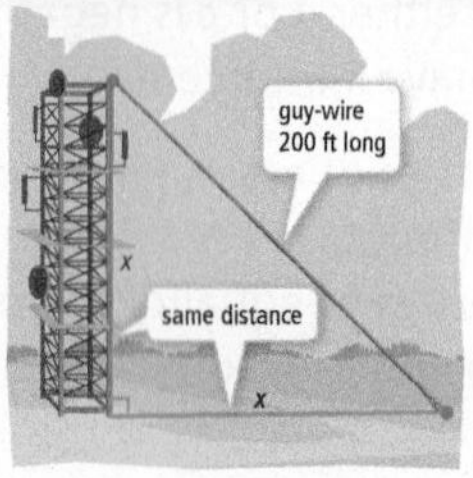
guy-wire
200 ft long
x
same distance
x

Formulate Write an equation that relates the lengths of the sides of the triangle formed by the guy-wire, the tower, and the distance on the ground from the tower to where the guy-wire is secured.

Let x represent the height of the tower and the distance on the ground.

$$x^2 + x^2 = 200^2$$

Use x in the Pythagorean Theorem for the side lengths since the two lengths are the same.

Compute Solve the equation for x.

$$x^2 + x^2 = 200^2$$
$$2x^2 = 40{,}000$$
$$x^2 = 20{,}000$$
$$\sqrt{x^2} = \sqrt{20{,}000}$$
$$x = \sqrt{2 \cdot 100 \cdot 100}$$
$$x = \pm 100\sqrt{2}$$

Rewrite 20,000 using 100 as a factor.

Interpret The height of the tower must be positive, so the solution is $100\sqrt{2} \approx 141$.

The height of the cell phone tower is approximately 141 ft.

Try It! 4. Find the distance from the base of the tower to the midpoint of the guy-wire.

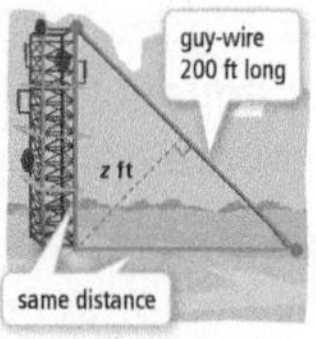
guy-wire
200 ft long
z ft
same distance

378 TOPIC 9 Solving Quadratic Equations Go Online | PearsonRealize.com

ELL English Language Learners *(Use with* **EXAMPLE 4***)*

WRITING BEGINNING Have the students look at the picture of the tower. The example states that the guy-wire is *secured* on the ground. Explain the meaning of *secured* as being safely attached.

Q: Write down three examples of things that are *secured* in your everyday life.
[me when I wear a seatbelt, the locks on my house, the dog's leash to its collar]

Q: Write down three words that are the opposite of *secure*.
[unstable, unfastened, loose]

SPEAKING INTERMEDIATE Display the words *tower, tow,* and *now* on the board. Discuss the pronunciation of the word *tower,* the difference between the sounds of *tower* and *tow,* and the similarity between the words *tower* and *now.* Then display the following pairs of words. With a partner, have students discuss the pronunciations of each pair and whether they sound the same or different.

Q: flower and flow
[different]

Q: mower and mow
[same]

Q: lower and low
[same]

Q: shower and show
[different]

READING ADVANCED Have students read the definition of *guy-wire* from the dictionary. Then have students research the following questions.

Q: What language is the term *guy* in *guy-wire* derived from?
[It comes from the old French word *guier,* meaning "to guide."]

Q: Find terms similar to term *guy-wire* where the word *wire* is replaced with a different word.
[guy-cable, guy-rope]

CONCEPT SUMMARY Solving Quadratics Using Square Roots

Q: How is solving an equation of the form $ax^2 + b = c$ similar to solving an equation of the form $x^2 = a$?
[Once you isolate the variable on one side of the equation, the new equation is of the form $x^2 = a$. Therefore, both can be solved by taking the square root of each side of the equation.]

Do You UNDERSTAND? | Do You KNOW HOW?

Common Error

Exercise 6 Students may only write the positive solution to this equation. Have students substitute both the positive and negative solutions into the original equation and simplify. Students will see that both solutions satisfy the equation.

Answers

1. If you have—or can simplify—a quadratic equation so that it is in the form $ax^2 = c$, where there is no linear term, then you can divide both sides by a and take the square root to solve.
2. no solutions; If you divide both sides by a, you will get x^2 on one side and a negative number on the other.
3. If there are two solutions, and no real-world context, use $\pm$. If there are fewer than two solutions, or if a solution such as a negative number does not make sense, do not use it.
4. No; there are 2 solutions, −7 and 7.
5. For both types of equations the last two steps are to divide by a and take the square root of the value. For equations in the form $ax^2 \pm b = c$, you first need to add or subtract b to/from c.
6. $x = \pm 20$
7. no solution
8. $x = \pm\frac{20\sqrt{3}}{3}$
9. $x = \pm\sqrt{6}$
10. $x = \pm 2\sqrt{3}$
11. $x = \pm\frac{3\sqrt{10}}{2}$
12. $x =$ no solution
13. $x = \pm\frac{7}{2}$
14. $x = \pm\sqrt{30}$
15. $x = \pm 3$
16. $x = 7$
17. $x = 5\sqrt{2}$

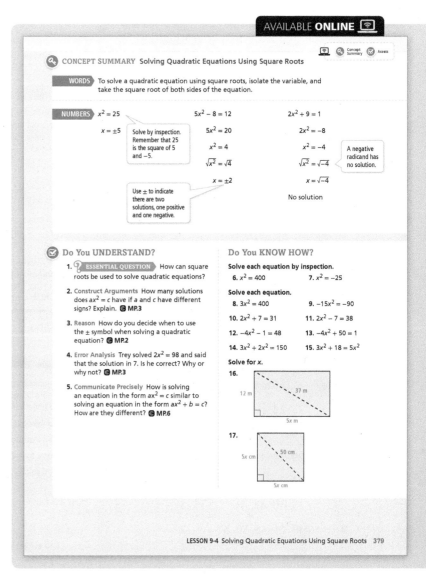

AVAILABLE **ONLINE**

Concept Summary Assess

CONCEPT SUMMARY Solving Quadratic Equations Using Square Roots

WORDS To solve a quadratic equation using square roots, isolate the variable, and take the square root of both sides of the equation.

NUMBERS

$x^2 = 25$
$x = \pm 5$

Solve by inspection. Remember that 25 is the square of 5 and −5.

$5x^2 - 8 = 12$
$5x^2 = 20$
$x^2 = 4$
$\sqrt{x^2} = \sqrt{4}$
$x = \pm 2$

Use $\pm$ to indicate there are two solutions, one positive and one negative.

$2x^2 + 9 = 1$
$2x^2 = -8$
$x^2 = -4$
$\sqrt{x^2} = \sqrt{-4}$
$x = \sqrt{-4}$
No solution

A negative radicand has no solution.

Do You UNDERSTAND?

1. ESSENTIAL QUESTION How can square roots be used to solve quadratic equations?
2. **Construct Arguments** How many solutions does $ax^2 = c$ have if a and c have different signs? Explain. MP.3
3. **Reason** How do you decide when to use the $\pm$ symbol when solving a quadratic equation? MP.2
4. **Error Analysis** Trey solved $2x^2 = 98$ and said that the solution in 7. Is he correct? Why or why not? MP.3
5. **Communicate Precisely** How is solving an equation in the form $ax^2 = c$ similar to solving an equation in the form $ax^2 + b = c$? How are they different? MP.6

Do You KNOW HOW?

Solve each equation by inspection.

6. $x^2 = 400$
7. $x^2 = -25$

Solve each equation.

8. $3x^2 = 400$
9. $-15x^2 = -90$
10. $2x^2 + 7 = 31$
11. $2x^2 - 7 = 38$
12. $-4x^2 - 1 = 48$
13. $-4x^2 + 50 = 1$
14. $3x^2 + 2x^2 = 150$
15. $3x^2 + 18 = 5x^2$

Solve for x.

16.
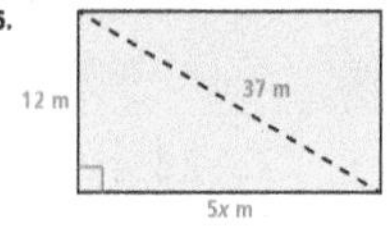

12 m
37 m
5x m

17.
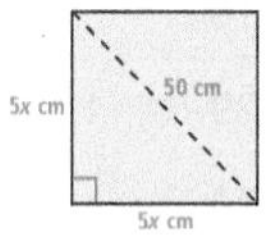

5x cm
50 cm
5x cm

LESSON 9-4 Solving Quadratic Equations Using Square Roots 379

PRACTICE & PROBLEM SOLVING

AVAILABLE ONLINE

Lesson Practice You may opt to have students complete the automatically scored Practice and Problem Solving items online powered by MathXL for School.

Choose from: **Lesson Practice**

Adaptive Practice

You may also take advantage of the bank of exercises for assigning additional practice.

Assignment Guide

Basic	Advanced
18–38, 41, 44–52	18–23, 26–28, 31–52

Item Analysis

Example	Items	DOK
1	23–28	1
	18	2
2	29–34, 41, 42	1
	20	2
3	35–40, 43, 44	1
	19, 21, 45, 50, 51	2
	22	3
4	46–49	2
	52	3

Answers

18. $(-3.74, 7), (3.74, 7); \frac{1}{2}x^2 = 7$

19. The equation has no solution; It tried to take the square root of a negative number.

20. **a.** when c divided by a is the square of a rational number

b. when c divided by a is nonnegative but not the square of a rational number

c. when c is 0

d. when c divided by a is negative

21. The student took the square root of 4 in the next to last step and did not include $\pm$.

$$-4x^2 + 19 = 3$$
$$-4x^2 + 19 - 19 = 3 - 19$$
$$-4x^2 = -16$$
$$x^2 = 4$$
$$x = \pm 2$$

See answers for 22, 43–45 on next page.

AVAILABLE ONLINE

PRACTICE & PROBLEM SOLVING

Scan for Multimedia

Practice Tutorial

Additional Exercises Available Online

UNDERSTAND

18. Make Sense and Persevere Where will the parabola intersect the line? What equation did you solve to find the intersection? MP.1

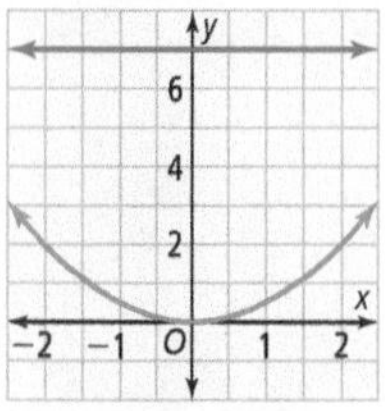

y
6
4
2
x
−2
−1
O
1
2

19. Use Appropriate Tools When solving an equation of the form $ax^2 + b = c$, what does the error message indicate? What situation may cause this error? MP.5

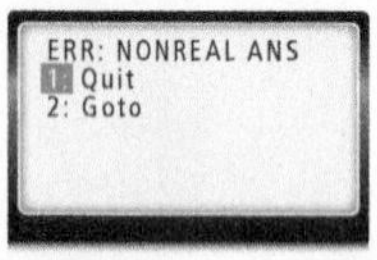

ERR: NONREAL ANS
1: Quit
2: Goto

20. Communicate Precisely When does solving a quadratic equation of the form $ax^2 = c$ yield the given result? MP.6

a. a rational solution

b. an irrational solution

c. one solution

d. no solutions

21. Error Analysis Describe and correct the errors a student made in solving $-4x^2 + 19 = 3$. MP.3

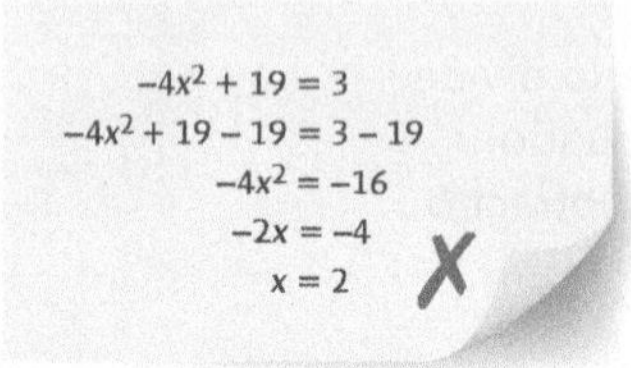

−4x² + 19 = 3
−4x² + 19 − 19 = 3 − 19
−4x² = −16
−2x = −4
x = 2

22. Higher Order Thinking

a. Solve $(x - 5)^2 - 100 = 0$. Show the steps for your solution.

b. Explain how you could solve an equation of the form $(x - d)^2 - c = 0$ for x.

PRACTICE

Solve each equation by inspection. SEE EXAMPLE 1

23. $x^2 = 256$ ± 16

24. $x^2 = 144$ ± 12

25. $x^2 = -20$ no solution

26. $x^2 = -27$ no solution

27. $x^2 = 91$ $\pm\sqrt{91} \approx \pm 9.54$

28. $x^2 = 0.25$ ± 0.5

Solve each equation. SEE EXAMPLE 2

29. $12x^2 = 300$ ± 5

30. $-x^2 = 0$ 0

31. $0.1x^2 = 100$ $\pm 10\sqrt{10}$

32. $227x^2 = 1{,}816$ $\pm 2\sqrt{2}$

33. $-36x^2 = -36$ ± 1

34. $-16x^2 = 200$ no solution

Solve each equation. SEE EXAMPLE 3

35. $x^2 + 65 = 90$ ± 5

36. $x^2 - 65 = 90$ $\pm\sqrt{155}$

37. $3x^2 + 8 = 56$ ± 4

38. $3x^2 - 8 = 56$ $\pm\frac{8\sqrt{3}}{3}$

39. $\frac{4x^2 + 10}{2} = 5$ 0

40. $\frac{8x^2 - 40}{4} = 470$ $\pm 4\sqrt{15}$

Solve each equation. Approximate irrational solutions to the nearest hundredth. SEE EXAMPLE 4

41. $6x^2 + 2x^2 = 80$ $\pm\sqrt{10} \approx \pm 3.16$

42. $6x^2 + (2x)^2 = 80$ $\pm 2\sqrt{2} \approx \pm 2.83$

Solve for x. Then find the side lengths of each triangle to the nearest tenth. SEE EXAMPLE 4

43.

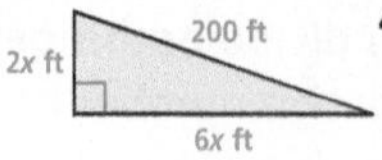

200 ft
2x ft
6x ft

44.

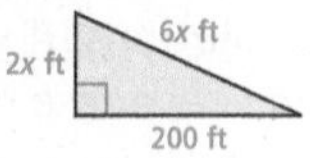

6x ft
2x ft
200 ft

45. Use two methods to solve $x^2 - 900 = 0$. Explain.

46. At a certain time of day, the sun shines on a large flagpole causing a shadow that is twice as long as the flagpole is tall. What is the height of the flagpole to the nearest tenth of a foot? 93.9 ft

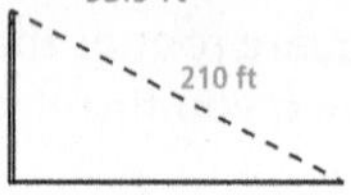

210 ft

Answers

22. a.

$$(x-5)^2-100=0$$
$$(x-5)^2=100$$
$$(x-5)=\pm 10$$
So $(x-5)=10$ or $(x-5)=-10$
$$x-5=10 \text{ or } x-5=-10$$
$$x=15 \text{ or } x=-5$$

b. Get the variable expression $(x-d)^2$ by itself by adding c to both sides, then take the square root of both sides, simplify each resulting expression, and use the Zero Product Property to solve.

43. $10\sqrt{10}$ ft; $6x = 189.74$ ft; $2x = 63.25$ ft

44. $25\sqrt{2}$ ft; $6x = 212.13$ ft; $2x = 70.71$ ft

45. Solve algebraically using square roots:

$$x^2-900=0$$
$$x^2=900$$
$$\sqrt{x^2}=\pm\sqrt{900}$$
$$x=\pm 30$$

Solve using the table function on a graphing calculator:

Enter $y = x^2 - 900$ into a graphing calculator.

Use the table function to find the values for which $y = 0$.

$x = \pm 30$

47. Part a. $-16t^2 + 67 - 3 = 0$

Part b. 2 s; $-16t^2 + 67 - 3 = 0$, so $-16t^2 = -64$; $t^2 = 4$, $t = 2$

48. 5 mi

49. 48 ft

52. Part A 120 mi; 216 mi

Part B $x^2 + 120^2 = 216^2$; $x \approx 180$ mi

Part C 1.5 h

AVAILABLE ONLINE

PRACTICE & PROBLEM SOLVING

Practice Tutorial
Mixed Review Available Online

APPLY

47. A test weight is dropped from the top of a fire department training tower onto a net three feet off of the ground. Use $-16t^2$ for the change in height per second. MP.4

67 ft

a. Write an equation to determine the time it takes for the test weight to drop on to the net.

b. How long does it take before the test weight is caught by the net? Explain.

48. Make Sense and Persevere Calculate the distance in miles between the two points shown on the map. MP.1

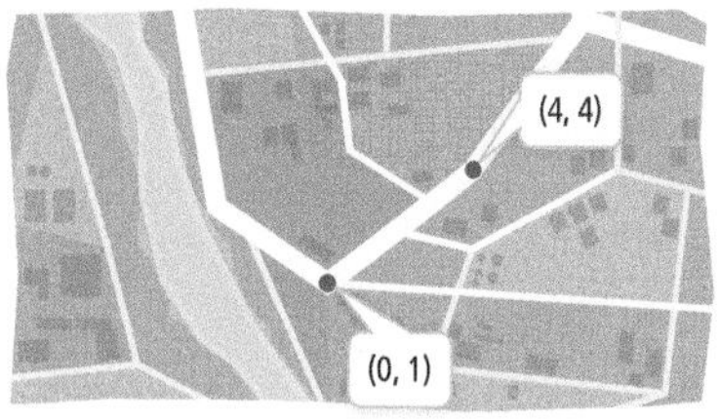
(4, 4)
(0, 1)

49. Make Sense and Persevere The evacuation slide from an aircraft is shown. If the slide is 73 feet long, what is its height at the top in feet? MP.1

x ft
55 ft

ASSESSMENT PRACTICE

50. Fill in the solutions of $2{,}900 - 5x^2 = 840$.

$+\underline{2\sqrt{103}}$ and $-\underline{2\sqrt{103}}$

51. SAT/ACT A park has an area of 280 m². A rectangular region with a length three times its width will be added to give the park a total area of 435 m². Which equation can be solved to find the width of the region?

Ⓐ $x + 3x + 280 = 435$
Ⓑ $(x \cdot 3x) + 280 = 435$
Ⓒ $(x^2 + 3x) + 280 = 435$
Ⓓ $x^2 + (3x)^2 + 280 = 435$

52. Performance Task A CEO flies to three different company locations. The flight times for two of her legs are shown.

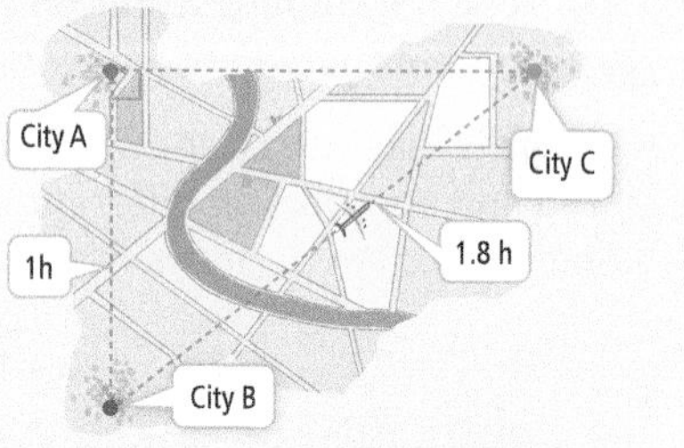
City A
City C
1h
1.8 h
City B

Part A The plane travels at an average speed of 120 mph. Find the distance between City A and City B and the distance between City B and City C.

Part B Write and solve a quadratic equation that can be used to find the distance between City A and City C.

Part C How long will the flight between City C and City A last?

Assess Tutorials Worksheets

LESSON QUIZ

Use the Lesson Quiz to assess students' understanding of the mathematics in the lesson.

Students can take the Lesson Quiz online or you can download a printable copy from **SavvasRealize.com**. The Lesson Quiz is also available in the *Assessment Resources* book.

Item Analysis

Item	DOK	Standards
1	1	HSA.REI.B.4.B, HSA.SSE.A.2
2	2	HSA.REI.B.4.B
3	1	HSA.REI.B.4.B, HSA.SSE.A.2
4	1	HSA.SSE.A.2
5	2	HSA.CED.A.1

RtI Use the student scores on the Lesson Quiz to prescribe differentiated assignments.

If students take the Lesson Quiz online, it will be automatically scored and appropriate differentiated practice will be assigned based on student performance.

I Intervention	0–3 points	• Reteach to Build Understanding • Mathematical Literacy and Vocabulary • Additional Practice
O On-Level	4 points	• Mathematical Literacy and Vocabulary • Additional Practice • Enrichment
A Advanced	5 points	• Enrichment

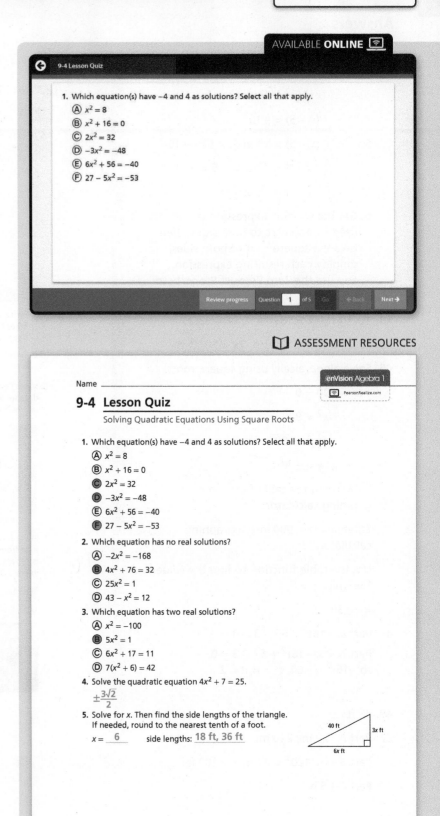

AVAILABLE **ONLINE**

9-4 Lesson Quiz

1. Which equation(s) have −4 and 4 as solutions? Select all that apply.
   - Ⓐ $x^2 = 8$
   - Ⓑ $x^2 + 16 = 0$
   - Ⓒ $2x^2 = 32$
   - Ⓓ $-3x^2 = -48$
   - Ⓔ $6x^2 + 56 = -40$
   - Ⓕ $27 - 5x^2 = -53$

Review progress Question 1 of 5 Go ← Back Next →

ASSESSMENT RESOURCES

Name ____________

enVision Algebra 1

PearsonRealize.com

9-4 Lesson Quiz

Solving Quadratic Equations Using Square Roots

1. Which equation(s) have −4 and 4 as solutions? Select all that apply.
   - Ⓐ $x^2 = 8$
   - Ⓑ $x^2 + 16 = 0$
   - Ⓒ $2x^2 = 32$
   - Ⓓ $-3x^2 = -48$
   - Ⓔ $6x^2 + 56 = -40$
   - Ⓕ $27 - 5x^2 = -53$
2. Which equation has no real solutions?
   - Ⓐ $-2x^2 = -168$
   - Ⓑ $4x^2 + 76 = 32$
   - Ⓒ $25x^2 = 1$
   - Ⓓ $43 - x^2 = 12$
3. Which equation has two real solutions?
   - Ⓐ $x^2 = -100$
   - Ⓑ $5x^2 = 1$
   - Ⓒ $6x^2 + 17 = 11$
   - Ⓓ $7(x^2 + 6) = 42$
4. Solve the quadratic equation $4x^2 + 7 = 25$.
   $\pm\frac{3\sqrt{2}}{2}$
5. Solve for x. Then find the side lengths of the triangle. If needed, round to the nearest tenth of a foot.
   $x =$ 6   side lengths: 18 ft, 36 ft

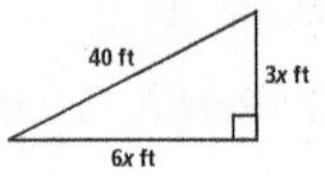
40 ft
3x ft
6x ft

enVision™ **Algebra 1** • Assessment Resources

SavvasRealize.com

Assess | Tutorials | Worksheets

DIFFERENTIATED RESOURCES

I = Intervention O = On-Level A = Advanced

⚙ = This activity is available as a digital assignment powered by MathXL® for School.

AVAILABLE ONLINE

Reteach to Build Understanding I ⚙

Provides scaffolded reteaching for the key lesson concepts.

Name ______ enVision Algebra 1 PearsonRealize.com

9-4 Reteach to Build Understanding

Solving Quadratic Equations Using Square Roots

1. Match each equation with its solution(s).

$x^2 = 9$ — $x = \pm 3$
$7x^2 - 6 = 15$ — $x = \pm\sqrt{3}$
$4x^2 + 19 = 7$ — no solution
$3x^2 + 4 = 4$ — $x = 0$

2. A student made an error when solving the quadratic equation. Find and correct the error the student made.

$-5x^2 + 11 = -14$
$-5x^2 + 11 - 11 = -14 - 11$
$-5x^2 = -25$
$x^2 = 5$
$x = \sqrt{5}$ The student forgot to include the negative square root. The correct answer is $x = \pm\sqrt{5}$.

3. Find the solution of the quadratic equation $9x^2 - 4 = 23$ using square roots. Approximate if necessary.

Write in the form $x^2 = a$, where a is a real number. $9x^2 - 4 + 4 = 23 + 4$
$9x^2 = 27$
$x^2 = 3$
Take the square root of each side. $\sqrt{x^2} = \sqrt{3}$
$x = \pm\sqrt{3}$

The approximate solutions of the quadratic equation $9x^2 - 4 = 23$ would be between ± 1 and ± 2, since $\pm\sqrt{3}$ is between $\pm\sqrt{1}$ and $\pm\sqrt{4}$.

enVision™ Algebra 1 • Teaching Resources

Additional Practice I O ⚙

Provides extra practice for each lesson.

Name ______ enVision Algebra 1 PearsonRealize.com

9-4 Additional Practice

Solving Quadratic Equations Using Square Roots

Solve each equation by inspection.

1. $x^2 = 64$ $-8, 8$
2. $x^2 = -169$ no solution
3. $x^2 = 108$ $-6\sqrt{3}, 6\sqrt{3}$
4. $x^2 = 200$ $-10\sqrt{2}, 10\sqrt{2}$

Solve each equation.

5. $4x^2 = 81$ $-\frac{9}{2}, \frac{9}{2}$
6. $-3x^2 = -54$ $-3\sqrt{2}, 3\sqrt{2}$
7. $-7x^2 = 49$ no solution
8. $\frac{1}{5}x^2 = 80$ $-20, 20$
9. $2x^2 - 3 = 11$ $-\sqrt{7}, \sqrt{7}$
10. $-3x^2 + 4 = -104$ $-6, 6$
11. $\frac{1}{2}x^2 - 3 = 37$ $-4\sqrt{5}, 4\sqrt{5}$
12. $3x^2 + 5 = -145$ no solution
13. How can you solve $ax^2 = c$ and $ax^2 + b = c$? Assume $a \neq c$. What is the solution to each equation?
Sample answer: In both equations, you use properties of equality to solve for x. After you solve for the variable expression, you have the additional step of applying square roots on both sides. In the second equation, $x = \pm\sqrt{\frac{c-b}{a}}$, while in the first equation $x = \pm\sqrt{\frac{c}{a}}$.
14. The formula for the volume of a cylinder is $V = \pi r^2 h$. What is the radius for a cylinder that has a volume of 160π m^3 and a height of 8 m? Express your answer in simplest radical form and as a decimal rounded to the nearest tenth.
$2\sqrt{5}$ m, 4.5 m

enVision™ Algebra 1 • Teaching Resources

Enrichment O A ⚙

Presents engaging problems and activities that extend the lesson concepts.

Name ______ enVision Algebra 1 PearsonRealize.com

9-4 Enrichment

Solving Quadratic Equations Using Square Roots

Solve the equations. Indicate if there is no solution.

1. $2x^2 - 12 = 20$ ± 4
2. $4x^2 + 5 = 30$ $\pm\frac{5}{2}$
3. $3x^2 + 10 = 49$ $\pm\sqrt{13}$
4. $3x^2 + 10 = 7$ no solution
5. $-3x^2 = -108$ ± 6
6. $x^2 + 20 = 21$ ± 1
7. $9x^2 - 5 = 44$ $\pm\frac{7}{3}$
8. $2x^2 - 141 = 59$ ± 10
9. $11x^2 = 11^2$ $\pm\sqrt{11}$
10. $5x^2 - 15 = 70$ $\pm\sqrt{17}$
11. $-3x^2 - 139 = 104$ no solution
12. $9x^2 + 11 = 12$ $\pm\frac{1}{3}$
13. $-x^2 - 1 = -1$ 0
14. $4x^2 + 24 = -40$ no solution
15. $16x^2 + 1 = 122$ $\pm\frac{11}{4}$
16. $4 = 16x^2 - 5$ $\pm\frac{3}{4}$
17. $-3x^2 - 5 = 0$ no solution
18. $13x^2 - 16 = 10$ $\pm\sqrt{2}$

Sort the equations from Exercises 1–18 by answering the following questions.

- Which equations have no real number solution?
- Which equations have one or two distinct integer solutions?
- Which equations have rational solutions that are *not* integers?
- Which equations have solutions that are *not* rational?

Complete the diagram by writing each item number in the appropriate space. Use each item number one time.

Rational Solutions: 2, 7, 12, 15, 16
Integer Solutions: 1, 5, 6, 8, 13
Irrational Solutions: 3, 9, 10, 18
No Real Solutions: 4, 11, 14, 17

enVision™ Algebra 1 • Teaching Resources

Mathematical Literacy and Vocabulary I O

Helps students develop and reinforce understanding of key terms and concepts.

Name ______ enVision Algebra 1 PearsonRealize.com

9-4 Mathematical Literacy and Vocabulary

Solving Quadratic Equations Using Square Roots

Theodore is trying to solve $5x^2 + 2 = 17$. He wrote the steps and the explanations on note cards, but they got mixed up. Help Theodore write the steps in the correct order.

$5x^2 + 2 - 2 = 17 - 2$
$\sqrt{x^2} = \sqrt{3}$
Solve for x.
Divide both sides by 5.
Subtract 2 from each side of the equation.
$x = \pm\sqrt{3}$
Isolate the variable by taking the square root of each side of the equation.
$\frac{5x^2}{5} = \frac{15}{5}$

Write the steps from the note cards in the correct order.

Steps	Explanation
1. $5x^2 + 2 - 2 = 17 - 2$	Subtract 2 from each side of the equation.
2. $\frac{5x^2}{5} = \frac{15}{5}$	Divide both sides by 5.
3. $\sqrt{x^2} = \sqrt{3}$	Isolate the variable by taking the square root of each side of the equation.
4. $x = \pm\sqrt{3}$	Solve for x.

enVision™ Algebra 1 • Teaching Resources

Digital Resources and Video Tutorials I O A ⚙

The **Reteach to Build Understanding, Additional Practice**, and **Enrichment** activities are available as digital assignments powered by MathXL for School. These activities are automatically assigned when students complete the lesson quiz online and are automatically scored.

Students can access instructional tutorials using the **Virtual Nerd app**.

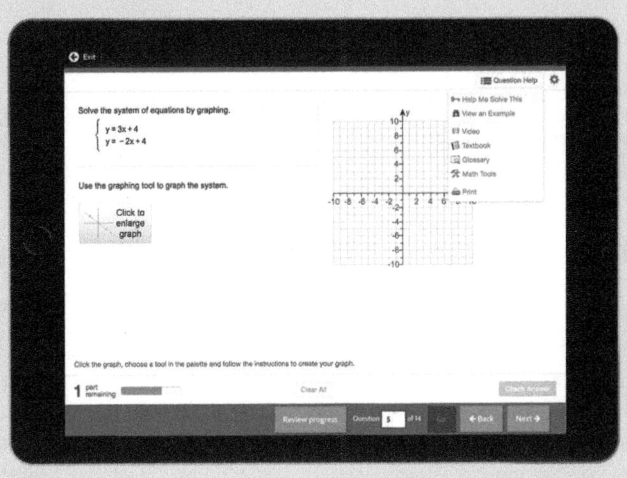

Solve the system of equations by graphing.
Use the graphing tool to graph the system.
Click to enlarge graph
Question Help
Review progress

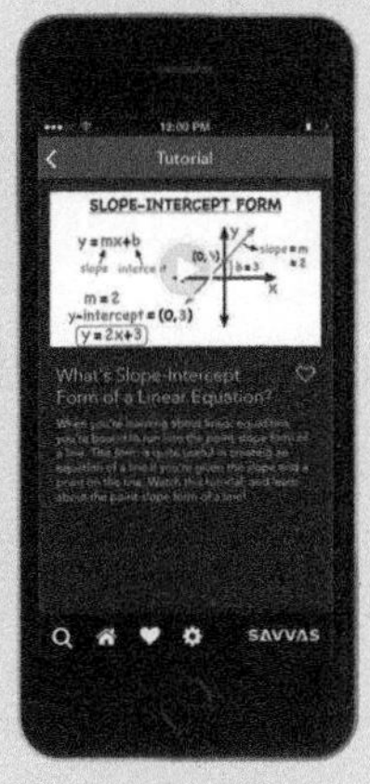

Tutorial
SLOPE-INTERCEPT FORM
SAVVAS

Students can also access Virtual Nerd videos using the **BouncePages app** to scan exercise pages marked with this icon. Students can download both apps for free in their mobile devices' app store.

Lesson Overview

FOCUS

Objective

Students will be able to:

✔ Solve a quadratic trinomial by completing the square to transform a quadratic equation into a perfect square trinomial.

✔ Use completing the square to write a quadratic equation in vertex form.

Essential Understanding

To complete the square, add the square of half of the coefficient of x to each side of the equation. Completing the square is useful when solving quadratic equations that are not factorable.

COHERENCE

Previously in this topic, students:

- Solved quadratic equations by graphing, using tables and graphing technology, factoring, and taking square roots.
- Found the binomial factors of perfect square trinomials.

In this lesson, students:

- Solve quadratic equations by completing the square to create perfect square trinomials and then finding the binomial factors.

Later in this topic students will:

- Solve quadratic equations using the quadratic formula.

RIGOR

This lesson emphasizes a blend of *conceptual understanding* and *application.*

- Students understand that a perfect square trinomial will create a square when represented with algebra tiles.
- Students complete the square for a quadratic equation in standard form, $ax^2 + bx + c = 0$, by subtracting c from both sides of the equation and then adding $\left(\frac{b}{2}\right)^2$ to both sides of the equation.

Vocabulary Builder

A-Z

REVIEW VOCABULARY

English | *Spanish*

- **binomial factor** | *factor binomio*
- **perfect square trinomial** | *trinomio cuadrado perfecto*
- **vertex form** | *forma vértice*

NEW VOCABULARY

- **completing the square** | *completer el caudrado*

VOCABULARY ACTIVITY

Review the term *perfect square trinomial.* Explain that *completing the square* is a method used to create a perfect square trinomial when a quadratic equation is not factorable. Each expression on the left has two terms. Have students match it to the third term on the right, so that the three terms create a *perfect square trinomial.*

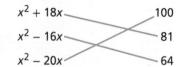

$x^2 + 18x$	100	$[x^2 + 18x + 81 = (x + 9)^2]$
$x^2 - 16x$	81	$[x^2 - 16x + 64 = (x - 8)^2]$
$x^2 - 20x$	64	$[x^2 - 20x + 100 = (x - 10)^2]$

Student Companion

Students can do their in-class work for the lesson on pages 205–208 of their *Student Companion* or in Savvas Realize.

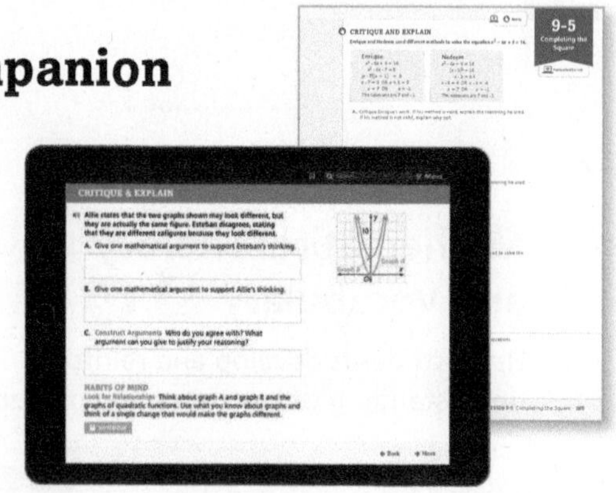

Mathematics Overview

COMMON CORE STANDARDS

Content Standards

In this lesson, students focus on these standards:

HSA.REI.B.4.A Use the method of completing the square to transform any quadratic equation in x into an equation of the form $(x - p)^2 = q$ that has the same solutions. Derive the quadratic formula from this form.

HSA.SSE.B.3.B Complete the square in a quadratic expression to reveal the maximum or minimum value of the function it defines.

They also work with concepts related to this standard:
HSF.IF.C.8.A

Mathematical Practice Standards

These standards are highlighted in this lesson:

MP.2 Reason Abstractly and Quantitatively

Students understand the meaning of quantities when they consider the possible values for c in the standard form of a quadratic equation. They think about whether c can have a negative value in a perfect square trinomial.

MP.7 Look For and Make Use of Structure

Students determine how changing the value of the coefficient of x in a quadratic equation would affect the arrangement of algebra tiles that represents the equation.

CRITIQUE & EXPLAIN

INSTRUCTIONAL FOCUS Students analyze two methods of solving a quadratic equation. This introduces them to completing the square, and provides an opportunity for them to validate the method as a way of solving quadratic equations.

STUDENT COMPANION Students can complete the *Critique & Explain* activity on page 205 of their *Student Companion.*

Before WHOLE CLASS

Implement Tasks that Promote Reasoning and Problem Solving ETP

Q: What do you notice about the initial equation when comparing each side?
[Both sides of the equation are perfect squares.]

During SMALL GROUP

Support Productive Struggle in Learning Mathematics ETP

Q: What method of solving the quadratic equation is Enrique using?
[Enrique solved the quadratic by factoring.]

Q: What method of solving the quadratic equation is Nadeem using?
[Nadeem solved the quadratic by extracting roots.]

For Early Finishers

Q: What determines when you can use Nadeem's method for solving a quadratic equation? List 4 trinomials and their factored binomial squares that would allow you to use this method.
[If the trinomial on one side of the equation is a binomial squared, then you can take the square root of each side of the equation. Check students' work.]

After WHOLE CLASS

Facilitate Meaningful Mathematical Discourse ETP

Q: What can you do if a quadratic equation cannot be solved by factoring, but contains a perfect square trinomial?
[You can solve the quadratic equation by taking the square roots of each side of the equation.]

Q: When solving any type of equation, what allows you to manipulate the expression on each side to find a solution?
[The properties of equality allow you to carry out any operation on each side of an equation and maintain equality.]

HABITS OF MIND *Use with* **CRITIQUE & EXPLAIN**

Reason Explain how the properties of equality are used to solve equations. MP.2

[The properties of equality allow addition, subtraction, and multiplication/division of values without changing the equality between expressions.]

AVAILABLE **ONLINE**

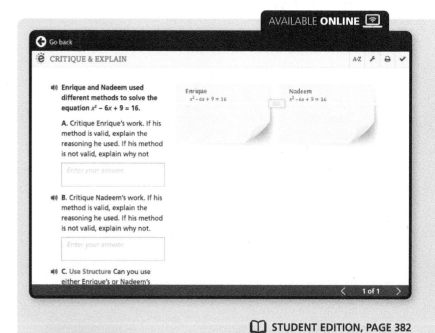

Go back

CRITIQUE & EXPLAIN

Enrique and Nadeem used different methods to solve the equation $x^2 - 6x + 9 = 16$.

Enrique $x^2 - 6x + 9 = 16$

Nadeem $x^2 - 6x + 9 = 16$

A. Critique Enrique's work. If his method is valid, explain the reasoning he used. If his method is not valid, explain why not

Enter your answer.

B. Critique Nadeem's work. If his method is valid, explain the reasoning he used. If his method is not valid, explain why not.

Enter your answer.

C. Use Structure Can you use either Enrique's or Nadeem's

1 of 1

STUDENT EDITION, PAGE 382

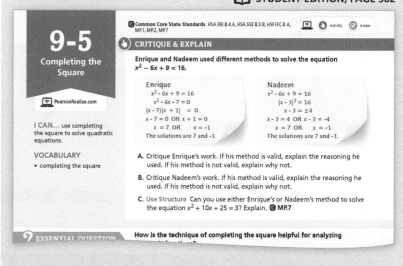

9-5 Completing the Square

PearsonRealize.com

I CAN… use completing the square to solve quadratic equations.

VOCABULARY
- completing the square

Common Core State Standards HSA.REI.B.4.A, HSA.SSE.B.3.B, HSF.IF.C.8.A, MP.1, MP.2, MP.7

Activity Assess

CRITIQUE & EXPLAIN

Enrique and Nadeem used different methods to solve the equation $x^2 - 6x + 9 = 16$.

Enrique
$x^2 - 6x + 9 = 16$
$x^2 - 6x - 7 = 0$
$(x - 7)(x + 1) = 0$
$x - 7 = 0$ OR $x + 1 = 0$
$x = 7$ OR $x = -1$
The solutions are 7 and -1.

Nadeem
$x^2 - 6x + 9 = 16$
$(x - 3)^2 = 16$
$x - 3 = \pm 4$
$x - 3 = 4$ OR $x - 3 = -4$
$x = 7$ OR $x = -1$
The solutions are 7 and -1.

A. Critique Enrique's work. If his method is valid, explain the reasoning he used. If his method is not valid, explain why not.

B. Critique Nadeem's work. If his method is valid, explain the reasoning he used. If his method is not valid, explain why not.

C. Use Structure Can you use either Enrique's or Nadeem's method to solve the equation $x^2 + 10x + 25 = 3$? Explain. MP.7

ESSENTIAL QUESTION How is the technique of completing the square helpful for analyzing

SAMPLE STUDENT WORK

A. Enrique's work is correct, and his method is valid. Enrique subtracted 16 from both sides so that one side would be equal to 0. Then he factored to find the solutions.

B. Nadeem's work is correct, and his method is valid. Nadeem used the fact that the trinomial is a perfect square trinomial to rewrite it as a square. Then he took the square root of both sides to find the solutions.

C. No, only Nadeem's method works. If you subtract 3 from both sides, then the trinomial on the left becomes unfactorable.

INTRODUCE THE ESSENTIAL QUESTION

Establish Mathematics Goals to Focus Learning ETP

Students learn that some quadratic equations cannot be factored and other means of solving them are needed. They use the properties of equality to perform operations on each side of an equation that help them find a solution. Students learn the technique of completing the square by utilizing the properties of equality to create a perfect square trinomial, in order to extract the roots and solve the quadratic equation.

AVAILABLE ONLINE

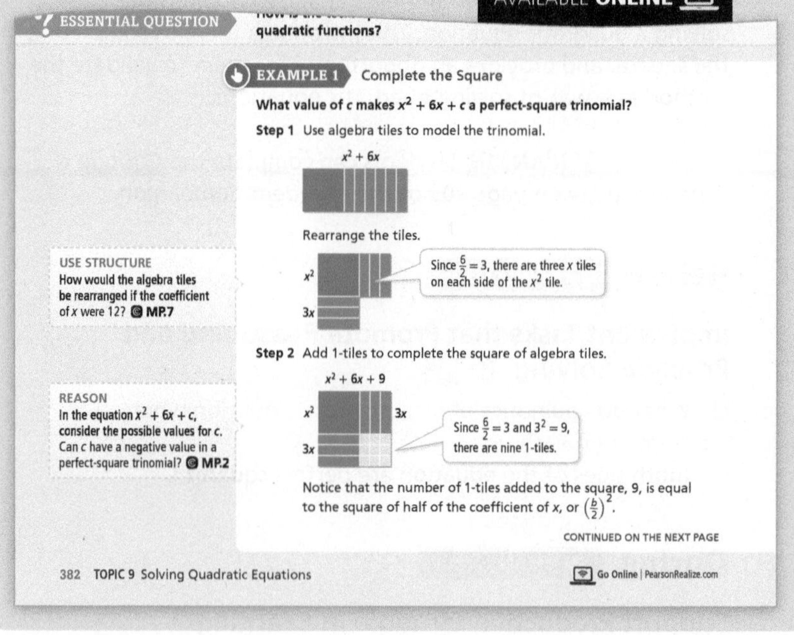
ESSENTIAL QUESTION quadratic functions?

EXAMPLE 1 Complete the Square

What value of c makes $x^2 + 6x + c$ a perfect-square trinomial?

Step 1 Use algebra tiles to model the trinomial.

$x^2 + 6x$

Rearrange the tiles.

x^2
$3x$
Since $\frac{6}{2} = 3$, there are three x tiles on each side of the x^2 tile.

USE STRUCTURE
How would the algebra tiles be rearranged if the coefficient of x were 12? MP.7

Step 2 Add 1-tiles to complete the square of algebra tiles.

$x^2 + 6x + 9$
x^2
$3x$
$3x$
Since $\frac{6}{2} = 3$ and $3^2 = 9$, there are nine 1-tiles.

REASON
In the equation $x^2 + 6x + c$, consider the possible values for c. Can c have a negative value in a perfect-square trinomial? MP.2

Notice that the number of 1-tiles added to the square, 9, is equal to the square of half of the coefficient of x, or $\left(\frac{b}{2}\right)^2$.

CONTINUED ON THE NEXT PAGE

382 TOPIC 9 Solving Quadratic Equations Go Online | PearsonRealize.com

EXAMPLE 1 Complete the Square

Pose Purposeful Questions ETP

Q: How do you use the algebra tiles to determine what is needed to create a perfect square trinomial?
[The algebra tiles need to be rearranged to form a square. Then you can determine how many units are needed to complete the square.]

Q: What do you know about the missing part of the algebra tile model?
[The missing part is a square and needs to be filled in with individual units.]

Use and Connect Mathematical Representations ETP

Q: Why do you always take half of b when completing the square?
[When using algebra tiles, x^2 is a square; therefore, you must add exactly the same amount of x-tiles to the height and base in order to keep the shape of a square.]

ADDITIONAL EXAMPLES

AVAILABLE ONLINE

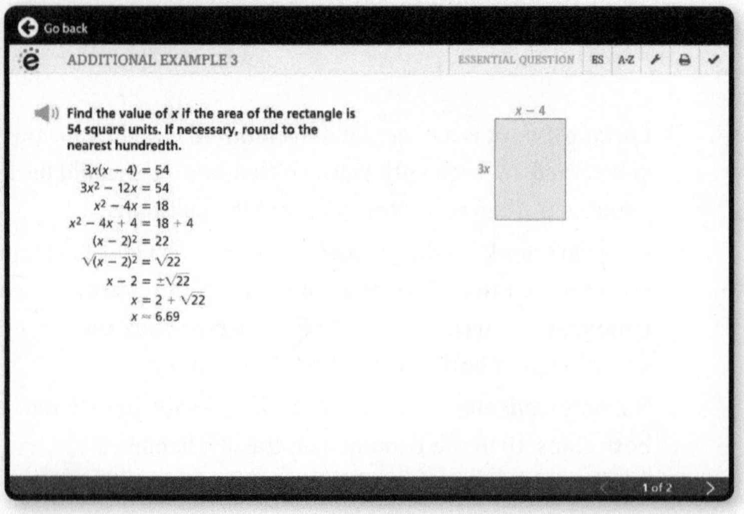
Go back

ADDITIONAL EXAMPLE 3 ESSENTIAL QUESTION ES A-Z

Find the value of x if the area of the rectangle is 54 square units. If necessary, round to the nearest hundredth.

$3x(x - 4) = 54$
$3x^2 - 12x = 54$
$x^2 - 4x = 18$
$x^2 - 4x + 4 = 18 + 4$
$(x - 2)^2 = 22$
$\sqrt{(x - 2)^2} = \sqrt{22}$
$x - 2 = \pm\sqrt{22}$
$x = 2 + \sqrt{22}$
$x \approx 6.69$

$x - 4$
$3x$

1 of 2

Example 3 Students practice setting up a quadratic equation and solving the equation by completing the square.

Q: With the application of area, what must be done before starting to complete the square?
[You have to multiply the expressions that represent the length and width to get a trinomial in standard form.]

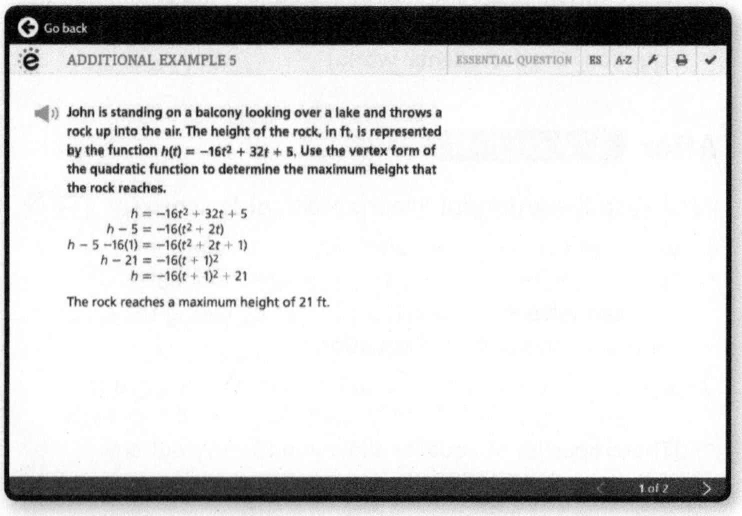
Go back

ADDITIONAL EXAMPLE 5 ESSENTIAL QUESTION ES A-Z

John is standing on a balcony looking over a lake and throws a rock up into the air. The height of the rock, in ft, is represented by the function $h(t) = -16t^2 + 32t + 5$. Use the vertex form of the quadratic function to determine the maximum height that the rock reaches.

$h = -16t^2 + 32t + 5$
$h - 5 = -16(t^2 + 2t)$
$h - 5 - 16(1) = -16(t^2 + 2t + 1)$
$h - 21 = -16(t + 1)^2$
$h = -16(t + 1)^2 + 21$

The rock reaches a maximum height of 21 ft.

1 of 2

Example 5 Students practice completing the square to write in vertex form with a real-world application.

Q: When $a \neq 1$, what must be done in order to start the completing the square process?
[The coefficient of x^2 must be factored out to leave you with a $(x^2 + bx)$.]

Try It! Answers

1. a. 36 b. 16

Elicit and Use Evidence of Student Thinking ETP

Q: How can you check to be sure that you have found the correct value of c?
[You can factor the trinomial to make sure it is a form of $(a + b)^2$.]

AVAILABLE **ONLINE**

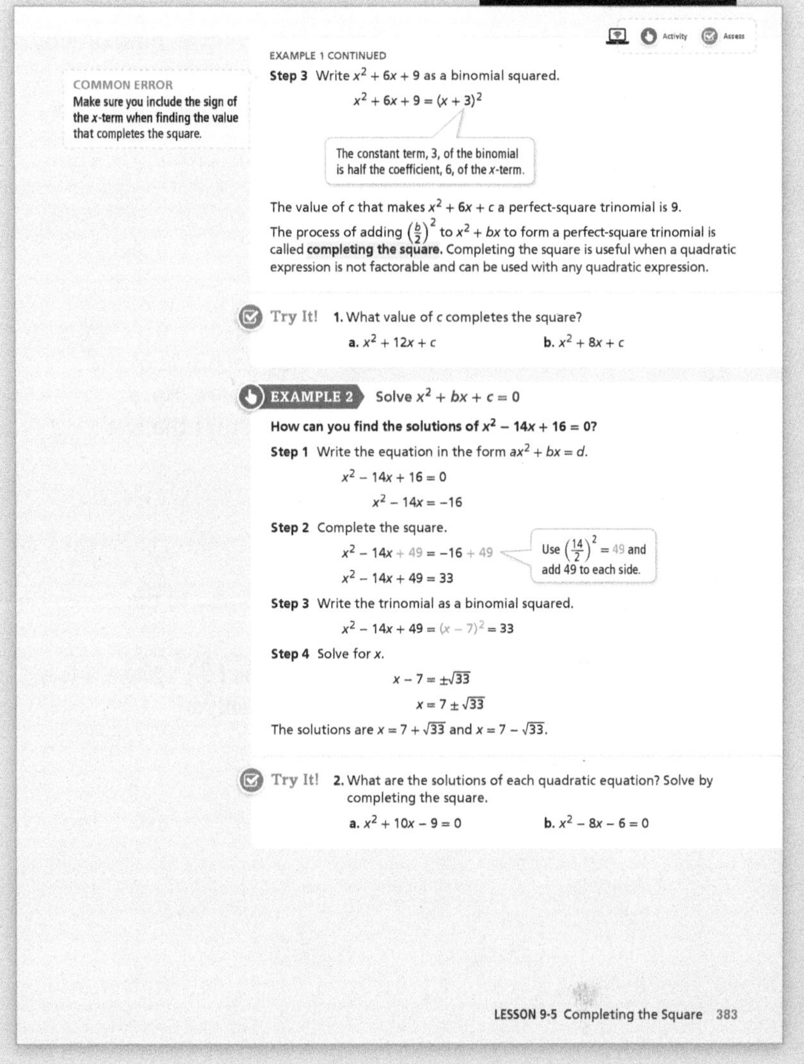

EXAMPLE 1 CONTINUED

COMMON ERROR
Make sure you include the sign of the x-term when finding the value that completes the square.

Step 3 Write $x^2 + 6x + 9$ as a binomial squared.

$x^2 + 6x + 9 = (x + 3)^2$

The constant term, 3, of the binomial is half the coefficient, 6, of the x-term.

The value of c that makes $x^2 + 6x + c$ a perfect-square trinomial is 9.

The process of adding $\left(\frac{b}{2}\right)^2$ to $x^2 + bx$ to form a perfect-square trinomial is called **completing the square.** Completing the square is useful when a quadratic expression is not factorable and can be used with any quadratic expression.

Try It! **1.** What value of c completes the square?
a. $x^2 + 12x + c$ **b.** $x^2 + 8x + c$

EXAMPLE 2 Solve $x^2 + bx + c = 0$

How can you find the solutions of $x^2 - 14x + 16 = 0$?

Step 1 Write the equation in the form $ax^2 + bx = d$.

$x^2 - 14x + 16 = 0$
$x^2 - 14x = -16$

Step 2 Complete the square.

$x^2 - 14x + 49 = -16 + 49$
$x^2 - 14x + 49 = 33$

Use $\left(\frac{14}{2}\right)^2 = 49$ and add 49 to each side.

Step 3 Write the trinomial as a binomial squared.

$x^2 - 14x + 49 = (x - 7)^2 = 33$

Step 4 Solve for x.

$x - 7 = \pm\sqrt{33}$
$x = 7 \pm \sqrt{33}$

The solutions are $x = 7 + \sqrt{33}$ and $x = 7 - \sqrt{33}$.

Try It! **2.** What are the solutions of each quadratic equation? Solve by completing the square.
a. $x^2 + 10x - 9 = 0$ **b.** $x^2 - 8x - 6 = 0$

LESSON 9-5 Completing the Square 383

EXAMPLE 2 Solve $x^2 + bx + c = 0$

Pose Purposeful Questions ETP

Q: After finding $\left(\frac{b}{2}\right)^2$, why do you add it on each side of the equation?
[When working with equations, you must always follow the properties of equality; what you do to one side must be done to the other.]

Q: When the original constant is moved to form $ax^2 + bx = d$, why does it become d?
[The standard form of a trinomial is $ax^2 + bx + c$. When it is moved, it is no longer considered a part of the trinomial; therefore, you can complete the square by creating a new c.]

Try It! Answers

2. a. $-5 + \sqrt{34}$ and $-5 - \sqrt{34}$
b. $4 + \sqrt{22}$ and $4 - \sqrt{22}$

ADV Advanced Students

USE WITH EXAMPLE 2 Students that grasp the process of completing the square can investigate examples that require more steps and have rational numbers in the form of decimals and fractions.

- Use the completing the square process to investigate how it works with different types of values.

1. $x^2 + 17.5x + 4 = 0$
[$x = -8.75 \pm \sqrt{72.5625}$]

2. $x^2 + \frac{3}{5}x - \frac{4}{5} = \frac{2}{5}$
[$x = -\frac{3}{10} \pm \frac{\sqrt{129}}{10}$]

Q: How is it possible to complete the square with any rational number?
[All perfect square trinomials are in the form of $x^2 + bx + c$, where $c = \left(\frac{b}{2}\right)^2$.]

Activity Assess

EXAMPLE 3 Complete the Square When $a \neq 1$

Pose Purposeful Questions ETP

Q: What must be done differently when solving an equation by completing the square if $a \neq 1$?
[After rewriting in the correct form, divide each side of the equation by the coefficient a.]

Try It! Answer

3. about 51.5 yd by 103 yd

Common Error

Try It 3 Students may forget to divide each side of the equation by 2 before completing the square. Have students square their binomial to check that the two expressions are equivalent.

HABITS OF MIND

Use with **EXAMPLES 1–3**

Reason Is it possible for the value used to complete the square to be negative? Explain. **MP.2**

[No; the value used to complete the square is $\left(\frac{b}{2}\right)^2$. Since it is a value that has been squared, it is always positive.]

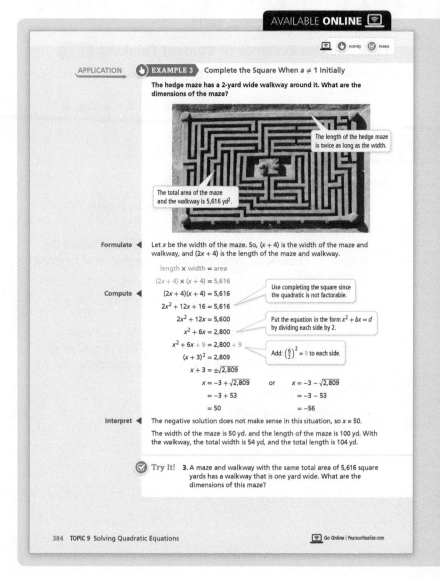

AVAILABLE **ONLINE**

Activity Assess

APPLICATION

EXAMPLE 3 Complete the Square When $a \neq 1$ Initially

The hedge maze has a 2-yard wide walkway around it. What are the dimensions of the maze?

The length of the hedge maze is twice as long as the width.
The total area of the maze and the walkway is 5,616 yd².

Formulate Let x be the width of the maze. So, $(x + 4)$ is the width of the maze and walkway, and $(2x + 4)$ is the length of the maze and walkway.

length × width = area

$(2x + 4) \times (x + 4) = 5{,}616$

Compute

$(2x + 4)(x + 4) = 5{,}616$

$2x^2 + 12x + 16 = 5{,}616$ — Use completing the square since the quadratic is not factorable.

$2x^2 + 12x = 5{,}600$

$x^2 + 6x = 2{,}800$ — Put the equation in the form $x^2 + bx = d$ by dividing each side by 2.

$x^2 + 6x + 9 = 2{,}800 + 9$ — Add: $\left(\frac{6}{2}\right)^2 = 9$ to each side.

$(x + 3)^2 = 2{,}809$

$x + 3 = \pm\sqrt{2{,}809}$

$x = -3 + \sqrt{2{,}809}$ or $x = -3 - \sqrt{2{,}809}$

$= -3 + 53$ $\quad$ $= -3 - 53$

$= 50$ $\quad$ $= -56$

Interpret The negative solution does not make sense in this situation, so $x = 50$.

The width of the maze is 50 yd. and the length of the maze is 100 yd. With the walkway, the total width is 54 yd, and the total length is 104 yd.

Try It! **3.** A maze and walkway with the same total area of 5,616 square yards has a walkway that is one yard wide. What are the dimensions of this maze?

384 TOPIC 9 Solving Quadratic Equations — Go Online | PearsonRealize.com

Struggling Students

USE WITH EXAMPLE 3 Students may need extra support with the process of completing the square when $a \neq 1$.

- Show students the following example, which details the process. Then have students do the exercises.

$$2x^2 + 28x + 36 = 54$$
$$2x^2 + 28x + 36 - 36 = 54 - 36$$
$$2x^2 + 28x = 18$$
$$\frac{2x^2}{2} + \frac{28x}{2} = \frac{18}{2}$$
$$x^2 + 14x = 9$$
$$x^2 + 14x + 49 = 9 + 49$$
$$x^2 + 14x + 49 = 58$$

1. $3x^2 + 18x - 3 = 18$ $[x^2 + 6x + 9 = 16]$

2. $5x^2 + 20x - 5 = 25$ $[x^2 + 4x + 4 = 10]$

Q: Why must you divide the equation by a?
[In order to find the square root of the trinomial, the coefficient of the x^2 term must be 1.]

SavvasRealize.com
Activity Assess

EXAMPLE 4 Use Completing the Square to Write Vertex Form

Use and Connect Mathematical Representation ETP

Q: How is this similar to solving a trinomial equation?
[You add $\left(\frac{b}{2}\right)^2$ to each side.]

Q: What form does the equation need to be in before being able to complete the square?
[$x^2 + bx$ is isolated before completing the square.]

Try It! Answers

4. a. $y = (x - 1)^2 + 2$ b. $y = (x + 3)^2 + 16$

EXAMPLE 5 Write Vertex Form When $a \neq 1$

Pose Purposeful Questions ETP

Q: After *a* is factored out, why is it multiplied by the number that is added to the left side?
[It is multiplied because the actual number that is added to the trinomial is the product of *a* and the new *c*.]

Q: Why is it helpful to keep the −5 on the side of the equation with the perfect square?
[To solve the problem, the −5 would need to be moved back to this side of the equation, so it saves steps.]

Try It! Answer

5. −903

HABITS OF MIND

Use with **EXAMPLES 4 & 5**

Communicate Precisely How is completing the square related to writing the vertex form of a function? Explain. **MP.6**

[Completing the square allows you to write one part of the equation as $(x - h)^2$, which is then used in the vertex form of the function.]

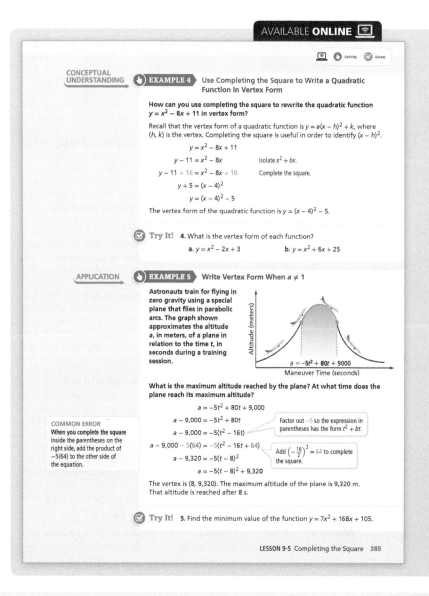

AVAILABLE **ONLINE**

Activity Assess

CONCEPTUAL UNDERSTANDING

EXAMPLE 4 Use Completing the Square to Write a Quadratic Function In Vertex Form

How can you use completing the square to rewrite the quadratic function $y = x^2 - 8x + 11$ in vertex form?

Recall that the vertex form of a quadratic function is $y = a(x - h)^2 + k$, where (h, k) is the vertex. Completing the square is useful in order to identify $(x - h)^2$.

$y = x^2 - 8x + 11$

$y - 11 = x^2 - 8x$ Isolate $x^2 + bx$.

$y - 11 + 16 = x^2 - 8x + 16$ Complete the square.

$y + 5 = (x - 4)^2$

$y = (x - 4)^2 - 5$

The vertex form of the quadratic function is $y = (x - 4)^2 - 5$.

Try It! 4. What is the vertex form of each function?

a. $y = x^2 - 2x + 3$ b. $y = x^2 + 6x + 25$

APPLICATION

EXAMPLE 5 Write Vertex Form When $a \neq 1$

Astronauts train for flying in zero gravity using a special plane that flies in parabolic arcs. The graph shown approximates the altitude *a*, in meters, of a plane in relation to the time *t*, in seconds during a training session.

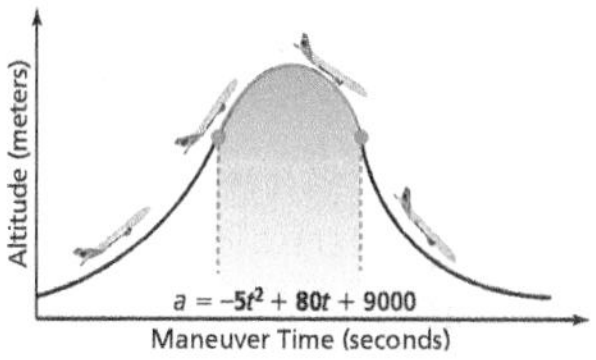
Altitude (meters)
a = −5t² + 80t + 9000
Maneuver Time (seconds)

What is the maximum altitude reached by the plane? At what time does the plane reach its maximum altitude?

$a = -5t^2 + 80t + 9{,}000$

$a - 9{,}000 = -5t^2 + 80t$

$a - 9{,}000 = -5(t^2 - 16t)$ Factor out −5 so the expression in parentheses has the form $t^2 + bt$.

$a - 9{,}000 - 5(64) = -5(t^2 - 16t + 64)$ Add $\left(-\frac{16}{2}\right)^2 = 64$ to complete the square.

$a - 9{,}320 = -5(t - 8)^2$

$a = -5(t - 8)^2 + 9{,}320$

The vertex is (8, 9,320). The maximum altitude of the plane is 9,320 m. That altitude is reached after 8 s.

COMMON ERROR
When you complete the square inside the parentheses on the right side, add the product of −5(64) to the other side of the equation.

Try It! 5. Find the minimum value of the function $y = 7x^2 + 168x + 105$.

LESSON 9-5 Completing the Square 385

ELL English Language Learners (*Use with* EXAMPLE 5)

SPEAKING INTERMEDIATE Display a jar of marbles and ask students to guess the number of marbles in the jar. Then have them count the marbles and compare the actual number to their estimates.

Q: How did your guess compare to the actual number of marbles in the jar?
[Check students' work.]

Q: Was your guess an exact measurement or an approximation?
[an approximation]

Q: Describe a situation in which an approximation is sufficient and one in which you need an exact answer.
[calculating the amount of time a trip takes; naming a plane's location in the sky so that it does not crash with another plane]

WRITING ADVANCED *Parentheses* are symbols used to mark off, or separate, content.

Q: Place parentheses in two different ways around the expression $3x + 7y - 24$ to create two new expressions.
[$3(x + 7y) - 24$, $3x + 7y - 2(4)$]

Q: Explain in writing what each new expression means.
[3 times the quantity $x + 7y$, minus 24; $3x + 7y$ minus the product of 2 times 4, or 8]

Q: Why are the parentheses introduced in the third line of solving the equation in the example?
[-5 is factored out of the expression $-5t^2 + 80t$. If parentheses were not used, it would appear that $-5t^2 + 80t$ was equal to $-5t^2 - 16t$.]

READING BEGINNING In small groups, have students take turns reading the example. While each classmate is reading, have the other students follow along the graph until they are pointing at the maximum point, (8, 9,320).

Q: Using the graph as a context clue, what does *maximum* mean?
[the highest point]

Q: What other word is used in the example as a synonym for *altitude*?
[height]

Q: How is the vertex used to answer both questions in the example?
[The *x*-coordinate gives the number of seconds it takes the plane to reach its maximum height, and the *y*-coordinate gives the maximum height.]

CONCEPT SUMMARY Completing the Square

Q: How is completing the square useful when working with quadratics?
[Completing the square allows you to solve quadratic equations that cannot be factored and write functions in vertex form in order to interpret features of the graph.]

Do You UNDERSTAND? | Do You KNOW HOW?

Common Error

Exercise 10 Students may incorrectly add 144 to both sides of the equation. Explain that in order to complete the square, the purpose is to create a perfect square trinomial where $a = 1$. Therefore, dividing both sides by a must be done before adding the new c.

Answers

1. The technique of completing the square can be applied to any quadratic equation with integer coefficients that has real number solutions. This includes finding solutions that are not rational.
2. When you add 25 to $x^2 + 10x$, the binomial becomes a perfect square trinomial.
3. The student neglected to add 16 to the right side, so the equation is no longer equivalent to the original equation.
4. It is like completing the square because you write one side as a perfect square trinomial. It is different because you are dealing with a function instead of an equation and so are not finding solutions.
5. It is easier to write the trinomial as a binomial squared when the coefficient of a is 1.
6. 169
7. 1
8. 81
9. $x = -4 \pm \sqrt{15}$
10. $x = 6 \pm \sqrt{38}$
11. $x = 2 \pm \sqrt{11}$
12. $y = (x + 2)^2 - 9$
13. $y = 5(x - 1)^2 + 2$
14. $y = (x + 4)^2 - 31$

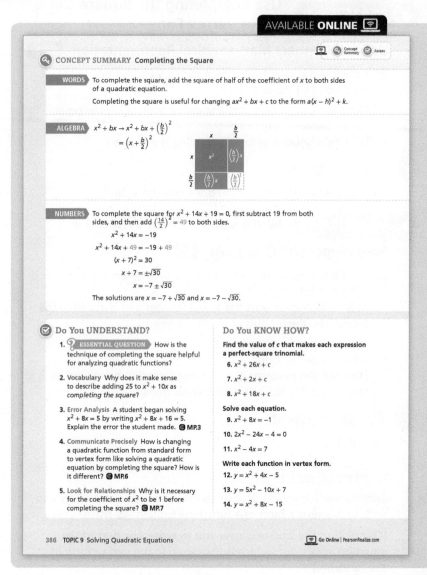

AVAILABLE **ONLINE**

Concept Summary Assess

CONCEPT SUMMARY Completing the Square

WORDS To complete the square, add the square of half of the coefficient of x to both sides of a quadratic equation.

Completing the square is useful for changing $ax^2 + bx + c$ to the form $a(x - h)^2 + k$.

ALGEBRA $x^2 + bx \rightarrow x^2 + bx + \left(\frac{b}{2}\right)^2$

$= \left(x + \frac{b}{2}\right)^2$

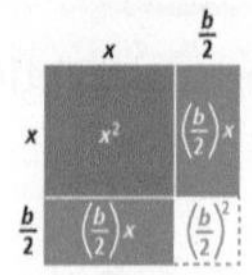
x
b/2
x
x²
(b/2)x
b/2
(b/2)x
(b/2)²

NUMBERS To complete the square for $x^2 + 14x + 19 = 0$, first subtract 19 from both sides, and then add $\left(\frac{14}{2}\right)^2 = 49$ to both sides.

$$x^2 + 14x = -19$$
$$x^2 + 14x + 49 = -19 + 49$$
$$(x + 7)^2 = 30$$
$$x + 7 = \pm\sqrt{30}$$
$$x = -7 \pm \sqrt{30}$$

The solutions are $x = -7 + \sqrt{30}$ and $x = -7 - \sqrt{30}$.

Do You UNDERSTAND?

1. ESSENTIAL QUESTION How is the technique of completing the square helpful for analyzing quadratic functions?
2. Vocabulary Why does it make sense to describe adding 25 to $x^2 + 10x$ as *completing the square*?
3. Error Analysis A student began solving $x^2 + 8x = 5$ by writing $x^2 + 8x + 16 = 5$. Explain the error the student made. MP.3
4. Communicate Precisely How is changing a quadratic function from standard form to vertex form like solving a quadratic equation by completing the square? How is it different? MP.6
5. Look for Relationships Why is it necessary for the coefficient of x^2 to be 1 before completing the square? MP.7

Do You KNOW HOW?

Find the value of c that makes each expression a perfect-square trinomial.

6. $x^2 + 26x + c$
7. $x^2 + 2x + c$
8. $x^2 + 18x + c$

Solve each equation.

9. $x^2 + 8x = -1$
10. $2x^2 - 24x - 4 = 0$
11. $x^2 - 4x = 7$

Write each function in vertex form.

12. $y = x^2 + 4x - 5$
13. $y = 5x^2 - 10x + 7$
14. $y = x^2 + 8x - 15$

386 TOPIC 9 Solving Quadratic Equations — Go Online | PearsonRealize.com

SavvasRealize.com

Practice | Tutorials | Math Tools

PRACTICE & PROBLEM SOLVING

AVAILABLE ONLINE

Lesson Practice You may opt to have students complete the automatically scored Practice and Problem Solving items online powered by MathXL for School.

Choose from: **Lesson Practice**

Adaptive Practice

You may also take advantage of the bank of exercises for assigning additional practice.

Assignment Guide

Basic	Advanced
15–23, 28–51	15–39, 44–51

Item Analysis

Example	Items	DOK
1	15, 20–25	1
	50	2
2	18, 26–29	1
	16, 19	2
	46	3
3	30–33	1
	34, 35, 49, 51	2
4	36–39	1
	44, 47	2
5	40–43	1
	17, 45	2
	48	3

AVAILABLE ONLINE

PRACTICE & PROBLEM SOLVING

Scan for Multimedia | Practice | Tutorial | Additional Exercises Available Online

UNDERSTAND

15. Use Structure What value of c completes the square for each area model below? Represent the area model as a perfect-square trinomial and as a binomial squared. MP.7

a.

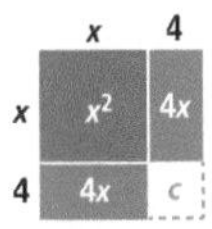

x
4
x
x²
4x
4
4x
c

b.

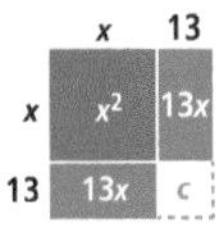

x
13
x
x²
13x
13
13x
c

16. Construct Arguments To solve the equation $x^2 - 7x - 9 = 0$, would you use graphing, factoring, or completing the square if you want exact solutions? Explain. MP.3

17. Error Analysis Describe and correct the error a student made in writing the quadratic function $y = 2x^2 + 12x + 1$ in vertex form. MP.3

$$y = 2x^2 + 12x + 1$$
$$y = 2(x^2 + 6x) + 1$$
$$y + 9 = 2(x^2 + 6x + 9) + 1$$
$$y + 9 = 2(x + 3)^2 + 1$$
$$y = 2(x + 3)^2 - 8$$
✗

18. Reason Find the solution to the equation $x^2 + 4x = -12$. Explain your reasoning. MP.2

19. Mathematical Connections Use the graph of $f(x) = x^2 - 2x - 1$ to estimate the solutions of $f(x) = 5$. Then find the exact solutions.

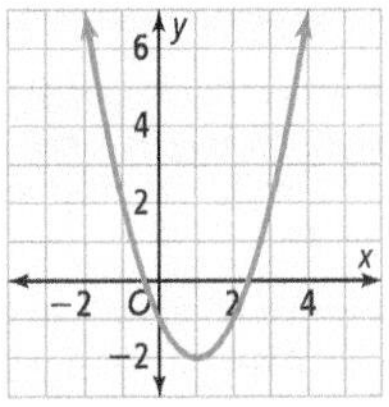

y
6
4
2
x
−2
O
2
4
−2

PRACTICE

Find the value of c that makes each expression a perfect-square trinomial. Write each expression as a binomial squared. SEE EXAMPLE 1

20. $x^2 + 16x + c$ **21.** $x^2 + 22x + c$

22. $p^2 - 30p + c$ **23.** $k^2 - 5k + c$

24. $g^2 + 17g + c$ **25.** $q^2 - 48q + c$

Solve each equation by completing the square. SEE EXAMPLES 2 AND 3

26. $x^2 + 6x = 144$ $-3 \pm \sqrt{153}$ **27.** $x^2 - 4x = 30$ $2 \pm \sqrt{34}$

28. $m^2 + 16m = -59$ $-8 \pm \sqrt{5}$ **29.** $x^2 - 2x - 35 = 0$ -5 and 7

30. $5n^2 - 3n - 15 = 0$ $0.3 \pm \sqrt{3.09}$ **31.** $4w^2 + 12w - 44 = 0$ $-1.5 \pm \sqrt{13.25}$

32. $3r^2 + 18r = 21$ -7 and 1 **33.** $2v^2 - 10v - 20 = 8$ -2 and 7

Find the value of x. If necessary, round to the nearest hundredth. SEE EXAMPLE 3

34. Area of triangle = 8 2.47

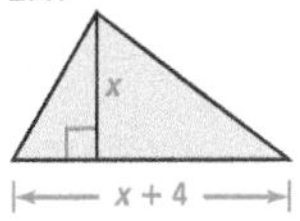

x
x + 4

35. Area of rectangle = 50 6.4

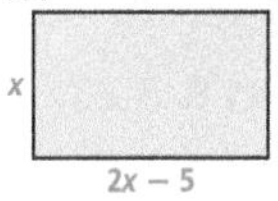

x
2x − 5

Write each function in vertex form, and identify the vertex. SEE EXAMPLES 4 AND 5

36. $y = x^2 + 4x - 3$ **37.** $y = x^2 + 12x + 27$

38. $y = x^2 - 6x + 12$ **39.** $y = x^2 - 14x - 1$

40. $y = 3x^2 - 6x - 2$ **41.** $y = 2x^2 - 20x + 35$

42. $y = -x^2 - 8x - 7$ **43.** $y = -4x^2 + 16x + 5$

Write each function in vertex form. Tell whether each graph could represent the function.

44. $y = x^2 + 6x + 3$

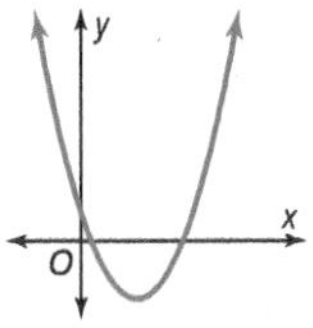

y
x
O

45. $f(x) = -x^2 - 10x - 21$

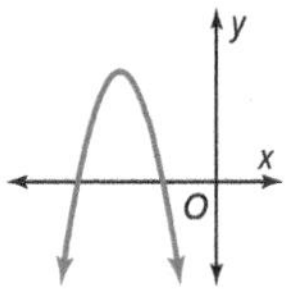

y
x
O

LESSON 9-5 Completing the Square 387

Answers

15. a. 16; $x^2 + 8x + 16$; $(x + 4)^2$

b. 169; $x^2 + 26x + 169$; $(x + 13)^2$

16. completing the square; The trinomial is not factorable, and the solutions are not integers, so to find the exact solutions, you will need to use completing the square.

17. The student added 9 to the left side of the equation instead of adding 18. The correct answer is $y = 2(x + 3)^2 - 17$.

18. There is no solution because $(x + 2)^2 = -8$ and the square root of a negative number is undefined.

19. −1.6 and 3.6; $1 \pm \sqrt{7}$

20. 64; $(x + 8)^2$

21. 121; $(x + 11)^2$

22. 225; $(x - 15)^2$

23. 6.25; $(x - 2.5)^2$

24. 72.25; $(x + 8.5)^2$

25. 576; $(x - 24)^2$

36. $y = (x + 2)^2 - 7$; $(-2, -7)$

37. $y = (x + 6)^2 - 9$; $(-6, -9)$

38. $y = (x - 3)^2 + 3$; $(3, 3)$

39. $y = (x - 7)^2 - 50$; $(7, -50)$

40. $y = 3(x - 1)^2 - 5$; $(1, -5)$

41. $y = 2(x - 5)^2 - 15$; $(5, -15)$

42. $y = -(x + 4)^2 + 9$; $(-4, 9)$

43. $y = -4(x - 2)^2 + 21$; $(2, 21)$

44. $y = (x + 3)^2 - 6$; no

45. $f(x) = -(x + 5)^2 + 4$; yes

Answers

46. about 7.08 ft by 7.08 ft

47. 4 m; The vertex form of the function is $f(x) = (x - 2)^2 + 14$. So the vertex is (2, 14). This means that the lowest point of the dish is 14 m above the ground. The graph of the parabola has points (0, 18) and (4, 18), so the width of the dish at 18 m off the ground is 4 m.

48. a. The vertex form of the function is $h = -16\left(t - \frac{v_0}{32}\right)^2 + \left(h_0 + \frac{(v_0)^2}{64}\right)$. This means that the maximum height occurs at $h_0 + \frac{(v_0)^2}{64}$.

b. no; The maximum height increases by a factor of 4 because the initial velocity is squared. So if the initial velocity is doubled, the maximum height is multiplied by 4.

51. Part A $w = 0.5625h$; $A = (0.5625h + 0.4)(h + 1.2)$

Part B 5.23 in.

Part C 5.23 in. and 2.94 in.; 6.43 in. and 3.34 in.

AVAILABLE **ONLINE**

PRACTICE & PROBLEM SOLVING

Practice Tutorial
Mixed Review Available Online

APPLY

46. Model With Mathematics You are designing a square banner for a school assembly. You want the banner to be gold with vertical purple bars as shown. You have enough material to make the area of the rectangular gold section 36 ft². What are the dimensions of the banner? MP.4

1ft
1ft
GO
PANTHERS

47. Reason The profile of a satellite dish is shaped like a parabola. The bottom of the dish can be modeled by the function shown, where x and $f(x)$ are measured in meters. Use the vertex form of the quadratic function to determine the vertex or the lowest point of the dish. How wide is the dish at 18 m off of the ground? Explain. MP.2

f(x) = x² − 4x + 18

48. Higher Order Thinking The kicker on a football team uses the function, $h = -16t^2 + v_0t + h_0$, to model the height of a football being kicked into the air.

a. Show that for any values of v_0 and h_0, the maximum height of the object is $\frac{(v_0)^2}{64} + h_0$.

b. The kicker performs an experiment. He thinks if he can double the initial upward velocity of the football kicked from the ground, the maximum height will also double. Is the kicker correct? If not, how does the maximum height change? Explain.

ASSESSMENT PRACTICE

49. A rectangle is 8 cm longer than it is wide. Its area is 250 cm². The width of the rectangle is about ______. The rectangle's perimeter is about ______. 12.3 cm; 65.2 cm

50. SAT/ACT The expressions $f(x) = x^2 + 12x + c$ and $g(x) = x^2 - 20x + d$ are perfect-square trinomials. What is the value of $f(0) - g(0)$?

Ⓐ −256
Ⓑ −64
Ⓒ 0
Ⓓ 32

51. Performance Task An electronics manufacturer designs a smartphone with an aspect ratio (the ratio of the screen's height h to its width w) of 16 : 9.

0.6 in.
10:15
Thursday
h
0.2 in.
w

Part A Write the width in terms of h. What is the area of the phone, including the border, in terms of h?

Part B The total area of the screen and border is about 21.48 in.². What is the value of h?

Part C What are the height and width of the screen? What is the total height and width of the phone including the border?

LESSON QUIZ

Use the Lesson Quiz to assess students' understanding of the mathematics in the lesson.

Students can take the Lesson Quiz online or you can download a printable copy from **SavvasRealize.com**. The Lesson Quiz is also available in the *Assessment Resources* book.

Item Analysis

Item	DOK	Standards
1	2	HSA.REI.B.4.A
2	1	HSA.REI.B.4.A
3	1	HSA.REI.B.4.A
4	2	HSA.SSE.B.3.B, HSF.IF.C.8.A
5	2	HSA.SSE.B.3.B, HSF.IF.C.8.A

RtI Use the student scores on the Lesson Quiz to prescribe differentiated assignments.

If students take the Lesson Quiz online, it will be automatically scored and appropriate differentiated practice will be assigned based on student performance.

I Intervention	0–3 points	• Reteach to Build Understanding • Mathematical Literacy and Vocabulary • Additional Practice
O On-Level	4 points	• Mathematical Literacy and Vocabulary • Additional Practice • Enrichment
A Advanced	5 points	• Enrichment

AVAILABLE **ONLINE**

9-5 Lesson Quiz

1. Which value of c completes the square in the expression $x^2 + 14x + c$?

Ⓐ −49

Ⓑ −7

Ⓒ 7

Ⓓ 49

Review progress | Question 1 of 5 | Go | ← Back | Next →

ASSESSMENT RESOURCES

Name ________

enVision Algebra 1

PearsonRealize.com

9-5 Lesson Quiz

Completing the Square

1. Which value of c completes the square in the expression $x^2 + 14x + c$?

Ⓐ −49

Ⓑ −7

Ⓒ 7

Ⓓ 49

2. Use completing the square to determine which of the following gives the solutions to $3x^2 - 24x + 40 = 28$.

Ⓐ $2 \pm 4\sqrt{3}$

Ⓑ $4 \pm 2\sqrt{3}$

Ⓒ $3 \pm 3\sqrt{2}$

Ⓓ $6 \pm 2\sqrt{5}$

3. Solve the quadratic equation $x^2 + 12x + 8 = 0$ by completing the square. Select *Yes* or *No* to to tell whether each value is a possible solution to the equation.

	Yes	No
$-6 + \sqrt{7}$	☐	☑
$-6 + 2\sqrt{7}$	☑	☐
$6 - 2\sqrt{7}$	☐	☑
$-6 - \sqrt{7}$	☐	☑
$-6 - 2\sqrt{7}$	☑	☐

4. Write the function $f(x) = 3x^2 - 30x + 71$ in vertex form. What is the vertex of the function?

vertex form: $f(x) =$ $3(x - 5)^2 - 4$ vertex: $(5, -4)$

5. The function $a = -2x^2 + 8x + 5$ models the altitude a in feet of a ball thrown in the air and the horizontal distance in feet that the ball travels. Rewrite the function in vertex form. What is the maximum altitude reached by the ball?

vertex form: $a = -2(x - 2)^2 + 13$ maximum altitude: 13 ft

enVision™ **Algebra 1** • Assessment Resources

DIFFERENTIATED RESOURCES

I = Intervention **O** = On-Level **A** = Advanced

⚙ = This activity is available as a digital assignment powered by MathXL® for School.

Assess | Tutorials | Worksheets

AVAILABLE **ONLINE**

Reteach to Build Understanding I ⚙

Provides scaffolded reteaching for the key lesson concepts.

Name ______________ enVision Algebra 1 PearsonRealize.com

9-5 Reteach to Build Understanding

Completing the Square

1. Label each part of the diagram to show how to complete the square.

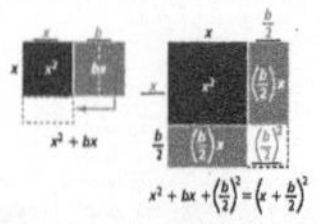

$x^2 + bx + \left(\frac{b}{2}\right)^2 = \left(x + \frac{b}{2}\right)^2$

2. Fill in the blanks to find the solutions of $x^2 - 18x + 15 = 0$ by completing the square.

Write the equation in the form $ax^2 + bx = d$. $x^2 - 18x =$ -15

Complete the square. $x^2 - 18x +$ 81 $=$ -15 $+$ 81

$x^2 - 18x +$ 81 $=$ 66

Write the trinomial as a binomial squared. $(x -$ 9 $)^2 =$ 66

Solve for x. $x -$ 9 $= \pm\sqrt{66}$

$x =$ 9 $\pm$ $\sqrt{66}$

3. The side lengths of a rectangle are given as $x + 8$ and $x - 2$. Reece calculated the area of the rectangle by completing the square. Find and correct her error.

$(x + 8)(x - 2) = x^2 + 6x - 16$

$x^2 + 6x = 16$

$x^2 + 6x + 9 = 16 + 9$

$x^2 + 6x + 9 = 25$

$(x + 3)^2 = 25$

$x + 3 - 3 = 25 - 3$ X

$x = 22$

Reece did not take the square root of each side of the equation. The correct answer should be $x = 2$. After taking the square root of 25, which is 5, and subtracting 3, the result is 2.

enVision™ Algebra 1 • Teaching Resources

Additional Practice I O ⚙

Provides extra practice for each lesson.

Name ______________ enVision Algebra 1 PearsonRealize.com

9-5 Additional Practice

Completing the Square

Find the value of c that makes each expression a perfect square trinomial.

1. $x^2 + 18x + c$ — 81
2. $x^2 - 32x + c$ — 256
3. $x^2 + 13x + c$ — $\frac{169}{4}$

Solve each equation by completing the square.

4. $x^2 + 8x + 5 = 0$ — $-4 \pm \sqrt{11}$
5. $x^2 - 4x - 14 = 0$ — $2 \pm 3\sqrt{2}$
6. $x^2 + 5x - 9 = 0$ — $-\frac{5}{2} \pm \frac{\sqrt{61}}{2}$
7. $4x^2 - 16x = -8$ — $2 \pm \sqrt{2}$
8. $4x^2 + 8x = 32$ — $-4, 2$
9. $x^2 - 8x = 9$ — $-1, 9$

Write each function in vertex form and identify the vertex.

10. $f(x) = x^2 - 16x + 3$
$f(x) = (x - 8)^2 - 61$
Vertex is at $(8, -61)$.
11. $f(x) = 4x^2 + 24x - 7$
$f(x) = 4(x + 3)^2 - 43$
Vertex is at $(-3, -43)$.
12. $f(x) = -2x^2 - 8x + 9$
$f(x) = -2(x + 2)^2 + 17$
Vertex is at $(-2, 17)$.
13. Is $x^2 + 2bx - b^2$ a perfect square trinomial? Explain. If not, what is an expression for the last term that will make it a perfect square trinomial?
No; Sample answer: The last term cannot be negative, since it is the square of b. The square of any real number must be nonnegative. The last term must be $+ b^2$.
14. A rectangle with sides measuring x in. and $4x - 1$ in. has an area of 663 in.². What are the dimensions of the rectangle?
13 in. by 51 in.

enVision™ Algebra 1 • Teaching Resources

Enrichment O A ⚙

Presents engaging problems and activities that extend the lesson concepts.

Name ______________ enVision Algebra 1 PearsonRealize.com

9-5 Enrichment

Completing the Square

The graph of a quadratic function is a parabola. When the equation for the parabola is expressed in vertex form, $y = a(x - h)^2 + k$, you can easily identify the coordinates of the parabola's vertex. It lies at the point (h, k).

Complete the square of an equation for a parabola and express it in vertex form. Determine the coordinates of its vertex. *Note*: The value of h is the opposite of the constant in the term being squared, but the value of k has the same sign as it does in the expression.

Example:

For the parabola $y = x^2 + 14x + 9$, determine the coordinates of its vertex.

$y + 7^2 = x^2 + 14x + 7^2 + 9$	Square half the coefficient of the x-term and add to both sides.
$y + 49 = (x^2 + 14x + 49) + 9$	Simplify.
$y + 49 = (x + 7)^2 + 9$	Factor.
$y = (x + 7)^2 - 40$	Solve for y.

The vertex is at $(-7, -40)$.

Determine the vertex of the parabola by completing the square to write each equation in vertex form. Graph to check.

1. $y = x^2 - 6x + 17$

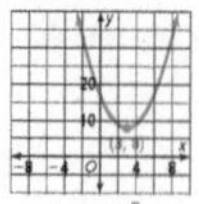

$y = (x - 3)^2 + 8$

The vertex is at $(3, 8)$.

2. $y = x^2 + 24x + 124$

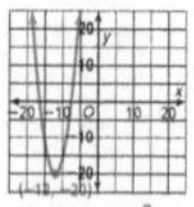

$y = (x + 12)^2 - 20$

The vertex is at $(-12, -20)$.

enVision™ Algebra 1 • Teaching Resources

Mathematical Literacy and Vocabulary I O

Helps students develop and reinforce understanding of key terms and concepts.

Name ______________ enVision Algebra 1 PearsonRealize.com

9-5 Mathematical Literacy and Vocabulary

Completing the Square

There are two sets of note cards that show how to find the solutions of the equation $g^2 - 4g = 45$. The set on the left explains the thinking. The set on the right shows the steps. Write the thinking and the steps in the correct order.

Think Cards	Write Cards
Add 2 to each side.	$(g - 2)^2 = 49$
Write as two equations.	$g = 9$ or $g = -5$
Simplify the right side.	$g - 2 = 7$ or $g - 2 = -7$
Add $\left(\frac{b}{2}\right)^2$ or 4 to each side.	$g^2 - 4g + 4 = 45 + 4$
Take the square root of each side.	$g - 2 = \pm\sqrt{49}$
Write $g^2 - 4g + 4$ as a square.	$(g - 2)^2 = 45 + 4$

Think	Write
First, add $\left(\frac{b}{2}\right)^2$ or 4 to each side.	Step 1 $g^2 - 4g + 4 = 45 + 4$
Second, write $g^2 - 4g + 4$ as a square.	Step 2 $(g - 2)^2 = 45 + 4$
Third, simplify the right side.	Step 3 $(g - 2)^2 = 49$
Next, take the square root of each side.	Step 4 $g - 2 = \pm\sqrt{49}$
Then, write as two equations.	Step 5 $g - 2 = 7$ or $g - 2 = -7$
Finally, add 2 to each side.	Step 6 $g = 9$ or $g = -5$

enVision™ Algebra 1 • Teaching Resources

Digital Resources and Video Tutorials I O A ⚙

The **Reteach to Build Understanding, Additional Practice,** and **Enrichment** activities are available as digital assignments powered by MathXL for School. These activities are automatically assigned when students complete the lesson quiz online and are automatically scored.

Students can access instructional tutorials using the **Virtual Nerd app.**

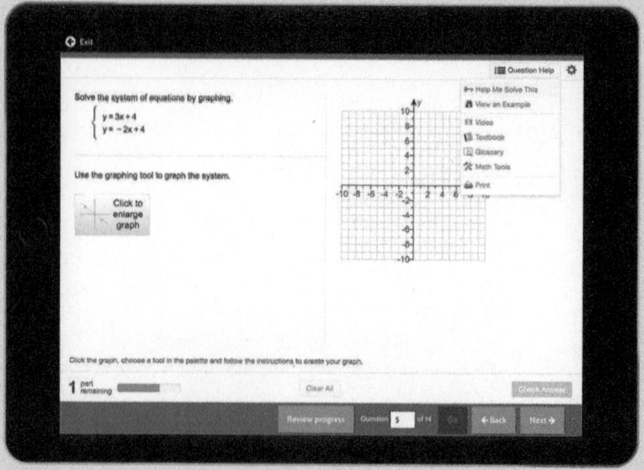

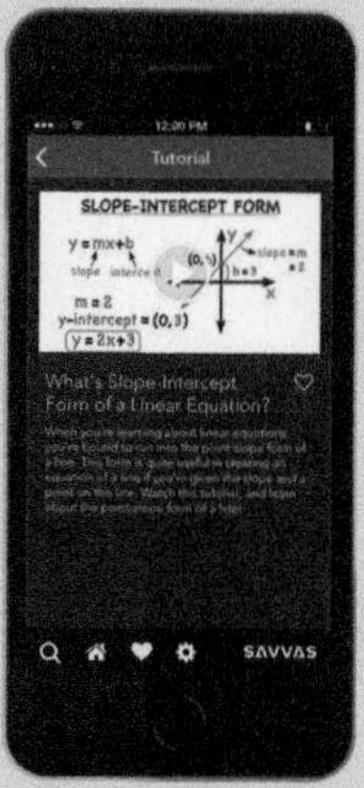
Tutorial
SLOPE-INTERCEPT FORM
What's Slope-Intercept Form of a Linear Equation?
SAVVAS

Students can also access Virtual Nerd videos using the **BouncePages app** to scan exercise pages marked with this icon. Students can download both apps for free in their mobile devices' app store.

SavvasRealize.com

A-Z Glossary

LESSON 9-6
The Quadratic Formula and the Discriminant

Lesson Overview

FOCUS

Objective

Students will be able to:

✔ Derive the quadratic formula by completing the square.

✔ Solve quadratic equations in one variable by using the quadratic formula.

✔ Use the discriminant to determine the number and type of solutions to a quadratic equation.

Essential Understanding

The quadratic formula can be used to solve every quadratic equation and is particularly useful for those that cannot be easily factored. The discriminant of the quadratic formula indicates the number of solutions of the equation.

COHERENCE

Previously in this course, students:

- Solved quadratic equations by factoring.
- Solved quadratic equations by completing the square.

In this lesson, students:

- Derive the quadratic formula and use it to solve quadratic equations.

Later in this topic, students will:

- Solve systems of quadratic equations.

RIGOR

This lesson emphasizes a blend of *conceptual understanding* and *application.*

- Students derive the quadratic formula and learn to interpret the value of the discriminant.
- Students use the quadratic formula to solve a real-world problems, such as the time it takes for a frog to land after jumping.

A-Z Vocabulary Builder

NEW VOCABULARY — **English** | *Spanish*

- **discriminant** | *discriminante*
- **quadratic formula** | *fórmula cuadrática*
- **root** | *raíz*

VOCABULARY ACTIVITY

Throughout this lesson, have students pay close attention to the use of the terms zeros, x-intercepts, solutions, and roots. Students often use these terms interchangeably, but each has a specific meaning.

Functions have zeros. The real zeros of a function are identical to its x-intercepts. Equations have solutions. When an equation is in the form $f(x) = 0$, these solutions are called roots. Zeros of the function f are the roots of the equation $f(x) = 0$. We graph quadratic functions, and we solve quadratic equations.

1. For a quadratic equation in the form $ax^2 + bx + c = 0$, this value can be used to determine the number of solutions to a quadratic equation. **[discriminant]**
2. a formula that can be used to solve any quadratic equation in the form $ax^2 + bx + c = 0$ **[quadratic formula]**
3. the input value that makes an equation true **[root]**

Student Companion

Students can do their in-class work for the lesson on pages 209–212 of their *Student Companion* or in Savvas Realize.

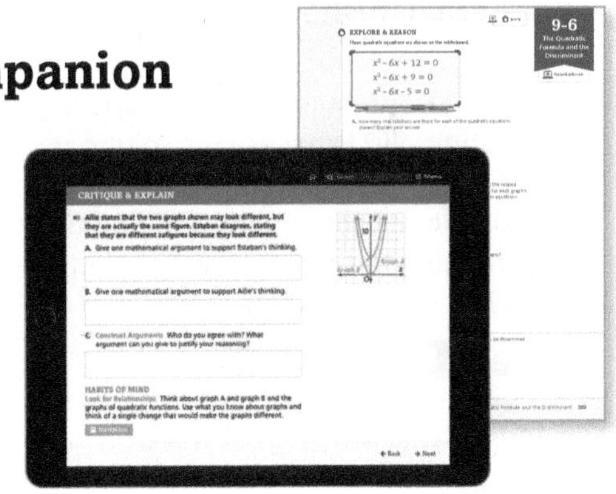

Mathematics Overview — COMMON CORE STANDARDS

Content Standards

In this lesson, students focus on these standards:

HSA.REI.B.4.A Use completing the square to derive the quadratic formula.

HSA.REI.B.4.B Solve quadratic equations using the quadratic formula.

HSA.SSE.B.3 Rewrite quadratic equations in equivalent forms using completing the square to derive the quadratic formula.

They also work with concepts related to **HSA.CED.A.1.**

Mathematical Practice Standards

These standards are highlighted in this lesson:

MP.6 Communicate Precisely

Students describe the meaning of the variables and symbols in the quadratic formula.

MP.7 Look For and Make Use of Structure

Students look for the relationship between the structure of a quadratic equation and the number of solutions it has.

Activity

EXPLORE & REASON

INSTRUCTIONAL FOCUS Students use their knowledge of quadratic functions to predict the number of solutions of a quadratic equation and how that relates to the features of the equation. This prepares them to determine the number of solutions of a quadratic equation using the discriminant.

STUDENT COMPANION Students can complete the *Explore & Reason* activity on page 209 of their *Student Companion*.

Before WHOLE CLASS

Implement Tasks that Promote Reasoning and Problem Solving ETP

Q: What are some ways to describe the solution of a quadratic equation?
[the roots of the equation; the zeros of the equation; the input values that give you an output value of zero; the points where the graph of the function crosses the *x*-axis]

During SMALL GROUP

Support Productive Struggle in Learning Mathematics ETP

Q: How do you transform a function so that it is reflected across the *x*-axis?
[Multiply the entire function by –1; change the sign of each term in the function.]

For Early Finishers

Q: How many solutions does the equation $x^2 + 5.8x - 10.08 = 0$ have? How could you determine the answer algebraically and graphically? What are the solutions?
[2 solutions, 1.4 and –7.2; Find the answers algebraically by completing the square, and find the answers graphically by graphing the function and noting where it crosses the *x*-axis.]

After WHOLE CLASS

Facilitate Meaningful Mathematical Discourse ETP

Q: Compare the solutions of each equation with the solutions for its reflection across the *x*-axis. What do you notice?
[The value of the solutions are the same for the original equations and the reflection over the *x*-axis, and the number of solutions is the same for both equations.]

Q: Is it possible to solve a quadratic equation that is not factorable? Explain.
[Yes; Graph the related function; use completing the square.]

HABITS OF MIND

Use with **EXPLORE & REASON**

Reason How can the number of solutions of a quadratic equation be determined by inspecting its graph? **MP.2**

[The number of solutions of a quadratic equation is the same as the number of *x*-intercepts of the graph of the related function.]

AVAILABLE **ONLINE**

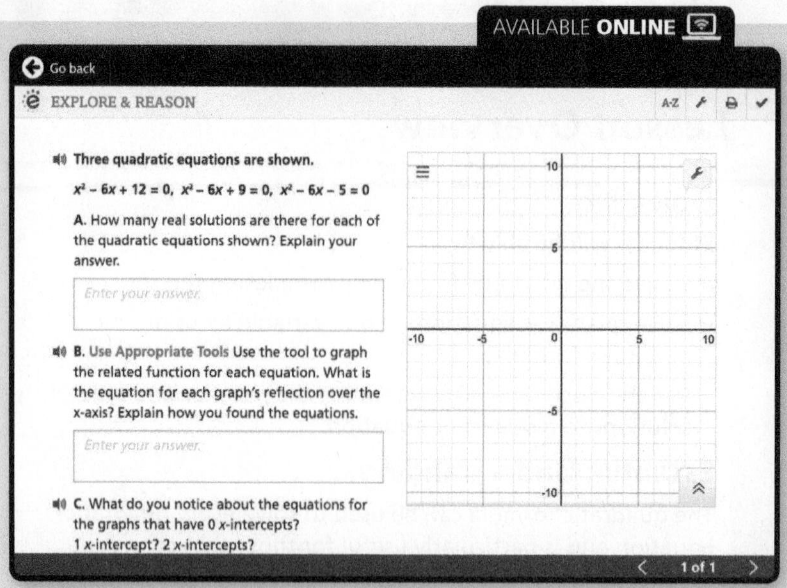

Go back
EXPLORE & REASON
Three quadratic equations are shown.
x² – 6x + 12 = 0, x² – 6x + 9 = 0, x² – 6x – 5 = 0
A. How many real solutions are there for each of the quadratic equations shown? Explain your answer.
Enter your answer.
B. Use Appropriate Tools Use the tool to graph the related function for each equation. What is the equation for each graph's reflection over the x-axis? Explain how you found the equations.
Enter your answer.
C. What do you notice about the equations for the graphs that have 0 x-intercepts? 1 x-intercept? 2 x-intercepts?
1 of 1

STUDENT EDITION, PAGE 389

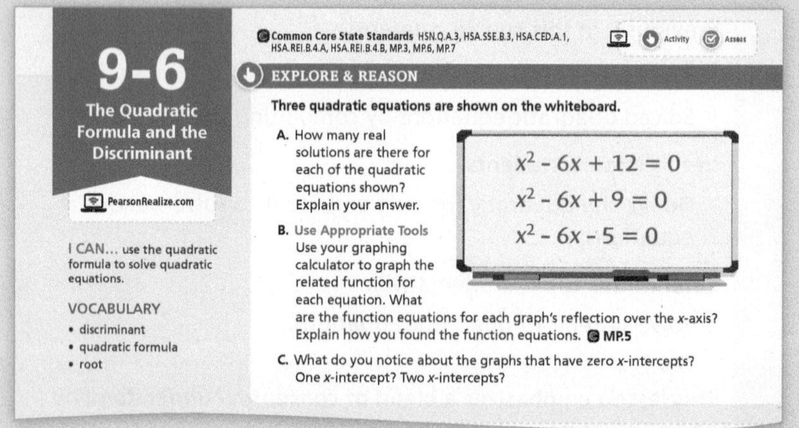

Common Core State Standards HSN.Q.A.3, HSA.SSE.B.3, HSA.CED.A.1, HSA.REI.B.4.A, HSA.REI.B.4.B, MP.3, MP.6, MP.7

9-6 The Quadratic Formula and the Discriminant

PearsonRealize.com

I CAN… use the quadratic formula to solve quadratic equations.

VOCABULARY
- discriminant
- quadratic formula
- root

EXPLORE & REASON

Three quadratic equations are shown on the whiteboard.

$x^2 - 6x + 12 = 0$
$x^2 - 6x + 9 = 0$
$x^2 - 6x - 5 = 0$

A. How many real solutions are there for each of the quadratic equations shown? Explain your answer.

B. Use Appropriate Tools Use your graphing calculator to graph the related function for each equation. What are the function equations for each graph's reflection over the *x*-axis? Explain how you found the function equations. MP.5

C. What do you notice about the graphs that have zero *x*-intercepts? One *x*-intercept? Two *x*-intercepts?

SAMPLE STUDENT WORK

A. 0; 1; 2; The equation $0 = x^2 - 6x + 9$ has a solution of 3;
The equation $0 = x^2 - 6x + 12$ has no solutions;
The equation $0 = x^2 - 6x - 5$ is not factorable.

B.

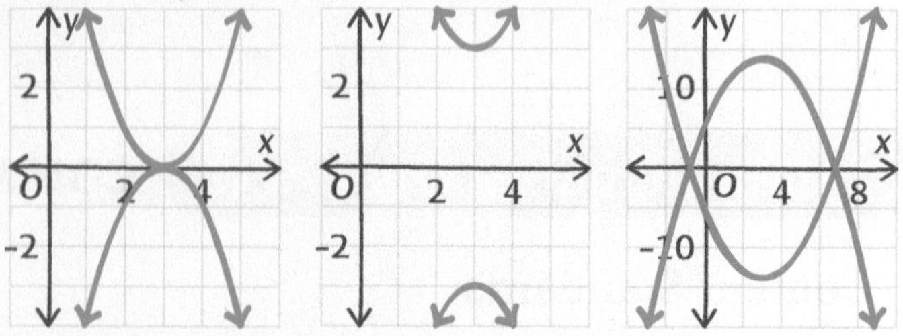

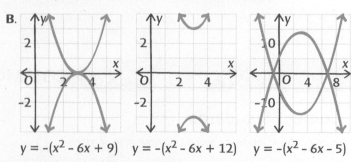

$y = -(x^2 - 6x + 9)$ $y = -(x^2 - 6x + 12)$ $y = -(x^2 - 6x - 5)$

I multiplied each equation by -1.

C. Equations for graphs that have 0 *x*-intercepts have no real factors. Equations for graphs that have 1 *x*-intercept have two identical real factors. Equations for graphs that have 2 *x*-intercepts have two unique real factors.

INTRODUCE THE ESSENTIAL QUESTION

Establish Mathematics Goals to Focus Learning ETP

Students learn to derive and use the quadratic formula. Students learn that the quadratic formula can be used to find the solution or solutions for any quadratic equation. Students understand and use the discriminant of the quadratic formula to determine the number of possible solutions for a given quadratic equation.

EXAMPLE 1 Derive the Quadratic Formula

Use and Connect Mathematical Representations ETP

Q: When deriving the quadratic formula, what term should you solve for?
[You should solve for *x*. The solution of a quadratic equation is the value of *x* that makes the equation equal to 0.]

Q: Why must *a* not be equal to zero?
[If *a* is equal to zero, then there is no x^2 term and it is not a quadratic equation; the first step of completing the square is to divide every term by *a*, and you cannot divide by zero.]

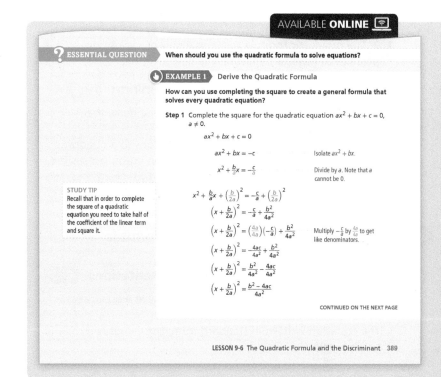

AVAILABLE ONLINE

ESSENTIAL QUESTION **When should you use the quadratic formula to solve equations?**

EXAMPLE 1 Derive the Quadratic Formula

How can you use completing the square to create a general formula that solves every quadratic equation?

Step 1 Complete the square for the quadratic equation $ax^2 + bx + c = 0$, $a \neq 0$.

$$ax^2 + bx + c = 0$$

$$ax^2 + bx = -c$$ Isolate $ax^2 + bx$.

$$x^2 + \frac{b}{a}x = -\frac{c}{a}$$ Divide by *a*. Note that *a* cannot be 0.

$$x^2 + \frac{b}{a}x + \left(\frac{b}{2a}\right)^2 = -\frac{c}{a} + \left(\frac{b}{2a}\right)^2$$

$$\left(x + \frac{b}{2a}\right)^2 = -\frac{c}{a} + \frac{b^2}{4a^2}$$

$$\left(x + \frac{b}{2a}\right)^2 = \left(\frac{4a}{4a}\right)\left(-\frac{c}{a}\right) + \frac{b^2}{4a^2}$$ Multiply $-\frac{c}{a}$ by $\frac{4a}{4a}$ to get like denominators.

$$\left(x + \frac{b}{2a}\right)^2 = -\frac{4ac}{4a^2} + \frac{b^2}{4a^2}$$

$$\left(x + \frac{b}{2a}\right)^2 = \frac{b^2}{4a^2} - \frac{4ac}{4a^2}$$

$$\left(x + \frac{b}{2a}\right)^2 = \frac{b^2 - 4ac}{4a^2}$$

STUDY TIP
Recall that in order to complete the square of a quadratic equation you need to take half of the coefficient of the linear term and square it.

CONTINUED ON THE NEXT PAGE

LESSON 9-6 The Quadratic Formula and the Discriminant 389

ADDITIONAL EXAMPLES

AVAILABLE ONLINE

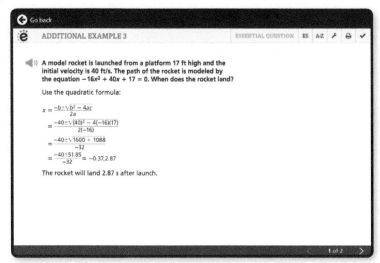

Go back

ADDITIONAL EXAMPLE 3 ESSENTIAL QUESTION ES A-Z

A model rocket is launched from a platform 17 ft high and the initial velocity is 40 ft/s. The path of the rocket is modeled by the equation $-16x^2 + 40x + 17 = 0$. When does the rocket land?

Use the quadratic formula:

$$x = \frac{-b \pm \sqrt{b^2 - 4ac}}{2a}$$
$$= \frac{-40 \pm \sqrt{(40)^2 - 4(-16)(17)}}{2(-16)}$$
$$= \frac{-40 \pm \sqrt{1600 + 1088}}{-32}$$
$$= \frac{-40 \pm 51.85}{-32} = -0.37, 2.87$$

The rocket will land 2.87 s after launch.

1 of 2

Go back

ADDITIONAL EXAMPLE 4 ESSENTIAL QUESTION ES A-Z

How many solutions are there to the following quadratic equation? Use the discriminant to determine your answer.

$12x^2 - 5x + 10 = 0$

Find the discriminant.

$b^2 - 4ac = (-5)^2 - 4(12)(10)$
$= 25 - 480$
$= -455$

The discriminant is less than 0, so there are 0 real solutions.

1 of 2

Example 3 Students practice solving real-world problems using the quadratic formula with this additional example.

Q: If the rocket were launched from a platform that was 32 ft high instead, how long would it take the rocket to reach the ground?
[3.14 seconds]

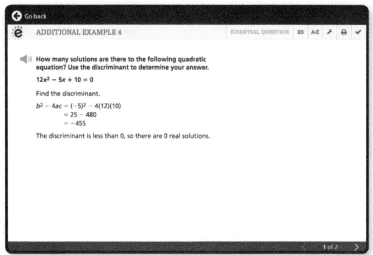

Example 4 Students practice using the discriminant to determine the number of solutions of a quadratic equation with this additional example.

Q: What does it mean if a quadratic equation has no solutions?
[The graph of the related function does not cross the *x*-axis.]

EXAMPLE 1 CONTINUED

Try It! Answer

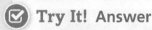

1. 2; The quadratic formula contains a plus or minus sign, so it is possible to have two solutions.

Elicit and Use Evidence of Student Thinking ETP

Q: Why does the quadratic formula not provide more than two solutions?
[The quadratic formula provides the solutions to a quadratic equation, which are the x-values where the graph crosses the x-axis. A parabola can only cross the x-axis 0, 1, or 2 times, so the quadratic formula can only provide 0, 1, or 2 solutions.]

EXAMPLE 2 Use the Quadratic Formula

Use and Connect Mathematical Representations ETP

Q: In order to use the quadratic formula to solve a quadratic equation, what information do you need?
[the equation written in standard form; the values of a, b, and c with $a \neq 0$]

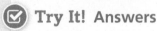

Try It! Answers

2. a. −7, 3
   b. 6, −4

Elicit and Use Evidence of Student Thinking ETP

Q: Is it necessary for the value of a to be positive?
[No, it just makes the numbers easier to use.]

Q: What are the values for a, b, and c in Try It 2a? What steps were required to get these values?
[$a = 1$; $b = 4$; $c = -21$;
Answers may vary. Sample: You must rewrite the equation to get it into standard form. If you want the value of a to be positive, you add $4x$ and subtract 21 from each side.]

HABITS OF MIND

Use with **EXAMPLES 1 & 2**

Look for Relationships Using the quadratic formula, how can you tell when a quadratic equation has only one solution? MP.7

[If the term under the square root simplifies to zero, the quadratic equation has only one solution.]

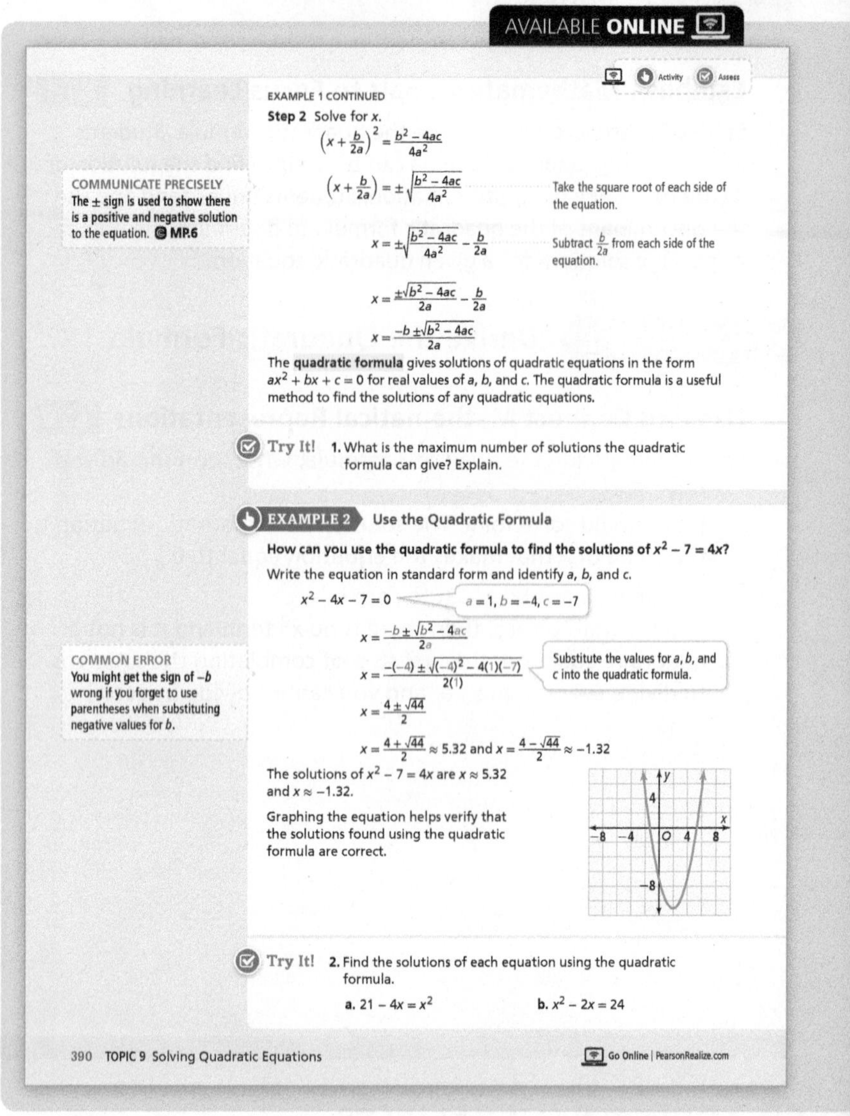

AVAILABLE ONLINE

Activity Assess

EXAMPLE 1 CONTINUED

Step 2 Solve for x.

$$\left(x+\frac{b}{2a}\right)^2=\frac{b^2-4ac}{4a^2}$$

$$\left(x+\frac{b}{2a}\right)=\pm\sqrt{\frac{b^2-4ac}{4a^2}}$$ Take the square root of each side of the equation.

$$x=\pm\sqrt{\frac{b^2-4ac}{4a^2}}-\frac{b}{2a}$$ Subtract $\frac{b}{2a}$ from each side of the equation.

$$x=\frac{\pm\sqrt{b^2-4ac}}{2a}-\frac{b}{2a}$$

$$x=\frac{-b\pm\sqrt{b^2-4ac}}{2a}$$

COMMUNICATE PRECISELY
The ± sign is used to show there is a positive and negative solution to the equation. MP.6

The **quadratic formula** gives solutions of quadratic equations in the form $ax^2 + bx + c = 0$ for real values of a, b, and c. The quadratic formula is a useful method to find the solutions of any quadratic equations.

Try It! 1. What is the maximum number of solutions the quadratic formula can give? Explain.

EXAMPLE 2 Use the Quadratic Formula

How can you use the quadratic formula to find the solutions of $x^2 - 7 = 4x$?

Write the equation in standard form and identify a, b, and c.

$x^2 - 4x - 7 = 0$ — $a = 1, b = -4, c = -7$

$$x=\frac{-b\pm\sqrt{b^2-4ac}}{2a}$$

$$x=\frac{-(-4)\pm\sqrt{(-4)^2-4(1)(-7)}}{2(1)}$$ Substitute the values for a, b, and c into the quadratic formula.

$$x=\frac{4\pm\sqrt{44}}{2}$$

$$x=\frac{4+\sqrt{44}}{2}\approx 5.32 \text{ and } x=\frac{4-\sqrt{44}}{2}\approx -1.32$$

COMMON ERROR
You might get the sign of $-b$ wrong if you forget to use parentheses when substituting negative values for b.

The solutions of $x^2 - 7 = 4x$ are $x \approx 5.32$ and $x \approx -1.32$.

Graphing the equation helps verify that the solutions found using the quadratic formula are correct.

y
4
x
−8
−4
O
4
8
−8

Try It! 2. Find the solutions of each equation using the quadratic formula.
a. $21 - 4x = x^2$
b. $x^2 - 2x = 24$

390 TOPIC 9 Solving Quadratic Equations Go Online | PearsonRealize.com

Struggling Students

USE WITH EXAMPLE 2 Provide this additional example about using the quadratic formula to students who need more practice.

- Solve the following quadratic equation.

$14x^2 + 7 = 21x$

1. What is the equation in standard form?
   [$14x^2 - 21x + 7 = 0$]
2. What are the values for a, b, and c?
   [$a = 14$; $b = -21$; $c = 7$]

Q: What is the solution of the given quadratic equation? [1 and 0.5]

EXAMPLE 3 Find Approximate Solutions

Use and Connect Mathematical Representations ETP

Q: In this context, why do you want to find the value for x when $y = 0$?
[The y-value is a measure of height, so when the height of the frog is zero, he has landed on the ground.]

Q: How does the equation indicate that there are 2 solutions?
[The plus or minus symbol indicates there will be 2 different answers as long as the number under the square root sign is not equal to 0.]

Try It! Answer

3. 0.65 seconds

Elicit and Use Evidence of Student Thinking ETP

Q: What is the related equation for this function?
[$-16x^2 + 10x + 0.3 = 0$]

Common Error

Try It! 3 Some students may forget to include the negative sign for the coefficient –16. Remind the student that the values for *a, b,* and *c* always include the sign of the value. Have students practice naming the coefficients in the following equations:

a. $-3x^2 + 5x - 12 = 0$ [$a = -3$; $b = 5$; $c = -12$]
b. $2x^2 - 9x + 1 = 0$ [$a = 2$; $b = -9$; $c = 1$]
c. $x^2 - 7x - 10 = 0$ [$a = 1$; $b = -7$; $c = -10$]

AVAILABLE **ONLINE**

Activity Assess

APPLICATION

EXAMPLE 3 Find Approximate Solutions

The function shown represents the height of a frog x seconds after it jumps off a rock. How many seconds is the frog in the air before it lands on the ground?

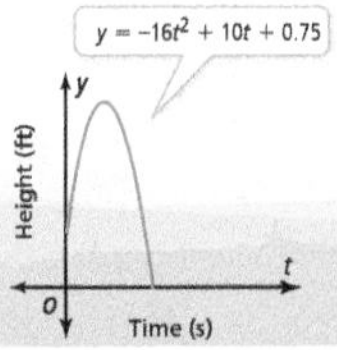
$y = -16t^2 + 10t + 0.75$
y
Height (ft)
t
O
Time (s)

Formulate ◀ Write a related quadratic equation with $y = 0$ to find when the frog lands on the ground. Although the path of the frog's jump is a parabolic curve, you are being asked to find the time of the jump and not the distance of the jump. The function representing the time of the jump is also parabolic, but the parabola is not the same.

$-16t^2 + 10t + 0.75 = 0$

Find the values of a, b, and c in the equation.
$a = -16$, $b = 10$, $c = 0.75$

Compute ◀ Substitute the values of a, b, and c into the quadratic formula.

$$t = \frac{-(10) \pm \sqrt{(10)^2 - 4(-16)(0.75)}}{2(-16)}$$
$$= \frac{-10 \pm \sqrt{148}}{-32}$$
$$= \frac{-10 \pm 12.17}{-32}$$
$$t = \frac{-10 + 12.17}{-32} = -\frac{2.17}{32} \approx -0.068 \text{ and}$$
$$t = \frac{-10 - 12.17}{-32} = \frac{-22.17}{-32} \approx 0.693$$

Interpret ◀ The negative value for t is not a realistic answer in this situation because time is positive.

The frog is in the air about 0.7 s before it lands on the ground.

Try It! **3.** The height of another frog over time is modeled by the function $y = -16t^2 + 10t + 0.3$. How many seconds is this frog in the air before landing on the ground? Round your answer to the nearest hundredth.

ADV Advanced Students

USE WITH EXAMPLE 3 Expand on using the quadratic formula to solve real-world problems with the following example.

- The profit for a company is modeled by the function $f(x) = -10x^2 + 120x + 300$, where x is the cost in dollars and $f(x)$ is the profit.

At what cost does the company not make any profit?
[$14.12; The profit will be $0 when the graph of the function crosses the x-axis, or when $f(x)$ is equal to 0.]

Q: Why is there only 1 solution even though the quadratic formula gives you 2?
[The other answer is negative, and an item cannot have a negative price.]

Activity Assess

EXAMPLE 4 Understand and Use the Discriminant

Use and Connect Mathematical Representations ETP

Q: Why are there 2 real roots when the discriminant is greater than 0?
[If the discriminant is greater than zero, then the square root of the discriminant is both the positive and negative roots. Therefore, there are two possible value for *x*.]

Q: Why is there only 1 real root when the discriminant is equal to zero?
[If the discriminant is equal to zero, then the square root of zero can only be equal to zero, and therefore there is only one solution to the equation.]

Q: Why are there no real solutions when the discriminant is less than zero?
[You cannot take the square root of a negative number.]

Try It! Answers

4. a. 0; 1 root

   b. −4; no roots

Elicit and Use Evidence of Student Thinking ETP

Q: What are the values for *a*, *b*, and *c* in Try It 4b?
[$a = -1$; $b = -6$; $c = -10$]

HABITS OF MIND

Use with **EXAMPLES 3 & 4**

Reason If the equation $4x^2 - bx + 9 = 0$ has only 1 solution, what is the value of *b*? MP.2

[$b = 12$]

AVAILABLE **ONLINE**

Activity Assess

CONCEPTUAL UNDERSTANDING

EXAMPLE 4 Understand and Use the Discriminant

How can you determine the number of solutions of a quadratic equation without solving it?

In the quadratic formula $x = \frac{-b \pm \sqrt{b^2 - 4ac}}{2a}$, the **discriminant** is the expression $b^2 - 4ac$. The discriminant indicates the number of real solutions of the equation. The solutions of a quadratic equation are also called its **roots**. Roots are the input values for which the related function is zero.

If $b^2 - 4ac > 0$, there are two real solutions.
If $b^2 - 4ac = 0$, there is one real solution.
If $b^2 - 4ac < 0$, there are no real solutions.

LOOK FOR RELATIONSHIPS
What does the graph of the related function look like when a quadratic equation has two real solutions? One real solution? No real solutions? MP.7

A. Find the number of solutions for $x^2 - 4x + 3 = 0$.

$x^2 - 4x + 3 = 0$
$(-4)^2 - 4(1)(3) = 4$

The discriminant is > 0, so there are two real roots.

$y = x^2 - 4x + 3$

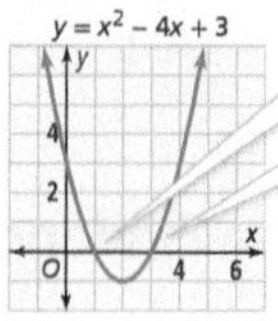

y
4
2
x
O
4
6

The graph of the related function intersects the *x*-axis at two points.

B. Find the solutions for $-x^2 + 4x - 4 = 0$.

$-x^2 + 4x - 4 = 0$
$(4)^2 - 4(-1)(-4) = 0$

The discriminant is 0, so there is one real root.

$y = -x^2 + 4x - 4$

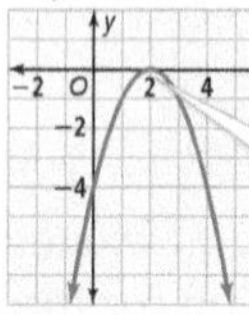

y
x
−2
O
2
4
6
−2
−4

The graph of the related function intersects the *x*-axis at one point.

C. Find the solutions for $x^2 - 4x + 5 = 0$.

$x^2 - 4x + 5 = 0$
$(-4)^2 - 4(1)(5) = -4$

The discriminant is < 0, so there are no real roots.

$y = x^2 - 4x + 5$

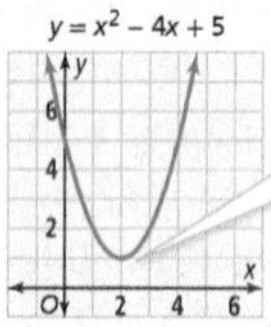

y
6
4
2
x
O
2
4
6

The graph of the related function does not intersect the *x*-axis.

Try It! 4. Use the discriminant to find the number of roots of each equation.

a. $x^2 - 10x + 25 = 0$ b. $-x^2 - 6x - 10 = 0$

392 TOPIC 9 Solving Quadratic Equations Go Online | PearsonRealize.com

ELL English Language Learners *(Use with* **EXAMPLE 4***)*

READING BEGINNING Have students read the following synonyms for the word *root*: *solution, essence, core, foundation, ancestor, clap,* or *cheer.* Then have students read the sentence from the example in which the word *root* is highlighted.

Q: Which synonyms apply to the use of *root* in this sentence?
[*Solution, essence, core,* and *foundation* are all implied.]

Q: What clues in the sentence point to these synonyms?
[*solutions* and *related*]

SPEAKING INTERMEDIATE Display the quadratic formula. In small groups, have students discuss the following questions about formulas.

Q: What are some characteristics of *formulas*?
[equations, use meaningful variables to represent different quantities, have real-world applications]

Q: What is the purpose of the *quadratic formula*?
[to solve any quadratic equation, especially those that are not easy to factor]

Q: Is $b^2 - 4ac$ a *formula*?
[No, it is not an equation. It is an algebra expression that is part of a formula.]

LISTENING ADVANCED Distribute notecards with *True* on one side and *False* on the other. Ask students to listen to the following statements about the term *zero.* Have them hold up the correct side of the card to indicate whether each statement is true or false.

Q: Zero is a positive number. [false]

Q: The origin is labeled with coordinates of zero. [true]

Q: Points with *x*-values of zero are always roots of an equation. [false]

Q: Points with *y*-values of zero are roots of an equation. [true]

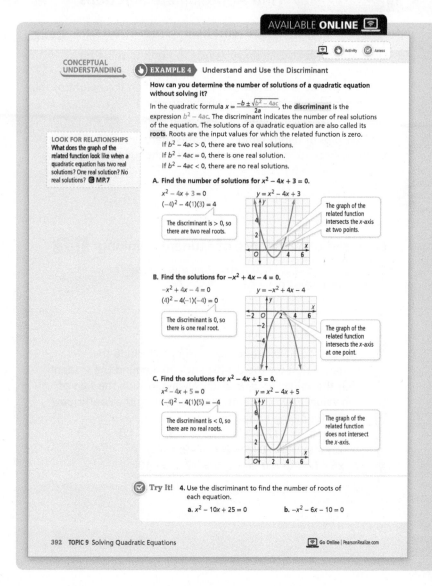

CONCEPT SUMMARY Using the Quadratic Formula

Q: When is the quadratic formula useful?
[when a quadratic equation is not factorable; when you need to approximate the answer to a real-world situation involving a quadratic equation]

Do You UNDERSTAND? | Do You KNOW HOW?

Common Error

Exercise 8 Some students may mistakenly think that $a = 0$ because there is no visible value for a. Ask students to add $a + 2a$. What is the result? [$3a$] What coefficient did they use for the first term? [1] Have students write the number 1 in front of all variables that do not show a coefficient.

Answers

1. Use the quadratic formula when you cannot factor easily and when completing the square would result in many fractions.
2. $4ac$; When the discriminant is 0, there is one real solution. For the discriminant $b^2 - 4ac$ to be 0, b^2 must equal $4ac$.
3. The discriminant tells you the number of roots.
4. Although the equation has no x-term, you can still use the quadratic formula. Just use $b = 0$.
5. Completing the square is better than using the quadratic formula when $a = 1$ and b is an even number, so the number to complete the square is a positive integer.
6. $a = 4$, $b = 2$, $c = -1$
7. $a = -1$, $b = 31$, $c = 7$
8. $a = 2$, $b = -10$, $c = -3$
9. $a = 1$, $b = 1$, $c = -1$
10. 2
11. 0
12. 1
13. 2

AVAILABLE **ONLINE**

Concept Summary Assess

CONCEPT SUMMARY Using the Quadratic Formula

	Equation	Quadratic Formula	Discriminant
ALGEBRA	$ax^2 + bx + c = 0$	$x = \frac{-b \pm \sqrt{b^2 - 4ac}}{2a}$	$b^2 - 4ac$
NUMBERS	$2x^2 - 3x - 1 = 0$	$x = \frac{-(-3) \pm \sqrt{(-3)^2 - 4(2)(-1)}}{2(2)}$ $x = \frac{3 + \sqrt{17}}{4} \approx 1.78$ and $x = \frac{3 - \sqrt{17}}{4} \approx -0.28$	$(-3)^2 - 4(2)(-1) = 17$ $17 > 0$, two real solutions
	Related Function		
GRAPH	$y = 2x^2 - 3x - 1$ 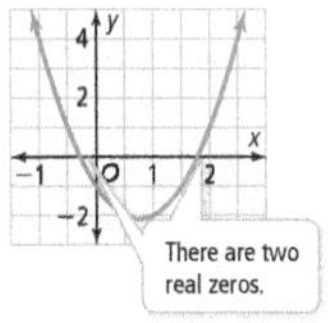		The discriminant of the related equation is > 0.

y
4
2
x
−1
O
1
2
−2
There are two real zeros.

Do You UNDERSTAND?

1. ESSENTIAL QUESTION When should you use the quadratic formula to solve equations?
2. Reason What value of b^2 is needed for there to be exactly one real solution of a quadratic equation? Explain. MP.2
3. Vocabulary How are the *roots* of a quadratic equation related to its *discriminant*?
4. Error Analysis A student says that the quadratic formula cannot be used to solve $-23x^2 + 5 = 0$. Explain the error the student made. MP.3
5. Reason When is completing the square better than using the quadratic formula? MP.2

Do You KNOW HOW?

Identify *a*, *b*, and *c* in each of the quadratic equations.

6. $4x^2 + 2x - 1 = 0$
7. $-x^2 + 31x + 7 = 0$
8. $2x^2 - 10x - 3 = 0$
9. $x^2 + x - 1 = 0$

Given the discriminant of a quadratic equation, determine the number of real solutions.

10. 8
11. −3
12. 0
13. 1

LESSON 9-6 The Quadratic Formula and the Discriminant 393

PRACTICE & PROBLEM SOLVING

AVAILABLE ONLINE

Lesson Practice You may opt to have students complete the automatically scored Practice and Problem Solving items online powered by MathXL for School.

Choose from: **Lesson Practice**

Adaptive Practice

You may also take advantage of the bank of exercises for assigning additional practice.

Assignment Guide

Basic	Advanced
14–32, 37–44	14–18, 23–44

Item Analysis

Example	Items	DOK
1	14	1
2	19–28	1
	15–17	2
3	39–41, 44	2
4	29–38, 42, 43	1
	18	3

AVAILABLE ONLINE

PRACTICE & PROBLEM SOLVING

Scan for Multimedia

Practice Tutorial

Additional Exercises Available Online

UNDERSTAND

14. Mathematical Connections Why does a quadratic equation have to be in standard form before applying the quadratic formula to find solutions?

15. Error Analysis Describe and correct the error a student made in solving $3x^2 + 9x - 4 = 0$. MP.3

$a = 3, b = 9, c = -4$

$x = \frac{-9 + \sqrt{9^2 - 4(3)(-4)}}{2(3)}$

$= \frac{-9 + \sqrt{129}}{6}$

≈ 0.39

✗

16. Reason Which method would you use to solve each equation? Explain. MP.2

a. $x^2 + 9x = 0$

b. $11x^2 - 4 = 0$

c. $7x^2 + 11x - 6 = 0$

17. Use Structure The graph of a quadratic function is shown below. Describe how you could change the graph so that the discriminant of the new related quadratic equation is positive. MP.7

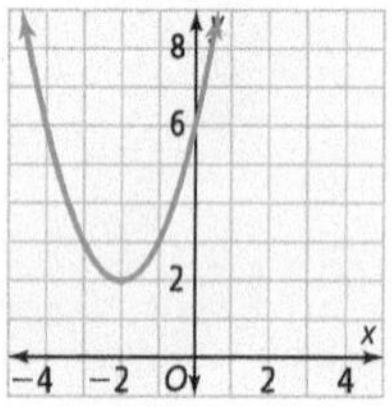

18. Higher Order Thinking Use the quadratic formula to prove the axis of symmetry can be found using $-\frac{b}{2a}$. What does the discriminant of a quadratic equation tell you about the vertex of the graph of the related function?

PRACTICE

Solve each equation using the quadratic formula. Round to the nearest hundredth.
SEE EXAMPLES 1, 2, AND 3

19. $-2x^2 + 12x - 5 = 0$ $x \approx 0.45$ and $x \approx 5.55$

20. $x^2 + 19x - 7 = 0$ $x \approx 0.36$ and $x \approx -19.36$

21. $3x^2 + 18x - 27 = 0$ $x \approx 1.24$ and $x \approx -7.24$

22. $-7x^2 + 2x + 1 = 0$ $x \approx -0.26$ and $x \approx 0.55$

23. $2x^2 + 9x + 7 = 0$ $x = -1$ and $x = -3.5$

24. $-x^2 + 9x + 5 = -3$ $x \approx -0.82$ and $x \approx 9.82$

25. $4x^2 + 17x - 5 = 4$ $x \approx 0.48$ and $x \approx -4.73$

26. $5x^2 + 10x + 7 = 2$ $x = -1$

27. $-6x^2 + 5x - 2 = -11$ $x \approx -0.88$ and $x \approx 1.71$

28. $-2x^2 + 4x + 9 = -3$ $x \approx -1.65$ and $x \approx 3.65$

Use the discriminant to determine the real roots for each equation. SEE EXAMPLE 4

29. $3x^2 - 9x - 16 = 0$ 273; 2

30. $-4x^2 + 7x - 11 = 0$ −127; 0

31. $2x^2 - 6x + 3 = 0$ 12; 2

32. $5x^2 - 20x + 20 = 0$ 0; 1

33. $7x^2 - 14x + 12 = 5$ 0; 1

34. $9x^2 + 5x - 2 = -4$ −47; 0

35. $-8x^2 - 3x - 1 = 5$ −183; 0

36. $2x^2 - 21x - 7 = 4$ 529; 2

For each graph, determine the number of roots the related quadratic equation has. Then determine whether its discriminant is greater than, equal to, or less than zero. SEE EXAMPLE 4

37.

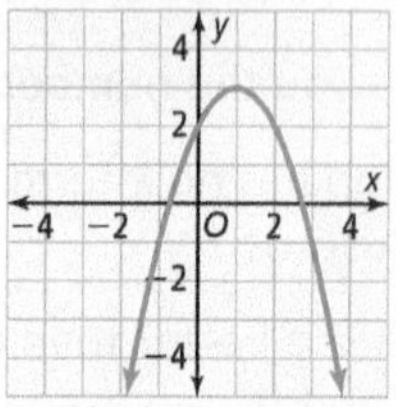

2 real solutions; greater than 0

38.

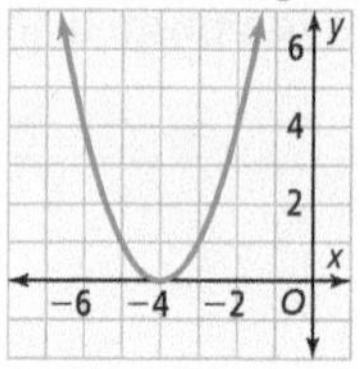

1 real solution; equal to 0

394 TOPIC 9 Solving Quadratic Equations

Go Online | PearsonRealize.com

Answers

14. The Quadratic Formula is derived by solving the general standard form quadratic equation $ax^2 + bx + c = 0$. So, the Quadratic Formula works only if the a, b, and c you use have the same meaning that they did in the original derivation.

15. The student used a plus sign instead of a plus or minus sign. In addition to the solution $x = 0.39$, there is also the solution $x = -3.39$.

16. a. factoring; The terms in this equation have a common factor.

b. square root; In this equation, there is no x-term, so taking the square root of both sides after isolating the x^2-term is efficient.

c. quadratic formula; The left side of the equation is not factorable. Although you could use completing the square to solve this equation, it would involve many fractions. So, using the quadratic formula is easier.

17. Shift the parabola down by 3 units. Then it will cross the x-axis twice, which means it will have 2 roots. When a quadratic function has 2 roots, the discriminant is positive.

18. By setting the discriminant equal to zero, you can find the x-value that is associated with the vertex. This gives the equation $x = \frac{-b \pm \sqrt{0}}{2a} = \frac{-b}{2a}$. If the discriminant is 0, then the vertex lies on the x-axis. This is the only way for a parabola to touch the x-axis only once that corresponds to one root.

Answers

39. The discriminant must be greater than 0. The graph of the function that models the height of an object over time is a parabola that opens down. Because a height of 0 represents the ground, eventually the object will hit the ground. Unless the object is launched from the ground, one of the roots will be negative, which can be discarded in the context of the problem since time is not negative.

40. a. $-16x^2 + 64x + 5 = 20$

b. 2

c. $x = 0.25$ and $x = 3.75$

41. a. $1{,}250 = -5n^2 + 85n + 1{,}000$

b. $x = 3.78$, $x = 13.22$; The two prices that will result in the student council exactly meeting their goal are \$11.78 and \$21.22.

44. Part A Check students' answers.

Part B 3.29 seconds

Part C 3.23 seconds

Part D Check students' answers.

AVAILABLE **ONLINE**

PRACTICE & PROBLEM SOLVING

Practice Tutorial

Mixed Review Available Online

APPLY

39. Reason A quadratic function can be used to model the height y of an object that is thrown over time x. What are the values of the discriminant of the related equation of the function $f(x) = -16t^2 + 35t + 5$, which models a ball being thrown into the air? **MP.2**

40. Model With Mathematics The function $f(x) = -16x^2 + 64x + 5$ models the height y, in feet, of a watermelon from a watermelon launcher after x seconds. **MP.4**

(x, y)

a. Write a quadratic equation that can be used to determine when the watermelon reaches 20 ft.

b. Use the discriminant to predict the number of solutions to the equation from part (a).

c. What are the approximate solutions of the equation you wrote in part a?

41. Make Sense and Persevere The student council is raising money for school dances by selling spirit T-shirts. The function $R = -5n^2 + 85n + 1{,}000$ models the revenue R in dollars they expect per increase of n dollars over the original price of each T-shirt. The goal is \$1,250. **MP.1**

Go Tigers!
$8.00

a. Write a quadratic equation to find the dollar increase n in price needed to meet this goal.

b. Solve the equation using the quadratic formula. What price(s) will result in the student council meeting their goal?

ASSESSMENT PRACTICE

42. A quadratic equation has no real solutions. Choose *Yes* or *No* to tell whether each is a possible value of the discriminant.

	Yes	No
−4	■	☐
−2	■	☐
0	☐	■
2	☐	■
4	☐	■

43. SAT/ACT What is the discriminant of $x^2 - x - 3 = 0$?

Ⓐ −11
Ⓑ 0
Ⓒ 11
Ⓓ 13
Ⓔ −13

44. Performance Task A skier made 2 jumps that were recorded by her coach. A function that models the height y, in meters, at x seconds for each jump is shown.

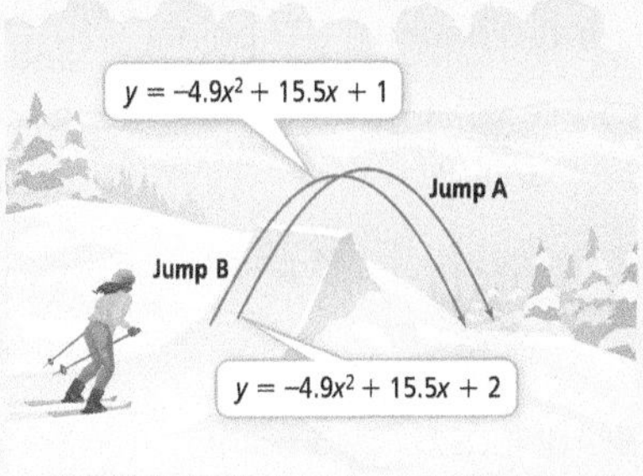
y = −4.9x² + 15.5x + 1
Jump A
Jump B
y = −4.9x² + 15.5x + 2

Part A Predict which jump kept the skier in the air for the greatest number of seconds.

Part B Use the quadratic formula to find how long the skier was in the air during Jump A.

Part C Use the quadratic formula to find how long the skier was in the air during Jump B.

Part D Do your results support your prediction? Explain.

LESSON QUIZ

Use the Lesson Quiz to assess students' understanding of the mathematics in the lesson.

Students can take the Lesson Quiz online or you can download a printable copy from **SavvasRealize.com**. The Lesson Quiz is also available in the *Assessment Resources* book.

Item Analysis

Item	DOK	Standards
1	1	HSA.REI.B.4.B, HSA.SSE.B.3
2	1	HSA.REI.B.4.B, HSA.SSE.B.3
3	1	HSA.REI.B.4.B
4	1	HSA.REI.B.4.B
5	1	HSA.CED.A.1

RtI Use the student scores on the Lesson Quiz to prescribe differentiated assignments.

If students take the Lesson Quiz online, it will be automatically scored and appropriate differentiated practice will be assigned based on student performance.

I Intervention	0–3 points	• Reteach to Build Understanding • Mathematical Literacy and Vocabulary • Additional Practice
O On-Level	4 points	• Mathematical Literacy and Vocabulary • Additional Practice • Enrichment
A Advanced	5 points	• Enrichment

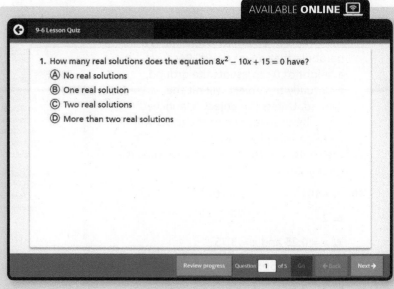

AVAILABLE **ONLINE**

9-6 Lesson Quiz

1. How many real solutions does the equation $8x^2 - 10x + 15 = 0$ have?
   Ⓐ No real solutions
   Ⓑ One real solution
   Ⓒ Two real solutions
   Ⓓ More than two real solutions

Review progress Question 1 of 5 Go Back Next

ASSESSMENT RESOURCES

Name ______________________

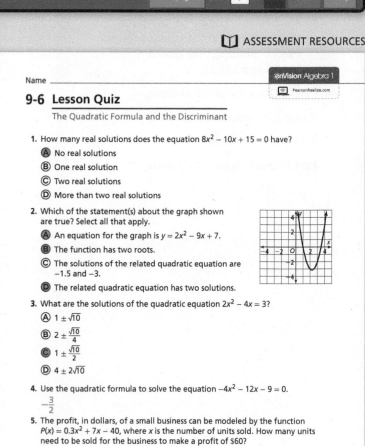

enVision Algebra 1 PearsonRealize.com

9-6 Lesson Quiz

The Quadratic Formula and the Discriminant

1. How many real solutions does the equation $8x^2 - 10x + 15 = 0$ have?
   Ⓐ No real solutions
   Ⓑ One real solution
   Ⓒ Two real solutions
   Ⓓ More than two real solutions

2. Which of the statement(s) about the graph shown are true? Select all that apply.

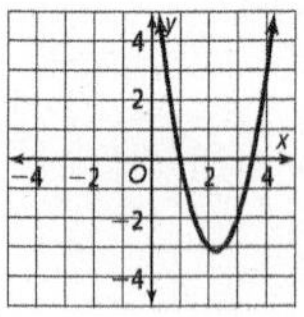

4
2
x
−4
−2
O
2
4
−2
−4
y

   Ⓐ An equation for the graph is $y = 2x^2 - 9x + 7$.
   Ⓑ The function has two roots.
   Ⓒ The solutions of the related quadratic equation are −1.5 and −3.
   Ⓓ The related quadratic equation has two solutions.

3. What are the solutions of the quadratic equation $2x^2 - 4x = 3$?
   Ⓐ $1 \pm \sqrt{10}$
   Ⓑ $2 \pm \frac{\sqrt{10}}{4}$
   Ⓒ $1 \pm \frac{\sqrt{10}}{2}$
   Ⓓ $4 \pm 2\sqrt{10}$

4. Use the quadratic formula to solve the equation $-4x^2 - 12x - 9 = 0$.
   $-\frac{3}{2}$

5. The profit, in dollars, of a small business can be modeled by the function $P(x) = 0.3x^2 + 7x - 40$, where x is the number of units sold. How many units need to be sold for the business to make a profit of $60?
   10 units

enVision™ **Algebra 1** • Assessment Resources

DIFFERENTIATED RESOURCES

I = Intervention O = On-Level A = Advanced

= This activity is available as a digital assignment powered by MathXL® for School.

AVAILABLE ONLINE

Reteach to Build Understanding I

Provides scaffolded reteaching for the key lesson concepts.

Name

9-6 Reteach to Build Understanding

The Quadratic Formula and the Discriminant

1. Fill in the blanks to complete the statements.

   For a quadratic equation $ax^2 + bx + c = 0$, the quadratic formula gives the solutions of the equation as $x = \frac{-b \pm \sqrt{b^2 - 4ac}}{2a}$. The discriminant is $b^2 - 4ac$.

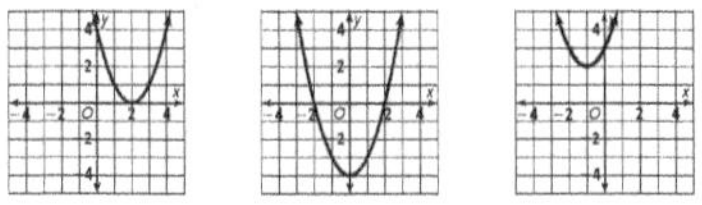

When the discriminant is 0, there is one real root. | When the discriminant is positive, there are two real roots. | When the discriminant is negative, there are no real roots.

2. Fill in the blanks with numbers to find the solutions of $x^2 - 5 = 3x$ using the quadratic formula.

   Step 1 Write the equation in standard form and identify a, b, and c.

   $x^2 - 3x - 5 = 0$

   $a = 1$, $b = -3$, $c = -5$

   Step 2 Substitute the values for a, b, and c into the quadratic formula.

   $x = \frac{-b \pm \sqrt{b^2 - 4ac}}{2a}$

   $x = \frac{-(-3) \pm \sqrt{(-3)^2 - 4(1)(-5)}}{2(1)}$

   Step 3 Simplify.

   $x = \frac{3 \pm \sqrt{29}}{2}$

   $x = \frac{3 + \sqrt{29}}{2} \approx 4.19$ or $x = \frac{3 - \sqrt{29}}{2} \approx -1.19$

   The solutions of $x^2 - 5 = 3x$ are $x \approx 4.19$ and $x \approx -1.19$.

3. A student says that she can use the discriminant to find the solutions of an equation. Explain the error the student made.

   The discriminant can be used to find the number of x-intercepts or to find the number of solutions of an equation, not the actual solutions or x-intercepts.

enVision™ Algebra 1 • Teaching Resources

Additional Practice I O

Provides extra practice for each lesson.

Name

9-6 Additional Practice

The Quadratic Formula and the Discriminant

Solve each equation using the quadratic formula. If necessary, round any answers to the nearest hundredth.

1. $7x^2 + 8x + 1 = 0$ — $-1, -\frac{1}{7}$
2. $2x^2 - 28x = -98$ — 7
3. $2x^2 - 3x = -1$ — $\frac{1}{2}, 1$
4. $2x^2 - 6x + 4 = 0$ — 1, 2
5. $2x^2 - 6x - 8 = 0$ — $-1, 4$
6. $4x^2 + 3 = 8x$ — $\frac{1}{2}, \frac{3}{2}$
7. $x^2 - 2x = 2$ — $-0.73, 2.73$
8. $-x^2 - 4x + 2 = 0$ — $-4.45, 0.45$
9. $3x^2 + 10x = 5$ — $-3.77, 0.44$

Use the discriminant to find the number of roots of each equation.

10. $x^2 - 8x - 3 = 0$ — two
11. $-x^2 - 2x = 10$ — none
12. $4x^2 = 20x - 25$ — one
13. When is the quadratic formula useful for solving equations?

    Sample answer: The quadratic formula is useful if the equation is not factorable or when factoring or completing the square is very difficult.
14. Leroy shoots a basketball through the air in an attempt to score two points. The height h of the ball in feet as a function of the distance d in feet that the ball travels horizontally is given by $h = -d^2 + 10d + 5$. How far horizontally from Leroy will the ball land on the ground if it does not hit the backboard or the rim of the basket?

    about 10.48 ft

enVision™ Algebra 1 • Teaching Resources

Enrichment O A

Presents engaging problems and activities that extend the lesson concepts.

Name

9-6 Enrichment

The Quadratic Formula and the Discriminant

The discriminant tells the number of real solutions of a quadratic equation $ax^2 + bx + c = 0$. When the quadratic equation is used to define a function, $f(x) = ax^2 + bx + c$, the discriminant lets you predict the number of x-intercepts of the function's graph.

Discriminant	Positive Discriminant $b^2 - 4ac > 0$	Discriminant Zero $b^2 - 4ac = 0$	Negative Discriminant $b^2 - 4ac < 0$
$b^2 - 4ac$	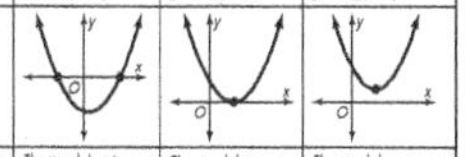		
Number of x-intercepts of graph of related function	The graph has two x-intercepts.	The graph has one x-intercept.	The graph has no x-intercepts.

Use the discriminant of the related quadratic equation to determine the number of x-intercepts of the graph of the function. Then make one change to the equation so that the number of x-intercepts changes from 2 to 0, 0 to 1, or 1 to 2. The first one has been done for you.

1. $y = x^2 - 3x - 8$
   Discriminant = 41
   2 x-intercepts
   $y = x^2 - 3x + 8$ (change to + 8)
   Discriminant = −23
   0 x-intercepts
2. $y = x^2 + 2x + 9$
   Discriminant = −32
   0 x-intercept(s)
   $y = x^2 + 6x + 9$
   Discriminant = 0
   1 x-intercept(s)
3. $y = 2x^2 + 28x + 98$
   Discriminant = 0
   1 x-intercept(s)
   $y = x^2 + 28x + 98$
   Discriminant = 392
   2 x-intercept(s)
4. $y = x^2 - 7x - 15$
   Discriminant = 109
   2 x-intercept(s)
   $y = x^2 - 7x + 15$
   Discriminant = −11
   0 x-intercept(s)

enVision™ Algebra 1 • Teaching Resources

Mathematical Literacy and Vocabulary I O

Helps students develop and reinforce understanding of key terms and concepts.

Name

9-6 Mathematical Literacy and Vocabulary

The Quadratic Formula and the Discriminant

Complete the table by filling in the missing information.

Word or Word Phrase	Definition	Example
quadratic equation	An equation that can be written in the standard form $ax^2 + bx + c = 0$, where $a \neq 0$.	$x^2 - 2x + 5 = 0$
quadratic formula	A formula that gives solutions of quadratic equations of the form $ax^2 + bx + c = 0$.	1. $x = \frac{-b \pm \sqrt{b^2 - 4ac}}{2a}$
discriminant	2. The expression $b^2 - 4ac$ in the quadratic formula.	The discriminant of $4x^2 + 6x - 5 = 0$ is 116.
root	The input value(s) for which the related function is 0.	3. Sample: The roots of $y = x^2 + 13x + 42$ are −7 and −6.

enVision™ Algebra 1 • Teaching Resources

Digital Resources and Video Tutorials I O A

The **Reteach to Build Understanding**, **Additional Practice**, and **Enrichment** activities are available as digital assignments powered by MathXL for School. These activities are automatically assigned when students complete the lesson quiz online and are automatically scored.

Students can access instructional tutorials using the **Virtual Nerd app**.

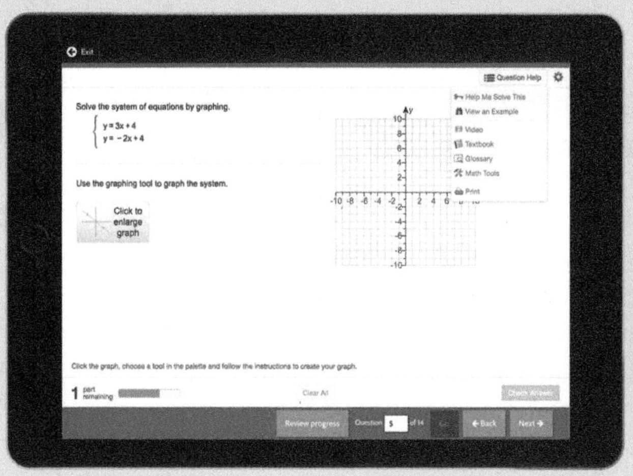

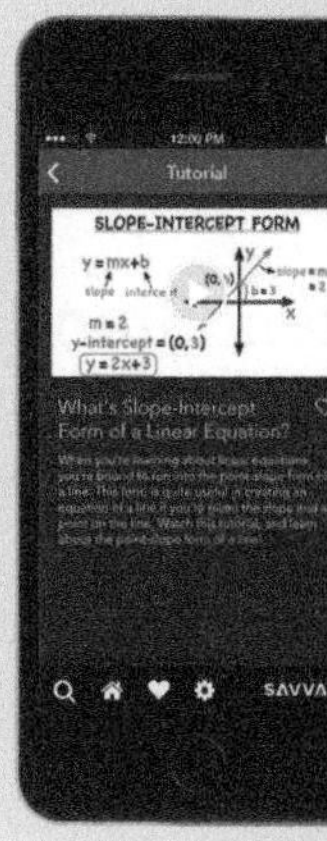

Students can also access Virtual Nerd videos using the **BouncePages app** to scan exercise pages marked with this icon. Students can download both apps for free in their mobile devices' app store.

SavvasRealize.com

Video

TOPIC 9
Mathematical Modeling in 3 Acts: Unwrapping Change

Lesson Overview

FOCUS

Objective

Students will be able to:

✓ Use mathematical modeling to represent a problem situation.

✓ Test and verify the appropriateness of their math models.

✓ Explain why the results might not exactly match the problem situation.

Essential Understanding

Many real-world problem situations can be represented with a mathematical model, but that model might not represent the real-world situation exactly.

COHERENCE

Earlier in this topic, students:

- Solved quadratic equations using a variety of methods.

In this lesson, students:

- Develop a mathematical model to represent and propose a solution to a problem situation involving quadratic equations.

Later in this topic, students will:

- Refine their mathematical modeling skills using linear-quadratic systems.

RIGOR

This mathematical modeling lesson focuses on application of both math content and math practices and processes.

- Students draw on their understanding of concepts related to quadratic equations to develop a representative model.
- Students apply their mathematical model to test and validate its applicability to similar problem situations.

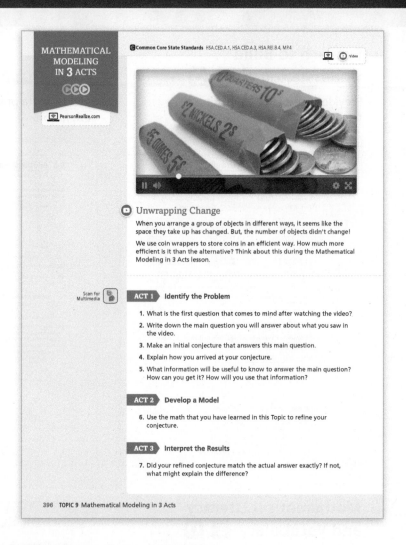

MATHEMATICAL MODELING IN 3 ACTS

PearsonRealize.com

Common Core State Standards HSA.CED.A.1, HSA.CED.A.3, HSA.REI.B.4, MP.4

Video

QUARTERS 10$
$2 NICKELS 2S
$5 DIMES 5S

Unwrapping Change

When you arrange a group of objects in different ways, it seems like the space they take up has changed. But, the number of objects didn't change!

We use coin wrappers to store coins in an efficient way. How much more efficient is it than the alternative? Think about this during the Mathematical Modeling in 3 Acts lesson.

Scan for Multimedia

ACT 1 Identify the Problem

1. What is the first question that comes to mind after watching the video?
2. Write down the main question you will answer about what you saw in the video.
3. Make an initial conjecture that answers this main question.
4. Explain how you arrived at your conjecture.
5. What information will be useful to know to answer the main question? How can you get it? How will you use that information?

ACT 2 Develop a Model

6. Use the math that you have learned in this Topic to refine your conjecture.

ACT 3 Interpret the Results

7. Did your refined conjecture match the actual answer exactly? If not, what might explain the difference?

396 TOPIC 9 Mathematical Modeling in 3 Acts

Student Companion

Students can do their work for the task on pages 213–214 of their *Student Companion* or on **SavvasRealize.com**.

Mathematics Overview COMMON CORE STANDARDS

Content Standards

In this lesson, students apply concepts and skills related to Common Core Standards **HSA.CED.A.1**, **HSA.CED.A.3**, and **HSA.REI.B.4**.

HSA.CED.A.1 Create equations and inequalities in one variable and use them to solve problems.

HSA.CED.A.3 Represent constraints by equations or inequalities, and by systems of equations and/or inequalities, and interpret solutions as viable or nonviable options in a modeling context.

HSA.REI.B.4 Solve quadratic equations in one variable.

Mathematical Practice Standards

MP.4 Model with Mathematics

To solve the problem presented, students identify variables and the relationship among them, develop a model that represents the situation, and use the model to propose a solution. Students interpret their solutions and propose explanations for why their answer may not match the real-world answer.

Students also engage in sense-making (**MP.1**), abstract and quantitative reasoning (**MP.2**), and mathematical communication and argumentation (**MP.3**). In testing their models, students look for patterns in the structure of their models (**MP.7, MP.8**).

SavvasRealize.com

Video

Unwrapping Change

In this mathematical modeling task, students analyze the relationship between the length of a coin wrapper and the area of the coins inside it. They need to determine what the amount of money is when the perimeter of a circle of coins is identical to the length of the corresponding wrappers. To do so, they apply concepts they study in Topic 9.

ACT 1 The Hook

Play the video. The video shows a student emptying rolls of coins and laying the coins and wrappers in a pattern. The first two rolls of coins are shown.

After the question brainstorming, present to students the main question they will be tasked with answering. Remind students to write down their questions and conjectures.

MAIN QUESTION

What is the value of the coins when the length of the wrappers is exactly the circumference of the coin circle?

ACT 2 Modeling With Math

Think about the task. Ask students to speculate how they can determine the total value of the coins. Then have them think about what information they need.

Reveal the information. The images show information about the dimensions of the coins and wrappers, as well as sample data.

What's the connection? Give students time to struggle as they think about how to connect their ideas to what they learned in this topic about quadratic functions. Which measure on a circle can you model with a quadratic function? How are circumference and area of a circle related?

Before showing the answers, find out where there is disagreement. Allow students to argue their cases and update their conjectures.

INTERESTING MOMENTS WITH STUDENTS

Students may incorrectly assume that circumference and area scale similarly. Students may suppose that if 5 wrappers form half the circumference of 5 rolls of coins, then the answer is 10 rolls. Address their misconception by having them find the areas of two circles, one with twice the radius of the other.

Consider what variables to use before writing equations. Students may think that there are too many variables to solve the problem. Remind them that some of the "variables" they are thinking about are actually unknown quantities. The only true variables are the number of rolls, and the area of the circle.

Necessary Information

Coin Roll

number of coins: 50 pennies

length: 3.875 in.

Diameters

1 roll: 6 in.

2 rolls: 8.5 in.

ACT 3 The Solution

Play the video. The final video shows the completion of the activity. The total value of the coins is revealed. Offer praise to the students whose conjectures are closest to the actual answer.

MAIN QUESTION ANSWER

\$12.50 (25 rolls)

Do the "post-game" analysis. Help students understand why the actual result might differ, even slightly, from the mathematical answer. There will always be error when fitting a quadratic model to data, such as the areas of the circles. The actual area and circumference of the circle also depend on how tightly you pack the coins.

ONE POSSIBLE SOLUTION

The length of x coin wrappers is $3.875x$ in.
The area of x coin rolls is about $9\pi x$ in.^{2}.

When the length of the wrappers is equal to the circumference of the circle, then $3.875x = 2\pi r$, and $9\pi x = \pi r^2$.

Solve the system. It is easier to isolate x in both equations than to isolate r.

$$x = \frac{2\pi r}{3.875} \qquad x = \frac{\pi r^2}{9\pi}$$

$$\frac{2\pi r}{3.875} = \frac{\pi r^2}{9\pi}$$

$$0 = \frac{\pi r^2}{9\pi} - \frac{2\pi r}{3.875}$$

$$0 = r\left(\frac{\pi r}{9\pi} - \frac{2\pi}{3.875}\right)$$

$$r = 0 \text{ or } \frac{r}{9} - \frac{2\pi}{3.875} = 0$$

$$\frac{r}{9} = \frac{2\pi}{3.875}$$

$$r \approx 14.59$$

Substitute r into either equation.

$$x = \frac{2\pi r}{3.875}$$

$$\approx \frac{2\pi(14.59)}{3.875}$$

$$\approx 23.66$$

The wrappers will surround the coins after about 24 rolls.
24 rolls × \$.50 = \$12

INTERESTING MOMENTS WITH STUDENTS

It's not enough to set circumference and area formulas equal. Students may want to set the formula for circumference equal to the formula for area. Point out that the circumference and area are not the same; they don't even use the same units. Actually, you are looking for when a length measurement is equal to the circumference for a circle with a particular area.

Using the 2-roll circle data is an added layer of difficulty. You can challenge students to use only the 2-roll circle or reconcile both circles before solving. They need to use half the area of the 2-roll circle, which is $\left(\frac{4.25^2}{2}\right)\pi$. Since $\frac{4.25^2}{2} \approx 9.03$, the mathematical answer will still be between 23 and 24 rolls of pennies.

SEQUEL

As students finish, reveal a roll of nickels spread out in a circle. Ask them how they can reuse their solution method for nickel rolls. [Answers will vary. Students' descriptions should include that the unit length of a roll and the area of a roll of nickels will change, but the solution method is the same. They should also notice that a roll has only 40 nickels instead of 50. The value will be around \$38.]

SavvasRealize.com

A-Z Glossary

LESSON 9-7
Solving Systems of Linear and Quadratic Equations

Lesson Overview

FOCUS

Objective

Students will be able to:

✔ Describe a linear-quadratic system of equations.

✔ Solve a linear-quadratic system of equations by graphing, elimination, or substitution.

Essential Understanding

For any system of two equations in two variables, the solution consists of the ordered pairs that satisfy both equations.

COHERENCE

Previously in this course, students:

- Solved systems of linear equations using the methods of graphing, substitution, and elimination.

In this lesson, students:

- Solve linear-quadratic systems of equations using the methods of graphing, substitution, and elimination.

Later in this course, students will:

- Solve systems of quadratic equations.
- Solve linear-quadratic systems of inequalities.

RIGOR

This lesson emphasizes a blend of *conceptual understanding* and *procedural skill and fluency.*

- Students describe and illustrate the different ways a line and a parabola can intersect, and relate those to the possible number of solutions of a linear-quadratic system of equations.
- Students describe and carry out the steps of solving a linear-quadratic system of equations by different methods.

Vocabulary Builder

REVIEW VOCABULARY **English** | *Spanish*

- **elimination method** | *eliminacion*
- **substitution method** | *methodo de sustitucion*

NEW VOCABULARY

- **linear-quadratic system** | *sistema lineal cuadratico*

VOCABULARY ACTIVITY

Review the *elimination method* and the *substitution method* with the students. Name the method that was used for each set of steps. Then order the steps.

System of equations	Method 1	Method 2
$\begin{cases} 2x + 3y = 7 \\ 4x + y = -1 \end{cases}$	A. $2x + 3(-4x - 1) = 7$	A. $\begin{cases} 2x + 3y = 7 \\ 12x + 3y = -3 \end{cases}$
	B. $y = -4x - 1$	B. $x = -1$
	C. $-10x = 10$	C. $-10x = 10$
	D. $2x - 12x - 3 = 7$	D. $y = -1 + 4 = 3$
	E. $y = -4(-1) - 1 = 4 - 1 = 3$	E. $4(-1) + y = -1$
	F. $x = -1$	F. $-4 + y = -1$
	[substitution; B, A, D, C, F, E]	**[elimination; A, C, B, E, F, D]**

Student Companion

Students can do their in-class work for the lesson on pages 215–218 of their *Student Companion* or in Savvas Realize.

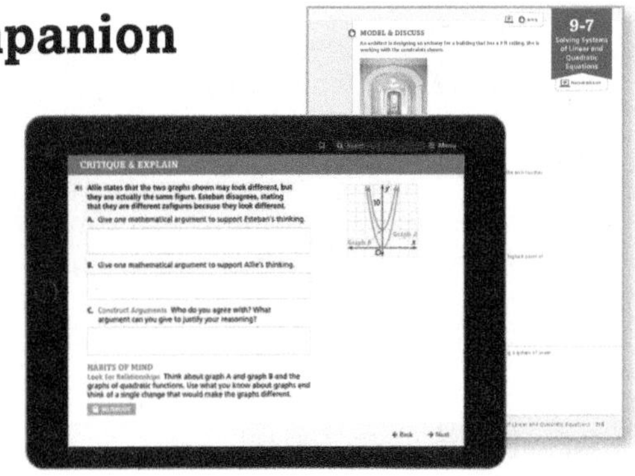

Mathematics Overview COMMON CORE STANDARDS

Content Standards

In this lesson, students focus on this standard:

HSA.REI.C.7 Solve a simple system consisting of a linear equation and a quadratic equation in two variables algebraically and graphically.

They also work with concepts related to this standard: **HSA.REI.D.11**

Mathematical Practice Standards

These standards are highlighted in this lesson:

MP.1 Make Sense of Problems and Persevere in Solving Them

Students persevere when they plan, perform, and describe how to solve a linear-quadratic system of equations by graphing, elimination, or substitution.

MP.7 Look For and Make Use of Structure

For the elimination method, students change the structure of an equation so one variable has the same or opposite coefficients and can thus be eliminated.

Activity

MODEL & DISCUSS

INSTRUCTIONAL FOCUS Students write a model for an archway that reaches the ceiling. Then students describe how to modify their equation so that the archway does not reach the ceiling. This prepares students to recognize that in a plane, a parabola could intersect a line in one point or not at all, which helps them solve linear-quadratic systems of equations.

STUDENT COMPANION Students can complete the *Model & Discuss* activity on page 215 of their *Student Companion.*

Before WHOLE CLASS

Implement Tasks that Promote Reasoning and Problem Solving ETP

Q: What do you know about the height of the archway that can help you write a model?
[The maximum height is 9 ft because that is the height of the ceiling. The maximum height occurs in the center of the archway, and because the opening is 5 ft wide, the vertex is (2.5, 9).]

During SMALL GROUP

Support Productive Struggle in Learning Mathematics ETP

Q: How can you write a quadratic equation that models this situation?
[Identify 3 points on the parabola formed by the archway. Then write a system of quadratic equations in 3 variables and solve the system for *a*, *b*, and *c*.]

Q: Name 3 points on the parabola formed by the archway.
[(0, 7), (2.5, 9), and (5, 7)]

For Early Finishers

Q: Write a model for another archway that is 8 ft wide and touches the ceiling that is 12 ft high if the arch begins to curve $\frac{3}{4}$ of the way up.
[$y = -0.1875x^2 + 1.5x + 9$]

After WHOLE CLASS

Facilitate Meaningful Mathematical Discourse ETP

Q: Why does decreasing the value of *c* cause the archway to no longer reach the ceiling?
[You can decrease the value of *c* by adding a negative constant to the output of the function, causing a vertical shift of the entire parabola downward. When the entire parabola is shifted downward, the highest point will no longer reach the ceiling.]

AVAILABLE **ONLINE**

Go back

MODEL & DISCUSS

An architect is designing entryways for a building that have a maximum height of 9 feet. She is working with the constraints shown in the image, and wants the top of each entryway to be an arch.

A. Find a quadratic model for the arches if the highest point of the arch reaches the maximum height.

Enter your answer.

B. Construct Arguments Describe how to change the model so the highest point of the arch does not reach the maximum height.

Enter your answer.

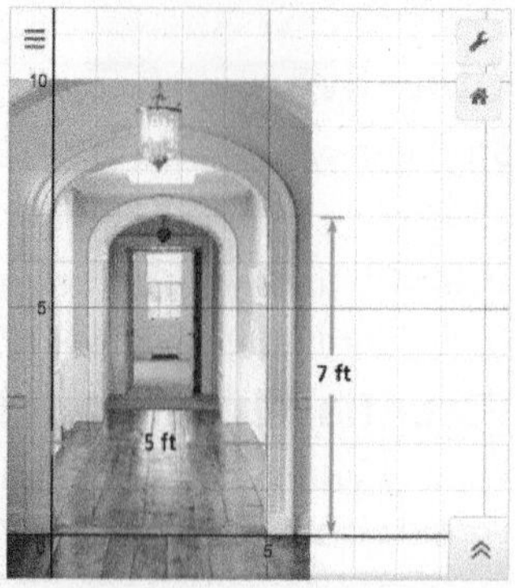

10
5
7 ft
5 ft
0
5

1 of 1

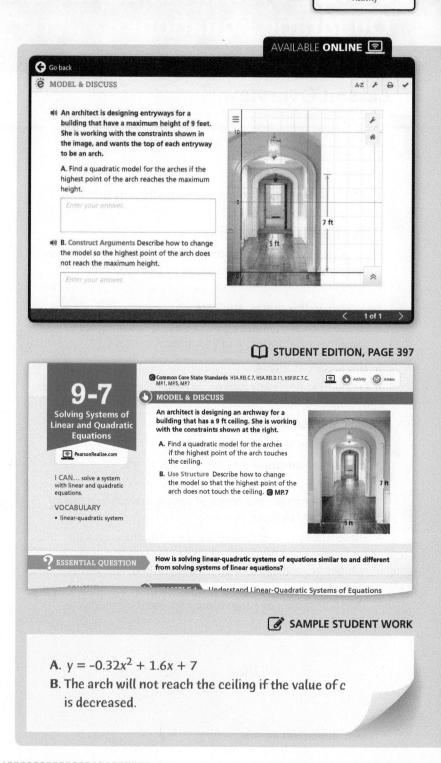

STUDENT EDITION, PAGE 397

9-7 Solving Systems of Linear and Quadratic Equations

PearsonRealize.com

Common Core State Standards HSA.REI.C.7, HSA.REI.D.11, HSF.IF.C.7.C, MP.1, MP.5, MP.7

I CAN… solve a system with linear and quadratic equations.

VOCABULARY
- linear-quadratic system

MODEL & DISCUSS

An architect is designing an archway for a building that has a 9 ft ceiling. She is working with the constraints shown at the right.

A. Find a quadratic model for the arches if the highest point of the arch touches the ceiling.

B. Use Structure Describe how to change the model so that the highest point of the arch does not touch the ceiling. MP.7

7 ft
5 ft

ESSENTIAL QUESTION How is solving linear-quadratic systems of equations similar to and different from solving systems of linear equations?

Understand Linear-Quadratic Systems of Equations

SAMPLE STUDENT WORK

A. $y = -0.32x^2 + 1.6x + 7$

B. The arch will not reach the ceiling if the value of c is decreased.

HABITS OF MIND

Use with **MODEL & DISCUSS**

Use Appropriate Tools What information would you need to determine the method that is used to solve a system of linear equations? Explain. **MP.5**

[When one of the equations is solved for one of the variables, substitution is the best method. When the coefficients or constants are very large, graphing may be the best method. When the coefficients of one of the variables are multiples of each other, elimination is the best method.]

SavvasRealize.com

Activity Assess

INTRODUCE THE ESSENTIAL QUESTION

Establish Mathematics Goals to Focus Learning ETP

Students learn that in a linear-quadratic system of equations, one equation is linear and one equation is quadratic. Students also learn that for any system of two-variable equations, the solution consists of all the (x, y) ordered pairs that satisfy both equations.

EXAMPLE 1 Understand Linear-Quadratic Systems of Equations

Build Procedural Fluency From Conceptual Understanding ETP

Q: How does the graph on the left represent a linear-quadratic system of equations?
[The linear part of the system is the x-axis, $y = 0$.]

Q: If the line in a linear-quadratic system of equations is a vertical line, how many solutions are there?
[one solution; A vertical line has the equation $x = a$, and substituting a for x into the quadratic function always results in exactly one value of y.]

Try It! Answer

1. 2; The graph of $y = x$ intersects the graph of $y = x^2$ at two points: (0, 0) and (1, 1).

AVAILABLE ONLINE

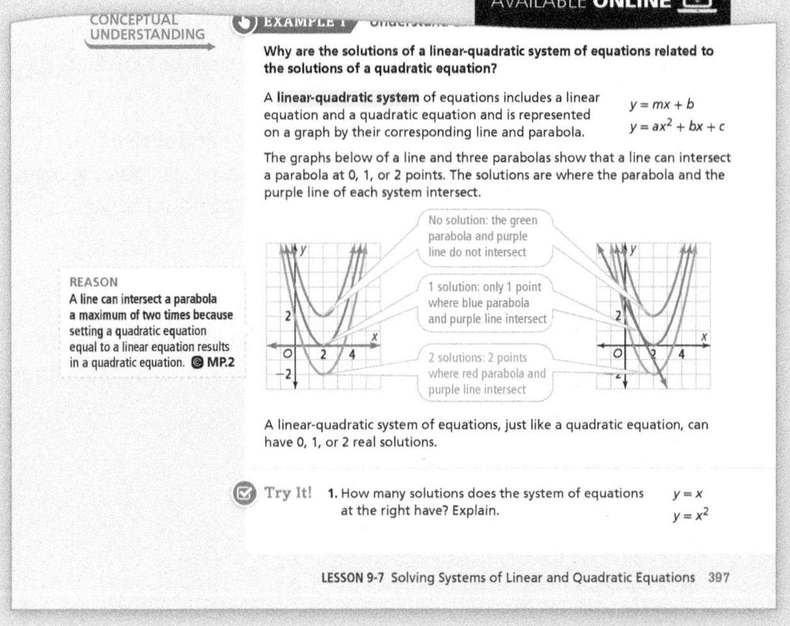

CONCEPTUAL UNDERSTANDING

EXAMPLE 1

Why are the solutions of a linear-quadratic system of equations related to the solutions of a quadratic equation?

A **linear-quadratic system** of equations includes a linear equation and a quadratic equation and is represented on a graph by their corresponding line and parabola.

$y = mx + b$
$y = ax^2 + bx + c$

The graphs below of a line and three parabolas show that a line can intersect a parabola at 0, 1, or 2 points. The solutions are where the parabola and the purple line of each system intersect.

REASON
A line can intersect a parabola a maximum of two times because setting a quadratic equation equal to a linear equation results in a quadratic equation. MP.2

No solution: the green parabola and purple line do not intersect
1 solution: only 1 point where blue parabola and purple line intersect
2 solutions: 2 points where red parabola and purple line intersect
y
x
O
2
4
-2

A linear-quadratic system of equations, just like a quadratic equation, can have 0, 1, or 2 real solutions.

Try It! 1. How many solutions does the system of equations at the right have? Explain.

$y = x$
$y = x^2$

LESSON 9-7 Solving Systems of Linear and Quadratic Equations 397

Elicit and Use Evidence of Student Thinking ETP

Q: How could you use technology to solve the problem?
[Use a graphing calculator to display the graphs of the two equations and count the number of intersections of the graphs.]

AVAILABLE ONLINE

ADDITIONAL EXAMPLES

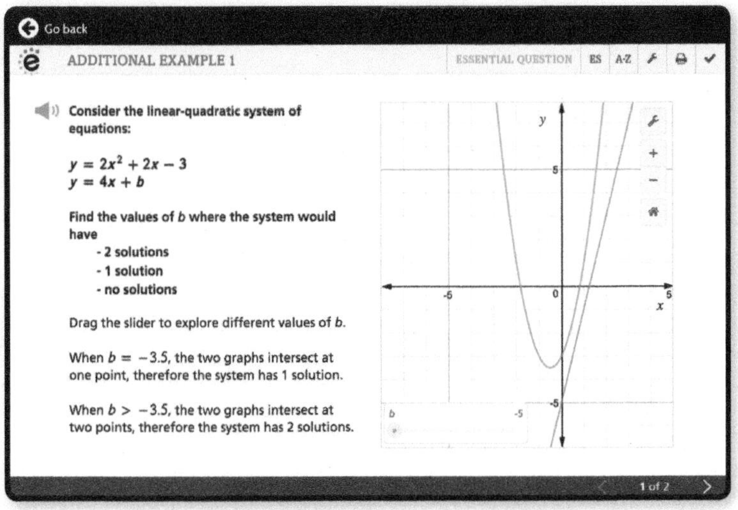

Go back
ADDITIONAL EXAMPLE 1
ESSENTIAL QUESTION
ES
A-Z
Consider the linear-quadratic system of equations:
y = 2x² + 2x − 3
y = 4x + b
Find the values of b where the system would have
- 2 solutions
- 1 solution
- no solutions
Drag the slider to explore different values of b.
When b = −3.5, the two graphs intersect at one point, therefore the system has 1 solution.
When b > −3.5, the two graphs intersect at two points, therefore the system has 2 solutions.
y
x
5
-5
0
b
1 of 2

Example 1 Students practice modifying a linear-quadratic system so that it has 1,2, or no solutions.

Q: Suppose the line intersects the parabola for the original linear-quadratic system of equations. What can you do so the line just touches the parabola?
[Move the line up or down by adjusting the constant in the linear equation until the line just touches the parabola.]

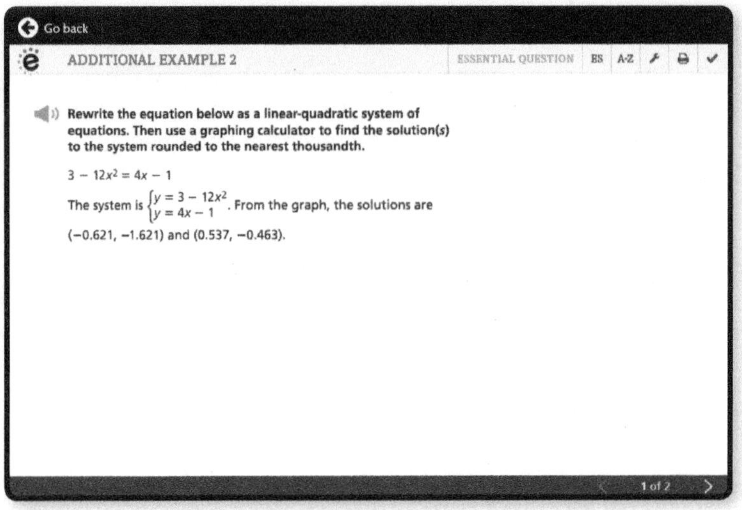

Go back
ADDITIONAL EXAMPLE 2
ESSENTIAL QUESTION
ES
A-Z
Rewrite the equation below as a linear-quadratic system of equations. Then use a graphing calculator to find the solution(s) to the system rounded to the nearest thousandth.
3 − 12x² = 4x − 1
The system is {y = 3 − 12x², y = 4x − 1. From the graph, the solutions are
(−0.621, −1.621) and (0.537, −0.463).
1 of 2

Example 2 Students practice: (1) rewriting a linear-quadratic equation as a linear-quadratic system of equations and (2) using a graphing calculator to find solutions to a linear-quadratic system of equations.

Q: How do you know that the original equation, which has only one variable, requires a two-variable solution?
[The direction line indicates that the problem represents a linear-quadratic system of equations, and that system has two variables.]

Activity Assess

EXAMPLE 2 Solve a Linear-Quadratic Equation by Graphing

Use and Connect Mathematical Representations ETP

Q: What makes it possible to graph this equation?
[Transitive Property; If $5 - x^2$ and $x + 3$ are equal to each other, then they can be set equal to the same variable, y. You can then graph the two equations, each set equal to y.]

Q: How is a linear-quadratic equation related to a linear-quadratic system of equations?
[In a linear-quadratic equation, a linear expression is set equal to a quadratic expression. The two expressions can be rewritten as a linear-quadratic system of equations by setting each side of the equation equal to y.]

Try It! Answers

2. a. $y = x^2 + 1$, $y = x + 3$; -1 and 2

b. $y = 5 - 0.5x^2$, $y = -0.5x + 2$; -2 and 3

HABITS OF MIND

Use with **EXAMPLES 1 & 2**

Communicate Precisely How could you use a table to solve a system of linear and quadratic equations? When does it make sense to use this method? Explain. MP.6

[Use a sketch to find approximate ordered pairs for the point(s) of intersection. Then, using the TABLE feature of a graphing calculator and ranges for x and y from the sketch, find (x, y) values that satisfy both equations. This method can be useful if the equations contain multi-digit decimal coefficients.]

EXAMPLE 3 Solve Systems of Equations Using Elimination

Use and Connect Mathematical Representations ETP

Q: Why is there a space between the equal sign and the first term in the second equation?
[There is not an x^2 term in the second equation, so a space is left to ensure like terms are properly aligned.]

Q: In Step 1, what could you do to the linear-quadratic system of equations in order to use addition rather than subtraction? [Multiply each side of one equation by -1.]

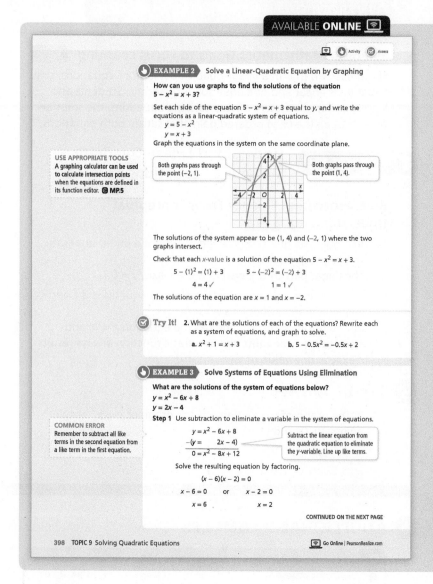

AVAILABLE ONLINE

Activity Assess

EXAMPLE 2 Solve a Linear-Quadratic Equation by Graphing

How can you use graphs to find the solutions of the equation $5 - x^2 = x + 3$?

Set each side of the equation $5 - x^2 = x + 3$ equal to y, and write the equations as a linear-quadratic system of equations.

$y = 5 - x^2$
$y = x + 3$

Graph the equations in the system on the same coordinate plane.

USE APPROPRIATE TOOLS
A graphing calculator can be used to calculate intersection points when the equations are defined in its function editor. MP.5

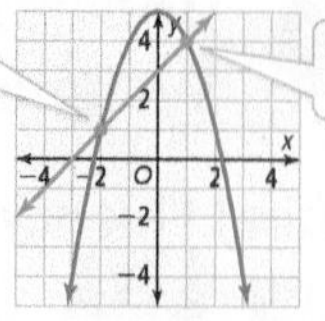

Both graphs pass through the point (–2, 1).
Both graphs pass through the point (1, 4).
y
x
4
2
–4
–2
O
2
4
–2
–4

The solutions of the system appear to be (1, 4) and (–2, 1) where the two graphs intersect.

Check that each x-value is a solution of the equation $5 - x^2 = x + 3$.

$5 - (1)^2 = (1) + 3$ $\quad$ $5 - (-2)^2 = (-2) + 3$
$4 = 4$ ✓ $\quad$ $1 = 1$ ✓

The solutions of the equation are $x = 1$ and $x = -2$.

Try It! 2. What are the solutions of each of the equations? Rewrite each as a system of equations, and graph to solve.

a. $x^2 + 1 = x + 3$ **b.** $5 - 0.5x^2 = -0.5x + 2$

EXAMPLE 3 Solve Systems of Equations Using Elimination

What are the solutions of the system of equations below?
$y = x^2 - 6x + 8$
$y = 2x - 4$

Step 1 Use subtraction to eliminate a variable in the system of equations.

COMMON ERROR
Remember to subtract all like terms in the second equation from a like term in the first equation.

$y = x^2 - 6x + 8$
$-(y = \quad 2x - 4)$
$0 = x^2 - 8x + 12$

Subtract the linear equation from the quadratic equation to eliminate the y-variable. Line up like terms.

Solve the resulting equation by factoring.

$(x - 6)(x - 2) = 0$
$x - 6 = 0$ or $x - 2 = 0$
$x = 6$ $\quad$ $x = 2$

CONTINUED ON THE NEXT PAGE

398 TOPIC 9 Solving Quadratic Equations Go Online | PearsonRealize.com

Struggling Students

USE WITH EXAMPLE 2 Have students use a graphing calculator to graph the equations and find their points of intersection.

Q: How can you use a graphing calculator to graph the two equations in a linear-quadratic system of equations?
[Enter the two equations on a single coordinate grid.]

Q: How can you use a graphing calculator to find the solution(s) of the system of equations?
[Use the Intersection and Trace features to find the coordinates of the points of intersection of the graphs.]

ADV Advanced Students

USE WITH EXAMPLE 3 Ask students to explain when and how the Transitive Property of Equality can be used to eliminate one variable in a system of equations.

Q: How can you use the Transitive Property of Equality to eliminate a variable in Example 3?
[Rewrite the first equation as $x^2 - 6x + 8 = y$. Then apply the Transitive Property to write $x^2 - 6x + 8 = 2x - 4$.]

Q: Do the original equations have to be in a specific form to use the Transitive Property of Equality? [Yes; each equation must have "$y =$" (or some other pair of identical expressions) on one side.]

Try It! Answers

3. a. (−3, 7) and (2, 2)

b. (0, 2) and (5, −3)

Elicit and Use Evidence of Student Thinking ETP

Q: Could you eliminate the *x*-variable in the linear-quadratic system of equations?
[No; because there is a quadratic *x*-term in one equation, but not in the other, there are no multiples of the two equations that could be added to eliminate the *x*-variable.]

Common Error

Try It! 3 Some students may make errors when they use subtraction to eliminate one of the variables. Tell students to multiply each side of one of the equations by −1, and then add to eliminate one of the variables.

AVAILABLE ONLINE

Activity Assess

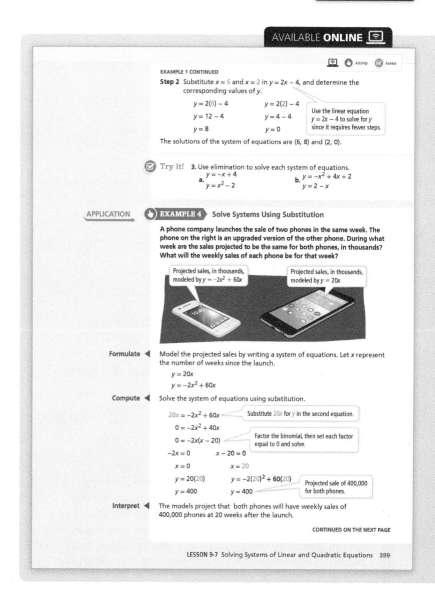

EXAMPLE 1 CONTINUED

Step 2 Substitute $x = 6$ and $x = 2$ in $y = 2x - 4$, and determine the corresponding values of *y*.

$y = 2(6) - 4$ $y = 2(2) - 4$

$y = 12 - 4$ $y = 4 - 4$

$y = 8$ $y = 0$

Use the linear equation $y = 2x - 4$ to solve for *y* since it requires fewer steps.

The solutions of the system of equations are (6, 8) and (2, 0).

Try It! 3. Use elimination to solve each system of equations.

a. $y = -x + 4$, $y = x^2 - 2$ b. $y = -x^2 + 4x + 2$, $y = 2 - x$

APPLICATION

EXAMPLE 4 Solve Systems Using Substitution

A phone company launches the sale of two phones in the same week. The phone on the right is an upgraded version of the other phone. During what week are the sales projected to be the same for both phones, in thousands? What will the weekly sales of each phone be for that week?

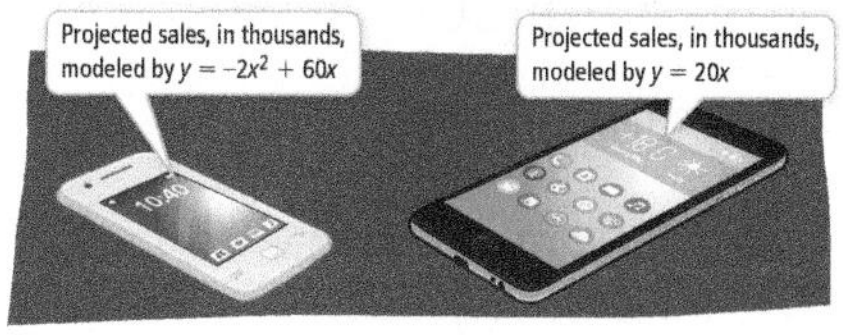
Projected sales, in thousands, modeled by $y = -2x^2 + 60x$
Projected sales, in thousands, modeled by $y = 20x$

Formulate Model the projected sales by writing a system of equations. Let *x* represent the number of weeks since the launch.

$y = 20x$

$y = -2x^2 + 60x$

Compute Solve the system of equations using substitution.

$20x = -2x^2 + 60x$ — Substitute 20*x* for *y* in the second equation.

$0 = -2x^2 + 40x$

$0 = -2x(x - 20)$ — Factor the binomial, then set each factor equal to 0 and solve.

$-2x = 0$ $x - 20 = 0$

$x = 0$ $x = 20$

$y = 20(20)$ $y = -2(20)^2 + 60(20)$

$y = 400$ $y = 400$ — Projected sale of 400,000 for both phones.

Interpret The models project that both phones will have weekly sales of 400,000 phones at 20 weeks after the launch.

CONTINUED ON THE NEXT PAGE

LESSON 9-7 Solving Systems of Linear and Quadratic Equations 399

EXAMPLE 4 Solve Systems Using Substitution

Pose Purposeful Questions ETP

Q: Could you substitute for the *x*-variable to solve this linear-quadratic system of equations?
[Yes, you could rewrite the first equation as $x = \frac{y}{20}$ and substitute that into the second equation. However, that results in an equation that is more difficult to solve.]

ELL English Language Learners *(Use with* **EXAMPLE 4***)*

SPEAKING BEGINNING Display the word *project.* Explain that when *project* is pronounced pROH-ject, it is a verb that means to forecast something in the future. When pronounced as pRAH-ject, it is a noun that means a large undertaking. Have students read the following sentences aloud with a partner, using the correct pronunciation of the word *project.*

Q: Brian has a big science project due on Monday. [pRAH-ject]

Q: The news station refused to project the winner of the election. [pROH-ject]

Q: Read the statement next to the *Interpret* tab. What is the correct pronunciation of the word *project* in the statement? [pROH-ject]

LISTENING INTERMEDIATE Have students listen aloud as you read the first sentence of the example several times. Point out the words *sale, two,* and *week.* Discuss the differences between *sale/sail, two/to,* and *week/weak.* Distribute three cards to students with pairs of homophones written on each side. Read the following sentences aloud and have students hold up the side with the correct homophone.

Q: The traveler was weak with thirst after crossing the desert. [weak]

Q: Henri made his first sale at the new company. [sale]

Q: You will be asked to fill out the questionnaire. [to]

READING ADVANCED Have students read the second sentence of the example.

Q: What does it mean that one phone is an upgraded version of the other phone?
[One phone is a slightly different form of the other with more and better features.]

Q: Name other electronics that can have upgraded versions.
[computers, gaming systems, music systems]

Q: Read the definition of *version* from the dictionary. Name some things besides electronics that can have different *versions.*
[translations of books, stories, accounts of events, film adaptations of novels]

EXAMPLE 4 CONTINUED

Try It! Answer

4. Yes, any method for solving a system of equations would work.

Use with **EXAMPLES 3 & 4**

HABITS OF MIND

Construct Arguments Explain when a solution to a linear-quadratic system of equations is not included as part of the solution to a problem. MP.3

[When a negative value for one of the variables does not satisfy the real-world situation, it is not included in the solution.]

CONCEPT SUMMARY Solving Linear-Quadratic Systems of Equations

Q: What is a linear-quadratic system, and what methods can be used to solve this system?
[A linear-quadratic system is a system of equations that includes a linear equation and a quadratic equation. Any of the three methods—elimination, substitution, or graphing—can be used to solve a linear-quadratic system of equations.]

Do You UNDERSTAND? | Do You KNOW HOW?

Common Error

Exercises 9–10 Students may stop after they find one solution to a linear-quadratic system of equations. Have them start the solution to every linear-quadratic system of equations by making a sketch of the graphs. The sketch will remind them that there may be 0, 1, or 2 solutions; it can also serve as a rough check if the graphing method is used.

AVAILABLE ONLINE

Concept Summary Assess

EXAMPLE 4 CONTINUED

Try It! 4. Could you have used elimination or graphing to solve this linear-quadratic system of equations? Explain.

CONCEPT SUMMARY Solving Linear-Quadratic Systems of Equations

WORDS A system of equations composed of a linear equation and a quadratic equation has 0, 1, or 2 solutions. The system of equations can be solved using elimination, substitution, or graphing.

$y = mx + b$
$y = ax^2 + bx + c$

	Elimination	Substitution	Graphing
ALGEBRA	$y = x^2 + x$ $y = x - 1$	$y = -2x + 3$ $y = -x^2 + 2$	$y = \frac{1}{2}x + 1$ $y = -x^2 - 8x - 14$
	$y = x^2 + x$ $-y = -x + 1$ $0 = x^2 + 1$ $x^2 = -1$ No solution	$-2x + 3 = -x^2 + 2$ $x^2 - 2x + 1 = 0$ $(x - 1)^2 = 0$ $x - 1 = 0$ $x = 1$ $y = -2(1) + 3 = 1$ Solution is (1, 1)	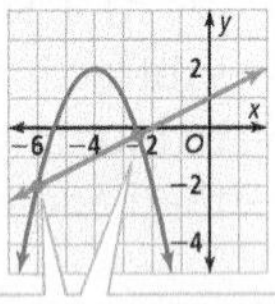 The solutions are where the line and parabola intersect at (–6, –2) and (–2.5, –0.25).

y
2
x
–6
–4
–2
O
–2
–4

Do You UNDERSTAND?

1. ESSENTIAL QUESTION How is solving linear-quadratic systems of equations similar to and different from solving systems of linear equations?

2. Error Analysis A student claims that a linear-quadratic system of equations has three solutions. Explain the error the student made. MP.3

3. Vocabulary What are the characteristics of a *linear-quadratic system* of equations?

4. Reason What system of equations could you use to solve the equation $x^2 - 3 = 7$? Explain. MP.2

Do You KNOW HOW?

Rewrite each equation as a system of equations.

5. $3 = x^2 + 2x$
6. $x = x^2 - 5$
7. $2x^2 - 5 = x + 7$
8. $x^2 - 2x + 3 = x + 4$

Find the solution of each system of equations.

9. $\begin{cases} y = x^2 + 3x + 1 \\ y = -x + 1 \end{cases}$
10. $\begin{cases} y = x^2 + 1 \\ y = -2x \end{cases}$

11.
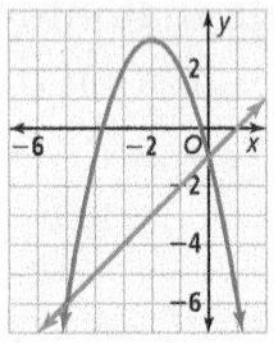

y
2
–6
–2
O
x
2
–4
–6

400 TOPIC 9 Solving Quadratic Equations   Go Online | PearsonRealize.com

Answers

1. It is similar because you can use the same methods to solve: graphing, elimination, or substitution. It is different because linear-quadratic systems have 0, 1, or 2 solutions. Linear systems have 0, 1, or infinitely many solutions.
2. Linear-quadratic systems can have only 0, 1, or 2 solutions. So the student incorrectly calculated the number of solutions.
3. It is composed of a linear equation and a quadratic equation, each in two variables.
4. $y = x^2 - 3$ and $y = 7$; To rewrite an equation as a system, set each side of the original equation as a separate equation equal to y.
5. $y = x^2 + 2x$
   $y = 3$
6. $y = x^2 - 5$
   $y = x$
7. $y = 2x^2 - 5$
   $y = x + 7$
8. $y = x^2 - 2x + 3$
   $y = x + 4$
9. (0, 1) and –4, 5)
10. (–1, 2)
11. (–5, –6) and (0, –1)
12. A linear-quadratic system includes a parabola and a line, but a linear system includes the graphs of two lines. They are similar because the graphs of the equations can intersect at their solutions.
13. The system has only one solution because the graphs of the two equations have only one point of intersection.
15. When the student used the elimination method, he or she subtracted an x-term from an x^2-term. Instead of getting $0 = -x^2 + 2$, the student should have gotten $0 = 2x^2 - 3x + 2$. Use the quadratic formula to solve. Because the discriminant of the equation is negative (–7) the equation and the system have no solutions.

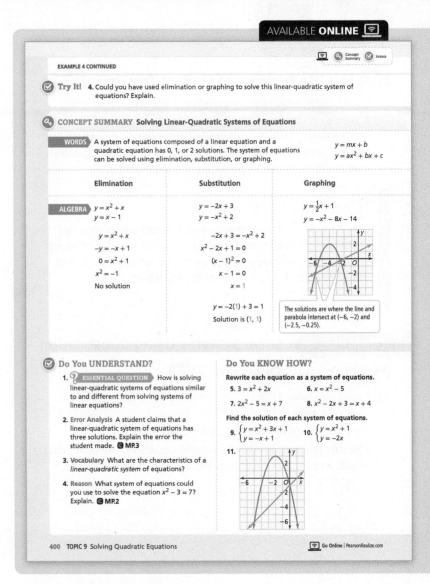

PRACTICE & PROBLEM SOLVING

AVAILABLE ONLINE

Lesson Practice You may opt to have students complete the automatically scored Practice and Problem Solving items online powered by MathXL for School.

Choose from: **Lesson Practice**

Adaptive Practice

You may also take advantage of the bank of exercises for assigning additional practice.

Assignment Guide

Basic	Advanced
12–29, 32–38	12–17, 20–38

Item Analysis

Example	Items	DOK
1	20	2
	13, 14	3
2	18, 19, 21–24	1
	17, 34, 37	2
	12	3
3	27–29, 31, 36	1
	33	2
	15, 38	3
4	25, 26, 30	1
	32, 35	2
	16	3

Answers

See answers for Exercises 12, 13, and 15 on previous page.

16. Look at the terms in the equations of the system. If the equations would be easy to graph and intersect at grid lines, then graphing is a good choice. Elimination is a good choice when it will reduce the number of terms you have to deal with. Substitution works in any situation.

17. $y = x^2 + 2$
$y = \frac{1}{3}x + 3$

AVAILABLE ONLINE

Scan for Multimedia | Practice | Tutorial | Additional Exercises Available Online

UNDERSTAND

12. Mathematical Connections How is the graph of a linear-quadratic system of equations different from the graph of a linear system of equations? How are the graphs similar?

13. Look for Relationships What does the graph of the system of equations tell you about its solution? MP.7
$y = 3x^2 - 4x + 2$
$y = 8x - 10$

14. Higher Order Thinking Given the equation $y = x^2 + 3x + 2$, write an equation for a line that intersects the parabola the given number of times.
a. 0 Check students work.
b. 1 Check students work.
c. 2 Check students work.

15. Error Analysis Describe and correct the error a student made in solving the system of equations. MP.3
$y = 2x^2 + 3$
$y = 3x + 1$

$y = 2x^2 + 3$
$-(y = 3x + 1)$
$0 = -x^2 + 2$
$x^2 = 2$
$x = \pm\sqrt{2} \approx \pm 1.41$ ✗

16. Use Appropriate Tools How do you select the appropriate method for solving a linear-quadratic system? Describe when you would use graphing, elimination, and substitution. MP.5

17. Use Structure Write the linear-quadratic system of equations that is represented by the graph. MP.7

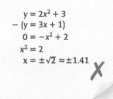

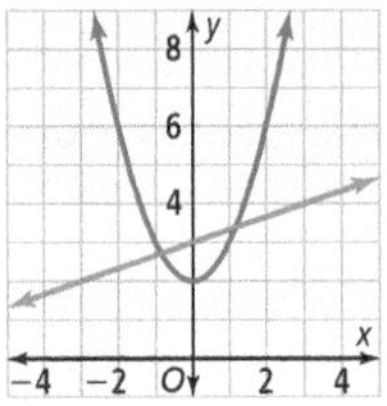
y
8
6
4
x
−4
−2
O
2
4

PRACTICE

Rewrite each equation as a system of equations, and then use a graph to solve. SEE EXAMPLES 1 AND 2

18. $\frac{1}{3}x^2 + 2 = -x + 8$ $x = -6$ and $x = 3$

19. $2x^2 - 3x = -2x + 1$ $x = 1$ and $x = -\frac{1}{2}$

20. $5x^2 = 3x - 7$ no solutions

21. $x^2 - 2x = 2x - 4$ $x = 2$

Rewrite each equation as a system of equations and graph to solve. SEE EXAMPLE 2

22. $x^2 - 4 = x + 2$

23. $-2x + 4 = -0.5x^2 + 4$

Find the solution of each system of equations. SEE EXAMPLES 1–4

24. $y = x^2 + 3x - 2$, $y = 2x$ (−2, −4) and (1, 2)

25. $y = -4x^2 + x + 1$, $y = -7x + 1$ (0, 1) and (2, −13)

26. $y = 0.5x^2 - 8x + 13$, $y = x - 3$ (2, −1) and (16, 13)

27. $y = 7x^2 + 12$, $y = 14x + 5$ (1, 19)

28. $y = -x^2 - 2x + 9$, $y = 3x + 20$ no solution

29. $y = -5x^2 + 6x - 3$, $y = -4x - 3$ (0, −3) and (2, −11)

30. $y = 0.75x^2 + 4x - 5$, $y = 4x - 5$ (0, −5)

31. $y = -2x^2 + 6x + 7$, $y = 13 - 2x$ (1, 11) and (3, 7)

32. A ropes course facility offers two types of courses, a low ropes course and a high ropes course. The price of a high ropes adventure is five times as much as a low ropes adventure. Eight members of the high school adventure club choose to participate in the low ropes course, and 15 members choose the high ropes course. The total cost is $1,411. What is the price of each type of ropes course adventure? low ropes course: $17; high ropes course: $85

LESSON 9-7 Solving Systems of Linear and Quadratic Equations 401

22.

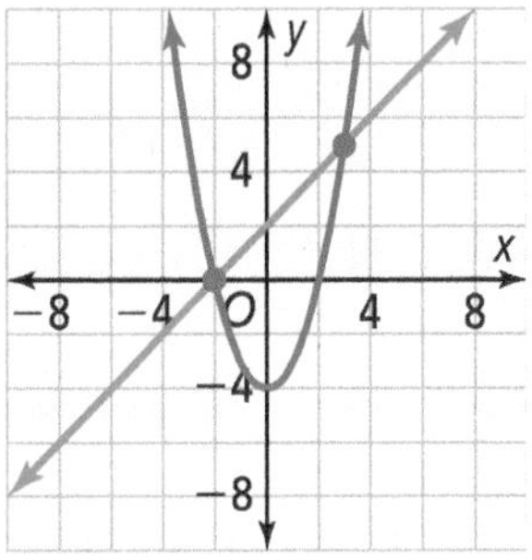
y
8
4
x
−8
−4
O
4
8
−4
−8

(−2, 0) and (3, 5)

23.

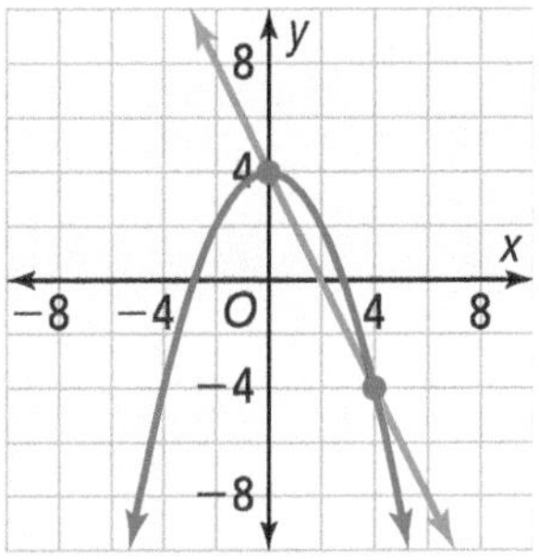
y
8
4
x
−8
−4
O
4
8
−4
−8

(0, 4) and (4, −4)

Practice Tutorials Math Tools

Answers

33. $y = -16x^2 + 30$
$y = 14$; 1 second

34. 4; Write a system of equations and then solve. The solutions are (−2, 2) and (4, 8). Because time cannot be negative, discard (−2, 2). The solution (4, 8) tells you that in 4 minutes both the car and the truck will be 8 miles from the stop sign. This is when the car will pass the truck.

35. **a.** $y = -\frac{1}{7}x^2 + 2x + 10$
$y = 2x + 3$; $-\frac{1}{7}x^2 + 2x + 10 = 2x + 3$

b. day 7

c. 17 people rock climbing and 17 people zip lining

38. **Part A** $y = 0.25x^2 + 3$
$y = 0.5x + 5$; 4 days

Part B 1; Although the system has 2 solutions, only the solution with a positive x-value makes sense in this situation.

Part C no; The graphs of these two equations never intersect, so there is no solution. This means that the songs are never played the same number of times on the same day.

AVAILABLE **ONLINE**

PRACTICE & PROBLEM SOLVING

Practice Tutorial
Mixed Review Available Online

APPLY

33. Make Sense and Persevere An equation that models the height of an object dropped from the top of a building is $y = -16x^2 + 30$ where x is time in sec. Another equation $y = 14$ models the path of a bird flying in the air. Write a system of equations and then solve to find how many seconds the object is in the air before it crosses the bird's path. **MP.1**

34. Reason A car accelerates after being completely stopped at a stop sign and enters the highway. The distance the car has traveled in miles after x minutes is represented by $y = 0.5x^2$. A truck is traveling in the same direction at a constant speed so that its distance in miles from the same stop sign after x minutes is represented by $y = x + 4$. After how many minutes will the car pass the truck? Explain. **MP.2**

35. Model With Mathematics At the beginning of a month, the number of people rock climbing increases and then decreases by the end of the month. The number of people zip-lining steadily increases throughout the same month. The models show the number of people y for each type of activity based on the number of days x since the beginning of the month. **MP.4**

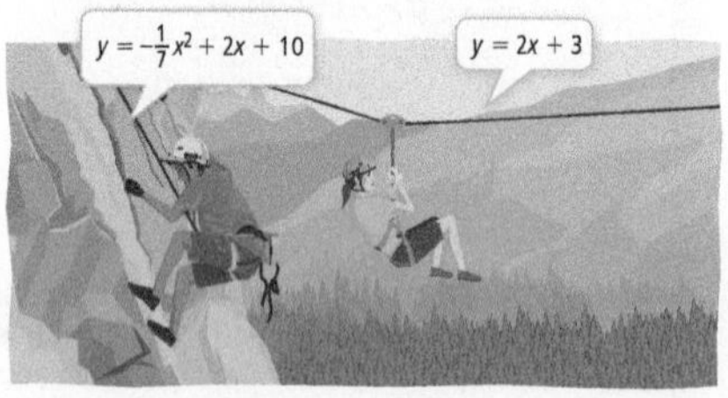

$y = -\frac{1}{7}x^2 + 2x + 10$
$y = 2x + 3$

a. Write a system of equations that represents this situation.

b. On what day or days were the same number of people rock climbing and zip-lining?

c. How many people were participating in each activity on that day or days?

ASSESSMENT PRACTICE

36. What is the solution of the system of equations?
$y = x^2 - 5x - 8$
$y = -2x - 4$ (−1, −2), (4, −12)

37. SAT/ACT What is the solution of the system of equations?
$y = 6x^2 + 3x - 11$
$y = 3x - 5$

Ⓐ (1, −2), (−1, −8)
Ⓑ (1, −1)
Ⓒ (−2, 1), (−8, −1)
Ⓓ (−1, −8)

38. Performance Task A music streaming service tracks the number of times songs are played. Two different songs are released on the same day. The functions model the number of times y, in thousands, each song is played x days following their release.

Song A is modeled by $y = 0.25x^2 + 3$.
Song B is modeled by $y = 0.5x + 5$.

Part A Write and solve a system of equations to find the number of days since the release when both songs are played the same number of times.

Part B How many solutions are there? Explain.

Part C A third song is released on the same day as the other two. The number of times this song is played is modeled by $y = 0.5x + 2$. Is there a day when the same number of people listen to the third song and the first song? Explain.

Go Online | PearsonRealize.com

LESSON QUIZ

Use the Lesson Quiz to assess students' understanding of the mathematics in the lesson.

Students can take the Lesson Quiz online or you can download a printable copy from **SavvasRealize.com**. The Lesson Quiz is also available in the *Assessment Resources* book.

Item Analysis

Item	DOK	Standards
1	1	HSA.REI.D.11
2	2	HSA.REI.D.11, HSA.REI.C.7
3	2	HSA.REI.D.11, HSA.REI.C.7
4	1	HSA.REI.C.7
5	1	HSA.REI.C.7

RtI Use the student scores on the Lesson Quiz to prescribe differentiated assignments.

If students take the Lesson Quiz online, it will be automatically scored and appropriate differentiated practice will be assigned based on student performance.

I Intervention	0–3 points	• Reteach to Build Understanding • Mathematical Literacy and Vocabulary • Additional Practice
O On-Level	4 points	• Mathematical Literacy and Vocabulary • Additional Practice • Enrichment
A Advanced	5 points	• Enrichment

AVAILABLE **ONLINE**

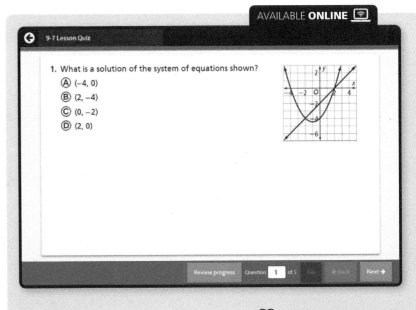

9-7 Lesson Quiz

1. What is a solution of the system of equations shown?
Ⓐ (−4, 0)
Ⓑ (2, −4)
Ⓒ (0, −2)
Ⓓ (2, 0)

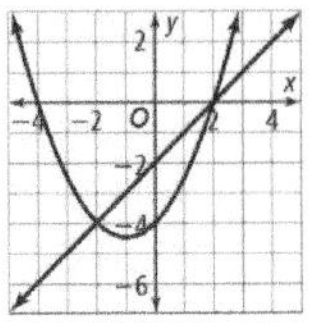

Review progress Question 1 of 5 Go ← Back Next →

ASSESSMENT RESOURCES

Name ________________

enVision Algebra 1
PearsonRealize.com

9-7 Lesson Quiz

Solving Systems of Linear and Quadratic Equations

1. What is a solution of the system of equations shown?
Ⓐ (−4, 0)
Ⓑ (2, −4)
Ⓒ (0, −2)
Ⓓ (2, 0)

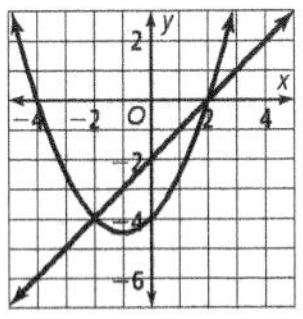

2. Which of the following has a graph that does NOT intersect with the graph of $y = x^2 + 3$?
Ⓐ $y = 2x - 5$
Ⓑ $y = -2x + 2$
Ⓒ $y = 3x + 3$
Ⓓ $y = -3x + 5$

3. Write the equation $-x^2 + 2x + 3 = x + 1$ as a system of equations. Then graph to solve the equation.

system: $\begin{cases} y = -x^2 + 2x + 3 \\ y = x + 1 \end{cases}$

solution: $x = -1, x = 2$

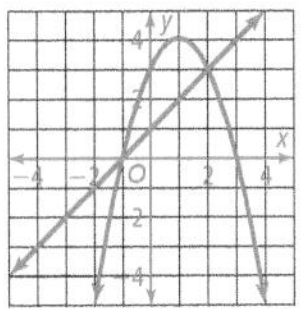

4. Use elimination to solve the system of equations.
$y = x^2 - 3x + 16$
$y = 9x - 20$
(6, 34)

5. Use substitution to solve the system of equations.
$y = x^2 - 7x - 5$
$y = -2x + 19$
(8, 3) and (−3, 25)

enVision™ **Algebra 1** • Assessment Resources

DIFFERENTIATED RESOURCES

I = Intervention O = On-Level A = Advanced

= This activity is available as a digital assignment powered by MathXL® for School.

AVAILABLE ONLINE

Reteach to Build Understanding I

Provides scaffolded reteaching for the key lesson concepts.

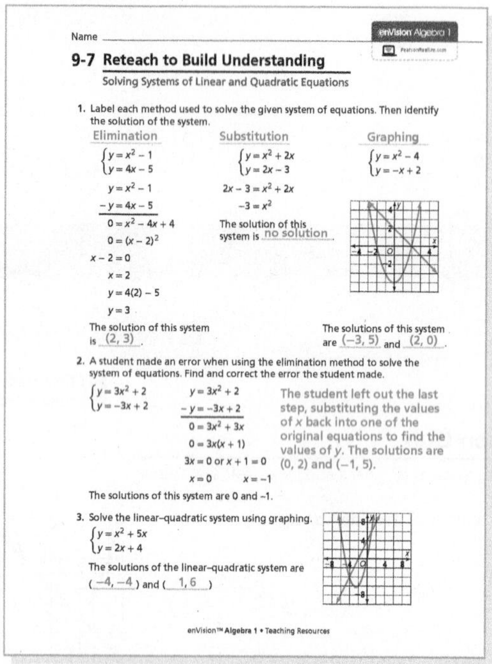

Name
enVision Algebra 1

9-7 Reteach to Build Understanding
Solving Systems of Linear and Quadratic Equations

1. Label each method used to solve the given system of equations. Then identify the solution of the system.

Elimination: $\begin{cases} y = x^2 - 1 \\ y = 4x - 5 \end{cases}$
$y = x^2 - 1$
$-y = 4x - 5$
$0 = x^2 - 4x + 4$
$0 = (x - 2)^2$
$x - 2 = 0$
$x = 2$
$y = 4(2) - 5$
$y = 3$
The solution of this system is (2, 3).

Substitution: $\begin{cases} y = x^2 + 2x \\ y = 2x - 3 \end{cases}$
$2x - 3 = x^2 + 2x$
$-3 = x^2$
The solution of this system is no solution.

Graphing: $\begin{cases} y = x^2 - 4 \\ y = -x + 2 \end{cases}$
The solutions of this system are (−3, 5) and (2, 0).

2. A student made an error when using the elimination method to solve the system of equations. Find and correct the error the student made.

$\begin{cases} y = 3x^2 + 2 \\ y = -3x + 2 \end{cases}$
$y = 3x^2 + 2$
$-y = -3x + 2$
$0 = 3x^2 + 3x$
$0 = 3x(x + 1)$
$3x = 0$ or $x + 1 = 0$
$x = 0$ $x = -1$
The solutions of this system are 0 and −1.

The student left out the last step, substituting the values of x back into one of the original equations to find the values of y. The solutions are (0, 2) and (−1, 5).

3. Solve the linear-quadratic system using graphing.
$\begin{cases} y = x^2 + 5x \\ y = 2x + 4 \end{cases}$
The solutions of the linear-quadratic system are (−4, −4) and (1, 6).

enVision™ Algebra 1 • Teaching Resources

Additional Practice I O

Provides extra practice for each lesson.

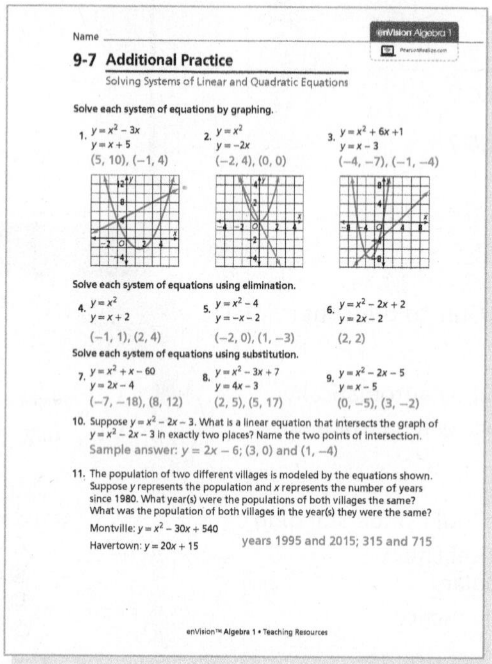

Name
enVision Algebra 1

9-7 Additional Practice
Solving Systems of Linear and Quadratic Equations

Solve each system of equations by graphing.

1. $y = x^2 - 3x$, $y = x + 5$ — (5, 10), (−1, 4)
2. $y = x^2$, $y = -2x$ — (−2, 4), (0, 0)
3. $y = x^2 + 6x + 1$, $y = x - 3$ — (−4, −7), (−1, −4)

Solve each system of equations using elimination.

4. $y = x^2$, $y = x + 2$ — (−1, 1), (2, 4)
5. $y = x^2 - 4$, $y = -x - 2$ — (−2, 0), (1, −3)
6. $y = x^2 - 2x + 2$, $y = 2x - 2$ — (2, 2)

Solve each system of equations using substitution.

7. $y = x^2 + x - 60$, $y = 2x - 4$ — (−7, −18), (8, 12)
8. $y = x^2 - 3x + 7$, $y = 4x - 3$ — (2, 5), (5, 17)
9. $y = x^2 - 2x - 5$, $y = x - 5$ — (0, −5), (3, −2)

10. Suppose $y = x^2 - 2x - 3$. What is a linear equation that intersects the graph of $y = x^2 - 2x - 3$ in exactly two places? Name the two points of intersection.
Sample answer: $y = 2x - 6$; (3, 0) and (1, −4)

11. The population of two different villages is modeled by the equations shown. Suppose y represents the population and x represents the number of years since 1980. What year(s) were the populations of both villages the same? What was the population of both villages in the year(s) they were the same?
Montville: $y = x^2 - 30x + 540$
Havertown: $y = 20x + 15$
years 1995 and 2015; 315 and 715

enVision™ Algebra 1 • Teaching Resources

Enrichment O A

Presents engaging problems and activities that extend the lesson concepts.

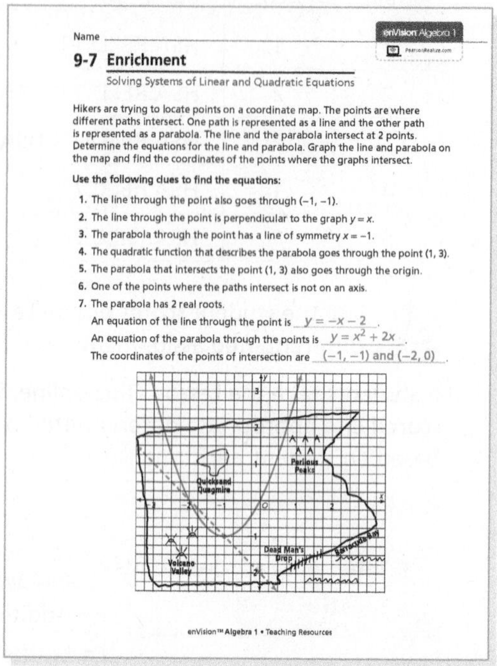

Name
enVision Algebra 1

9-7 Enrichment
Solving Systems of Linear and Quadratic Equations

Hikers are trying to locate points on a coordinate map. The points are where different paths intersect. One path is represented as a line and the other path is represented as a parabola. The line and the parabola intersect at 2 points. Determine the equations for the line and parabola. Graph the line and parabola on the map and find the coordinates of the points where the graphs intersect.

Use the following clues to find the equations:

1. The line through the point also goes through (−1, −1).
2. The line through the point is perpendicular to the graph $y = x$.
3. The parabola through the point has a line of symmetry $x = -1$.
4. The quadratic function that describes the parabola goes through the point (1, 3).
5. The parabola that intersects the point (1, 3) also goes through the origin.
6. One of the points where the paths intersect is not on an axis.
7. The parabola has 2 real roots.

An equation of the line through the point is $y = -x - 2$.
An equation of the parabola through the points is $y = x^2 + 2x$.
The coordinates of the points of intersection are (−1, −1) and (−2, 0).

Perilous Peaks
Quicksand Quagmire
Dead Man's Drop
Volcano Valley

enVision™ Algebra 1 • Teaching Resources

Mathematical Literacy and Vocabulary I O

Helps students develop and reinforce understanding of key terms and concepts.

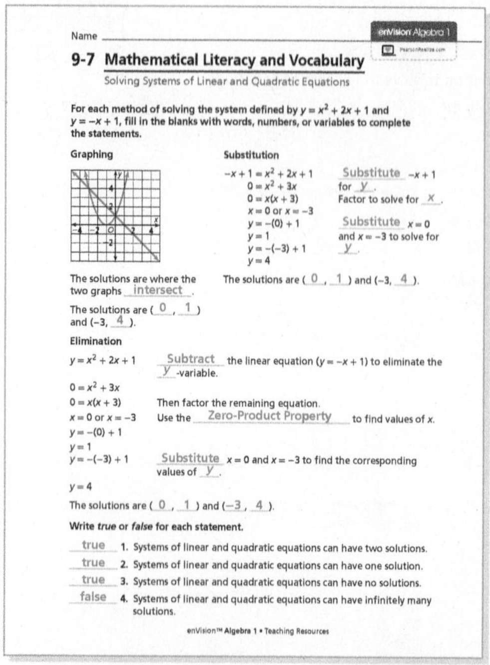

Name
enVision Algebra 1

9-7 Mathematical Literacy and Vocabulary
Solving Systems of Linear and Quadratic Equations

For each method of solving the system defined by $y = x^2 + 2x + 1$ and $y = -x + 1$, fill in the blanks with words, numbers, or variables to complete the statements.

Graphing

The solutions are where the two graphs intersect.
The solutions are (0, 1) and (−3, 4).

Substitution

$-x + 1 = x^2 + 2x + 1$ — Substitute $-x + 1$ for y.
$0 = x^2 + 3x$
$0 = x(x + 3)$ — Factor to solve for x.
$x = 0$ or $x = -3$
$y = -(0) + 1$ — Substitute $x = 0$ and $x = -3$ to solve for y.
$y = 1$
$y = -(-3) + 1$
$y = 4$
The solutions are (0, 1) and (−3, 4).

Elimination

$y = x^2 + 2x + 1$ — Subtract the linear equation ($y = -x + 1$) to eliminate the y-variable.
$0 = x^2 + 3x$
$0 = x(x + 3)$ — Then factor the remaining equation.
$x = 0$ or $x = -3$ — Use the Zero-Product Property to find values of x.
$y = -(0) + 1$
$y = 1$
$y = -(-3) + 1$ — Substitute $x = 0$ and $x = -3$ to find the corresponding values of y.
$y = 4$
The solutions are (0, 1) and (−3, 4).

Write *true* or *false* for each statement.

true 1. Systems of linear and quadratic equations can have two solutions.
true 2. Systems of linear and quadratic equations can have one solution.
true 3. Systems of linear and quadratic equations can have no solutions.
false 4. Systems of linear and quadratic equations can have infinitely many solutions.

enVision™ Algebra 1 • Teaching Resources

Digital Resources and Video Tutorials I O A

The **Reteach to Build Understanding, Additional Practice,** and **Enrichment** activities are available as digital assignments powered by MathXL for School. These activities are automatically assigned when students complete the lesson quiz online and are automatically scored.

Students can access instructional tutorials using the **Virtual Nerd app.**

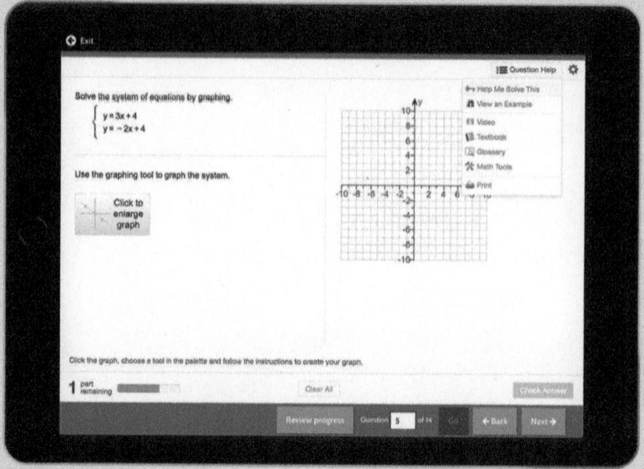

Exit
Question Help
Help Me Solve This
View an Example
Video
Textbook
Glossary
Math Tools
Print
Solve the system of equations by graphing.
y = 3x + 4
y = −2x + 4
Use the graphing tool to graph the system.
Click to enlarge graph
Click the graph, choose a tool in the palette and follow the instructions to create your graph.
Clear All
Check Answer
Review progress
Back
Next

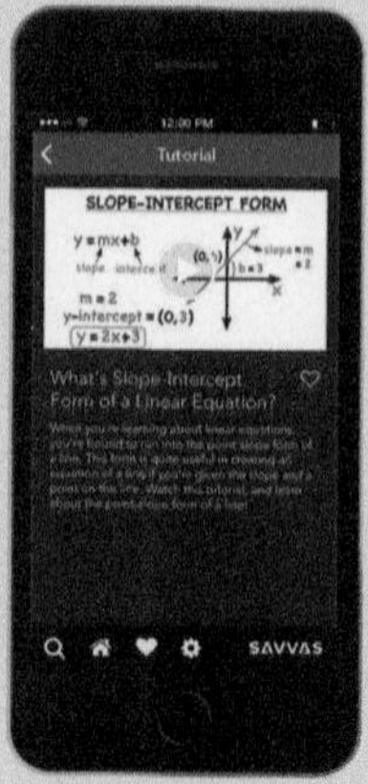

Tutorial
SLOPE-INTERCEPT FORM
What's Slope-Intercept Form of a Linear Equation?
SAVVAS

Students can also access Virtual Nerd videos using the **BouncePages app** to scan exercise pages marked with this icon. Students can download both apps for free in their mobile devices' app store.

TOPIC 9
Solving Quadratic Equations

TOPIC REVIEW

TOPIC ESSENTIAL QUESTION

How do you use quadratic equations to model situations and solve problems?

As students answer the Essential Question in writing, encourage them to include examples that support their answers. Look for the following points to come out while discussing students' answers.

- Quadratic equations can be used to model area problems. The solutions of the equations can be used to determine missing side lengths of an object.
- The amount of time an object is in the air can be estimated by graphing the function and identifying where the graph crosses the x-axis. An exact solution can be found by solving a quadratic equation.
- Rewriting radical expressions is useful when solving problems using the Pythagorean Theorem.
- Revenue problems can be modeled by writing a system of equations, using substitution, and solving the resulting quadratic equation to project sales.

Answers

2. standard form of a quadratic equation
3. completing the square
4. zeros of a function
5. Product Property of Square Roots
6. Zero-Product Property
7. –4, 4

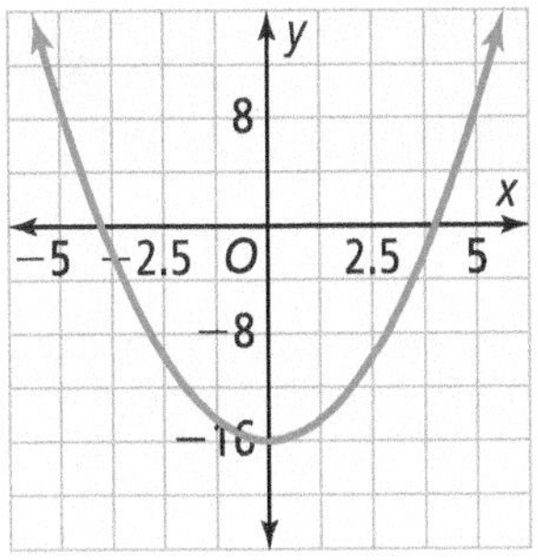
y
8
x
–5
–2.5
O
2.5
5
–8
–16

8. 3

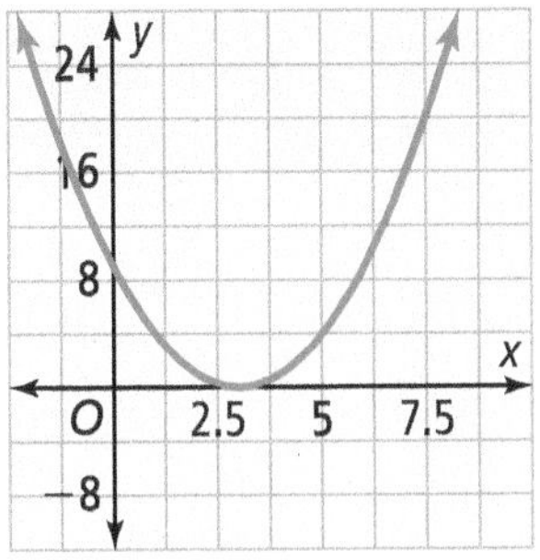
y
24
16
8
x
O
2.5
5
7.5
–8

9. no solution

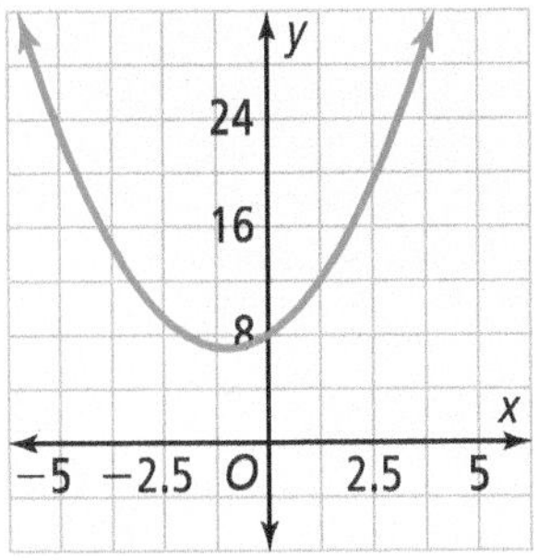
y
24
16
8
x
–5
–2.5
O
2.5
5

10. $\frac{1}{2}$, 5

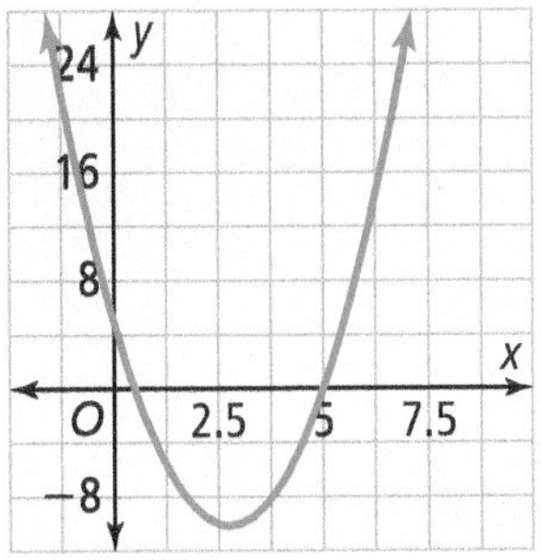
y
24
16
8
x
O
2.5
5
7.5
–8

See answers for 11–13 on next page

AVAILABLE ONLINE

TOPIC 9

Topic Review

TOPIC ESSENTIAL QUESTION

1. How do you use quadratic equations to model situations and solve problems?

Vocabulary Review

Choose the correct term to complete each sentence.

2. The ________ is $ax^2 + bx + c = 0$, where $a \neq 0$.
3. The process of adding $\left(\frac{b}{2}\right)^2$ to $x^2 + bx$ to form a perfect-square trinomial is called ________.
4. The x-intercepts of the graph of the function are also called the ________.
5. The ________ states that $\sqrt{ab} = \sqrt{a} \cdot \sqrt{b}$, where both a and b are greater than or equal to 0.
6. The ________ states that for all real numbers a and b, if $ab = 0$, then either $a = 0$ or $b = 0$.

- completing the square
- discriminant
- Product Property of Square Roots
- quadratic equation
- quadratic formula
- standard form of a quadratic equation
- Zero-Product Property
- zeros of a function

Concepts & Skills Review

LESSON 9-1 Solving Quadratic Equations Using Graphs and Tables

Quick Review

A **quadratic equation** is an equation of the second degree. A quadratic equation can have 0, 1 or 2 solutions, which are known as the **zeros of the related function.**

Example

Find the solutions of $0 = x^2 + x - 2$.

The x-intercepts of the related function are –2, and 1, so the equation has two real solutions.

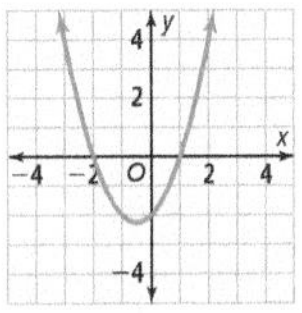
y
4
2
x
–4
–2
O
2
4
–4

From the graph, the solutions of the equation $x^2 + x - 2 = 0$ appear to be $x = -2$ and $x = 1$.

It is important to verify those solutions by substituting into the equation.

$(-2)^2 + (-2) - 2 = 0$ $\quad 1^2 + 1 - 2 = 0$

$0 = 0$ $\quad 0 = 0$

Practice & Problem Solving

Solve each quadratic equation by graphing.

7. $x^2 - 16 = 0$
8. $x^2 - 6x + 9 = 0$
9. $x^2 + 2x + 8 = 0$
10. $2x^2 - 11x + 5 = 0$

Find the solutions for each equation using a table. Round to the nearest tenth.

11. $x^2 - 64 = 0$
12. $x^2 - 6x - 16 = 0$
13. Model With Mathematics A video game company uses the profit model $P(x) = -x^2 + 14x - 39$, where x is the number of video games sold, in thousands, and $P(x)$ is the profit earned in millions of dollars. How many video games would the company have to sell to earn a maximum profit? How many video games would the company have to sell to not show a profit? MP.4

TOPIC 9 REVIEW

AVAILABLE ONLINE

Go online at **SavvasRealize.com** for additional practice and mixed review.

TOPIC REVIEW

Answers

11. −8, 8

x	−8	−4	−2	0	2	4	8
$f(x)$	0	−48	−60	−64	−60	−48	0

12. −2, 8

x	−2	0	2	4	6	8
$f(x)$	0	−16	−24	−24	−16	0

13. 7,000 video games; about 3,838 video games or about 10,162 video games

14. $x = -3$

15. $x = -2$ or $x = 5$

16. $x = 0$ or $x = 12$

17. $x = -1.5$ or $x = 5$

18. $(x - 10)(x - 2) = 0$; vertex is $(6, -16)$

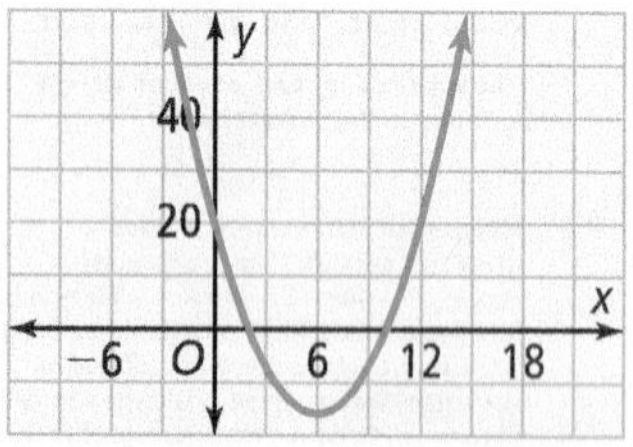
y
40
20
x
−6
O
6
12
18

19. $(x - 3)(x - 5) = 0$; vertex is $(4, -1)$

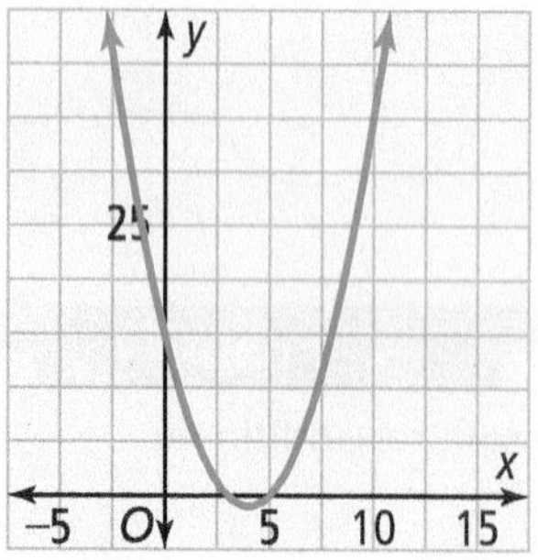
y
25
x
−5
O
5
10
15

20. The student did not change the sign when finding the value of x.

$$2x^2 - 8x + 8 = 0$$
$$2(x^2 - 4x + 4) = 0$$
$$2(x - 2)(x - 2) = 0$$
$$x = 2$$

The solution is $x = 2$.

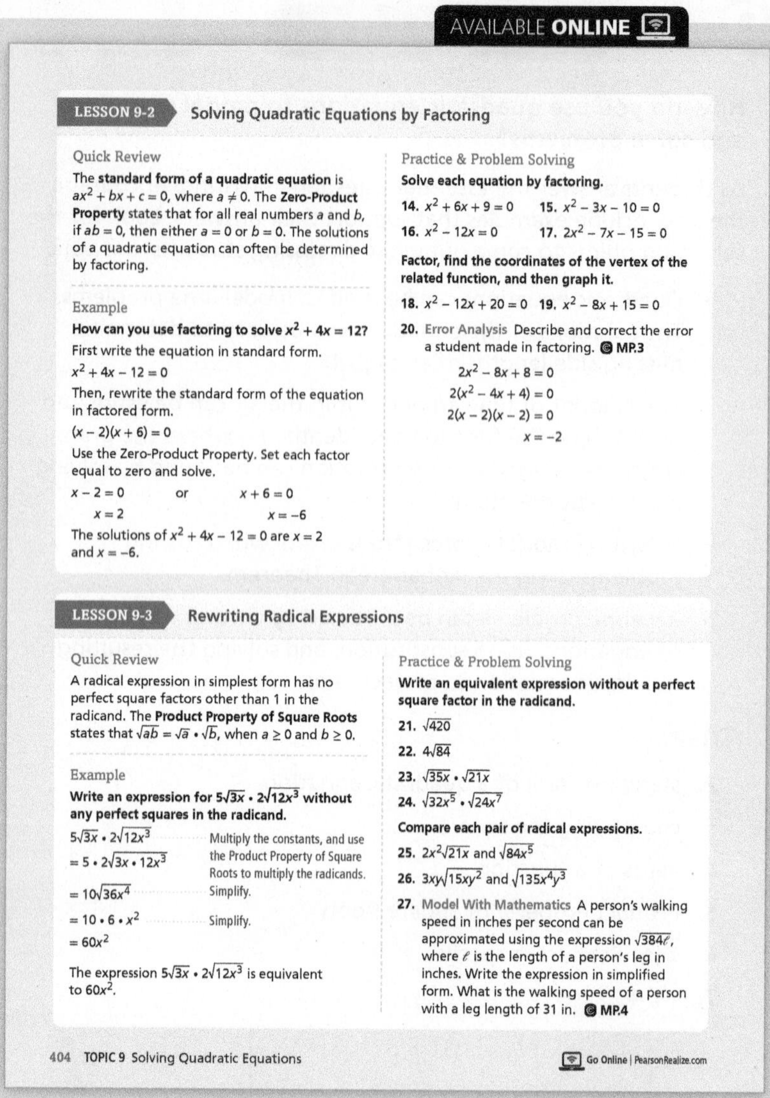

AVAILABLE **ONLINE**

LESSON 9-2 **Solving Quadratic Equations by Factoring**

Quick Review

The **standard form of a quadratic equation** is $ax^2 + bx + c = 0$, where $a \neq 0$. The **Zero-Product Property** states that for all real numbers a and b, if $ab = 0$, then either $a = 0$ or $b = 0$. The solutions of a quadratic equation can often be determined by factoring.

Example

How can you use factoring to solve $x^2 + 4x = 12$?

First write the equation in standard form.

$x^2 + 4x - 12 = 0$

Then, rewrite the standard form of the equation in factored form.

$(x - 2)(x + 6) = 0$

Use the Zero-Product Property. Set each factor equal to zero and solve.

$x - 2 = 0$ or $x + 6 = 0$

$x = 2$ $\quad x = -6$

The solutions of $x^2 + 4x - 12 = 0$ are $x = 2$ and $x = -6$.

Practice & Problem Solving

Solve each equation by factoring.

14. $x^2 + 6x + 9 = 0$
15. $x^2 - 3x - 10 = 0$
16. $x^2 - 12x = 0$
17. $2x^2 - 7x - 15 = 0$

Factor, find the coordinates of the vertex of the related function, and then graph it.

18. $x^2 - 12x + 20 = 0$
19. $x^2 - 8x + 15 = 0$
20. Error Analysis Describe and correct the error a student made in factoring. **MP.3**

$$2x^2 - 8x + 8 = 0$$
$$2(x^2 - 4x + 4) = 0$$
$$2(x - 2)(x - 2) = 0$$
$$x = -2$$

LESSON 9-3 **Rewriting Radical Expressions**

Quick Review

A radical expression in simplest form has no perfect square factors other than 1 in the radicand. The **Product Property of Square Roots** states that $\sqrt{ab} = \sqrt{a} \cdot \sqrt{b}$, when $a \geq 0$ and $b \geq 0$.

Example

Write an expression for $5\sqrt{3x} \cdot 2\sqrt{12x^3}$ without any perfect squares in the radicand.

$5\sqrt{3x} \cdot 2\sqrt{12x^3}$ Multiply the constants, and use the Product Property of Square Roots to multiply the radicands.

$= 5 \cdot 2\sqrt{3x \cdot 12x^3}$

$= 10\sqrt{36x^4}$ Simplify.

$= 10 \cdot 6 \cdot x^2$ Simplify.

$= 60x^2$

The expression $5\sqrt{3x} \cdot 2\sqrt{12x^3}$ is equivalent to $60x^2$.

Practice & Problem Solving

Write an equivalent expression without a perfect square factor in the radicand.

21. $\sqrt{420}$
22. $4\sqrt{84}$
23. $\sqrt{35x} \cdot \sqrt{21x}$
24. $\sqrt{32x^5} \cdot \sqrt{24x^7}$

Compare each pair of radical expressions.

25. $2x^2\sqrt{21x}$ and $\sqrt{84x^5}$
26. $3xy\sqrt{15xy^2}$ and $\sqrt{135x^4y^3}$
27. Model With Mathematics A person's walking speed in inches per second can be approximated using the expression $\sqrt{384\ell}$, where ℓ is the length of a person's leg in inches. Write the expression in simplified form. What is the walking speed of a person with a leg length of 31 in. **MP.4**

404 TOPIC 9 Solving Quadratic Equations

Go Online | PearsonRealize.com

21. $2\sqrt{105}$

22. $8\sqrt{21}$

23. $7x\sqrt{15}$

24. $16x^6\sqrt{3}$

25. The expressions are equal.

26. The expressions are not equal; $\sqrt{135x^4y^3} = 3x^2y\sqrt{15y}$

27. $8\sqrt{6l}$, 109.1 in./s

TOPIC 9
Solving Quadratic Equations

SavvasRealize.com

A-Z Glossary | Tutorials | Math Tools

TOPIC REVIEW

Answers

28. $-17, 17$
29. no solution
30. $-\sqrt{155}, \sqrt{155}$
31. $-0.8, 0.8$
32. $-8, 8$
33. $-20, 20$
34. $-5, 5$
35. $-5, 13$
$$(x-4)^2 - 81 = 0$$
$$(x-4)^2 = 81$$
$$\sqrt{(x-4)^2} = \sqrt{81}$$
$$x - 4 = \pm 9$$
$$x = \pm 9 + 4$$
$$x = 13 \text{ or } x = -5$$
36. $\sqrt{74}$ units
37. $81, (x+9)^2$
38. $9, (x-3)^2$
39. $56.25, (x-7.5)^2$
40. $144, (x+12)^2$
41. $-9+\sqrt{105}, -9-\sqrt{105}$
42. $5+\sqrt{71}, 5-\sqrt{71}$
43. $-11+\sqrt{82}, -11-\sqrt{82}$
44. $-7+\sqrt{34}, -7-\sqrt{34}$
45. Completing the square provides an exact solution. You cannot factor the equation, and graphing does not provide an exact solution. The solutions are $4.5+\sqrt{35.25}$ and $4.5-\sqrt{35.25}$.

AVAILABLE ONLINE

LESSON 9-4 Solving Quadratic Equations Using Square Roots

Quick Review

To solve a quadratic equation using square roots, isolate the variable and find the square root of both sides of the equation.

Example

Use the properties of equality to solve the quadratic equation $4x^2 - 7 = 57$.

Rewrite the equation in the form $x^2 = a$.

$4x^2 - 7 = 57$

$4x^2 = 64$ — Rewrite using the form $x^2 = a$, where a is a real number.

$x^2 = 16$

$\sqrt{x^2} = \sqrt{16}$ — Take the square root of each side of the equation.

$x = \pm 4$

Since 16 is perfect square, there are two integer answers. The solutions of the quadratic equation $4x^2 - 7 = 57$ are $x = -4$ and $x = 4$.

Practice & Problem Solving

Solve each equation by inspection.

28. $x^2 = 289$
29. $x^2 = -36$
30. $x^2 = 155$
31. $x^2 = 0.64$

Solve each equation.

32. $5x^2 = 320$
33. $x^2 - 42 = 358$
34. $4x^2 - 18 = 82$
35. Higher Order Thinking Solve $(x-4)^2 - 81 = 0$. Explain the steps in your solution.
36. Communicate Precisely Use the equation $d = \sqrt{(12-5)^2 + (8-3)^2}$ to calculate the distance between the points (3, 5) and (8, 12). What is the distance? MP.6

LESSON 9-5 Completing the Square

Quick Review

The process of adding $\left(\frac{b}{2}\right)^2$ to $x^2 + bx$ to form a perfect-square trinomial is called **completing the square.** This is useful for changing $ax^2 + bx + c$ to the form $a(x-h)^2 + k$.

Example

Find the solutions of $x^2 - 16x + 12 = 0$.

First, write the equation in the form $ax^2 + bx = d$.

$x^2 - 16x = -12$

Complete the square.

$b = -16$, so $\left(\frac{-16}{2}\right)^2 = 64$

$x^2 - 16x + 64 = -12 + 64$

$x^2 - 16x + 64 = 52$

Write the trinomial as a binomial squared.

$(x-8)^2 = 52$

Solve for x.

$x - 8 = \sqrt{52}$

$x = 8 \pm 2\sqrt{13}$

$x = 8 + 2\sqrt{13}$ and $x = 8 - 2\sqrt{13}$.

Practice & Problem Solving

Find the value of c that makes each expression a perfect-square trinomial. Then write the expression as a binomial squared.

37. $x^2 + 18x + c$
38. $x^2 - 6x + c$
39. $x^2 - 15x + c$
40. $x^2 + 24x + c$

Solve each equation by completing the square.

41. $x^2 + 18x = 24$
42. $x^2 - 10x = 46$
43. $x^2 + 22x = -39$
44. $3x^2 + 42x + 45 = 0$
45. Construct Arguments To solve the equation $x^2 - 9x - 15 = 0$, would you use graphing, factoring, or completing the square if you want exact solutions? Explain. MP.3

TOPIC 9 REVIEW

TOPIC 9 Topic Review 405

TOPIC REVIEW

Answers

46. $x = 1$ and $x = -2.5$

47. $x = 2$ and $x = -\frac{6}{5}$

48. $x = -2.63$ and $x = 0.63$

49. $x = -0.63$ and $x = -2.37$

50. 2 solutions

51. 2 solutions

52. 1 solution

53. no solution

54. The student had the wrong sign for *c*.

$a = 3,\ b = -5,\ c = -8$

$$x = \frac{-5 \pm \sqrt{(-5)^2 - 4(3)(-8)}}{2(3)}$$

$$= \frac{-5 \pm \sqrt{121}}{6}$$

$x = 1$ or $x = -2.67$

55. The solutions of the related equation are approximately 1.87 and –5.87. The negative solution is discarded because a height cannot be negative. The only possible value is 5.87.

AVAILABLE **ONLINE**

LESSON 9-6 **The Quadratic Formula and the Discriminant**

Quick Review

The **quadratic formula,** $x = \frac{-b \pm \sqrt{b^2 - 4ac}}{2a}$, gives solutions of quadratic equations in the form $ax^2 + bx + c = 0$ for real values of *a*, *b*, and *c* where $a \neq 0$. The quadratic formula is a useful method to find the solutions of quadratic equations that are not factorable.

The **discriminant** is the expression $b^2 - 4ac$, which indicates the number of solutions of the equation. The solutions of a quadratic equation are also called its **roots,** which are the input values when the related function's output value is zero.

If $b^2 - 4ac > 0$, there are 2 real solutions.

If $b^2 - 4ac = 0$, there is 1 real solution.

If $b^2 - 4ac < 0$, there are no real solutions.

Example

Use the quadratic formula to find the solutions of $x^2 - 9 = 5x$.

Write the equation in standard form $ax^2 + bx + c = 0$ and identify *a*, *b* and *c*.

$x^2 - 5x - 9 = 0$

$a = 1,\ b = -5,\ c = -9$

$$x = \frac{-b \pm \sqrt{b^2 - 4ac}}{2a}$$

$$= \frac{-5 \pm \sqrt{(-5)^2 - 4(1)(-9)}}{2(1)}$$

$$= \frac{5 \pm \sqrt{61}}{2}$$

$$x = \frac{5 + \sqrt{61}}{2} \approx 6.41 \text{ and}$$

$$= \frac{5 - \sqrt{61}}{2} \approx -1.41$$

The approximate solutions of $x^2 - 9 = 5x$ are $x \approx 6.41$ and $x \approx -1.41$.

Practice & Problem Solving

Solve each equation using the quadratic formula.

46. $2x^2 + 3x - 5 = 0$

47. $-5x^2 + 4x + 12 = 0$

48. $3x^2 + 6x - 1 = 4$

49. $4x^2 + 12x + 6 = 0$

Use the discriminant to determine the number of real solutions for each equation.

50. $3x^2 - 8x + 2 = 0$

51. $-4x^2 - 6x - 1 = 0$

52. $7x^2 + 14x + 7 = 0$

53. $2x^2 + 5x + 3 = -5$

54. Error Analysis Describe and correct the error a student made in solving $3x^2 - 5x - 8 = 0$. **MP.3**

$a = 3,\ b = -5,\ c = 8$

$$x = \frac{-5 \pm \sqrt{(-5)^2 - 4(3)(8)}}{2(3)}$$

$$= \frac{-5 \pm \sqrt{-71}}{6}$$

There are no real solutions.

55. Reason The function $f(x) = -5x^2 + 20x + 55$ models the height of a ball *x* seconds after it is thrown into the air. What are the possible solutions to the related equation? Explain. **MP.2**

Go Online | PearsonRealize.com

TOPIC 9
Solving Quadratic Equations

TOPIC REVIEW

Answers

56. no solution

57. (0.5, 2) and (–1, –1)

58. (4, –8)

59. (–8, 0) and (–3, –7.5)

60. no solution

61. (–5, 15)

62. (0, 1)

63. (3.5, 12), (–5, –5)

64. Answers may vary. Sample: $y = x - 4$

65. $3

AVAILABLE **ONLINE**

LESSON 9-7 Solving Systems of Linear and Quadratic Equations

Quick Review

A **linear-quadratic system** of equations includes a linear equation and a quadratic equation. The graph of the system of equations is a line and a parabola.

$y = mx + b$

$y = ax^2 + bx + c$

You can solve a linear-quadratic system of equations by graphing, elimination, or substitution.

Example

What are the solutions of the system of equations?

$y = x^2 - 5x + 4$

$y = x - 4$

Graph the equations in the system on the same coordinate plane.

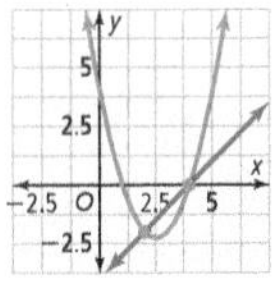
y
5
2.5
x
–2.5
O
2.5
5
–2.5

The solutions are where the parabola and the line intersect, which appear be at the points (2, –2) and (4, 0).

Check that the ordered pairs are solutions of the equations $y = x^2 - 5x + 4$ and $y = x - 4$.

$-2 = (2)^2 - 5(2) + 4$

$-2 = 4 - 10 + 4$

$-2 = -2$

and

$0 = (4)^2 - 5(4) + 4$

$0 = 16 - 20 + 4$

$0 = 0$

$0 = 4 - 4$

$0 = 0$

and

$-2 = 2 - 4$

$-2 = -2$

The solutions of the system are (2, –2) and (4, 0).

Practice & Problem Solving

Rewrite each equation as a system of equations, and then use a graph to solve.

56. $4x^2 = 2x - 5$

57. $2x^2 + 3x = 2x + 1$

58. $x^2 - 6x = 2x - 16$

59. $0.5x^2 + 4x = -12 - 1.5x$

Find the solution(s) of each system of equations.

60. $y = x^2 + 6x + 9$
$y = 3x$

61. $y = x^2 + 8x + 30$
$y = 5 - 2x$

62. $y = 3x^2 + 2x + 1$
$y = 2x + 1$

63. $y = 2x^2 + 5x - 30$
$y = 2x + 5$

64. Make Sense and Persevere Write an equation for a line that does not intersect the graph of the equation $y = x^2 + 6x + 9$. MP.1

65. Reason A theater company uses the revenue function $R(x) = -50x^2 + 250x$, where x is the ticket price in dollars. The cost function of the production is $C(x) = 450 - 50x$. What ticket price is needed for the theater to break even? MP.2

TOPIC 9 REVIEW

TOPIC ASSESSMENT Form A

AVAILABLE ONLINE

Name ______________________

enVision Algebra 1

PearsonRealize.com

9 Topic Assessment Form A

1. Solve $2x^2 + x - 3 = 0$ by factoring.
   $1, -\frac{3}{2}$

2. Find the solutions of $2 - x^2 = -x$ by graphing.

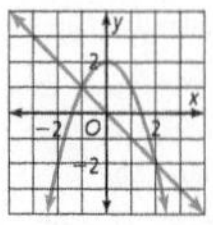

y
x
2
−2
O
2
−2

   Solutions: $-1, 2$

3. What are the coordinates of the vertex of the graph of $y = x^2 + 8x + 1$?
   Ⓐ $(-8, 1)$ Ⓒ $(4, 49)$
   Ⓑ $(-4, -15)$ Ⓓ $(8, 129)$

4. Write an expression for $\sqrt{140}$ without a perfect square factor in the radicand. $2\sqrt{35}$

5. Which equation(s) have only one real solution? Select all that apply.
   Ⓐ $x^2 + 6x + 7 = 6x + 7$
   Ⓑ $3x^2 + x - 5 = x + 5$
   Ⓒ $7x^2 = 5$
   Ⓓ $3x^2 + 2x = 2x$

6. What is the solution of $x^2 + 4x = 3$?
   Ⓐ $-2 \pm \sqrt{7}$ Ⓒ $2 \pm \sqrt{3}$
   Ⓑ $2 \pm \sqrt{7}$ Ⓓ $-2 \pm \sqrt{3}$

7. Solve the system of equations:
   $\begin{cases} y = 5x \\ y = x^2 + 5x - 9 \end{cases}$ $(3, 15)$ $(-3, -15)$

8. Which line(s) intersect the parabola $y = x^2 - 3x + 4$ at two points? Select all that apply.
   Ⓐ $y = -3x + 2$ Ⓒ $y = -3x + 5$
   Ⓑ $y = -3x + 3$ Ⓓ $y = -3x + 6$

9. The graph of a quadratic function passes through the points $(0, -22)$ and one of its zeros is $(-2, 0)$. What is the other zero of the function? -2

10. What is the value of x in the diagram below?

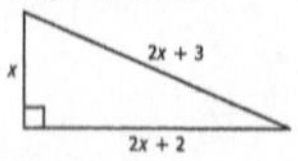

2x + 3
x
2x + 2

   5

11. Which is equivalent to $(\sqrt{16x^5})(5\sqrt{9x^3})$?
   Ⓐ $60x^4$ Ⓒ $12x^8$
   Ⓑ $60x^8$ Ⓓ $12x^4$

12. Solve $\frac{1}{x^2 - 1} = 1$
   $\pm\sqrt{2}$

13. Solve $5x^2 + 2x - 3 = 0$ by factoring.
   $-1, \frac{3}{5}$

enVision™ Algebra 1 • Assessment Resources

14. The profit from a business is described by the function $P(x) = -4x^2 + 16x + 25$, where x is the number of items made, in thousands, and $P(x)$ is the profit in dollars. How many items will maximize the profit?
   Ⓐ 1,000 Ⓒ 3,000
   Ⓑ 2,000 Ⓓ 4,000

15. Solve $(2x - 1)^2 = 25$.
   $3, -2$

16. Use the Quadratic Formula to solve $2x^2 + 6x = -3$. Which of the following gives the solutions to the nearest hundredth?
   Ⓐ 2.37 and 0.63
   Ⓑ 2.37 and −0.63
   Ⓒ −2.37 and 0.63
   Ⓓ −2.37 and −0.63

17. Which of the following are factors of $x^4 - 81$? Select all that apply.
   Ⓐ $x^2 + 9$ Ⓒ $x^2 + 27$
   Ⓑ $x^2 + 3$ Ⓓ $x + 3$

18. The quadratic function $d = -3x^2 + 16$ models a skateboarder's distance, in feet, from the bottom of a hill x seconds after the skateboarder starts moving down the hill. After how many seconds is the skateboarder 8 ft from the bottom of the hill?
   Ⓐ 3.6 s Ⓒ 1.6 s
   Ⓑ 2.6 s Ⓓ 0.6 s

19. Find the value of c that makes $9x^2 + 12x + c$ a perfect square trinomial.
   Ⓐ 4 Ⓒ 12
   Ⓑ 8 Ⓓ 16

20. Rewrite the expression $(\sqrt{4x^5})(\sqrt{8x^4})$, where x is positive, without a perfect square factor in the radicand.
   Ⓐ $8x^5\sqrt{2x}$ Ⓒ $2x^4\sqrt{2x}$
   Ⓑ $4x^4\sqrt{2x}$ Ⓓ $4x^5\sqrt{2x}$

21. Find the value of $\sqrt{(18 - 6)^2 + (17 - 1)^2}$. 20

22. The zeros of a quadratic function are −7 and 3. Which of the following could be the function? Select all that apply.
   Ⓐ $f(x) = x^2 + 4x - 21$
   Ⓑ $f(x) = x^2 - 4x - 21$
   Ⓒ $f(x) = 2x^2 - 8x - 42$
   Ⓓ $f(x) = 5x^2 + 20x - 105$

23. An outfielder throws a ball to home plate. The ball's path is modeled by the graph of $y = \frac{x}{5} - \frac{x^2}{1,000}$, where x represents the horizontal distance of the ball from the outfielder, and y represents the ball's vertical distance above the ground. What are the coordinates of the vertex of the ball's path?
   $(100, 10)$

24. What is the discriminant of the equation $2x^2 - 3x + 1 = 0$?
   Ⓐ −17 Ⓒ 1
   Ⓑ −1 Ⓓ 17

enVision™ Algebra 1 • Assessment Resources

AVAILABLE ONLINE

Topic Assessment Assess students' understanding of topic concepts and skills using the Topic Assessment found at **SavvasRealize.com.** These auto-scored online assessments provide students with a breadth of technology-enhanced item types.

There are two versions of the Topic Assessment, Form A and Form B. These two versions, available in print and at **SavvasRealize.com,** are parallel tests that assess the same content item for item. The Item Analysis chart on the next page can be used for both versions.

TOPIC 9
Solving Quadratic Equations

TOPIC ASSESSMENT Form B

AVAILABLE ONLINE

Name ____________________

enVision Algebra 1

PearsonRealize.com

9 Topic Assessment Form B

1. Solve $2x^2 + 7x - 4 = 0$ by factoring.
   −4, 0.5

2. Find the solutions of $x^2 - 2x = x$ by graphing.

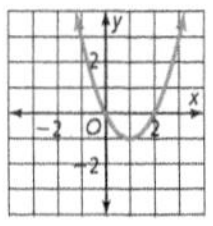

y
x
2
−2
O
2
−2

   Solutions: 0, 3

3. What are the coordinates of the vertex of the graph of $y = x^2 + 2x + 8$?
   Ⓐ (−1, −7)
   Ⓑ (−1, 7)
   Ⓒ (1, 9)
   Ⓓ (1, 10)

4. Write an expression for $\sqrt{128}$ without a perfect square factor in the radicand. $8\sqrt{2}$

5. Which equation(s) have only one real solution? Select all that apply.
   Ⓐ $4x^2 + 4x + 1 = 4x + 1$
   Ⓑ $2x^2 + x + 1 = x + 1$
   Ⓒ $4x^2 = 1$
   Ⓓ $4x^2 - x - 1 = 0$

6. What is the solution of $x^2 - 6x = 11$?
   Ⓐ $3 \pm 2\sqrt{5}$
   Ⓑ $-3 \pm 2\sqrt{5}$
   Ⓒ $-3 \pm \sqrt{5}$
   Ⓓ $3 \pm 5\sqrt{5}$

7. Solve the system of equations:
   $\begin{cases} y = x \\ y = x^2 - 3x \end{cases}$ (0, 0), (4, 4)

8. Which line(s) intersect the parabola $y = x^2 - x + 3$ at two points? Select all that apply.
   Ⓐ $y = -x + 2$
   Ⓑ $y = -x + 3$
   Ⓒ $y = -x + 4$
   Ⓓ $y = -x + 5$

9. The graph of a quadratic function passes through the points (0, −4) and (−2, 0). What is a zero of the function? −2

10. What is the value of x in the diagram below?

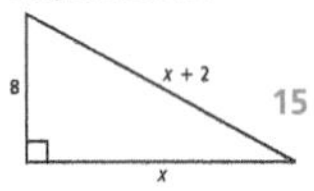

8
x + 2
x

   15

11. Which is equivalent to $(3\sqrt{2x^3})(\sqrt{8x^5})$?
   Ⓐ $12x^4$
   Ⓑ $12x^8$
   Ⓒ $24x^8$
   Ⓓ $6x^4$

12. Solve $x(12 - x) = 3(4x - 3)$
   ±3

13. Solve $x^2 - 5x = 84$ by factoring.
   −7, 12

enVision™ **Algebra 1** • Assessment Resources

14. The profit from a business is described by the function $P(x) = -3x^2 + 12x + 75$, where x is the number of items made, in thousands, and $P(x)$ is the profit in dollars. How many items will maximize the profit?
   Ⓐ 1,000
   Ⓑ 2,000
   Ⓒ 4,000
   Ⓓ 6,000

15. Solve $(x + 7)^2 = 49$.
   0, −14

16. Use the Quadratic Formula to solve $x^2 + 14x + 44 = 0$. Which of the following are the solutions to the nearest hundredth?
   Ⓐ −9.24 and −4.76
   Ⓑ −9.24 and 4.76
   Ⓒ 9.23 and 4.76
   Ⓓ 16.64 and −2.64

17. Which of the following are factors of $x^6 - 16$? Select all that apply.
   Ⓐ $x^3 - 4$
   Ⓑ $x^3 - 2$
   Ⓒ $x^3 - 8$
   Ⓓ $x^3 + 4$

18. The quadratic function $d = -2x^2 + 10$ models a skateboarder's distance, in feet, from the bottom of a hill x seconds after the skateboarder starts moving down the hill. After how many seconds is the skateboarder 1 ft from the bottom of the hill?
   Ⓐ 2.1 s
   Ⓑ 4.1 s
   Ⓒ 8.0 s
   Ⓓ 10.0 s

19. Find the value of c that makes $25x^2 + 70x + c$ a perfect square trinomial.
   Ⓐ 36
   Ⓑ 49
   Ⓒ 64
   Ⓓ 81

20. Rewrite the expression $(2\sqrt{6x^3})(\sqrt{18x^5})$, where x is positive, without a perfect square factor in the radicand.
   Ⓐ $12x^8\sqrt{3}$
   Ⓑ $6x^8\sqrt{3}$
   Ⓒ $12x^4\sqrt{3}$
   Ⓓ $6x^4\sqrt{3}$

21. Find the value of $\sqrt{(3 + 2)^2 + (16 - 4)^2}$. 13

22. The zeros of a quadratic function are 9 and −4. Which of the following could be the function? Select all that apply.
   Ⓐ $f(x) = x^2 - 5x + 36$
   Ⓑ $f(x) = x^2 + 5x - 36$
   Ⓒ $f(x) = x^2 - 5x - 36$
   Ⓓ $f(x) = \frac{x^2 - 5x - 36}{5}$

23. An outfielder throws a ball to home plate. The ball's path is modeled by the graph of $y = \frac{2x}{5} - \frac{x^2}{500}$, where x represents the horizontal distance of the ball from the outfielder, and y represents the ball's vertical distance above the ground. What are the coordinates of the vertex of the ball's path?
   (100, 20)

24. What is the discriminant of the equation $2x^2 + 3x + 4 = 0$?
   Ⓐ 41
   Ⓑ −24
   Ⓒ −23
   Ⓓ 23

enVision™ **Algebra 1** • Assessment Resources

Item Analysis

Item	DOK	Standard	Item	DOK	Standard	Item	DOK	Standard
1	2	HSA.SSE.B.3.A, HSA.APR.B.3	9	2	HSA.CED.A.1, HSA.SSE.B.3	17	2	HSA.SSE.A.2
2	3	HSA.CED.A.2	10	3	HSA.CED.A.1	18	3	HSA.REI.B.4.B
3	3	HSA.SSE.B.3.B	11	2	HSN.RN.A.2	19	3	HSA.REI.B.4.A, HSA.SSE.B.3.B
4	2	HSN.RN.A.2	12	2	HSA.REI.B.4.B	20	3	HSN.RN.A.2
5	2	HSA.REI.B.4.A	13	2	HSA.REI.B.4.B	21	2	HSN.RN.A.2
6	2	HSA.REI.B.4.A	14	2	HSA.SSE.B.3.B, HSF.IF.C.8.A	22	3	HAS.CED.A.2, HSA.APR.B.3
7	3	HSA.REI.D.11, HSA.REI.C.7	15	2	HSA.REI.B.4.B	23	2	HSA.SSE.B.3.B, HSF.IF.C.8.A
8	3	HSA.REI.C.7	16	2	HSA.REI.B.4.B	24	2	HSA.REI.B.4.B

TOPIC PERFORMANCE ASSESSMENT Form A

AVAILABLE **ONLINE**

Name ______________________ enVision Algebra 1 PearsonRealize.com

9 Performance Assessment Form A

How far will a car travel before coming to a full stop after the driver applies the brakes? How do accident investigators determine whether cars involved in accidents were traveling at safe speeds? They consider variables such as a car's speed, the driver's reaction time, the type of road, the weather conditions, and the effectiveness of the brakes.

1. Suppose a car is traveling on a dry, level road and the driver has average reaction time. The formula $y = 0.048x^2 + 0.37x$ relates the car's approximate stopping distance y, in feet, to the speed of the car x, in miles per hour.

Part A

Graph the formula. Label axes and use appropriate scales for the axes.

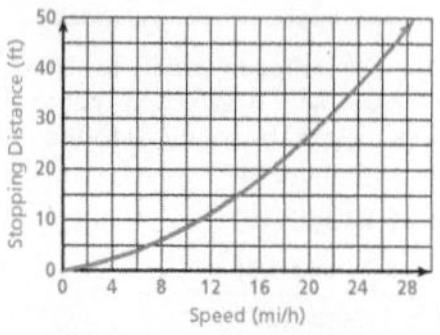
Stopping Distance (ft)
50
40
30
20
10
0
0 4 8 12 16 20 24 28
Speed (mi/h)

Part B

At about what speed should a driver travel to guarantee a stopping distance of 50 ft or less? Use the quadratic formula to find the speed. Explain each step.

About 28.6 mi/h or less. Solutions may vary. Sample:

$0.048x^2 + 0.37x = 50$	Write original equation.
$1{,}000(0.048x^2 + 0.37x) = 50(1{,}000)$	Multiply each side by 1000.
$48x^2 + 370x = 50{,}000$	Simplify.
$48x^2 + 370x - 50{,}000 = 0$	Write the equation in standard form and identify a, b, and c.
$x = \frac{-370 \pm \sqrt{(370)^2 - 4(48)(-50{,}000)}}{2(48)}$	Substitute values for a, b, and c into the quadratic formula.
$x \approx 28.6$	Simplify. The negative solution does not make sense in this situation.

enVision™ Algebra 1 • Assessment Resources

Part C

Explain how you can find the speed you found in Part B by using a graphing calculator to graph two functions.

Answers will vary. Sample: Graph $y = 0.048x^2 + 0.37x$ and $y = 50$. Then find the points of intersection of the two functions. Choose the point that has positive values for x and y.

2. When a driver applies the brakes, the car's tires leave skid marks on the road that can be used to estimate the car's speed before braking. On a dry, level road, the expression $3\sqrt{3} \cdot \sqrt{d}$ can be used to estimate the speed, in miles per hour, that a car leaving a skid mark d feet long was traveling when the brakes were applied. If a car skids for 60 ft before stopping, what is an expression for the speed it was traveling? Write your answer so there are no perfect square factors in the radicand, and then approximate your answer to the nearest tenth of a mile per hour. Show your work.

$18\sqrt{5} \approx 40.2$

$3\sqrt{3} \cdot \sqrt{d} = 3\sqrt{3} \cdot \sqrt{60}$

$= 18\sqrt{5}$

3. Suppose an automobile company tests the brakes of its sports model car in two types of road conditions. On a dry road, the car traveling x miles per hour leaves a skid mark f feet long, according to $f(x) = \frac{x^2}{27}$. On a wet road, the car traveling x miles per hour leaves a skid mark w feet long, according to the table shown. Compare the functions. What do the results tell you about the effects of weather? Should you drive more slowly or more quickly in the rain?

x(mi/h)	$w(x)$(ft)
0	0
5	1.9
10	7.4
15	16.7
20	29.6
25	46.3

Answers will vary. Sample: At similar speeds, cars skid for longer distances on wet roads versus dry roads. When roads are wet, drivers should drive more slowly and leave more distance between themselves and cars in front of them.

4. For a new road-surface design, the equation $y = \frac{x^2}{20} - \frac{1}{2}x + 10$ relates a car's stopping distance y, in feet, to its speed before braking x, in miles per hour. Suppose a car takes 300 feet to stop after applying the brakes. Use completing the square to rewrite $\frac{x^2}{20} - \frac{1}{2}x + 10 = 300$ in the form $(x + p)^2 = q$. Then estimate how fast the car was going when the brakes were applied. Show your work.

$(x - 5)^2 = 5{,}825$; 81.32 mph

$\frac{x^2}{20} - \frac{1}{2}x + 10 = 300$

$x^2 - 10x + 200 = 6{,}000$

$x^2 - 10x + 25 = 5{,}800 + 25$

$(x - 5)^2 = 5{,}825$

$\sqrt{(x-5)^2} = \sqrt{5{,}825}$

$x - 5 \approx 76.32$

$x \approx 81.32$

enVision™ Algebra 1 • Assessment Resources

AVAILABLE **ONLINE**

Topic Performance Assessment Assess students' ability to apply the topic concepts and skills using the Topic Performance Assessments found at **SavvasRealize.com.** These online assessments include a breadth of technology-enhanced item types.

Item Analysis and Scoring Guide

Item	DOK	2-Point Responses	1-Point Responses	Standards
1A	2	Correct answer	Partially correct graph	HSA.CED.A.2, HSF.IF.C.7.A
1B	3	Correct answer and solution steps	Correct answer only	HSA.REI.B.4.B, HSA.CED.A.1, HSA.SSE.B.3
1C	2	Correct answer and explanation	Correct answer and partially correct explanation	HSA.REI.D.11
2	2	Correct answer	Partially correct answer	HSN.RN.A.2
3	3	Correct explanation	Partially correct explanation	HSA.CED.A.2, HSF.IF.C.9
4	3	Correct answer and solution steps	Correct answer only	HSA.REI.B.4.A, HSA.REI.B.4.B, HSA.SSE.A.2

SavvasRealize.com

Assess

TOPIC 9
Solving Quadratic Equations

TOPIC PERFORMANCE ASSESSMENT Form B

AVAILABLE ONLINE

Name ______________________________ enVision Algebra 1

PearsonRealize.com

9 Performance Assessment Form B

When an archer shoots an arrow, the arrow follows a parabolic path through the air. That parabola can be represented by a quadratic function, where x represents the arrow's horizontal distance from the archer, and y represents the arrow's height above the ground.

1. Philip releases an arrow from a shoulder height of 4 ft. The arrow reaches a maximum height of 40 ft before it begins to fall. It lands on the ground about 160 ft away from where he is standing. Philip models this situation with a quadratic function. What is a zero of the function? What is the y-intercept of the graph of the function? Construct a rough graph of the situation based on your findings, where y represents the vertical height, in feet, and x represents the horizontal distance, in feet.

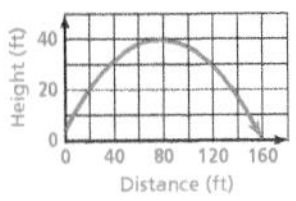

Height (ft)
40
20
0
0 40 80 120 160
Distance (ft)

zero: 160; y-intercept: 4; Graphs will vary. Sample shown above.

2. Philip shoots an arrow from the top of a hill onto the ground. The flight of the arrow can be modeled with the quadratic function $y = -5x^2 + 15x + 90$, where y represents the vertical height of the arrow, in meters, and x represents the time, in seconds. Use factoring to find the positive zero of the function. What does this zero represent? Then find the maximum value of the function by completing the square. What does the maximum value represent? Explain each step in your answer.

zero: 6; The arrow lands 6 s after it is released. (1.5, 101.25); The arrow reaches a maximum height of 101.25 m above the ground 1.5 s after it is released.

Factor $-5x^2 + 15x + 90 = 0$.

$(-1)(-5x^2 + 15x + 90) = (-1)(0)$	Multiply each side by -1.
$5x^2 - 15x - 90 = 0$	Simplify.
$(5x + 15)(x - 6) = 0$	Factor.
$x = -3, 6$	Solve. Choose $x = 6$ because all values are positive.

To find the maximum value, find the value at the vertex.

$y = -5x^2 + 15x + 90$	
$y - 90 = -5x^2 + 15x$	Isolate $ax^2 + bx$.
$y - 90 = -5(x^2 - 3x)$	Factor -5, so the expression in parenthesis is $x^2 + bx$.
$y - 90 - 5(2.25) = -5(x^2 - 3x + 2.25)$	Add $\left(\frac{-3}{2}\right)^2$ to complete the square.
$y = -5(x^2 - 1.5)^2 + 101.25$	The vertex is (1.5, 101.25).

3. Target shooters use the angle of their aim to control the distance their arrows travel. They need to aim their arrows at a point above the center of the target to offset the distance the arrow will drop due to gravity. With his current angle of aim, Philip estimates the following values for his arrow's height y, in meters, and horizontal distance x, in meters.
   - At $x = 0$ m, $y = 1.4$ m (shoulder height)
   - At $x = 90$ m, $y = 1.2$ m (height of the center of the target)
   - At $x = 95$ m, $y = 0$ m (the distance the arrow would travel if the target were not there)

Part A

Use a graphing calculator and Philip's estimated points to find a model that represents this situation. Explain.

$y \approx -0.002503x^2 + 0.2230x + 1.4$; Sample: Use a graphing calculator to find a, b, and c and write an equation for the function. Use the 3 points given, (0, 1.4), (90, 1.2), and (95, 0). Using regression, $a \approx -0.002503$, $b \approx 0.2230$ and $c = 1.4$, so $y \approx -0.002503x^2 + 0.2230x + 1.4$.

Part B

Use a graphing calculator to find the maximum height reached by Philip's arrow and the horizontal distance of the arrow from Philip at that point.

maximum height $\approx$ 6.4 m; horizontal distance $\approx$ 44.5 m

4. Philip releases an arrow at a moving target. The model for the arrow's path is $y = -0.02x^2 + x + 4$, and the model for the path of the target is $y = 0.3x$. For both models, x and y represent horizontal and vertical distances in feet. When the arrow hits the target, what is the arrow's horizontal distance from Philip, and what is the arrow's height from the ground? (Assume that the two objects reach the intersection point at the same time.) Use a graph to estimate answers to this problem. Then use algebra to solve the problem. Explain.

horizontal distance = 40 ft

height above ground = 12 ft

Solve $\begin{cases} y = -0.02x^2 + x + 4 \\ y = 0.3x \end{cases}$

$-0.02x^2 + x + 4 = 0.3x$

$x^2 - 50x - 200 = -15x$

$x^2 - 35x - 200 = 0$

$x = \frac{35 \pm \sqrt{(-35)^2 - 4(1)(-200)}}{2(1)} = \frac{35 \pm 45}{2}$

$x = 40, -5$. Ignore -5, because all values in this context are positive. So $x = 40$. Substituting $x = 40$ into either of the two equations in the system gives $y = 12$.

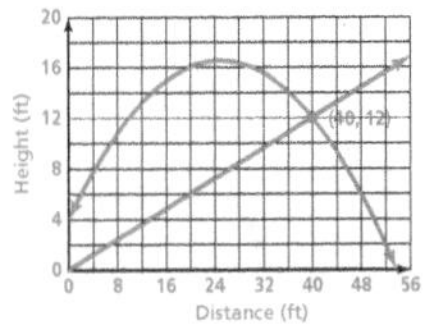

Height (ft)
20
16
12
8
4
0
(40, 12)
0 8 16 24 32 40 48 56
Distance (ft)

AVAILABLE ONLINE

Topic Performance Assessment Assess students' ability to apply the topic concepts and skills using the Topic Performance Assessments found at **SavvasRealize.com.** These online assessments include a breadth of technology-enhanced item types.

Item Analysis and Scoring Guide

Item	DOK	2-Point Responses	1-Point Responses	Standards
1	3	Correct answers and graph	Correct answers only	HSA.APR.B.3
2	4	Correct answers, steps, and explanation	Correct answers only	HSA.SSE.B.3.A, HSA.SSE.B.3.B, HSF.IF.C.8.A, HSA.APR.B.3
3A	3	Correct answer and explanation	Correct answer only	HSS.ID.B.6.A
3B	2	Two correct answers	One correct answer only	HSF.IF.C.7
4	4	Correct answer, graph, and explanation	Partially correct answer	HSA.REI.C.7

MATH BACKGROUND FOCUS

Topic 10 extends students' knowledge of functions to include radical functions. Students identify the key features of the graphs of radical functions. They also learn to transform functions, combine functions, and find inverse functions.

Transformations of Functions

Key Features of Functions Students learn to recognize the key features of functions. They identify the domain and range, maximum and minimum values, axis of symmetry, and end behavior of functions.

Vertical and Horizontal Translations Students understand the conditions that cause graphs of functions to shift up and down and to the left and right. They also learn to represent these translations in function notation.

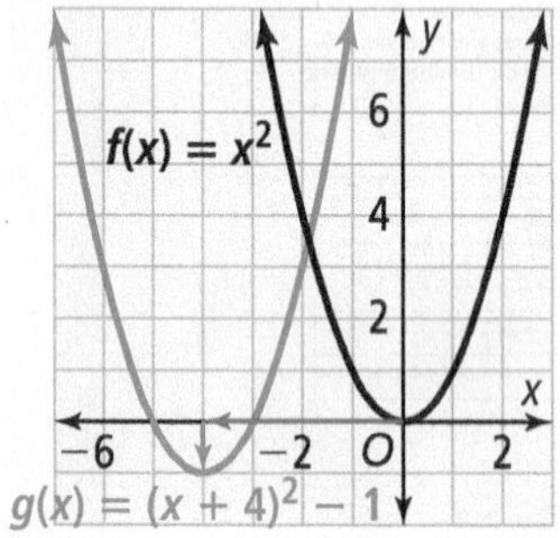

y
f(x) = x²
6
4
2
x
−6
−2
O
2
g(x) = (x + 4)² − 1

Stretches and Compressions of Graphs Students learn about stretching and compressing functions vertically and horizontally. They also represent the stretches and compressions in function notation.

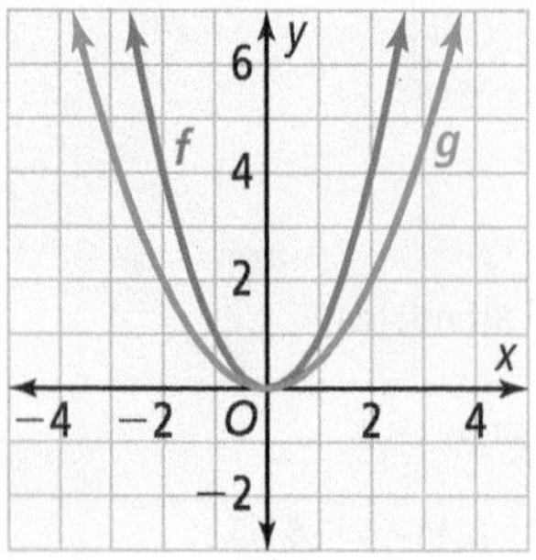

y
6
f
4
g
2
x
−4
−2
O
2
4
−2

Function Operations

Adding and Subtracting Functions Students learn to add and subtract functions and to identify the domain and the range of the new function.

Multiplying Functions Students learn to multiply functions and to identify the domain and the range of the new function.

Inverse Functions Students understand the relationship between a function and its inverse. They learn to graph inverse functions and find inverse functions algebraically. Students also interpret and use inverse functions to solve problems.

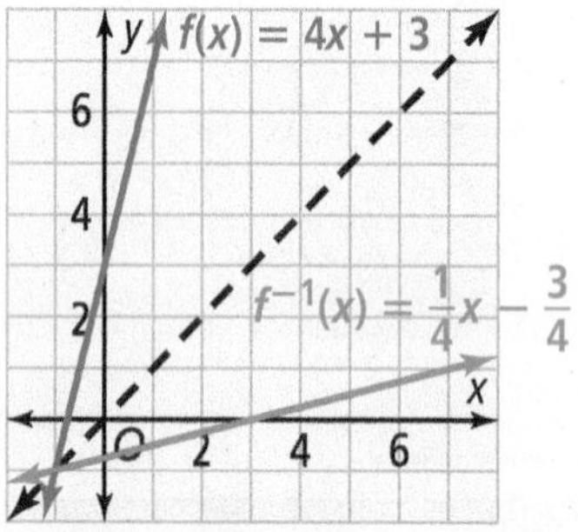

y
f(x) = 4x + 3
6
4
2
f⁻¹(x) = ¼x − ¾
x
O
2
4
6

TOPIC 10

Working With Functions

MATH BACKGROUND COHERENCE

Students learn best when concepts are connected through the curriculum. This coherence is achieved within topics, across topics, across domains, and across grade levels.

MAKING MATHEMATICAL CONNECTIONS

Looking Back

How does Topic 10 connect to what students learned earlier?

TOPIC 5

- **Translations of Functions** Students learned to translate absolute value functions. In Topic 10, they learn to translate any type of function.

TOPIC 6

- **Key Features of Functions** Students learned to identify the key features of exponential functions. In Topic 10, they identify the key features of square root and cube root functions.

TOPIC 8

- **Average Rate of Change** Students learned to calculate the average rate of change over an interval of a quadratic function. In Topic 10, they calculate the average rate of change of square root and cube root functions over intervals.

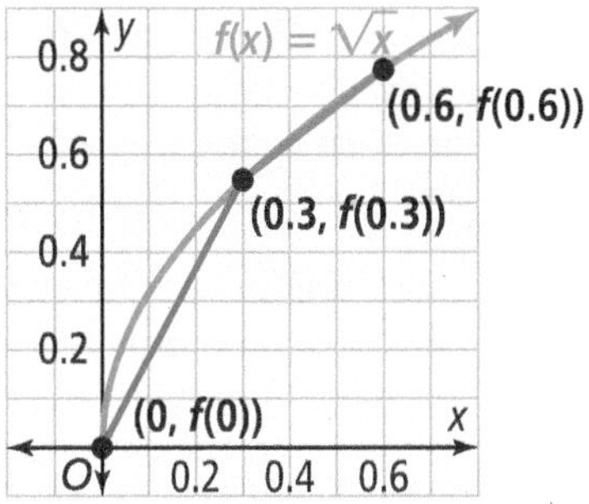

f(x) = √x
y
0.8
0.6
0.4
0.2
(0.6, f(0.6))
(0.3, f(0.3))
(0, f(0))
x
O
0.2
0.4
0.6

IN THIS TOPIC

How is content connected within Topic 10?

- **Transformations of Functions** In Lessons 10-1 and 10-2, students learn to translate square root functions and cube root functions. In Lesson 10-4, they learn to graph and analyze translations of absolute value, exponential, quadratic, and radical functions. In Lesson 10-5, students transform absolute value, exponential, quadratic, and radical functions by stretching and compressing their graphs.

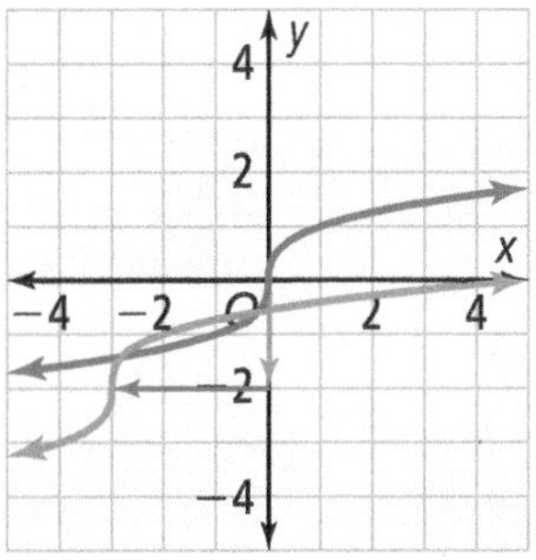

y
4
2
x
−4
−2
O
2
4
−2
−4

- **Analyzing Key Features of Functions** In Lessons 10-1 and 10-2, students identify the key features of square root functions and cube root functions including the domain, range, maximum and minimum values, and end behavior. In Lesson 10-3, they use the key features of functions to compare them. In Lesson 10-6, students perform operations on functions and determine how the operations affect the domain and the range of the new functions. In Lesson 10-7, they find inverse functions and determine the key features of the inverse functions.

MAKING MATHEMATICAL CONNECTIONS

Looking Ahead

How does Topic 10 connect to what students will learn later?

ALGEBRA 2

- **Exponential and Logarithmic Functions** In Lesson 10-7, students learn to find inverse functions for linear, quadratic, and radical functions. In Algebra 2, they will learn to find inverse functions for exponential and logarithmic functions.
- **Function Operations** In Lesson 10-6, students learn to add, subtract, and multiply functions. In Algebra 2, they will learn to divide functions and will find the composition of functions.
- **Graphing Radical Functions** Students learn to graph and identify the key features of square root and cube root functions. In Algebra 2, they will graph and identify the key features of other radical functions.

A rigorous curriculum emphasizes conceptual understanding, procedural skill and fluency, and applications.

Conceptual Understanding

- **Key Features of a Function** Students understand that key features of a function, including the domain, range, maximum and minimum values, axis of symmetry, and end behavior, can be used to identify and compare functions.
- **Translations of Functions** Students recognize that for all functions, adding a constant to the output translates a graph vertically and subtracting a constant from the input translates a graph horizontally.

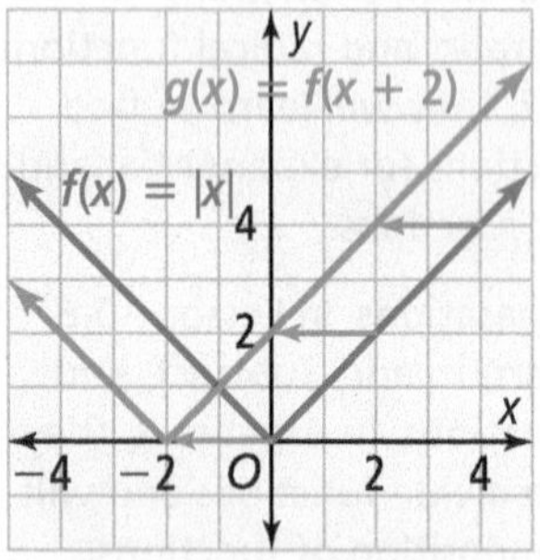
y
g(x) = f(x + 2)
f(x) = |x|
4
2
x
−4
−2
O
2
4

- **Compressions and Stretches of Functions** Students understand that multiplying the output of a function by a factor of k stretches or compresses the graph vertically, and multiplying the input of a function by a factor of k stretches or compresses the graph horizontally.

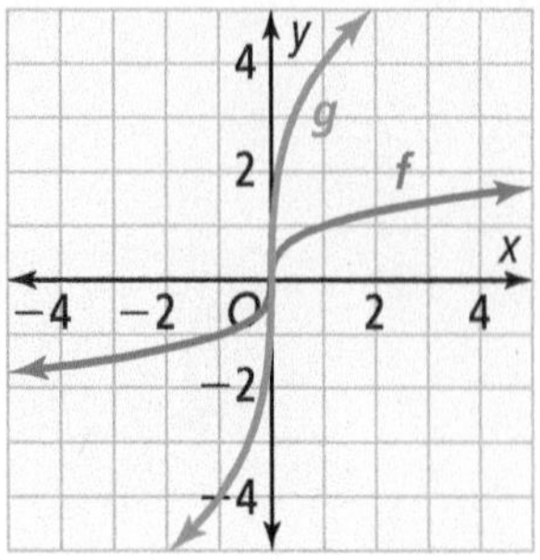
y
4
g
2
f
x
−4
−2
O
2
4
−2
−4

Procedural Skill and Fluency

- **Average Rate of Change** Students calculate the average rate of change of a square root or cube root function for a specified interval by finding the ratio of the change in y to the change in x for the points at the beginning and the end of an interval.
- **Reflections of Functions** Students reflect the graph of a function across the x-axis when the output of the function is multiplied by –1.

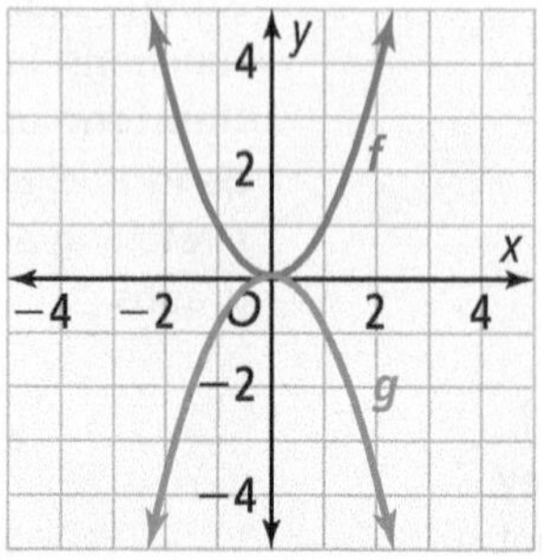
y
4
2
f
x
−4
−2
O
2
4
−2
g
−4

- **Inverse Functions** Students find the equations for the inverse of linear functions and for restricted-domain quadratic functions. Students use the notation for inverse functions.

Applications

- **Function Operations** Students can use function operations to model real-world problems, such as finding the surface area of a cylindrical container.
- **Model With a Cube Root Function** Students discover that they can apply a cube root function to determine the increase in volume of a cube-shaped package due to an increase in side length.
- **Interpret Inverse Functions** Students interpret inverse functions when they determine how much money must be charged to a credit card in order to earn enough airline miles to purchase a plane ticket.

TOPIC 10

Working With Functions

MATH PRACTICES & PROCESSES

Math Practices Within Topic 10 Lessons

The math practices describe the behaviors and habits of mind that mathematically proficient students demonstrate when actively engaged in mathematics work. Opportunities to develop expertise with these important behaviors and thinking habits exist throughout the topic and program. Here we focus on *using appropriate tools* and *being precise*.

As students create, graph, and solve functions, look for the following behaviors to assess and identify students who demonstrate proficiency with these math practices.

Highlighted Math Practices Within Topic 10 Lessons

Use Appropriate Tools Strategically **MP.5**	Attend to Precision **MP.6**
Mathematically proficient students:	Mathematically proficient students:
• Recognize the strengths of available tools when they choose to use a graphing calculator to graph a square root function and identify the domain and range.	• Label quantities appropriately when they describe the x- and y-values with respect to the maximum or minimum values of the function.
• Use mathematical models for visualizing and analyzing information when they graph the sums of functions and make observations about how the new graph relates to the graphs of the addends.	• Determine the mathematical terms and definitions that apply when explaining why $y = 3$ cannot be an axis of symmetry for a function.
• Identify relevant external resources for solving problems when they choose to use a graph to identify the domain and range of a combined function.	• Communicate precisely when explaining the steps to calculate the value of a radical function for a specific value of x.
• Adjust the method or approach they use to compare functions based on the types of functions used and the information that is given.	• Use precision when determining which terms apply—*vertical, horizontal, stretch,* and *compression*—for describing specific transformations.

Help students become more proficient at using appropriate tools and being precise.

If students do not understand how to identify and use appropriate strategies for understanding and solving problems involving functions, then use these questioning strategies to help them develop their proficiency at using appropriate tools and being precise as they solve problems throughout the topic.

Q: What approach could you use to find the inverse of a function?

Q: What mathematical tools could you use to visualize transformations of functions?

Q: Why is it helpful to use a table to find the inverse of a function?

Q: What do you know when graphing a square root function?

Q: How can you check that you graphed a transformation of a function correctly?

Q: When finding the average rate of change of a function over an interval, how do you know that your answer is reasonable?

Q: What mathematical terms do you use when finding the key features of a graph of a function?

Q: What mathematical notation is important when writing an inverse function?

TOPIC PLANNER

Lesson	New Vocabulary	Objective	Essential Understanding	Standards
10-1 2 DAYS The Square Root Function	• square root function	• Graph translations of the square root function. • Calculate and interpret the average rate of change for a square root function over a specified interval.	A square root function contains a square root symbol with the independent variable in the radicand.	HSF.IF.B.4, HSF.IF.B.6, HSF.IF.C.7.B **Mathematical Practices** MP.5, MP.6, MP.7
10-2 2 DAYS The Cube Root Function	• cube root function	• Identify key features of the graph of cube root functions and graph translations of them. • Model real-world situations using the cube root function. • Calculate and interpret the average rate of change of a cube root function over a specified interval.	The general form of a cube root function is $f(x) = \sqrt[3]{x}$. It intersects both axes at the origin, and the domain and range are all real numbers.	HSF.IF.B.4, HSF.IF.B.6, HSF.IF.C.7.B **Mathematical Practices** MP.4, MP.7, MP.8
10-3 2 DAYS Analyzing Functions Graphically	none	• Relate the domain and range of a function to its graph. • Analyze the key features of the graph of a function to identify the type of function it represents.	The key features of the graphs of functions—including the domain, range, maximum and minimum values, axis of symmetry, and end behavior—are used to identify and compare functions.	HSF.IF.B.4, HSF.IF.B.5 **Mathematical Practices** MP.4, MP.6, MP.7
10-4 2 DAYS Translations of Functions	none	• Graph translations of absolute value, exponential, quadratic, and radical functions. • Determine how combining translations affects the key features of the graph of a function.	Changes to the input and output of a function in the form $f(x - h) + k$ result in a translation of the graph of the function. Adding a constant k to the output of the function shifts the graph vertically. Subtracting a constant h from the input of the function shifts the graph horizontally.	HSF.IF.B.4, HSF.BF.B.3, HSF.IF.C.7.B **Mathematical Practices** MP.1, MP.7, MP.8

Lesson Resources

Digital
Print

Student Edition

Student Companion

Assessment Resource Book
- Lesson Quiz

Digital

Digital Lesson Courseware
- Examples with Embedded Interactives
- Additional Examples
- Online Practice powered by MathXL for School
- Virtual Nerd Tutorials
- English/Spanish Glossary
- Digital Math Tools
- Mathematical Modeling in 3 Acts

Teaching Resources
- Reteach to Build Understanding
- Mathematical Literacy and Vocabulary
- Additional Practice
- Enrichment

Lesson Support for Teachers
- Professional Development Video
- Lesson Plans

SavvasRealize.com

Digital

The suggested pacing for each lesson is shown for a 45-minute class.
In addition allow 1 day for the Topic Review and 1 day for the Topic Assessment.

TOPIC PLANNER

Lesson	New Vocabulary	Objective	Essential Understanding	Standards
10-5 2 DAYS Compressions and Stretches of Functions	none	• Identify the effect on the graph of a function of multiplying the output by −1. • Identify the effect on the graph of a function of replacing $f(x)$ by $kf(x)$ or $f(kx)$ for specific values of k.	The graphs of functions are transformed when the input and output are multiplied by varying factors of k. Multiplying the output by a factor of k stretches or compresses the graph vertically. Multiplying the input by a factor of k stretches or compresses the graph horizontally.	HSF.BF.B.3 **Mathematical Practices** MP.2, MP.6, MP.7
Mathematical Modeling in 3 Acts: Edgy Tiles 1 DAY	none	• Use mathematical modeling to represent a problem situation and to propose a solution. • Test and verify the appropriateness of their math models. • Explain why the results from their mathematical models might not align exactly with the problem situation.	Many real-world problem situations can be represented with a mathematical model, but that model might not represent the real-world situation exactly.	HSF.IF.B.4, HSF.IF.C.7.B **Mathematical Practices** MP.4
10-6 2 DAYS Operations With Functions	none	• Combine functions using arithmetic operations, including addition, subtraction, and multiplication. • Combine functions to solve real-world problems.	Functions can be combined in the same way as numbers, expressions, and polynomials. Addition, subtraction, and multiplication can be used to find $(f + g)(x)$, $(f - g)(x)$, and $(f \cdot g)(x)$.	HSF.BF.A.1.B **Mathematical Practices** MP.3, MP.5, MP.7
10-7 2 DAYS Inverse Functions	• inverse of a function	• Write an equation for the inverse of a linear function. • Write the inverse of a quadratic function after restricting the domain so the original function is one-to-one.	A one-to-one function is a function for which each range value corresponds to exactly one domain value. For these functions, it is possible to describe an *inverse function,* which reverses the order of the outputs and inputs of the function.	HSF.BF.B.4, HSF.BF.B.4.A **Mathematical Practices** MP.2, MP.3, MP.7

Topic Resources

Digital

Print

Student Edition
- enVision STEM
- Mathematical Modeling in 3 Acts
- Topic Review

Digital Lesson Courseware
- Topic Readiness Assessment
- Topic Assessment
- Topic Performance Assessment

Digital

Teaching Resources
- enVision STEM
- Graphing Technology Activities

Topic Support for Teachers
- Mathematical Modeling in 3 Acts
- ExamView
- Answers and Solutions

TOPIC READINESS ASSESSMENT

AVAILABLE ONLINE

Name ____________________ enVision Algebra 1 · PearsonRealize.com

10 Readiness Assessment

1. If $f(x) = x$ and $g(x) = x + 4$, which statement(s) about the graphs of the functions are true? Select all that apply.
   - **(A)** g is a translation 4 units up of f.
   - (B) g is a translation 4 units down of f.
   - **(C)** The x-intercept of g is 4 units less than the x-intercept of f.
   - (D) The x-intercept of g is 4 units greater than the x-intercept of f.

2. Function h is a translation 2 units left of the function $g(x) = 3x$. Which is an equation of function h?
   - (A) $h(x) = 3x - 2$
   - (B) $h(x) = 3(x - 2)$
   - (C) $h(x) = 3x + 2$
   - **(D)** $h(x) = 3(x + 2)$

3. If g is a reflection of $f(x) = \frac{1}{2}x - 5$ across the x-axis, what is an equation for g?
   $g(x) = -\left(\frac{1}{2}x - 5\right)$ or $g(x) = -\frac{1}{2}x + 5$

4. Function g is a translation 1 unit down of $f(x) = |x - 1|$. Which equation represents function g?
   - (A) $g(x) = |x - 2|$
   - (B) $g(x) = |x|$
   - **(C)** $g(x) = |x - 1| - 1$
   - (D) $g(x) = |x - 1| + 1$

5. Which function(s) are translations of $h(x) = |x|$? Select all that apply.
   - (A) $j(x) = \left|\frac{1}{4}x\right|$
   - **(B)** $j(x) = |x + 4|$
   - **(C)** $j(x) = |x| - 4$
   - (D) $j(x) = 4|x|$

6. How does the vertex of the function $g(x) = \left|\frac{1}{2}x - 1\right| + 2$ compare to the vertex of $f(x) = \left|\frac{1}{2}x + 2\right| - 2$?
   - **(A)** The vertex of g is 6 units to the right and 4 units above the vertex of f.
   - (B) The vertex of g is 6 units to the left and 4 units below the vertex of f.
   - (C) The vertex of g is 4 units to the right and 6 units above the vertex of f.
   - (D) The vertex of g is 4 units to the left and 6 units below the vertex of f.

7. What is the solution of the system of equations $\begin{cases} y = 10x - 4 \\ y = 8x + 2 \end{cases}$? Write your answer as an ordered pair.
   (3, 26)

8. What is the y-value of the solution of the system of equations $\begin{cases} 2x + y = 6 \\ y = 4x - 3 \end{cases}$?
   - (A) $-\frac{9}{2}$
   - (B) $\frac{3}{2}$
   - **(C)** 3
   - (D) 15

9. Substitution is used to solve the system shown. Which of the following could be a step in the solution?
   $\begin{cases} y = 3x + 6 \\ x - y = -2 \end{cases}$?
   - (A) $x - 3x = -2$
   - (B) $x - 3x + 6 = -2$
   - **(C)** $x - 3x - 6 = -2$
   - (D) $3x + 6 = -2$

10. What is the slope of the graph of $7x - 2y = 14$? 3.5 or $\frac{7}{2}$

11. Which function's graph has a vertex at $(-3, 5)$?
   - **(A)** $f(x) = |x + 3| + 5$
   - (B) $f(x) = |x - 3| + 5$
   - (C) $f(x) = |x + 3| - 5$
   - (D) $f(x) = |x - 3| - 5$

12. What is the y-intercept of the graph of $h(x) = |2x - 8|$? 8

13. Over which interval is the function $f(x) = -5x^2 + 5$ positive?
   - (A) $x > 0$
   - (B) $x < 0$
   - (C) $-5 < x < 0$
   - **(D)** $-1 < x < 1$

14. Over which interval is the function $g(x) = |x + 2|$ decreasing?
   - (A) $x > -2$
   - **(B)** $x < -2$
   - (C) $x > 2$
   - (D) $0 < x < 2$

15. Does the relation in the table represent a function?

x	y
−2	12
−1	3
0	0
1	3
2	12

Yes

16. Does the graph represent a function?

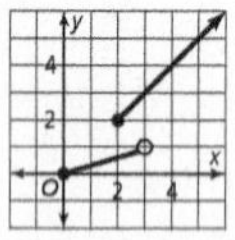

y
4
2
O
2
4
x

No

17. What are the domain and range of the function $f(x) = 3|x - 4| + 2$?
   - **(A)** domain: all real numbers; range: $y \geq 2$
   - (B) domain: $x > 2$; range: $y > 2$
   - (C) domain: $x \geq 2$; range: all real numbers
   - (D) domain: all real numbers; range: all real numbers

18. Which statement about the graph of $x = 2$ is true?
   - (A) The graph represents a linear function.
   - (B) The graph represents a nonlinear function.
   - (C) The graph represents a function.
   - **(D)** The graph does not represent

AVAILABLE ONLINE

Topic Readiness Assessment Assess students' understanding of prerequisite concepts and skills using the Topic Readiness Assessment found at **SavvasRealize.com.** These auto-scored online assessments provide students with a breadth of technology-enhanced item types.

Individualized Study Plan Based on their performance, students will be assigned a study plan tailored to their specific learning needs.

RtI Item Analysis for Diagnosis and Intervention

Item	DOK	Standard	Item	DOK	Standard
1	2	HSF.BF.B.3	10	2	HSF.IF.B.4
2	2	HSF.BF.B.3	11	2	HSF.IF.B.4
3	2	HSF.BF.B.3	12	2	HSF.IF.B.4
4	2	HSF.BF.B.3	13	2	HSF.IF.B.4
5	2	HSF.BF.B.3	14	2	HSF.IF.B.4
6	2	HSF.BF.B.3	15	1	HSF.IF.A.1
7	2	HSA.REI.C.6	16	1	HSF.IF.A.1
8	2	HSA.REI.C.6	17	2	HSF.IF.A.1
9	2	HSA.REI.C.6	18	2	HSF.IF.A.1

TOPIC 10
Working With Functions

TOPIC OPENER

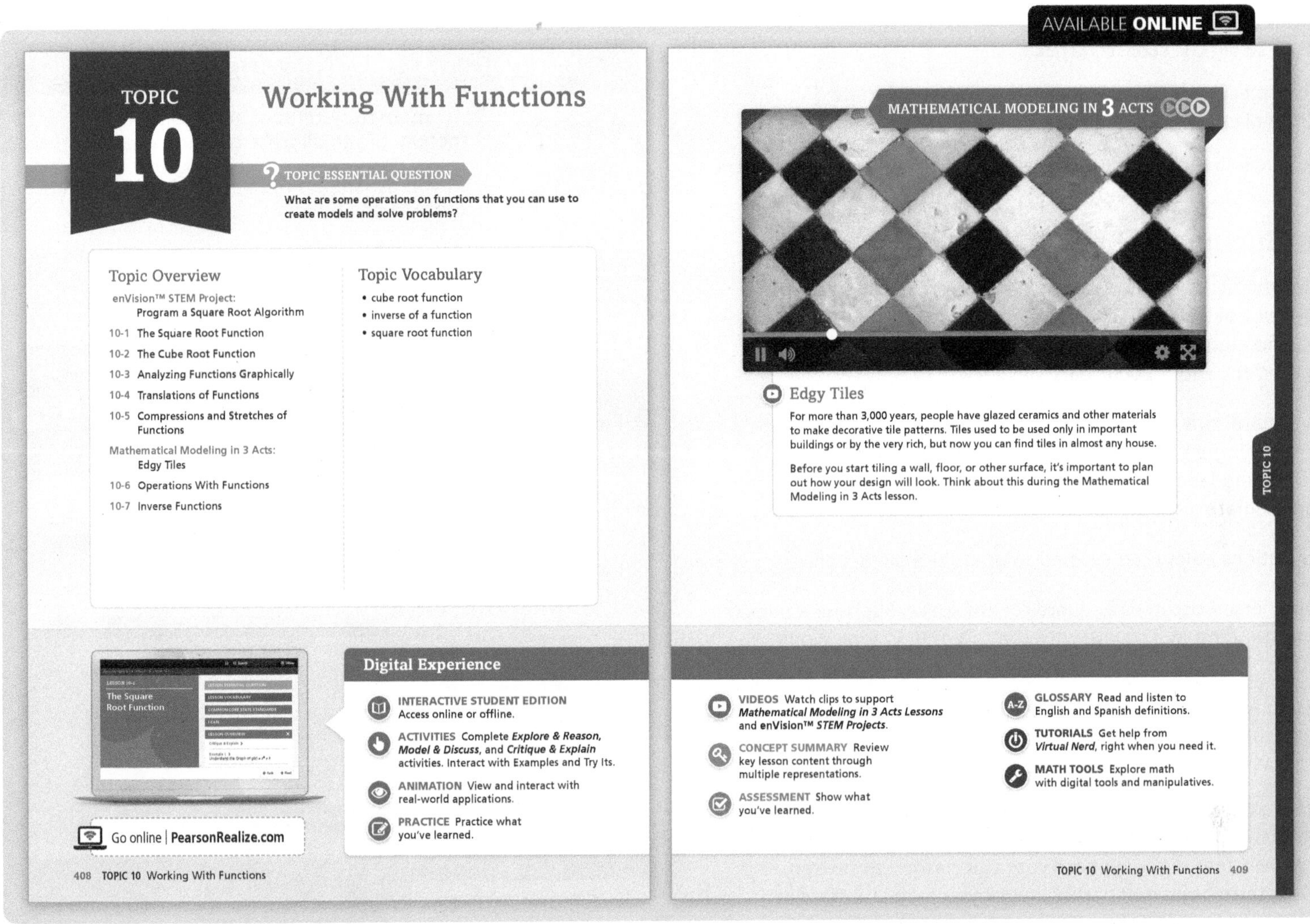

AVAILABLE ONLINE

TOPIC 10

Working With Functions

TOPIC ESSENTIAL QUESTION

What are some operations on functions that you can use to create models and solve problems?

Topic Overview

Topic Vocabulary

- cube root function
- inverse of a function
- square root function

Digital Experience

Go online | PearsonRealize.com

INTERACTIVE STUDENT EDITION Access online or offline.

ACTIVITIES Complete *Explore & Reason, Model & Discuss*, and *Critique & Explain* activities. Interact with Examples and Try Its.

ANIMATION View and interact with real-world applications.

PRACTICE Practice what you've learned.

MATHEMATICAL MODELING IN 3 ACTS

Edgy Tiles

For more than 3,000 years, people have glazed ceramics and other materials to make decorative tile patterns. Tiles used to be used only in important buildings or by the very rich, but now you can find tiles in almost any house.

Before you start tiling a wall, floor, or other surface, it's important to plan out how your design will look. Think about this during the Mathematical Modeling in 3 Acts lesson.

VIDEOS Watch clips to support *Mathematical Modeling in 3 Acts Lessons* and enVision™ *STEM Projects*.

CONCEPT SUMMARY Review key lesson content through multiple representations.

ASSESSMENT Show what you've learned.

GLOSSARY Read and listen to English and Spanish definitions.

TUTORIALS Get help from *Virtual Nerd*, right when you need it.

MATH TOOLS Explore math with digital tools and manipulatives.

Topic Essential Question

What are some operations on functions that you can use to create models and solve problems?

Revisit the Topic Essential Question throughout the topic. See page 457 (Topic Review) for notes about answering the Topic Essential Question.

Mathematical Modeling in 3 Acts

Generate excitement about the upcoming Mathematical Modeling in 3 Acts lesson by having students read about the math modeling problem for this topic.

See pages 444, 444A, and 444B for notes about how to use the lesson video in your classroom.

:ënVision™ STEM **Project**

Overview of the Project

In this project, students will learn how to approximate a square root to a given degree of accuracy.

Note: Students should *not* use calculator square roots for this project.

Introducing the Project

Present the situation by discussing that approximations for the square root of 2 have been used since Egyptian and Babylonian times, and algorithms for approximating any square root have been used for about 2000 years.

Many square root algorithms are recursive, taking an answer and producing a better one. Graphing calculators, phones, and programming languages may each be using a different algorithm to approximate a square root.

The questions below can be used to guide the discussion.

Q: One person occupies 2 square feet of space. Suppose a person was standing in a square with that area. How long would one side of the square be? [$\sqrt{2}$ feet]

Q: If you had to give the length of the side of the square in feet without using a square root symbol, how would you do it? [Use a calculator and round to the nearest tenth or hundredth.]

Q: Now suppose you had a crowd of people to fit into a square building, still keeping in mind that each person occupies 2 square feet. Also, suppose your calculator was broken, and the internet was down. How might you calculate the side length of one side of the building? [Steer students away from a specific number of people in a crowd and toward a process that would work for any number.]

Have students read the task they will be asked to complete.

Implementing the Project

Show the Topic 10 STEM video to generate interest in the project.

You can download blackline masters for use with the project from the Teacher Resource Center.

You may want to research unusual square root algorithms, to answer questions from students and to make available for students who want to extend the project.

Finishing the Project

You may wish to plan a day when students share their completed programs and building plans. Encourage students to explain their process as well as their results.

MAKING MATHEMATICAL CONNECTIONS	
In Topic 4 ...	... you used systems of equations and inequalities to allocate crops on a farm.
In this Topic ...	... you use square roots to determine square footage in a building.
In Topic 11 ...	... you will gather and analyze data about reducing energy consumption.

AVAILABLE **ONLINE**

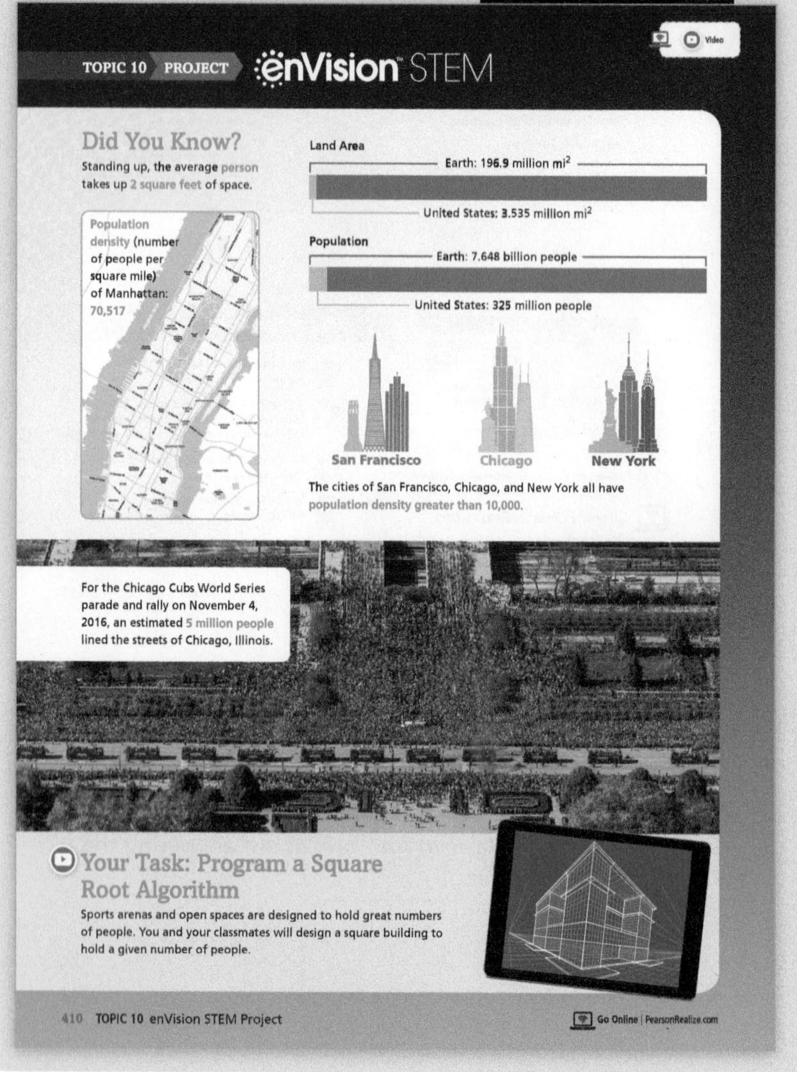

TOPIC 10 PROJECT
ënVision STEM
Video
Did You Know?
Standing up, the average person takes up 2 square feet of space.
Population density (number of people per square mile) of Manhattan: 70,517
Land Area
Earth: 196.9 million mi²
United States: 3.535 million mi²
Population
Earth: 7.648 billion people
United States: 325 million people
San Francisco
Chicago
New York
The cities of San Francisco, Chicago, and New York all have population density greater than 10,000.
For the Chicago Cubs World Series parade and rally on November 4, 2016, an estimated 5 million people lined the streets of Chicago, Illinois.
Your Task: Program a Square Root Algorithm
Sports arenas and open spaces are designed to hold great numbers of people. You and your classmates will design a square building to hold a given number of people.
410 TOPIC 10 enVision STEM Project
Go Online | PearsonRealize.com

Common Core Standards HSF.IF.A.3, HSF.BF.A.1, HSN.RN.B.3

Mathematical Practices MP.1, MP.6, MP.8

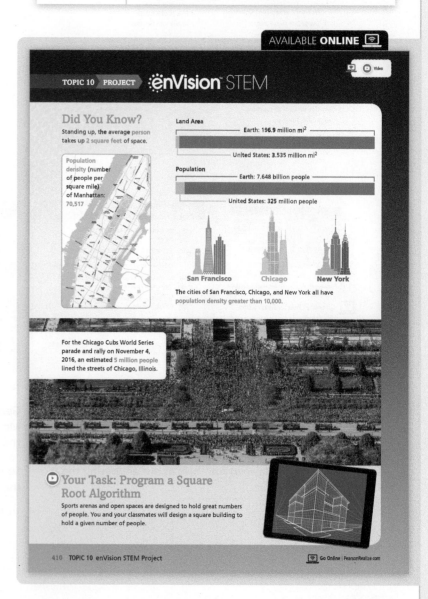

A-Z Glossary

LESSON 10-1
The Square Root Function

Lesson Overview

FOCUS

Objective
Students will be able to:

✔ Graph translations of the square root function.

✔ Calculate and interpret the average rate of change for a square root function over a specified interval.

✔ Solve real-world problems by evaluating and comparing two square root functions.

Essential Understanding
A square root function contains a square root symbol with the independent variable in the radicand.

COHERENCE

Previously in this course, students:
- Graphed linear, quadratic, exponential, and absolute value functions and translations of the functions.
- Calculated the average rate of change of linear, quadratic, exponential, and absolute value functions.

In this lesson, students:
- Graph square root functions and translations of the functions.
- Calculate the average rate of change of square root functions.

Later in this topic, students will:
- Graph cube root functions and translations of the functions.
- Calculate the average rate of change of cube root functions.

RIGOR

This lesson emphasizes a blend of *conceptual understanding* and *application.*
- Students understand the general characteristics of a square root function.
- Students evaluate and compare real-world square root functions, such as finding which ride at an amusement park spins at a faster rate.

Vocabulary Builder

REVIEW VOCABULARY — **English** | *Spanish*
- **average rate of change** | *tasa promedio de cambio*
- **interval** | *intervalo*

NEW VOCABULARY
- **square root function** | *función raíz cuadrada*

VOCABULARY ACTIVITY

Display a graph of the square root function. Then have students fill in the blanks to remind them of the difference between rate of change and slope.

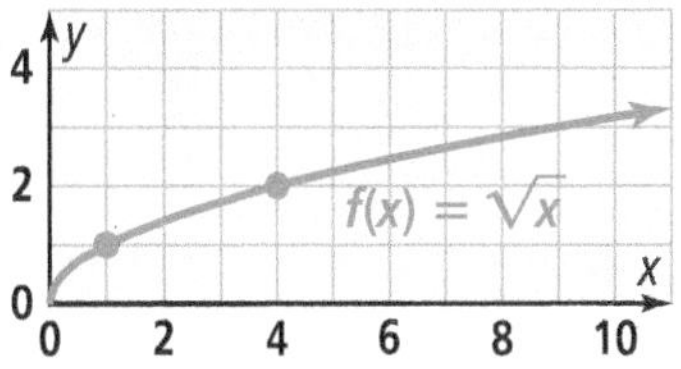
y
4
2
0
x
0
2
4
6
8
10
f(x) = √x

Q: ______ is defined as the ratio of the change in output values to the change in input values. [slope]

Q: You can find the slope of the line for any ______ function. [linear]

Q: When you use the ______ to calculate the slope between two points on a curved function, it is called the ______. [slope formula, average rate of change]

Student Companion

Students can do their in-class work for the lesson on pages 219–222 of their *Student Companion* or in Savvas Realize.

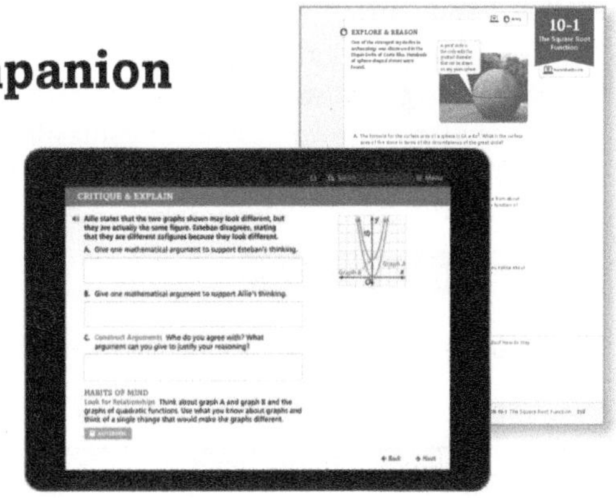
10-1
CRITIQUE & EXPLAIN

Mathematics Overview — COMMON CORE STANDARDS

Content Standards
In this lesson, students focus on these standards:

HSF.IF.B.6 Calculate and interpret the average rate of change of a function (presented symbolically or as a table) over a specified interval. Estimate the rate of change from a graph.*

HSF.IF.C.7.B Graph square root, cube root, and piecewise-defined functions, including step functions and absolute value functions.

They also work with concepts related to this standard:
HSF.IF.B.4

Mathematical Practice Standards
These standards are highlighted in this lesson:

MP.5 Use Appropriate Tools Strategically
Students use available tools such as a graphing calculator to graph a square root function and identify the domain and range.

MP.6 Attend to Precision
Students communicate precisely when explaining the steps for calculating the value of a square root function for a specific value of *x*.

Activity

EXPLORE & REASON

INSTRUCTIONAL FOCUS Students explore the relationship between the surface area of a sphere and the radius of a great circle. Students graph the relationship and compare it to the graph of a quadratic function in preparation for understanding the square root function.

STUDENT COMPANION Students can complete the *Explore & Reason* activity on page 219 of their *Student Companion*.

Before WHOLE CLASS

Implement Tasks that Promote Reasoning and Problem Solving ETP

Q: What do you notice about the sphere and the great circle associated with it?
[The radius of the sphere and the radius of the great circle are the same.]

During SMALL GROUP

Support Productive Struggle in Learning Mathematics ETP

Q: How can the coordinate pairs for the graph be determined?
[First, rewrite the equation from Part A to give the circumference based on the surface area. The first coordinate of each ordered pair would be surface area, and the second coordinate of each ordered pair would be the calculated circumference.]

For Early Finishers

Q: Use your equation from Part A to find the approximate surface areas of spheres with circumferences of 10 cm and 20 cm. Do these values match values from your graph?
[≈ 31.8 cm^2 and ≈ 127.3 cm^2; yes]

After WHOLE CLASS

Facilitate Meaningful Mathematical Discourse ETP

Q: How could you describe the average rate of change of the graph as the surface area increases?
[The average rate of change of the graph decreases as the surface area increases.]

Q: Why is the graph only the top half of a sideways parabola?
[The measurements of surface area and radius can have only positive values.]

HABITS OF MIND *Use with* **EXPLORE & REASON**

Look for Relationships What are the domain and range of the circumference function? How do they compare to the domain and range of a quadratic function? MP.7

[The domain and range of the circumference function contain all real numbers greater than or equal to 0. This is different from the domain and range of a quadratic function, both of which include all real numbers.]

AVAILABLE **ONLINE**

Go back

EXPLORE & REASON

One of the strangest mysteries in archaeology was discovered in the Diquís Delta of Costa Rica. Hundreds of sphere-shaped stones were discovered.

A. The formula for the surface area of a sphere is $SA = 4\pi r^2$. What is the surface area of the stone in terms of the circumference of the great circle?

Enter your answer.

A great circle is the circle with the greatest diameter that can be drawn on any given sphere.

1 of 2

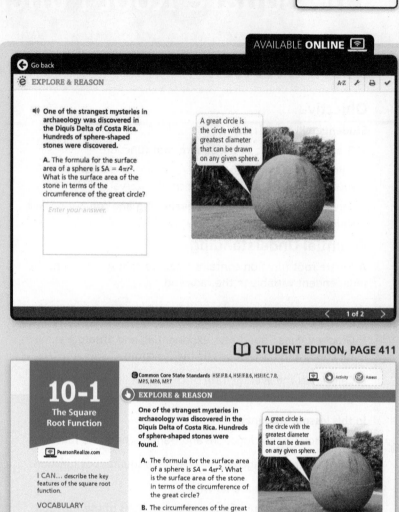

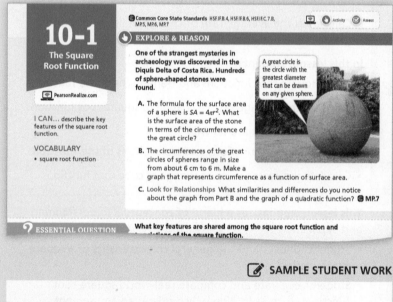

STUDENT EDITION, PAGE 411

Common Core State Standards HSF.IF.B.4, HSF.IF.B.6, HSF.IF.C.7.B, MP.5, MP.6, MP.7

Activity Assess

10-1 The Square Root Function

PearsonRealize.com

I CAN… describe the key features of the square root function.

VOCABULARY
- square root function

EXPLORE & REASON

One of the strangest mysteries in archaeology was discovered in the Diquís Delta of Costa Rica. Hundreds of sphere-shaped stones were found.

A great circle is the circle with the greatest diameter that can be drawn on any given sphere.

A. The formula for the surface area of a sphere is $SA = 4\pi r^2$. What is the surface area of the stone in terms of the circumference of the great circle?

B. The circumferences of the great circles of spheres range in size from about 6 cm to 6 m. Make a graph that represents circumference as a function of surface area.

C. Look for Relationships What similarities and differences do you notice about the graph from Part B and the graph of a quadratic function? MP.7

ESSENTIAL QUESTION What key features are shared among the square root function and translations of the square function.

SAMPLE STUDENT WORK

A. $SA = \frac{C^2}{\pi}$

B.

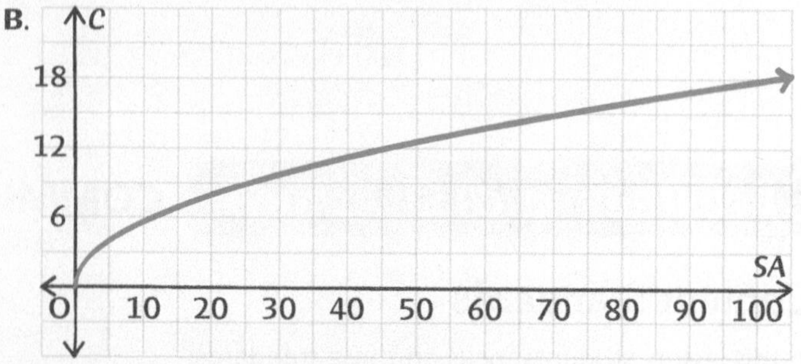

C
18
12
6
O
10
20
30
40
50
60
70
80
90
100
SA

C. The graph appears to be half of a sideways parabola that opens to the right instead of up or down.

INTRODUCE THE ESSENTIAL QUESTION

AVAILABLE ONLINE

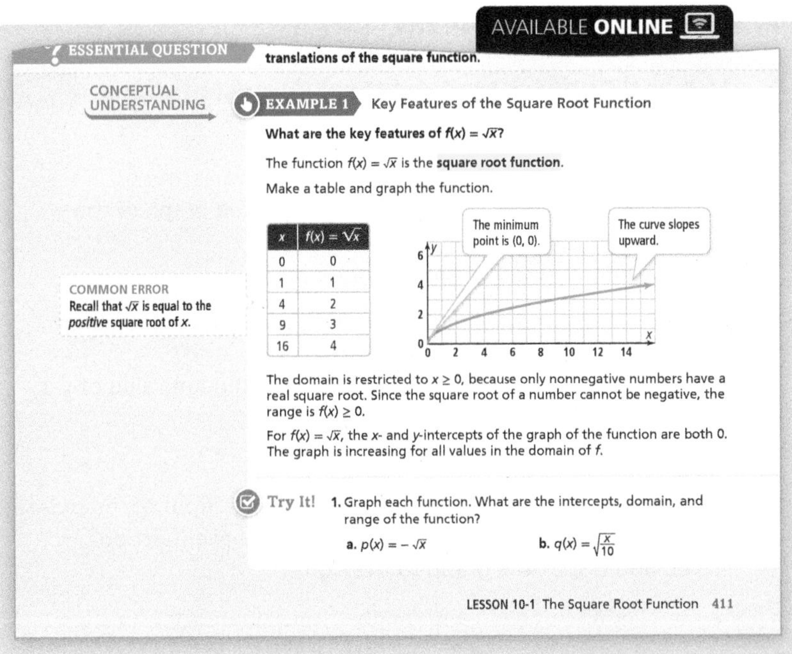
ESSENTIAL QUESTION translations of the square function.

CONCEPTUAL UNDERSTANDING

EXAMPLE 1 Key Features of the Square Root Function

What are the key features of $f(x) = \sqrt{x}$?

The function $f(x) = \sqrt{x}$ is the **square root function**.

Make a table and graph the function.

x	$f(x) = \sqrt{x}$
0	0
1	1
4	2
9	3
16	4

The minimum point is (0, 0).
The curve slopes upward.

COMMON ERROR
Recall that $\sqrt{x}$ is equal to the *positive* square root of *x*.

The domain is restricted to $x \geq 0$, because only nonnegative numbers have a real square root. Since the square root of a number cannot be negative, the range is $f(x) \geq 0$.

For $f(x) = \sqrt{x}$, the *x*- and *y*-intercepts of the graph of the function are both 0. The graph is increasing for all values in the domain of *f*.

Try It! 1. Graph each function. What are the intercepts, domain, and range of the function?

a. $p(x) = -\sqrt{x}$ b. $q(x) = \sqrt{\frac{x}{10}}$

LESSON 10-1 The Square Root Function 411

Establish Mathematics Goals to Focus Learning ETP

Introduce the square root function $f(x) = \sqrt{x}$. Like other function families, square root functions can be transformed by adding a constant to the input or output, or by multiplying the input or output by a constant.

EXAMPLE 1 Key Features of the Square Root Function

Build Procedural Fluency From Conceptual Understanding ETP

Q: Why are the *x*-values 0, 1, 4, 9, and 16 used in the table?
[They are perfect squares, so their square roots are integers.]

Try It! Answers

1. a.

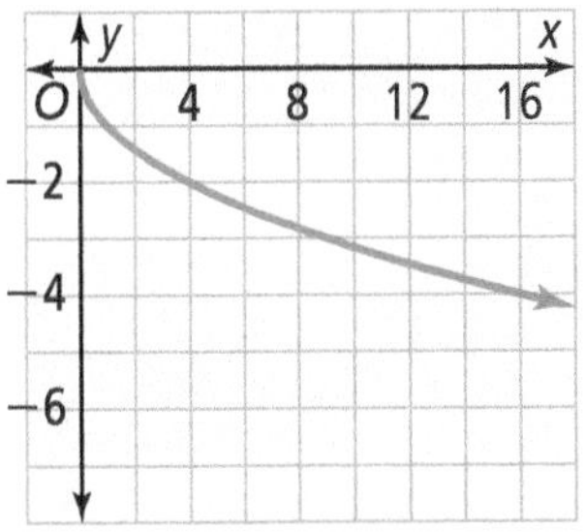

x- and *y*-intercepts: (0, 0); domain: $x \geq 0$; range: $y \leq 0$

b.

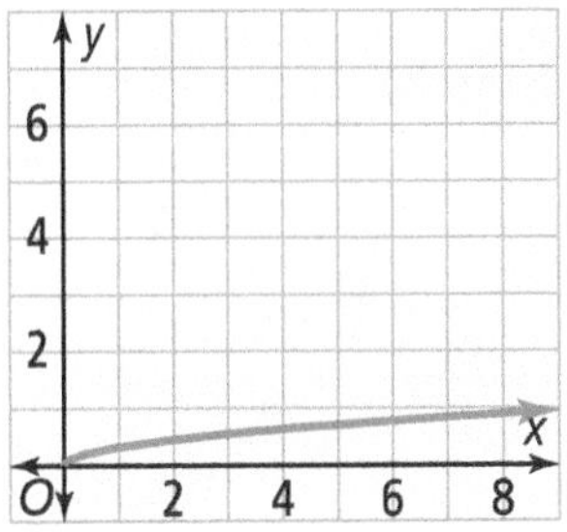

x- and *y*-intercepts: (0, 0); domain: $x \geq 0$; range: $y \geq 0$

AVAILABLE ONLINE

ADDITIONAL EXAMPLES

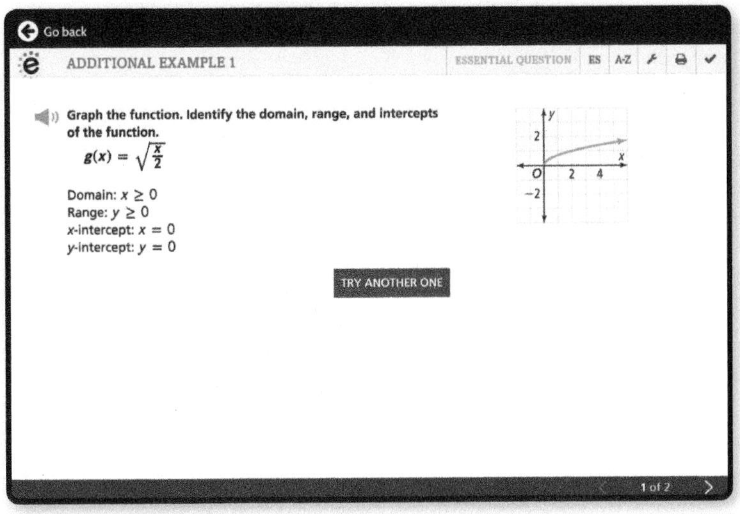
Go back
ADDITIONAL EXAMPLE 1
ESSENTIAL QUESTION
Graph the function. Identify the domain, range, and intercepts of the function.
$g(x) = \sqrt{\frac{x}{2}}$
Domain: $x \geq 0$
Range: $y \geq 0$
x-intercept: $x = 0$
y-intercept: $y = 0$
TRY ANOTHER ONE
1 of 2

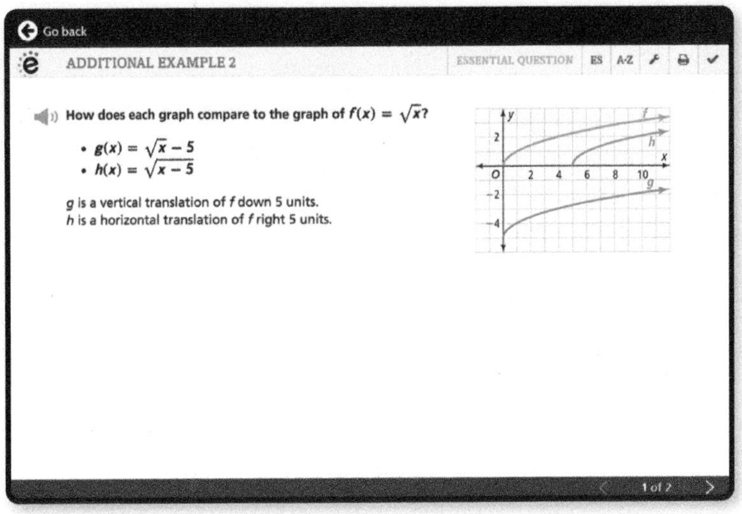
Go back
ADDITIONAL EXAMPLE 2
ESSENTIAL QUESTION
How does each graph compare to the graph of $f(x) = \sqrt{x}$?
• $g(x) = \sqrt{x} - 5$
• $h(x) = \sqrt{x - 5}$
g is a vertical translation of f down 5 units.
h is a horizontal translation of f right 5 units.
1 of 2

Example 1 Students graph a square root function.

Q: Does the graph of $f(x) = \sqrt{\frac{x}{a}}$ have *x*- and *y*-intercepts?
[Yes, the graph starts at the origin so the *x*-intercept is 0 and the *y*-intercept is also 0.]

Example 2 Students compare the graphs of translated square root functions.

Q: Is the graph $g(x) = \sqrt{x} - a$ the same as the graph of $h(x) = \sqrt{x - a}$ for the same value of *a*?
[No, the graph $g(x) = \sqrt{x} - a$ is a vertical translation of $f(x) = \sqrt{x}$ while the graph of $h(x) = \sqrt{x - a}$ is a horizontal translation of $f(x) = \sqrt{x}$.]

Activity Assess

EXAMPLE 2 Translations of the Square Root Function

Use and Connect Mathematical Representations ETP

PART A

Q: How would adding a negative value to the output of the square root function $f(x) = \sqrt{x}$ affect the graph of the function?
[It would shift the graph down.]

Q: How do the domain and range of the square root function $f(x) = \sqrt{x}$ change when it is vertically translated?
[The domain remains unchanged. The minimum value of y is changed by the value of the constant.]

PART B

Q: How would adding a negative value to the input of the square root function $f(x) = \sqrt{x}$ affect the graph of the function?
[It would shift the graph to the right.]

Q: How do the domain and range of the square root function $f(x) = \sqrt{x}$ change when it is horizontally translated?
[The range remains unchanged. The minimum value of the domain is changed by the value of the constant.]

Try It! Answers

2. a. $g(x)$ is the graph of $f(x)$ translated 4 units down.

   b. $p(x)$ is the graph of $f(x)$ translated 10 units right.

Common Error

Try It 2 Some students may think that subtracting a positive constant from the input of the function would shift the function to the left. Have students create a table of values to check that they plotted the correct points for each graph.

HABITS OF MIND

Use with **EXAMPLES 1 & 2**

Communicate Precisely Name the different types of transformations that can be made to the graph of $f(x) = \sqrt{x}$ and describe how they affect the graph. MP.6

[Adding a positive constant to the output of the function translates the graph up, while adding a negative constant to the output translates the graph down. Subtracting a positive constant from the input of the function translates the graph right, while subtracting a negative constant from the input translates the graph left.]

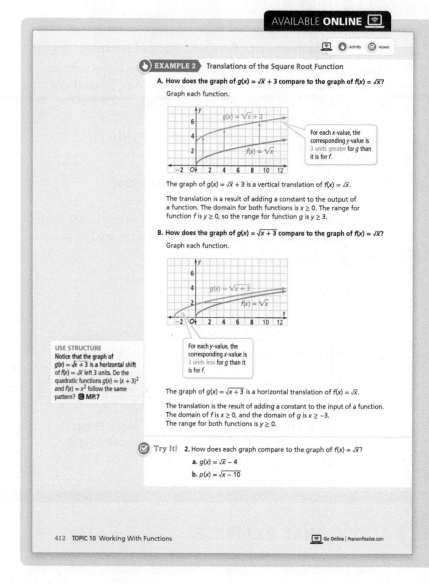

AVAILABLE ONLINE

Activity Assess

EXAMPLE 2 Translations of the Square Root Function

A. How does the graph of $g(x) = \sqrt{x} + 3$ compare to the graph of $f(x) = \sqrt{x}$?

Graph each function.

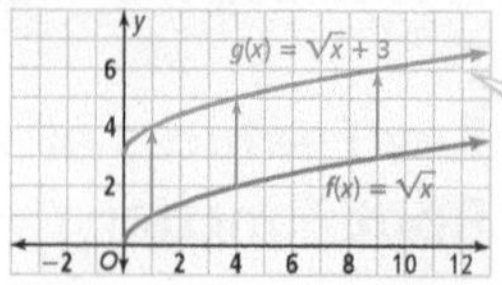

y
$g(x) = \sqrt{x} + 3$
$f(x) = \sqrt{x}$
6
4
2
−2 O 2 4 6 8 10 12

For each x-value, the corresponding y-value is 3 units greater for g than it is for f.

The graph of $g(x) = \sqrt{x} + 3$ is a vertical translation of $f(x) = \sqrt{x}$.

The translation is a result of adding a constant to the output of a function. The domain for both functions is $x \geq 0$. The range for function f is $y \geq 0$, so the range for function g is $y \geq 3$.

B. How does the graph of $g(x) = \sqrt{x + 3}$ compare to the graph of $f(x) = \sqrt{x}$?

Graph each function.

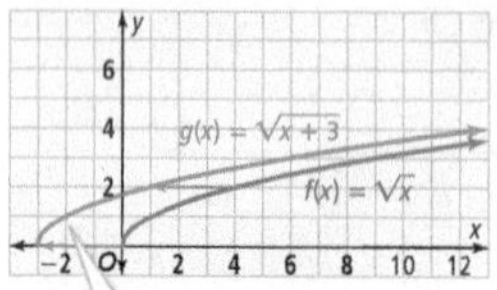

y
$g(x) = \sqrt{x + 3}$
$f(x) = \sqrt{x}$
6
4
2
x
−2 O 2 4 6 8 10 12

For each y-value, the corresponding x-value is 3 units less for g than it is for f.

USE STRUCTURE
Notice that the graph of $g(x) = \sqrt{x + 3}$ is a horizontal shift of $f(x) = \sqrt{x}$ left 3 units. Do the quadratic functions $g(x) = (x + 3)^2$ and $f(x) = x^2$ follow the same pattern? MP.7

The graph of $g(x) = \sqrt{x + 3}$ is a horizontal translation of $f(x) = \sqrt{x}$.

The translation is the result of adding a constant to the input of a function. The domain of f is $x \geq 0$, and the domain of g is $x \geq -3$. The range for both functions is $y \geq 0$.

Try It! 2. How does each graph compare to the graph of $f(x) = \sqrt{x}$?

a. $g(x) = \sqrt{x} - 4$

b. $p(x) = \sqrt{x - 10}$

EXAMPLE 3 Rate of Change of the Square Root Function

Use and Connect Mathematical Representations ETP

Q: What does the average rate of change between two points represent?
[the slope of the straight line that connects the two points]

Q: Why is the rate of change of the segment from $x = 0$ to $x = 0.3$ greater than that of the segment from $x = 0.3$ to $x = 0.6$?
[For greater values of x, the value of y increases more slowly in square root functions.]

Try It! Answers

3. $h(8) = 4$, $h(10) \approx 4.47$, $h(12) \approx 4.90$;

a. 0.2$\dot{3}$5

b. 0.215

Elicit and Use Evidence of Student Thinking ETP

Q: How is the numerator for the average rate of change for $8 \leq x \leq 10$ calculated? What does it represent?
[It is the difference between $h(10)$ and $h(8)$. It represents the change in the y-values of the function between $x = 10$ and $x = 8$.]

AVAILABLE ONLINE

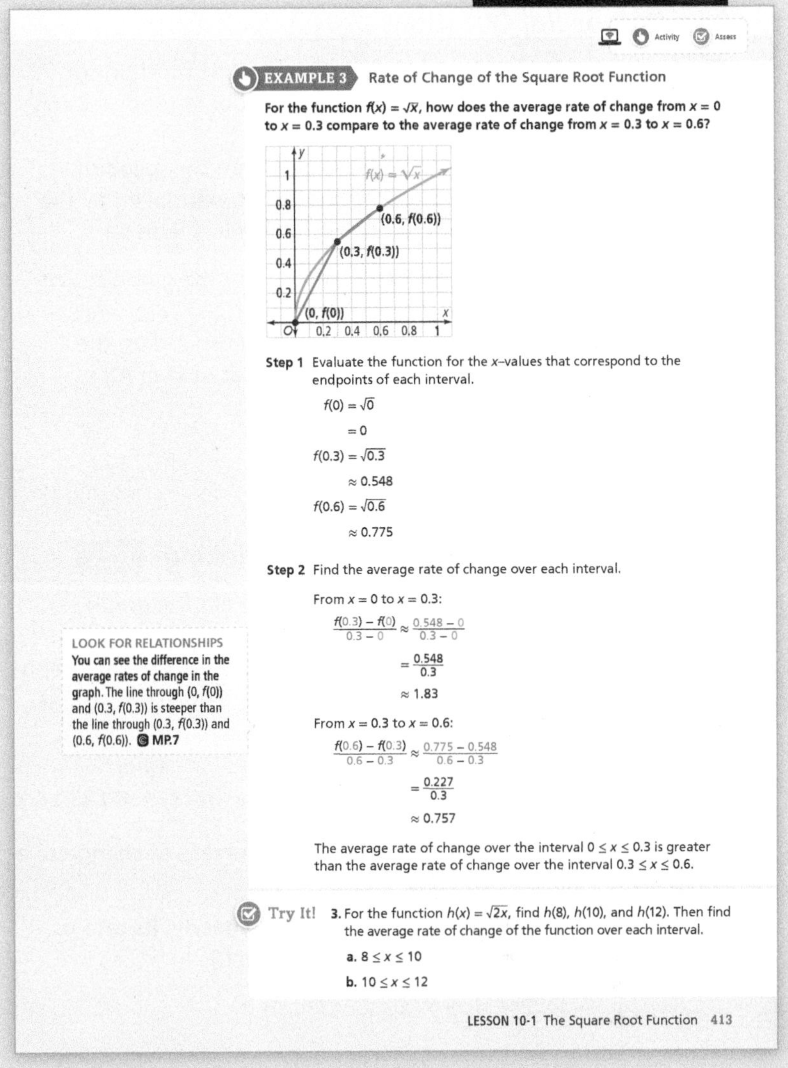

Activity Assess

EXAMPLE 3 Rate of Change of the Square Root Function

For the function $f(x) = \sqrt{x}$, how does the average rate of change from $x = 0$ to $x = 0.3$ compare to the average rate of change from $x = 0.3$ to $x = 0.6$?

y
$f(x) = \sqrt{x}$
(0.6, f(0.6))
(0.3, f(0.3))
(0, f(0))
x
O
0.2 0.4 0.6 0.8 1

Step 1 Evaluate the function for the x-values that correspond to the endpoints of each interval.

$f(0) = \sqrt{0}$
$= 0$

$f(0.3) = \sqrt{0.3}$
≈ 0.548

$f(0.6) = \sqrt{0.6}$
≈ 0.775

Step 2 Find the average rate of change over each interval.

From $x = 0$ to $x = 0.3$:

$\frac{f(0.3) - f(0)}{0.3 - 0} \approx \frac{0.548 - 0}{0.3 - 0}$
$= \frac{0.548}{0.3}$
≈ 1.83

From $x = 0.3$ to $x = 0.6$:

$\frac{f(0.6) - f(0.3)}{0.6 - 0.3} \approx \frac{0.775 - 0.548}{0.6 - 0.3}$
$= \frac{0.227}{0.3}$
≈ 0.757

The average rate of change over the interval $0 \leq x \leq 0.3$ is greater than the average rate of change over the interval $0.3 \leq x \leq 0.6$.

LOOK FOR RELATIONSHIPS
You can see the difference in the average rates of change in the graph. The line through (0, $f(0)$) and (0.3, $f(0.3)$) is steeper than the line through (0.3, $f(0.3)$) and (0.6, $f(0.6)$). MP.7

Try It! 3. For the function $h(x) = \sqrt{2x}$, find $h(8)$, $h(10)$, and $h(12)$. Then find the average rate of change of the function over each interval.
a. $8 \leq x \leq 10$
b. $10 \leq x \leq 12$

LESSON 10-1 The Square Root Function 413

RtI Struggling Students

USE WITH EXAMPLE 3 Students practice finding the average rate of change for $f(x) = \sqrt{x}$ over specific intervals that will yield whole-number values.

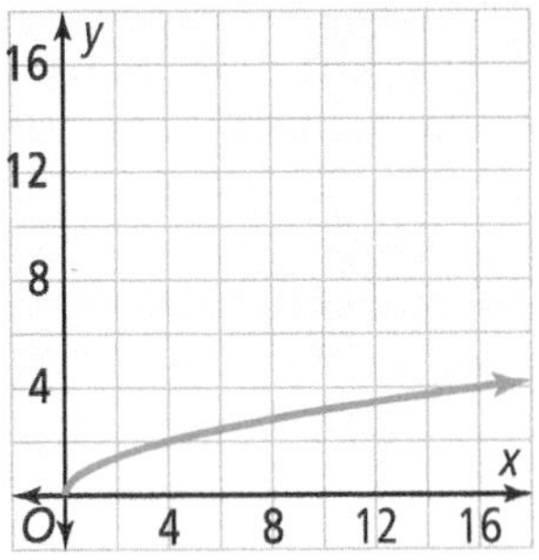
y
16
12
8
4
x
O
4 8 12 16

1. Find the average rate of change over the intervals $0 \leq x \leq 4$ and $4 \leq x \leq 16$. [$\frac{1}{2}$; $\frac{1}{6}$]

Q: What do the rates of change of the different intervals of the graph tell you about the square root function?
[The slope of the graph decreases as x increases.]

ADV Advanced Students

USE WITH EXAMPLE 4 Students determine relative radii of two circles based on area.

Levi is purchasing rims and tires for his vehicle. The area available for each tire is approximately 350 square inches. The outer radius of the tire he is considering is 1.5 times larger than the radius of the rim.

- Formula for the area of a circle: $A = \pi r^2$

1. Write functions to find the radii of the rims and tires.
[rims: $\left(\frac{1}{1.5}\right) \times \sqrt{\frac{A}{\pi}}$; tires: $r = \sqrt{\frac{A}{\pi}}$]

Q: What are the maximum radii of the rims and the tires Levi could purchase if sizes were limited to half-inch increments?
[rim: 7 in.; tire: 10.5 in.]

EXAMPLE 4 Compare Functions

Pose Purposeful Questions ETP

Q: How would the coefficient in the square root function for Plan A differ from the coefficient in the square root function for Plan B?
[Because the speed of Plan B is greater than the speed of Plan A for any given radius, the coefficient multiplied by the square root function of Plan A is probably less than 5.]

Q: How would the graph of Plan B differ from the graph shown for Plan A?
[Since the speed of Plan A is less for any given radius, the graph of Plan B would be steeper than that of Plan A.]

Try It! Answers

4. **a.** 0.412
   b. 1.304

Elicit and Use Evidence of Student Thinking ETP

Q: How would the graphs of v and w differ from the graph of $f(x) = \sqrt{x}$?
[$v(x) = \frac{1}{10}f(x)$, so the graph of v is a vertical shrink of the graph of f. $w(x) = f\left(\frac{x}{10}\right)$, so the graph of w is a horizontal stretch of the graph of f.]

HABITS OF MIND

Use with **EXAMPLES 3 & 4**

Reason Why does the given interval affect the rate of change of a square root function? MP.2

[The square root function does not increase linearly. Its rate of change varies depending on the given interval.]

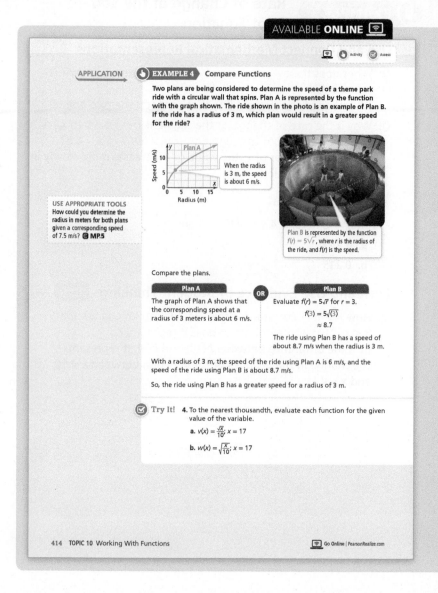

AVAILABLE ONLINE

Activity Assess

APPLICATION

EXAMPLE 4 Compare Functions

Two plans are being considered to determine the speed of a theme park ride with a circular wall that spins. Plan A is represented by the function with the graph shown. The ride shown in the photo is an example of Plan B. If the ride has a radius of 3 m, which plan would result in a greater speed for the ride?

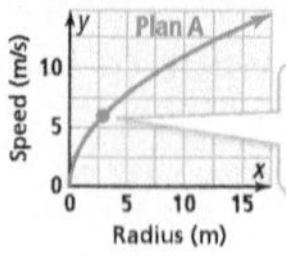

Plan A
y
Speed (m/s)
10
5
0
0 5 10 15
x
Radius (m)

When the radius is 3 m, the speed is about 6 m/s.

Plan B is represented by the function $f(r) = 5\sqrt{r}$, where r is the radius of the ride, and $f(r)$ is the speed.

USE APPROPRIATE TOOLS How could you determine the radius in meters for both plans given a corresponding speed of 7.5 m/s? MP.5

Compare the plans.

Plan A

The graph of Plan A shows that the corresponding speed at a radius of 3 meters is about 6 m/s.

OR

Plan B

Evaluate $f(r) = 5\sqrt{r}$ for $r = 3$.

$$f(3) = 5\sqrt{(3)}$$
$$\approx 8.7$$

The ride using Plan B has a speed of about 8.7 m/s when the radius is 3 m.

With a radius of 3 m, the speed of the ride using Plan A is 6 m/s, and the speed of the ride using Plan B is about 8.7 m/s.

So, the ride using Plan B has a greater speed for a radius of 3 m.

Try It! 4. To the nearest thousandth, evaluate each function for the given value of the variable.

a. $v(x) = \frac{\sqrt{x}}{10}$; $x = 17$

b. $w(x) = \sqrt{\frac{x}{10}}$; $x = 17$

Go Online | PearsonRealize.com

ELL English Language Learners (*Use with* EXAMPLE 4)

LISTENING BEGINNING Ask students if they've ever heard someone describe the location of something as being within a 2-mile radius. Explain that a radius is the distance from the central point of a circle to any point on the circle's circumference. Have pairs of students each hold an end of a 2-foot string. Instruct one student to stand still while the other student moves around, keeping the string stretched taut. Explain that they just marked off a 2-foot radius.

Q: What shape is made as you marked off the 2-foot radius? [a circle]

Q: How could you define a radius in terms of a circle? [It is the length from the center of a circle to any point along the edge of the circle.]

SPEAKING INTERMEDIATE Ask students to talk about what *speed* means and when and how they have heard the word used. Students may talk about speed limits, Internet speed, a speedboat, top speeds of animals, different speeds of a bike, etc.

Q: Looking at the graph in the example, how would you describe how speed is measured?
[as a ratio of distance over time]

Q: How does the radius of the theme park ride relate to the speed of the ride?
[the greater the radius, the faster the speed of the ride]

WRITING ADVANCED In math, the word *about* usually indicates that a value is close to an amount, such as an estimated or rounded number. Other meanings for *about* include describing when something is concerning a particular subject ("what is the story about") and describing movement or location ("the papers were strewn about the desk"). Challenge students to write sentences using *about* in different ways, and have a partner guess which meaning is intended.

Q: What is a synonym for *about* as it is used in this example? [approximately]

Q: What is a synonym for *about* that is used to indicate motion or location? [around]

CONCEPT SUMMARY Square Root Functions

Q: How is a vertical translation of the square root function represented differently in the equation than a horizontal translation?
[A vertical translation results from adding a constant to the output of the function, while a horizontal translation results from subtracting a constant from the input of the function.]

Do You UNDERSTAND? | Do You KNOW HOW?

Common Error

Exercise 6 Some students may think the graph that results from subtracting 5 from the input will be a vertical translation. Have students calculate the value of x when $y = 0$ for f and for h. Then ask students to identify the direction of the translation.

Answers

1. The graph of the square root function and its translations are one branch of a parabola with a horizontal axis. The domain and range always have a minimum value.
2. a. No; multiplying the radical by 2 changes the shape of the graph.
   b. Yes; the graph of g is the graph of f shifted 2 units left and 3 units down.
3. The ordered pairs have the values reversed. If $x = 12$, then $y = \sqrt{36} = 6$, so (12, 6) satisfies the function. Similarly, if $x = 27$, then $y = \sqrt{81} = 9$, so (27, 9) satisfies the function.
4. The domain is $x \geq -3$.
5. It is a vertical translation of the graph of f by 2 units down.
6. It is a horizontal translation of the graph of f by 5 units right.
7. It is a vertical translation of the graph of f by 5 units up.
8. It is a horizontal translation of the graph of f by 7 units left.
9. 0.14
10. 0.18
11. 0.45

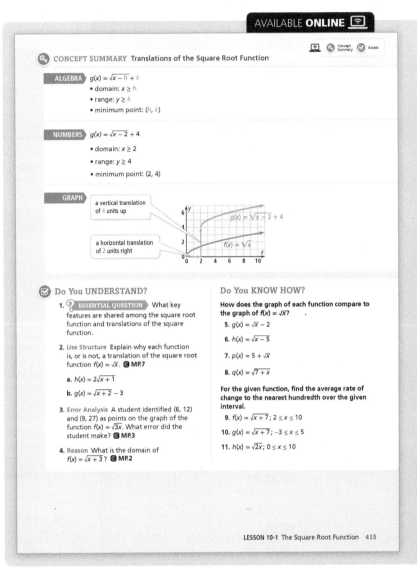

AVAILABLE ONLINE

Concept Summary Assess

CONCEPT SUMMARY Translations of the Square Root Function

ALGEBRA $g(x) = \sqrt{x - h} + k$
- domain: $x \geq h$
- range: $y \geq k$
- minimum point: (h, k)

NUMBERS $g(x) = \sqrt{x - 2} + 4$
- domain: $x \geq 2$
- range: $y \geq 4$
- minimum point: (2, 4)

GRAPH

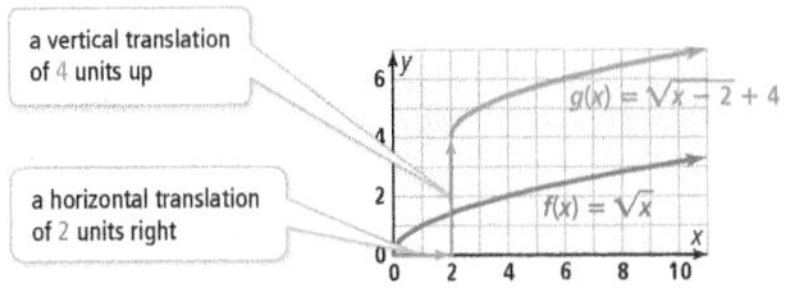
a vertical translation of 4 units up
a horizontal translation of 2 units right
y
x
0
2
4
6
8
10
g(x) = √x − 2 + 4
f(x) = √x

Do You UNDERSTAND?

1. ESSENTIAL QUESTION What key features are shared among the square root function and translations of the square function.
2. **Use Structure** Explain why each function is, or is not, a translation of the square root function $f(x) = \sqrt{x}$. MP.7
   a. $h(x) = 2\sqrt{x + 1}$
   b. $g(x) = \sqrt{x + 2} - 3$
3. **Error Analysis** A student identified (6, 12) and (9, 27) as points on the graph of the function $f(x) = \sqrt{3x}$. What error did the student make? MP.3
4. **Reason** What is the domain of $f(x) = \sqrt{x + 3}$? MP.2

Do You KNOW HOW?

How does the graph of each function compare to the graph of $f(x) = \sqrt{x}$?

5. $g(x) = \sqrt{x} - 2$
6. $h(x) = \sqrt{x - 5}$
7. $p(x) = 5 + \sqrt{x}$
8. $q(x) = \sqrt{7 + x}$

For the given function, find the average rate of change to the nearest hundredth over the given interval.

9. $f(x) = \sqrt{x + 7}$; $2 \leq x \leq 10$
10. $g(x) = \sqrt{x + 7}$; $-3 \leq x \leq 5$
11. $h(x) = \sqrt{2x}$; $0 \leq x \leq 10$

PRACTICE & PROBLEM SOLVING

AVAILABLE **ONLINE**

Lesson Practice You may opt to have students complete the automatically scored Practice and Problem Solving items online powered by MathXL for School.

Choose from: **Lesson Practice**

Adaptive Practice

You may also take advantage of the bank of exercises for assigning additional practice.

Assignment Guide

Basic	Advanced
12–30, 35–42	12–19, 24–42

Item Analysis

Example	Items	DOK
1	12, 16, 18–21, 33–36	1
2	13, 22–28, 40	1
	14	2
3	29–32, 41	1
	15	2
4	17, 37	1
	38, 39, 42	2

AVAILABLE **ONLINE**

PRACTICE & PROBLEM SOLVING

Scan for Multimedia

Practice Tutorial

Additional Exercises Available Online

UNDERSTAND

12. **Use Appropriate Tools** Use a graphing calculator to graph $f(x) = -\sqrt{x+7}$. Describe the domain and range of the function. **MP.5**

13. **Error Analysis** Describe and correct the error a student made when comparing the graph of $g(x) = \sqrt{x+3}$ to the graph of $f(x) = \sqrt{x}$. **MP.3**

    1. The expression under the radical in $g(x)$ is $x + 3$.
    2. $x + 3$ is to the right of x, so the graph of g is a translation of the graph of f by 3 units to the right.

    ✗

14. **Higher Order Thinking** Write a function involving a square root expression with domain $x \geq \frac{7}{2}$ and range $y \leq 2$.

15. **Mathematical Connections** Consider the two functions $f(x) = \sqrt{x}$ and $g(x) = -\sqrt{x}$.

    a. What is the average rate of change for each function from $x = 4$ to $x = 9$?

    b. How are the two values in part (a) related to each other?

    c. Suppose the average rate of change for $f(x)$ between two values of x is 0.32. What is the rate of change for $g(x)$ between the same two values of x?

16. **Use Structure** For a function of the form $f(x) = a\sqrt{x-h} + k$, why are some real numbers excluded from the domain and the range? **MP.7**

17. **Communicate Precisely** Explain the steps of each calculation. **MP.6**

    a. Find $f(10)$ if $f(x) = \frac{\sqrt{2x}}{7}$.

    b. Find $f(10)$ if $f(x) = \sqrt{\frac{2x}{7}}$.

PRACTICE

Find the x- and y-intercepts of each function. If there is no intercept, write *Does not exist.* SEE EXAMPLE 1

18. $f(x) = \sqrt{x} - 2$

19. $g(x) = \sqrt{x-9}$

20. $h(x) = \sqrt{x+9}$

21. $k(x) = \sqrt{x+4} - 9$

How does each graph compare to the graph of $f(x) = \sqrt{x}$? SEE EXAMPLE 2

22. $q(x) = \sqrt{x} + 11$

23. $r(x) = \sqrt{x+11}$

24. $s(x) = \sqrt{x-2} + 5$

25. $t(x) = \sqrt{x+3} - 6$

Write an expression for each function. SEE EXAMPLE 2

26. a translation by 6 units up of $f(x) = \sqrt{x}$.

27. a translation by $\frac{1}{2}$ unit to the right of $f(x) = \sqrt{x}$.

28. a translation by 2 units down and 1 unit to the left of $f(x) = \sqrt{x}$.

Find the value of the given function at each end of the range of values of the variable. Then calculate the average rate of change of the function between the two values of the variable. SEE EXAMPLES 3 AND 4

29. $p(x) = \sqrt{15x}$; $0.01 \leq x \leq 1.01$ 0.39; 3.89; 3.50

30. $q(x) = \sqrt{x+11}$; $-3 \leq x \leq 0$ 2.824; 3.317; 0.163

31. $r(x) = \sqrt{2x-7}$; $5 \leq x \leq 10$ 1.732; 3.6056; 0.375

32. $t(x) = \sqrt{\frac{x-4}{2}}$; $4 \leq x \leq 8$ 0; 1.414; 0.354

Describe the domain and range for each function. SEE EXAMPLE 1

33. Function p from Exercise 29

34. Function q from Exercise 30

35. Function r from Exercise 31

36. function t from Exercise 32

Answers

12. Domain: $x \geq -7$; Range: $y \leq 0$

13. The expression under the radical is $x + 3$, so the radicand has a minimum value when $x = -3$. That means the x-intercept is at the point $(-3, 0)$ and the graph is a translation of $f(x) = \sqrt{x}$ by 3 units to the left.

14. $f(x) = -\sqrt{2x-7} + 2$

15. a. For $f(x)$, the average rate of change is 0.2; for $g(x)$, the average rate of change is –0.2.

    b. The two values are opposites.

    c. –0.32

16. The domain is restricted because the radicand cannot be negative. Since the value of the radicand cannot be negative, the value of the function is restricted, which restricts the range.

17. a. The steps are to multiply 10 by 2 to get 20, find the square root of 20, and then divide that value by 7.

    b. The steps are to multiply 10 by 2 to get 20, divide that value by 7, and then find the square root of the result.

18. x-intercept = 4; y-intercept = –2

19. x-intercept = 9; y-intercept does not exist

20. x-intercept = –9; y-intercept = 3

21. x-intercept = 77; y-intercept –7

22. It is a vertical translation of the graph of f by 11 units up.

23. It is a horizontal translation of the graph of f by 11 units to the left.

24. It is a horizontal translation of the graph of f by 2 units to the right and a vertical translation by 5 units up.

25. It is a horizontal translation of the graph of f by 3 units to the left and a vertical translation by 6 units down.

See answers for Exercises 26–28 and 33–36 on next page.

Answers

26. $g(x) = \sqrt{x} + 6$

27. $g(x) = \sqrt{x - \frac{1}{2}}$

28. $g(x) = \sqrt{x + 1} - 2$

33. domain: $x \geq 0$; range: $y \geq 0$

34. domain: $x \geq -11$; range: $y \geq 0$

35. domain: $x \geq 3.5$; range: $y \geq 0$

36. domain: $x \geq 4$; range: $y \geq 0$

37. 70, 65, 74, 85

38. a.

x	1	10	15	18.5	25	50
d	1.41	10.05	15.03	18.53	25.02	50.01

b. $d = \sqrt{x^2 + 1}$, so $10.2 = \sqrt{x^2 + 1}$. Then $104.04 = x^2 + 1$, $x^2 = 103.04$, and $x = 10.15$ mi. They have already hiked 5 mi, so they need to travel another 5.15 mi.

39. about 8.97 mi

42. Part A 0.0739

Part B 0.0729

Part C 0.0728; 0.0728

Part D The two points are getting closer and closer to $x = 15$, with one point on either side of $x = 15$. As the points get closer and closer together, with one point on each side of $x = 15$, the rate of change for the function is stabilizing at about 0.0728.

AVAILABLE ONLINE

PRACTICE & PROBLEM SOLVING

Practice Tutorial

Mixed Review Available Online

APPLY

37. Model With Mathematics A teacher adjusts the grades of an exam using a curve. If a student's raw score on a test is x, the score based on the curve is given by the function $c(x) = 10\sqrt{x}$.

Five students received raw scores of 49, 42, 55, and 72. What are their scores according to the curve? MP.4

38. Make Sense and Persevere A group of campers leave Camp 2 and hike x miles along the path to Camp 3. The distance d between the group of campers and Camp 1 is given by $d(x) = \sqrt{x^2 + 1}$. MP.1

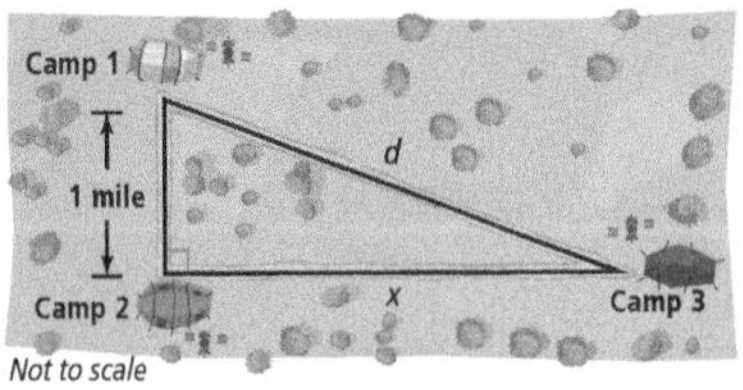
Camp 1
1 mile
d
Camp 2
x
Camp 3

Not to scale

a. Use the function to find the distance d of the campers when $x = 1$, 10, 15, 18.5, 25, and 50.

b. When the campers have hiked 5 miles from Camp 2, their distance from Camp 1 is $\sqrt{5^2 + 1} = \sqrt{26} \approx 5.1$ miles. How much farther do they need to hike until they double their distance from Camp 1? Show your work.

39. Communicate Precisely The distance to the horizon is a function of height above sea level. If the height h above sea level is measured in feet and the distance d to the horizon is measured in miles, then $d(h) \approx 1.22\sqrt{h}$.

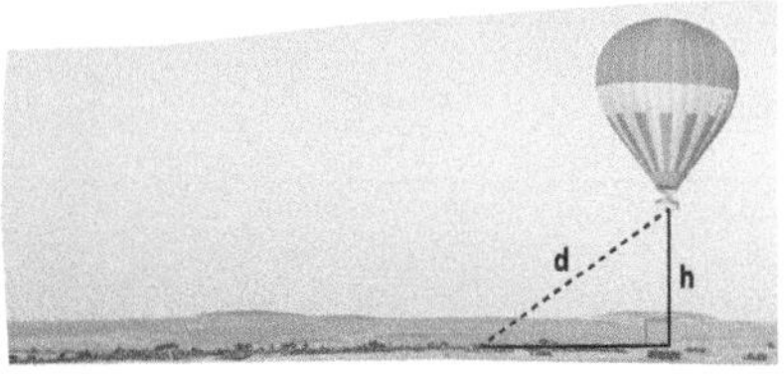
d
h

On a hot-air balloon ride, a passenger looks out from 54 ft above sea level. What is the distance from the passenger to the horizon? MP.6

ASSESSMENT PRACTICE

40. Which of the following functions are vertical translations of $f(x) = \sqrt{x}$? Select all that apply.

Ⓐ $g(x) = \sqrt{x} - 4$

Ⓑ $h(x) = 3 + \sqrt{x}$

Ⓒ $k(x) = \sqrt{-5 + x}$

Ⓓ $m(x) = \sqrt{5x}$

Ⓔ $n(x) = -7 + \sqrt{x}$

41. SAT/ACT For the square root function $p(x) = \sqrt{x}$, the average rate of change between $x = 13$ and $x = a$ is 0.155. What is the value of a?

Ⓐ −4

Ⓑ 0

Ⓒ 5

Ⓓ 8

Ⓔ 11

42. Performance Task The relationship between the surface area A and the diameter D of each glass sphere can be described using the equation shown.

$D = \sqrt{\frac{A}{\pi}}$

PART A Find the average rate of change in the diameter for surface areas between 20 in.^{2} and 10 in.^{2}.

PART B Find the average rate of change in the diameter when the surface area decreases from 16 in.^{2} to 14 in.^{2}.

PART C Find the average rate of change in D when A increases from 14.9 to 15.1 in.^{2}, and find the average rate of change in D when A increases from 14.99 to 15.01 in.^{2}.

PART D Describe a pattern in parts A, B, and C.

LESSON QUIZ

Use the Lesson Quiz to assess students' understanding of the mathematics in the lesson.

Students can take the Lesson Quiz online or you can download a printable copy from **SavvasRealize.com**. The Lesson Quiz is also available in the *Assessment Resources* book.

Item Analysis

Item	DOK	Standards
1	1	HSF.IF.B.4
2	2	HSF.IF.B.6
3	1	HSF.IF.C.7.B
4	2	HSF.IF.C.7.B
5	2	HSF.IF.B.6

RtI Use the student scores on the Lesson Quiz to prescribe differentiated assignments.

If students take the Lesson Quiz online, it will be automatically scored and appropriate differentiated practice will be assigned based on student performance.

I Intervention	0–3 points	• Reteach to Build Understanding • Mathematical Literacy and Vocabulary • Additional Practice
O On-Level	4 points	• Mathematical Literacy and Vocabulary • Additional Practice • Enrichment
A Advanced	5 points	• Enrichment

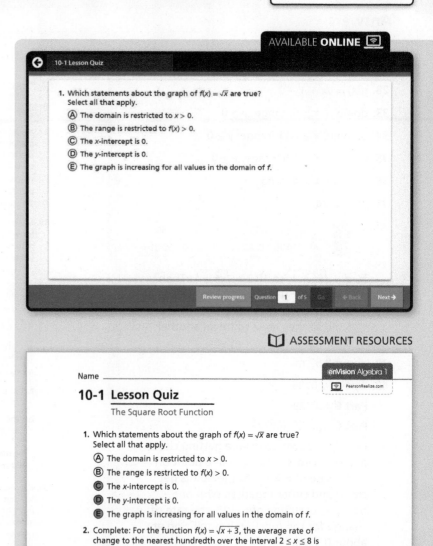

AVAILABLE **ONLINE**

10-1 Lesson Quiz

1. Which statements about the graph of $f(x) = \sqrt{x}$ are true? Select all that apply.

Ⓐ The domain is restricted to $x > 0$.
Ⓑ The range is restricted to $f(x) > 0$.
Ⓒ The x-intercept is 0.
Ⓓ The y-intercept is 0.
Ⓔ The graph is increasing for all values in the domain of f.

Review progress Question 1 of 5 Go ← Back Next →

ASSESSMENT RESOURCES

Name ____________

enVision Algebra 1
PearsonRealize.com

10-1 Lesson Quiz

The Square Root Function

1. Which statements about the graph of $f(x) = \sqrt{x}$ are true? Select all that apply.
   Ⓐ The domain is restricted to $x > 0$.
   Ⓑ The range is restricted to $f(x) > 0$.
   Ⓒ The x-intercept is 0.
   Ⓓ The y-intercept is 0.
   Ⓔ The graph is increasing for all values in the domain of f.
2. Complete: For the function $f(x) = \sqrt{x + 3}$, the average rate of change to the nearest hundredth over the interval $2 \le x \le 8$ is 0.18.
3. The graph of g is a translation 3 units down and 5 units left of the graph of $f(x) = \sqrt{x}$. What is the equation for g?
   Ⓐ $g(x) = \sqrt{x + 3} - 5$
   Ⓑ $g(x) = \sqrt{x - 3} - 5$
   Ⓒ $g(x) = \sqrt{x - 5} - 3$
   Ⓓ $g(x) = \sqrt{x + 5} - 3$
4. Which function is represented by the graph?

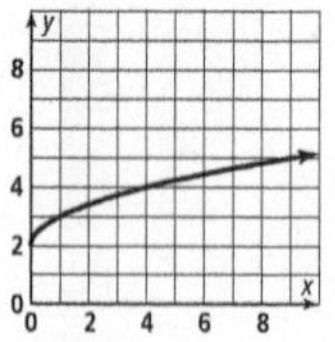

y
8
6
4
2
0
x
0 2 4 6 8

   Ⓐ $f(x) = \sqrt{x + 2} + 2$
   Ⓑ $f(x) = \sqrt{x + 2}$
   Ⓒ $f(x) = \sqrt{x} + 2$
   Ⓓ $f(x) = \sqrt{x - 2}$
5. The function $f(x) = \sqrt{\frac{x}{\pi}}$ gives the diameter, in inches, of a proposed spherical sculpture with a surface area of x square inches. The artist making the sculpture wants to know how the diameter changes if the surface area is increased. What is the average rate of change for the function as the surface area changes from 12.6 in.^{2} to 28.3 in.^{2}? Round your answer to the nearest hundredth of an inch.
   0.06 in.

enVision™ **Algebra 1** • Assessment Resources

SavvasRealize.com

Assess Tutorials Worksheets

DIFFERENTIATED RESOURCES

I = Intervention   O = On-Level   A = Advanced

= This activity is available as a digital assignment powered by MathXL® for School.

AVAILABLE ONLINE

Reteach to Build Understanding I

Provides scaffolded reteaching for the key lesson concepts.

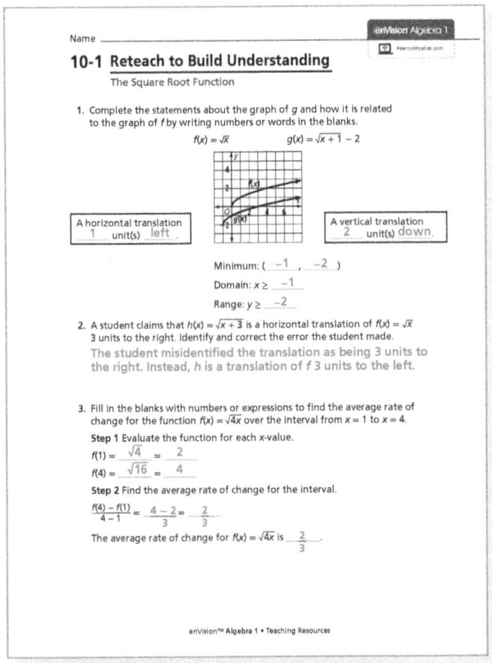

Name

10-1 Reteach to Build Understanding

The Square Root Function

1. Complete the statements about the graph of g and how it is related to the graph of f by writing numbers or words in the blanks.

$f(x) = \sqrt{x}$ $g(x) = \sqrt{x+1} - 2$

A horizontal translation 1 unit(s) left

A vertical translation 2 unit(s) down

Minimum: (−1 , −2)

Domain: $x \geq$ −1

Range: $y \geq$ −2

2. A student claims that $h(x) = \sqrt{x+3}$ is a horizontal translation of $f(x) = \sqrt{x}$ 3 units to the right. Identify and correct the error the student made.

The student misidentified the translation as being 3 units to the right. Instead, h is a translation of f 3 units to the left.

3. Fill in the blanks with numbers or expressions to find the average rate of change for the function $f(x) = \sqrt{4x}$ over the interval from $x = 1$ to $x = 4$.

Step 1 Evaluate the function for each x-value.

$f(1) = \sqrt{4} = 2$

$f(4) = \sqrt{16} = 4$

Step 2 Find the average rate of change for the interval.

$\frac{f(4) - f(1)}{4 - 1} = \frac{4 - 2}{3} = \frac{2}{3}$

The average rate of change for $f(x) = \sqrt{4x}$ is $\frac{2}{3}$.

enVision™ Algebra 1 • Teaching Resources

Additional Practice I O

Provides extra practice for each lesson.

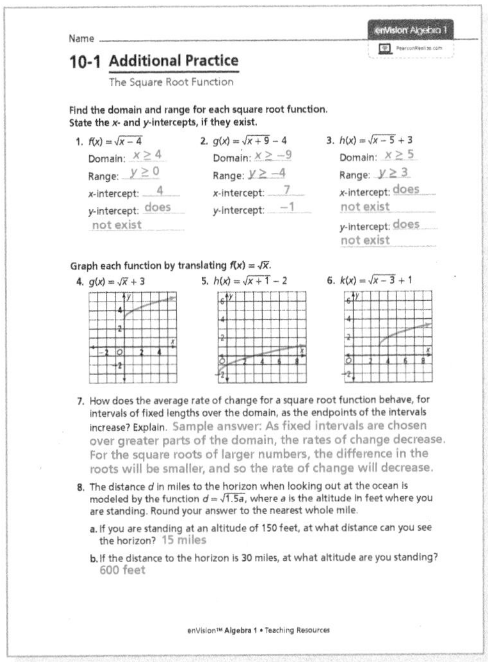

Name

10-1 Additional Practice

The Square Root Function

Find the domain and range for each square root function. State the x- and y-intercepts, if they exist.

1. $f(x) = \sqrt{x-4}$ Domain: $x \geq 4$ Range: $y \geq 0$ x-intercept: 4 y-intercept: does not exist

2. $g(x) = \sqrt{x+9} - 4$ Domain: $x \geq -9$ Range: $y \geq -4$ x-intercept: 7 y-intercept: −1

3. $h(x) = \sqrt{x-5} + 3$ Domain: $x \geq 5$ Range: $y \geq 3$ x-intercept: does not exist y-intercept: does not exist

Graph each function by translating $f(x) = \sqrt{x}$.

4. $g(x) = \sqrt{x} + 3$ 5. $h(x) = \sqrt{x+1} - 2$ 6. $k(x) = \sqrt{x-3} + 1$

7. How does the average rate of change for a square root function behave, for intervals of fixed lengths over the domain, as the endpoints of the intervals increase? Explain. Sample answer: As fixed intervals are chosen over greater parts of the domain, the rates of change decrease. For the square roots of larger numbers, the difference in the roots will be smaller, and so the rate of change will decrease.

8. The distance d in miles to the horizon when looking out at the ocean is modeled by the function $d = \sqrt{1.5a}$, where a is the altitude in feet where you are standing. Round your answer to the nearest whole mile.

a. If you are standing at an altitude of 150 feet, at what distance can you see the horizon? 15 miles

b. If the distance to the horizon is 30 miles, at what altitude are you standing? 600 feet

enVision™ Algebra 1 • Teaching Resources

Enrichment O A

Presents engaging problems and activities that extend the lesson concepts.

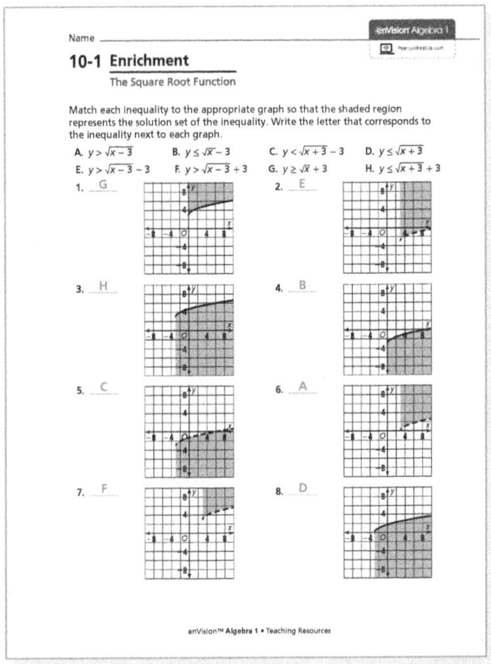

Name

10-1 Enrichment

The Square Root Function

Match each inequality to the appropriate graph so that the shaded region represents the solution set of the inequality. Write the letter that corresponds to the inequality next to each graph.

A. $y > \sqrt{x-3}$ B. $y \leq \sqrt{x} - 3$ C. $y < \sqrt{x+3} - 3$ D. $y \leq \sqrt{x+3}$

E. $y > \sqrt{x-3} - 3$ F. $y > \sqrt{x-3} + 3$ G. $y \geq \sqrt{x} + 3$ H. $y \leq \sqrt{x+3} + 3$

1. G   2. E   3. H   4. B   5. C   6. A   7. F   8. D

enVision™ Algebra 1 • Teaching Resources

Mathematical Literacy and Vocabulary I O

Helps students develop and reinforce understanding of key terms and concepts.

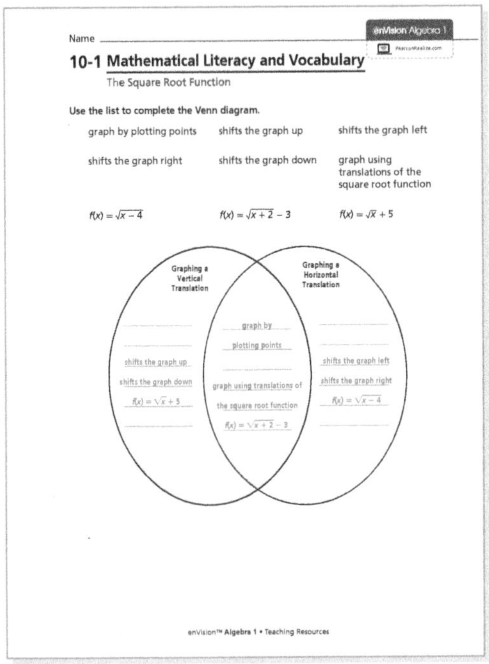

Name

10-1 Mathematical Literacy and Vocabulary

The Square Root Function

Use the list to complete the Venn diagram.

graph by plotting points   shifts the graph up   shifts the graph left

shifts the graph right   shifts the graph down   graph using translations of the square root function

$f(x) = \sqrt{x-4}$ $f(x) = \sqrt{x+2} - 3$ $f(x) = \sqrt{x} + 5$

Graphing a Vertical Translation: shifts the graph up; shifts the graph down; $f(x) = \sqrt{x} + 5$

Both: graph by plotting points; graph using translations of the square root function; $f(x) = \sqrt{x+2} - 3$

Graphing a Horizontal Translation: shifts the graph left; shifts the graph right; $f(x) = \sqrt{x-4}$

enVision™ Algebra 1 • Teaching Resources

Digital Resources and Video Tutorials I O A

The **Reteach to Build Understanding, Additional Practice**, and **Enrichment** activities are available as digital assignments powered by MathXL for School. These activities are automatically assigned when students complete the lesson quiz online and are automatically scored.

Students can access instructional tutorials using the **Virtual Nerd app**.

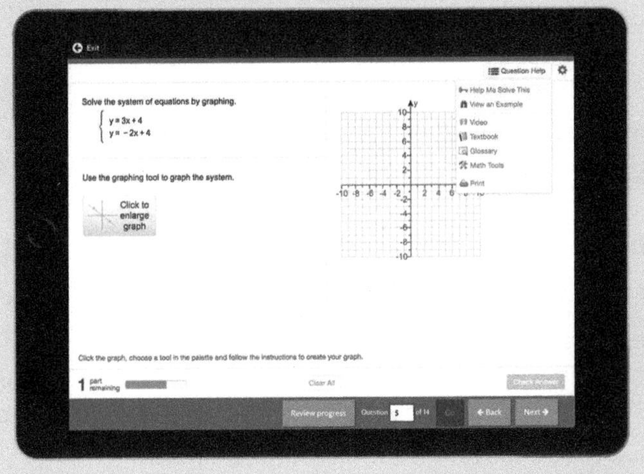

Solve the system of equations by graphing.
y = 3x + 4
y = −2x + 4
Use the graphing tool to graph the system.
Click to enlarge graph
Question Help
Help Me Solve This
View an Example
Video
Textbook
Glossary
Math Tools
Print
Review progress
Back
Next

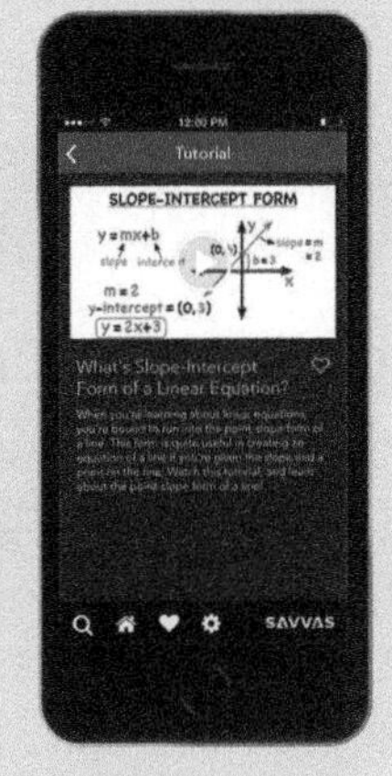

Tutorial
SLOPE-INTERCEPT FORM
What's Slope-Intercept Form of a Linear Equation?
SAVVAS

Students can also access Virtual Nerd videos using the **BouncePages app** to scan exercise pages marked with this icon. Students can download both apps for free in their mobile devices' app store.

Lesson Overview

FOCUS

Objective

Students will be able to:

✔ Identify key features of the graph of cube root functions and graph translations of them.

✔ Model real-world situations using the cube root function.

✔ Calculate and interpret the average rate of change of a cube root function over a specified interval.

Essential Understanding

The general form of a cube root function is $f(x) = \sqrt[3]{x}$. It intersects both axes at the origin, and the domain and range are all real numbers.

COHERENCE

Previously in this topic, students:

- Identified the key features of the square root function.
- Calculated the average rate of change of the square root function over a specified interval.

In this lesson, students:

- Identify the key features of the cube root function.
- Calculate the average rate of change of the cube root function over a specified interval.

Later in this topic, students will:

- Analyze key features of graphs of exponential, quadratic, and absolute value functions.

RIGOR

This lesson emphasizes a blend of *procedural skill and fluency* and *application.*

- Students calculate the average rate of change of a cube root function for a specified interval.
- Students interpret the key features of cube root functions that model real-world problems, such as finding the maximum side length of a package given its volume.

A-Z Vocabulary Builder

REVIEW VOCABULARY — **English** | *Spanish*

- **average rate of change** | *tasa promedio de cambio*
- **interval** | *intervalo*

NEW VOCABULARY

- **cube root function** | *función raíz cúbica*

VOCABULARY ACTIVITY

Review cube roots with students by comparing square roots and cube roots. Make sure that students understand that although both have a variable under a radical symbol, the square root symbol has an empty index, while a cube root has a 3 for the index. Have students identify which of the functions shown are cube root functions.

$f(x) = \sqrt{x} + 4$ [no]

$f(x) = \sqrt[3]{x - 3}$ [yes]

$f(x) = 4\sqrt[3]{x}$ [yes]

$f(x) = 3\sqrt{x - 2}$ [no]

Student Companion

Students can do their in-class work for the lesson on pages 223–226 of their *Student Companion* or in Savvas Realize.

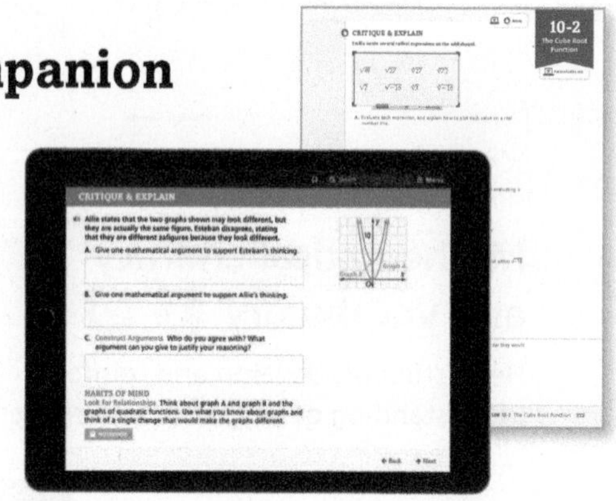

Mathematics Overview — COMMON CORE STANDARDS

Content Standards

In this lesson, students focus on these standards:

HSF.IF.B.6 Calculate and interpret the average rate of change of a function (presented symbolically or as a table) over a specified interval. Estimate the rate of change from a graph.

HSF.IF.C.7.B Graph square root, cube root, and piecewise-defined functions, including step functions and absolute value functions.

They also work with concepts related to this standard:
HSF.IF.B.4

Mathematical Practice Standards

These standards are highlighted in this lesson:

MP.4 Model With Mathematics

Students understand how mathematics can solve problems in everyday life when they recognize that creating mathematical models for manufacturing can prevent costly mistakes in production.

MP.8 Look For and Express Regularity in Repeated Reasoning

Students look for generalizations when they determine that the end points of the domain can always be used to find the maximum and minimum values of a cube root function.

STEP 1 | Explore

CRITIQUE & EXPLAIN

INSTRUCTIONAL FOCUS Students analyze the values for which a cube root can be calculated to prepare them for identifying and describing the domain of a cube root function.

STUDENT COMPANION Students can complete the *Critique & Explain* activity on page 223 of their *Student Companion.*

Before WHOLE CLASS

Implement Tasks that Promote Reasoning and Problem Solving ETP

Q: How can you estimate the value of a square root or a cube root that is not a perfect square or perfect cube?
[Find a perfect square or cube that is less than the number and another that is greater than the number. The estimate is between those two integers.]

During SMALL GROUP

Support Productive Struggle in Learning Mathematics ETP

Q: For what values is the square root function undefined?
[The square root function is undefined for $x < 0$.]

Q: For what values is the cube root function undefined?
[None; the cube root function is defined for all real numbers.]

For Early Finishers

Q: Use what you know about cube roots to predict what you think the graph of a cube root function will look like. Sketch the graph and explain.
[When $x < 0$, the graph will be a curve under the x-axis because the cube root of a negative number is always negative. When $x > 0$, the graph will be a curve above the x-axis because the cube root of a positive number is always positive.]

After WHOLE CLASS

Facilitate Meaningful Mathematical Discourse ETP

Q: Explain how you would plot $-\sqrt{30}$ and $\sqrt{-30}$ on a real number line.
[To plot $-\sqrt{30}$, estimate $\sqrt{30}$ to be 5.5 and plot the opposite of it, −5.5. $\sqrt{-30}$ cannot be plotted on a real number line because it is not a real number.]

Q: Explain how you would plot $-\sqrt[3]{30}$ and $\sqrt[3]{-30}$ on a real number line. What do you notice about the points?
[To plot $-\sqrt[3]{30}$, estimate $\sqrt[3]{30}$ to be 3.1 and plot the opposite of it, −3.1. Estimating $\sqrt[3]{-30}$ also results in −3.1. The points are the same.]

Use with **CRITIQUE & EXPLAIN**

HABITS OF MIND

Make Sense and Persevere Write the following numbers in the order they would appear from left to right on a real number line: $\sqrt{8}$, $\sqrt[3]{8}$, $\sqrt[3]{-8}$, $\sqrt{16}$. MP.1

[$\sqrt[3]{-8}$, $\sqrt[3]{8}$, $\sqrt{8}$, $\sqrt{16}$]

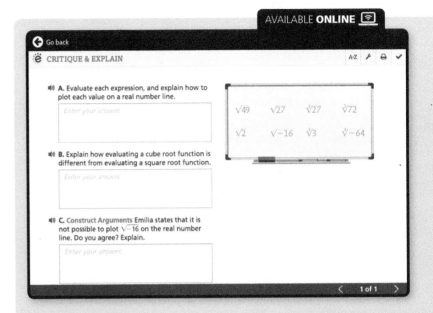

AVAILABLE **ONLINE**

Go back

CRITIQUE & EXPLAIN

A. Evaluate each expression, and explain how to plot each value on a real number line.

Enter your answer.

B. Explain how evaluating a cube root function is different from evaluating a square root function.

Enter your answer.

C. Construct Arguments Emilia states that it is not possible to plot $\sqrt{-16}$ on the real number line. Do you agree? Explain.

Enter your answer.

$\sqrt{49}$ $\sqrt{27}$ $\sqrt[3]{27}$ $\sqrt[3]{72}$

$\sqrt{2}$ $\sqrt{-16}$ $\sqrt[3]{3}$ $\sqrt[3]{-64}$

1 of 1

STUDENT EDITION, PAGE 418

10-2 The Cube Root Function

Common Core State Standards HSF.IF.B.4, HSF.IF.B.6, HSF.IF.C.7.B, MP. 4, MP. 7, MP.8

PearsonRealize.com

Activity Assess

I CAN… identify the key features of the cube root function.

VOCABULARY
- cube root function

CRITIQUE & EXPLAIN

Emilia wrote several radical expressions on the whiteboard.

$\sqrt{49}$ $\sqrt{27}$ $\sqrt[3]{27}$ $\sqrt[3]{72}$

$\sqrt{2}$ $\sqrt{-16}$ $\sqrt[3]{3}$ $\sqrt[3]{-16}$

A. Evaluate each expression, and explain how to plot each value on a real number line.

B. Explain how evaluating a cube root function is different from evaluating a square root function.

C. Construct Arguments Emilia states that it is not possible to plot either $\sqrt{-16}$ or $\sqrt[3]{-16}$ on the real number line. Do you agree? Explain. MP.3

ESSENTIAL QUESTION **What are the key features of the cube root function?**

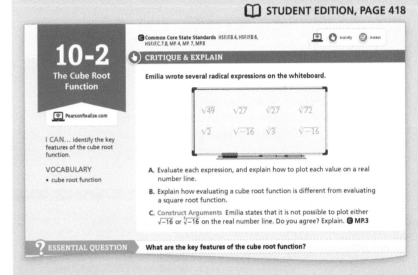

SAMPLE STUDENT WORK

A. 7, plot at 7; $3\sqrt{3}$, plot between 5 and 6; 3, plot at 3; $2\sqrt[3]{9}$, plot between 4 and 5; $\sqrt{2}$, plot between 1 and 2; nonreal value, cannot be plotted; $\sqrt[3]{3}$, plot between 1 and 2; $-2\sqrt[3]{2}$, plot between -3 and -2.

B. Cube roots can be evaluated for all real numbers, whereas square roots can only be evaluated for positive real numbers and 0.

C. No; the square root of a negative number will always be a nonreal value, so $\sqrt{-16}$ cannot be plotted on the real number line. The cube root function is defined for all real numbers, so $\sqrt[3]{-16}$ can be plotted between -3 and -2.

Activity Assess

INTRODUCE THE ESSENTIAL QUESTION

Establish Mathematics Goals to Focus Learning ETP

Introduce students to the cube root function. Remind students of the definitions of a function and of a function family. Explain that they will analyze the key features of a cube root function.

EXAMPLE 1 Key Features of the Cube Root Function

Build Procedural Fluency From Conceptual Understanding ETP

PART A

Q: What do you notice about the values of the cube root function in the table?
[When the *x*-values are negative, the *y*-values are negative. When $x = 0$, $y = 0$. When the *x*-values are positive, the *y*-values are positive.]

Q: How does the table show symmetry in the function?
[For *x*-values with the same absolute value, the *y*-values are opposite.]

Q: Why are there no restrictions on the domain or range of the cube root function?
[The cube root of any real number can be calculated. As *x* increases or decreases, the cube root of *x* increases or decreases, so there is no restriction on the range.]

AVAILABLE ONLINE

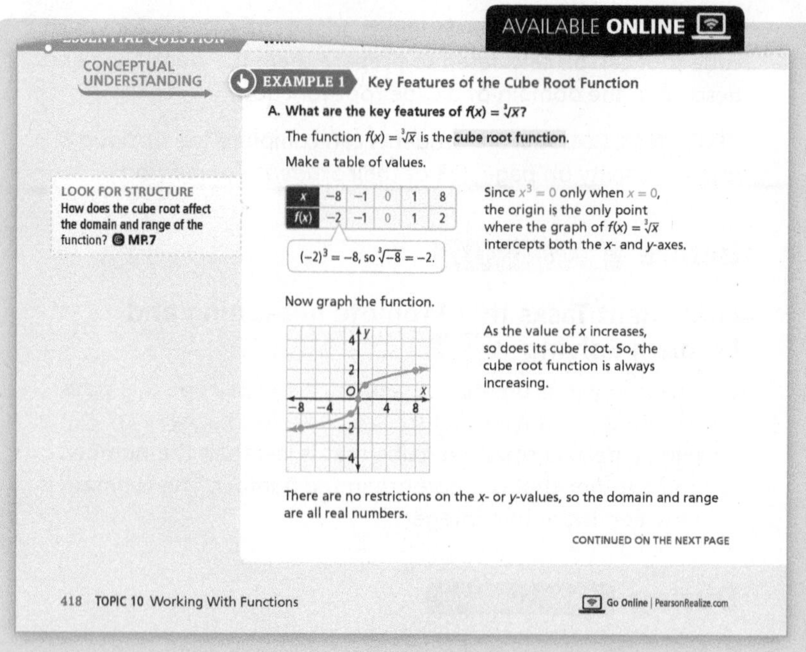
CONCEPTUAL UNDERSTANDING

EXAMPLE 1 Key Features of the Cube Root Function

A. What are the key features of $f(x) = \sqrt[3]{x}$?

The function $f(x) = \sqrt[3]{x}$ is the **cube root function**.

Make a table of values.

LOOK FOR STRUCTURE
How does the cube root affect the domain and range of the function? MP.7

x	−8	−1	0	1	8
$f(x)$	−2	−1	0	1	2

$(-2)^3 = -8$, so $\sqrt[3]{-8} = -2$.

Since $x^3 = 0$ only when $x = 0$, the origin is the only point where the graph of $f(x) = \sqrt[3]{x}$ intercepts both the *x*- and *y*-axes.

Now graph the function.

As the value of *x* increases, so does its cube root. So, the cube root function is always increasing.

There are no restrictions on the *x*- or *y*-values, so the domain and range are all real numbers.

CONTINUED ON THE NEXT PAGE

418 TOPIC 10 Working With Functions

Go Online | PearsonRealize.com

ADDITIONAL EXAMPLES

AVAILABLE ONLINE

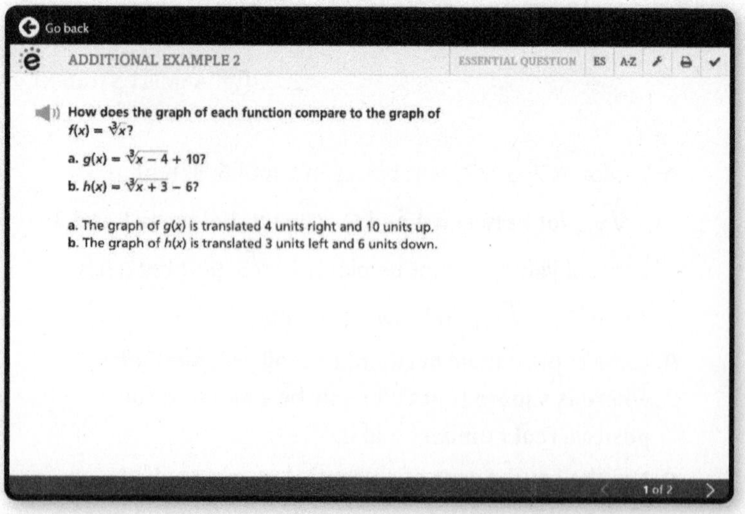
Go back

ADDITIONAL EXAMPLE 2

ESSENTIAL QUESTION ES A-Z

How does the graph of each function compare to the graph of $f(x) = \sqrt[3]{x}$?

a. $g(x) = \sqrt[3]{x - 4} + 10$?

b. $h(x) = \sqrt[3]{x + 3} - 6$?

a. The graph of $g(x)$ is translated 4 units right and 10 units up.
b. The graph of $h(x)$ is translated 3 units left and 6 units down.

1 of 2

Example 2 Students continue working with vertical and horizontal translations of the cube root function.

Q: How does performing two translations affect the graph of the cube root function?
[They move the graph both vertically and horizontally, which appears to be a diagonal move on the coordinate plane.]

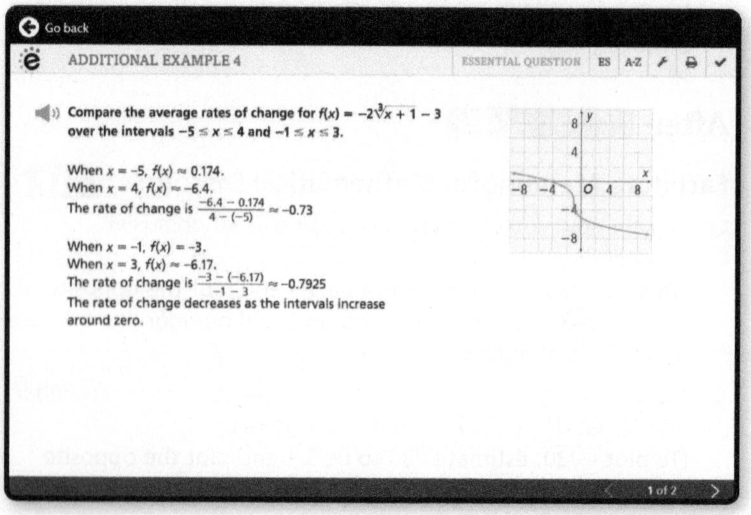
Go back

ADDITIONAL EXAMPLE 4

ESSENTIAL QUESTION ES A-Z

Compare the average rates of change for $f(x) = -2\sqrt[3]{x + 1} - 3$ over the intervals $-5 \leq x \leq 4$ and $-1 \leq x \leq 3$.

When $x = -5$, $f(x) \approx 0.174$.
When $x = 4$, $f(x) \approx -6.4$.
The rate of change is $\frac{-6.4 - 0.174}{4 - (-5)} \approx -0.73$

When $x = -1$, $f(x) = -3$.
When $x = 3$, $f(x) \approx -6.17$.
The rate of change is $\frac{-3 - (-6.17)}{-1 - 3} \approx -0.7925$
The rate of change decreases as the intervals increase around zero.

1 of 2

Example 4 Some students may need more practice working with the rate of change of a function.

Q: Why does the steeper part of the graph have the lesser rate of change?
[Because the graph is falling, the rates of change are negative. The lesser rate of change has the greater absolute value, indicating the steeper part of the graph.]

SavvasRealize.com

Activity Assess

PART B

Q: Why do the maximum and minimum have to be defined on an interval?
[The function continues infinitely, so there is no absolute maximum or minimum value.]

Try It! Answer

1. minimum is −3 when $x = -27$;
maximum is 3 when $x = 27$

EXAMPLE 2 Translations of the Cube Root Function

Use and Connect Mathematical Representations ETP

PART A

Q: How can you tell that the graph has been shifted up by looking at the equation?
[There is a number added to the output of the function.]

Q: Why does a vertical shift have no effect on the domain and range of the function?
[The domain and range are both all real numbers. When the graph of the function is vertically shifted, the domain and range are both still all real numbers.]

PART B

Q: How can you tell that the graph of g is a horizontal translation of the graph of the cube root function?
[The graph passes through (−6, 0), which is 6 units to the left of the origin, and has the same shape as the cube root function.]

Try It! Answers

2. a. shifted down 2 units
b. shifted left 1 unit

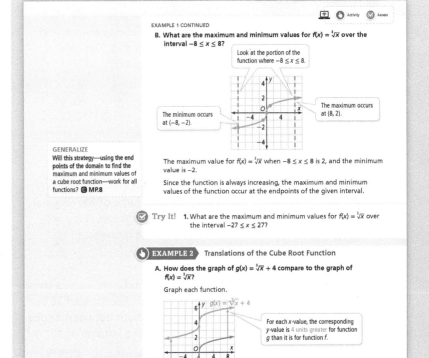

AVAILABLE ONLINE

Activity Assess

EXAMPLE 1 CONTINUED

B. What are the maximum and minimum values for $f(x) = \sqrt[3]{x}$ over the interval $-8 \le x \le 8$?

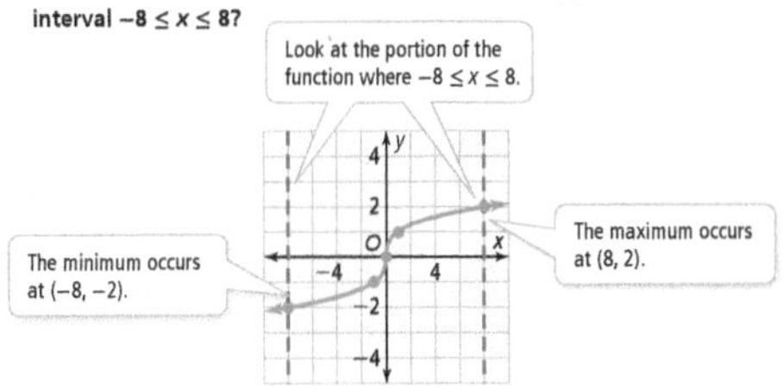
Look at the portion of the function where $-8 \le x \le 8$.
The minimum occurs at (−8, −2).
The maximum occurs at (8, 2).
y
4
2
O
x
−4
4
−2
−4

GENERALIZE
Will this strategy—using the end points of the domain to find the maximum and minimum values of a cube root function—work for all functions? MP.8

The maximum value for $f(x) = \sqrt[3]{x}$ when $-8 \le x \le 8$ is 2, and the minimum value is −2.

Since the function is always increasing, the maximum and minimum values of the function occur at the endpoints of the given interval.

Try It! 1. What are the maximum and minimum values for $f(x) = \sqrt[3]{x}$ over the interval $-27 \le x \le 27$?

EXAMPLE 2 Translations of the Cube Root Function

A. How does the graph of $g(x) = \sqrt[3]{x} + 4$ compare to the graph of $f(x) = \sqrt[3]{x}$?

Graph each function.

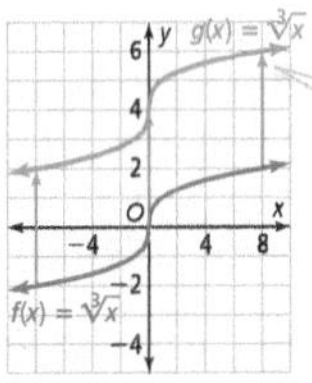
$g(x) = \sqrt[3]{x} + 4$
$f(x) = \sqrt[3]{x}$
y
6
4
2
O
x
−4
4
8
−2
−4
For each x-value, the corresponding y-value is 4 units greater for function g than it is for function f.

The graph of $g(x) = \sqrt[3]{x} + 4$ is a vertical translation of the graph of $f(x) = \sqrt[3]{x}$.

As with other functions you have studied, when you add a constant to the output of the cube root function $f(x) = \sqrt[3]{x}$, the graph of the resulting function, $g(x) = \sqrt[3]{x} + k$, is a vertical translation of the graph of f. The domain and the range for both functions are all real numbers.

CONTINUED ON THE NEXT PAGE

LESSON 10-2 The Cube Root Function 419

ADV Advanced Students

USE WITH EXAMPLE 1 Students expand their understanding of translations by writing equations that map a periodic function back to itself.

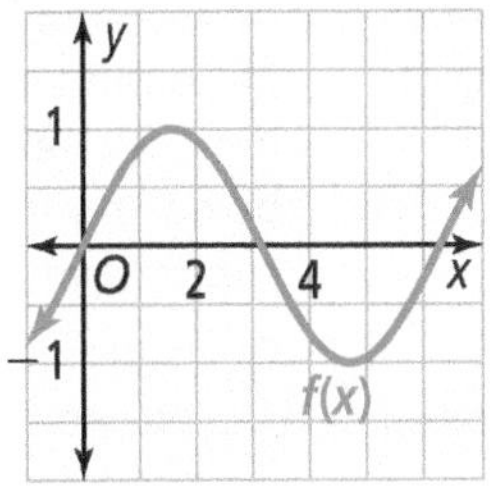
y
1
O
2
4
x
−1
f(x)

Q: Write as many translated functions of f as you can that are equivalent to f and result in the same graph.
[$y = f(x - 6.28)$, $y = f(x + 6.28)$, $y = -f(x - 3.14)$, $y = -f(x + 3.14)$, $y = f(x + 12.56)$]

Q: Do a search for *sine graphs* on the Internet. List at least one example of how the sine function is useful in science.
[sound waves, tides]

Common Error

Try It! 2 Some students may translate the graph horizontally in the opposite direction because of the sign they see under the radical sign. Have students always find the new x-intercept by substituting 0 for $f(x)$. The new x-intercept indicates the direction of the shift.

EXAMPLE 3 Model a Problem Using the Cube Root Function

Pose Purposeful Questions ETP

Q: How is the volume of the original package represented in the equation and on the graph? [The volume of the original package is the 8 in the expression. On the graph, it is $x = 0$, because that is where there is no increase in the size.]

Try It! Answer

3. $f(14)$ represents the difference in side length between a cube with a volume of 14 cm^3 and a cube with a volume of 10 cm^3. $f(19)$ represents the difference in side length between a cube with a volume of 19 cm^3 and a cube with a volume of 10 cm^3.

Elicit and Use Evidence of Student Thinking ETP

Q: When are the domain and the range of a cube root function restricted? Give an example. [The domain and range can be restricted in a real-world application. For example, many measurements cannot have a negative value.]

HABITS OF MIND

Use with **EXAMPLES 1–3**

Communicate Precisely How is transforming cube root functions similar to transforming square root functions? How is it different? MP.6

[They are similar in that adding to an input results in a horizontal translation and adding to an output results in a vertical translation. Transforming a cube root function does not affect domain and range of the function.]

Activity Assess

AVAILABLE **ONLINE**

Activity Assess

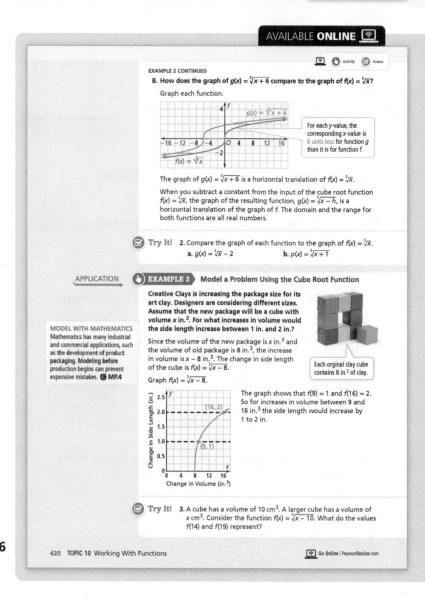

EXAMPLE 2 CONTINUED

B. How does the graph of $g(x) = \sqrt[3]{x+6}$ compare to the graph of $f(x) = \sqrt[3]{x}$?

Graph each function.

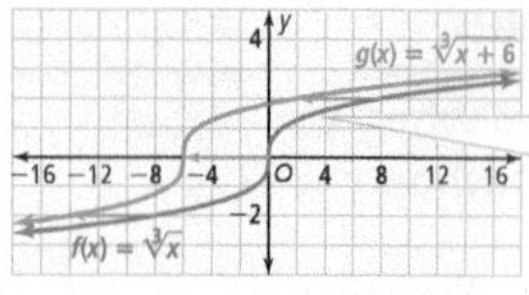

y
4
$g(x) = \sqrt[3]{x+6}$
−16 −12 −8 −4 O 4 8 12 16
−2
$f(x) = \sqrt[3]{x}$

For each y-value, the corresponding x-value is 6 units less for function g than it is for function f.

The graph of $g(x) = \sqrt[3]{x+6}$ is a horizontal translation of $f(x) = \sqrt[3]{x}$.

When you subtract a constant from the input of the cube root function $f(x) = \sqrt[3]{x}$, the graph of the resulting function, $g(x) = \sqrt[3]{x-h}$, is a horizontal translation of the graph of f. The domain and the range for both functions are all real numbers.

Try It! 2. Compare the graph of each function to the graph of $f(x) = \sqrt[3]{x}$.

a. $g(x) = \sqrt[3]{x} - 2$

b. $p(x) = \sqrt[3]{x+1}$

APPLICATION

EXAMPLE 3 Model a Problem Using the Cube Root Function

Creative Clays is increasing the package size for its art clay. Designers are considering different sizes. Assume that the new package will be a cube with volume x in.^{3}. For what increases in volume would the side length increase between 1 in. and 2 in.?

Each orginal clay cube contains 8 in.^{3} of clay.

MODEL WITH MATHEMATICS
Mathematics has many industrial and commercial applications, such as the development of product packaging. Modeling before production begins can prevent expensive mistakes. MP.4

Since the volume of the new package is x in.^{3} and the volume of old package is 8 in.^{3}, the increase in volume is $x - 8$ in.^{3}. The change in side length of the cube is $f(x) = \sqrt[3]{x-8}$.

Graph $f(x) = \sqrt[3]{x-8}$.

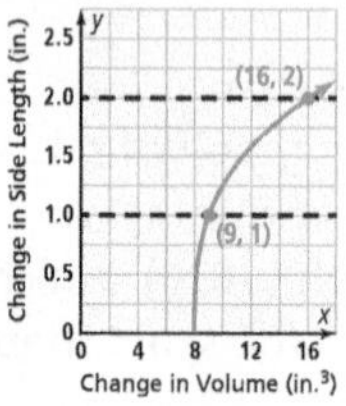

y
2.5
2.0
1.5
1.0
0.5
0
(16, 2)
(9, 1)
x
0 4 8 12 16
Change in Volume (in.^{3})
Change in Side Length (in.)

The graph shows that $f(9) = 1$ and $f(16) = 2$. So for increases in volume between 9 and 16 in.^{3} the side length would increase by 1 to 2 in.

Try It! 3. A cube has a volume of 10 cm^3. A larger cube has a volume of x cm^3. Consider the function $f(x) = \sqrt[3]{x-10}$. What do the values $f(14)$ and $f(19)$ represent?

420 TOPIC 10 Working With Functions

Go Online | PearsonRealize.com

ELL English Language Learners *(Use with* EXAMPLE 3*)*

READING BEGINNING Have students read the first sentence of the example along with you as you read it aloud.

Q: In the example, is the word *clays* the plural of *clay*? Explain. [No; *Clays* is part of the name of the business, and art clay is the product they are selling.]

Display the definition of *clay* and have students read it along with you: "earth; a type of mud made of very fine particles that stick together when wet."

Q: Is Creative Clays selling mud? [No, they are selling art clay, which has a similar consistency as mud, but it is man-made.]

SPEAKING INTERMEDIATE Remind students that *volume* is the amount of space that an object takes up. In small groups, have students discuss how the volume of solid material is calculated and how that is related to the graph in the example.

Q: How do you find the volume of a cube? [Multiply the side length by itself 3 times.]

Q: How does knowing how to calculate the volume of a cube help you understand the graph? [Instead of calculating the volume given the side length of a cube, the graph shows how to find the change in side length given the change in volume.]

WRITING ADVANCED Help students understand that the term *cubic inches* can be used as a unit of measure for any three-dimensional shape, not only for cubes. Start by having students write the definition for *cubic*: having three dimensions.

Q: List as many three-dimensional shapes as you can. [cube, cone, pyramid]

Q: Is a cone measured in *conic* inches? [No, the term *cubic* is different from the term *cube*. Cones meet the definition of *cubic*, having three dimensions, so their volume can be measured in cubic inches.]

EXAMPLE 4 Compare Rates of Change of a Function

Pose Purposeful Questions ETP

Q: Why must the average rate of change be used?
[Because the function is not linear, the rate of change is not constant. Therefore, the average rate of change must be calculated over different intervals.]

Q: How does the average rate of change relate to the graph of the function?
[If the average rate of change is positive, the graph is increasing. If the average rate of change is negative, the graph is decreasing. The greater the absolute value of the average rate of change, the steeper the graph.]

Try It! Answer

4. For $-12 \le x \le -8$, the average rate of change is about 0.121; for $-4 \le x \le 0$, the average rate of change is about 0.235.

Elicit and Use Evidence of Student Thinking ETP

Q: How can you describe the average rate of change for the cube root function?
[It is always positive. For intervals close to the origin, the average rate of change is greater. For intervals farther from the origin, the average rate of change decreases.]

EXAMPLE 5 Compare Rates of Change of Two Functions

Use and Connect Mathematical Representations ETP

Q: How can you compare the rates of change for functions in different forms? [Use two points from each function and the slope formula to find the average rate of change.]

Q: If the function from the table was shown as a graph as well, how would the two graphs be the same over the given interval? How would they be different?
[Both graphs would have a positive slope. The graph of the second function, *h*, would have a steeper slope because the rate of change is greater.]

Try It! Answer

5. The average rate of change of the first function over $-5 \le x \le 0$ is 0.163, and the average rate of change of *r* over the same interval is 0.342, so *r* has the greater rate of change.

AVAILABLE **ONLINE**

Activity Assess

EXAMPLE 4 Compare Rates of Change of a Function

For the function $f(x) = \sqrt[3]{x-1}$, how does the average rate of change from $x = 1$ to $x = 5$ compare to the average rate of change from $x = 5$ to $x = 9$?

Step 1 Evaluate the function for the *x*-values that correspond to the endpoints of each interval.

Interval: $1 \le x \le 5$

$f(1) = \sqrt[3]{1-1} = 0$ $\quad f(5) = \sqrt[3]{5-1} \approx 1.59$

Interval: $5 \le x \le 9$

$f(5) = \sqrt[3]{5-1} \approx 1.59$ $\quad f(9) = \sqrt[3]{9-1} = 2$

Step 2 Find the average rate of change over each interval.

$$\frac{f(5)-f(1)}{5-1} \approx \frac{1.59-0}{5-1} \approx 0.40 \qquad \frac{f(9)-f(5)}{9-5} \approx \frac{2-1.59}{9-5} \approx 0.10$$

The average rate of change of the function $f(x) = \sqrt[3]{x-1}$ appears to decrease when $x \ge 1$ and as the *x*-values corresponding to the endpoints of the interval increase. This is consistent with the curve becoming less steep when $x \ge 1$ and *x* increases.

Try It! 4. Compare the average rates of change for $f(x) = 2\sqrt[3]{x-3}$ over the intervals $-12 \le x \le -8$ and $-4 \le x \le 0$.

EXAMPLE 5 Compare Rates of Change of Two Functions

The graph and table represent translations of the cube root function $f(x) = \sqrt[3]{x}$. Values in the table are rounded to the nearest hundredth. Which function has a greater average rate of change over the interval $2 \le x \le 4$?

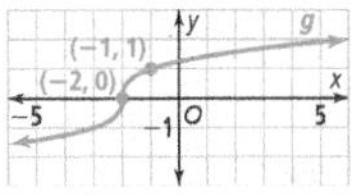

y
g
(−1, 1)
(−2, 0)
x
−5
−1
O
5

x	h(x)
0	1.22
1	2.22
2	2.48
3	2.66
4	2.81

COMMON ERROR
You may be tempted to express calculated values to a higher precision. This is misleading with estimated data. For reasonable comparisons, express both values in the same level of precision.

The function *g* is *f* translated to the left 2 units, so $g(x) = \sqrt[3]{x+2}$. Use this function to find the average rate of change in the interval $2 \le x \le 4$.

$$\frac{g(4)-g(2)}{4-2} \approx \frac{1.82-1.59}{4-2} = 0.115$$

To find the average rate of change for $h(x)$, use the values in the table directly.

$$\frac{h(4)-h(2)}{4-2} \approx \frac{2.81-2.48}{4-2} = 0.165$$

The average rate of change of $h(x)$ is greater than the average rate of change of $g(x)$ on the interval $2 \le x \le 4$.

CONTINUED ON THE NEXT PAGE

LESSON 10-2 The Cube Root Function 421

HABITS OF MIND

Use with **EXAMPLES 4 & 5**

Use Appropriate Tools Which method of comparing functions do you prefer? Justify your answer. MP.5

[I prefer comparing functions using the rate of change, because it shows which function is increasing or decreasing at a faster rate.]

Struggling Students

USE WITH EXAMPLE 5 Provide practice with finding the rate of change given two points.

- Find the average rate of change between the given points.

1. (2, 5), (−1, −4) [3]
2. (−3, 0), (2, −6) [−1.2]
3. (−1, −2), (−3, 5) [−3.5]
4. (0, 4), (−1, −3) [7]

Q: How do you know in which order to subtract the coordinates?
[The *x*- and *y*-coordinates must be subtracted in the same order, but it does not matter which is first.]

Q: How are average rate of change and slope related?
[The average rate of change between two points is the slope of the line that can be drawn between them.]

CONCEPT SUMMARY The Cube Root Function $f(x) = \sqrt[3]{x}$

Q: What are the key features of the cube root function $f(x) = \sqrt[3]{x}$?

[The x- and y-intercepts are both 0. The domain and range are both all real numbers. The graph is always increasing.]

Do You UNDERSTAND? | Do You KNOW HOW?

Common Error

Exercise 8 Some students may think that because the cube root function has neither a vertical nor a horizontal line of symmetry, it is not symmetric. Have students graph the function and then trace it on a translucent page. Ask them to rotate the function until it lies on top of itself again to recognize the 180° rotational symmetry of a cube root function.

Answers

1. domain: $-\infty < x < \infty$; range: $-\infty < y < \infty$; increasing everywhere (no max/min values); intercepts axes at (0, 0), rotational symmetry about the origin
2. Timothy limits his view to what the calculator displays. He does not realize that the function increases without bound as x increases and decreases without bound as x decreases. Therefore, the range is all real numbers.
3. One graph is the reflection of the other across the x-axis.
4. domain: $-\infty < x < \infty$; range: $-\infty < y < \infty$
5. The graphs have the same shape; the graph of f is the result of shifting the graph of g down 3 units.
6. The minimum is $\sqrt[3]{-3} \approx -1.44$ when $x = -2$; the maximum is 2 when $x = 9$.
7. about 0.109
8. g is translated 4 units to the right of f.

AVAILABLE **ONLINE**

Concept Summary Assess

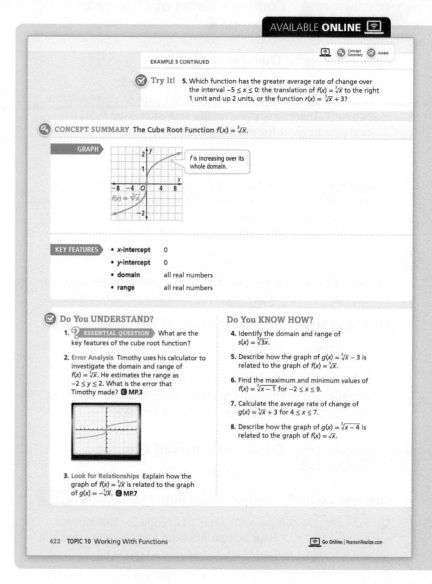

EXAMPLE 5 CONTINUED

Try It! **5.** Which function has the greater average rate of change over the interval $-5 \le x \le 0$: the translation of $f(x) = \sqrt[3]{x}$ to the right 1 unit and up 2 units, or the function $r(x) = \sqrt[3]{x} + 3$?

CONCEPT SUMMARY **The Cube Root Function $f(x) = \sqrt[3]{x}$.**

GRAPH

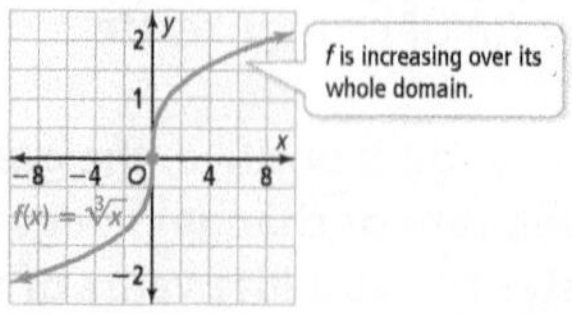

y
2
1
x
−8
−4
O
4
8
f(x) = ∛x
−2
f is increasing over its whole domain.

KEY FEATURES

- **x-intercept** 0
- **y-intercept** 0
- **domain** all real numbers
- **range** all real numbers

Do You UNDERSTAND?

1. ESSENTIAL QUESTION What are the key features of the cube root function?
2. **Error Analysis** Timothy uses his calculator to investigate the domain and range of $f(x) = \sqrt[3]{x}$. He estimates the range as $-2 \le y \le 2$. What is the error that Timothy made? MP.3

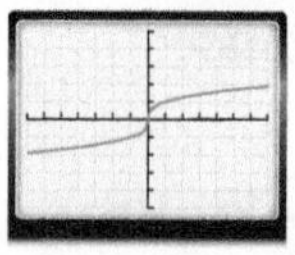

3. **Look for Relationships** Explain how the graph of $f(x) = \sqrt[3]{x}$ is related to the graph of $g(x) = -\sqrt[3]{x}$. MP.7

Do You KNOW HOW?

4. Identify the domain and range of $s(x) = \sqrt[3]{3x}$.
5. Describe how the graph of $g(x) = \sqrt[3]{x} - 3$ is related to the graph of $f(x) = \sqrt[3]{x}$.
6. Find the maximum and minimum values of $f(x) = \sqrt[3]{x-1}$ for $-2 \le x \le 9$.
7. Calculate the average rate of change of $g(x) = \sqrt[3]{x} + 3$ for $4 \le x \le 7$.
8. Describe how the graph of $g(x) = \sqrt[3]{x-4}$ is related to the graph of $f(x) = \sqrt{x}$.

422 TOPIC 10 Working With Functions

Go Online | PearsonRealize.com

SavvasRealize.com

Practice Tutorials Math Tools

PRACTICE & PROBLEM SOLVING

AVAILABLE **ONLINE**

Lesson Practice You may opt to have students complete the automatically scored Practice and Problem Solving items online powered by MathXL for School.

Choose from: **Lesson Practice**

Adaptive Practice

You may also take advantage of the bank of exercises for assigning additional practice.

Assignment Guide

Basic	Advanced
9–23, 26, 27, 29–34, 36–40	9–19, 22–31, 35–40

Item Analysis

Example	Items	DOK
1	16–19	1
	9, 38	2
2	20–25	1
	15	2
3	26–28	2
	35–37	3
	40	4
4	29–31, 39	1
	11–14	3
5	32–34	1
	10	2

AVAILABLE **ONLINE**

PRACTICE & PROBLEM SOLVING

Scan for Multimedia

Practice Tutorial

Additional Exercises Available Online

UNDERSTAND

9. **Reason** Explain why the x- and y-intercepts of $f(x) = \sqrt[3]{x}$ are the same. MP.2

10. **Look for Relationships** Compare the average rates of change for $f(x) = \sqrt[3]{x}$ and $f(x) = \sqrt[3]{x} + 5$ for $0 \leq x \leq 4$. MP.7

11. **Error Analysis** Hugo calculated that the average rate of change of $f(x) = \sqrt[3]{3x}$ for $0 \leq x \leq 5$ is 1.026. Explain the error that Hugo made. MP.3

$$\frac{\sqrt[3]{3(5)} - \sqrt[3]{3(0)}}{5 - 0}$$

$$= \frac{3(\sqrt[3]{5} - \sqrt[3]{0})}{5 - 0}$$

$$\approx 1.026 \quad ✗$$

12. **Use Appropriate Tools** Find the average rate of change of $f(x) = \sqrt[3]{x}$ for $0 \leq x \leq 4$. Use the symmetry of the function to predict its average rate of change for $-4 \leq x \leq 0$. MP.5

13. **Reason** Which gives a better approximation of the rate of change of $f(x) = \sqrt[3]{x}$ near $x = 1$: the average rate of change for $-1 \leq x \leq 3$ or for $\frac{1}{2} \leq x \leq \frac{3}{2}$? Explain your reasoning. MP.2

14. **Higher Order Thinking** Consider the function $f(x) = x^3$. How can you find two different intervals that have the same average rate of change? Explain how you can generalize your statement.

15. **Use Structure** For each condition, describe a translation or pair of translations of $f(x) = \sqrt[3]{x}$ that results in the graph of function g. MP.7

    a. The y-intercept of the graph of g is -2.

    b. The graph of g passes through the point $(3, 5)$.

    c. The x-intercept of the graph of g is -1.

PRACTICE

For each function, identify domain, range, and intercepts. SEE EXAMPLE 1

16. $f(x) = \sqrt[3]{x - 3}$
17. $f(x) = \sqrt[3]{2x}$
18. $f(x) = \sqrt[3]{x} - 1$
19. $f(x) = \sqrt[3]{x + 2}$

Describe translations that transform the graph of $f(x) = \sqrt[3]{x}$ into the graph of the given function. SEE EXAMPLE 2

20. $g(x) = \sqrt[3]{x - 3}$ shift right 3 units
21. $p(x) = \sqrt[3]{x} + 2$ shift up 2 units
22. $p(x) = \sqrt[3]{x} - 10$
23. $q(x) = \sqrt[3]{x + 7}$
24. $j(x) = \sqrt[3]{x + 4} - 8$
25. $k(x) = \sqrt[3]{\frac{1}{2} + x} - \frac{3}{4}$

Graph each function. Use the graph to estimate the values of x that satisfy each condition. SEE EXAMPLE 3

26. $f(x) = \sqrt[3]{x};\ 1 \leq f(x) \leq 2$

27. $g(x) = \sqrt[3]{x - 2};\ 1 \leq g(x) \leq 2$

28. $p(x) = \sqrt[3]{x - 1} + 3;\ 2 \leq p(x) \leq 5$

Calculate the average rate of change for each function over the given interval. SEE EXAMPLE 4

29. $f(x) = \sqrt[3]{x}$ for $3 \leq x \leq 10$ 0.102

30. $g(x) = \sqrt[3]{x} + 2$ for $-4 \leq x \leq 0$ 0.397

31. $p(x) = \sqrt[3]{4x + 5}$ for $-1 \leq x \leq 1$ 0.540

Let $f(x) = \sqrt[3]{x}$. The function g is shown in the graph. For each function, use <, >, or = to complete each of the statements. SEE EXAMPLE 5

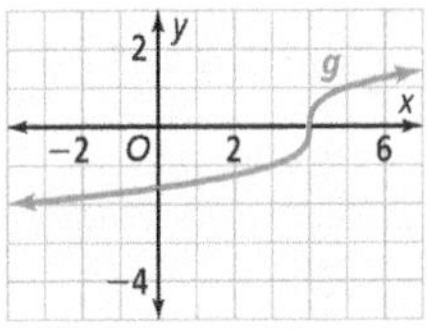

y
2
g
x
−2
O
2
6
−4

32. $f(3)$ __>__ $g(3)$

33. x-intercept of f __<__ x-intercept of g

34. y-intercept of f __>__ y-intercept of g

LESSON 10-2 The Cube Root Function 423

Answers

9. The graph crosses the axes at the origin, (0, 0), so the x-intercept and the y-intercept are the same.

10. The rates of change are the same.

11. Hugo incorrectly factors 3. The correct common factor is $\sqrt[3]{3}$.

12. approximately 0.397; The rate of change is the same for $-4 \leq x \leq 0$ as for $0 \leq x \leq 4$ due to rotational symmetry.

13. The smaller interval provides the better approximation.

14. Just like the cube root function, the cube function has 180° rotational symmetry about the origin. Also, the cube function is always increasing. So, when the endpoints of one interval are the same distance apart as the endpoints of another interval and have the same absolute value, but are on opposite sides of 0, the cube function has the same rate of change over those intervals. For example, the average rate of change is the same over $-4 \leq x \leq -2$ and $2 \leq x \leq 4$.

15. a. translation down 2 units

    b. translation right 3 units and up 5 units

    c. translation left 1 unit

16. domain: $-\infty < x < \infty$; range: $-\infty < y < \infty$; x-intercept: (3, 0); y-intercept: $(0, -\sqrt[3]{3})$ rotational symmetry about the point (3, 0)

17–19, 22–28. See next page.

Answers

17. domain: $-\infty < x < \infty$; range: $-\infty < y < \infty$; x-intercept/ y-intercept: (0, 0); rotational symmetry about the origin

18. domain: $-\infty \le x \le \infty$; range: $-\infty \le y \le \infty$; x-intercept: (1, 0); y-intercept: (0, −1); rotational symmetry about the point (0, −1)

19. domain: $-\infty \le x \le \infty$; range: $-\infty \le y \le \infty$; x-intercept: (−2, 0); y-intercept: $(0, \sqrt[3]{2})$; rotational symmetry about the point (−2, 0)

22. shift down 10 units

23. shift left 7 units

24. shift left 4 units and down 8 units

25. shift left $\frac{1}{2}$ unit and down $\frac{3}{4}$ unit

26.

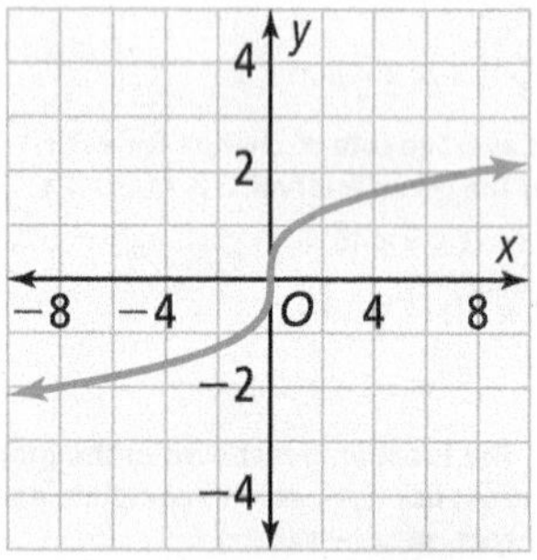

y
x
4
2
−2
−4
−8
−4
O
4
8

$1 \le x \le 8$ when $1 \le f(x) \le 2$

27.

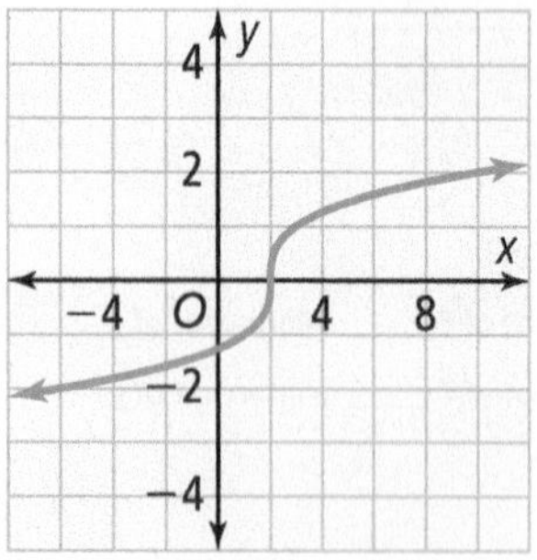

y
x
4
2
−2
−4
−4
O
4
8

$3 \le x \le 10$ when $1 \le g(x) \le 2$

28.

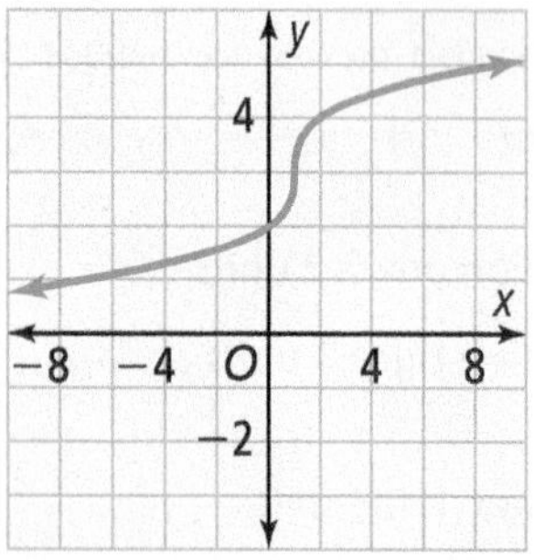

y
x
4
−2
−8
−4
O
4
8

$0 \le x \le 9$ when $2 \le p(x) \le 5$

AVAILABLE **ONLINE**

PRACTICE & PROBLEM SOLVING

Practice Tutorial
Mixed Review Available Online

APPLY

35. Model With Mathematics Tamika's Auto Sales opened recently. Weekly sales are shown in the table.

Week	1	2	3	4	5	6
Cars Sold	9	13	14	15	17	18

Plot the sales on a graph and write a cube root function that approximately models the sales. Explain what the features of the cube root function mean for the dealer's sales in the long run. MP.4

36. Communicate Precisely Max Wax Company packages colored wax to make homemade candles in cube-shaped containers. The production line needs to plan sizes of the containers based on the associated costs. Write a cube root function that tells the side lengths of the container, x, in inches for a given cost, C. MP.6

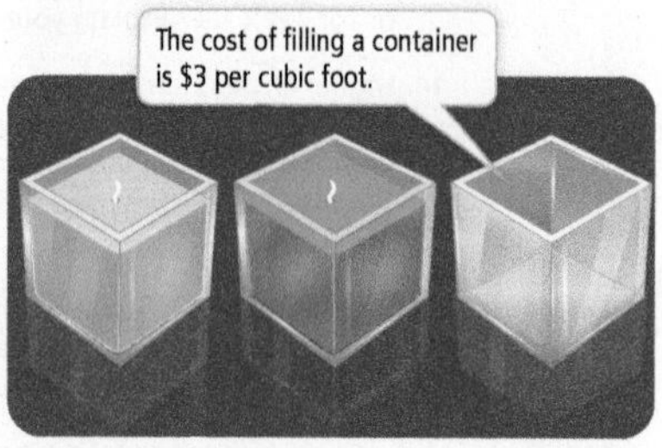

The cost of filling a container is $3 per cubic foot.

37. Mathematical Connections A cube has the same volume as a box that is 4 ft 5 in. long, 3 ft 2 in. wide, and 4 ft 3 in. deep.

a. Write an expression that models the length of one side of the cube.

b. Find the side length of the cube.

c. Does the cube or the box have a greater surface area? How much greater?

ASSESSMENT PRACTICE

38. Analyze the key features of $g(x) = \sqrt[3]{x-8} + 4$. Which of the following are true? Select all that apply.

Ⓐ The domain of g is $x \ge 8$.
Ⓑ The range of g is the set of all real numbers.
Ⓒ As x approaches infinity, $g(x)$ approaches infinity.
Ⓓ The graph of g is a translation of the graph of $f(x) = \sqrt[3]{x}$ left 8 units and up 4 units.
Ⓔ The function has an absolute minimum at $x = 8$.

39. SAT/ACT Which shows the average rate of change of $f(x) = \sqrt[3]{x} - 2$ over $1 \le x \le 4$?

Ⓐ 0.47
Ⓑ 0.20
Ⓒ −0.20
Ⓓ −0.47
Ⓔ −1.53

40. Performance Task Paul is filling spherical water balloons for an experiment. It is important that each balloon holds exactly the same volume of water, but Paul does not have a good instrument for measuring capacity.

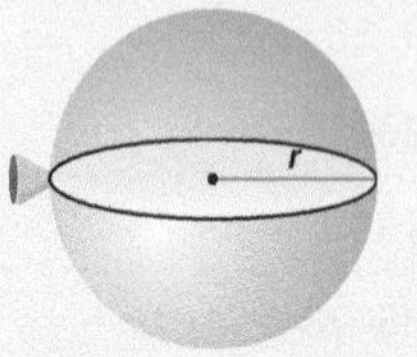

r

Part A Write a cube root function that allows Paul to predict the radius associated with a given volume using $V = \frac{4}{3}\pi r^3$.

Part B Describe a reasonable domain and range.

Part C If each balloon should have a volume of 72 in.^{3}, what radius should the balloon have?

424 TOPIC 10 Working With Functions

Go Online | PearsonRealize.com

35.

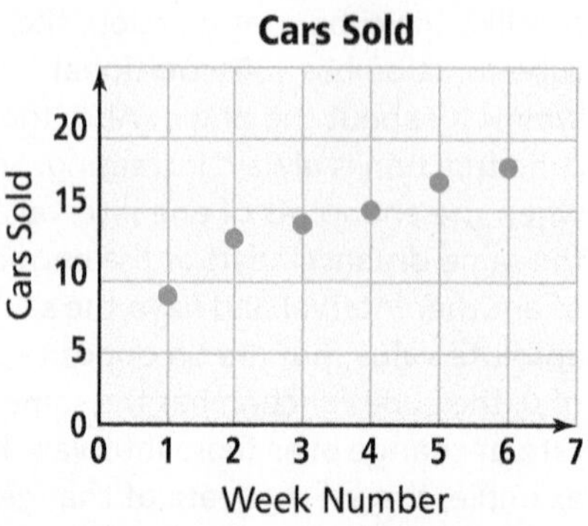

Cars Sold
Cars Sold
Week Number
0
5
10
15
20
0
1
2
3
4
5
6
7

$f(x) = 10\sqrt[3]{x}$

Sales will continue to increase, but at a decreasing rate.

36. $S(C) = 12\sqrt[3]{\frac{C}{3}}$

37. a. $x^3 = 102{,}714$

b. about 46.8 in.

c. the box; about 170 in.^{2} more surface area

40. Part A $r = \sqrt[3]{\frac{3V}{4\pi}}$

Part B Sample: $1 \le r \le 4$; $4 \le V \le 270$

Part C about 2.58 inches

LESSON QUIZ

Use the Lesson Quiz to assess students' understanding of the mathematics in the lesson.

Students can take the Lesson Quiz online or you can download a printable copy from **SavvasRealize.com**. The Lesson Quiz is also available in the *Assessment Resources* book.

Item Analysis

Item	DOK	Standards
1	1	HSF.IF.B.4
2	2	HSF.IF.B.6
3	2	HSF.IF.C.7.B
4	1	HSF.IF.C.7.B
5	2	HSF.IF.B.6

RtI Use the student scores on the Lesson Quiz to prescribe differentiated assignments.

If students take the Lesson Quiz online, it will be automatically scored and appropriate differentiated practice will be assigned based on student performance.

I Intervention	0–3 points	• Reteach to Build Understanding • Mathematical Literacy and Vocabulary • Additional Practice
O On-Level	4 points	• Mathematical Literacy and Vocabulary • Additional Practice • Enrichment
A Advanced	5 points	• Enrichment

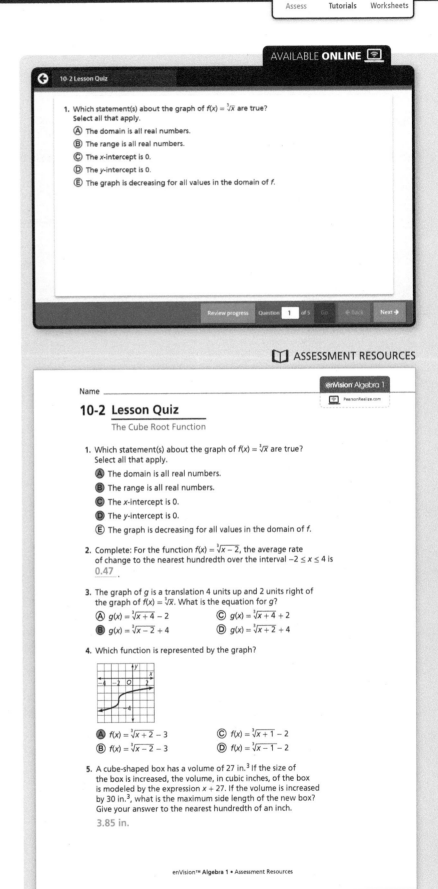

AVAILABLE **ONLINE**

10-2 Lesson Quiz

1. Which statement(s) about the graph of $f(x) = \sqrt[3]{x}$ are true? Select all that apply.
   Ⓐ The domain is all real numbers.
   Ⓑ The range is all real numbers.
   Ⓒ The x-intercept is 0.
   Ⓓ The y-intercept is 0.
   Ⓔ The graph is decreasing for all values in the domain of f.

Review progress Question 1 of 5 Go ← Back Next →

ASSESSMENT RESOURCES

Name ______________________ enVision Algebra 1 PearsonRealize.com

10-2 Lesson Quiz

The Cube Root Function

1. Which statement(s) about the graph of $f(x) = \sqrt[3]{x}$ are true? Select all that apply.
   Ⓐ The domain is all real numbers.
   Ⓑ The range is all real numbers.
   Ⓒ The x-intercept is 0.
   Ⓓ The y-intercept is 0.
   Ⓔ The graph is decreasing for all values in the domain of f.

2. Complete: For the function $f(x) = \sqrt[3]{x-2}$, the average rate of change to the nearest hundredth over the interval $-2 \le x \le 4$ is 0.47.

3. The graph of g is a translation 4 units up and 2 units right of the graph of $f(x) = \sqrt[3]{x}$. What is the equation for g?
   Ⓐ $g(x) = \sqrt[3]{x+4} - 2$
   Ⓑ $g(x) = \sqrt[3]{x-2} + 4$
   Ⓒ $g(x) = \sqrt[3]{x+4} + 2$
   Ⓓ $g(x) = \sqrt[3]{x+2} + 4$

4. Which function is represented by the graph?

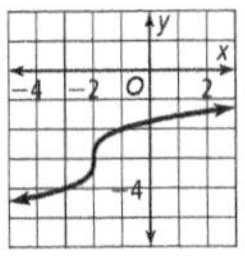
y
x
−4
−2
O
2
−4

   Ⓐ $f(x) = \sqrt[3]{x+2} - 3$
   Ⓑ $f(x) = \sqrt[3]{x-2} - 3$
   Ⓒ $f(x) = \sqrt[3]{x+1} - 2$
   Ⓓ $f(x) = \sqrt[3]{x-1} - 2$

5. A cube-shaped box has a volume of 27 in.^{3} If the size of the box is increased, the volume, in cubic inches, of the box is modeled by the expression $x + 27$. If the volume is increased by 30 in.^{3}, what is the maximum side length of the new box? Give your answer to the nearest hundredth of an inch.
   3.85 in.

enVision™ **Algebra 1** • Assessment Resources

DIFFERENTIATED RESOURCES

I = Intervention **O** = On-Level **A** = Advanced

⚙ = This activity is available as a digital assignment powered by MathXL® for School.

AVAILABLE **ONLINE**

Reteach to Build Understanding I ⚙

Provides scaffolded reteaching for the key lesson concepts.

Name

enVision Algebra 1 | PearsonRealize.com

10-2 Reteach to Build Understanding

The Cube Root Function

1. Complete the statements about the graph of f by writing numbers, expressions, or words in the blanks.

$f(x) =$ $\sqrt[3]{x}$

Domain: all real numbers

Range: all real numbers

x-intercept: 0

y-intercept: 0

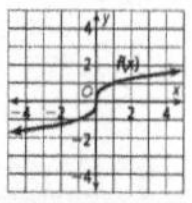

2. Greg made two incorrect statements about the function $f(x) = \sqrt[3]{x+2}$. Put an X next to the incorrect statements. Correct his errors.

The domain is $x \geq -2$. X

The range is all real numbers.

The function does not have a minimum.

The function is a vertical translation of $g(x) = \sqrt[3]{x}$. X

The function passes through the point (6, 2).

Sample: Greg incorrectly identified the domain of the function. The correct domain is all real numbers. Greg also incorrectly identified the function as being a vertical translation of $g(x) = \sqrt[3]{x}$. Instead, it is a horizontal translation 2 units left of $g(x) = \sqrt[3]{x}$.

3. For the function $f(x) = \sqrt[3]{x}$, which interval, $1 \leq x \leq 4$ or $4 \leq x \leq 7$, has a greater average rate of change? List the average rates of change.

Complete the work to answer the question.

$1 \leq x \leq 4$

$\frac{f(4) - f(1)}{4 - 1} \approx \frac{1.59 - 1}{3}$

≈ 0.197

$4 \leq x \leq 7$

$\frac{f(7) - f(4)}{7 - 4} \approx \frac{1.91 - 1.59}{3}$

≈ 0.107

The interval $1 \leq x \leq 4$ has a greater average rate of change.

enVision™ Algebra 1 • Teaching Resources

Additional Practice I O ⚙

Provides extra practice for each lesson.

Name

enVision Algebra 1 | PearsonRealize.com

10-2 Additional Practice

The Cube Root Function

For each function, identify the domain, range, and intercepts.

1. $f(x) = \sqrt[3]{x-8}$
Domain: all real numbers
Range: all real numbers
x-intercept: 8
y-intercept: −2

2. $g(x) = \sqrt[3]{x} - 1$
Domain: all real numbers
Range: all real numbers
x-intercept: 1
y-intercept: −1

3. $h(x) = \sqrt[3]{x+8} - 3$
Domain: all real numbers
Range: all real numbers
x-intercept: 19
y-intercept: −1

Graph each function by translating $f(x) = \sqrt[3]{x}$.

4. $g(x) = \sqrt[3]{x} - 2$

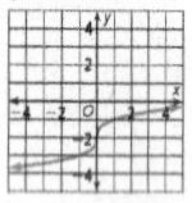

5. $h(x) = \sqrt{x+6}$

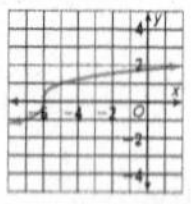

6. $k(x) = \sqrt[3]{x-1} + 2$

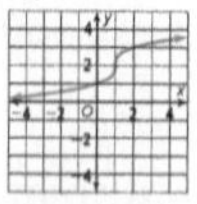

7. Compare the average rates of change for $f(x) = \sqrt[3]{x} + c$ and $g(x) = k\sqrt[3]{x} + c$ over the interval $[a, b]$. Express the average rate of change for $g(x)$ in terms of the rate of change for $f(x)$ over $[a, b]$.

Sample answer: The rate of change for $f(x)$ is $\frac{\sqrt[3]{b} - \sqrt[3]{a}}{b - a}$, and for $g(x)$, it is $\frac{k\sqrt[3]{b} - k\sqrt[3]{a}}{b - a}$. For $g(x)$, the rate is $k\left(\frac{\sqrt[3]{b} - \sqrt[3]{a}}{b - a}\right)$.

8. A cube container, with original volume 64 in.^{3}, is being redesigned to increase its capacity. The expression $x + 64$ in.^{3} models the volume of the new cube. If the volume can increase by a maximum of 100 in.^{3}, what is the maximum measurement of the edge of the larger cube, rounded to the nearest tenth?
5.5 in.

enVision™ Algebra 1 • Teaching Resources

Enrichment O A ⚙

Presents engaging problems and activities that extend the lesson concepts.

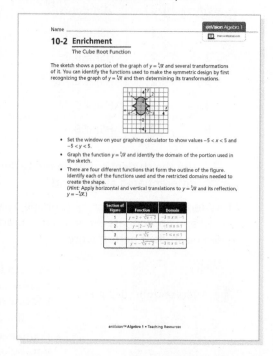

Name

enVision Algebra 1 | PearsonRealize.com

10-2 Enrichment

The Cube Root Function

The sketch shows a portion of the graph of $y = \sqrt[3]{x}$ and several transformations of it. You can identify the functions used to make the symmetric design by first recognizing the graph of $y = \sqrt[3]{x}$ and then determining its transformations.

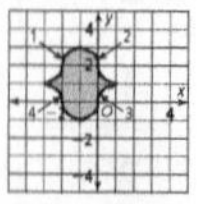

- Set the window on your graphing calculator to show values $-5 < x < 5$ and $-5 < y < 5$.
- Graph the function $y = \sqrt[3]{x}$ and identify the domain of the portion used in the sketch.
- There are four different functions that form the outline of the figure. Identify each of the functions used and the restricted domains needed to create the shape.
(*Hint:* Apply horizontal and vertical translations to $y = \sqrt[3]{x}$ and its reflection, $y = -\sqrt[3]{x}$.)

Section of Figure	Function	Domain
1	$y = 2 + \sqrt[3]{x+2}$	$-3 \leq x \leq -1$
2	$y = 2 - \sqrt[3]{x}$	$-1 \leq x \leq 1$
3	$y = \sqrt[3]{x}$	$-1 \leq x \leq 1$
4	$y = -\sqrt[3]{x+2}$	$-3 \leq x \leq -1$

enVision™ Algebra 1 • Teaching Resources

Mathematical Literacy and Vocabulary I O

Helps students develop and reinforce understanding of key terms and concepts.

Name

enVision Algebra 1 | PearsonRealize.com

10-2 Mathematical Literacy and Vocabulary

The Cube Root Function

Problem

For the function $f(x) = \sqrt[3]{x+2}$, what is the average rate of change from $x = 1$ to $x = 6$? Explain your work.

Explain	Work
First, evaluate the function at $x = 1$.	$x_1 = 1$ $f(1) = \sqrt[3]{1+2} \approx 1.44$
Second, evaluate the function at $x = 6$.	$x_2 = 6$ $f(6) = \sqrt[3]{6+2} = 2$
Third, find the average rate of change.	$\frac{f(x_2) - f(x_1)}{x_2 - x_1} = \frac{2 - 1.44}{6 - 1}$
Then, simplify to get the answer.	$\frac{2 - 1.44}{6 - 1} = 0.112$

Exercise

For the function $f(x) = \sqrt[3]{x-3}$, what is the average rate of change from $x = 2$ to $x = 4$? Explain your work.

Explain	Work
Evaluate the function at $x = 2$.	$x_1 = 2$ $f(2) = \sqrt[3]{2-3} = -1$
Evaluate the function at $x = 4$.	$x_2 = 4$ $f(4) = \sqrt[3]{4-3} = 1$
Find the average rate of change.	$\frac{f(x_2) - f(x_1)}{x_2 - x_1} = \frac{1 - (-1)}{4 - 2}$
Simplify to get the answer.	$\frac{1 - (-1)}{4 - 2} = 1$

enVision™ Algebra 1 • Teaching Resources

Digital Resources and Video Tutorials I O A ⚙

The **Reteach to Build Understanding, Additional Practice,** and **Enrichment** activities are available as digital assignments powered by MathXL for School. These activities are automatically assigned when students complete the lesson quiz online and are automatically scored.

Students can access instructional tutorials using the **Virtual Nerd app.**

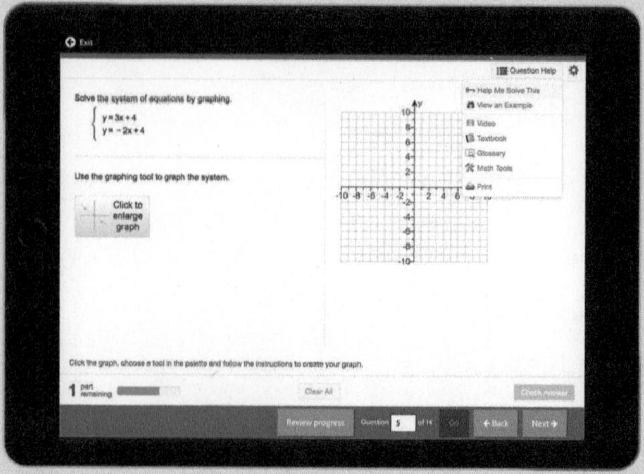
Solve the system of equations by graphing.
Use the graphing tool to graph the system.
Click to enlarge graph
Clear All
Check Answer
Review progress
Back
Next

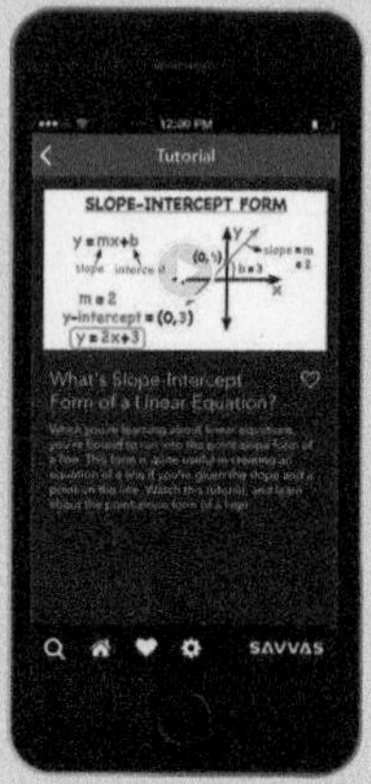
Tutorial
SLOPE-INTERCEPT FORM
SAVVAS

Students can also access Virtual Nerd videos using the **BouncePages app** to scan exercise pages marked with this icon. Students can download both apps for free in their mobile devices' app store.

SavvasRealize.com

A-Z Glossary

LESSON 10-3

Analyzing Functions Graphically

Lesson Overview

FOCUS

Objective

Students will be able to:

✔ Relate the domain and range of a function to its graph.

✔ Analyze the key features of the graph of a function—including the domain, range, maximum and minimum values, axis of symmetry, and end behavior—to identify the type of function it represents.

Essential Understanding

The key features of the graphs of functions—including the domain, range, maximum and minimum values, axis of symmetry, and end behavior—are used to identify and compare functions.

COHERENCE

Previously in this course, students:

- Created and graphed linear, exponential, absolute value, quadratic, and square root functions.

In this lesson, students:

- Identify the key features of the graph of a function and use them to compare functions.

Later in this topic, students will:

- Determine whether horizontal and vertical translations work the same way for all types of functions.

RIGOR

This lesson emphasizes a blend of *conceptual understanding* and *procedural skill and fluency.*

- Students understand that the key features of a function—including the domain, range, maximum and minimum values, axis of symmetry, and end behavior—can be used to identify and compare functions.
- Students identify the axis of symmetry for a graph by determining where to fold the paper so the halves coincide.

A-Z Vocabulary Builder

REVIEW VOCABULARY — **English** | *Spanish*

- **absolute value function** | *función de valor absoluto*
- **exponential function** | *función exponencial*
- **linear function** | *función lineal*
- **quadratic function** | *función cuadratica*
- **square root function** | *función de raíz caudrada*

VOCABULARY ACTIVITY

Review types of functions that students have learned about. Differentiate between exponential and quadratic functions by explaining that the prefix *quad-* means four, as in the four sides of a square, since the quadratic function has an independent variable that is squared. In an exponential function, the independent variable is in the exponent. Have students match the terms to the functions.

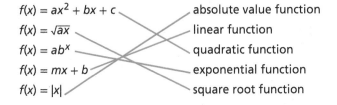

$f(x) = ax^2 + bx + c$	absolute value function
$f(x) = \sqrt{ax}$	linear function
$f(x) = ab^x$	quadratic function
$f(x) = mx + b$	exponential function
$f(x) = \lvert x \rvert$	square root function

Student Companion

Students can do their in-class work for the lesson on pages 227–230 of their *Student Companion* or in Savvas Realize.

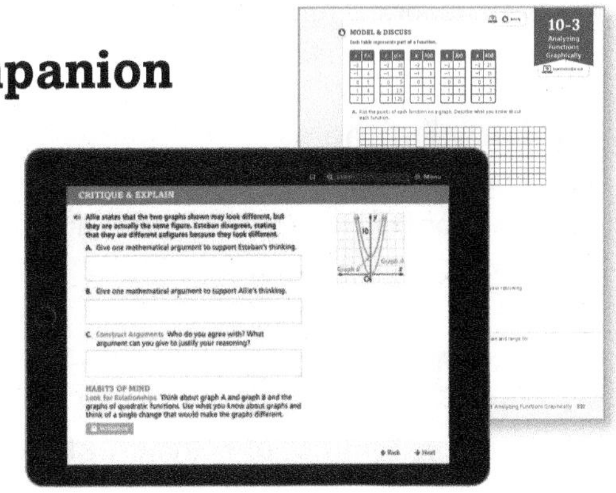
10-3
CRITIQUE & EXPLAIN

Mathematics Overview COMMON CORE STANDARDS

Content Standards

In this lesson, students focus on these standards:

HSF.IF.B.4 For a function that models a relationship between two quantities, interpret key features of graphs and tables in terms of the quantities, and sketch graphs showing key features given a verbal description of the relationship.

HSF.IF.B.5 Relate the domain of a function to its graph and, where applicable, to the quantitative relationship it describes.

Mathematical Practice Standards

These standards are highlighted in this lesson:

MP.4 Model With Mathematics

Students understand how the features of graphs used to model real-world situations can be interpreted within the context.

MP.6 Attend to Precision

Students label quantities appropriately when they determine what the *x*- and *y*-values describe with respect to the maximum or minimum values of a function.

MODEL & DISCUSS

INSTRUCTIONAL FOCUS Students use patterns to understand tables and graphs of linear, exponential, quadratic, and absolute value functions. This prepares students to recognize domains, ranges, maximum and minimum values, axes of symmetry, and end behaviors of graphs.

STUDENT COMPANION Students can complete the *Model & Discuss* activity on page 227 of their *Student Companion.*

Before WHOLE CLASS

Implement Tasks that Promote Reasoning and Problem Solving ETP

Q: What do you notice about the tables?
[The x-values are the same for all the tables. The values of $f(x)$ and $j(x)$ show symmetry about $x = 0$. The values of $g(x)$ and $h(x)$ appear to decrease when the x-values increase.]

During SMALL GROUP

Support Productive Struggle in Learning Mathematics ETP

Q: How are the graphs of the functions similar, and how are they different?
[Functions h and j are similar to each other since h is a linear function and an absolute value function can be considered a combination of two linear segments. Functions f and k are both quadratic functions, but one has a maximum value while the other has a minimum value.]

For Early Finishers

Q: Make three more tables that follow patterns similar to those of any of the functions provided. Graph each function.
[Check students' work.]

After WHOLE CLASS

Facilitate Meaningful Mathematical Discourse ETP

Q: What observations can you make about linear, quadratic, absolute value, and exponential functions?
[Quadratic functions and absolute value functions have a minimum or maximum value and a line of symmetry, but linear and exponential functions do not.]

HABITS OF MIND *Use with* **MODEL & DISCUSS**

Use Structure Based on the given points, guess a reasonable domain and range for each function. **MP.7**

[Domains for all are all real numbers; range of f: $y \leq 5$; range of g: $y > 0$; range of h: all real numbers; range of j: $y \geq 0$; range of k: $y \geq 3$]

AVAILABLE ONLINE

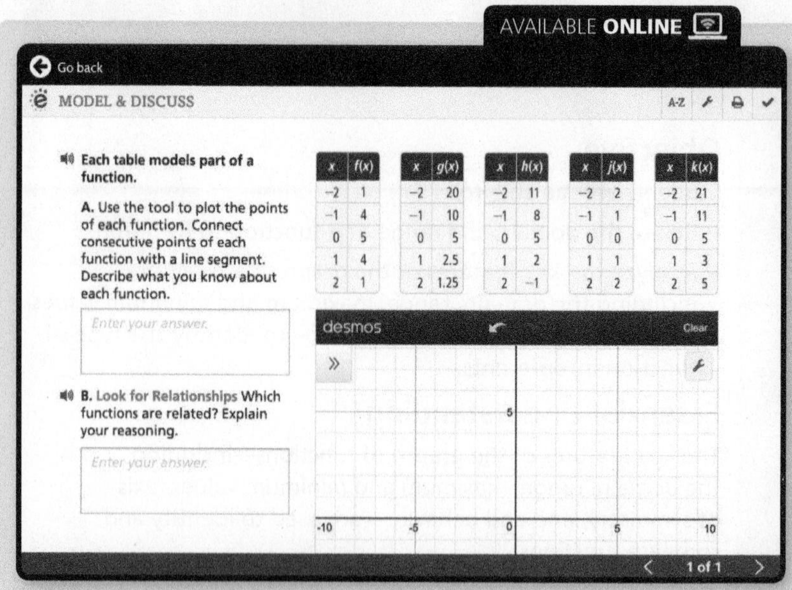

Go back

MODEL & DISCUSS

Each table models part of a function.

x	$f(x)$
−2	1
−1	4
0	5
1	4
2	1

x	$g(x)$
−2	20
−1	10
0	5
1	2.5
2	1.25

x	$h(x)$
−2	11
−1	8
0	5
1	2
2	−1

x	$j(x)$
−2	2
−1	1
0	0
1	1
2	2

x	$k(x)$
−2	21
−1	11
0	5
1	3
2	5

A. Use the tool to plot the points of each function. Connect consecutive points of each function with a line segment. Describe what you know about each function.

Enter your answer.

B. Look for Relationships Which functions are related? Explain your reasoning.

Enter your answer.

desmos
Clear
5
-10
-5
0
5
10

1 of 1

STUDENT EDITION, PAGE 425

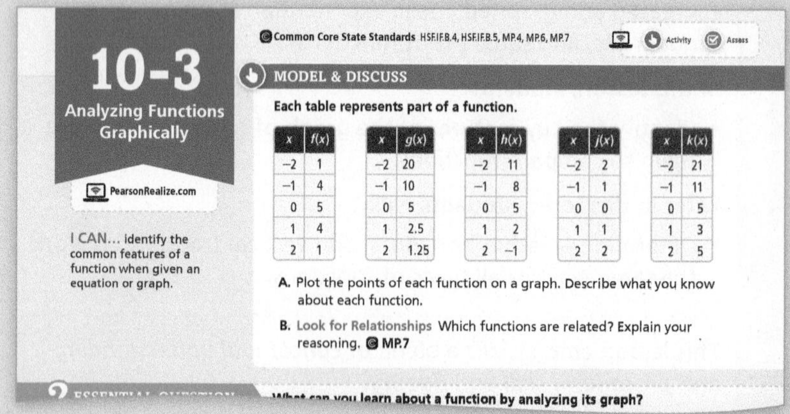

Common Core State Standards HSF.IF.B.4, HSF.IF.B.5, MP.4, MP.6, MP.7

10-3 Analyzing Functions Graphically

PearsonRealize.com

I CAN… identify the common features of a function when given an equation or graph.

MODEL & DISCUSS

Each table represents part of a function.

x	$f(x)$
−2	1
−1	4
0	5
1	4
2	1

x	$g(x)$
−2	20
−1	10
0	5
1	2.5
2	1.25

x	$h(x)$
−2	11
−1	8
0	5
1	2
2	−1

x	$j(x)$
−2	2
−1	1
0	0
1	1
2	2

x	$k(x)$
−2	21
−1	11
0	5
1	3
2	5

A. Plot the points of each function on a graph. Describe what you know about each function.

B. Look for Relationships Which functions are related? Explain your reasoning. MP.7

ESSENTIAL QUESTION What can you learn about a function by analyzing its graph?

SAMPLE STUDENT WORK

A.

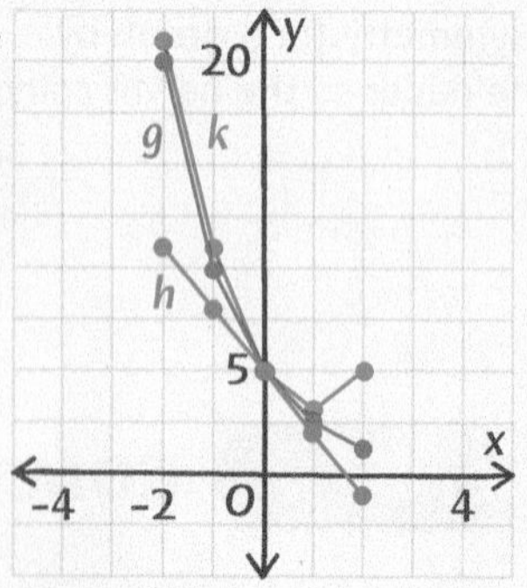

y
20
g
k
h
5
x
-4
-2
0
4

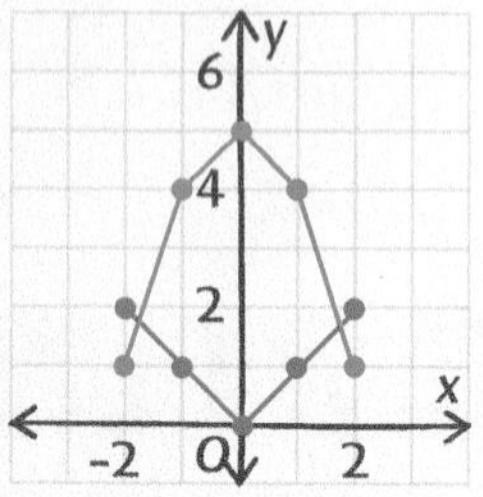

y
6
4
2
x
-2
0
2

Function k is red. Appears parabolic.
Function g is blue. Appears exponential
Function h is green. Appears linear.

Function f is red. Appears parabolic.
Function j is blue. Appears to be absolute value.

B. Functions f and k are most closely related—they are the only two that have a quadratic shape.

INTRODUCE THE ESSENTIAL QUESTION

Establish Mathematics Goals to Focus Learning ETP

Introduce students to graphs of quadratic, absolute value, and exponential functions. Remind students how to uncover the domain and range of a function, and the maximum and minimum values. Explain that they can learn a lot about a function by observing its graph.

AVAILABLE ONLINE

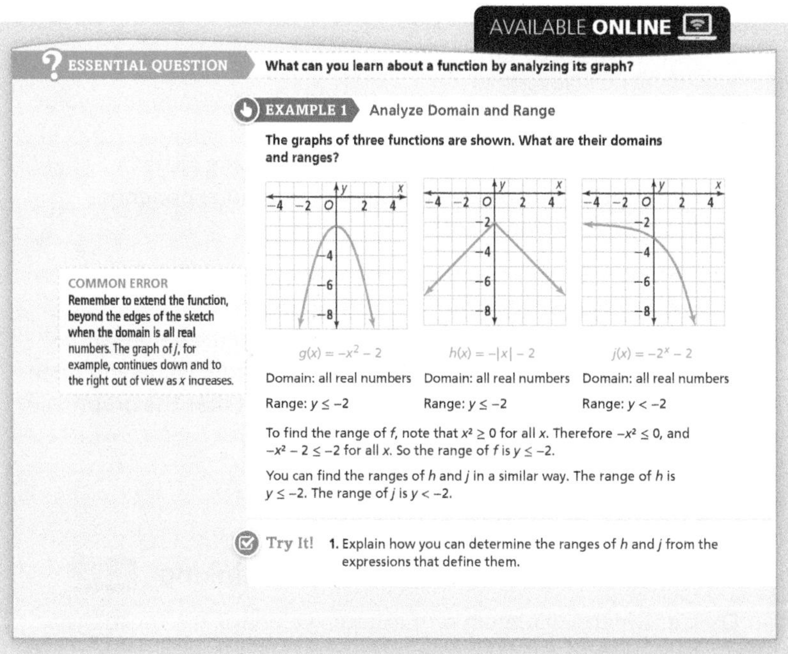
ESSENTIAL QUESTION What can you learn about a function by analyzing its graph?
EXAMPLE 1 Analyze Domain and Range
The graphs of three functions are shown. What are their domains and ranges?
COMMON ERROR
Remember to extend the function, beyond the edges of the sketch when the domain is all real numbers. The graph of j, for example, continues down and to the right out of view as x increases.
g(x) = −x² − 2
h(x) = −|x| − 2
j(x) = −2ˣ − 2
Domain: all real numbers
Range: y ≤ −2
Domain: all real numbers
Range: y ≤ −2
Domain: all real numbers
Range: y < −2
To find the range of f, note that x² ≥ 0 for all x. Therefore −x² ≤ 0, and −x² − 2 ≤ −2 for all x. So the range of f is y ≤ −2.
You can find the ranges of h and j in a similar way. The range of h is y ≤ −2. The range of j is y < −2.
Try It! 1. Explain how you can determine the ranges of h and j from the expressions that define them.

EXAMPLE 1 Analyze Domain and Range

Pose Purposeful Questions ETP

Q: What are the domain and range of a function?
[The domain is the set of all possible x-values, or input values. The range is the set of all possible y-values, or output values.]

Q: Why is the domain all real numbers for all three of the graphs?
[All real numbers are allowed to be x-coordinates of the points on the graph.]

Try It! Answer

1. The expression for $h(x)$ is the opposite of an absolute value minus 2. The absolute value of any number is greater than or equal to 0, so the opposite is less than or equal to 0. By subtracting 2, the range becomes $y \leq -2$. The expression for $j(x)$ is the opposite of an exponential value minus 2. The exponential value must be positive, so the opposite is negative. By subtracting 2, the range becomes $y < -2$.

Elicit and Use Evidence of Student Thinking ETP

Q: Can you determine the range of a function by looking only at its graph? [On some occasions, the graph of a function may tell you its range. You may not be able to see exactly what y-value the graph is approaching, however, so you may also need to look at the function itself to determine the range.]

AVAILABLE ONLINE

ADDITIONAL EXAMPLES

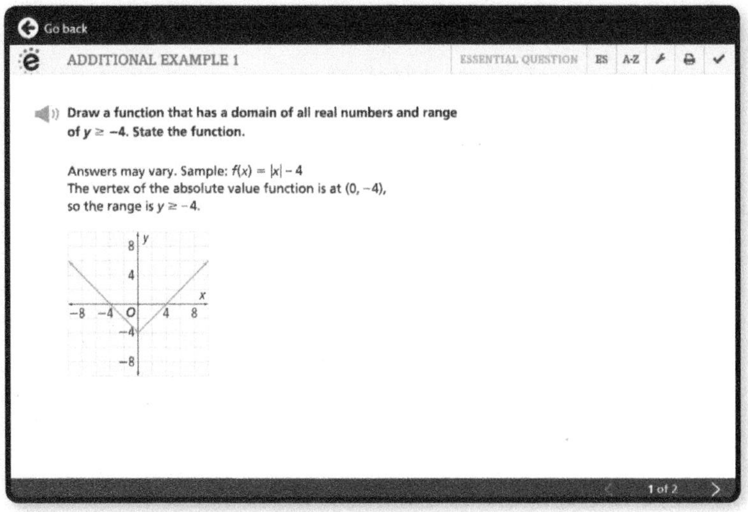
Go back
ADDITIONAL EXAMPLE 1
Draw a function that has a domain of all real numbers and range of y ≥ −4. State the function.
Answers may vary. Sample: f(x) = |x| − 4
The vertex of the absolute value function is at (0, −4), so the range is y ≥ −4.
1 of 2

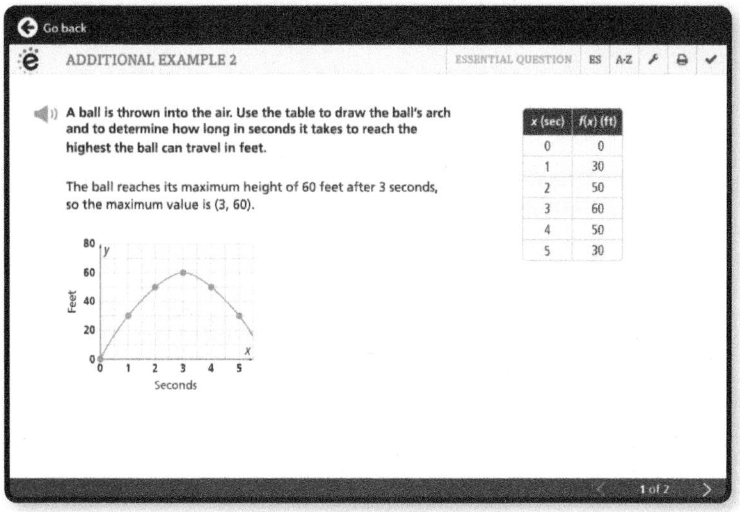
Go back
ADDITIONAL EXAMPLE 2
A ball is thrown into the air. Use the table to draw the ball's arch and to determine how long in seconds it takes to reach the highest the ball can travel in feet.
The ball reaches its maximum height of 60 feet after 3 seconds, so the maximum value is (3, 60).
x (sec) | f(x) (ft)
0 | 0
1 | 30
2 | 50
3 | 60
4 | 50
5 | 30
Feet
Seconds
1 of 2

Example 1 Students write and graph functions based on the domain and range.

Q: How does the range influence the graph of the function?
[The range indicates whether the graph of the function has a minimum, a maximum, or an asymptote.]

Example 2 Students discover the maximum value of a real-world problem using a table.

Q: What type of function does the problem represent?
[quadratic function; The trajectory of the ball is a parabola.]

EXAMPLE 2 Analyze Maximum and Minimum Values

Pose Purposeful Questions ETP

Q: Name two functions that have a maximum or minimum value and two functions that do not.
[Absolute value and quadratic functions have either a maxiumum or a minimum value. Linear and exponential functions have neither.]

Q: Do you need the graph to determine whether an absolute value function has a maximum or minimum value?
[No, a negative coefficient before the absolute value symbol indicates that the graph will have a maximum value and open downward. A positive coefficient indicates that the graph will have a minimum value and open upward.]

Try It! Answers

2. a. yes **b.** yes **c.** no

Elicit and Use Evidence of Student Thinking ETP

Q: Identify the minimum or maximum value for the functions that have them. [The graph for part (a) has a minimum of −1.25 and the graph for part (b) has a minimum of 0.]

Common Error

Try It! 2 Some students may assume a cube root function has a minimum or maximum value because a square root function does. Encourage students to graph the functions to determine whether a function has a maximum or minimum value.

HABITS OF MIND

Use with **EXAMPLES 1 & 2**

Look for Relationships What do the graphs of the functions in parts (b) and (c) have in common? **MP.7**

[Both functions increase when $x > 0$.]

AVAILABLE **ONLINE**

Activity Assess

EXAMPLE 2 Analyze Maximum and Minimum Values

Which of these functions has a maximum value and/or a minimum value?

$f(x) = 2x - 3$ $g(x) = -\left(\frac{1}{2}\right)^x + 4$ $h(x) = |x + 1| + 2$

Consider the graphs of a linear function, an exponential function, and a translation of the absolute value function.

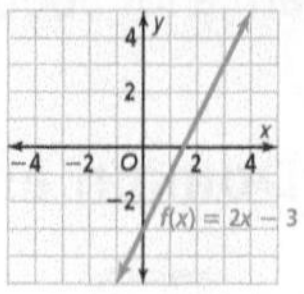
y
x
4
2
−4 −2 O 2 4
−2
f(x) = 2x − 3

The graph of the linear function f increases at a constant rate. There is no maximum or minimum value.

As the x-value increases the y-value approaches 4, but it never reaches 4.

The graph of the function g is a translation of an exponential function. It is bounded above by the asymptote $y = 4$ which means that $g(x) < 4$. However it has no maximum because it is always increasing.

The function g also has no minimum. As x decreases, $g(x)$ decreases.

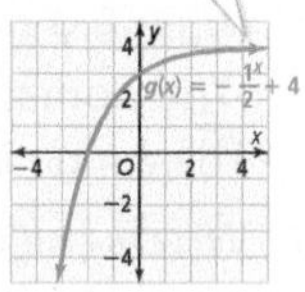
y
x
4
2
−4 O 2 4
−2
−4
g(x) = −(1/2)^x + 4

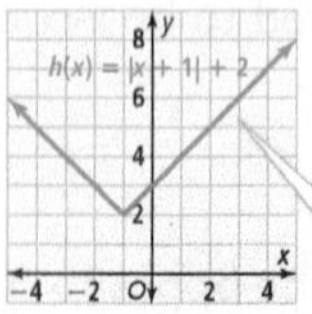
y
x
8
6
4
2
−4 −2 O 2 4
h(x) = |x + 1| + 2

The graph of h is a translation of the absolute value function. It opens upward so the function has a minimum value of 2 at the vertex (−1, 2).

If the function were instead $h(x) = -|x + 1| + 2$, the absolute value function would open down. It would then have a maximum value instead of a minimum value.

COMMUNICATE PRECISELY
The maximum or minimum value is a y-value of the function. What value tells you *where* the maximum or minimum is found? **MP.6**

Try It! **2.** Does each function have a maximum value and/or a minimum value? Sketch the graph of each function to help you.

a. $f(x) = x^2 - 3x + 1$ yes

b. $g(x) = 2\sqrt{x + 1}$ yes

c. $h(x) = \sqrt[3]{8(x - 1)} + 5$ no

Go Online | PearsonRealize.com

RtI Struggling Students

USE WITH EXAMPLE 2 Help students who struggle with describing the values different types of functions can have.

Q: Complete the table to show whether each type of function has a maximum or a minimum value, and to explain why.

	Linear	Quadratic	Square Root	Exponential
Maximum or Minimum	☐	☑	☑	☐
Explanation	The graph continually increases or decreases at a constant rate.	The graph has a minimum or maximum value at its vertex, where it changes direction.	The graph starts at a point that is either the minimum or maximum value.	The graph is always increasing or decreasing as it approaches an asymptote.

EXAMPLE 3 Understand Axes of Symmetry

Build Procedural Fluency From Conceptual Understanding ETP

Q: How can you use the graph of a function to determine whether the function has an axis of symmetry?
[If you can fold the function at a point and the two parts of the function coincide, then the function has an axis of symmetry.]

Q: Can the tables help you determine whether a function has an axis of symmetry?
[Yes, if the table shows duplicate *y*-values starting from an *x*-value (such as the *y*-values for *g*: 9, 4, 1, 0, 1, 4, 9), and the corresponding *x*-values are the same number of units apart, then you can tell that the function has an axis of symmetry.]

Try It! Answers

3. a. no

b. no

Elicit and Use Evidence of Student Thinking ETP

Q: Why is it useful to identify whether or not a function has an axis of symmetry?
[A function with an axis of symmetry can be graphed using half the points, with the other half being mirrored across the axis of symmetry.]

AVAILABLE ONLINE

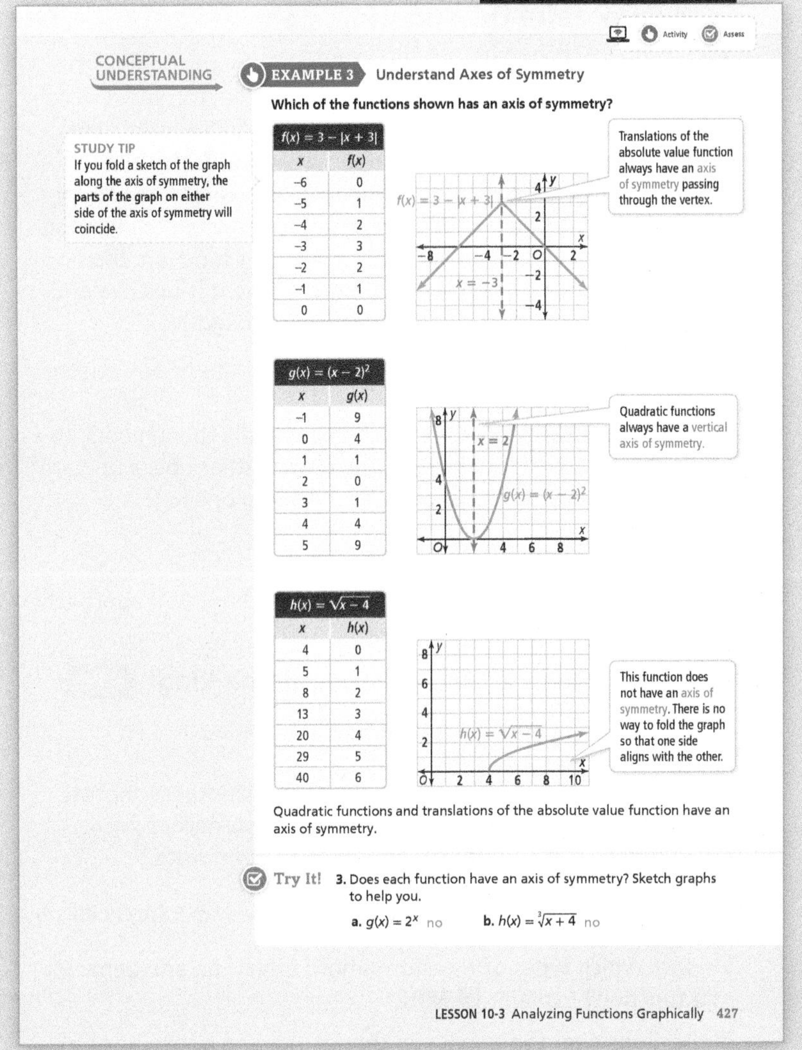

Activity Assess

CONCEPTUAL UNDERSTANDING

EXAMPLE 3 Understand Axes of Symmetry

Which of the functions shown has an axis of symmetry?

STUDY TIP
If you fold a sketch of the graph along the axis of symmetry, the parts of the graph on either side of the axis of symmetry will coincide.

$f(x) = 3 - \lvert x + 3 \rvert$	
x	*f*(*x*)
−6	0
−5	1
−4	2
−3	3
−2	2
−1	1
0	0

f(x) = 3 − |x + 3|
x = −3
Translations of the absolute value function always have an axis of symmetry passing through the vertex.

$g(x) = (x - 2)^2$	
x	*g*(*x*)
−1	9
0	4
1	1
2	0
3	1
4	4
5	9

x = 2
g(x) = (x − 2)²
Quadratic functions always have a vertical axis of symmetry.

$h(x) = \sqrt{x - 4}$	
x	*h*(*x*)
4	0
5	1
8	2
13	3
20	4
29	5
40	6

h(x) = √(x − 4)
This function does not have an axis of symmetry. There is no way to fold the graph so that one side aligns with the other.

Quadratic functions and translations of the absolute value function have an axis of symmetry.

Try It! 3. Does each function have an axis of symmetry? Sketch graphs to help you.
a. $g(x) = 2^x$ no
b. $h(x) = \sqrt[3]{x + 4}$ no

LESSON 10-3 Analyzing Functions Graphically 427

ELL English Language Learners (Use with EXAMPLE 3)

LISTENING BEGINNING Read the first sentence of the example aloud as the students listen. Explain that *symmetry* is a noun, and *symmetric* is the related adjective. Distribute notecards to students with *symmetry* on one side and *symmetric* on the other. Ask students to listen as you read the following sentences, and instruct them to hold up the side of the card showing the word that correctly completes each sentence.

Q: The painting is a beautiful example of ________. [symmetry]

Q: The lack of ________ in the placement of the photos on the wall disturbed the homeowner. [symmetry]

Q: The letter H is an example of one of the letters in the alphabet that is ________. [symmetric]

WRITING INTERMEDIATE Have the students duplicate the first graph from the example on a piece of graph paper. Tell them to fold the piece of paper vertically along the dotted line.

Q: Rewrite the Study Tip by replacing the word *coincide* with a word or phrase that you think means the same thing.
[If you fold a sketch of the graph along the axis of symmetry, the parts of the graph on either side of the axis of symmetry will *match up exactly*.]

Display: Dan's visit to his parents' house will be at the same time as their anniversary party.

Q: Rewrite the sentence by replacing a word or phrase with the words *coincide with*. [Dan's visit to his parents' house will *coincide with* their anniversary party.]

READING ADVANCED Have students read the title of the example. Then have them read the Study Tip.

Q: What is the difference between *axes of symmetry* and *axis of symmetry*?
[*Axes* is plural and *axis* is singular.]

Q: Read the definition of *axes* in the dictionary. Determine the other two words that *axes* is the plural form of.
[*ax* and *axe*]

Display:
Earth rotates on its axes and orbits the sun.

Q: Is the use of the word *axes* correct in the sentence?
[No, *axes* should be replaced with *axis*, because Earth only rotates around one axis.]

Activity Assess

EXAMPLE 4 Analyze End Behaviors of Graphs

Pose Purposeful Questions ETP

Q: How does the leading term of a function predict the end behavior of the graph?
[For the quadratic function, a negative leading coefficient indicates that the graph will open downwards. For the exponential function, the graph increases when the leading coefficient is greater than 1 and decreases when the leading coefficient is less than 1. For the cube root function, the graph increases when the leading coefficient is positive and decreases when the leading coefficent is negative.]

Q: How do the end behaviors of x and $f(x)$ relate to one another for a quadratic function?
[For a quadratic function, the domain is all real numbers, so x approaches both ∞ and $-\infty$. The graph either opens upward or downward, so $f(x)$ approaches either ∞ or $-\infty$.]

Try It! Answer

4. As x approaches ∞, $f(x)$ and $h(x)$ approach ∞. As x approaches $-\infty$, $g(x)$ and $h(x)$ approach ∞.

Elicit and Use Evidence of Student Thinking ETP

Q: How do you know whether a function approaches an asymptote?
[Exponential functions always have a horizontal asymptote. The function f approaches $y = 0$, and g approaches $y = 4$. Quadratic functions never approach an asymptote.]

HABITS OF MIND

Use with **EXAMPLES 3 & 4**

Reason Which types of transformations affect the end behavior of a function? Explain. **MP.2**

[Reflections over the x-axis can change the end behavior of a function.]

AVAILABLE **ONLINE**

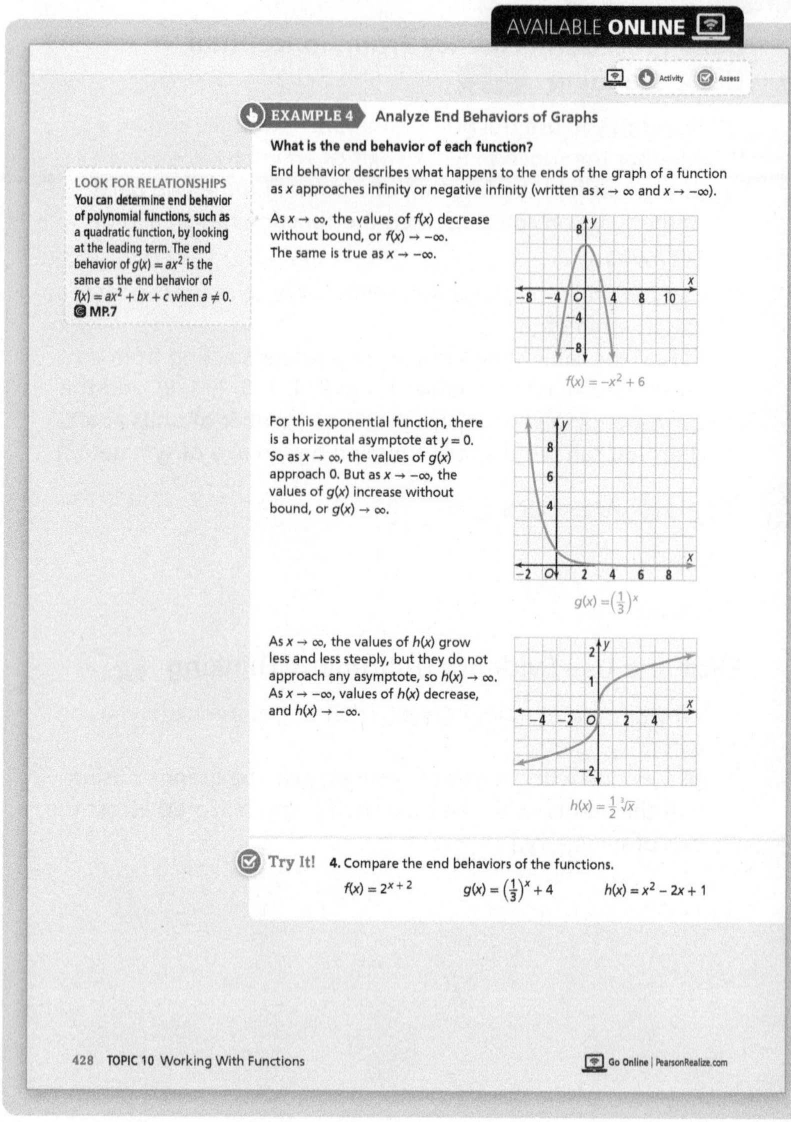

Activity Assess

EXAMPLE 4 Analyze End Behaviors of Graphs

What is the end behavior of each function?

End behavior describes what happens to the ends of the graph of a function as x approaches infinity or negative infinity (written as $x \to \infty$ and $x \to -\infty$).

LOOK FOR RELATIONSHIPS
You can determine end behavior of polynomial functions, such as a quadratic function, by looking at the leading term. The end behavior of $g(x) = ax^2$ is the same as the end behavior of $f(x) = ax^2 + bx + c$ when $a \neq 0$.
MP.7

As $x \to \infty$, the values of $f(x)$ decrease without bound, or $f(x) \to -\infty$. The same is true as $x \to -\infty$.

$f(x) = -x^2 + 6$

For this exponential function, there is a horizontal asymptote at $y = 0$. So as $x \to \infty$, the values of $g(x)$ approach 0. But as $x \to -\infty$, the values of $g(x)$ increase without bound, or $g(x) \to \infty$.

$g(x) = \left(\frac{1}{3}\right)^x$

As $x \to \infty$, the values of $h(x)$ grow less and less steeply, but they do not approach any asymptote, so $h(x) \to \infty$. As $x \to -\infty$, values of $h(x)$ decrease, and $h(x) \to -\infty$.

$h(x) = \frac{1}{2}\sqrt[3]{x}$

Try It! 4. Compare the end behaviors of the functions.
$f(x) = 2^{x+2}$ $g(x) = \left(\frac{1}{3}\right)^x + 4$ $h(x) = x^2 - 2x + 1$

428 TOPIC 10 Working With Functions

Go Online | PearsonRealize.com

ADV Advanced Students

USE WITH EXAMPLE 4 Students show their understanding of end behaviors of graphs by finding the errors of others.

Q: Margie describes the end behavior of $f(x) = \sqrt[3]{x + 4}$ in the following manner: As $x \to \infty$, $f(x) \to 3$, and as $x \to -\infty$, $f(x) \to -3$. Is Margie correct? Explain.
[No, it may look like the function approaches an asymptote when graphed over a limited domain, but cube root functions do not have asymptotes. For the function f, as x approaches infinity, $f(x)$ also approaches infinity. And as x approaches negative infinity, $f(x)$ also approaches negative infinity.]

STEP 2 | Understand & Apply

Concept Summary Assess

CONCEPT SUMMARY Common Features of Functions

Q: How can key features of the graph of a function help you to identify whether a graph is linear, exponential, absolute value, quadratic, or square root?
[Graphs with an axis of symmetry represent quadratic or absolute value functions. Graphs that have a minimum or maximum value, but no axis of symmetry, represent square root functions. Graphs that approach infinity in one direction and a horizontal line in the other direction represent exponential functions.]

Do You UNDERSTAND? | Do You KNOW HOW?

Common Error

Exercise 4 Some students may mistake the minimum value of $f(x)$ as 5 instead of 0. Encourage students to graph the function, so they can verify the behavior of the graph.

Answers

1. the domain and range of the function, the maximum and minimum values, asymptotes, the axis of symmetry, and end behavior
2. There is no value x with $-2^x = 0$. As $x \to -\infty$, $f(x) \to 0$, but the function value is never equal to 0, so there is no maximum.
3. Both types of functions change direction from increasing to decreasing or from decreasing to increasing. Both have an axis of symmetry, and the end behaviors of both graphs go in the same direction.
4. domain: $x \geq 5$, range: $f(x) \geq 0$; minimum value is 0 when $x = 5$; no maximum value; no axis of symmetry; as $x \to \infty$, $y \to \infty$
5. domain: all real numbers, range: $f(x) \geq 0$; minimum value is 0 when $x = -1$; no maximum value; axis of symmetry: $x = -1$; as $x \to -\infty$, $y \to \infty$; as $x \to \infty$, $y \to \infty$
6. domain: all real numbers, range: $f(x) \leq 2$; no minimum value; maximum value is 2 when $x = -6$; axis of symmetry: $x = -6$; as $x \to -\infty$, $y \to -\infty$; as $x \to \infty$, $y \to -\infty$

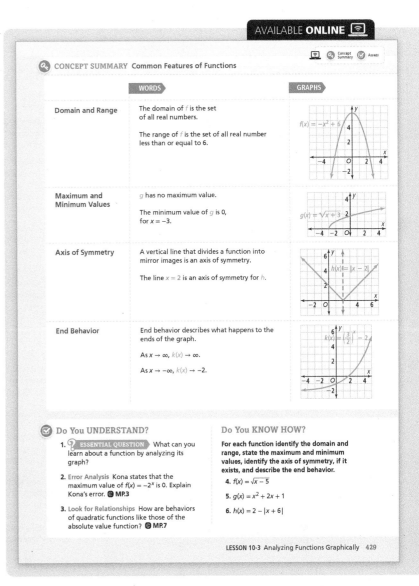

AVAILABLE ONLINE

Concept Summary Assess

CONCEPT SUMMARY Common Features of Functions

	WORDS	GRAPHS
Domain and Range	The domain of f is the set of all real numbers. The range of f is the set of all real number less than or equal to 6.	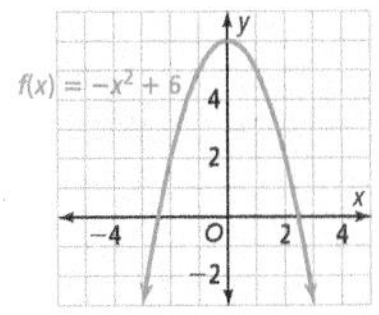
Maximum and Minimum Values	g has no maximum value. The minimum value of g is 0, for $x = -3$.	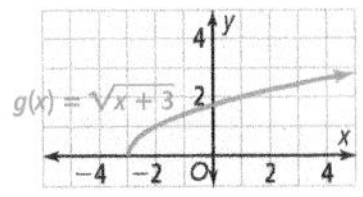
Axis of Symmetry	A vertical line that divides a function into mirror images is an axis of symmetry. The line $x = 2$ is an axis of symmetry for h.	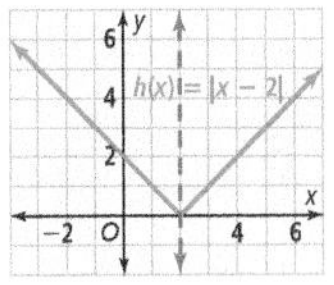
End Behavior	End behavior describes what happens to the ends of the graph. As $x \to \infty$, $k(x) \to \infty$. As $x \to -\infty$, $k(x) \to -2$.	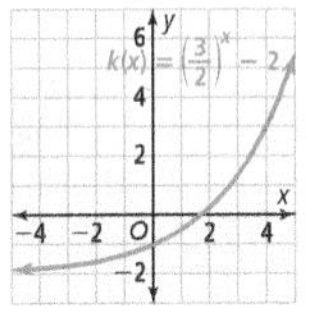

$f(x) = -x^2 + 6$
y
x
4
2
-4
O
2
4
-2

$g(x) = \sqrt{x+3}$
y
x
4
2
-4
-2
O
2
4

$h(x) = |x - 2|$
y
x
6
4
2
-2
O
4
6

$k(x) = \left(\frac{3}{2}\right)^x - 2$
y
x
6
4
2
-4
-2
O
2
4
-2

Do You UNDERSTAND?

1. ESSENTIAL QUESTION What can you learn about a function by analyzing its graph?
2. Error Analysis Kona states that the maximum value of $f(x) = -2^x$ is 0. Explain Kona's error. MP.3
3. Look for Relationships How are behaviors of quadratic functions like those of the absolute value function? MP.7

Do You KNOW HOW?

For each function identify the domain and range, state the maximum and minimum values, identify the axis of symmetry, if it exists, and describe the end behavior.

4. $f(x) = \sqrt{x - 5}$
5. $g(x) = x^2 + 2x + 1$
6. $h(x) = 2 - |x + 6|$

LESSON 10-3 Analyzing Functions Graphically 429

PRACTICE & PROBLEM SOLVING

AVAILABLE ONLINE

Lesson Practice You may opt to have students complete the automatically scored Practice and Problem Solving items online powered by MathXL for School.

Choose from: **Lesson Practice**

Adaptive Practice

You may also take advantage of the bank of exercises for assigning additional practice.

Assignment Guide

Basic	Advanced
7–23, 26–36	7–15, 18–36

Item Analysis

Example	Items	DOK
1	14–17	1
	7, 31, 32	2
	11, 12	3
2	18–21	1
	8	2
3	22–24, 34	1
	10	2
	13	3
4	25–30, 35	1
	9	2
	33, 36	3

AVAILABLE ONLINE

PRACTICE & PROBLEM SOLVING

Scan for Multimedia

Practice Tutorial

Additional Exercises Available Online

UNDERSTAND

7. **Look for Relationships** Without sketching the graph, how can you identify the domain and range of $f(x) = 4 - \sqrt{2x - 5}$? MP.7

8. **Mathematical Connections** The function $f(x) = \sqrt[3]{x}$ has a domain of all real numbers and has neither a maximum nor a minimum value. How can you redefine the domain so that f has a maximum of 8 and a minimum of −8?

9. **Error Analysis** Describe and correct the error a student made in describing the end behavior of the function $y = 1{,}000{,}000 - x^2$. MP.3

Every number that I enter for x gives a great big value for y, so as $x \to \infty$, $y \to \infty$.

✗

10. **Communicate Precisely** Explain why the line $y = 3$ cannot be an axis of symmetry for a function. MP.6

11. **Higher Order Thinking** The domain of a function, f, is the set of all real numbers. Its axis of symmetry is the line $x = 4$. As x approaches infinity, y approaches infinity. Can the range of f be all real numbers? Explain your reasoning.

12. **Error Analysis** If a function is increasing throughout its domain, the y-values are greater and greater as x approaches infinity. Libby claims that any function that has all real numbers as its domain and is increasing everywhere must have all real numbers as its range as well. Is Libby correct? Explain why or why not. MP.3

13. **Use Structure** For what values of a and b would the graph of f have an axis of symmetry? MP.7

$$f(x) = \begin{cases} a\sqrt[3]{x}, & x \le b \\ \sqrt[3]{x}, & x > b \end{cases}$$

PRACTICE

Sketch the graph of each function and identify its domain and range. SEE EXAMPLE 1

14. $f(x) = x^2 - 2$

15. $f(x) = \sqrt{x - 3}$

16. $f(x) = 5^x$

17. $f(x) = 3 - |x - 4|$

Use the graph of each function to help you identify its maximum and minimum values, if they exist. SEE EXAMPLE 2

18. $f(x) = 3 - x^2$

19. $f(x) = \sqrt[3]{x}$

20. $f(x) = -2^x$

21. $f(x) = 5|x| - 8$

State the equation of the axis of symmetry for each function, if it exists. SEE EXAMPLE 3

22. 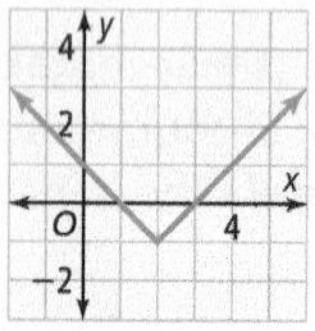

y
4
2
x
O
4
−2

$x = 2$

23. 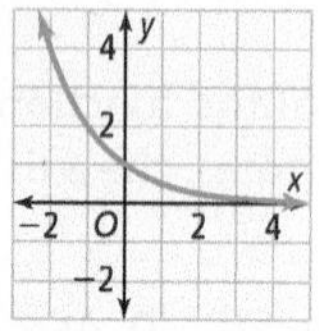

y
4
2
x
−2
O
2
4
−2

no axis of symmetry

24. 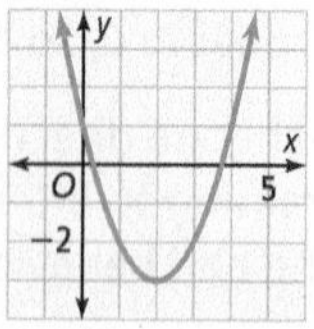

y
x
O
5
−2

$x = 2$

Describe the end behavior of each function. SEE EXAMPLE 4

25. $f(x) = 1 - 3x$

26. $f(x) = x^2 + 2$

27. $f(x) = -7^x$

28. $f(x) = |x + 2| - 8$

29. $f(x) = -3(x + 4)^2$

30. $f(x) = \sqrt{x} - 5$

Answers

7. The radicand must be nonnegative: $2x - 5 \ge 0$, so $x \ge \frac{5}{2}$. The domain is $x \ge \frac{5}{2}$.

   The radical indicates the positive root, so it will not be less than 0. All values of $f(x)$, then, must be less than or equal to 4. The range is $(-\infty, 4]$

8. $f(x) = 8$ when $x = 512$, and $f(x) = -8$ when $x = -512$. Restrict the domain to be $-512 \le x \le 512$.

9. The student is distracted by the large constant. As $x \to \infty$, the leading term $-x^2$ will, from some point on, be less than $-1{,}000{,}000$. Looking at the leading term shows $x \to \infty$, $y \to -\infty$.

10. If the line $y = 3$ is an axis of symmetry for a graph, then any point above the axis must have a matching point below. So, for example, if (1, 4) is a point on the graph, then the point (1, 2) must also be on the graph. The graph cannot represent a function.

11. No, the left side of the function is a mirror image of the side to the right of the axis of symmetry. Because the domain is the set of all real numbers, there is no vertical asymptote. Since $y \to \infty$ when $x \to \pm\infty$, the graph must change directions at some point, having a minimum value. The range cannot be the set of all real numbers.

12. Libby is not correct. The exponential function $y = -2^x$ meets these criteria, but has range $y < 0$.

13. $a = -1$, $b = 0$

See answers for Exercises 14–21 and 25–30 on next page.

Answers

14.

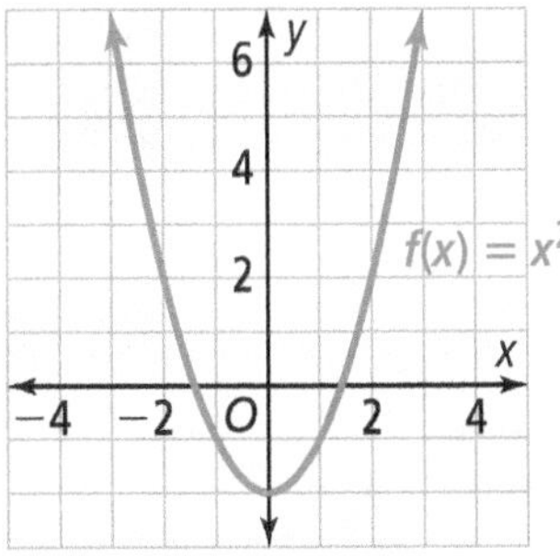
y
6
4
2
f(x) = x² − 2
x
−4 −2 O 2 4

domain: all real numbers, range: $f(x) \geq -2$

15.

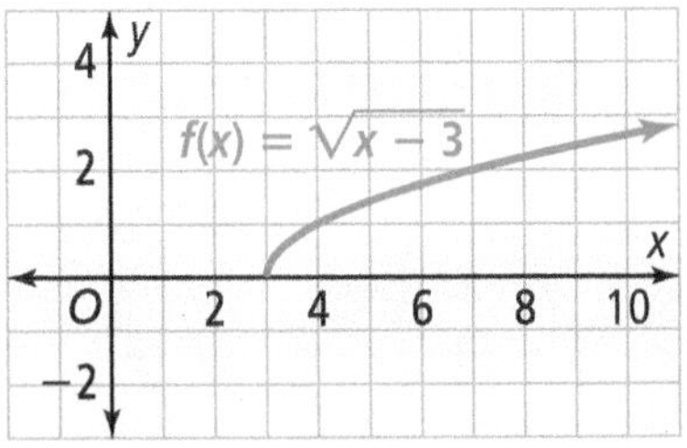
y
4
2
f(x) = √x − 3
x
O 2 4 6 8 10
−2

domain: $x \geq 3$, range: $f(x) \geq 0$

16.

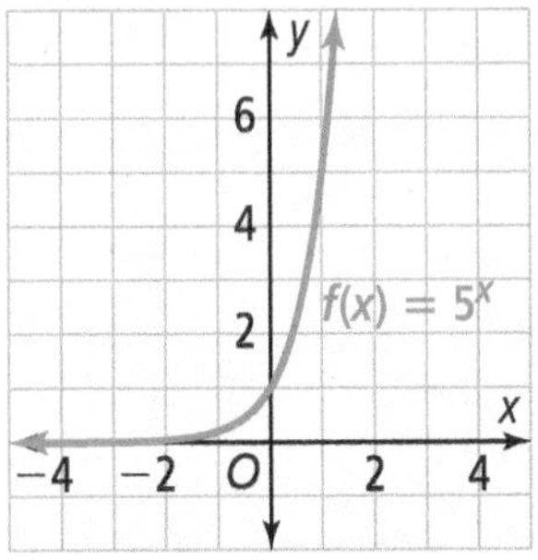
y
6
4
2
f(x) = 5ˣ
x
−4 −2 O 2 4

domain: all real numbers, range: $f(x) > 0$

17.

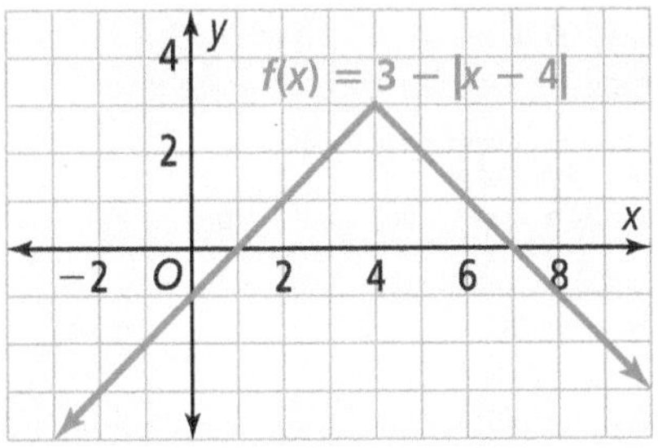
y
4
2
f(x) = 3 − |x − 4|
x
−2 O 2 4 6 8

domain: all real numbers, range: $f(x) \leq 3$

18. maximum is 3 when $x = 0$; no minimum value

19. no maximum or minimum value

20. no maximum or minimum value

21. minimum is –8 when $x = 0$; no maximum value

25. As $x \to -\infty$, $y \to \infty$; as $x \to \infty$, $y \to -\infty$.

26. As $x \to -\infty$, $y \to \infty$; as $x \to \infty$, $y \to \infty$.

27. As $x \to -\infty$, $y \to 0$; as $x \to \infty$, $y \to -\infty$.

28. As $x \to -\infty$, $y \to \infty$; as $x \to \infty$, $y \to \infty$.

29. As $x \to -\infty$, $y \to -\infty$; as $x \to \infty$, $y \to -\infty$

30. As $x \to \infty$, $y \to \infty$

AVAILABLE **ONLINE**

Practice Tutorial
Mixed Review Available Online

PRACTICE & PROBLEM SOLVING

APPLY

31. Model With Mathematics The average high temperatures for four different cities, Anchorage, AK, Kansas City, MO, Miami, FL, and New York, NY, have been used to create the graph. Use information about maximum and minimum values to complete the legend for the graph. Explain your reasoning. MP.4

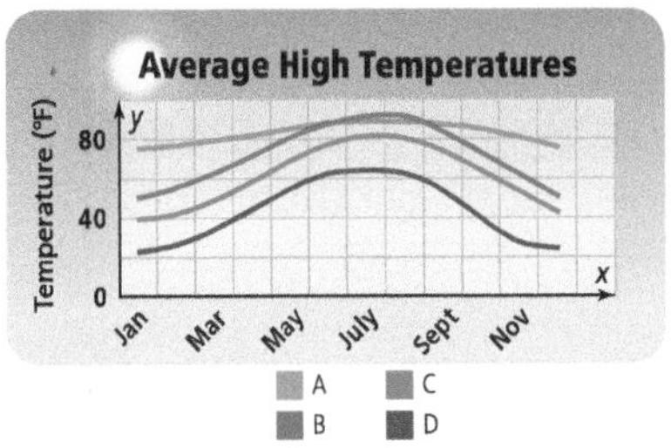
Average High Temperatures
Temperature (°F)
y
80
40
0
x
Jan
Mar
May
July
Sept
Nov
A
B
C
D

32. Make Sense and Persevere A marketing company is designing a new package for a box of cereal. They have determined that the function $C(x) = 4.5x^2$ models the cost of a box with side lengths as shown (measured in inches). Identify a reasonable domain and range for the function. MP.1

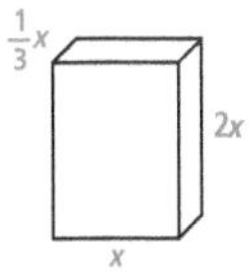
1/3 x
2x
x

33. Model With Mathematics Yumiko is an animator. She uses computer-generated imagery (CGI) to create scenes for a movie. The shapes and features she uses are defined by functions. Which features of functions will be useful for Yumiko, and how can she use them in her work? MP.4

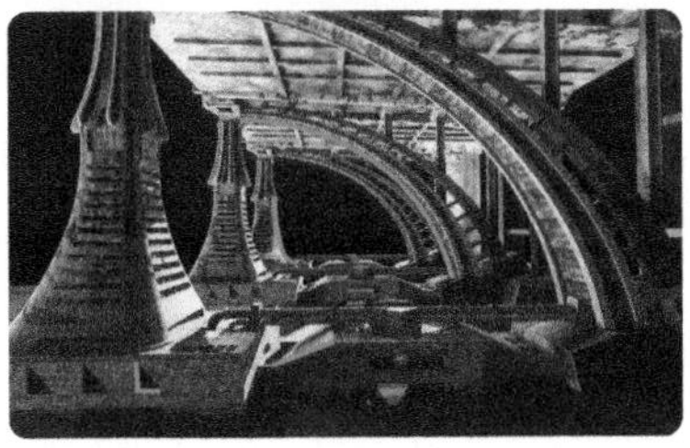

ASSESSMENT PRACTICE

34. Analyze the behavior of $f(x) = x^2 - 2x + 5$. Which of the following are true? Select all that apply.

Ⓐ As x approaches infinity, y approaches infinity.

Ⓑ As x approaches negative infinity, y approaches negative infinity.

Ⓒ f has an axis of symmetry at $x = 1$.

Ⓓ The domain of f is the set of all real numbers.

Ⓔ The maximum value of f is 4, for $x = 1$.

35. SAT/ACT Which function has an axis of symmetry at $x = 1$ and a maximum value of 3?

Ⓐ $y = 1 - |x - 3|$

Ⓑ $y = |x - 1| + 3$

Ⓒ $y = |x + 1| - 3$

Ⓓ $y = 3 - |x - 1|$

Ⓔ $y = |x - 3| + 1$

36. Performance Task Jack started a small business recently, and he has been tracking his monthly profits, summarized in the table below.

Jan	\$3	May	\$100
Feb	\$10	June	\$180
Mar	\$25	July	\$415
Apr	\$40	Aug	\$795

Part A Create a graph to show Jack's profits over time. Determine the type of function that will best model Jack's profits based on data collected so far.

Part B Evaluate features of the function that will be relevant to Jack's business. Explain what those features mean in this context.

Part C Write an equation that models the growth of Jack's business. Use your function to predict Jack's profits for August of the following year. Is your prediction reasonable? Explain why or why not.

LESSON 10-3 Analyzing Functions Graphically 431

31. A = Miami (relatively steady high temperatures all year)

B = Kansas City (max is highest of the four, min is less than Miami's)

C = New York City (max/min values are lower than those for KC)

D = Anchorage (lowest max temp/lowest min temp)

32. Domain: $0 < x \leq 12$, Range: $0 < f(x) \leq 648$ (x cannot be 0 or negative, and probably won't be greater than 12 inches. The range is determined using endpoints of the domain.)

33. Axes of symmetry will save Yumiko work because she can draw half of the image and then reflect it. Maximum and minimum values might be helpful in setting up edges of shapes.

36. *See back of book.*

LESSON QUIZ

Use the Lesson Quiz to assess students' understanding of the mathematics in the lesson.

Students can take the Lesson Quiz online or you can download a printable copy from **SavvasRealize.com**. The Lesson Quiz is also available in the *Assessment Resources* book.

Item Analysis

Item	DOK	Standards
1	1	HSF.IF.B.4
2	1	HSF.IF.B.4
3	2	HSF.IF.B.5
4	1	HSF.IF.B.4
5	2	HSF.IF.B.5

RtI Use the student scores on the Lesson Quiz to prescribe differentiated assignments.

If students take the Lesson Quiz online, it will be automatically scored and appropriate differentiated practice will be assigned based on student performance.

I Intervention	0–3 points	• Reteach to Build Understanding • Mathematical Literacy and Vocabulary • Additional Practice
O On-Level	4 points	• Mathematical Literacy and Vocabulary • Additional Practice • Enrichment
A Advanced	5 points	• Enrichment

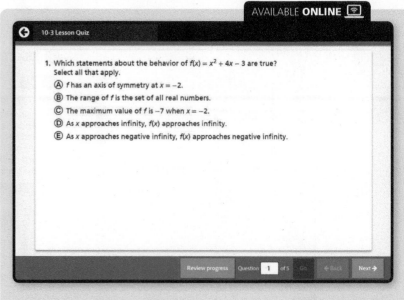

AVAILABLE **ONLINE**

10-3 Lesson Quiz

1. Which statements about the behavior of $f(x) = x^2 + 4x - 3$ are true? Select all that apply.

Ⓐ f has an axis of symmetry at $x = -2$.

Ⓑ The range of f is the set of all real numbers.

Ⓒ The maximum value of f is -7 when $x = -2$.

Ⓓ As x approaches infinity, $f(x)$ approaches infinity.

Ⓔ As x approaches negative infinity, $f(x)$ approaches negative infinity.

Review progress Question 1 of 5 Go ← Back Next →

ASSESSMENT RESOURCES

Name

enVision Algebra 1 PearsonRealize.com

10-3 Lesson Quiz

Analyzing Functions Graphically

1. Which statements about the behavior of $f(x) = x^2 + 4x - 3$ are true? Select all that apply.

Ⓐ f has an axis of symmetry at $x = -2$.

Ⓑ The range of f is the set of all real numbers.

Ⓒ The maximum value of f is -7 when $x = -2$.

Ⓓ As x approaches infinity, $f(x)$ approaches infinity.

Ⓔ As x approaches negative infinity, $f(x)$ approaches negative infinity.

2. Complete each sentence with *minimum* or *maximum* and the corresponding numeric values.

The maximum value of $f(x) = -|x - 4| - 5$ is -5 when $x = 4$.

The minimum value of $f(x) = x^2 - 2x + 1$ is 0 when $x = 1$.

3. The graph of g is a translation 2 units left of the graph of $f(x) = \sqrt{x}$. What is the domain of g?

Ⓐ all real numbers Ⓑ $x \geq -2$ Ⓒ $x \geq 0$ Ⓓ $x \geq 2$

4. What is the end behavior of the exponential function f represented by the graph?

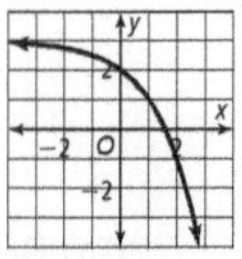

y
x
−2
O
−2

As $x \to \infty$, $f(x) \to -\infty$.

As $x \to -\infty$, $f(x) \to 3$.

5. The function $f(x) = 2.75x^2$ models the packaging costs, in cents, for shipping a book with the side lengths, in inches, shown in the diagram. What are reasonable domain and range values for this function?

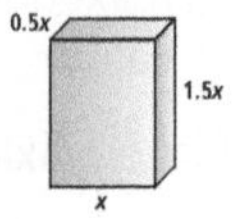

0.5x
1.5x
x

Ⓐ domain: $4 \leq x \leq 12$; range: $6 \leq f(x) \leq 18$

Ⓑ domain: $x \geq 4$; range: $f(x) \geq 44$

Ⓒ domain: $4 \leq x \leq 12$; range: $44 \leq f(x) \leq 396$

Ⓓ domain: $x \geq 0$; range: $f(x) > 0$

enVision™ **Algebra 1** • Assessment Resources

SavvasRealize.com

Assess Tutorials Worksheets

DIFFERENTIATED RESOURCES

I = Intervention O = On-Level A = Advanced

= This activity is available as a digital assignment powered by MathXL® for School.

AVAILABLE **ONLINE**

Reteach to Build Understanding I

Provides scaffolded reteaching for the key lesson concepts.

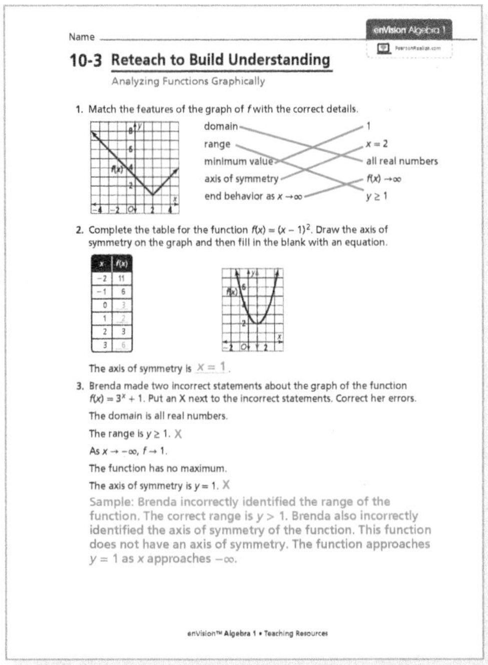

Name

10-3 Reteach to Build Understanding

Analyzing Functions Graphically

1. Match the features of the graph of f with the correct details.

domain — all real numbers; range — $y \geq 1$; minimum value — 1; axis of symmetry — $x = 2$; end behavior as $x \to -\infty$ — $f(x) \to \infty$

2. Complete the table for the function $f(x) = (x - 1)^2$. Draw the axis of symmetry on the graph and then fill in the blank with an equation.

x	f(x)
−2	11
−1	6
0	3
1	2
2	3
3	6

The axis of symmetry is $x = 1$.

3. Brenda made two incorrect statements about the graph of the function $f(x) = 3^x + 1$. Put an X next to the incorrect statements. Correct her errors.

The domain is all real numbers.

The range is $y \geq 1$. X

As $x \to -\infty$, $f \to 1$.

The function has no maximum.

The axis of symmetry is $y = 1$. X

Sample: Brenda incorrectly identified the range of the function. The correct range is $y > 1$. Brenda also incorrectly identified the axis of symmetry of the function. This function does not have an axis of symmetry. The function approaches $y = 1$ as x approaches $-\infty$.

enVision™ Algebra 1 • Teaching Resources

Additional Practice I O

Provides extra practice for each lesson.

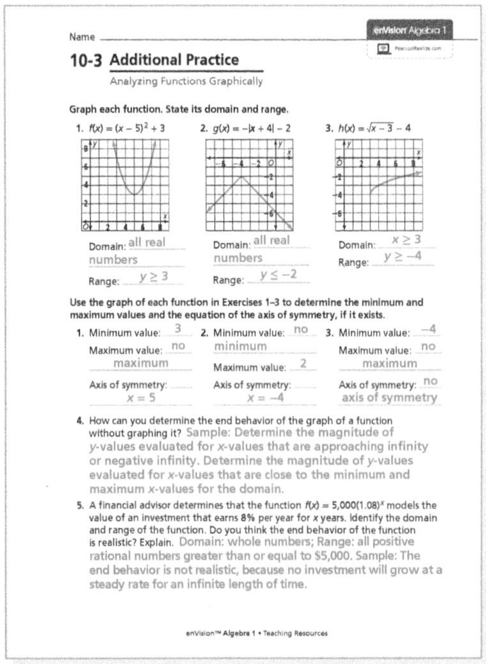

Name

10-3 Additional Practice

Analyzing Functions Graphically

Graph each function. State its domain and range.

1. $f(x) = (x - 5)^2 + 3$ Domain: all real numbers Range: $y \geq 3$

2. $g(x) = -|x + 4| - 2$ Domain: all real numbers Range: $y \leq -2$

3. $h(x) = \sqrt{x - 3} - 4$ Domain: $x \geq 3$ Range: $y \geq -4$

Use the graph of each function in Exercises 1–3 to determine the minimum and maximum values and the equation of the axis of symmetry, if it exists.

1. Minimum value: 3 Maximum value: no maximum Axis of symmetry: $x = 5$

2. Minimum value: no minimum Maximum value: −2 Axis of symmetry: $x = -4$

3. Minimum value: −4 Maximum value: no maximum Axis of symmetry: no axis of symmetry

4. How can you determine the end behavior of the graph of a function without graphing it? Sample: Determine the magnitude of y-values evaluated for x-values that are approaching infinity or negative infinity. Determine the magnitude of y-values evaluated for x-values that are close to the minimum and maximum x-values for the domain.

5. A financial advisor determines that the function $f(x) = 5{,}000(1.08)^x$ models the value of an investment that earns 8% per year for x years. Identify the domain and range of the function. Do you think the end behavior of the function is realistic? Explain. Domain: whole numbers; Range: all positive rational numbers greater than or equal to $5,000. Sample: The end behavior is not realistic, because no investment will grow at a steady rate for an infinite length of time.

enVision™ Algebra 1 • Teaching Resources

Enrichment O A

Presents engaging problems and activities that extend the lesson concepts.

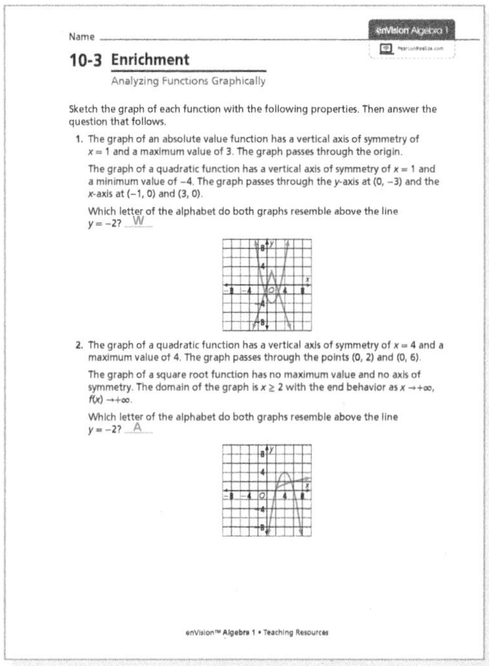

Name

10-3 Enrichment

Analyzing Functions Graphically

Sketch the graph of each function with the following properties. Then answer the question that follows.

1. The graph of an absolute value function has a vertical axis of symmetry of $x = 1$ and a maximum value of 3. The graph passes through the origin.

The graph of a quadratic function has a vertical axis of symmetry of $x = 1$ and a minimum value of −4. The graph passes through the y-axis at (0, −3) and the x-axis at (−1, 0) and (3, 0).

Which letter of the alphabet do both graphs resemble above the line $y = -2$? W

2. The graph of a quadratic function has a vertical axis of symmetry of $x = 4$ and a maximum value of 4. The graph passes through the points (0, 2) and (0, 6).

The graph of a square root function has no maximum value and no axis of symmetry. The domain of the graph is $x \geq 2$ with the end behavior as $x \to +\infty$, $f(x) \to +\infty$.

Which letter of the alphabet do both graphs resemble above the line $y = -2$? A

enVision™ Algebra 1 • Teaching Resources

Mathematical Literacy and Vocabulary I O

Helps students develop and reinforce understanding of key terms and concepts.

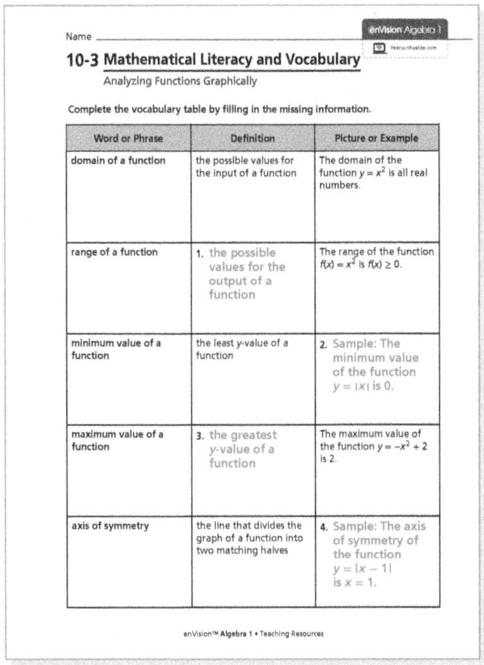

Name

10-3 Mathematical Literacy and Vocabulary

Analyzing Functions Graphically

Complete the vocabulary table by filling in the missing information.

Word or Phrase	Definition	Picture or Example
domain of a function	the possible values for the input of a function	The domain of the function $y = x^2$ is all real numbers.
range of a function	1. the possible values for the output of a function	The range of the function $f(x) = x^2$ is $f(x) \geq 0$.
minimum value of a function	the least y-value of a function	2. Sample: The minimum value of the function $y = \lvert x \rvert$ is 0.
maximum value of a function	3. the greatest y-value of a function	The maximum value of the function $y = -x^2 + 2$ is 2.
axis of symmetry	the line that divides the graph of a function into two matching halves	4. Sample: The axis of symmetry of the function $y = \lvert x - 1 \rvert$ is $x = 1$.

enVision™ Algebra 1 • Teaching Resources

Digital Resources and Video Tutorials I O A

The **Reteach to Build Understanding, Additional Practice**, and **Enrichment** activities are available as digital assignments powered by MathXL for School. These activities are automatically assigned when students complete the lesson quiz online and are automatically scored.

Students can access instructional tutorials using the **Virtual Nerd app**.

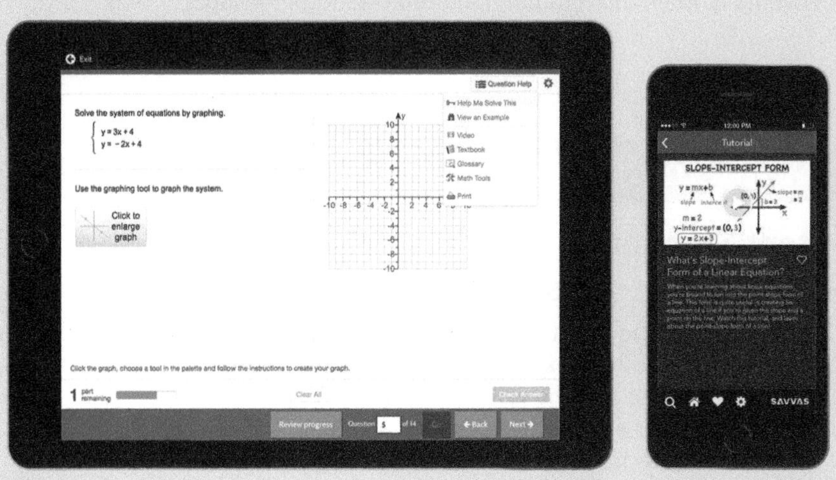
Solve the system of equations by graphing.
Use the graphing tool to graph the system.
Click to enlarge graph
Question Help
Review progress
Tutorial
SLOPE-INTERCEPT FORM
What's Slope-Intercept Form of a Linear Equation?
SAVVAS

Students can also access Virtual Nerd videos using the **BouncePages app** to scan exercise pages marked with this icon. Students can download both apps for free in their mobile devices' app store.

Lesson Overview

FOCUS

Objective

Students will be able to:

✔ Graph translations of absolute value, exponential, quadratic, and radical functions.

✔ Determine how combining translations affects the key features of the graph of a function.

Essential Understanding

Changes to the input and output of a function in the form $f(x - h) + k$ result in a translation of the graph of the function. Adding a constant k to the output of the function shifts the graph vertically. Subtracting a constant h from the input of the function shifts the graph horizontally.

COHERENCE

Previously in this topic, students:

- Graphed and identified the key features of the graphs of absolute value, exponential, quadratic, and radical functions.

In this lesson, students:

- Graph and analyze translations of absolute value, exponential, quadratic, and square root functions.

Later in this topic, students will:

- Graph and analyze vertical and horizontal stretches and compressions of the graphs of absolute value, exponential, quadratic, and square root functions.

RIGOR

This lesson emphasizes a blend of *conceptual understanding* and *procedural skill and fluency.*

- Students understand that for all functions, changing the input or output of the function shifts all of the points on the graph of the function, but does not change its shape.
- Students translate the graph of a function by shifting all points vertically when the constant k is added to the output and horizontally when the constant h is subtracted from the input.

A-Z Vocabulary Builder

REVIEW VOCABULARY

English | *Spanish*

- **constant** | *constante*
- **input** | *entrada*
- **output** | *salida*
- **translation** | *traslación*

VOCABULARY ACTIVITY

Review the terms *translation, constant, input,* and *output.* Explain that functions are translated, or shifted, when a change is made to the input or output. Have students identify whether a change is being made to the input or output of the functions shown.

$f(x) = \sqrt{x} + 1$ [output] $\quad f(x) = \sqrt{x + 1}$ [input]

$f(x) = |x - 1|$ [input] $\quad f(x) = |x| + 1$ [output]

$f(x) = 2^x - 1$ [output] $\quad f(x) = 2^{x+1}$ [input]

Student Companion

Students can do their in-class work for the lesson on pages 231–234 of their *Student Companion* or in Savvas Realize.

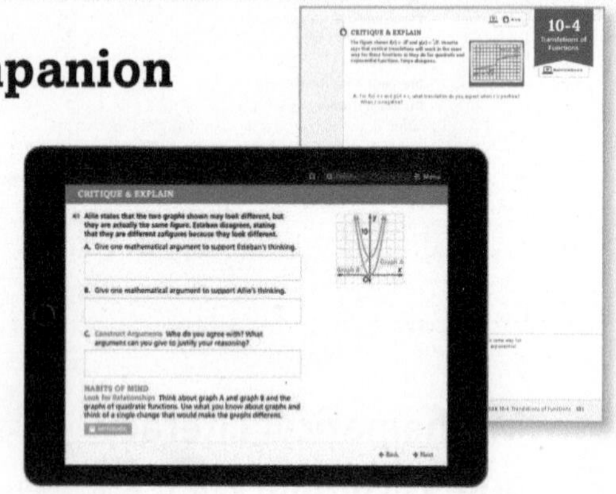

Mathematics Overview

COMMON CORE STANDARDS

Content Standards

In this lesson, students focus on this standard:

HSF.BF.B.3 Identify the effect on the graph of replacing $f(x)$ by $f(x) + k$, $kf(x)$, $f(kx)$, and $f(x + k)$ for specific values of k (both positive and negative); find the value of k given the graphs. Experiment with cases and illustrate an explanation of the effects on the graph using technology. Include recognizing even and odd functions from their graphs and algebraic expressions for them.

They also work with concepts related to these standards: **HSF.IF.B.4** and **HSF.IF.C.7.B**

Mathematical Practice Standards

These standards are highlighted in this lesson:

MP.1 Make Sense of Problems and Persevere in Solving Them

Students look for starting points when they consider what point to use as a reference point when translating the graph of a function.

MP.7 Look For and Make Use of Structure

Students look at the overall structure of a function in the form $f(x - h) + k$, and make the connection that if h is subtracted, the value of h is positive and shifts the graph right h units, and if h is added, the value of h is negative and shifts the graph left h units.

CRITIQUE & EXPLAIN

INSTRUCTIONAL FOCUS Students critique statements about the effect of vertical translations on the graphs of square root and cube root functions. This activity introduces students to the idea that adding a constant value to a function's output affects the graphs of all functions in the same way.

STUDENT COMPANION Students can complete the *Critique & Explain* activity on page 231 of their *Student Companion.*

Before WHOLE CLASS

Implement Tasks that Promote Reasoning and Problem Solving ETP

Q: What do you notice about the figure?
[The figure shows the graphs of $f(x) = \sqrt{x}$ and $g(x) = \sqrt[3]{x}$. The graphs of both functions pass through the points (0, 0) and (1, 1).]

During SMALL GROUP

Support Productive Struggle in Learning Mathematics ETP

Q: What happens to the output values of the functions after a constant is added?
[The new output values are equal to the old output values increased or decreased by the value of the constant.]

For Early Finishers

Q: For $f(x - c)$ and $g(x - c)$, what translation do you expect when c is positive? When c is negative?
[When c is positive, the functions are translated right c units. When c is negative, the functions are translated left $|c|$ units.]

After WHOLE CLASS

Facilitate Meaningful Mathematical Discourse ETP

Q: Does adding a constant value to the output change the shape of the graph of a function?
[No; adding the same constant value to each output value of a function shifts the graph of the function vertically, but the shape of the graph does not change.]

HABITS OF MIND

Use with **CRITIQUE & EXPLAIN**

Reason Do you think that horizontal translations will work in the same way for square root and cube root functions as they do for quadratic and exponential functions? Justify your answer. MP.2

[Yes; vertical translations work the same way, so it seems reasonable that horizontal translations would work the same way too. Tables of values could be created for $f(x - c)$ and $g(x - c)$ for different values of c to verify this.]

AVAILABLE **ONLINE**

Go back

CRITIQUE & EXPLAIN

The figure shows $f(x) = \sqrt{x}$ and $g(x) = \sqrt[3]{x}$. Venetta says that vertical translations will work in the same way for these functions as they do for quadratic and exponential functions. Tonya disagrees.

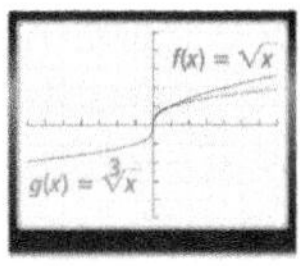
f(x) = √x
g(x) = ∛x

A. For $f(x) + c$ and $g(x) + c$, what translation do you expect when c is positive? When c is negative?

Enter your answer.

B. Generalize Which student is correct? Explain your answer.

Enter your answer.

1 of 1

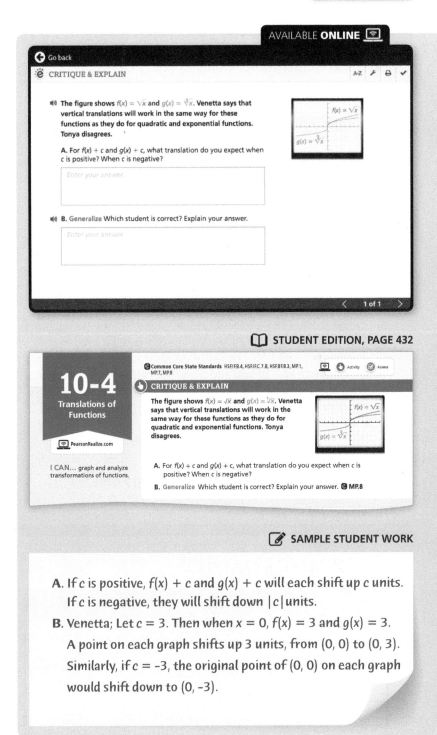

STUDENT EDITION, PAGE 432

10-4 Translations of Functions

PearsonRealize.com

I CAN… graph and analyze transformations of functions.

Common Core State Standards HSF.IF.B.4, HSF.IF.C.7.B, HSF.BF.B.3, MP.1, MP.7, MP.8

Activity Assess

CRITIQUE & EXPLAIN

The figure shows $f(x) = \sqrt{x}$ and $g(x) = \sqrt[3]{x}$. Venetta says that vertical translations will work in the same way for these functions as they do for quadratic and exponential functions. Tonya disagrees.

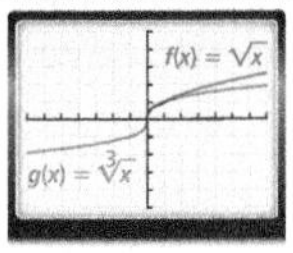
f(x) = √x
g(x) = ∛x

A. For $f(x) + c$ and $g(x) + c$, what translation do you expect when c is positive? When c is negative?

B. Generalize Which student is correct? Explain your answer. MP.8

SAMPLE STUDENT WORK

A. If c is positive, $f(x) + c$ and $g(x) + c$ will each shift up c units. If c is negative, they will shift down $|c|$ units.

B. Venetta; Let $c = 3$. Then when $x = 0$, $f(x) = 3$ and $g(x) = 3$. A point on each graph shifts up 3 units, from (0, 0) to (0, 3). Similarly, if $c = -3$, the original point of (0, 0) on each graph would shift down to (0, -3).

Activity Assess

INTRODUCE THE ESSENTIAL QUESTION

Establish Mathematics Goals to Focus Learning ETP

Introduce students to translations for all types of functions. Students learn that adding a constant k to the output of a function shifts the graph of the function vertically and subtracting a constant h from the input of a function shifts the graph of the function horizontally. Students apply a combination of translations when changes are made to both the input and the output of a function.

AVAILABLE ONLINE

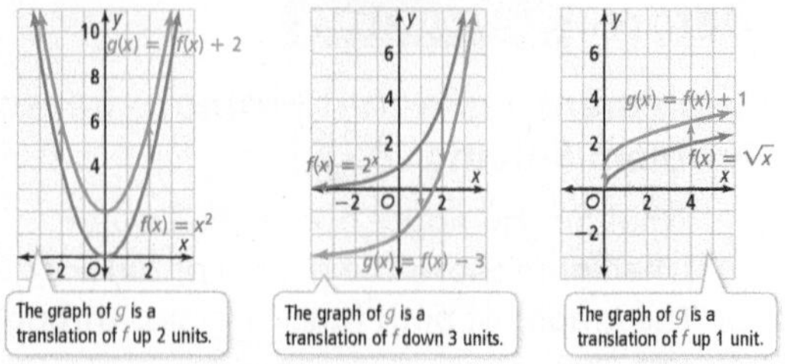

ESSENTIAL QUESTION Do horizontal and vertical translations work in the same way for all types of functions?

EXAMPLE 1 Vertical Translations

How does adding a constant value to the output change the graph of a function?

Consider how the value of the constant changes the graph of each function shown.

You can write this operation as $g(x) = f(x) + k$. This means that for a value of x, g takes the output of f and adds the constant k.

$g(x) = f(x) + 2$
$f(x) = x^2$
$f(x) = 2^x$
$g(x) = f(x) - 3$
$g(x) = f(x) + 1$
$f(x) = \sqrt{x}$

LOOK FOR RELATIONSHIPS Adding a negative constant k to a function decreases the function value by k, so it moves the graph down k units. MP.7

The graph of g is a translation of f up 2 units.

The graph of g is a translation of f down 3 units.

The graph of g is a translation of f up 1 unit.

Adding a positive constant translates the graph up, while adding a negative constant translates the graph down.

Try It! 1. For each function $g(x) = f(x) + k$, how does the value of k affect the graph of function f?

a. $g(x) = f(x) + 7$ b. $g(x) = f(x) - 9$

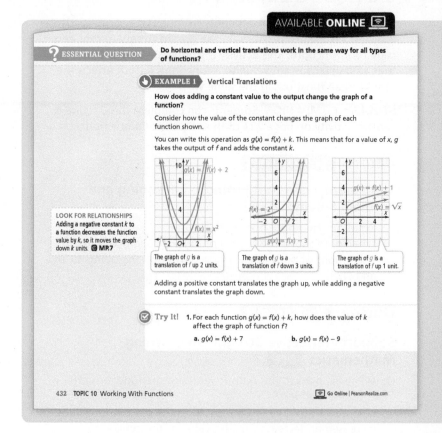

432 TOPIC 10 Working With Functions Go Online | PearsonRealize.com

EXAMPLE 1 Vertical Translations

Pose Purposeful Questions ETP

Q: Does the type of function you are translating vertically have an effect on the translation? [No, when translating a function vertically, all points move up or down the same distance, no matter what type of function you are translating.]

Q: Why does adding a positive constant to the output move the graph up and adding a negative constant to the output move the graph down? [If you add a positive constant, each output, or y-value, increases, so the graph moves up. If you add a negative constant, each output, or y-value, decreases, so the graph moves down.]

Try It! Answers

1. a. shift up 7 units b. shift down 9 units

AVAILABLE ONLINE

ADDITIONAL EXAMPLES

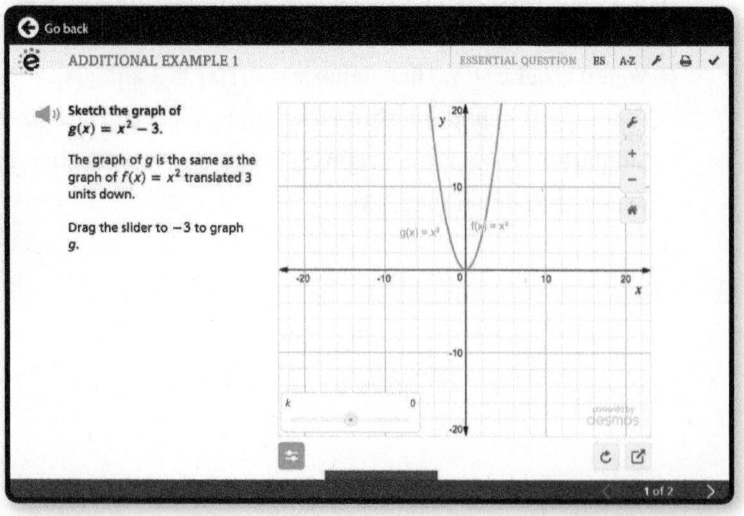

Go back
ADDITIONAL EXAMPLE 1
ESSENTIAL QUESTION ES A-Z
Sketch the graph of $g(x) = x^2 - 3$.
The graph of g is the same as the graph of $f(x) = x^2$ translated 3 units down.
Drag the slider to -3 to graph g.
$g(x) = x^2$
$f(x) = x^2$
desmos
1 of 2

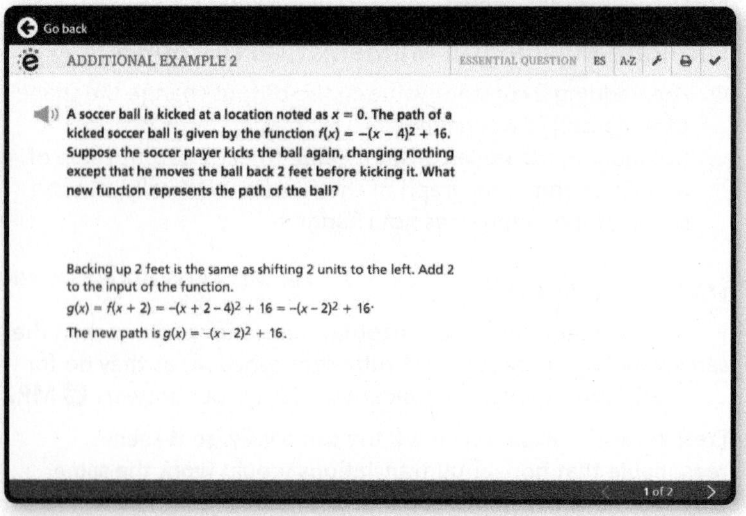

Go back
ADDITIONAL EXAMPLE 2
ESSENTIAL QUESTION ES A-Z
A soccer ball is kicked at a location noted as $x = 0$. The path of a kicked soccer ball is given by the function $f(x) = -(x - 4)^2 + 16$. Suppose the soccer player kicks the ball again, changing nothing except that he moves the ball back 2 feet before kicking it. What new function represents the path of the ball?
Backing up 2 feet is the same as shifting 2 units to the left. Add 2 to the input of the function.
$g(x) = f(x + 2) = -(x + 2 - 4)^2 + 16 = -(x - 2)^2 + 16$
The new path is $g(x) = -(x - 2)^2 + 16$.
1 of 2

Example 1 Students sketch the graph of a translation given the original function and number of units to shift the graph vertically.

Q: What does shifting the graph up or down tell you about k? [It tells you the sign of k. If the graph is shifted up, k is positive. If the graph is shifted down, k is negative.]

Example 2 Students solve real-life situations involving horizontal translations of functions.

Q: Does changing where the ball is kicked change the shape of the path of the ball? [No; the path that the ball travels is the same shape. The location where the ball lands also shifts the same distance that the starting point shifts.]

EXAMPLE 2 Analyze Horizontal Translations

Use and Connect Mathematical Representations ETP

Q: Does the type of function you are translating horizontally have an effect on the translation?
[No, when translating a function horizontally, all points move left or right the same distance, no matter what type of function you are translating.]

Q: How are horizontal translations represented in an equation differently than vertical translations?
[When performing a horizontal translation, you subtract a constant value from the input, and then evaluate the function. When performing a vertical translation, you evaluate the function, and then add a constant value to the output of the function.]

Explain why the expression $x + 3$ in the function $f(x + 3)$ shifts the graph of f horizontally in the negative direction rather than in the positive direction.
[You can think of $f(x + 3)$ as $f(x - (-3))$, which means that the constant is negative, and so the graph moves in the negative direction.]

Try It! Answers

2. a. shift right 8 units
   b. shift left 7 units

Common Error

Try It 2b Some students may state that the value of h is 7 and that the graph of g is a translation right 7 units. Have students rewrite the function in the form $g(x) = f(x - (-7))$ to see that the value of h is -7 and the translation is left 7 units.

HABITS OF MIND

Use with **EXAMPLES 1 & 2**

Communicate Precisely Why is it not necessary to know the function represented by f in Try It! problems 1 and 2? **MP.6**

[The transformation will affect the function in the same way regardless of what the function is.]

AVAILABLE **ONLINE**

Activity Assess

EXAMPLE 2 Analyze Horizontal Translations

How does subtracting a constant from the input change the graph of a function?

Consider how the value of the constant changes the graph of each function shown.

You can write this operation generally as $g(x) = f(x - h)$. This means that g takes the input of f and subtracts the constant h before applying function f.

To see what happens to the graph when you subtract a constant from the input, consider what inputs for g you would need to get the same output as f for a given input x.

For example, if $g(x) = f(x + 2)$, you would need an input x_1 that is 2 units *less* than x for $g(x_1) = f(x)$. So the graph of g is the graph of f shifted 2 units to the *left*.

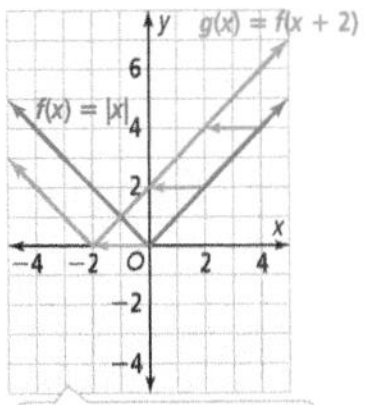
y
g(x) = f(x + 2)
f(x) = |x|
6
4
2
x
−4
−2
O
2
4
−2
−4

The graph of g is a translation of f left 2 units.

COMMON ERROR
The expression $x + 2$ in the function $f(x + 2)$ shifts the graph of $f(x)$ horizontally in the *negative* direction, not the positive direction. You can think of this as $f(x - (-2))$, so the constant is negative.

You can use the same reasoning to see how the graph changes for any function.

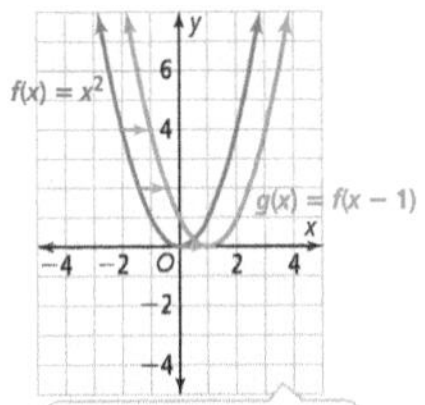
y
f(x) = x²
6
4
g(x) = f(x − 1)
x
−4
−2
O
2
4
−2
−4

The graph of g is a translation of f right 1 unit.

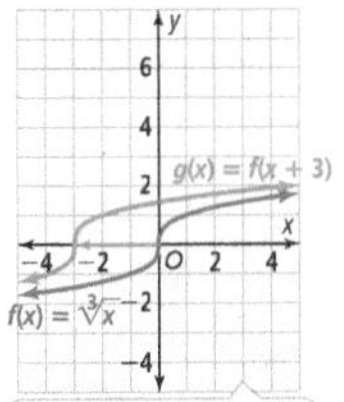
y
6
4
2
g(x) = f(x + 3)
x
−4
−2
O
2
4
f(x) = ∛x
−2
−4

The graph of g is a translation of f left 3 units.

Subtracting a positive constant from x translates the graph to the right, while subtracting a negative constant from x translates the graph to the left.

Try It! 2. For each function $g(x) = f(x - h)$, how does the value of h affect the graph of function f?

a. $g(x) = f(x - 8)$ b. $g(x) = f(x + 7)$

LESSON 10-4 Translations of Functions 433

Struggling Students

USE WITH EXAMPLE 2 Some students struggle with understanding horizontal translations. Have students practice by identifying the vertex of each horizontal translation of the graph of $f(x) = x^2$.

- **Identify the vertex of the function g. Tell how many units the vertex of the graph of g shifts and in what direction.**

1. $g(x) = f(x + 3)$
   [(−3, 0); left 3 units]
2. $g(x) = f(x - 6)$
   [(6, 0); right 6 units]
3. $g(x) = f(x + 1)$
   [(−1, 0); left 1 unit]

ADV Advanced Students

USE WITH EXAMPLE 3 Have students explore combining translations when the given function is $f(x) = x^2 + 2$.

- **Identify the the vertex of the function g. Explain.**

1. $g(x) = f(x - 4) + 3$
   [(4, 5); It is the vertex of f, (0, 2), shifted up 3 units and right 4 units.]
2. $g(x) = f(x + 1) + 6$
   [(−1, 8); It is the vertex of f, (0, 2), shifted up 6 units and left 1 unit.]
3. $g(x) = f(x + 4) - 2$
   [(−4, 0); It is the vertex of f, (0, 2), shifted down 2 units and left 4 units.]

EXAMPLE 3 Combine Translations

Build Procedural Fluency From Conceptual Understanding ETP

Q: When combining vertical and horizontal translations, does it matter in which order the translations occur?
[No; if you reverse the order and shift each graph down 1 unit first and then left 4 units, you would get the same result. The vertical and horizontal translations are independent of one another.]

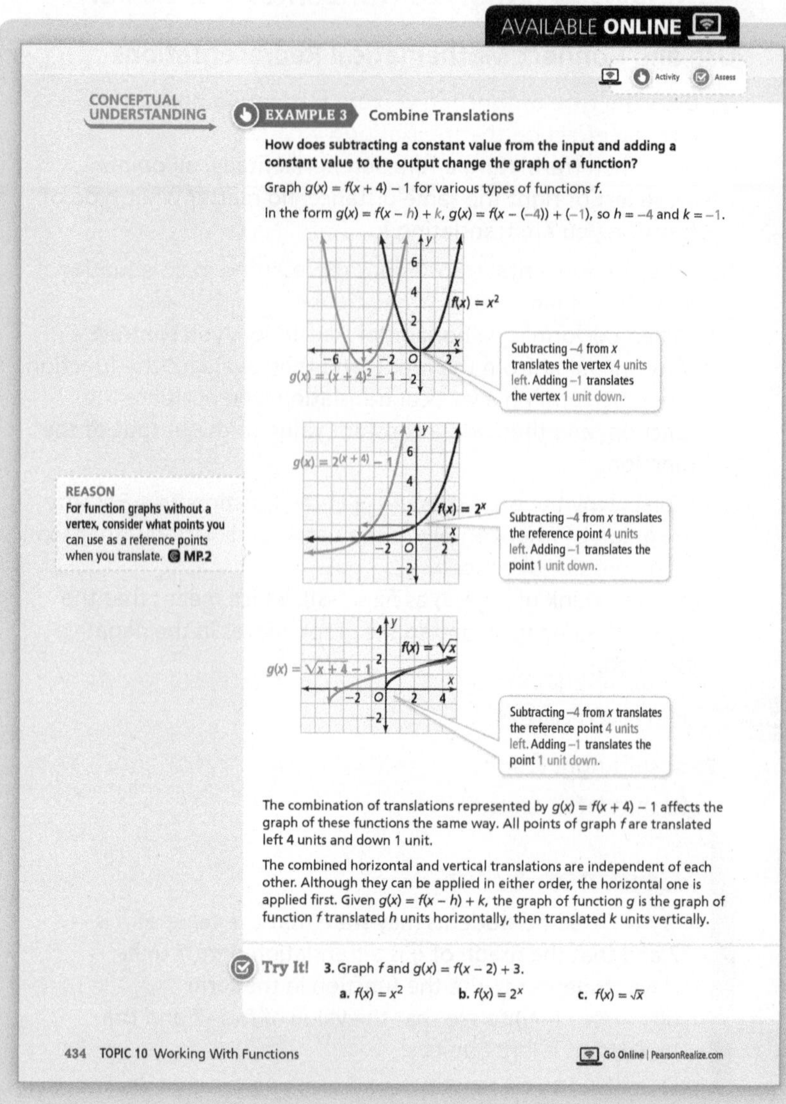

AVAILABLE **ONLINE**

Activity Assess

CONCEPTUAL UNDERSTANDING

EXAMPLE 3 Combine Translations

How does subtracting a constant value from the input and adding a constant value to the output change the graph of a function?

Graph $g(x) = f(x + 4) - 1$ for various types of functions f.

In the form $g(x) = f(x - h) + k$, $g(x) = f(x - (-4)) + (-1)$, so $h = -4$ and $k = -1$.

$f(x) = x^2$
$g(x) = (x + 4)^2 - 1$
Subtracting −4 from x translates the vertex 4 units left. Adding −1 translates the vertex 1 unit down.
$g(x) = 2^{(x+4)} - 1$
$f(x) = 2^x$
Subtracting −4 from x translates the reference point 4 units left. Adding −1 translates the point 1 unit down.
$f(x) = \sqrt{x}$
$g(x) = \sqrt{x + 4} - 1$
Subtracting −4 from x translates the reference point 4 units left. Adding −1 translates the point 1 unit down.

REASON
For function graphs without a vertex, consider what points you can use as a reference points when you translate. MP.2

The combination of translations represented by $g(x) = f(x + 4) - 1$ affects the graph of these functions the same way. All points of graph f are translated left 4 units and down 1 unit.

The combined horizontal and vertical translations are independent of each other. Although they can be applied in either order, the horizontal one is applied first. Given $g(x) = f(x - h) + k$, the graph of function g is the graph of function f translated h units horizontally, then translated k units vertically.

Try It! 3. Graph f and $g(x) = f(x - 2) + 3$.
a. $f(x) = x^2$ b. $f(x) = 2^x$ c. $f(x) = \sqrt{x}$

434 TOPIC 10 Working With Functions Go Online | PearsonRealize.com

Try It! Answers

3. a.

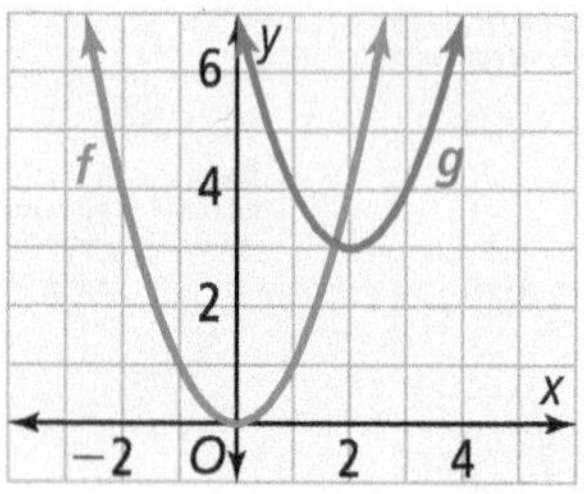

b.

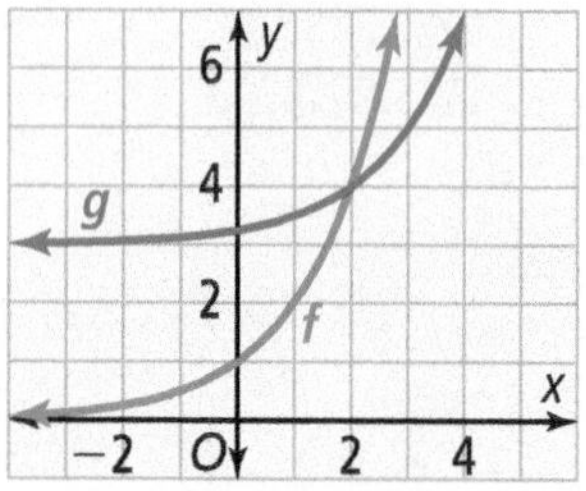

c.

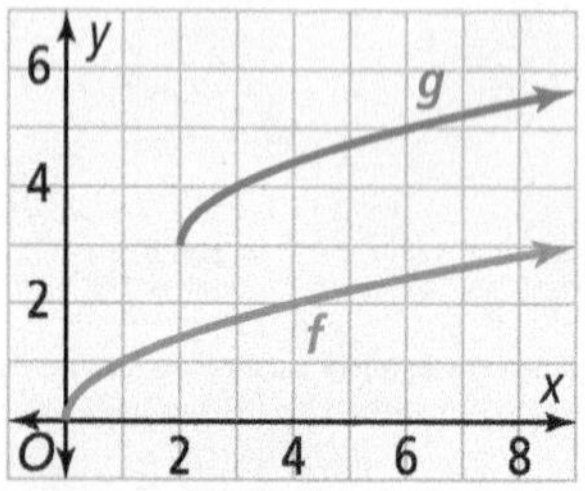

HABITS OF MIND

Use with **EXAMPLE 3**

Look for Relationships How do the domains and ranges of f and g compare when f is a quadratic, exponential, or square root function? MP.7

[For the quadratic and exponential functions, the domains of f and g are the same, but the range of g is shifted up. For the square root function, both the domain and the range of g are shifted.]

ELL English Language Learners (*Use with* EXAMPLE 3)

SPEAKING INTERMEDIATE Discuss with students the two definitions of *vertex*: (1) the intersection of two sides of a polygon, and (2) the highest or lowest point on a parabola. Then display several pictures with vertices highlighted. Ask students to respond with *one* or *two* to identify which definition applies.

Q: Name two types of functions whose graphs contain a vertex.
[quadratic and absolute value functions]

Q: Name some functions whose graphs do not contain a vertex.
[linear, cubic, exponential]

READING BEGINNING The words *affect* and *effect* are often confused. Display the definitions: *affect* (verb)—to act on or to produce a change in; *effect* (noun)—the result or consequence of an action. Ask students to read the given definitions and the following sentences and choose the word that best completes them.

Q: Cold weather _______ the crops. [affects]

Q: The mother's voice had an _______ on the baby's crying, as the baby calmed down immediately. [effect]

Q: The combined translation $f(x + 2) - 3$ _______ the graph of $f(x) = x^2$. [affects]

LISTENING BEGINNING People often give directions using a *reference point.* For example, to get to our school from the south, turn left at the green light and drive 3 more blocks. Challenge students to guess popular spots within your community by giving them verbal directions from a well-known reference point.

Q: What reference point do you use to graph (−2, 5) on a coordinate grid? [(0, 0)]

Q: How does using reference points help you to translate graphs?
[Identifying points and moving them all in the same way allows you to maintain the shape of the graph when you move it.]

CONCEPT SUMMARY Translations of Functions

Q: Why do the definitions of the translations use the absolute values of h and k?

[The signs of h and k determine the direction of the translation. The absolute values of h and k determine the number of units that the function is translated.]

AVAILABLE **ONLINE**

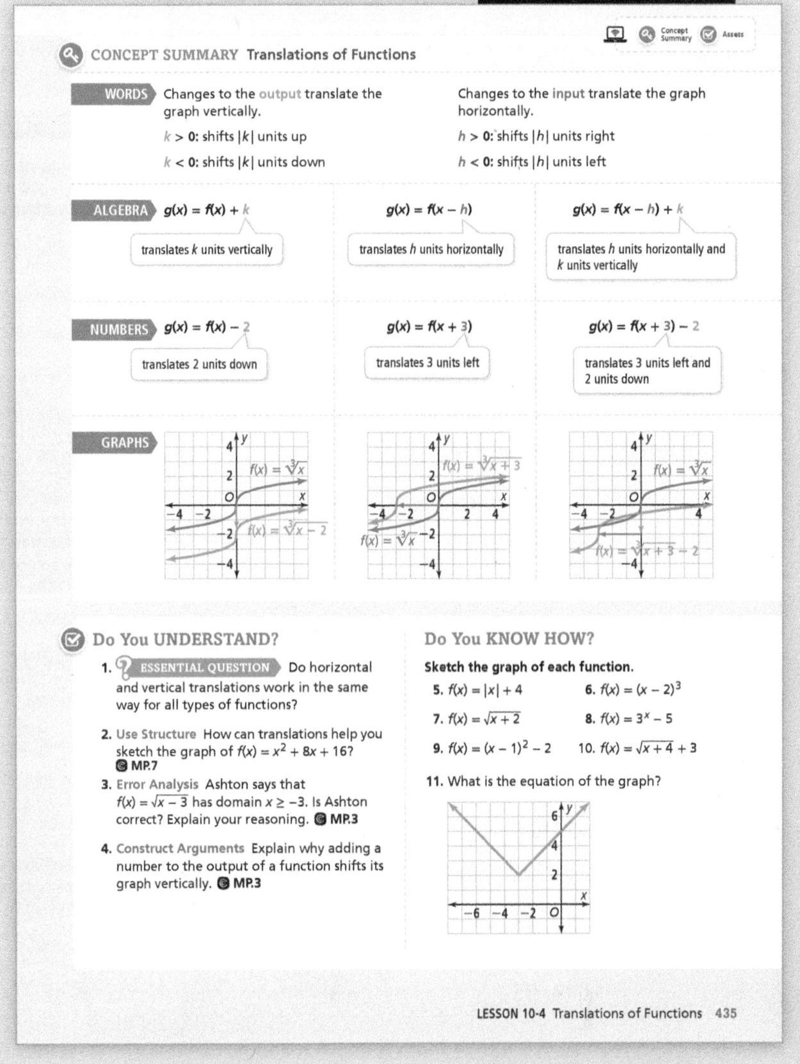

CONCEPT SUMMARY Translations of Functions

WORDS	Changes to the output translate the graph vertically. $k > 0$: shifts $\|k\|$ units up $k < 0$: shifts $\|k\|$ units down	Changes to the input translate the graph horizontally. $h > 0$: shifts $\|h\|$ units right $h < 0$: shifts $\|h\|$ units left	
ALGEBRA	$g(x) = f(x) + k$ translates k units vertically	$g(x) = f(x - h)$ translates h units horizontally	$g(x) = f(x - h) + k$ translates h units horizontally and k units vertically
NUMBERS	$g(x) = f(x) - 2$ translates 2 units down	$g(x) = f(x + 3)$ translates 3 units left	$g(x) = f(x + 3) - 2$ translates 3 units left and 2 units down
GRAPHS	$f(x) = \sqrt[3]{x}$, $f(x) = \sqrt[3]{x} - 2$	$f(x) = \sqrt[3]{x + 3}$, $f(x) = \sqrt[3]{x}$	$f(x) = \sqrt[3]{x}$, $f(x) = \sqrt[3]{x + 3} - 2$

Do You UNDERSTAND?

1. ESSENTIAL QUESTION Do horizontal and vertical translations work in the same way for all types of functions?
2. Use Structure How can translations help you sketch the graph of $f(x) = x^2 + 8x + 16$? MP.7
3. Error Analysis Ashton says that $f(x) = \sqrt{x - 3}$ has domain $x \geq -3$. Is Ashton correct? Explain your reasoning. MP.3
4. Construct Arguments Explain why adding a number to the output of a function shifts its graph vertically. MP.3

Do You KNOW HOW?

Sketch the graph of each function.

5. $f(x) = |x| + 4$
6. $f(x) = (x - 2)^3$
7. $f(x) = \sqrt{x + 2}$
8. $f(x) = 3^x - 5$
9. $f(x) = (x - 1)^2 - 2$
10. $f(x) = \sqrt{x + 4} + 3$
11. What is the equation of the graph?

LESSON 10-4 Translations of Functions 435

Do You UNDERSTAND? | Do You KNOW HOW?

Common Error

Exercise 11 Some students may write the equation of the graph as $y = |x - 3| + 2$. Have students identify the values of h and k and then substitute those values into the form $g(x) = f(x - h) + k$ and simplify.

Answers

1. Yes; subtracting h from the function input shifts the graph of the function horizontally h units. Adding k to the function output shifts the graph of the function vertically k units.
2. Rewrite the function as $y = (x + 4)^2$. Shift the graph of the function $y = x^2$ to the left 4 units.
3. Ashton is not correct. $y = \sqrt{x}$ has domain $0 \leq x < \infty$. The graph of $y = \sqrt{x - 3}$ is graph of $y = \sqrt{x}$ shifted right 3 units, so the new domain is $3 \leq x < \infty$.
4. The output is the result after the function has been evaluated. Adding a number to the output only changes the y-value, shifting the graph of the function vertically.

5.

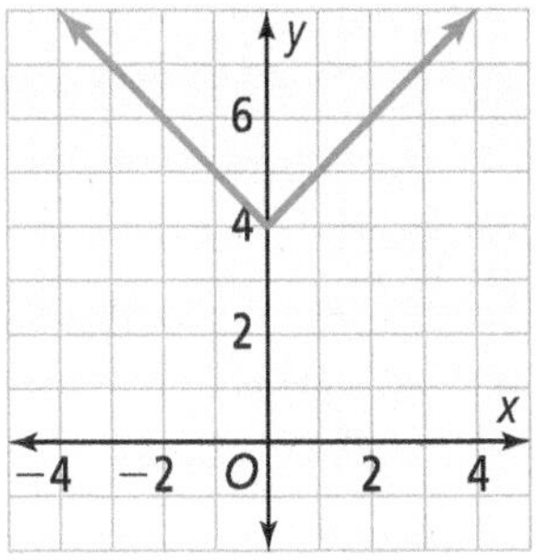

6.

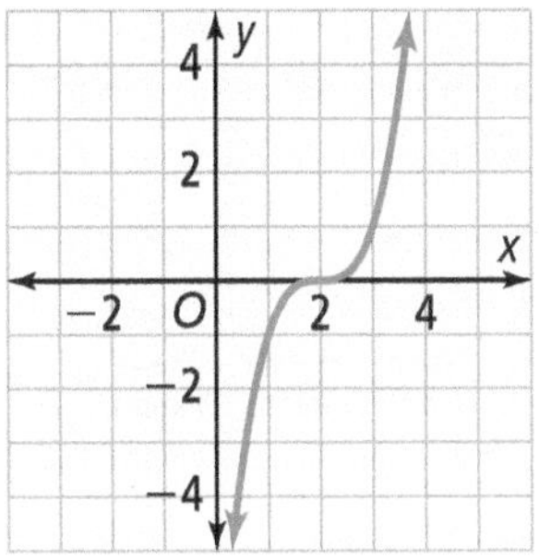

7.

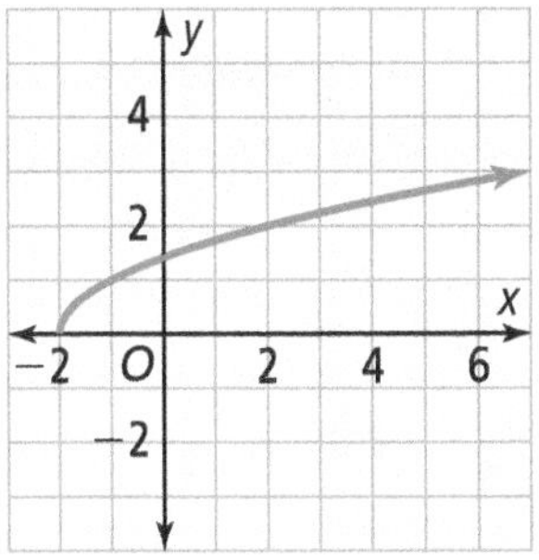

8.

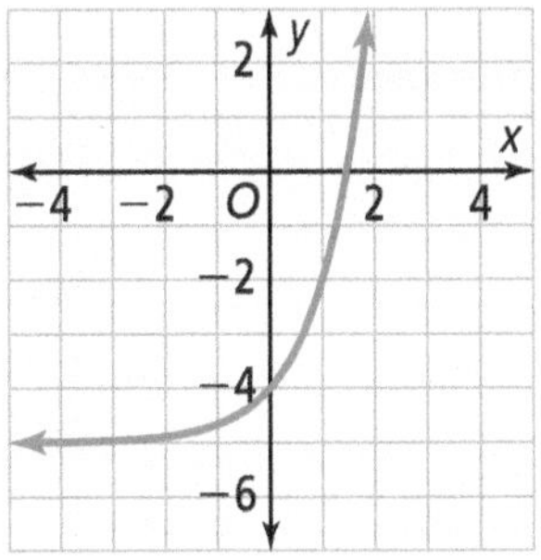

9.

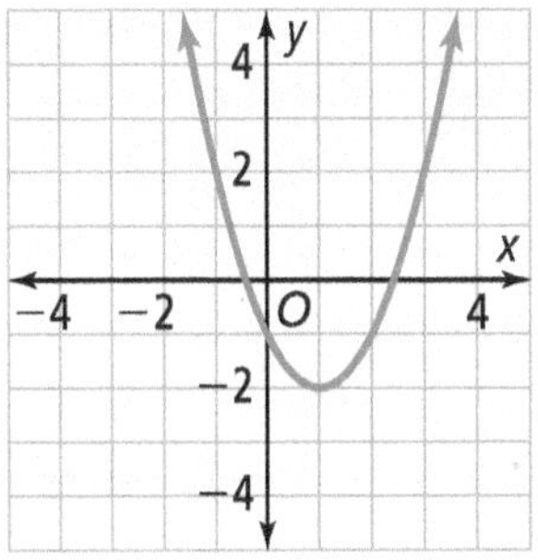

10.

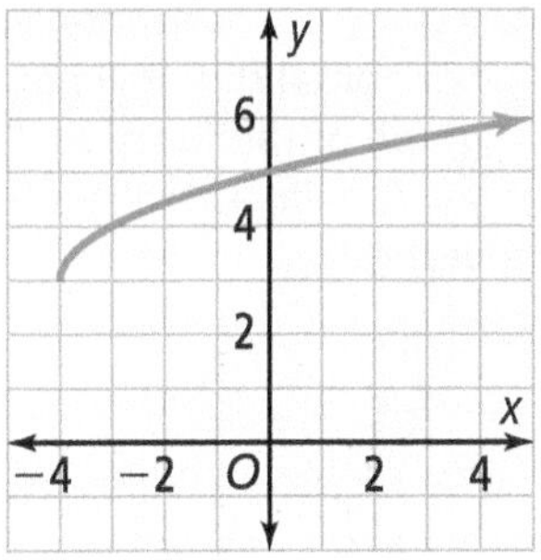

11. $y = |x + 3| + 2$

Practice | Tutorials | Math Tools

PRACTICE & PROBLEM SOLVING

AVAILABLE **ONLINE**

Lesson Practice You may opt to have students complete the automatically scored Practice and Problem Solving items online powered by MathXL for School.

Choose from: **Lesson Practice**

Adaptive Practice

You may also take advantage of the bank of exercises for assigning additional practice.

Assignment Guide

Basic	Advanced
12–27, 30–35	12–15, 18–35

Item Analysis

Example	Items	DOK
1	17–20	1
	32	2
2	21–28	1
	31	2
3	12, 13, 15, 16, 29, 30, 33, 34	2
	14, 35	3

Answers

12. $f(x) = 5$ is a horizontal line, so the horizontal shift will not change the graph of the function. For this function, $y = f(x - h) + k$ shifts the line $y = 5$ vertically k units.

13.

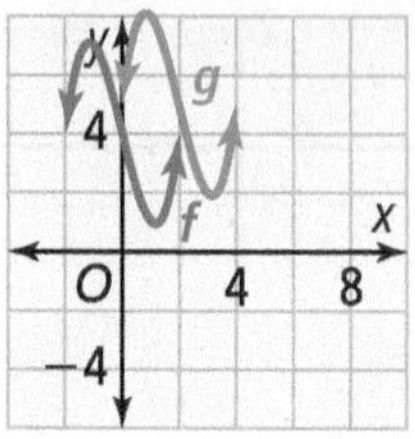

g
f
4
x
O
4
8
−4

14. Victor is not correct. He cannot remove −2 from the absolute value input.

15. If the graph is shifted the same integer number of units either up and right or down and left, the graph will appear unchanged. The new function is $f(x) = |x - a| + a$, where a is an integer.

AVAILABLE **ONLINE**

PRACTICE & PROBLEM SOLVING

Scan for Multimedia | Practice | Tutorial | Additional Exercises Available Online

UNDERSTAND

12. Reason How does the graph of $f(x) = 5$ change for $g(x) = f(x - h) + k$, where h and k are constants? MP.2

13. Use Structure The graph of $g(x) = f(x - 2) + 1$ is shown. Sketch the graph of f. MP.7

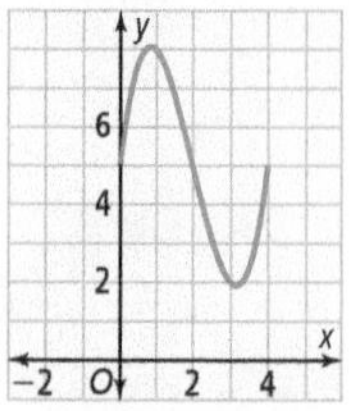

y
6
4
2
x
−2
O
2
4

14. Error Analysis Victor is asked to explain how the graph of $g(x) = |x - 2| + 2$ relates to the graph of $f(x) = |x|$. His work is shown below. Is Victor correct? Explain why or why not. MP.3

$f(x) = |x - 2| + 2$
$= |x| + (-2 + 2)$
$= |x|$
Graph of $f(x) = |x - 2| + 2$ is the same as the graph of $f(x) = |x|$, with vertex at (0, 0).

15. Use Structure Describe a combination of translations to apply to the floor function, $f(x) = \lfloor x \rfloor$, that leaves its graph appearing unchanged. Write the new equation. MP.7

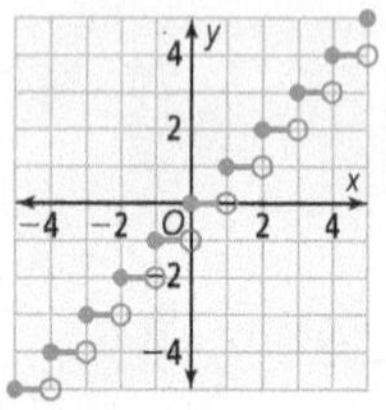

y
4
2
x
−4
−2
O
2
4
−2
−4

16. Higher Order Thinking Given $g(x) = f(x - 2) + 4$ and $j(x) = g(x + 5) - 3$, find the values of h and k in the equation $j(x) = f(x - h) + k$.

PRACTICE

Sketch the graph of each function.
SEE EXAMPLES 1 AND 2

17. $g(x) = |x| + 6$

18. $g(x) = x^2 - 3$

19. $g(x) = \frac{1}{3}x + 2$

20. $g(x) = \sqrt{x} - 8$

21. $g(x) = (x - 2)^2$

22. $g(x) = |x + 4|$

23. $g(x) = \sqrt{x + 3}$

24. $g(x) = \sqrt[3]{x - 5}$

Each graph is a translation of the given function. Write the function for the graph. SEE EXAMPLE 2

25. $f(x) = x^2$ $y = (x - 1)^2$

26. $f(x) = \sqrt[3]{x}$ $y = \sqrt[3]{x + 6}$

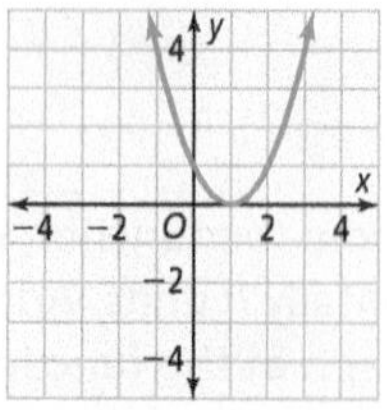

y
4
x
−4
−2
O
2
4
−2
−4

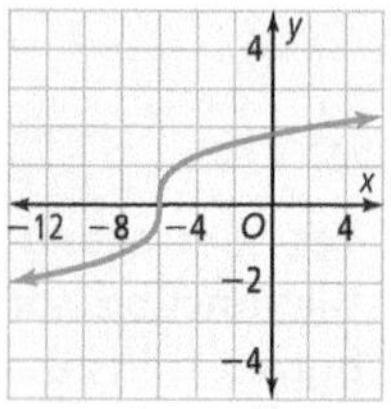

y
4
x
−12
−8
−4
O
4
−2
−4

27. $f(x) = |x|$ $y = |x + 10|$

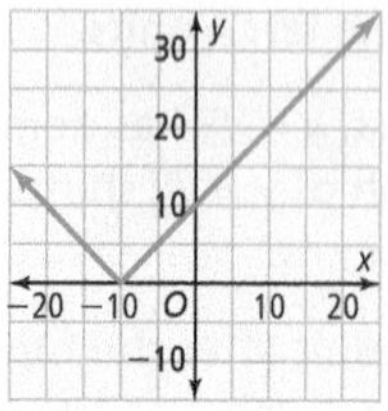

y
30
20
10
x
−20
−10
O
10
20
−10

28. $f(x) = \sqrt{x}$ $y = \sqrt{x - 5}$

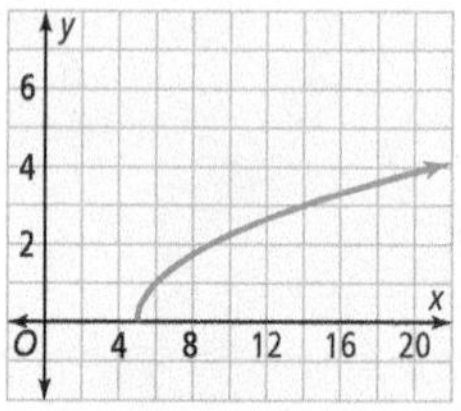

y
6
4
2
x
O
4
8
12
16
20

Sketch the graph of each function. SEE EXAMPLE 3

29. $g(x) = 2^{x+4} - 7$

30. $g(x) = |x + 4.3| - 2.7$

Go Online | PearsonRealize.com

16. $h = -3$, $k = 1$

17.

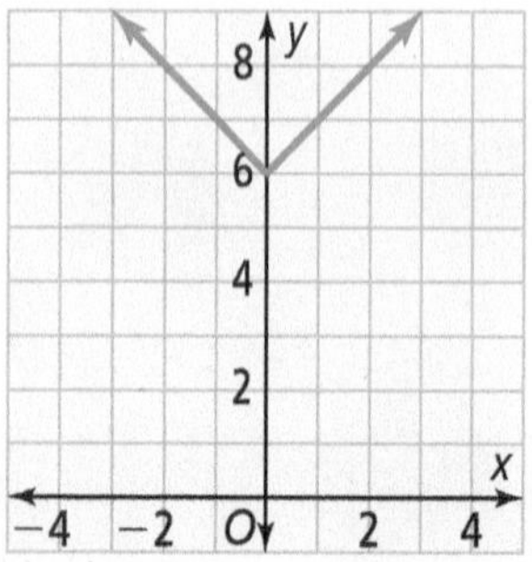

y
8
6
4
2
x
−4
−2
O
2
4

See answers for Exercises 18–24 on next page.

29–30. See back of book.

Answers

18.

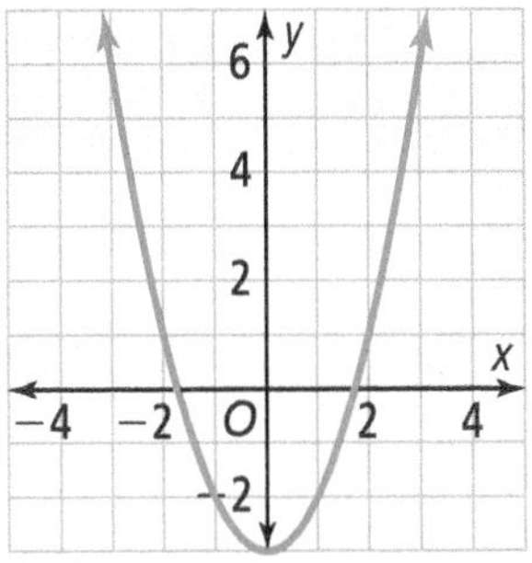

19.

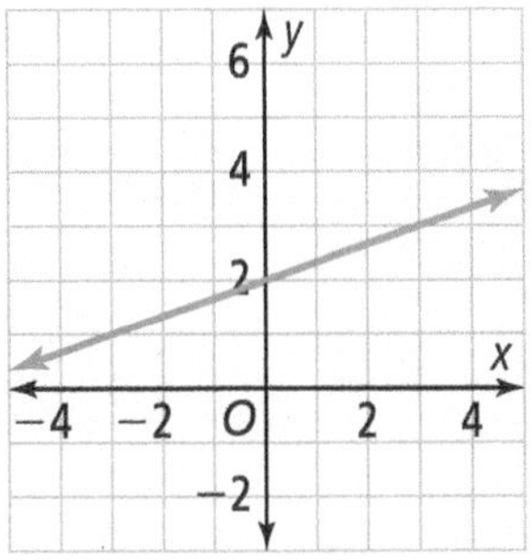

20.

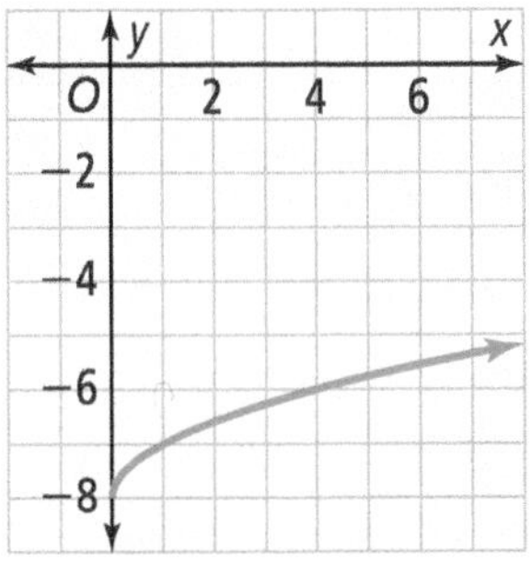

21.

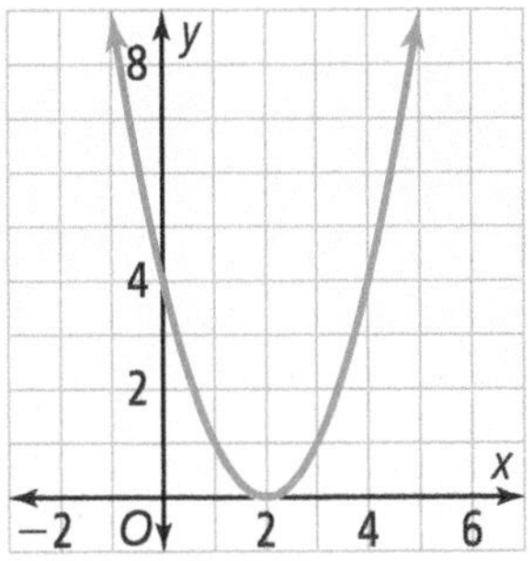

22.

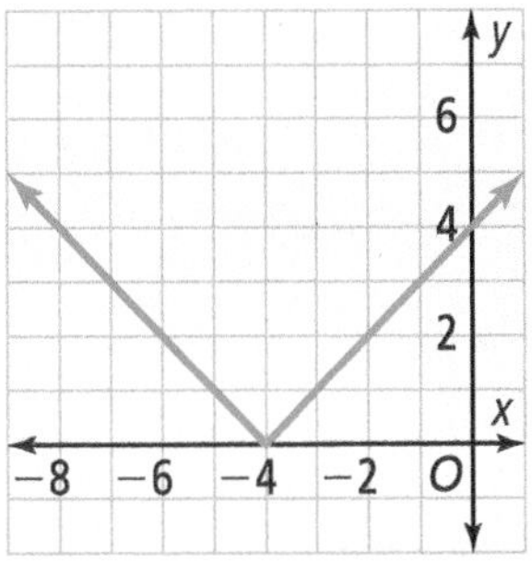

23.

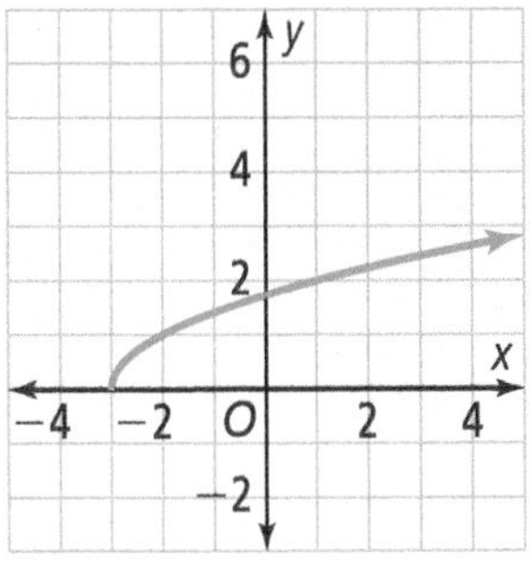

AVAILABLE **ONLINE**

PRACTICE & PROBLEM SOLVING

Practice Tutorial
Mixed Review Available Online

APPLY

31. Make Sense and Persevere The height, h, in meters of a Saturn V rocket t seconds after launch is modeled by the graph shown. Note that the graph is not the actual path of the rocket. A launch is delayed by 60 seconds by a technical problem. Describe the effect on $h(t)$ as a translation. Sketch the graph of the height of the rocket t seconds from the original launch time. **MP.1**

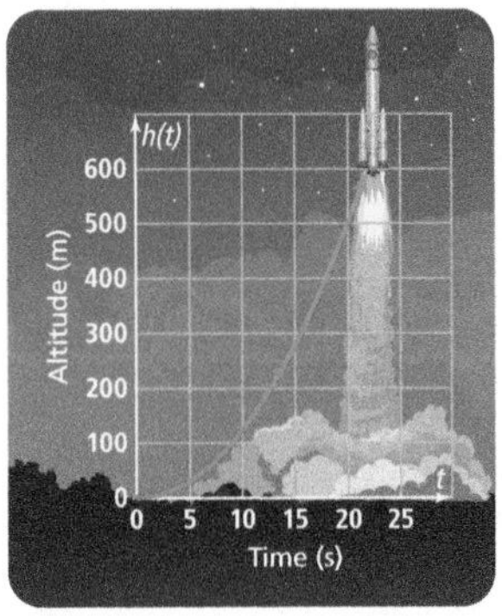
h(t)
Altitude (m)
600
500
400
300
200
100
0
0 5 10 15 20 25
t
Time (s)

32. Mathematical Connections The costs for a new publishing company can be classified as fixed costs, such as rent and insurance, or variable costs, such as materials and labor. Fixed costs are constant, while variable costs change as the number of items produced changes. The graph shows the weekly variable costs based on the number of books produced.

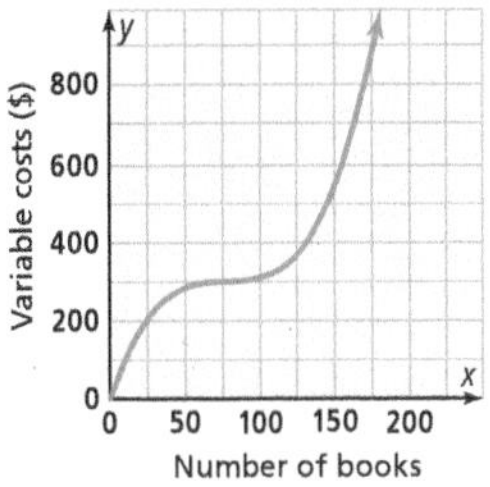
y
Variable costs ($)
800
600
400
200
0
0 50 100 150 200
x
Number of books

a. If weekly fixed costs are $300, sketch a graph showing total expenses for the week.

b. Find the total cost of producing 75 books in a week.

ASSESSMENT PRACTICE

33. Which is true about the graph of the function $f(x) = (x - 2)^2 - 3$? Select all that apply.

Ⓐ It is a parabola that opens upward.
Ⓑ It is a parabola that opens downward.
Ⓒ The vertex is (2, −3).
Ⓓ The vertex is (−2, −3).
Ⓔ The vertex is (2, 3).

34. SAT/ACT How is the function $f(x) = \sqrt{x}$ translated to obtain the graph of $g(x) = \sqrt{x + 5} + 6$?

Ⓐ Shift $f(x) = \sqrt{x}$ up 5 units and right 6 units.
Ⓑ Shift $f(x) = \sqrt{x}$ right 5 units and down 6 units.
Ⓒ Shift $f(x) = \sqrt{x}$ left 5 units and up 6 units.
Ⓓ Shift $f(x) = \sqrt{x}$ left 5 units and down 6 units.
Ⓔ Shift $f(x) = \sqrt{x}$ down 5 units and left 6 units.

35. Performance Task In a computer football game, you are attempting to kick a field goal. Every kick in the game can be modeled by a horizontal translation of the function shown. Assume the translations are to the nearest tenth of a yard. The goal post is 10 yards behind the goal line.

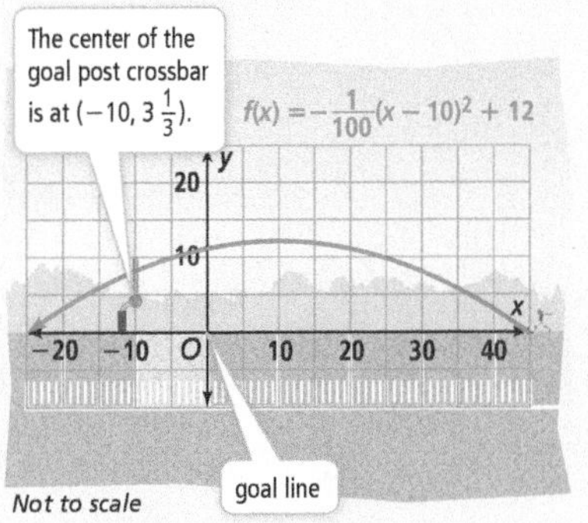
The center of the goal post crossbar is at $(-10, 3\frac{1}{3})$.
$f(x) = -\frac{1}{100}(x - 10)^2 + 12$
y
20
10
x
−20 −10 O 10 20 30 40
Not to scale
goal line

Part A How far from the goal line is the football placed in the figure shown? 44.6 yards

Part B What is the maximum distance from the goal line the football can be placed for the kick to clear the crossbar? 54.0 yards

Part C Write the function for the kick in Part B.
$g(x) = -\frac{1}{100}(x - 19.4)^2 + 12$

24.

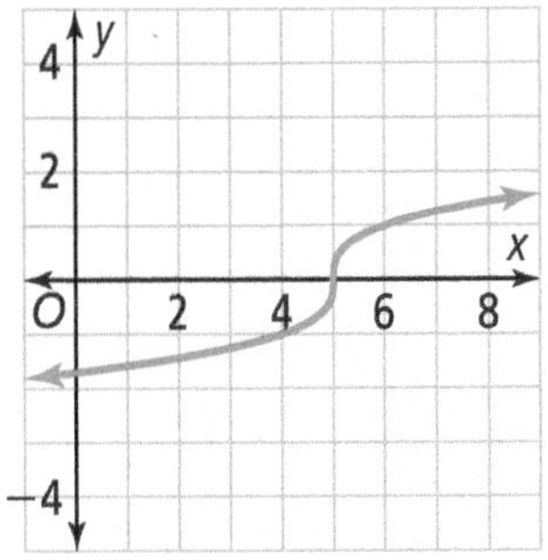

31. The delay represents a translation 60 units right.

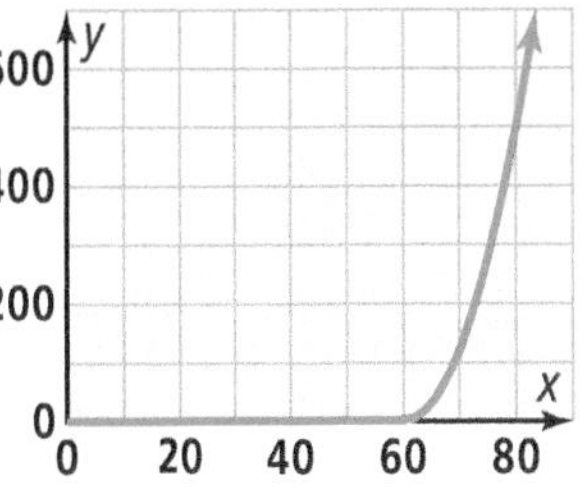

32. a.

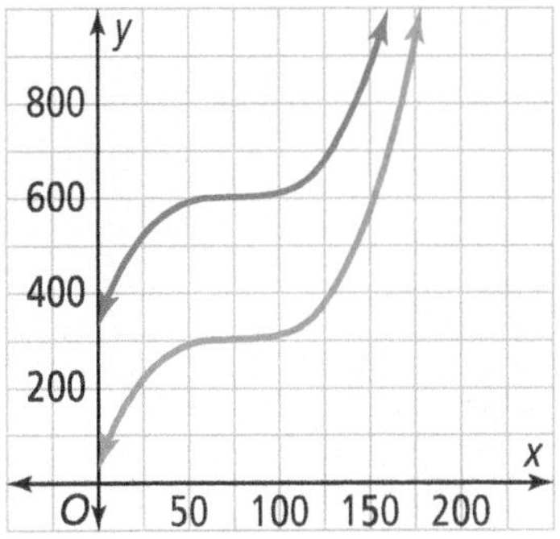

b. $600

LESSON QUIZ

Use the Lesson Quiz to assess students' understanding of the mathematics in the lesson.

Students can take the Lesson Quiz online or you can download a printable copy from **SavvasRealize.com**. The Lesson Quiz is also available in the *Assessment Resources* book.

Item Analysis

Item	DOK	Standards
1	2	HSF.IF.B.4
2	1	HSF.IF.B.4, HSF.BF.B.3
3	2	HSF.IF.B.5
4	1	HSF.IF.C.7.B
5	2	HSF.IF.B.4

RtI Use the student scores on the Lesson Quiz to prescribe differentiated assignments.

If students take the Lesson Quiz online, it will be automatically scored and appropriate differentiated practice will be assigned based on student performance.

I Intervention	0–3 points	• Reteach to Build Understanding • Mathematical Literacy and Vocabulary • Additional Practice
O On-Level	4 points	• Mathematical Literacy and Vocabulary • Additional Practice • Enrichment
A Advanced	5 points	• Enrichment

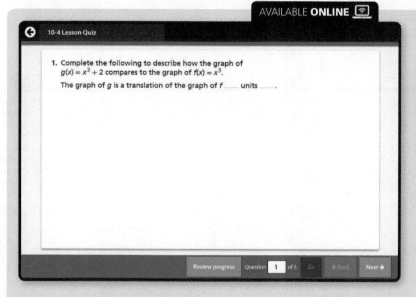

AVAILABLE **ONLINE**

10-4 Lesson Quiz

1. Complete the following to describe how the graph of $g(x) = x^3 + 2$ compares to the graph of $f(x) = x^3$.
The graph of g is a translation of the graph of f ___ units ___.

Review progress Question 1 of 5 Go ← Back Next →

ASSESSMENT RESOURCES

Name ______________

enVision Algebra 1
PearsonRealize.com

10-4 Lesson Quiz

Translations of Functions

1. Complete the following to describe how the graph of $g(x) = x^3 + 2$ compares to the graph of $f(x) = x^3$.
The graph of g is a translation of the graph of f 2 units up.

2. Which function has a graph that is a translation 4 units up and 6 units left of the graph of $f(x) = \sqrt{x}$?
Ⓐ $g(x) = \sqrt{x - 4} + 6$
Ⓑ $g(x) = \sqrt{x + 4} + 6$
Ⓒ $g(x) = \sqrt{x - 6} + 4$
Ⓓ $g(x) = \sqrt{x + 6} + 4$

3. The graph of g is a translation 2 units up of the graph of $f(x) = x^2 + 1$. What is the range of g?
Ⓐ all real numbers Ⓑ $f(x) \geq 1$ Ⓒ $f(x) \geq 2$ Ⓓ $f(x) \geq 3$

4. Graph $f(x) = (x - 1)^2 - 3$.

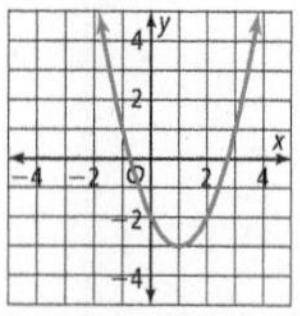

y
4
2
x
−4
−2
O
2
4
−2
−4

5. The graph of function g is a translation 2 units left of the graph of $f(x) = 2|x|$. Which statement(s) about the functions are true? Select all that apply.
Ⓐ The y-intercept of g is 4 greater than the y-intercept of f.
Ⓑ The x-intercept of g is 2 less than the y-intercept of f.
Ⓒ The graphs do not intersect.
Ⓓ An equation for g is $g(x) = 2|x + 2|$.
Ⓔ An equation for g is $g(x) = 2|x - 2|$.
Ⓕ An equation for g is $g(x) = 2|x| + 2$.

enVision™ Algebra 1 • Assessment Resources

SavvasRealize.com

Assess Tutorials Worksheets

DIFFERENTIATED RESOURCES

I = Intervention O = On-Level A = Advanced

= This activity is available as a digital assignment powered by MathXL® for School.

AVAILABLE ONLINE

Reteach to Build Understanding I

Provides scaffolded reteaching for the key lesson concepts.

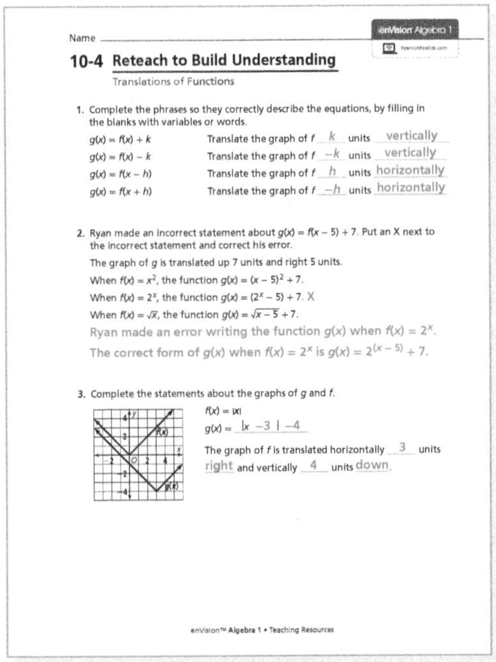

Name

10-4 Reteach to Build Understanding

Translations of Functions

1. Complete the phrases so they correctly describe the equations, by filling in the blanks with variables or words.

$g(x) = f(x) + k$ Translate the graph of f k units vertically

$g(x) = f(x) - k$ Translate the graph of f $-k$ units vertically

$g(x) = f(x - h)$ Translate the graph of f h units horizontally

$g(x) = f(x + h)$ Translate the graph of f $-h$ units horizontally

2. Ryan made an incorrect statement about $g(x) = f(x - 5) + 7$. Put an X next to the incorrect statement and correct his error.

The graph of g is translated up 7 units and right 5 units.

When $f(x) = x^2$, the function $g(x) = (x - 5)^2 + 7$.

When $f(x) = 2^x$, the function $g(x) = (2^x - 5) + 7$. X

When $f(x) = \sqrt{x}$, the function $g(x) = \sqrt{x - 5} + 7$.

Ryan made an error writing the function $g(x)$ when $f(x) = 2^x$. The correct form of $g(x)$ when $f(x) = 2^x$ is $g(x) = 2^{(x - 5)} + 7$.

3. Complete the statements about the graphs of g and f.

$f(x) = |x|$

$g(x) = |x - 3| - 4$

The graph of f is translated horizontally 3 units right and vertically 4 units down.

enVision™ Algebra 1 • Teaching Resources

Additional Practice I O

Provides extra practice for each lesson.

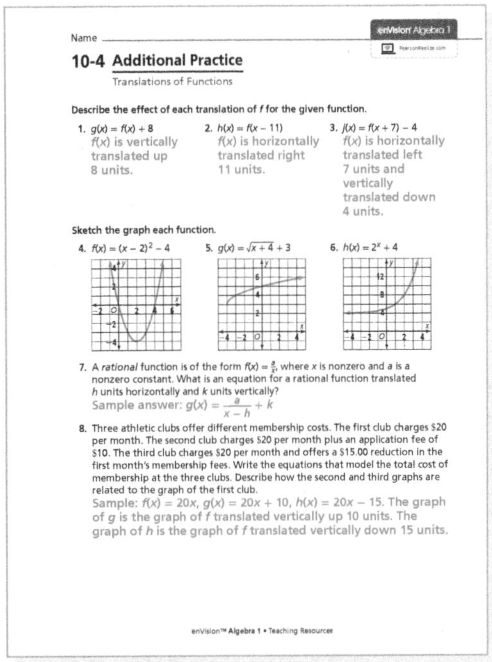

Name

10-4 Additional Practice

Translations of Functions

Describe the effect of each translation of f for the given function.

1. $g(x) = f(x) + 8$ $f(x)$ is vertically translated up 8 units.

2. $h(x) = f(x - 11)$ $f(x)$ is horizontally translated right 11 units.

3. $j(x) = f(x + 7) - 4$ $f(x)$ is horizontally translated left 7 units and vertically translated down 4 units.

Sketch the graph each function.

4. $f(x) = (x - 2)^2 - 4$

5. $g(x) = \sqrt{x + 4} + 3$

6. $h(x) = 2^x + 4$

7. A *rational* function is of the form $f(x) = \frac{a}{x}$, where x is nonzero and a is a nonzero constant. What is an equation for a rational function translated h units horizontally and k units vertically?

Sample answer: $g(x) = \frac{a}{x - h} + k$

8. Three athletic clubs offer different membership costs. The first club charges $20 per month. The second club charges $20 per month plus an application fee of $10. The third club charges $20 per month and offers a $15.00 reduction in the first month's membership fees. Write the equations that model the total cost of membership at the three clubs. Describe how the second and third graphs are related to the graph of the first club.

Sample: $f(x) = 20x$, $g(x) = 20x + 10$, $h(x) = 20x - 15$. The graph of g is the graph of f translated vertically up 10 units. The graph of h is the graph of f translated vertically down 15 units.

enVision™ Algebra 1 • Teaching Resources

Enrichment O A

Presents engaging problems and activities that extend the lesson concepts.

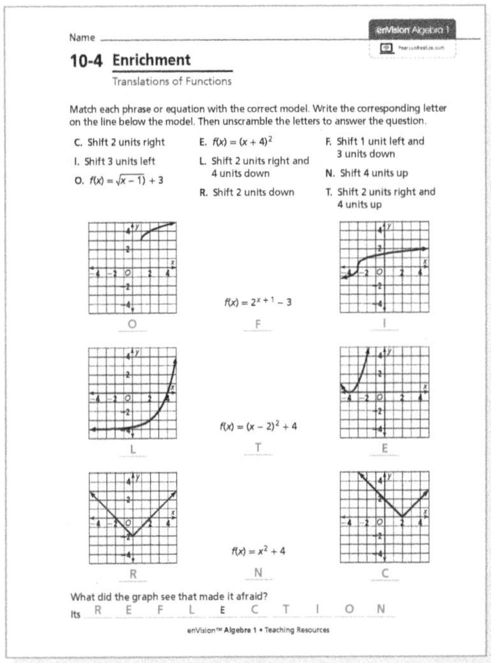

Name

10-4 Enrichment

Translations of Functions

Match each phrase or equation with the correct model. Write the corresponding letter on the line below the model. Then unscramble the letters to answer the question.

C. Shift 2 units right

I. Shift 3 units left

O. $f(x) = \sqrt{x - 1} + 3$

E. $f(x) = (x + 4)^2$

L. Shift 2 units right and 4 units down

R. Shift 2 units down

F. Shift 1 unit left and 3 units down

N. Shift 4 units up

T. Shift 2 units right and 4 units up

O $f(x) = 2^{x+1} - 3$ F I

L $f(x) = (x - 2)^2 + 4$ T E

R $f(x) = x^2 + 4$ N C

What did the graph see that made it afraid?

Its R E F L E C T I O N

enVision™ Algebra 1 • Teaching Resources

Mathematical Literacy and Vocabulary I O

Helps students develop and reinforce understanding of key terms and concepts.

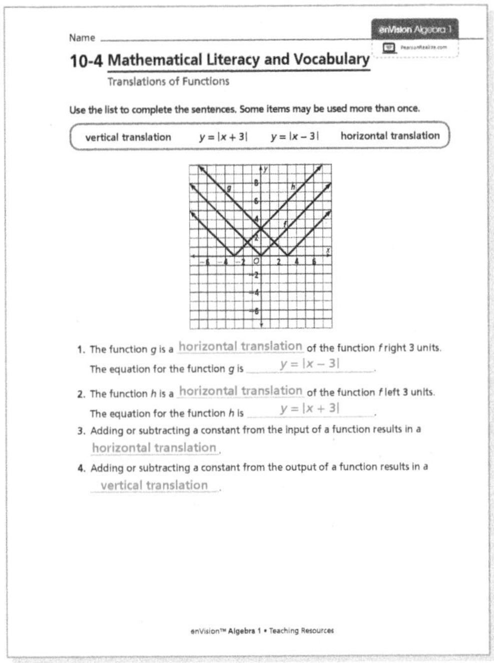

Name

10-4 Mathematical Literacy and Vocabulary

Translations of Functions

Use the list to complete the sentences. Some items may be used more than once.

vertical translation $y = |x + 3|$ $y = |x - 3|$ horizontal translation

1. The function g is a horizontal translation of the function f right 3 units. The equation for the function g is $y = |x - 3|$.

2. The function h is a horizontal translation of the function f left 3 units. The equation for the function h is $y = |x + 3|$.

3. Adding or subtracting a constant from the input of a function results in a horizontal translation.

4. Adding or subtracting a constant from the output of a function results in a vertical translation.

enVision™ Algebra 1 • Teaching Resources

Digital Resources and Video Tutorials I O A

The **Reteach to Build Understanding, Additional Practice**, and **Enrichment** activities are available as digital assignments powered by MathXL for School. These activities are automatically assigned when students complete the lesson quiz online and are automatically scored.

Students can access instructional tutorials using the **Virtual Nerd app**.

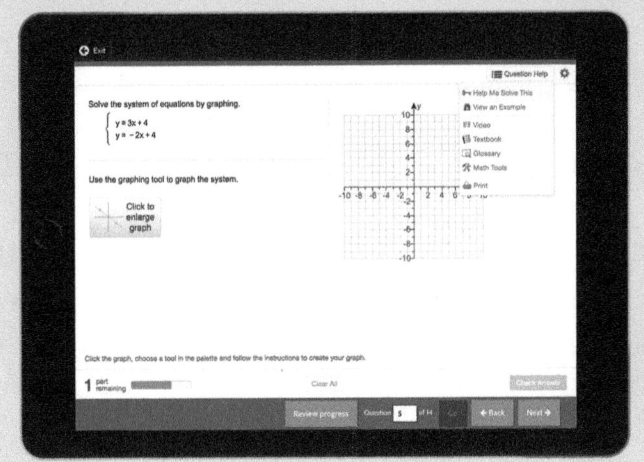
Exit
Question Help
Solve the system of equations by graphing.
y = 3x + 4
y = −2x + 4
Use the graphing tool to graph the system.
Click to enlarge graph
Help Me Solve This
View an Example
Video
Textbook
Glossary
Math Tools
Print
Click the graph, choose a tool in the palette and follow the instructions to create your graph.
Clear All
Check Answer
Review progress
Back
Next

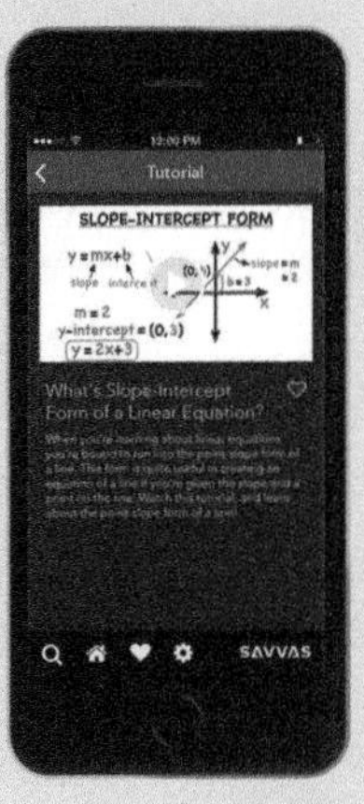
Tutorial
SLOPE-INTERCEPT FORM
What's Slope-Intercept Form of a Linear Equation?
SAVVAS

Students can also access Virtual Nerd videos using the **BouncePages app** to scan exercise pages marked with this icon. Students can download both apps for free in their mobile devices' app store.

Lesson Overview

FOCUS

Objective

Students will be able to:

✔ Identify the effect on the graph of a function of multiplying the output by −1.

✔ Identify the effect on the graph of a function of replacing $f(x)$ by $kf(x)$ or by $f(kx)$ for specific values of k.

Essential Understanding

The graphs of functions are transformed when the input and output are multiplied by varying factors of k. Multiplying the output by a factor of k stretches or compresses the graph vertically. Multiplying the input by a factor of k stretches or compresses the graph horizontally.

COHERENCE

Previously in this topic, students:

- Graphed and analyzed horizontal and vertical translations of absolute value, exponential, quadratic, and square root functions.

In this lesson, students:

- Graph and analyze vertical and horizontal stretches and compressions of absolute value, exponential, quadratic, and square root functions.

Later in this topic, students will:

- Add, subtract, and multiply functions and graph the results.

RIGOR

This lesson emphasizes a blend of *conceptual understanding* and *procedural skill and fluency.*

- Students understand that multiplying the output of a function by a factor of k stretches or compresses a graph vertically, and multiplying the input of a function by a factor of k stretches or compresses a graph horizontally.
- Students reflect the graph of a function across the x-axis when the output is multiplied by −1.

Vocabulary Builder

REVIEW VOCABULARY — **English** | *Spanish*

- **compression** | *compression*
- **horizontal** | *horizontal*
- **stretch** | *tramo*
- **vertical** | *vertical*

VOCABULARY ACTIVITY

The terms *compression* and *stretch* can be confusing because they can be applied both horizontally and vertically. The graph shows $g(x)$ and $h(x)$ as transformations of $f(x)$. Show and discuss with students the two sets of terms that describe the transformations.

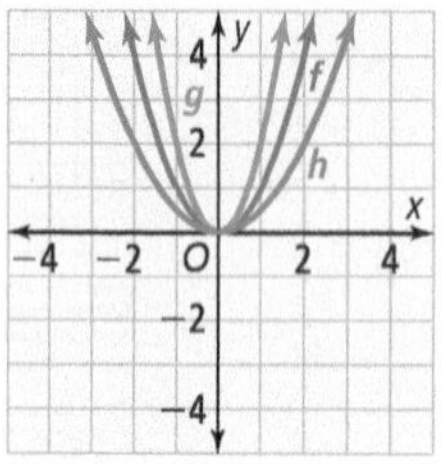

y
x
4
2
−4
−2
O
2
4
−2
−4
g
f
h

$g(x)$ can be described as a vertical stretch or a horizontal compression of $f(x)$.

$h(x)$ can be described as a horizontal stretch or a vertical compression of $f(x)$.

Q: What do you notice about the pairs of terms that describe the graphs?
[They are opposites of each other.]

Student Companion

Students can do their in-class work for the lesson on pages 235–238 of their *Student Companion* or in Savvas Realize.

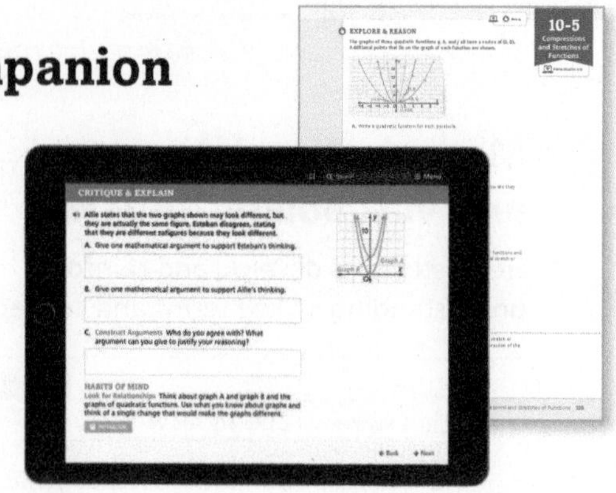

10-5
CRITIQUE & EXPLAIN

Mathematics Overview — COMMON CORE STANDARDS

Content Standards

In this lesson, students focus on this standard:

HSF.BF.B.3 Identify the effect on the graph of replacing $f(x)$ by $f(x) + k$, $kf(x)$, $f(kx)$, and $f(x + k)$ for specific values of k (both positive and negative); find the value of k given the graphs. Experiment with cases and illustrate an explanation of the effects on the graph using technology. Include recognizing even and odd functions from their graphs and algebraic expressions for them.

Mathematical Practice Standards

These standards are highlighted in this lesson:

MP.2 Reason Abstractly and Quantitatively

Students make sense of quantities and their relationships when they consider how the output values of a function change for the same input values when the output is multiplied by a constant with an absolute value greater than 1.

MP.6 Attend to Precision

Students communicate with precise mathematical vocabulary when using vertical, horizontal, stretch, and compression to describe transformations.

EXPLORE & REASON

INSTRUCTIONAL FOCUS Students make connections between the shapes of graphs and the expressions used to create the graphs.

STUDENT COMPANION Students can complete the *Explore & Reason* activity on page 235 of their *Student Companion.*

Before WHOLE CLASS

Implement Tasks that Promote Reasoning and Problem Solving ETP

Q: How are the graphs of the functions similar? How are they different?
[All of the graphs are parabolas and open upward. All of the graphs have different widths.]

During SMALL GROUP

Support Productive Struggle in Learning Mathematics ETP

Q: What can you determine about the graph of each function and its model? [Sample: Since the graphs are all parabolas, a change is being made to the expression x^2 when writing a quadratic expression for each function.]

For Early Finishers

Q: Describe how you can tell whether a function is increasing or decreasing at a faster rate by looking at its graph. What causes the rate change in the function? Test your conjecture using the parent function $f(x) = x^3$. [A graph that has a steeper incline or decline is changing at a faster rate. When a function is multiplied by a number greater than 1, the rate increases, and when a function is multiplied by a number between 0 and 1, the rate decreases. Check students' work.]

After WHOLE CLASS

Facilitate Meaningful Mathematical Discourse ETP

Q: How can you recognize a vertical compression?
[When a graph is compressed vertically, it gets wider and the rate of change decreases.]

Q: How can you recognize a vertical stretch?
[When a graph is stretched vertically, it gets narrower and the rate of change increases.]

HABITS OF MIND *Use with* **EXPLORE & REASON**

Reason Can you determine whether the graph of $g(x) = ax^2$ is a vertical stretch or compression of the graph of $f(x) = x^2$ or a horizontal stretch or compression of the graph of f? Explain. MP.2

[No, it could be either. For example, a horizontal compression of the graph of *f* toward the *y*-axis or a vertical stretch away from the *x*-axis would result in the same graph *g*.]

AVAILABLE **ONLINE**

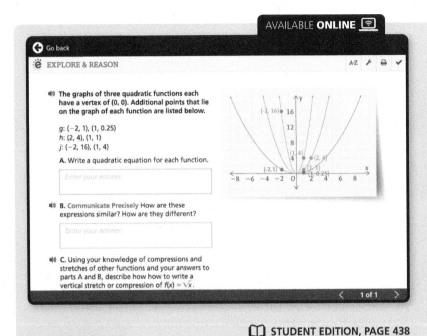

Go back

EXPLORE & REASON

The graphs of three quadratic functions each have a vertex of (0, 0). Additional points that lie on the graph of each function are listed below.

g: (−2, 1), (1, 0.25)
h: (2, 4), (1, 1)
j: (−2, 16), (1, 4)

A. Write a quadratic equation for each function.

Enter your answer.

B. Communicate Precisely How are these expressions similar? How are they different?

Enter your answer.

C. Using your knowledge of compressions and stretches of other functions and your answers to parts A and B, describe how how to write a vertical stretch or compression of $f(x) = \sqrt{x}$.

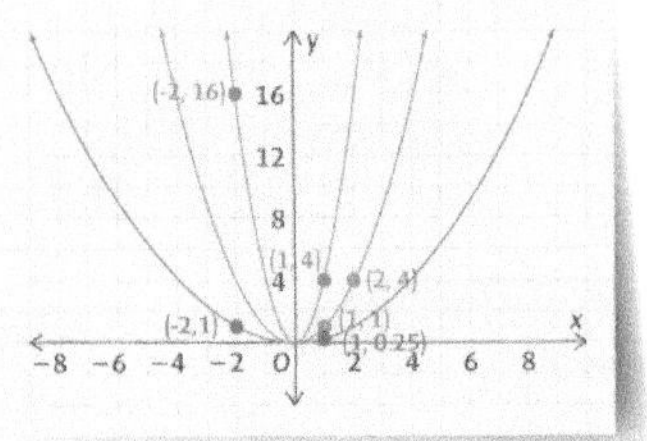
y
x
(−2, 16)
16
12
8
4
(1, 4)
(2, 4)
(1, 1)
(−2, 1)
(1, 0.25)
−8 −6 −4 −2 O 2 4 6 8

1 of 1

STUDENT EDITION, PAGE 438

10-5
Compressions and Stretches of Functions

PearsonRealize.com

I CAN… change functions to compress or stretch their graphs.

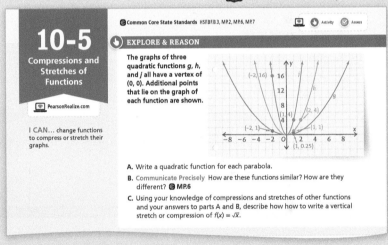

Common Core State Standards HSF.BF.B.3, MP.2, MP.6, MP.7

Activity Assess

EXPLORE & REASON

The graphs of three quadratic functions *g*, *h*, and *j* all have a vertex of (0, 0). Additional points that lie on the graph of each function are shown.

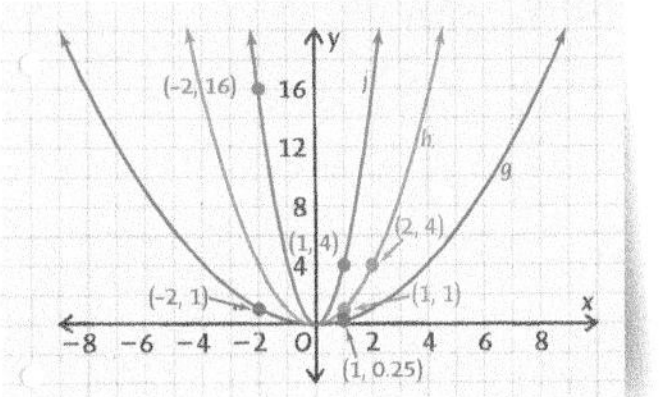
y
x
j
h
g
(−2, 16)
16
12
8
4
(1, 4)
(2, 4)
(−2, 1)
(1, 1)
(1, 0.25)
−8 −6 −4 −2 O 2 4 6 8

A. Write a quadratic function for each parabola.
B. Communicate Precisely How are these functions similar? How are they different? MP.6
C. Using your knowledge of compressions and stretches of other functions and your answers to parts A and B, describe how how to write a vertical stretch or compression of $f(x) = \sqrt{x}$.

SAMPLE STUDENT WORK

A. Function 1: $y = 0.25x^2$; Function 2: $y = x^2$;
Function 3: $y = 4x^2$

B. All of the equations are in the form $y = ax^2$. The equations have different values of a, which affect how wide the graphs of the functions open.

C. You could multiply $\sqrt{x}$ by different constants to make the graph of the function move closer to or farther from the x-axis.

INTRODUCE THE ESSENTIAL QUESTION

Establish Mathematics Goals to Focus Learning ETP

Review the changes to a function that result in horizontal or vertical translations. Explain that the shape of the graph of a function can be changed by multiplying the output by a constant. This prepares students to recognize vertical and horizontal stretches and compressions of graphs of functions.

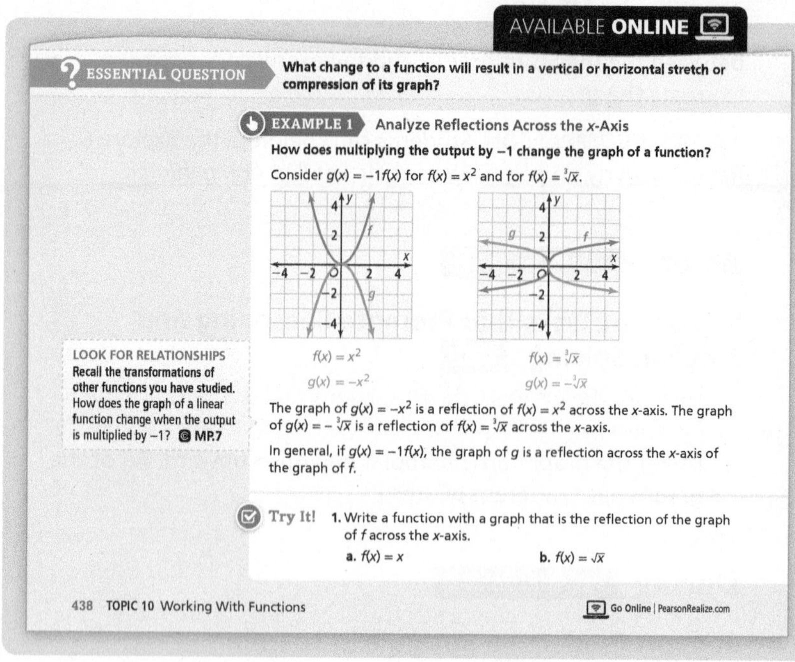
AVAILABLE ONLINE
ESSENTIAL QUESTION
What change to a function will result in a vertical or horizontal stretch or compression of its graph?
EXAMPLE 1 Analyze Reflections Across the x-Axis
How does multiplying the output by −1 change the graph of a function?
Consider g(x) = −1f(x) for f(x) = x² and for f(x) = ∛x.
f(x) = x²
g(x) = −x²
f(x) = ∛x
g(x) = −∛x
LOOK FOR RELATIONSHIPS
Recall the transformations of other functions you have studied. How does the graph of a linear function change when the output is multiplied by −1? MP.7
The graph of g(x) = −x² is a reflection of f(x) = x² across the x-axis. The graph of g(x) = −∛x is a reflection of f(x) = ∛x across the x-axis.
In general, if g(x) = −1f(x), the graph of g is a reflection across the x-axis of the graph of f.
Try It! 1. Write a function with a graph that is the reflection of the graph of f across the x-axis.
a. f(x) = x
b. f(x) = √x
438 TOPIC 10 Working With Functions
Go Online | PearsonRealize.com

EXAMPLE 1 Analyze Reflections Across the x-Axis

Use and Connect Mathematical Representations ETP

Q: In each graph, what do you notice about the graph of g compared to the graph of f?
[Sample: Both graphs have the same shape, but are mirror reflections across the x-axis.]

Q: Describe the graphs of the functions in terms of the distance from the x-axis after multiplying each output by -1.
[Each point of the function $-1f(x)$ will be the same distance from the x-axis, but in the opposite direction of $f(x)$.]

Try It! Answers

1. a. $g(x) = -x$
   b. $g(x) = -\sqrt{x}$

AVAILABLE ONLINE

ADDITIONAL EXAMPLES

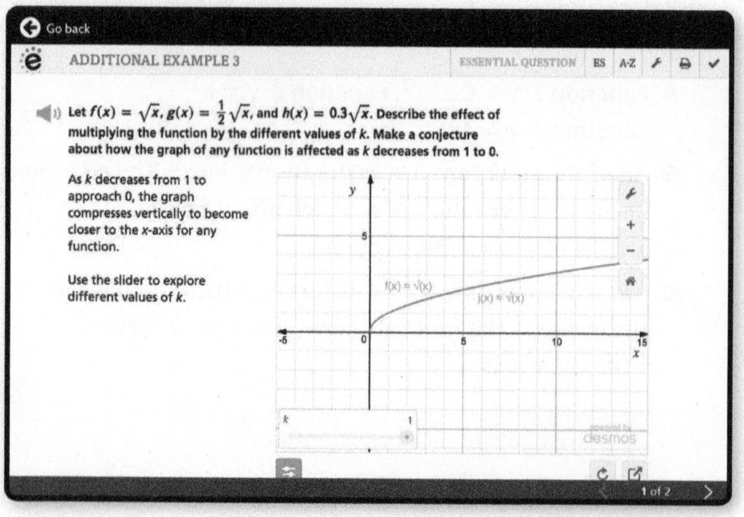
Go back
ADDITIONAL EXAMPLE 3
ESSENTIAL QUESTION ES A-Z
Let f(x) = √x, g(x) = ½√x, and h(x) = 0.3√x. Describe the effect of multiplying the function by the different values of k. Make a conjecture about how the graph of any function is affected as k decreases from 1 to 0.
As k decreases from 1 to approach 0, the graph compresses vertically to become closer to the x-axis for any function.
Use the slider to explore different values of k.
desmos
1 of 2

Example 3 Students investigate how the graph of a function is affected as the value of k changes in the function $f(x) = k\sqrt{x}$.

Q: What occurs as the value of k becomes smaller?
[As k becomes smaller, the output becomes smaller, therefore decreasing the distance from the x-axis.]

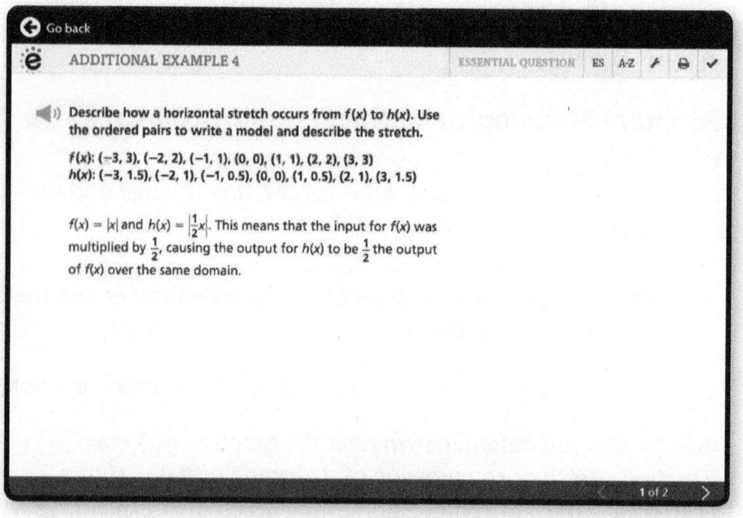
Go back
ADDITIONAL EXAMPLE 4
ESSENTIAL QUESTION ES A-Z
Describe how a horizontal stretch occurs from f(x) to h(x). Use the ordered pairs to write a model and describe the stretch.
f(x): (−3, 3), (−2, 2), (−1, 1), (0, 0), (1, 1), (2, 2), (3, 3)
h(x): (−3, 1.5), (−2, 1), (−1, 0.5), (0, 0), (1, 0.5), (2, 1), (3, 1.5)
f(x) = |x| and h(x) = |½x|. This means that the input for f(x) was multiplied by ½, causing the output for h(x) to be ½ the output of f(x) over the same domain.
1 of 2

Example 4 Students use sets of ordered pairs to find the model and define the horizontal stretch of a function.

Q: If you are defining a horizontal stretch, what do you know about the value of k?
[The value of k will be a number such that $0 < |k| < 1$.]

EXAMPLE 2 Analyze Vertical Stretches of Graphs

Pose Purposeful Questions ETP

Q: How do the output values of the function g change when the output of f is multiplied by a constant with an absolute value greater than 1?
[The output values of g change at a faster rate because multiplying the output of f by a number greater than 1 increases or decreases each output value by that factor.]

Q: Why is multiplying the output of a function by a constant with an absolute value greater than 1 considered a vertical stretch?
[$kf(x)$ for $|k| > 1$ increases the distance each point on the graph is from the x-axis.]

Try It! Answers

2. a. Sample: $g(x) = 12x$
   b. Sample: $g(x) = 5\sqrt{x}$

EXAMPLE 3 Analyze Vertical Compressions of Graphs

Use and Connect Mathematical Representations ETP

Q: Why is multiplying the output of a function by a constant with an absolute value between 0 and 1 considered a vertical compression?
[$kf(x)$ for $0 < |k| <1$ decreases the distance each point on the graph is from the x-axis, and the graph is a vertical compression toward the x-axis.]

Try It! Answers

3. a. Sample: $g(x) = \frac{2}{3}\sqrt{x}$
   b. Sample: $g(x) = -0.3|x|$

HABITS OF MIND

Use with **EXAMPLES 1–3**

Make Sense and Persevere Will the transformed function be wider or narrower than its parent function? MP.1

a. $f(x) = x^6$
   $g(x) = 0.1x^6$

b. $f(x) = \sqrt[3]{x^5}$
   $g(x) = \frac{12}{5}\sqrt[3]{x^5}$

[a. wider   b. narrower]

AVAILABLE **ONLINE**

Activity Assess

EXAMPLE 2 Analyze Vertical Stretches of Graphs

How does multiplying the output by a constant with an absolute value greater than 1 change the graph of a function?

Consider $g(x) = kf(x)$ for $|k| > 1$ when $f(x) = x^2$ and when $f(x) = \sqrt[3]{x}$.

$f(x) = x^2$ $g(x) = 2x^2$

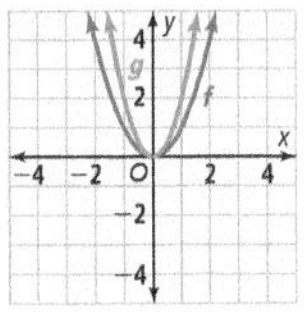

$f(x) = \sqrt[3]{x}$ $g(x) = 4\sqrt[3]{x}$

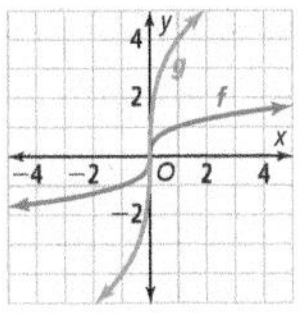

REASON
Think about how the y-values of the function change for the same input values when the output is multiplied by a constant greater than 1. MP.2

The graph of $g(x) = 2x^2$ is a vertical stretch of $f(x) = x^2$ away from the x-axis.
The graph of $g(x) = 4\sqrt[3]{x}$ is a vertical stretch of $f(x) = \sqrt[3]{x}$ away from the x-axis.

In general, if $g(x) = kf(x)$ for $|k| > 1$, the graph of g is a vertical stretch away from the x-axis of the graph of f.

Try It! 2. Write a function with a graph that is a vertical stretch of the graph of f, away from the x-axis.
a. $f(x) = x$ b. $f(x) = \sqrt{x}$

EXAMPLE 3 Analyze Vertical Compressions of Graphs

How does multiplying the output by a constant with an absolute value between 0 and 1 change the graph of a function?

Consider $g(x) = kf(x)$ for $0 < |k| < 1$ when $f(x) = |x + 1|$ and when $f(x) = x^2$.

$f(x) = |x + 1|$ $g(x) = \frac{1}{2}|x + 1|$

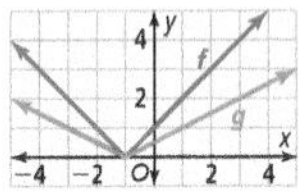

$f(x) = x^2$ $g(x) = \frac{1}{2}x^2$

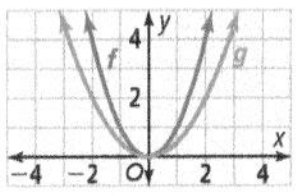

The graph of $g(x) = \frac{1}{2}|x + 1|$ is a vertical compression of $f(x) = |x + 1|$ toward the x-axis. The graph of $g(x) = \frac{1}{2}x^2$ is a vertical compression of $f(x) = x^2$ toward the x-axis.

In general, if $g(x) = kf(x)$ for $0 < |k| < 1$, the graph of g is a vertical compression toward the x-axis of the graph of f.

Try It! 3. Write a function with a graph that is a vertical compression of the graph of f, toward the x-axis.
a. $f(x) = \sqrt{x}$ b. $f(x) = |x|$

LESSON 10-5 Compressions and Stretches of Functions 439

Common Error

Try It! 3 Some students may not understand that multiplying by a negative constant results in a vertical compression. Ask students to compare the distance between each point of the new function and the x-axis and the distance between the corresponding point in the original function and the x-axis.

ADV Advanced Students

USE WITH EXAMPLE 1 Students investigate how negative coefficients other than –1 affect functions.

- Graph the following functions over the domain $[-4 \leq x \leq 4]$.
  1. $f(x) = -3|x|$ [Check students' work.]
  2. $g(x) = -\frac{1}{2}x^2$ [Check students' work.]

Q: What prediction can you make about a coefficient that is less than –1? Between –1 and 0?
[A coefficient less than –1 narrows the graph. A coefficient between –1 and 0 widens the graph.]

RtI Struggling Students

USE WITH EXAMPLE 2 Students see that a vertical stretch or compression is a change in the value of the slope of a function.

- Graph each function over the domain $[0 \leq x \leq 3]$ to determine if it is a vertical stretch of $f(x) = x^2$.
  1. $r(x) = 0.5x^2$ [not a vertical stretch]
  2. $g(x) = 5x^2$ [vertical stretch]

Q: What are the average rates of change for f, r, and g over $0 \leq x \leq 3$? [f: 3, r: 1.5, g: 15]

Activity Assess

EXAMPLE 4 Analyze Horizontal Stretches of Graphs

Build Procedural Fluency From Conceptual Understanding ETP

Q: How do the output values of the function g change when the input of f is multiplied by a constant with an absolute value between 0 and 1?
[Since the input values are smaller, the output values are less for g than for f, and they change at a slower rate.]

Q: How does multiplying the input of a function by a constant with an absolute value between 0 and 1 affect the shape of the graph?
[You now need a greater x-value to get the same y-value. The graph is wider and stretches away from the y-axis.]

Try It! Answer

4. When the input is multiplied by a value with an absolute value less than 1, the function is stretched.

EXAMPLE 5 Analyze Horizontal Compressions of Graphs

Use and Connect Mathematical Representations ETP

Q: Why is multiplying the input of a function by a constant with an absolute value greater than 1 considered a horizontal compression?
[$f(kx)$ for $|k| > 1$ decreases the distance that each point on the graph is from the y-axis, and the graph is a horizontal compression toward the y-axis.]

Try It! Answers

5. a. Answers may vary. Sample: $g(x) = \sqrt[3]{7x}$
b. Answers may vary. Sample: $g(x) = (3x)^2$

HABITS OF MIND

Use with **EXAMPLES 4 & 5**

Communicate Precisely Explain the different algebraic processes for stretching or compressing a graph vertically or horizontally. MP.6

[When you vertically stretch or compress a graph, you multiply the whole expression by a constant. When you horizontally stretch or compress a graph, you multiply x by a constant.]

AVAILABLE ONLINE

Activity Assess

CONCEPTUAL UNDERSTANDING

EXAMPLE 4 Analyze Horizontal Stretches of Graphs

Why does multiplying the input of the function stretch the graph horizontally?

Consider $g(x) = f(kx)$ for $0 < k < 1$ when $f(x) = x^2$.

x	$f(x)$	$g(x)$
−2	4	1
−1	1	0.25
0	0	0
1	1	0.25
2	4	1

$g(-2) = f(-1)$

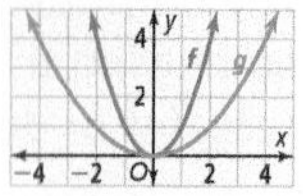

y
4
2
f
g
x
−4
−2
O
2
4

$f(x) = x^2$ $g(x) = \left(\frac{1}{2}x\right)^2$

LOOK FOR RELATIONSHIPS To get the same y-values from function g as from f, you must double the input x. The graph of g is a horizontal stretch of the graph of f away from y-axis by a scale factor of 2. MP.7

Multiplying the input of $f(x) = x^2$ by the constant $\frac{1}{2}$ yields $g(x) = \left(\frac{1}{2}x\right)^2$. To get y-values from function g that are equal to those from function f you need to input x-values into g that are farther away from the y-axis than the x-values you input into f. So the graph of g is a horizontal stretch away from the y-axis of the graph of f.

Try It! **4.** Why is $g(x) = 0.2x + 2$ a horizontal stretch of $f(x) = x + 2$?

EXAMPLE 5 Analyze Horizontal Compressions of Graphs

How does multiplying the input by a constant with an absolute value greater than 1 change the graph of a function?

Consider $g(x) = f(kx)$ for $|k| > 1$ when $f(x) = x^2 + 2$ and when $f(x) = |x + 1|$.

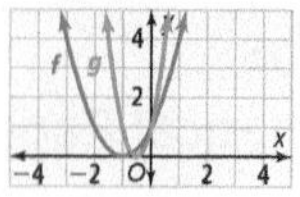

4
2
f
g
x
−4
−2
O
2
4

$f(x) = (x + 1)^2$
$g(x) = (2x + 1)^2$

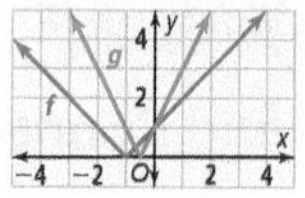

y
4
2
g
f
x
−4
−2
O
2
4

$f(x) = |x + 1|$
$g(x) = |2x + 1|$

COMMON ERROR You might think that as k increases the graph of the function $f(kx)$ would stretch horizontally. Instead, it compresses the graph horizontally as k increases.

The graph of $g(x) = (2x + 1)^2$ is a horizontal compression of $f(x) = (x + 1)^2$ toward the y-axis. The graph of $g(x) = |2x + 1|$ is a horizontal compression of $f(x) = |x + 1|$ toward the y-axis.

In general, when $g(x) = f(kx)$ for $|k| > 1$, the graph of g is a horizontal compression toward the y-axis of the graph of f.

Try It! **5.** Write a function with a graph that is a horizontal compression of the graph of f, toward the y-axis.

a. $f(x) = \sqrt[3]{x}$
b. $f(x) = x^2$

440 TOPIC 10 Working With Functions Go Online | PearsonRealize.com

ELL English Language Learners *(Use with* **EXAMPLE 5***)*

WRITING BEGINNING Create a two-column table with the headings *horizontal* and *vertical*. Have students add words to the appropriate columns. For example, a tabletop is horizontal and a lamppost is vertical.

Q: When multiplying by a constant with an absolute value greater than 1, the graph is a ________ compression toward the y-axis. [horizontal]

Q: When multiplying by a constant with an absolute value greater than 1, the graph is a ________ stretch away from the x-axis. [vertical]

LISTENING INTERMEDIATE Read the problem statement aloud. Read the meanings of the words *input* and *output* as they pertain to a vending machine.

Q: What would the input and output be when using the vending machine?
[money; a snack]

Have students identify which word describes each situation.

- ingredients [i]; muffins [o]
- seeds [i]; flowers [o]
- x-values [i]; y-values [o]

READING ADVANCED Ask students to read the title of the example.

Q: Which word could be replaced with the word *study* or *examine*?
[analyze]

Ask students to read through the entire example.

Q: Which sentence best describes the result of the analysis?
[In general, when $g(x) = f(kx)$ for $|k| > 1$, the graph of g is a horizontal compression toward the y-axis of the graph of f.]

CONCEPT SUMMARY Stretches and Compressions of Functions

Q: How can you distinguish between vertical stretches and compressions and horizontal stretches and compressions? [Vertical compressions and stretches result from k being multiplied by the output, $kf(x)$; horizontal compressions and stretches result from k being multiplied by the input, $f(kx)$.]

Do You UNDERSTAND? | Do You KNOW HOW?

Common Error

Exercise 4 Some students may relate the word *stretch* with getting larger and think that multiplying the input of a function by a constant value greater than 1 makes something larger. Explain that when working with horizontal transformations, you are describing the horizontal distance from the y-axis. Multiplying the input by a constant with an absolute value less than 1 increases that distance.

Answers

1. Multiplying the output by a constant either stretches or compresses the graph of the function vertically. Multiplying the input by a constant either stretches or compresses the graph of the function horizontally.
2. The student confused a vertical compression with a horizontal compression. Because the output of the function is being multiplied by a constant, the direction is vertical.
3. A vertical stretch causes the graph of a function to stretch away from the x-axis, and a horizontal stretch causes the graph of a function to stretch away from the y-axis.
4. $f(kx)$, for $0 < k < 1$
5. yes
6. no
7. horizontal compression
8. vertical stretch
9. horizontal compression

AVAILABLE ONLINE

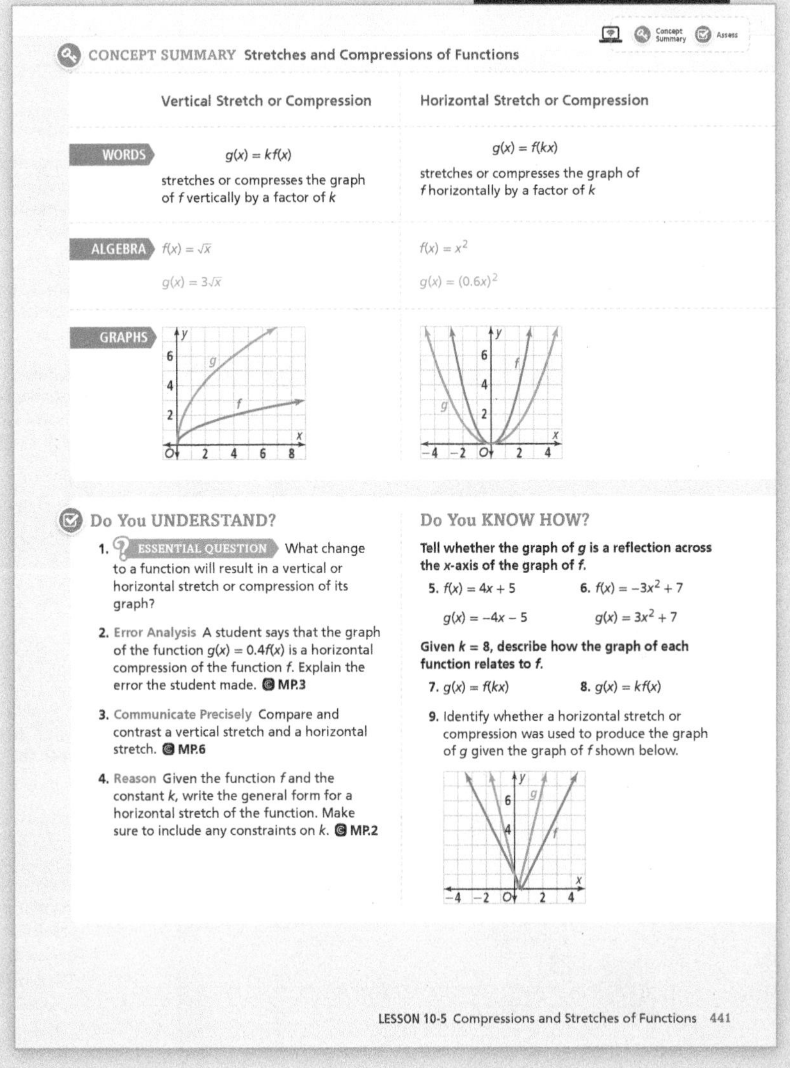

CONCEPT SUMMARY Stretches and Compressions of Functions

	Vertical Stretch or Compression	Horizontal Stretch or Compression
WORDS	$g(x) = kf(x)$ stretches or compresses the graph of f vertically by a factor of k	$g(x) = f(kx)$ stretches or compresses the graph of f horizontally by a factor of k
ALGEBRA	$f(x) = \sqrt{x}$ $g(x) = 3\sqrt{x}$	$f(x) = x^2$ $g(x) = (0.6x)^2$
GRAPHS		

Do You UNDERSTAND?

1. ESSENTIAL QUESTION What change to a function will result in a vertical or horizontal stretch or compression of its graph?
2. Error Analysis A student says that the graph of the function $g(x) = 0.4f(x)$ is a horizontal compression of the function f. Explain the error the student made. MP.3
3. Communicate Precisely Compare and contrast a vertical stretch and a horizontal stretch. MP.6
4. Reason Given the function f and the constant k, write the general form for a horizontal stretch of the function. Make sure to include any constraints on k. MP.2

Do You KNOW HOW?

Tell whether the graph of g is a reflection across the x-axis of the graph of f.

5. $f(x) = 4x + 5$; $g(x) = -4x - 5$
6. $f(x) = -3x^2 + 7$; $g(x) = 3x^2 + 7$

Given $k = 8$, describe how the graph of each function relates to f.

7. $g(x) = f(kx)$
8. $g(x) = kf(x)$
9. Identify whether a horizontal stretch or compression was used to produce the graph of g given the graph of f shown below.

LESSON 10-5 Compressions and Stretches of Functions 441

Practice Tutorials Math Tools

PRACTICE & PROBLEM SOLVING

AVAILABLE ONLINE

Lesson Practice You may opt to have students complete the automatically scored Practice and Problem Solving items online powered by MathXL for School.

Choose from: **Lesson Practice**

Adaptive Practice

You may also take advantage of the bank of exercises for assigning additional practice.

Assignment Guide

Basic	Advanced
10–24, 27–35	10–14, 17–35

Item Analysis

Example	Items	DOK
1	15–18	1
	27, 33	2
2	19, 25, 28, 32, 34	1
	29, 30	2
3	21, 24	1
4	23	1
	12, 13, 14	2
	35	3
5	11, 20, 22, 26	1
	10, 30, 31	2

AVAILABLE ONLINE

PRACTICE & PROBLEM SOLVING

Scan for Multimedia

Practice Tutorial

Additional Exercises Available Online

UNDERSTAND

10. Mathematical Connections Is the slope m of a line $y = mx + b$ related to vertical and horizontal compressions and stretches of the graph of the line? Explain.

11. Look for Relationships Graph $f(x) = \sqrt{x}$ and $g(x) = \sqrt{2x}$. Explain why you can consider the function g to be either a vertical stretch of f or a horizontal compression of f. MP.7

12. Make Sense and Persevere Two graphs of two quadratic functions $f(x)$ and $g(x) = f(kx)$ are shown below. What is the approximate value of k? MP.1 $\frac{1}{3}$

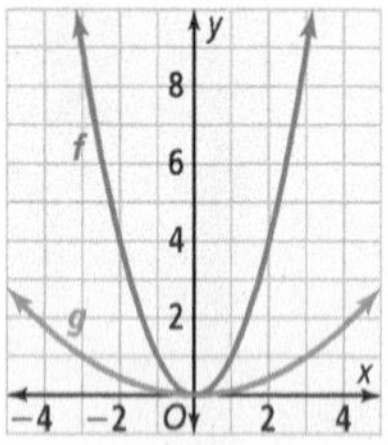

y
8
6
4
2
f
g
x
−4
−2
O
2
4

13. Error Analysis Describe and correct the error a student made in describing the relationship between the graphs of the two functions. MP.3

$f(x) = x^2 + 1$

$g(x) = (4x)^2 + 1$

> Because the input of f is being multiplied by a constant to get g, the graph of g is the graph of f being horizontally stretched or compressed. The constant is 4, which is greater than 1, so it is a horizontal stretch. ✗

14. Higher Order Thinking Describe the graph of g in terms of the graph of f for all values of k.

a. $g(x) = kf(x)$ for $0 < |k| < 1$

b. $g(x) = kf(x)$ for $1 < |k|$

c. $g(x) = f(kx)$ for $0 < |k| < 1$

PRACTICE

Write a function with a graph that is the reflection of the graph of f across the x-axis. SEE EXAMPLE 1

15. $f(x) = x^2 - 3$ $g(x) = -x^2 + 3$

16. $f(x) = |2x + 5|$ $g(x) = -|2x + 5|$

17. $f(x) = -\sqrt{2x}$ $g(x) = \sqrt{2x}$

18. $f(x) = -x + 4$ $g(x) = x - 4$

For each pair, tell whether the graph of g is a vertical or horizontal compression or stretch of the graph of f. SEE EXAMPLES 2, 3, 4 AND 5

19. $f(x) = |x + 3|$
$g(x) = 2|x + 3|$

20. $f(x) = x^2 - 4$
$g(x) = (0.5x)^2 - 4$

21. $f(x) = \sqrt{x + 1}$
$g(x) = 0.25\sqrt{x + 1}$

22. $f(x) = \sqrt[3]{x - 1}$
$g(x) = \sqrt[3]{2x - 1}$

23. $f(x) = x - 3$
$g(x) = 0.4x - 3$

24. $f(x) = |x - 2|$
$g(x) = \frac{2}{3}|x - 2|$

25. $f(x) = x^2 + 2$
$g(x) = 6x^2 + 12$

26. $f(x) = \sqrt{x}$
$g(x) = \sqrt{7x}$

For each graph, identify the transformation applied to f that results in g, and identify the value of k.

27.

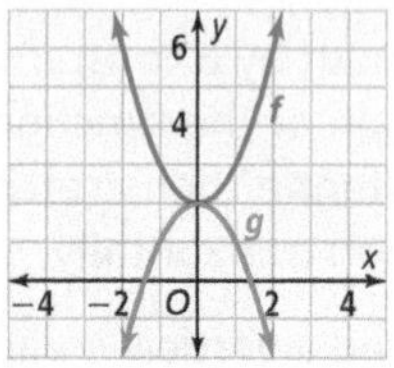

y
6
4
f
g
x
−4
−2
O
2
4

reflection across $y = 2$; $k = -1$

28.

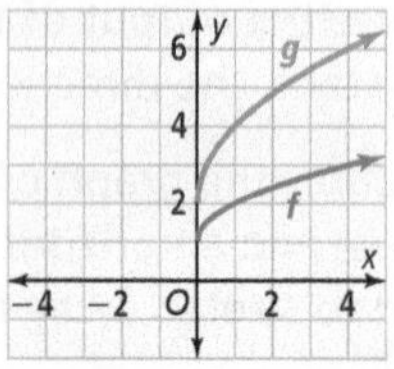

y
6
4
2
g
f
x
−4
−2
O
2
4

vertical stretch; $k = 2$

29. The graph of g is a reflection of the graph of $f(x) = \sqrt{x}$ across the x-axis and a vertical stretch of that graph by a factor of 3. Write the function g.

Go Online | PearsonRealize.com

Answers

10. Yes; the function $y = mx + b$ is a horizontal stretch or compression of the function $y = x + b$.

11.

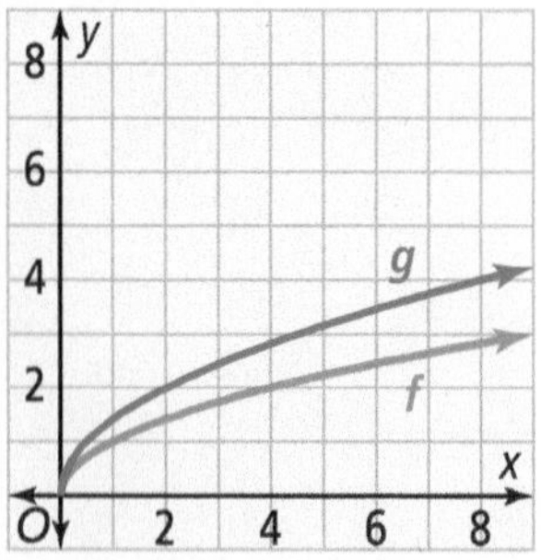

y
8
6
4
2
g
f
x
O
2
4
6
8

Based on the way the functions are written, it is a horizontal compression. But if you take the square root of 2 and put it in front of the radical, then it looks like a vertical stretch.

13. When the input is multiplied by $k > 1$, it is a horizontal compression, not a horizontal stretch.

14. a. vertical compression

b. vertical stretch

c. horizontal stretch

19. vertical stretch

20. horizontal stretch

21. vertical compression

22. horizontal compression

23. horizontal stretch

24. vertical compression

25. vertical stretch

26. horizontal compression

29. $g(x) = -3\sqrt{x}$

Answers

30. The output could be multiplied by a constant $k > 1$, which would stretch the graph away from the x-axis. Alternatively, the input could be multiplied by a constant $k > 1$, which would compress the graph toward the y-axis.

31. a.

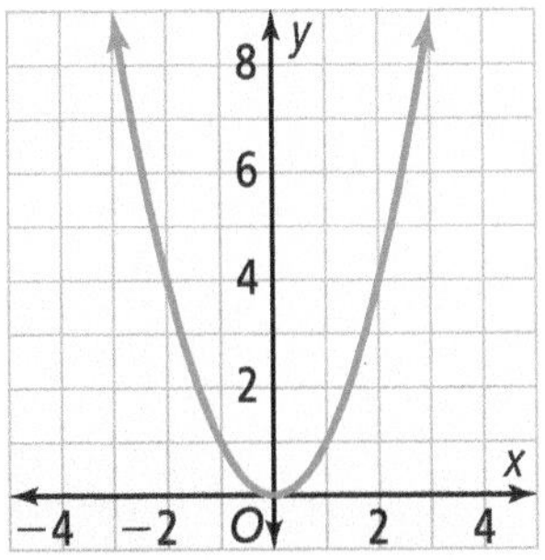

The graph is compressed horizontally.

b. $s = \sqrt{A}$

c.

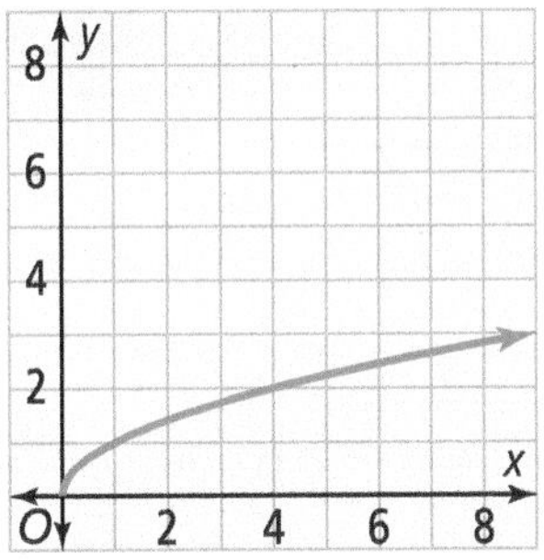

d. The graph is compressed vertically.

32. a.

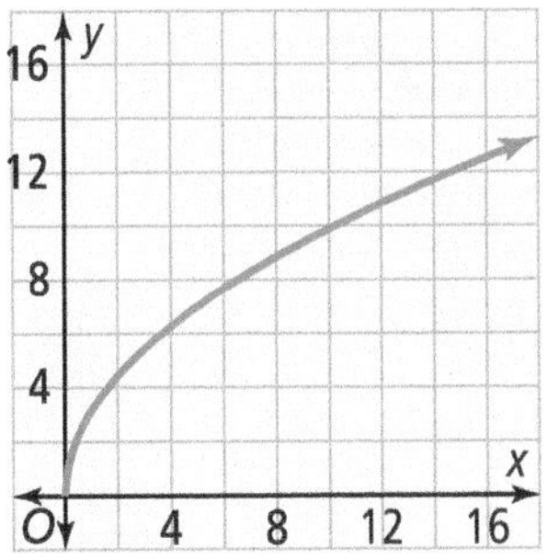

b. domain and range: $[0, \infty)$

c. about 9.9 m/s

35. Part A

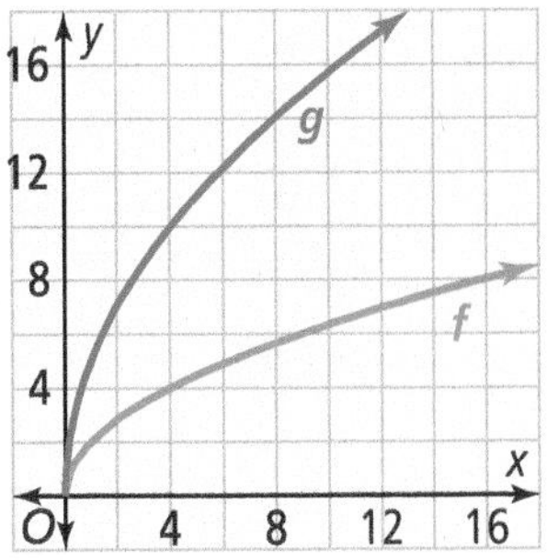

Part B $g(x) = \sqrt{6.125}\,f(x)$

Part C The period is longer on the moon than on Earth for a pendulum with the same length.

Part D The graph of g can be described as either a vertical stretch away from the x-axis or a horizontal compression toward the y-axis.

AVAILABLE **ONLINE**

PRACTICE & PROBLEM SOLVING

Practice Tutorial Mixed Review Available Online

APPLY

30. Make Sense and Persevere A company's logo is modeled by the function $f(x) = -|x| + 2$. For a new design, the company wants the logo to be narrower. What are two ways the function f could be altered so that the graph of the new function gives a narrower logo? Explain. MP.1

31. Reason The area A of a square is given by $A = s^2$, where s is a side length of the square. MP.2

a. Graph the function $A = s^2$ on a grid. How does the graph change when you double the side length of the square? Describe the changes in terms of stretches and compressions.

b. Write a function that gives the side length of a square in terms of its area.

c. Graph your function from part (b).

d. How does this graph change when you double the side length of the square? Describe the changes in terms of stretches and compressions.

32. Model With Mathematics The speed of a wave in the ocean in meters per second can be determined using the function $f(x) = 3.13\sqrt{x}$, where x represents the depth in meters of the water under the wave. MP.4

a. Graph the function.

b. Identify the domain and range.

c. How fast are the waves in the figure moving over the water?

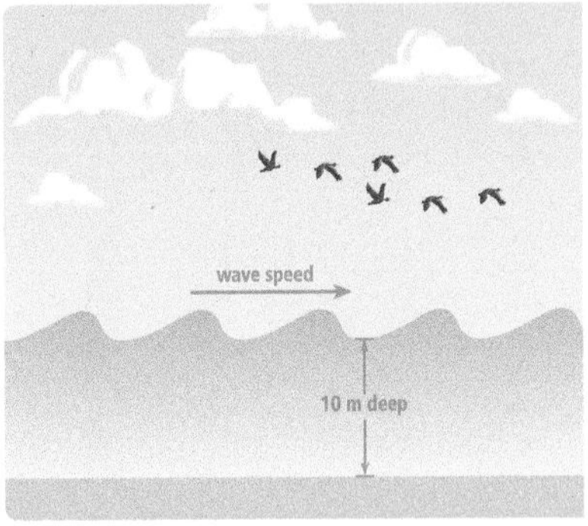
wave speed
10 m deep

ASSESSMENT PRACTICE

33. What is a function rule for g such that the graph of g is a reflection across the x-axis of the graph of $f(x) = |2x + 5|$? $g(x) = -|2x + 5|$

34. SAT/ACT Which function has a graph that is a vertical stretch of the graph of $f(x) = 4x^2 - 1$?

Ⓐ $g(x) = 6(4x^2 - 1)$
Ⓑ $g(x) = 0.6(4x^2 - 1)$
Ⓒ $g(x) = 4(6x)^2 - 1$
Ⓓ $g(x) = -(4x^2 - 1)$

35. Performance Task The period, in seconds, of a pendulum's swing on Earth is given by the function $f(x) = 2\pi\sqrt{\frac{x}{9.8}}$, where x is the length of the pendulum in meters. On the moon, the equation that gives the period of the pendulum is $g(x) = 2\pi\sqrt{\frac{x}{1.6}}$.

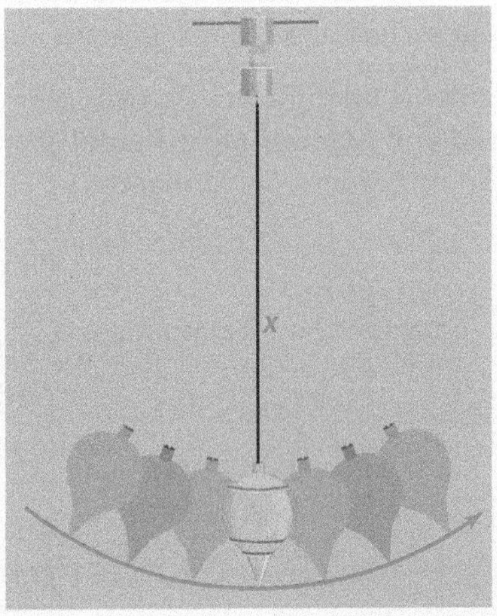
x

Part A Graph both functions on the same grid.

Part B Write the moon function in terms of $f(x)$.

Part C If $g(x) = kf(x)$, what does the value of k tell you about how a pendulum swings on the moon as compared to on Earth?

Part D Describe how the graph of g differs from the graph of f in terms of stretches and compressions.

LESSON QUIZ

Use the Lesson Quiz to assess students' understanding of the mathematics in the lesson.

Students can take the Lesson Quiz online or you can download a printable copy from **SavvasRealize.com**. The Lesson Quiz is also available in the *Assessment Resources* book.

Item Analysis

Item	DOK	Standards
1	1	HSF.BF.B.3
2	1	HSF.BF.B.3
3	1	HSF.BF.B.3
4	2	HSF.BF.B.3
5	2	HSF.BF.B.3

RtI Use the student scores on the Lesson Quiz to prescribe differentiated assignments.

If students take the Lesson Quiz online, it will be automatically scored and appropriate differentiated practice will be assigned based on student performance.

I Intervention	0–3 points	• Reteach to Build Understanding • Mathematical Literacy and Vocabulary • Additional Practice
O On-Level	4 points	• Mathematical Literacy and Vocabulary • Additional Practice • Enrichment
A Advanced	5 points	• Enrichment

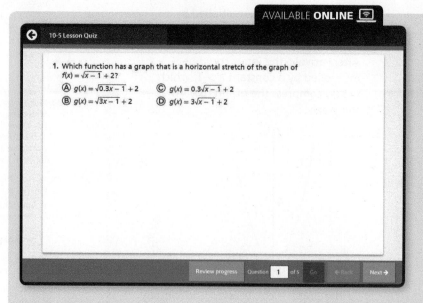

AVAILABLE **ONLINE**

10-5 Lesson Quiz

1. Which function has a graph that is a horizontal stretch of the graph of $f(x) = \sqrt{x-1} + 2$?

Ⓐ $g(x) = \sqrt{0.3x - 1} + 2$ Ⓒ $g(x) = 0.3\sqrt{x-1} + 2$

Ⓑ $g(x) = \sqrt{3x - 1} + 2$ Ⓓ $g(x) = 3\sqrt{x-1} + 2$

Review progress Question 1 of 5 Go ← Back Next →

ASSESSMENT RESOURCES

Name ______________________

enVision Algebra 1

PearsonRealize.com

10-5 Lesson Quiz

Compressions And Stretches of Functions

1. Which function has a graph that is a horizontal stretch of the graph of $f(x) = \sqrt{x-1} + 2$?

Ⓐ $g(x) = \sqrt{0.3x - 1} + 2$ Ⓒ $g(x) = 0.3\sqrt{x-1} + 2$

Ⓑ $g(x) = \sqrt{3x - 1} + 2$ Ⓓ $g(x) = 3\sqrt{x-1} + 2$

2. Complete each sentence with *horizontal stretch, vertical stretch, horizontal compression, vertical compression, x-axis,* or *y-axis.*

The graph of $h(x) = (2.5x)^3$ is a horizontal compression of the graph of $f(x) = x^3$ toward the y-axis.

The graph of $g(x) = \frac{1}{4}\sqrt{x}$ is a vertical compression of the graph of $f(x) = \sqrt{x}$ toward the x-axis.

3. How is the graph of $g(x) = f(kx)$ related to the graph of f when $k = 5$?

Ⓐ The graph of g is a horizontal stretch of the graph of f.

Ⓑ The graph of g is a vertical stretch of the graph of f.

Ⓒ The graph of g is a horizontal compression of the graph of f.

Ⓓ The graph of g is a vertical compression of the graph of f.

4. The graph of g is a stretch of the graph of f. Complete the sentence with *horizontal, vertical, x-axis,* or *y-axis.*

The graph of g is a vertical stretch of the graph of f away from the x-axis.

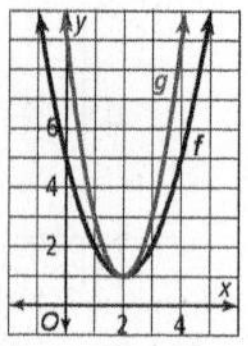

y
g
f
6
4
2
O
2
4
x

5. The graph of the function $f(x) = |x - 5| + 1$ models the shape of the cross-section of a V-shaped trough. Which function(s) model the cross-section of a trough with sides that are less steep than the sides of the trough modeled by function f? Select all that apply.

Ⓐ $g(x) = |3x - 5| + 1$ Ⓓ $g(x) = \frac{1}{3}|x - 5| + 1$

Ⓑ $g(x) = 2|x - 5| + 1$ Ⓔ $g(x) = -|x - 5| + 1$

Ⓒ $g(x) = \left|\frac{1}{2}x - 5\right| + 1$

enVision™ **Algebra 1** • Assessment Resources

DIFFERENTIATED RESOURCES

I = Intervention O = On-Level A = Advanced

⚙ = This activity is available as a digital assignment powered by MathXL® for School.

AVAILABLE ONLINE

Reteach to Build Understanding I ⚙

Provides scaffolded reteaching for the key lesson concepts.

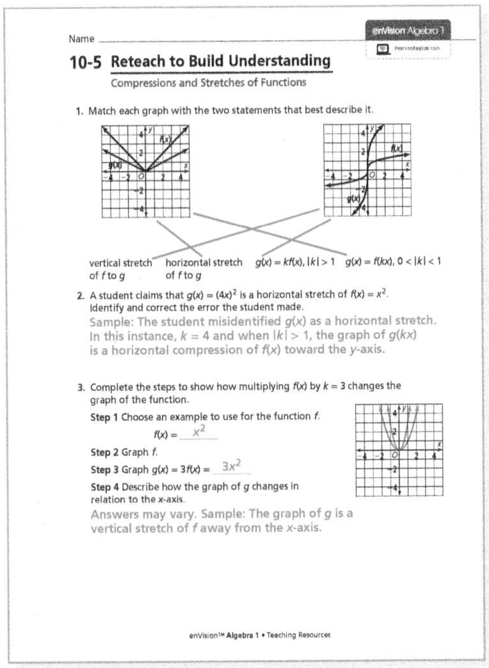

Name

10-5 Reteach to Build Understanding

Compressions and Stretches of Functions

1. Match each graph with the two statements that best describe it.

vertical stretch of f to g | horizontal stretch of f to g | $g(x) = kf(x), |k| > 1$ | $g(x) = f(kx), 0 < |k| < 1$

2. A student claims that $g(x) = (4x)^2$ is a horizontal stretch of $f(x) = x^2$. Identify and correct the error the student made.
Sample: The student misidentified $g(x)$ as a horizontal stretch. In this instance, $k = 4$ and when $|k| > 1$, the graph of $g(kx)$ is a horizontal compression of $f(x)$ toward the y-axis.

3. Complete the steps to show how multiplying $f(x)$ by $k = 3$ changes the graph of the function.
Step 1 Choose an example to use for the function f. $f(x) =$ x^2
Step 2 Graph f.
Step 3 Graph $g(x) = 3f(x) =$ $3x^2$
Step 4 Describe how the graph of g changes in relation to the x-axis.
Answers may vary. Sample: The graph of g is a vertical stretch of f away from the x-axis.

enVision™ Algebra 1 • Teaching Resources

Additional Practice I O ⚙

Provides extra practice for each lesson.

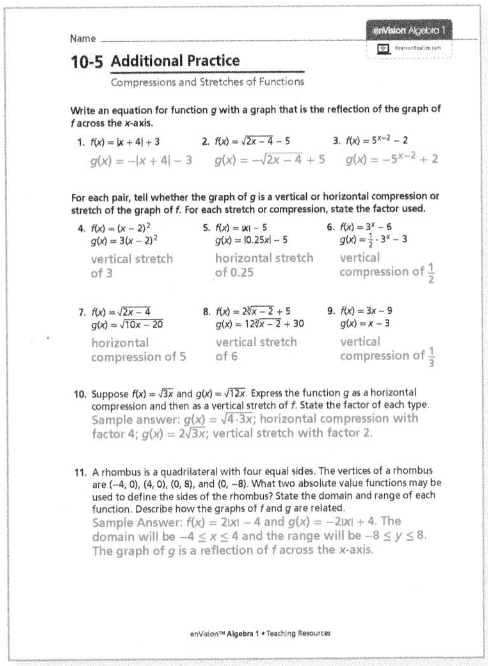

Name

10-5 Additional Practice

Compressions and Stretches of Functions

Write an equation for function g with a graph that is the reflection of the graph of f across the x-axis.

1. $f(x) = |x + 4| + 3$
$g(x) = -|x + 4| - 3$
2. $f(x) = \sqrt{2x - 4} - 5$
$g(x) = -\sqrt{2x - 4} + 5$
3. $f(x) = 5^{x-2} - 2$
$g(x) = -5^{x-2} + 2$

For each pair, tell whether the graph of g is a vertical or horizontal compression or stretch of the graph of f. For each stretch or compression, state the factor used.

4. $f(x) = (x - 2)^2$
$g(x) = 3(x - 2)^2$
vertical stretch of 3
5. $f(x) = |x| - 5$
$g(x) = |0.25x| - 5$
horizontal stretch of 0.25
6. $f(x) = 3^x - 6$
$g(x) = \frac{1}{2} \cdot 3^x - 3$
vertical compression of $\frac{1}{2}$
7. $f(x) = \sqrt{2x - 4}$
$g(x) = \sqrt{10x - 20}$
horizontal compression of 5
8. $f(x) = 2\sqrt[3]{x - 2} + 5$
$g(x) = 12\sqrt[3]{x - 2} + 30$
vertical stretch of 6
9. $f(x) = 3x - 9$
$g(x) = x - 3$
vertical compression of $\frac{1}{3}$

10. Suppose $f(x) = \sqrt{3x}$ and $g(x) = \sqrt{12x}$. Express the function g as a horizontal compression and then as a vertical stretch of f. State the factor of each type.
Sample answer: $g(x) = \sqrt{4 \cdot 3x}$; horizontal compression with factor 4; $g(x) = 2\sqrt{3x}$; vertical stretch with factor 2.

11. A rhombus is a quadrilateral with four equal sides. The vertices of a rhombus are (−4, 0), (4, 0), (0, 8), and (0, −8). What two absolute value functions may be used to define the sides of the rhombus? State the domain and range of each function. Describe how the graphs of f and g are related.
Sample Answer: $f(x) = 2|x| - 4$ and $g(x) = -2|x| + 4$. The domain will be $-4 \leq x \leq 4$ and the range will be $-8 \leq y \leq 8$. The graph of g is a reflection of f across the x-axis.

enVision™ Algebra 1 • Teaching Resources

Enrichment O A ⚙

Presents engaging problems and activities that extend the lesson concepts.

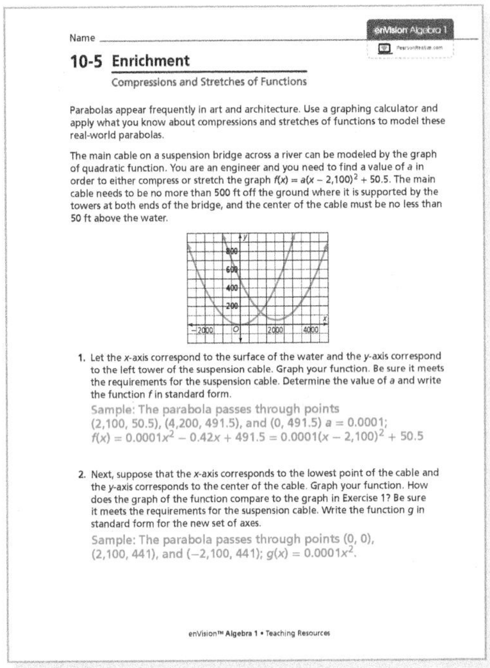

Name

10-5 Enrichment

Compressions and Stretches of Functions

Parabolas appear frequently in art and architecture. Use a graphing calculator and apply what you know about compressions and stretches of functions to model these real-world parabolas.

The main cable on a suspension bridge across a river can be modeled by the graph of quadratic function. You are an engineer and you need to find a value of a in order to either compress or stretch the graph $f(x) = a(x - 2{,}100)^2 + 50.5$. The main cable needs to be no more than 500 ft off the ground where it is supported by the towers at both ends of the bridge, and the center of the cable must be no less than 50 ft above the water.

1. Let the x-axis correspond to the surface of the water and the y-axis correspond to the left tower of the suspension cable. Graph your function. Be sure it meets the requirements for the suspension cable. Determine the value of a and write the function f in standard form.
Sample: The parabola passes through points (2,100, 50.5), (4,200, 491.5), and (0, 491.5) $a = 0.0001$; $f(x) = 0.0001x^2 - 0.42x + 491.5 = 0.0001(x - 2{,}100)^2 + 50.5$

2. Next, suppose that the x-axis corresponds to the lowest point of the cable and the y-axis corresponds to the center of the cable. Graph your function. How does the graph of the function compare to the graph in Exercise 1? Be sure it meets the requirements for the suspension cable. Write the function g in standard form for the new set of axes.
Sample: The parabola passes through points (0, 0), (2,100, 441), and (−2,100, 441); $g(x) = 0.0001x^2$.

enVision™ Algebra 1 • Teaching Resources

Mathematical Literacy and Vocabulary I O

Helps students develop and reinforce understanding of key terms and concepts.

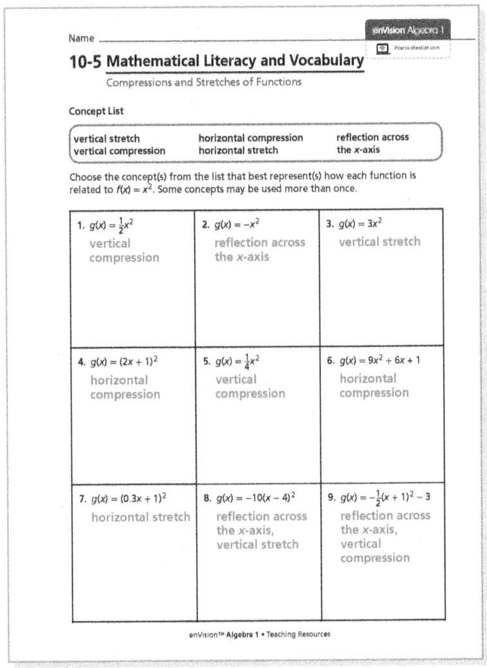

Name

10-5 Mathematical Literacy and Vocabulary

Compressions and Stretches of Functions

Concept List

vertical stretch	horizontal compression	reflection across
vertical compression	horizontal stretch	the x-axis

Choose the concept(s) from the list that best represent(s) how each function is related to $f(x) = x^2$. Some concepts may be used more than once.

1. $g(x) = \frac{1}{2}x^2$ vertical compression	2. $g(x) = -x^2$ reflection across the x-axis	3. $g(x) = 3x^2$ vertical stretch
4. $g(x) = (2x + 1)^2$ horizontal compression	5. $g(x) = \frac{1}{4}x^2$ vertical compression	6. $g(x) = 9x^2 + 6x + 1$ horizontal compression
7. $g(x) = (0.3x + 1)^2$ horizontal stretch	8. $g(x) = -10(x - 4)^2$ reflection across the x-axis, vertical stretch	9. $g(x) = -\frac{1}{2}(x + 1)^2 - 3$ reflection across the x-axis, vertical compression

enVision™ Algebra 1 • Teaching Resources

Digital Resources and Video Tutorials I O A ⚙

The **Reteach to Build Understanding, Additional Practice**, and **Enrichment** activities are available as digital assignments powered by MathXL for School. These activities are automatically assigned when students complete the lesson quiz online and are automatically scored.

Students can access instructional tutorials using the **Virtual Nerd app.**

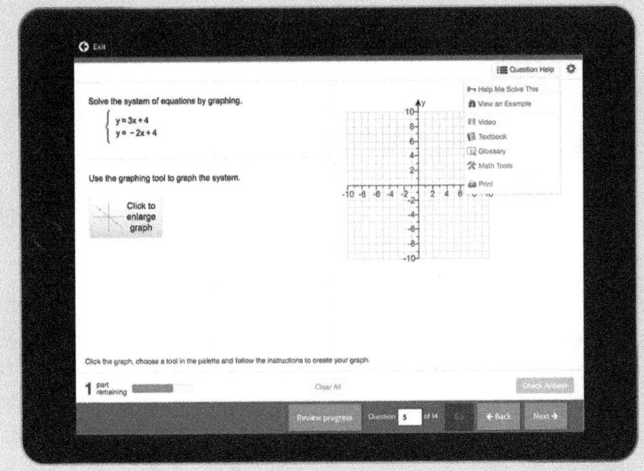
Solve the system of equations by graphing.
Use the graphing tool to graph the system.
Click to enlarge graph
Question Help
Help Me Solve This
View an Example
Video
Textbook
Glossary
Math Tools
Print
Review progress
Back
Next

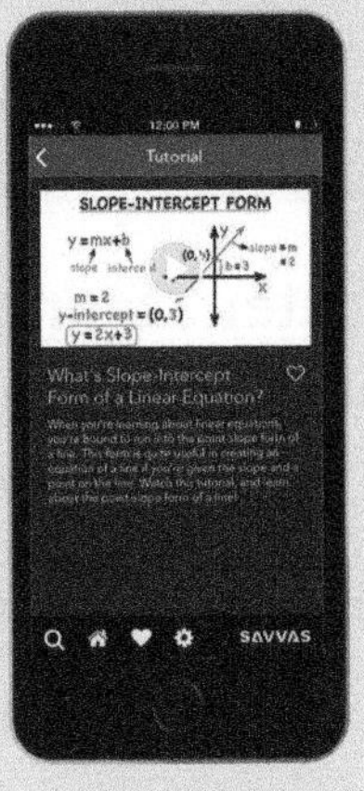
Tutorial
SLOPE-INTERCEPT FORM
What's Slope-Intercept Form of a Linear Equation?
SAVVAS

Students can also access Virtual Nerd videos using the **BouncePages app** to scan exercise pages marked with this icon. Students can download both apps for free in their mobile devices' app store.

Lesson Overview

FOCUS

Objective

Students will be able to:

✓ Use mathematical modeling to represent a problem situation and to propose a solution.

✓ Test and verify the appropriateness of their math models.

✓ Explain why the results from their mathematical models might not align exactly with the problem situation.

Essential Understanding

Many real-world problem situations can be represented with a mathematical model, but that model might not represent the real-world situation exactly.

COHERENCE

Earlier in this topic, students:

- Explored square root and cube root functions and transformed functions.

In this lesson, students:

- Develop a mathematical model to represent and propose a solution to a problem situation involving square root functions.

Later in this topic, students will:

- Refine their mathematical modeling skills using function operations and inverse functions.

RIGOR

This mathematical modeling lesson focuses on application of both math content and math practices and processes.

- Students draw on their understanding of concepts related to square root and cube root functions to develop a representative model.
- Students apply their mathematical model to test and validate its applicability to similar problem situations.

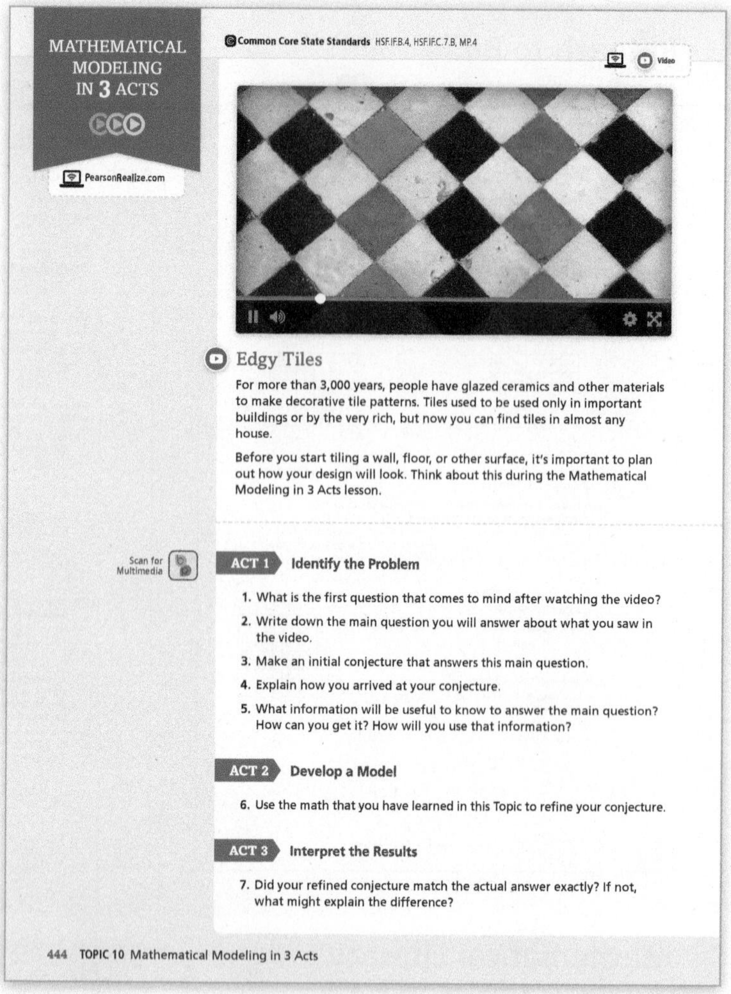
MATHEMATICAL MODELING IN 3 ACTS

PearsonRealize.com

Common Core State Standards HSF.IF.B.4, HSF.IF.C.7.B, MP.4

Video

Edgy Tiles

For more than 3,000 years, people have glazed ceramics and other materials to make decorative tile patterns. Tiles used to be used only in important buildings or by the very rich, but now you can find tiles in almost any house.

Before you start tiling a wall, floor, or other surface, it's important to plan out how your design will look. Think about this during the Mathematical Modeling in 3 Acts lesson.

Scan for Multimedia

ACT 1 Identify the Problem

1. What is the first question that comes to mind after watching the video?
2. Write down the main question you will answer about what you saw in the video.
3. Make an initial conjecture that answers this main question.
4. Explain how you arrived at your conjecture.
5. What information will be useful to know to answer the main question? How can you get it? How will you use that information?

ACT 2 Develop a Model

6. Use the math that you have learned in this Topic to refine your conjecture.

ACT 3 Interpret the Results

7. Did your refined conjecture match the actual answer exactly? If not, what might explain the difference?

444 TOPIC 10 Mathematical Modeling in 3 Acts

Student Companion

Students can do their work for the task on pages 239–240 of their *Student Companion* or on **SavvasRealize.com**.

Mathematics Overview COMMON CORE STANDARDS

Content Standards

In this lesson, students apply concepts and skills related to Common Core Standards **HSF.IF.B.4** and **HSF.IF.C.7.B**.

HSF.IF.B.4 For a function that models a relationship between two quantities, interpret key features of graphs in terms of the quantities, and sketch graphs showing key features given a verbal description of the relationship.

HSF.IF.C.7.B Graph square root, cube root, and piecewise-defined functions, including step functions and absolute value functions.

Mathematical Practice Standards

MP.4 Model With Mathematics

To solve the problem presented, students identify variables and the relationship among them, develop a model that represents the situation, and use the model to propose a solution. Students interpret their solutions and propose explanations for why their answer may not match the real-world answer.

Students also engage in sense-making **(MP.1)**, abstract and quantitative reasoning **(MP.2)**, and mathematical communication and argumentation **(MP.3)**. In testing their models, students look for patterns in the structure of their models **(MP.7, MP.8)**.

TOPIC 10 Mathematical Modeling in 3 Acts

Edgy Tiles

In this mathematical modeling task, students analyze a project to paint and assemble a square tile design. They need to determine the number of corner, edge, and interior tiles needed. To do so, they apply concepts they study in Topic 10.

ACT 1 The Hook

Play the video. The video shows a person making small tile designs, then planning a larger version of the same design. 3x3 and 4x4 designs are shown.

After the question brainstorming, present to students the Main Question they will be tasked with answering. Remind students to write down their questions and conjectures.

MAIN QUESTION

How many corners, edges, and interior tiles are needed for the large design?

ACT 2 Modeling With Math

Think about the task. Ask students to speculate how they can determine the number of each type of tile. Then have them think about what information they need.

Reveal the information. The images show information about the total number of tiles, which is not a square number, and the conditions for the large design. They also include information about the two smaller designs.

What's the connection? Give students time to struggle as they think about how to connect their ideas to what they learned in this topic about square root and cube root functions. Which type of function models how the side length of a square is dependent on its area?

Before showing the answers, find out where there is disagreement. Allow students to argue their cases and update their conjectures.

INTERESTING MOMENTS WITH STUDENTS

Students may not know how to interpret $\sqrt{432}$. You can discuss why the total number of tiles is not the same as the number of tiles that will be used in the design. Since each side of the design cannot be a fractional number of tiles, you need to round. You cannot round to the nearest square root, 441, because you don't have that many tiles. Round the square root down to the nearest integer: 20.

Necessary Information

First Design
Corner: 4
Edge: 4
Interior: 1
Total: 9

Second Design
Corner: 4
Edge: 8
Interior: 4
Total: 16

Total tiles: 432

The design will be a square.

The design will use the most tiles possible.

Video

ACT 3 The Solution

Play the video. The final video shows the entire process of painting and assembling the design. The numbers of each type of tile are tallied. Offer praise to the students whose conjectures are closest to the actual answer.

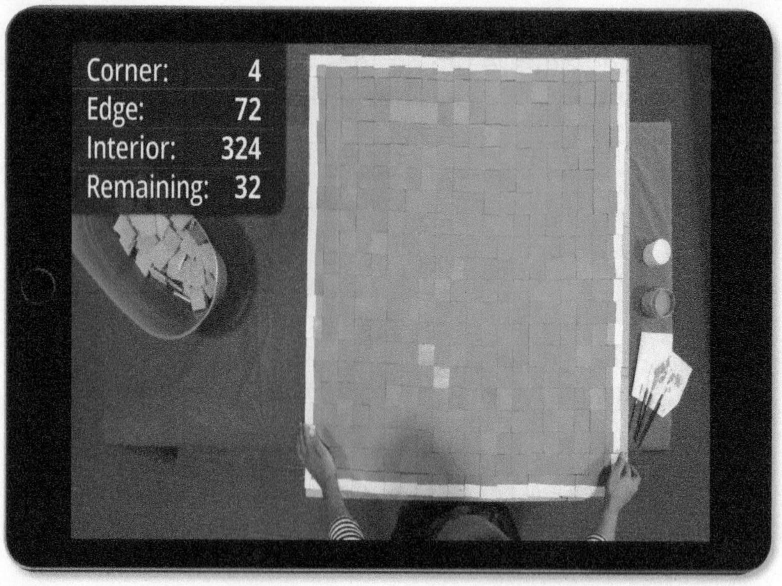
Corner: 4
Edge: 72
Interior: 324
Remaining: 32

MAIN QUESTION ANSWER

Corner: 4
Edge: 72
Interior: 324
Remaining: 32

Do the "post-game" analysis. Help students understand why the actual result might differ, even slightly, from the mathematical answer. The actual number of tiles used must be a square number, so the total tiles will add to 400, not 432. Students also may have incorrectly assumed that a 20×20 design has 80 tiles around the outside instead of 76.

ONE POSSIBLE SOLUTION

Write an equation to represent the situation.

Let T = total number of tiles.

Let s = number of tiles on each side of the design.

$$\sqrt{T} = s$$

$$\sqrt{432} = s$$

$$20.78 \approx s$$

Round down to the next integer. There will 20 tiles on each side of the design, for a total of 20^2, or 400 tiles.

Each side of the design has 2 corners and 18 edges between those corners.

There are 4 corner tiles.

There are $18 \times 4 = 72$ edge tiles.

There are $400 - (4 + 72) = 324$ interior tiles.

INTERESTING MOMENTS WITH STUDENTS

Students may try to write functions for each type of tile. Students may want to generalize and write formulas for each type of tile that depend on the total number of tiles T.

When T is a square number, the number of edges e is $e = 4(\sqrt{T} - 2)$.

The number of corner tiles c is a constant function $c = 4$.

The number of interior tiles i is $T - c - e$.

SEQUEL

As students finish, ask them to consider a design in the shape of a rectangle that uses every tile available. How would the answer change? [Answers will vary. Students' descriptions should include dimensions of the rectangle (6×71 is one option) and that a long rectangular design has significantly more edge tiles and fewer interior tiles (4 corners, 146 edges, 276 interior).]

LESSON 10-6
Operations With Functions

SavvasRealize.com

A-Z Glossary

Lesson Overview

FOCUS

Objective

Students will be able to:

✔ Combine functions using arithmetic operations, including addition, subtraction, and multiplication.

✔ Combine functions to solve real-world problems.

Essential Understanding

Functions can be combined in the same way as numbers, expressions, and polynomials. Addition, subtraction, and multiplication can be used to find $(f + g)(x)$, $(f - g)(x)$, and $(f \cdot g)(x)$.

COHERENCE

Previously in this course, students:

- Combined numbers, expressions, and polynomials using addition, subtraction, and multiplication.

In this lesson, students:

- Combine functions using addition, subtraction, and multiplication.

Later in this topic, students will:

- Find and interpret the inverse of a function.

RIGOR

This lesson emphasizes a blend of *conceptual understanding* and *application.*

- Students understand that just as you can add, subtract, and multiply numbers, expressions, and polynomials, functions can be combined using addition, subtraction, and multiplication.
- Students combine functions to solve real-world situations, which include writing and applying a function for the surface area of a cylinder that has a height twice its radius.

Vocabulary Builder

REVIEW VOCABULARY — **English** | *Spanish*

- **domain** | *dominio*
- **range** | *rango*

VOCABULARY ACTIVITY

Display graphs of linear, quadratic, and exponential functions on the board. Review what the *domain* and *range* of a function are and how to find them.

- Have students fill in the following sentences as needed.

1. The ________ of a function is the set of x-values, or inputs, that make the function true. **[domain]**
2. The ________ of a function is the set of y-values, or outputs, that make the function true. **[range]**

Student Companion

Students can do their in-class work for the lesson on pages 241–244 of their *Student Companion* or in Savvas Realize.

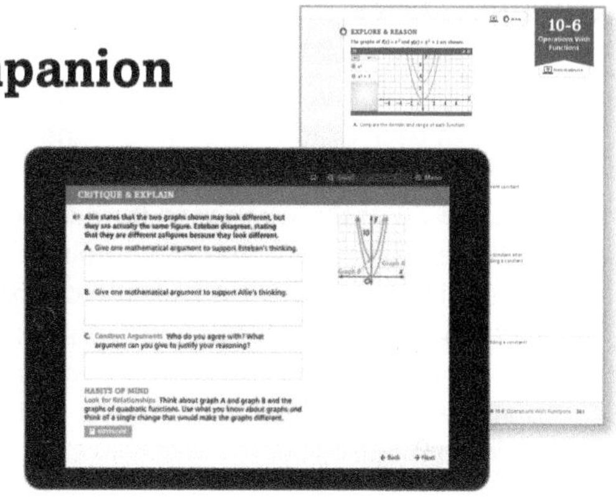

Mathematics Overview — COMMON CORE STANDARDS

Content Standards

In this lesson, students focus on this standard:

HSF.BF.A.1.B Combine standard function types—linear, quadratic, exponential, and square root functions—using addition, subtraction, and multiplication.

Mathematical Practice Standards

These standards are highlighted in this lesson:

MP.5 Use Appropriate Tools Strategically
Students graph functions either by hand or using technology both separately and then combined to make comparisons.

MP.7 Look For and Make Use of Structure
Students look for the structure in mathematics by using the Distributive Property when multiplying polynomials.

Activity

EXPLORE & REASON

INSTRUCTIONAL FOCUS Students use their knowledge of the domain and range of a function to see how adding a constant to the output of a function can affect its range, but not its domain. This leads students to use a graph to find the domain and range of two combined functions.

STUDENT COMPANION Students can complete the *Explore & Reason* activity on page 241 of their *Student Companion*.

Before WHOLE CLASS

Implement Tasks that Promote Reasoning and Problem Solving ETP

Q: What do you notice about the graphs of f and g?
[Both are parabolas. Both open upward. g is translated vertically up 3 units from f.]

During SMALL GROUP

Support Productive Struggle in Learning Mathematics ETP

Q: How can you find the domain and range of each function?
[Look at each graph to see where the function lies in the coordinate plane. The domain of the quadratic function includes all of the x-values in both directions. Then find the minimum or maximum point on the graph to determine the range. If the graph opens upward, the range is all the y-values greater than or equal to the y-coordinate of the minimum point. If the graph opens downward, the range is all the y-values less than or equal to the y-coordinate of the maximum point.]

For Early Finishers

Q: Give an example of a function that has a restricted domain and explain how you could modify the function to change its domain.
[The square root function $y = \sqrt{x}$ has a domain of $x \geq 0$. If you add a constant to the input, you can change the domain. For example, $y = \sqrt{x + 5}$ has a domain of $x \geq -5$.]

After WHOLE CLASS

Facilitate Meaningful Mathematical Discourse ETP

Q: In addition to adding a constant to the output of a function, how else could you use a constant to modify a function?
[Subtract, multiply, or divide the output of a function by a constant.]

HABITS OF MIND *Use with* **EXPLORE & REASON**

Use Structure What other key features of the graph change by adding a constant? **MP.7**

[The y-intercept of the graph changes by adding a constant.]

AVAILABLE ONLINE

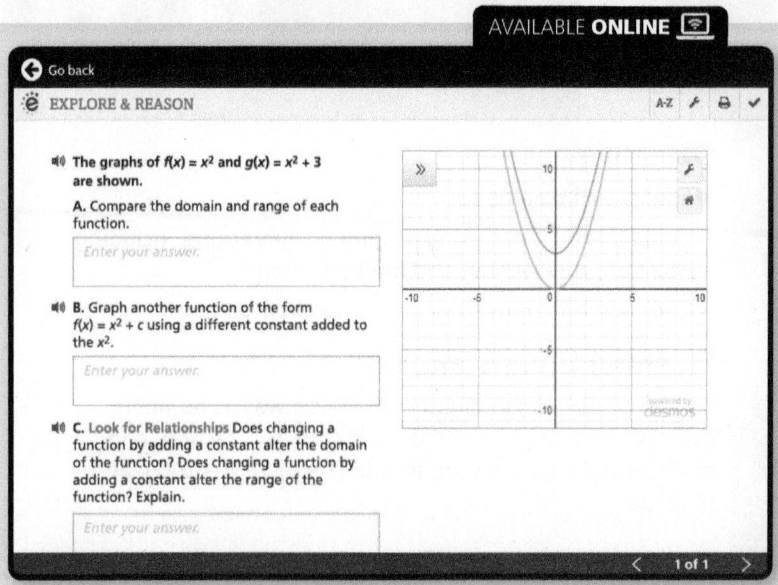

Go back
EXPLORE & REASON
The graphs of f(x) = x² and g(x) = x² + 3 are shown.
A. Compare the domain and range of each function.
Enter your answer.
B. Graph another function of the form f(x) = x² + c using a different constant added to the x².
Enter your answer.
C. Look for Relationships Does changing a function by adding a constant alter the domain of the function? Does changing a function by adding a constant alter the range of the function? Explain.
Enter your answer.
1 of 1

STUDENT EDITION, PAGE 445

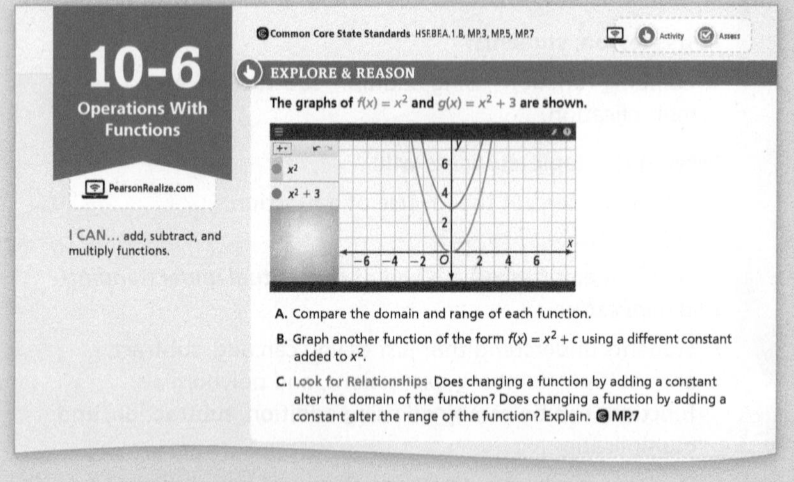

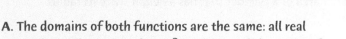

Common Core State Standards HSF.BF.A.1.B, MP.3, MP.5, MP.7
10-6
Operations With Functions
PearsonRealize.com
I CAN… add, subtract, and multiply functions.
EXPLORE & REASON
The graphs of f(x) = x² and g(x) = x² + 3 are shown.
A. Compare the domain and range of each function.
B. Graph another function of the form f(x) = x² + c using a different constant added to x².
C. Look for Relationships Does changing a function by adding a constant alter the domain of the function? Does changing a function by adding a constant alter the range of the function? Explain. MP.7

SAMPLE STUDENT WORK

A. The domains of both functions are the same: all real numbers. The range of $y = x^2$ is $y \geq 0$, and the range of $y = x^2 + 3$ is $y \geq 3$.

B. Answer may vary. Sample:

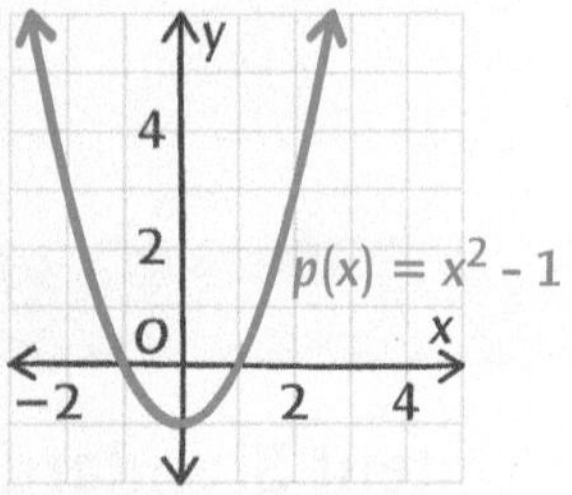

y
4
2
O
p(x) = x² - 1
x
−2
2
4

C. No; the domain of all three functions is the same. Yes; the lower limit of the range of the translated functions moves up or down according to the number added to the original function.

INTRODUCE THE ESSENTIAL QUESTION

Establish Mathematics Goals to Focus Learning ETP

Introduce students to combining functions. Explain that the same properties that are used to add, subtract, and multiply numbers, expressions, and polynomials can be used to add, subtract, and multiply functions.

EXAMPLE 1 Add and Subtract Functions

Build Procedural Fluency From Conceptual Understanding ETP

Q: What are like terms?
[combinable terms that have identical variable parts]

Q: What other properties of equality are helpful when adding functions?
[Associative Property of Equality, Commutative Property of Equality; when combining like terms, it is easier to change the order and regroup like terms together before adding.]

Q: In Part B, why is the Distributive Property important when subtracting one polynomial from another?
[You need to use this property to distribute, or multiply, each term of the second polynomial by –1.]

Try It! Answer

1. $(f - g)(x) = 15x^2 - 19x - 2$

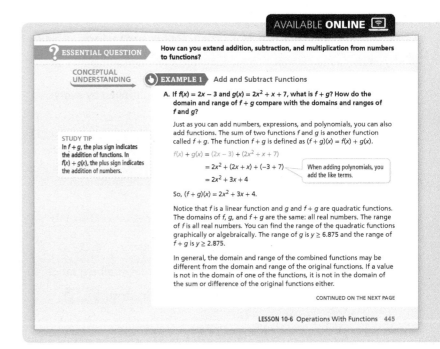

AVAILABLE ONLINE

ESSENTIAL QUESTION How can you extend addition, subtraction, and multiplication from numbers to functions?

CONCEPTUAL UNDERSTANDING

EXAMPLE 1 Add and Subtract Functions

A. If $f(x) = 2x - 3$ and $g(x) = 2x^2 + x + 7$, what is $f + g$? How do the domain and range of $f + g$ compare with the domains and ranges of f and g?

Just as you can add numbers, expressions, and polynomials, you can also add functions. The sum of two functions f and g is another function called $f + g$. The function $f + g$ is defined as $(f + g)(x) = f(x) + g(x)$.

STUDY TIP
In $f + g$, the plus sign indicates the addition of functions. In $f(x) + g(x)$, the plus sign indicates the addition of numbers.

$$f(x) + g(x) = (2x - 3) + (2x^2 + x + 7)$$
$$= 2x^2 + (2x + x) + (-3 + 7)$$
$$= 2x^2 + 3x + 4$$

When adding polynomials, you add the like terms.

So, $(f + g)(x) = 2x^2 + 3x + 4$.

Notice that f is a linear function and g and $f + g$ are quadratic functions. The domains of f, g, and $f + g$ are the same: all real numbers. The range of f is all real numbers. You can find the range of the quadratic functions graphically or algebraically. The range of g is $y \geq 6.875$ and the range of $f + g$ is $y \geq 2.875$.

In general, the domain and range of the combined functions may be different from the domain and range of the original functions. If a value is not in the domain of one of the functions, it is not in the domain of the sum or difference of the original functions either.

CONTINUED ON THE NEXT PAGE

LESSON 10-6 Operations With Functions 445

ADDITIONAL EXAMPLES

AVAILABLE ONLINE

Go back

ADDITIONAL EXAMPLE 2 ESSENTIAL QUESTION ES A-Z

What is the product of $f(x)$ and $g(x)$?
$f(x) = 5x^2 - 6x + 4$
$g(x) = -x^2 + 8$

$$f \circ g = (5x^2 - 6x + 4)(-x^2 + 8)$$
$$= (5x^2)(-x^2) + (5x^2)(8) + (-6x)(-x^2) + (-6x)(8) + (4)(-x^2) + (4)(8)$$
$$= -5x^4 + 40x^2 + 6x^3 - 48x - 4x^2 + 32$$
$$= -5x^4 + 6x^3 + 36x^2 - 48x + 32$$

1 of 2

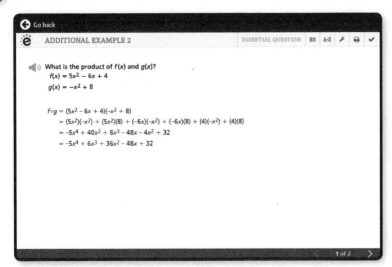

Example 2 Students multiply functions with these additional examples.

Q: What property can you use to multiply functions?
[the Distributive Property]

Go back

ADDITIONAL EXAMPLE 3 ESSENTIAL QUESTION ES A-Z

The population of two species of birds in a forest can be modeled by the functions, where x is the time in years:
$f(x) = -10x^2 + 102x + 950$
$g(x) = -5x^2 + 82x + 850$

What is the function for the combined populations and how many birds of both species will there be in 5 years?

$f(x) + g(x) = -10x^2 + 102x + 950 + -5x^2 + 82x + 850$
$f(x) + g(x) = -15x^2 + 184x + 1800$
After 5 years: $-15(5)^2 + 184(5) + 1800 = 2345$
In 5 years, there will be 2,345 birds.

1 of 2

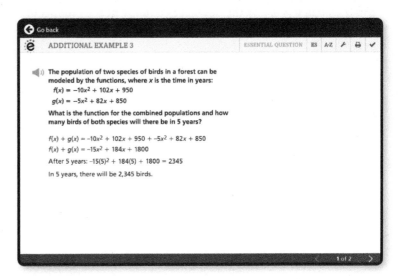

Example 3 Students apply function operations with this real-world bird species problem.

Q: What is the domain and range of the combined function?
[The domain is $x \geq 0$, because you cannot have a negative time. The range is $0 \leq y \leq 2{,}364.3$.]

EXAMPLE 2 Multiply Functions

Use and Connect Mathematical Representations ETP

Q: How is the Distributive Property used when multiplying polynomials?
[Every term in the second polynomial is multiplied by every term in the first polynomial.]

Q: What is the domain and range for any parabola?
[The domain is all real numbers. The range is y-values greater than or equal to the minimum for a parabola that opens upward and y-values less than or equal to the maximum for a parabola that opens downward.]

Try It! Answers

2. a. $(f \cdot g)(x) = 2x^{\frac{3}{2}} - \sqrt{x}$; domain: $x \geq 0$; range: $y > -0.27$

b. $(f \cdot g)(x) = 3x^2(2^x) + 2^{x+2}$; domain: all real numbers; range: $y > 0$

Elicit and Use Evidence of Student Thinking ETP

Q: How does $(4)(2^x) = 2^{x+2}$?
[$4 = 2^2$, so $(4)(2^x) = (2^2)(2^x) = 2^{x+2}$]

Common Error

Try It! 2 Some students may think $(2^x)(4) = 8^x$. Have them substitute a value for x into each expression and compare their values. For example, when $x = 3$, $2^3(4) = 32 \neq 512 = 8^3$.

HABITS OF MIND

Use with **EXAMPLES 1 & 2**

Construct Arguments A student claims that for any two functions, the domain and range of the product of the functions will be the same as the domain and range of the sum of the functions. Is the student correct? Explain. Provide a counterexample if the student is incorrect. MP.3

[No; $f(x) = \sqrt{x}$, $g(x) = 2\sqrt{x}$. The domain and range of the sum of f and g will be $y \geq 0$, and the domain and range of the product of f and g will be all real numbers.]

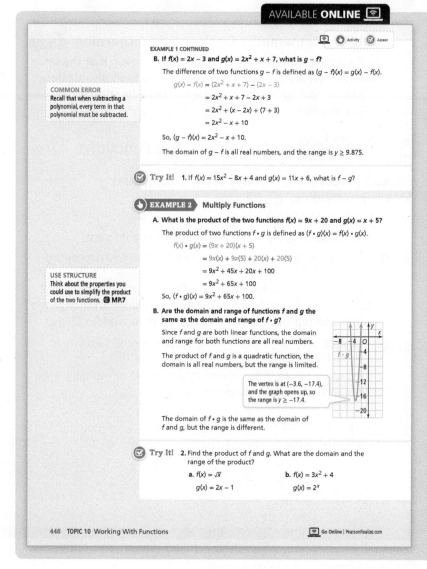

AVAILABLE ONLINE

Activity Assess

EXAMPLE 1 CONTINUED

B. If $f(x) = 2x - 3$ and $g(x) = 2x^2 + x + 7$, what is $g - f$?

The difference of two functions $g - f$ is defined as $(g - f)(x) = g(x) - f(x)$.

$$\begin{aligned} g(x) - f(x) &= (2x^2 + x + 7) - (2x - 3) \\ &= 2x^2 + x + 7 - 2x + 3 \\ &= 2x^2 + (x - 2x) + (7 + 3) \\ &= 2x^2 - x + 10 \end{aligned}$$

COMMON ERROR
Recall that when subtracting a polynomial, every term in that polynomial must be subtracted.

So, $(g - f)(x) = 2x^2 - x + 10$.

The domain of $g - f$ is all real numbers, and the range is $y \geq 9.875$.

Try It! 1. If $f(x) = 15x^2 - 8x + 4$ and $g(x) = 11x + 6$, what is $f - g$?

EXAMPLE 2 Multiply Functions

A. What is the product of the two functions $f(x) = 9x + 20$ and $g(x) = x + 5$?

The product of two functions $f \cdot g$ is defined as $(f \cdot g)(x) = f(x) \cdot g(x)$.

$$\begin{aligned} f(x) \cdot g(x) &= (9x + 20)(x + 5) \\ &= 9x(x) + 9x(5) + 20(x) + 20(5) \\ &= 9x^2 + 45x + 20x + 100 \\ &= 9x^2 + 65x + 100 \end{aligned}$$

USE STRUCTURE
Think about the properties you could use to simplify the product of the two functions. MP.7

So, $(f \cdot g)(x) = 9x^2 + 65x + 100$.

B. Are the domain and range of functions f and g the same as the domain and range of $f \cdot g$?

Since f and g are both linear functions, the domain and range for both functions are all real numbers.

The product of f and g is a quadratic function, the domain is all real numbers, but the range is limited.

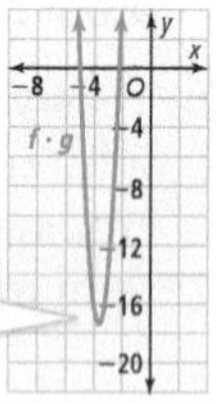
y
x
−8
−4
O
f · g
−4
−8
−12
−16
−20

The vertex is at (−3.6, −17.4), and the graph opens up, so the range is $y \geq -17.4$.

The domain of $f \cdot g$ is the same as the domain of f and g, but the range is different.

Try It! 2. Find the product of f and g. What are the domain and the range of the product?

a. $f(x) = \sqrt{x}$
$g(x) = 2x - 1$

b. $f(x) = 3x^2 + 4$
$g(x) = 2^x$

446 TOPIC 10 Working With Functions

Go Online | PearsonRealize.com

Struggling Students

USE WITH EXAMPLE 1 Some students may struggle to remember that when subtracting a polynomial, they need to distribute the negative sign to each term in the polynomial being subtracted.

- Have students practice subtracting $g(x)$ from $f(x)$.

1. $f(x) = 2x + 3$ and $g(x) = 6 - x$.
[$f(x) - g(x) = 3x - 3$]
2. $f(x) = 2x + 3$ and $g(x) = 5x + 7$.
[$f(x) - g(x) = -3x - 4$]

Q: Why do you distribute the negative sign to every term in the polynomial that is being subtracted?
[Sample: When you subtract a polynomial, you are subtracting every term in the polynomial.]

ADV Advanced Students

USE WITH EXAMPLE 2 Have students extend what they know about multiplying functions with this additional example.

- Find $f \cdot g$.

1. $f(x) = 2x^2 - 3x + 9$ and $g(x) = x^3 + 5x^2 - 1$.
[$f \cdot g = 2x^5 + 7x^4 - 6x^3 + 43x^2 + 3x - 9$]

Q: Using technology, what are the domain and range of f, g, and $f \cdot g$?
[f has a domain of all real numbers and a range of $y \geq 0$. Both g and $f \cdot g$ have a domain and a range of all real numbers.]

EXAMPLE 3 Apply Function Operations

Use and Connect Mathematical Representations ETP

Q: Why do you add $f(r)$ and $g(r)$?
[The value of $f(r)$ gives the combined area of the top and bottom of the cylinder, and the value of $g(r)$ gives the area of the side surface of the cylinder. To get a function for the total surface area, you must add the two functions.]

Q: Why don't you evaluate $(f + g)(120)$ to find the answer?
[You need to find the value of x such that $(f + g)(x) = 120$, which is not the same as $(f + g)(120)$.]

Try It! Answer

3. radius: 2.76 ft; height: 5.52 ft

HABITS OF MIND

Use with **EXAMPLE 3**

Make Sense and Persevere Compare the domains and ranges of f, g, and $f + g$. Explain why your answer makes sense for this context. **MP.1**

[The domain and range of f, g, and $f + g$ are $(0, \infty)$. This makes sense because all three are functions of the radius, and the radius must be positive.]

AVAILABLE ONLINE

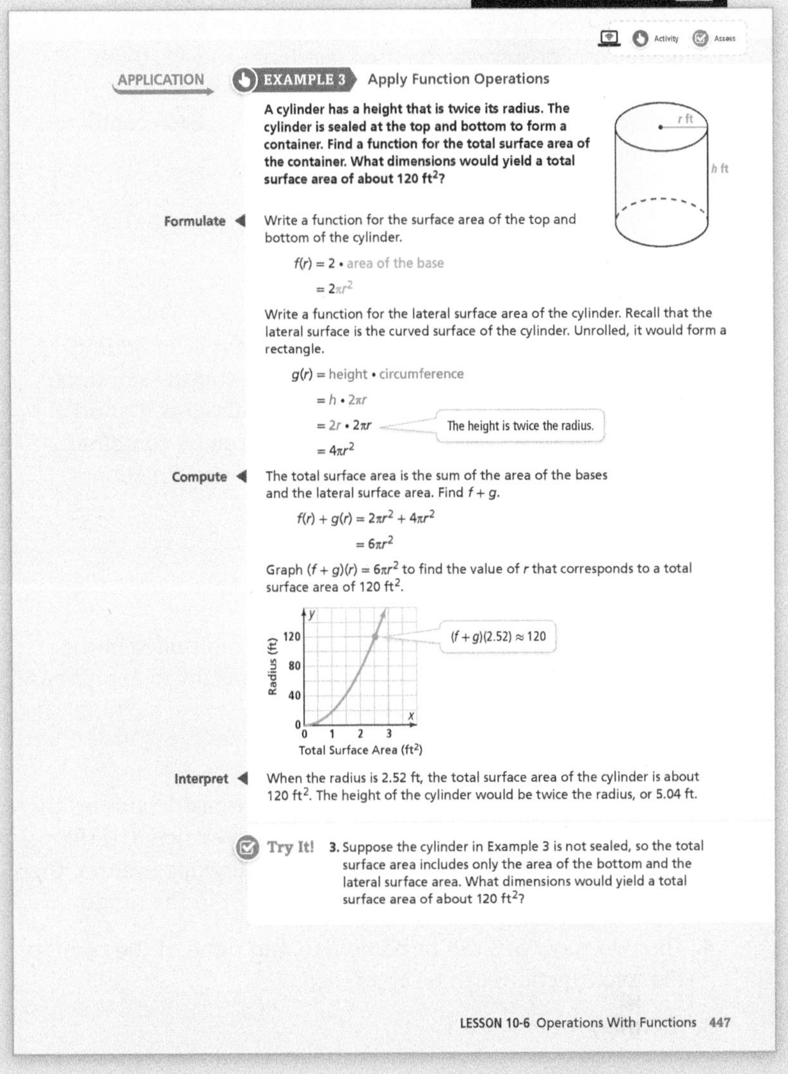

Activity Assess

APPLICATION

EXAMPLE 3 Apply Function Operations

A cylinder has a height that is twice its radius. The cylinder is sealed at the top and bottom to form a container. Find a function for the total surface area of the container. What dimensions would yield a total surface area of about 120 ft²?

r ft
h ft

Formulate Write a function for the surface area of the top and bottom of the cylinder.

$f(r) = 2 \cdot$ area of the base

$= 2\pi r^2$

Write a function for the lateral surface area of the cylinder. Recall that the lateral surface is the curved surface of the cylinder. Unrolled, it would form a rectangle.

$g(r) =$ height $\cdot$ circumference

$= h \cdot 2\pi r$

$= 2r \cdot 2\pi r$ (The height is twice the radius.)

$= 4\pi r^2$

Compute The total surface area is the sum of the area of the bases and the lateral surface area. Find $f + g$.

$f(r) + g(r) = 2\pi r^2 + 4\pi r^2$

$= 6\pi r^2$

Graph $(f + g)(r) = 6\pi r^2$ to find the value of r that corresponds to a total surface area of 120 ft².

y
120
80
40
0
Radius (ft)
x
0 1 2 3
Total Surface Area (ft²)
(f + g)(2.52) ≈ 120

Interpret When the radius is 2.52 ft, the total surface area of the cylinder is about 120 ft². The height of the cylinder would be twice the radius, or 5.04 ft.

Try It! **3.** Suppose the cylinder in Example 3 is not sealed, so the total surface area includes only the area of the bottom and the lateral surface area. What dimensions would yield a total surface area of about 120 ft²?

LESSON 10-6 Operations With Functions 447

ELL English Language Learners (*Use with* **EXAMPLE 3**)

LISTENING BEGINNING Show a cylinder to students. Explain that the *bases* of the cylinder are the circle-shaped sides on the top and the bottom. Explain that the *lateral surface* is the curved surface around the sides of the cylinder.

Q: How can you find the area of the bases?
[Find the area of one of the circles and multiply by 2.]

Q: Imagine cutting down the side of the cylinder and flattening out the lateral surface. What shape does the lateral surface have? [rectangle]

Q: How can you find the lateral surface area?
[Multiply its length and width. The length is the height of the cylinder, and the width is the circumference of the circle-shaped base.]

SPEAKING INTERMEDIATE Read the second sentence in the problem to students.

Q: What does "sealed at the top and bottom" mean?
[The top and bottom are connected to the sides so there are no leaks.]

Q: How does the fact that the cylinder is sealed at the top and bottom affect the problem of finding the surface area?
[It tells you that the top and bottom are surfaces, so you have to include their areas in the surface area of the cylinder.]

Q: What word do you see in the word *container*? How are these words related?
[contain; Contain means to hold something, so a container is something that can hold something else.]

WRITING ADVANCED Ask students to write an explanation of what the graph shows in terms of the problem situation. Encourage students to use the terms *radius, surface area, parabola,* and *quadratic* in their explanations.

Q: What do the numbers along the axes represent?
[x = radius in feet; y = total surface area in square feet]

Q: What is the shape of the graph? Why does it have that shape?
[Sample: The graph is half of a parabola. The function is a constant (6π) times r^2, so the function is quadratic. But since it represents a real-world scenario, the value of r cannot be negative.]

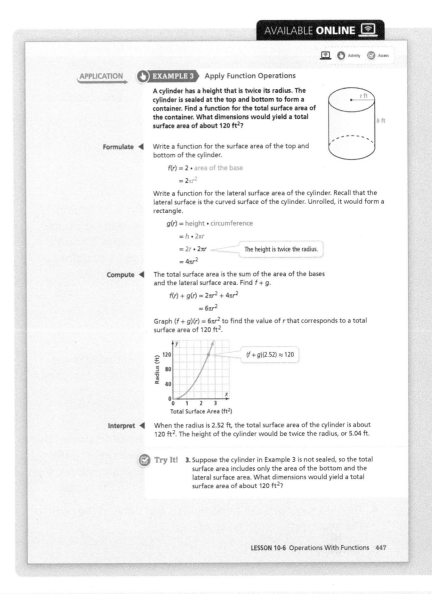

CONCEPT SUMMARY Function Operations

Q: Describe how to add, subtract, and multiply functions. [For addition, use the properties of equality to combine like terms. For subtraction, first distribute the −1, then use the properties of equality to combine like terms. For multiplication, use the Distributive Property, then combine like terms.]

Do You UNDERSTAND? | Do You KNOW HOW?

Common Error

Exercise 6 Some students might think that after adding *f* and *g*, the terms need to be combined and the solution needs to be further simplified. Remind students that only terms that have identical variable parts can be combined. If there are no like terms, then the combined function is already in simplest form.

Answers

1. Functions can be added, subtracted, and multiplied in the same way as numbers, however, it is important to apply the operation to all terms in the expression.
2. Distributive Property
3. Graph the combined function. If there are restrictions on the *x*-values of the graph, then the domain is restricted. If the graph of the function does not pass through all *y*-values, then the values it does not pass through are not in the range.
4. The two functions can be combined, but none of the terms of the two functions can be combined.
5. $(f+g)(x) = 2x^2 - x + 1$
6. $(f+g)(x) = x^2 + 3^x$
7. $(f-g)(x) = 3x^2 - 2x - 7$
8. $(f-g)(x) = 6x - \sqrt{2x} + 5$
9. $(f \cdot g)(x) = 3x^4 - 12x^3 - 2x^2 + 8x$
10. $(f \cdot g)(x) = 6x(8)^x$

AVAILABLE ONLINE

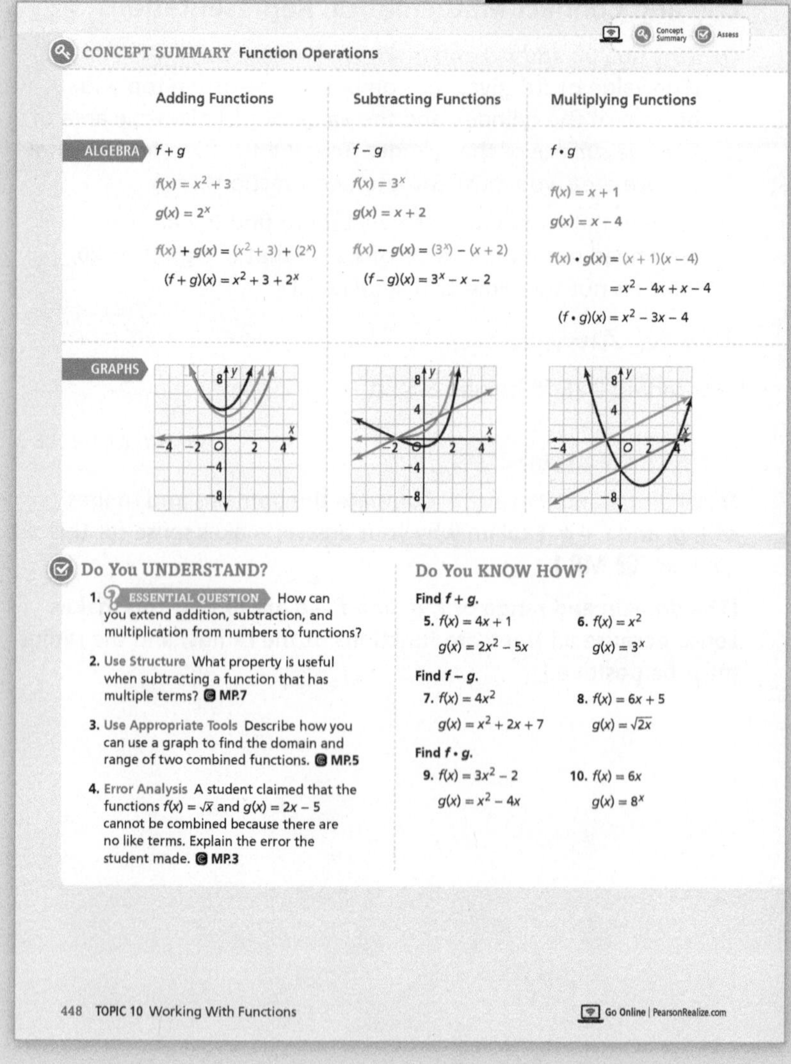

CONCEPT SUMMARY Function Operations

	Adding Functions	Subtracting Functions	Multiplying Functions
ALGEBRA	$f+g$ $f(x) = x^2 + 3$ $g(x) = 2^x$ $f(x) + g(x) = (x^2+3) + (2^x)$ $(f+g)(x) = x^2 + 3 + 2^x$	$f-g$ $f(x) = 3^x$ $g(x) = x + 2$ $f(x) - g(x) = (3^x) - (x+2)$ $(f-g)(x) = 3^x - x - 2$	$f \cdot g$ $f(x) = x + 1$ $g(x) = x - 4$ $f(x) \cdot g(x) = (x+1)(x-4)$ $= x^2 - 4x + x - 4$ $(f \cdot g)(x) = x^2 - 3x - 4$
GRAPHS			

Do You UNDERSTAND?

1. ESSENTIAL QUESTION How can you extend addition, subtraction, and multiplication from numbers to functions?
2. Use Structure What property is useful when subtracting a function that has multiple terms? MP.7
3. Use Appropriate Tools Describe how you can use a graph to find the domain and range of two combined functions. MP.5
4. Error Analysis A student claimed that the functions $f(x) = \sqrt{x}$ and $g(x) = 2x - 5$ cannot be combined because there are no like terms. Explain the error the student made. MP.3

Do You KNOW HOW?

Find $f + g$.

5. $f(x) = 4x + 1$, $g(x) = 2x^2 - 5x$
6. $f(x) = x^2$, $g(x) = 3^x$

Find $f - g$.

7. $f(x) = 4x^2$, $g(x) = x^2 + 2x + 7$
8. $f(x) = 6x + 5$, $g(x) = \sqrt{2x}$

Find $f \cdot g$.

9. $f(x) = 3x^2 - 2$, $g(x) = x^2 - 4x$
10. $f(x) = 6x$, $g(x) = 8^x$

448 TOPIC 10 Working With Functions

Go Online | PearsonRealize.com

SavvasRealize.com

Practice Tutorials Math Tools

PRACTICE & PROBLEM SOLVING

AVAILABLE ONLINE

Lesson Practice You may opt to have students complete the automatically scored Practice and Problem Solving items online powered by MathXL for School.

Choose from: **Lesson Practice**

Adaptive Practice

You may also take advantage of the bank of exercises for assigning additional practice.

Assignment Guide

Basic	Advanced
11–22, 25–32	11–18, 21–32

Item Analysis

Example	Items	DOK
1	16–19, 31	1
	11, 12, 27, 29	2
2	20–25	1
	13, 14, 28, 30	2
3	26	2
	15, 32	3

AVAILABLE ONLINE

PRACTICE & PROBLEM SOLVING

Scan for Multimedia

Practice Tutorial

Additional Exercises Available Online

UNDERSTAND

11. Mathematical Connections How is adding functions like adding polynomials? How is it different?

12. Look for Relationships Write two functions that, when combined by adding, have a different domain than at least one of the original functions. MP.7

13. Make Sense and Persevere Given the graphs of f and g, sketch the graphs of $f + g$ and $f \cdot g$. MP.1

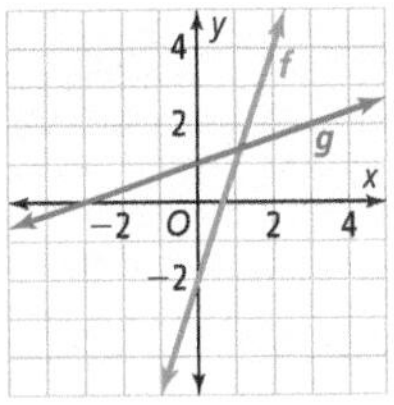
y
4
2
f
g
x
−2
O
2
4
−2

14. Error Analysis Describe and correct the error a student made in multiplying the two functions, $f(x) = x^3 + 3x^2 + 1$ and $g(x) = 2x - 1$. MP.3

$(x^3 + 3x^2 + 1)(2x - 1)$
$= x^3(2x) + 3x^2(2x) + 2x$
$= 2x^4 + 6x^3 + 2x$ ✗

15. Higher Order Thinking What two functions could you multiply to create the function shown in the graph? How do the domain and range of each of the functions compare to the domain and range of the graphed function?

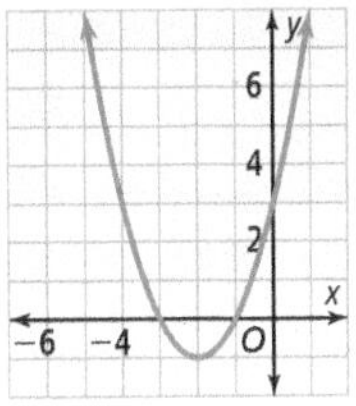
y
6
4
2
x
−6
−4
O

PRACTICE

Find $f + g$. SEE EXAMPLE 1

16. $f(x) = 6x^3 + 7x$
$g(x) = x^2 - 3x + 2$
$(f + g)(x) = 6x^3 + x^2 + 4x + 2$

17. $f(x) = 3\sqrt{x}$
$g(x) = -2x + 4$
$(f + g)(x) = -2x + 3\sqrt{x} + 4$

Find $f - g$. SEE EXAMPLE 1

18. $f(x) = 2x^3 + 2x^2 - 3$
$g(x) = 8x + 15$
$(f - g)(x) = 2x^3 + 2x^2 - 8x - 18$

19. $f(x) = 7^x$
$g(x) = 5x^2 - 2x - 4$
$(f - g)(x) = 7^x - 5x^2 + 2x + 4$

Find $f \cdot g$. SEE EXAMPLE 2

20. $f(x) = 9x - 2$
$g(x) = x^2 + 4x - 7$

21. $f(x) = 3x^2 + 8x + 2$
$g(x) = -6x + 1$

22. $f(x) = 3^x$
$g(x) = 5x^2 - 2$
$(f \cdot g)(x) = 5x^2(3^x) - 2(3^x)$

23. $f(x) = \sqrt{5x}$
$g(x) = 7x + 2$
$(f \cdot g)(x) = 7x\sqrt{5x} + 2\sqrt{5x}$

Given the graphs of f and g, graph $f + g$. Compare the domain and range of $f + g$ to the domains and ranges of f and g.

24.

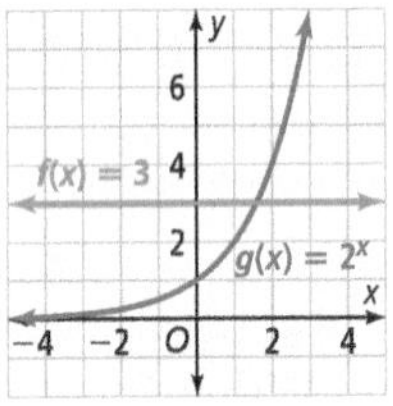
y
6
f(x) = 3
4
2
g(x) = 2^x
x
−4
−2
O
2
4

25.

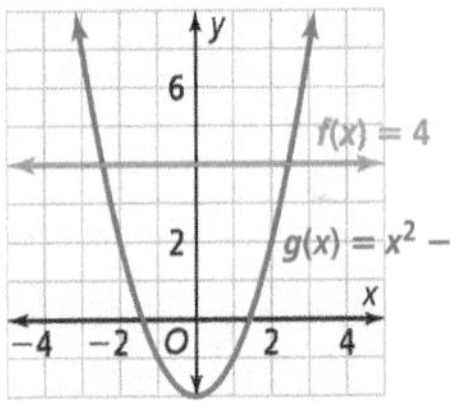
y
6
f(x) = 4
2
g(x) = x^2 − 2
x
−4
−2
O
2
4

26. A florist charges \$10 for delivery plus an additional \$2 per mile from the flower shop. The florist pays the delivery driver \$0.50 per mile and \$5 for gas per delivery. If x is the number of miles a delivery location is from the flower shop, what expression models the amount of money the florist earns for each delivery? SEE EXAMPLE 3
$f(x) = 1.5x + 5$

LESSON 10-6 Operations With Functions 449

Answers

11. When adding polynomials and functions, you combine any like terms. However, functions can include terms that cannot appear in a polynomial, such as radicals and terms with the variable in the exponent. Adding two polynomials results in another polynomial. Adding two functions results in another function, but not necessarily a type of function that matches either of the two original functions.

12. Sample: $f(x) = \sqrt{x}$ and $g(x) = x^2$

13.

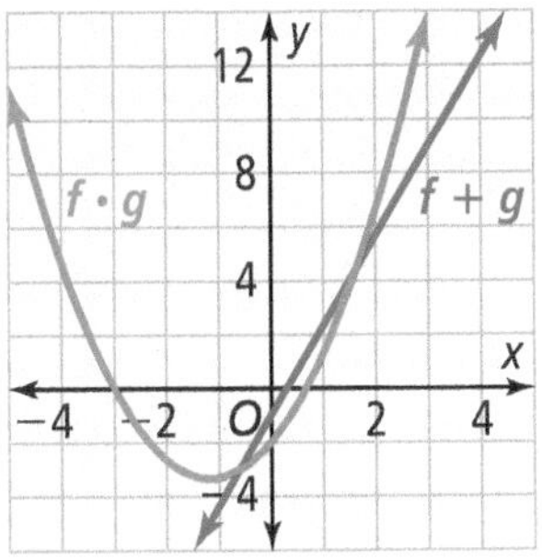
y
12
8
f • g
f + g
4
x
−4
−2
O
2
4
−4

14. The student did not multiply all the terms in the second function by the terms in the first function. The correct product of the two functions is $(f \cdot g)(x) = 2x^4 + 5x^3 - 3x^2 + 2x - 1$.

15. Sample: $f(x) = x + 3$, $g(x) = x + 1$, $(f \cdot g)(x) = x^2 + 4x + 3$. The domain and range of f and g are all real numbers. The domain for $f \cdot g$ also includes all real numbers, but the range changes. The range of $f \cdot g$ is $y \geq -1$.

20. $(f \cdot g)(x) = 9x^3 + 34x^2 - 71x + 14$

21. $(f \cdot g)(x) = -18x^3 - 45x^2 - 4x + 2$

See answers for Exercises 24–25 on next page.

Answers

24.

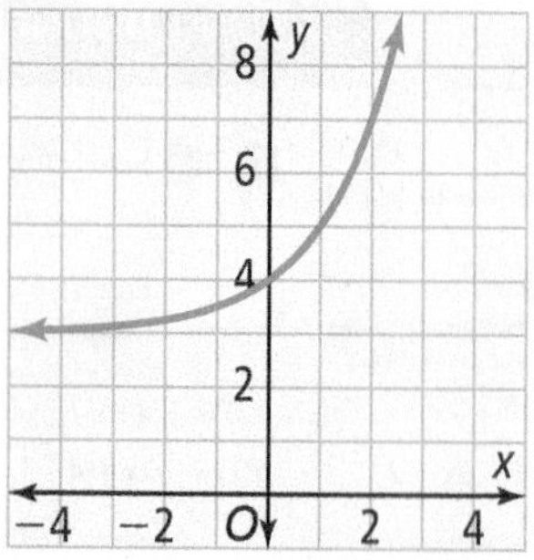

y
8
6
4
2
x
−4
−2
O
2
4

The domain of $f + g$ is the same as the domain of f and the domain of g. The range of $f + g$ is $y > 3$, but the range of f is 3 and the range of g is $y > 0$.

25.

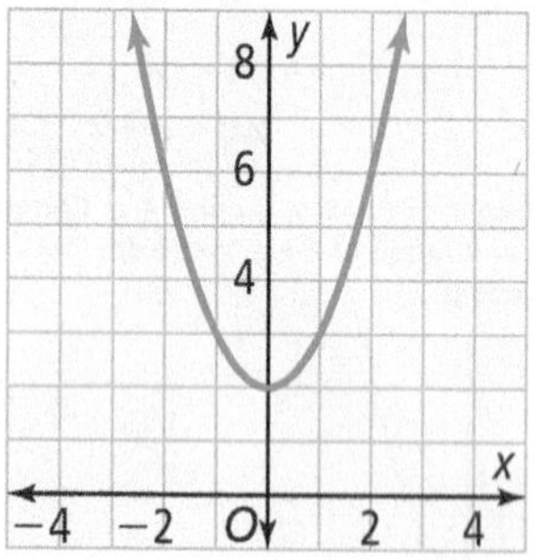

y
8
6
4
x
−4
−2
O
2
4

The domain of $f + g$ is the same as the domain of f and the domain of g. The range of $f + g$ is $y \geq 2$, but the range of f is 4 and the range of g is $y \geq -2$.

27. a. $f(x) = 75x + 50$

b. $g(x) = 36x$

c. $(f - g)(x) = 75x + 50 - 36x = 39x + 50$

28. a. $f(x) = 200$; constant

b. $g(x) = -20x^2 + 80x + 40$

c. \$6.24

29. a. $f(r) = 2\pi r^2$

b. $g(r) = 40\pi r$

c. $(f + g)(r) = 2\pi r^2 + 40\pi r$

32. Part A $f(x) = 24x$, $g(x) = 34x$

Part B Domain of f: 0 to 13 gal; Range of f: 0 to 312 mi; Domain of g: 0 to 13 gal; Range of g: 0 to 442 mi

Part C Answer may vary. Sample: $h(x) = \frac{1}{2}(24x + 34x)$

Part D Domain of h: 0 to 13 gal; Range of h: 0 to 312 mi

AVAILABLE **ONLINE**

PRACTICE & PROBLEM SOLVING

Practice Tutorial

Mixed Review Available Online

APPLY

27. Make Sense and Persevere A laser tag center charges \$50 to set up a party, and \$75 per hour. The center pays its employees that work the party a total of \$36 per hour. **MP.1**

a. Write a function f that represents the amount of revenue from a party that runs for x hours.

b. Write a function g that represents the expenses for a party that runs for x hours.

c. Write a combined function that represents the amount of profit the laser tag center makes on a party that runs x hours.

28. Reason A store is selling bumper stickers in support of a local sports team. The function $h(x) = -20x^2 + 80x + 240$ models the revenue, in dollars, the store expects to make by increasing the price of a bumper sticker x dollars over the original price of \$2. The store paid a total of \$200 for the bumper stickers. **MP.2**

a. Write a function that represents the amount of money the store paid for the bumper stickers. What kind of function is it?

b. What function models the store's profit from the bumper stickers?

c. What is the price per bumper sticker when the store makes a profit of \$20?

29. Model With Mathematics The surface of a cylindrical tank is being painted. The total surface area of a cylindrical tank is the sum of two area functions. **MP.4**

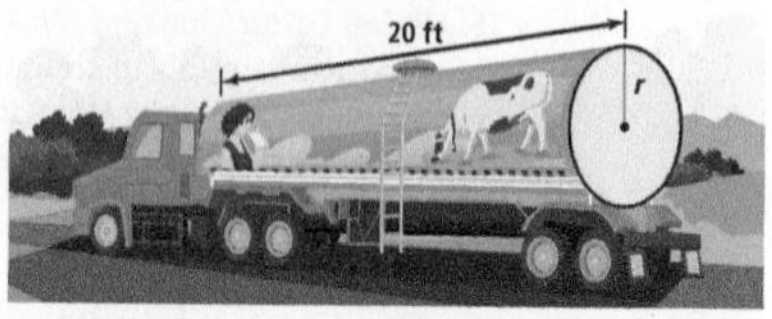

20 ft
r

a. Write a function that gives the total area of the two circular ends as a function of radius.

b. Write a function that gives the lateral surface area of the cylinder as a function of radius.

c. Combine the functions from parts (a) and (b) to get the total surface area of the cylinder as a function of radius.

ASSESSMENT PRACTICE

30. Given the functions $f(x) = x + 8$ and $g(x) = x^2 - 9$, which of the following are true statements about $f - g$? Select all that apply.

Ⓐ It is a linear function.
Ⓑ It is a quadratic function.
Ⓒ The domain is all real numbers.
Ⓓ The range is all real numbers.
Ⓔ The range is $y \geq 17$.

31. SAT/ACT The function h is the sum of the functions $f(x) = 3x + 5$ and $g(x) = 2x^2 - 6x - 2$. Which represents h?

Ⓐ $h(x) = 5x^2 - x - 2$
Ⓑ $h(x) = 2x^2 - 3x + 3$
Ⓒ $h(x) = 2x^2 + 9x + 7$
Ⓓ $h(x) = -3x + 3$

32. Performance Task A fuel-efficient car can travel 6 miles further per gallon than average while driving on the highway, and about 4 miles less than average while in the city.

Gas tank holds about 13 gallons.
averages 28 mpg

Part A Write two functions to determine the distance the driver could travel in the city or on the highway, using x gallons of gasoline.

Part B Assuming that the car has full tank of gas, what is the domain and range of each function?

Part C Suppose the driver does a combination of city and highway driving. Using the functions you found in Part A, write one function that could represent the distance traveled on x gallons of gasoline.

Part D Assume that the car has full tank of gas, what is the domain and range of the function you found in Part C?

Go Online | PearsonRealize.com

LESSON QUIZ

Use the Lesson Quiz to assess students' understanding of the mathematics in the lesson.

Students can take the Lesson Quiz online or you can download a printable copy from **SavvasRealize.com**. The Lesson Quiz is also available in the *Assessment Resources* book.

Item Analysis

Item	DOK	Standards
1	1	HSF.BF.A.1.B
2	1	HSF.BF.A.1.B
3	2	HSF.BF.A.1.B
4	1	HSF.BF.A.1.B
5	2	HSF.BF.A.1.B

RtI Use the student scores on the Lesson Quiz to prescribe differentiated assignments.

If students take the Lesson Quiz online, it will be automatically scored and appropriate differentiated practice will be assigned based on student performance.

I Intervention	0–3 points	• Reteach to Build Understanding • Mathematical Literacy and Vocabulary • Additional Practice
O On-Level	4 points	• Mathematical Literacy and Vocabulary • Additional Practice • Enrichment
A Advanced	5 points	• Enrichment

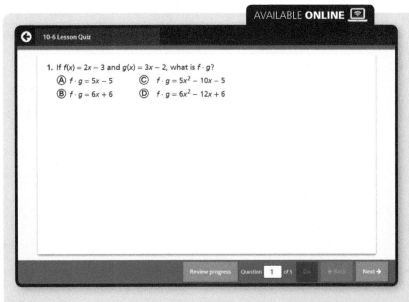

AVAILABLE **ONLINE**

10-6 Lesson Quiz

1. If $f(x) = 2x - 3$ and $g(x) = 3x - 2$, what is $f \cdot g$?

Ⓐ $f \cdot g = 5x - 5$ Ⓒ $f \cdot g = 5x^2 - 10x - 5$

Ⓑ $f \cdot g = 6x + 6$ Ⓓ $f \cdot g = 6x^2 - 12x + 6$

Review progress Question 1 of 5 Go Back Next

ASSESSMENT RESOURCES

Name ______________________

enVision Algebra 1

PearsonRealize.com

10-6 Lesson Quiz

Operations With Functions

1. If $f(x) = 2x - 3$ and $g(x) = 3x - 2$, what is $f \cdot g$?

Ⓐ $f(x) \cdot g(x) = 5x - 5$ Ⓒ $f(x) \cdot g(x) = 5x^2 - 10x - 5$

Ⓑ $f(x) \cdot g(x) = 6x + 6$ Ⓓ $f(x) \cdot g(x) = 6x^2 - 13x + 6$

2. If $f(x) = 3x^2 + 5x - 7$ and $g(x) = -x^2 + 2x + 1$, what is $f + g$?

$2x^2 + 7x - 6$

3. The functions $f(x) = -3x^2 - 1$ and $g(x) = 4x + 8$ are combined by subtracting g from f. Which of the following statements about $f - g$ are true? Select all that apply.

Ⓐ The domain is all real numbers.

Ⓑ The range is all real numbers.

Ⓒ The range is $y \geq 9$.

Ⓓ It is a linear function.

Ⓔ It is a quadratic function.

4. Complete the sentence with <, >, ≤, or ≥ and the correct value for the range.

If $f(x) = x^2 + 5$ and $g(x) = 6$, then the range of $f + g$ is y ≥ 11.

5. The surface area of a cylindrical can is given by the function $g(r) = 2\pi r^2 + 6\pi r$, where r is the radius. If $f(r) = 2\pi r^2$ gives the total area of the two circular ends, which combined function gives the surface area of the side of the cylinder?

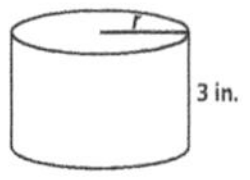
r
3 in.

Ⓐ $f + g$ Ⓒ $g - f$

Ⓑ $f - g$ Ⓓ $f \cdot g$

enVision™ Algebra 1 • Assessment Resources

DIFFERENTIATED RESOURCES

I = Intervention **O** = On-Level **A** = Advanced

= This activity is available as a digital assignment powered by MathXL® for School.

AVAILABLE **ONLINE**

Reteach to Build Understanding I

Provides scaffolded reteaching for the key lesson concepts.

Name ________ enVision Algebra 1 PearsonRealize.com

10-6 Reteach to Build Understanding

Operations With Functions

1. Match each expression with the correct combined form.
   $f(x) = x^2 - 2$ $g(x) = x + 5$ $h(x) = 2^x$
   - $f + g$ — $x^2 + x + 3$
   - $f - g$ — $x^2 - x - 7$
   - $g + h$ — $2^x + x + 5$
   - $f \cdot g$ — $x^3 + 5x^2 - 2x - 10$
   - $h - g$ — $2^x - x - 5$
2. A student incorrectly added $f(x) = 9x + 4$ and $g(x) = 8^x$. Find and correct the error.
   $f(x) + g(x) = 9x + 4 + 8^x$
   $= (9x + 8x) + 4$
   $= 17x + 4$
   Sample: The student incorrectly wrote 8^x as $8x$ in the second step. $9x$ and 8^x cannot be combined, so the correct answer is $8^x + 9x + 4$.
3. Complete the steps to find $f - g$, where $f(x) = 5x^2 + 3x - 1$ and $g(x) = 5x + 4$.
   $f(x) - g(x) = (5x^2 + 3x - 1) - \underline{(5x + 4)}$
   $= 5x^2 + 3x - 1 + \underline{(-5x)} + \underline{(-4)}$
   $= 5x^2 + (\underline{3x} + \underline{(-5x)}) + (\underline{(-1)} + \underline{(-4)})$
   $= 5x^2 + \underline{(-2x)} + \underline{(-5)}$
   So, $f(x) - g(x) = \underline{5x^2 - 2x - 5}$.

enVision™ Algebra 1 • Teaching Resources

Additional Practice I O

Provides extra practice for each lesson.

Name ________ enVision Algebra 1 PearsonRealize.com

10-6 Additional Practice

Operations With Functions

Find $f + g$ for each pair of functions.

1. $f(x) = 3x^3 - 6x$, $g(x) = x^2 + 8x - 9$
   $3x^3 + x^2 + 2x - 9$
2. $f(x) = x^2 - 6x + 7$, $g(x) = 2\sqrt{x - 2} + 10$
   $x^2 - 6x + 2\sqrt{x - 2} + 17$
3. $f(x) = 3^x - 6$, $g(x) = x^4 + 7x^2 - 9x + 3$
   $3^x + x^4 + 7x^2 - 9x - 3$

Find $f - g$ for each pair of functions.

4. $f(x) = 4^x - 7$, $g(x) = 2x^2 - 5x + 12$
   $4^x - 2x^2 + 5x - 19$
5. $f(x) = 3x - 8$, $g(x) = 4x^3 - x^2 + 4x - 3$
   $-4x^3 + x^2 - x - 5$
6. $f(x) = 3^x - 6$, $g(x) = 3\sqrt{x} + 9$
   $3^x - 3\sqrt{x} - 15$

Find $f \cdot g$ for each pair of functions.

7. $f(x) = 2x + 3$, $g(x) = x^2 - 3x - 6$
   $2x^3 - 3x^2 - 21x - 18$
8. $f(x) = 4^x - 5$, $g(x) = 2x + 8$
   $2x \cdot 4^x + 8 \cdot 4^x - 10x - 40$
9. $f(x) = x^2 - 2x + 1$, $g(x) = 2\sqrt{x} + 4$
   $2x^2\sqrt{x} + 4x^2 - 4x\sqrt{x} - 8x + 4$
10. How do you determine the domain for a sum, difference, or product of functions? Give an example.
    Sample answer: The domain of a sum, difference, or product will be a combination of the domains including the restrictions on both domains. For example, if $f(x) = \sqrt{x}$ and $g(x) = 2\sqrt{x}$, the sum and difference will contain $\sqrt{x}$, which is restricted to nonnegative real numbers.
11. A school hires an entertainment company to host a party. The company charges a setup fee of \$75, plus \$500 per hour. The same company pays 7 employees \$20 per hour. Write a function that models the amount of money the company will receive for hosting the party and another function that shows how much it will cost the company to host the party. Combine the two functions to show the amount of revenue the company will make for hosting the party. How much money will the company make if the party lasts 5 hours?
    Sample answer: $g(x) = 75 + 500x$; $h(x) = 7(-20x)$; $f(x) = (g + h)(x) = 75 + 360x$. The amount of money made after 5 hours will be \$1,875.

enVision™ Algebra 1 • Teaching Resources

Enrichment O A

Presents engaging problems and activities that extend the lesson concepts.

Name ________ enVision Algebra 1 PearsonRealize.com

10-6 Enrichment

Operations With Functions

The graphs of $f(x) = x + 4$ and $g(x) = x - 2$ are shown in each coordinate grid. For each grid, perform the indicated operation, write the new function, and sketch the graph of the resulting function. Label each function in the graph. Tell where the new function intersects each of the original functions.

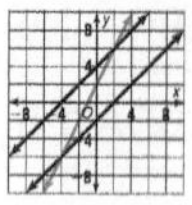

$f(x) + g(x) = \underline{2x + 2}$

Sample: The graph of $f + g$ intersects the graph of f at (2, 6), and it intersects the graph of g at (–4, 6).

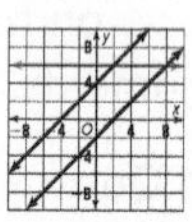

$f(x) - g(x) = \underline{6}$

Sample: The graph of $f - g$ intersects the graph of f at (2, 6) and it intersects the graph of g at (6, 6).

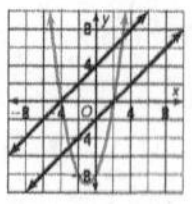

$f(x) \cdot g(x) = \underline{x^2 + 2x - 8}$

Sample: The graph of $f \cdot g$ intersects the graph of f at (–4, 0) and (3, 7) and it intersects the graph of g at (–3, –5) and (2, 0).

enVision™ Algebra 1 • Teaching Resources

Mathematical Literacy and Vocabulary I O

Helps students develop and reinforce understanding of key terms and concepts.

Name ________ enVision Algebra 1 PearsonRealize.com

10-6 Mathematical Literacy and Vocabulary

Operations With Functions

Use the properties of equality to combine the functions $f(x) = 3x^2 + 2x$ and $g(x) = 2x - 1$ through addition, subtraction, and multiplication. Write the explanation for each step.

Problem

$f(x) + g(x)$

$f(x) + g(x) = (3x^2 + 2x) + (2x - 1)$	Write the problem.
$= 3x^2 + (2x + 2x) - 1$	Combine like terms.
$= 3x^2 + 4x - 1$	Simplify.

Exercises

$f(x) - g(x)$

$f(x) - g(x) = (3x^2 + 2x) - (2x - 1)$	Write the problem.
$= 3x^2 + 2x - 2x + 1$	Use the Distributive Property.
$= 3x^2 + (2x - 2x) + 1$	Combine like terms.
$= 3x^2 + 1$	Simplify.

$f(x) \cdot g(x)$

$f(x) \cdot g(x) = (3x^2 + 2x)(2x - 1)$	Write the problem.
$= 3x^2(2x) + 3x^2(-1) + 2x(2x) + 2x(-1)$	Use the Distributive Property.
$= 6x^3 - 3x^2 + 4x^2 - 2x$	Multiply.
$= 6x^3 + (4x^2 - 3x^2) - 2x$	Combine like terms.
$= 6x^3 + x^2 - 2x$	Simplify.

enVision™ Algebra 1 • Teaching Resources

Digital Resources and Video Tutorials I O A

The **Reteach to Build Understanding, Additional Practice,** and **Enrichment** activities are available as digital assignments powered by MathXL for School. These activities are automatically assigned when students complete the lesson quiz online and are automatically scored.

Students can access instructional tutorials using the **Virtual Nerd app**.

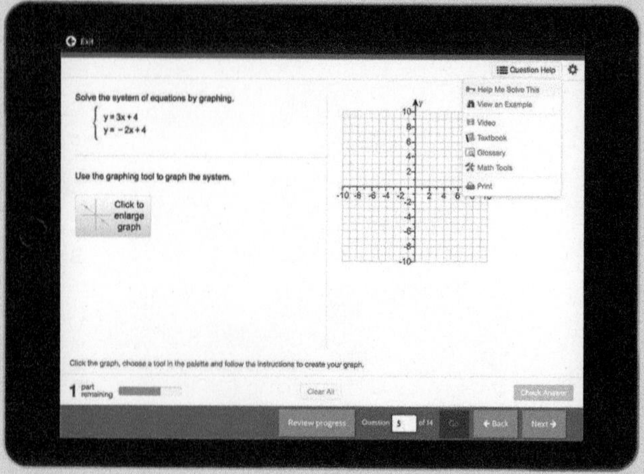
Solve the system of equations by graphing.
Use the graphing tool to graph the system.
Click to enlarge graph
Question Help
Help Me Solve This
View an Example
Video
Textbook
Glossary
Math Tools
Print
Clear All
Check Answer
Review progress
Back
Next

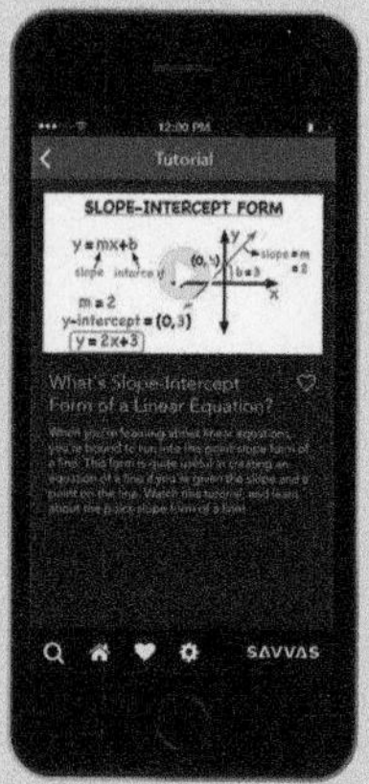
Tutorial
SLOPE-INTERCEPT FORM
SAVVAS

Students can also access Virtual Nerd videos using the **BouncePages app** to scan exercise pages marked with this icon. Students can download both apps for free in their mobile devices' app store.

SavvasRealize.com

A-Z Glossary

LESSON 10-7

Inverse Functions

Lesson Overview

FOCUS

Objective

Students will be able to:

✔ Write an equation for the inverse of a linear function.

✔ Write the inverse of a quadratic function after restricting the domain so the original function is one-to-one.

Essential Understanding

A one-to-one function is a function for which each range value corresponds to exactly one domain value. For these functions, it is possible to describe an *inverse function* which reverses the order of the outputs and inputs of the function.

COHERENCE

Previously in this course, students:

- Wrote and evaluated linear and quadratic functions using function notation.
- Graphed linear and quadratic functions and related the domain of a function to its graph.

In this lesson, students:

- Write the inverse of a function using function notation both algebraically and by using a table.
- Graph linear and quadratic inverse functions and restrict the domain of quadratic functions so they are one-to one.

In later courses, students will:

- Work with inverses of other types of functions.

RIGOR

This lesson emphasizes a blend of *conceptual understanding* and *procedural skill and fluency.*

- Students understand when it is necessary to restrict the domain of a quadratic function to identify its inverse function.
- Students use algebra, graphs, and tables to write inverse functions.

A-Z Vocabulary Builder

REVIEW VOCABULARY — **English** | *Spanish*

- **function** | *función*
- **function notation** | *notación de una función*
- **inverse operations** | *operaciones inversas*

NEW VOCABULARY

- **inverse of a function** | *función inversa*

VOCABULARY ACTIVITY

Review the terms *function* and *inverse.* Remind students that they have seen the term *inverse* when they learned about inverse operations—operations that undo or reverse each other. Introduce the term *inverse of a function.*

Show students the function $y = x - 7$. Switch x and y and then solve for y.

Match each function to its inverse.

1. $y = x + 2$ **[c]** a. $y = \frac{1}{2}x - 1$
2. $y = x - 2$ **[d]** b. $y = \frac{1}{2}x + 1$
3. $y = 2x + 2$ **[a]** c. $y = x - 2$
4. $y = 2x - 2$ **[b]** d. $y = x + 2$

Student Companion

Students can do their in-class work for the lesson on pages 245–248 of their *Student Companion* or in Savvas Realize.

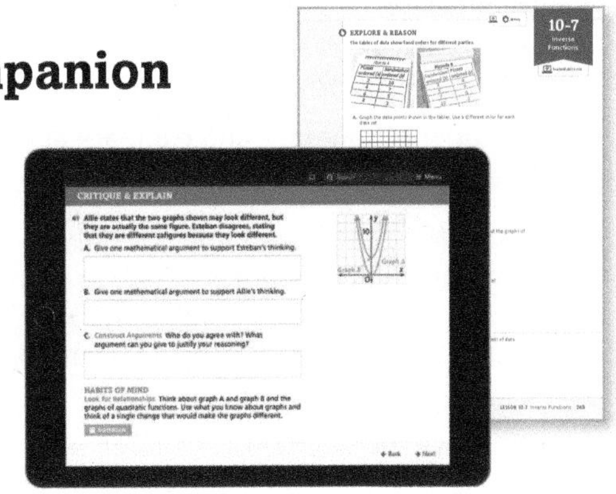

Mathematics Overview — COMMON CORE STANDARDS

Content Standards

In this lesson, students focus on this standard:

HSF.BF.B.4.A Solve an equation of the form $f(x) = c$ for a simple function f that has an inverse and write an expression for the inverse.

Mathematical Practice Standards

These standards are highlighted in this lesson:

MP.2 Reason Abstractly and Quantitatively

Students attend to the meaning of the relationship between quantities when they create tables of values for inverse functions and write equations to model those tables of values.

MP.7 Look For and Make Use of Structure

Students use the structure of a table or equation when they switch the x-values and y-values to find the inverse of a function.

EXPLORE & REASON

INSTRUCTIONAL FOCUS Students inspect two sets of ordered pairs and observe relationships between the two sets of data. This prepares the students to better understand inverse functions and to learn how to find an inverse function by using a table and reversing the order of the outputs and inputs.

STUDENT COMPANION Students can complete the *Explore & Reason* activity on page 245 of their *Student Companion.*

Before WHOLE CLASS

Implement Tasks that Promote Reasoning and Problem Solving ETP

Q: How can you use the terms *increasing* and *decreasing* to describe the data sets in the tables?
[For both pizzerias, when the x-values are increasing, the corresponding y-values are decreasing.]

During SMALL GROUP

Support Productive Struggle in Learning Mathematics ETP

Q: For each ordered pair in one data set, is there a related ordered pair in the other data set? If so, how are the ordered pairs related?
[Yes; for each ordered pair (a, b) in one data set, there is an ordered pair (b, a) in the other data set.]

For Early Finishers

Have students generate and compare another two sets of ordered pairs.

Q: Using the functions $x = 3n + 6$ and $y = (n - 1)(n + 1)$, write 5 ordered pairs (x, y) for $n = 1, 2, 3, 4$, and 5. Using the functions $x = n^2 - 1$ and $y = 3(n + 2)$, write 5 ordered pairs (x, y) for the same values of n. [(9, 0), (12, 3), (15, 8), (18, 15), (21, 24); (0, 9), (3, 12), (8, 15), (15, 18), (24, 21).]

Q: How are the two sets of ordered pairs related to each other?
[The x- and y-values are switched in the two sets of ordered pairs.]

Q: What do you notice about the expressions with n?
[Sample: $3n + 6 = 3(n + 2)$ and $(n - 1)(n + 1) = n^2 - 1$, so they generate the same results for each value of n.]

After WHOLE CLASS

Facilitate Meaningful Mathematical Discourse ETP

Q: Suppose you name 3 more ordered pairs from one pizzeria. Can you name 3 more ordered pairs from the other pizzeria?
[Yes; switch the x- and y-values.]

HABITS OF MIND *Use with* **EXPLORE & REASON**

Make Sense and Persevere Find a function to model each of the sets of data points. **MP.1**

[Sample: $y = -1.3x + 12.5$ and $y = -0.8x + 9.6$]

AVAILABLE **ONLINE**

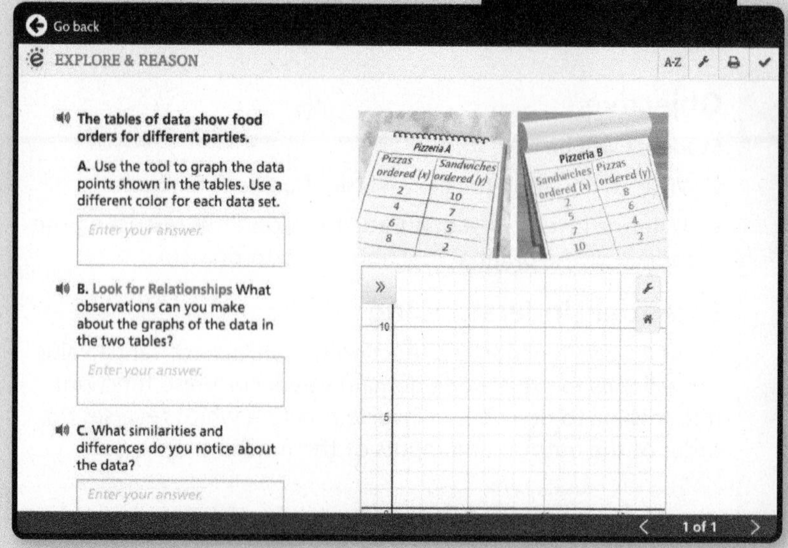
Go back
EXPLORE & REASON
The tables of data show food orders for different parties.
A. Use the tool to graph the data points shown in the tables. Use a different color for each data set.
Enter your answer.
B. Look for Relationships What observations can you make about the graphs of the data in the two tables?
Enter your answer.
C. What similarities and differences do you notice about the data?
Enter your answer.
1 of 1

STUDENT EDITION, PAGE 451

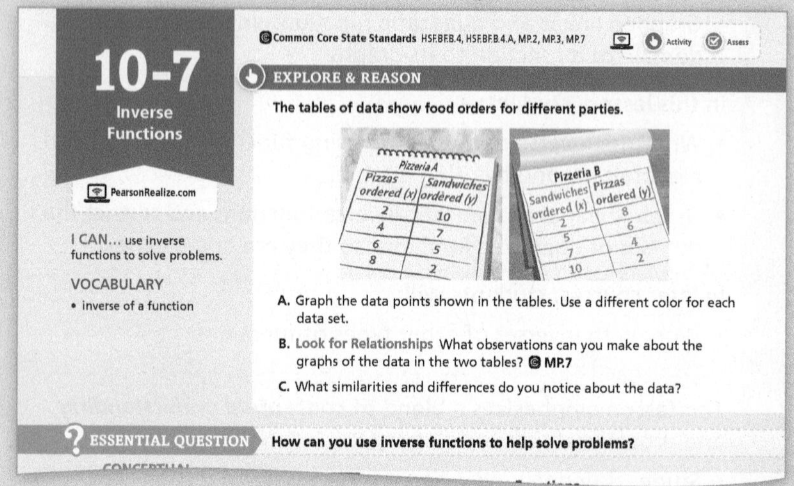
10-7 Inverse Functions

PearsonRealize.com

I CAN… use inverse functions to solve problems.

VOCABULARY
• inverse of a function

Common Core State Standards HSF.BF.B.4, HSF.BF.B.4.A, MP.2, MP.3, MP.7

EXPLORE & REASON

The tables of data show food orders for different parties.

Pizzeria A

Pizzas ordered (x)	Sandwiches ordered (y)
2	10
4	7
6	5
8	2

Pizzeria B

Sandwiches ordered (x)	Pizzas ordered (y)
2	8
5	6
7	4
10	2

A. Graph the data points shown in the tables. Use a different color for each data set.

B. Look for Relationships What observations can you make about the graphs of the data in the two tables? MP.7

C. What similarities and differences do you notice about the data?

ESSENTIAL QUESTION How can you use inverse functions to help solve problems?

SAMPLE STUDENT WORK

A.

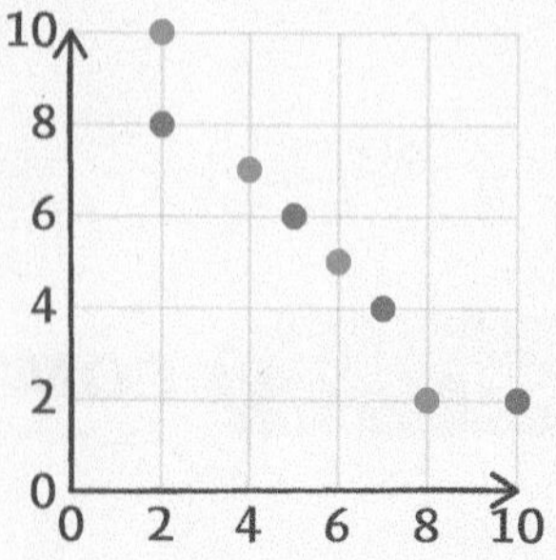

10
8
6
4
2
0
0
2
4
6
8
10

B. The two graphs look alike. They both appear to be linear.

C. The x-values and y-values in the two tables are reversed.

STEP 2 | Understand & Apply

INTRODUCE THE ESSENTIAL QUESTION

Establish Mathematics Goals to Focus Learning ETP

Students learn about inverse functions and ways to use inverse functions to help solve problems. The inverse of a function reverses the order of the outputs and inputs. A function f has an inverse function f^{-1} if and only if the original function is one-to-one. Students learn to find the inverse of a function algebraically and by using a table.

AVAILABLE ONLINE

CONCEPTUAL UNDERSTANDING

EXAMPLE 1 Understand Inverse Functions

What is the inverse of the function $f(x) = 2x + 6$?

The **inverse of a function** reverses the order of the outputs and inputs of a function. The inverse of a function f is usually written as f^{-1} (read "f inverse"). If $f(x) = y$, then $f^{-1}(y) = x$ for all x in the domain of f and all y in the range of f. A function f has an inverse function f^{-1} if and only if the original function f is one-to-one. The function f is also the inverse of f^{-1}.

VOCABULARY
Remember, a *one-to-one function* is a function for which each item in the range corresponds to exactly one item in the domain.

Make tables for the function and its inverse.

f: x	y
0	6
1	8
2	10
3	12

Switch the x-values and the y-values to find the inverse.

f^{-1}: x	y
6	0
8	1
10	2
12	3

The data in the table for the inverse function are linear. Write an equation for the inverse function.

$m = \frac{1-0}{8-6}$
$= \frac{1}{2}$

Identify the slope and then use point-slope form.

$y - y_1 = m(x - x_1)$
$y - 0 = \frac{1}{2}(x - 6)$
$y = \frac{1}{2}x - 3$

The inverse of the function is $f^{-1}(x) = \frac{1}{2}x - 3$.

Try It! 1. How is the slope of f^{-1} related to the slope of f?

LESSON 10-7 Inverse Functions 451

EXAMPLE 1 Understand Inverse Functions

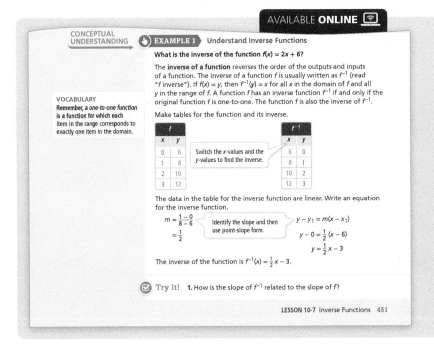

Build Procedural Fluency From Conceptual Understanding ETP

Q: How else is the word *inverse* used in math? How do you think these concepts are related?
[additive inverse, multiplicative inverse, inverse operation; All of these have something to do with things that are opposite each other or reverse each other in some way.]

Q: How are the domain and range of a function related to the domain and range of the inverse of the function?
[They are reversed.]

Elicit and Use Evidence of Student Thinking ETP

Q: What is a multiplicative inverse?
[The multiplicative inverse of a number is the reciprocal of the number. The product of a nonzero number and its reciprocal is 1.]

Try It! Answer

1. It is the multiplicative inverse.

AVAILABLE ONLINE

ADDITIONAL EXAMPLES

Go back
ADDITIONAL EXAMPLE 2 ESSENTIAL QUESTION ES A-Z

Write a table of values for the inverse function, g^{-1}. Then show the graphs of g and g^{-1} on the same axes. How is the graph of g^{-1} related to the graph of g?

x	$g(x)$
0	−1
0.5	−0.75
1	0
1.5	1.25
2	3

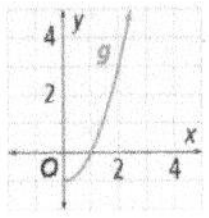
y
4
g
2
O
2
4
x

The graphs are reflections of each other across the line $y = x$.

x	$g^{-1}(x)$
−1	0
−0.75	0.5
0	1
1.25	1.5
3	2

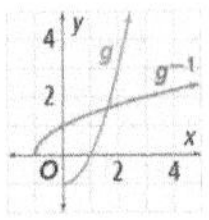
y
4
g
g^{-1}
2
O
2
4
x

1 of 2

Go back
ADDITIONAL EXAMPLE 4 ESSENTIAL QUESTION ES A-Z

Coach Grace orders swimsuits online for \$42/suit plust \$7.99 for shipping and handling. How many swimsuits can Coach Grace order if she has a budget of \$750?

The function $f(x) = 42x + 7.99$ represents the cost of ordering x suits.

The inverse function $f^{-1}(x) = \frac{x - 7.99}{42}$ represents the number of suits that can be purchased for x dollars.

$f^{-1}(750) = \frac{750 - 7.99}{42} \approx 17.67$

Coach Grace can purchase 17 suits within her budget of \$750.

1 of 2

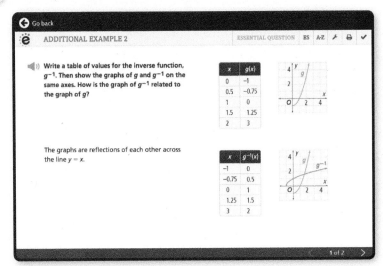

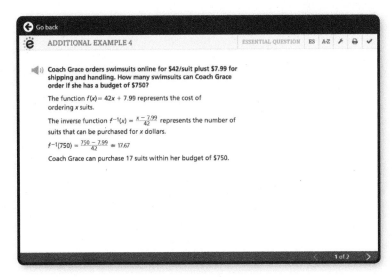

Example 2 Help students graph the inverse of a function from a table of values and identify the domain and range of the inverse.

Q: Where do the graphs of g and g^{-1} intersect?
[The graphs intersect on the line $y = x$.]

Q: How is the shape of the graph of g related to the restriction on the domain of g?
[The graph of g is part of a parabola, and the domain is restricted to points on one side of, and including, the maximum or minimum point of the parabola.]

Example 4 Help students understand how inverse functions can be used to solve real-world problems.

Q: What does the original function represent?
[cost, as a function of the number of suits purchased]

Q: What does the inverse function represent?
[the number of suits, as a function of the amount of money spent]

EXAMPLE 2 Graph Inverse Functions

Use and Connect Mathematical Representations ETP

Q: Why does the graph show only the values of the function when $x \geq 0$?
[The domain of the original function is restricted to make the inverse a one-to-one function.]

Try It! Answers

2. a.

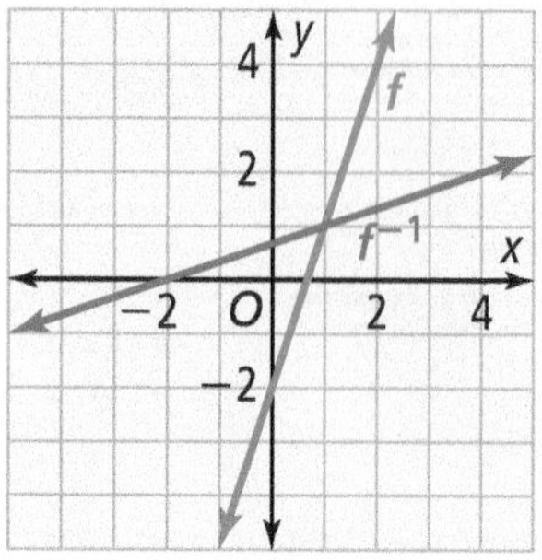

y
x
f
f^{-1}
4
2
−2
O
2
4
−2

b.

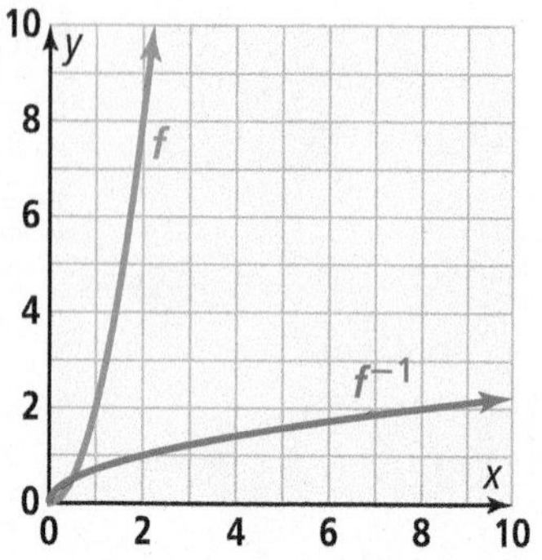

y
x
f
f^{-1}
10
8
6
4
2
0
0
2
4
6
8
10

HABITS OF MIND

Use with **EXAMPLES 1 & 2**

Communicate Precisely **Explain why the inverse of a function can be described as the reflection of the function across the line $y = x$. MP.6**

[The x-values of an inverse function are the y-values of the original function, and the y-values of an inverse function are the x-values of the original function, so the inverse of a function is the reflection of the function across $y = x$.]

EXAMPLE 3 Find the Inverse of a Function Algebraically

Pose Purposeful Questions ETP

Q: For a one-to-one function, how can you describe the process of finding the inverse of the function algebraically?
[Switch the x and y variables. Solve the resulting equation for y.]

AVAILABLE ONLINE

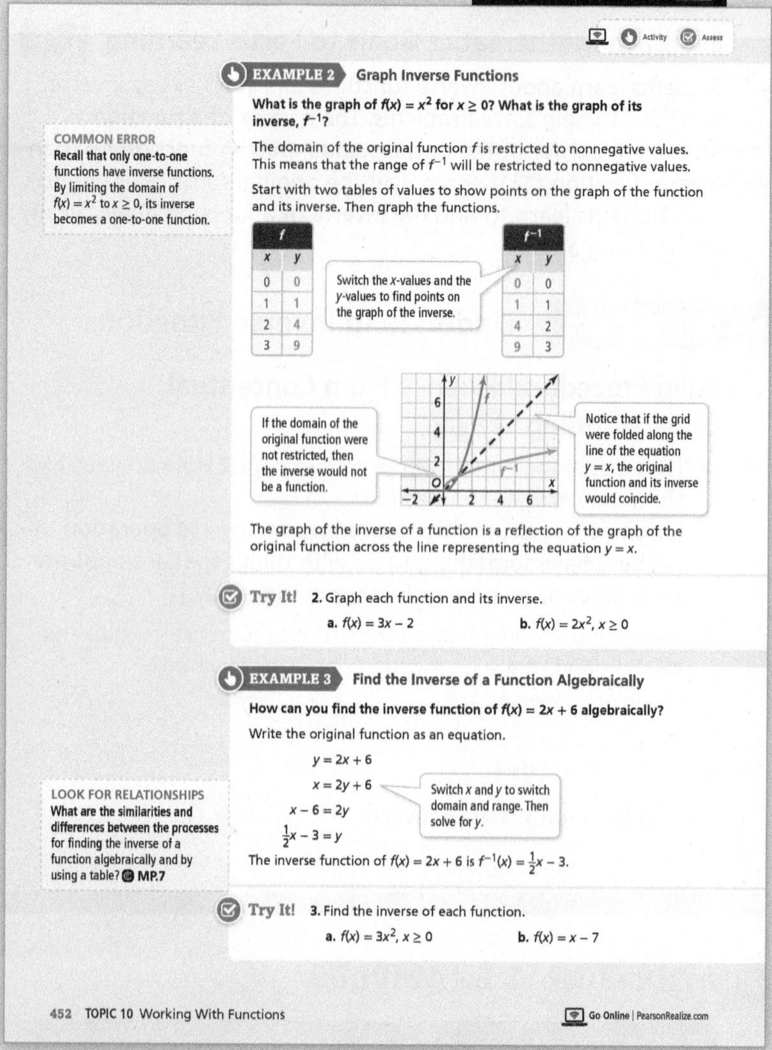
Activity Assess

EXAMPLE 2 **Graph Inverse Functions**

What is the graph of $f(x) = x^2$ for $x \geq 0$? What is the graph of its inverse, f^{-1}?

The domain of the original function f is restricted to nonnegative values. This means that the range of f^{-1} will be restricted to nonnegative values.

Start with two tables of values to show points on the graph of the function and its inverse. Then graph the functions.

f	
x	y
0	0
1	1
2	4
3	9

Switch the x-values and the y-values to find points on the graph of the inverse.

f^{-1}	
x	y
0	0
1	1
4	2
9	3

If the domain of the original function were not restricted, then the inverse would not be a function.

Notice that if the grid were folded along the line of the equation $y = x$, the original function and its inverse would coincide.

The graph of the inverse of a function is a reflection of the graph of the original function across the line representing the equation $y = x$.

COMMON ERROR
Recall that only one-to-one functions have inverse functions. By limiting the domain of $f(x) = x^2$ to $x \geq 0$, its inverse becomes a one-to-one function.

Try It! **2.** Graph each function and its inverse.

a. $f(x) = 3x - 2$ **b.** $f(x) = 2x^2, x \geq 0$

EXAMPLE 3 **Find the Inverse of a Function Algebraically**

How can you find the inverse function of $f(x) = 2x + 6$ algebraically?

Write the original function as an equation.

$$y = 2x + 6$$
$$x = 2y + 6$$
$$x - 6 = 2y$$
$$\frac{1}{2}x - 3 = y$$

Switch x and y to switch domain and range. Then solve for y.

The inverse function of $f(x) = 2x + 6$ is $f^{-1}(x) = \frac{1}{2}x - 3$.

LOOK FOR RELATIONSHIPS
What are the similarities and differences between the processes for finding the inverse of a function algebraically and by using a table? MP.7

Try It! **3.** Find the inverse of each function.

a. $f(x) = 3x^2, x \geq 0$ **b.** $f(x) = x - 7$

452 TOPIC 10 Working With Functions Go Online | PearsonRealize.com

Try It! Answers

3. a. $y = \sqrt{\frac{x}{3}}$ **b.** $y = x + 7$

ELL English Language Learners *(Use with* **EXAMPLE 2***)*

LISTENING BEGINNING Some students may interpret the prefix *non-* as meaning *the opposite of,* and therefore conclude that *nonnegative* is synonymous with *positive.* Have students listen as you read the first three sentences of the example aloud several times, stressing that x is greater than **or equal to** 0.

Q: Why does the example use the word *nonnegative* instead of the word *positive*?
[The domain includes 0, which is not a positive number.]

Q: What is the meaning of the prefix *non-*?
[not]

WRITING INTERMEDIATE To help students understand why the domain of f must be restricted, have them write the definition of *function* from the glossary.

Q: Make a table of values for the function f and its inverse f^{-1} for $-3 \leq x \leq 3$. Then graph the functions.
[Check students' work.]

Q: What is true about the graph of f^{-1}?
[It is not a function because the x-values greater than 0 are each mapped to two y-values.]

SPEAKING ADVANCED If you read the small print on a coupon, you may notice the sentence "Some *restrictions* apply." Have students discuss the questions with a partner and then share their answers with the class.

Q: Why would a company that issues a coupon place restrictions on it?
[Check students' work.]

Q: Why are the domain and the range *restricted*?
[The domain of f is restricted so that its inverse is a function. The range is restricted by the change in the domain.]

Activity Assess

EXAMPLE 4 Interpret Inverse Functions

Use and Connect Mathematical Representations ETP

Q: Is the original function linear or quadratic?
[Linear; the function is in the form $f(x) = mx + b$, which represents a linear function.]

Q: In the original function and the inverse function, what are the independent variables and what are the dependent variables?
[In the original function, the miles earned (dependent variable) is a function of the amount spent (independent variable). In the inverse function, the amount spent (dependent variable) is a function of the miles earned (independent variable).]

Try It! Answer

4. $4,776

Elicit and Use Evidence of Student Thinking ETP

Q: Are there restrictions on the domain and range for the function? For the inverse?
[Yes; the restrictions are that miles earned and amount spent must both be nonnegative values.]

HABITS OF MIND

Use with **EXAMPLES 3 & 4**

Use Appropriate Tools **Explain how you could use graphing to solve the previous problem. MP.5**

[Graph $y = 0.1x + 500$. Then reflect that graph across the line $y = x$ to get the graph of the inverse function. Using the graph of the inverse function, identify the value of y when $x = 1{,}097$.]

Common Error

Try It! 4 After switching the variables x and y, some students may make computational errors when they solve for y. Suggest to students that another approach would be to work with the original function and write an equivalent equation that has 1 for the coefficient of x. Then when they switch the variables, the coefficient of y will already be 1.

AVAILABLE ONLINE

Activity Assess

APPLICATION

EXAMPLE 4 Interpret Inverse Functions

Keenan plans to fly 1,097 miles from Miami to New York City to help assemble a dinosaur exhibit at a museum. He wants to use the miles he earns from his credit card purchases to pay for his flight. How much will Keenan need to spend in order to earn enough miles for the flight from Miami to New York City?

Turn your purchases into airline miles.
Earn 1 mile for every $10 you spend.
BONUS!
500 miles on your first purchase!

Formulate Find the function f that represents the balance of Keenan's airline miles.

miles balance = mile per dollar spent • amount spent + bonus miles

$f(x) = 0.1 \cdot x + 500$

Since Keenan earns 1 mile for every $10 he spends, he earns 0.1 mile for every $1 that he spends.

Find the inverse of the function.

$y = 0.1x + 500$

$x = 0.1y + 500$ — Reverse the variables and solve for y to find the inverse function.

$x - 500 = 0.1y$

$10(x - 500) = (0.1y)10$

$10x - 5{,}000 = y$

The inverse function is $f^{-1}(x) = 10x - 5{,}000$. The inverse function represents the amount Keenan spends, $f^{-1}(x)$, to earn x miles.

Compute Substitute 1,097 for x.

$f^{-1}(1{,}097) = 10(1{,}097) - 5{,}000$

$= 10{,}970 - 5{,}000$

$= 5{,}970$

Interpret Keenan needs to spend $5,970 to earn enough miles for his trip.

Try It! 4. Suppose the credit card company changes the program so Keenan earns 1 mile for every $8 he spends. How would that change the amount of money Keenan needs to spend to earn the miles for his trip?

LESSON 10-7 Inverse Functions 453

ADV Advanced Students

USE WITH EXAMPLE 3 Have students explore finding the inverse of the slope-intercept form of a linear equation, and then use that pattern to write the inverse of a linear equation.

Q: What is the inverse equation of $y = mx + b$? [$y = \frac{x - b}{m}$]

Q: How can you use your result to write the inverse of an equation such as $y = -3x - 17$?
[Because $m = -3$ and $b = -17$, the inverse equation is $y = \frac{x + 17}{-3}$.]

Q: Can you use $y = \frac{(x - b)}{m}$ if the original linear equation is not in slope-intercept form?
[Yes; start by rewriting the original equation in slope-intercept form.]

RtI Struggling Students

USE WITH EXAMPLE 4 Some students may struggle with solving for y to find the inverse function when the coefficient is a decimal. Help students practice simplifying the steps of writing an inverse function by removing decimals from the original equation.

Q: How can you remove decimals from the original related equation?
[Multiply each side of the equation by 10.]

Q: How does removing decimals affect the steps of finding an inverse function?
[Sample: Eliminating the decimals simplifies the steps of solving for y to find the inverse function.]

CONCEPT SUMMARY Finding the Inverse of a Function

Q: How is switching *x*- and *y*-values related to reflecting a graph across the line $y = x$?

[For any ordered pair (*a*, *b*) of a function, switching *x* and *y* results in (*b*, *a*). The line $y = x$ is the perpendicular bisector of the segment with endpoints (*a*, *b*) and (*b*, *a*), so another way to relate (*a*, *b*) and (*b*, *a*) is that they are images of each other across the line $y = x$.]

Do You UNDERSTAND? | Do You KNOW HOW?

Common Error

Exercise 8 Some students may forget to restrict a domain for the inverse function. Ask them to graph the original function and its reflection across the line $y = x$ in order to identify the domain of the inverse.

Answers

1. Sometimes when solving problems, you know data that is the output of a function. It may be easier to write the inverse of the function and use the data as the input instead.
2. The graph of the inverse of a function is a reflection across the line $y = x$, not across the *x*-axis.
3. No; the function $y = x^2$ does not have an inverse function unless the domain is restricted.
4. No; if a function crosses the *x*-axis twice, then it is not a one-to-one function. Therefore, it does not have an inverse function.

5.

x	y
0	3
1	1
2	−1
3	−3

x	y
3	0
1	1
−1	2
−3	3

6.

x	y
0	0
1	8
2	16
3	24

x	y
0	0
8	1
16	2
24	3

7. $f^{-1}(x) = 0.5x - 5.5$ 8. $f^{-1}(x) = x^2, x \geq 0$

9. The inverse of a function is similar to inverse operations because both are, in some ways, the "opposite" of the original function or operation. They are different because inverse functions involve switching the input and output, and inverse operations are used along with the properties of equality to solve equations.

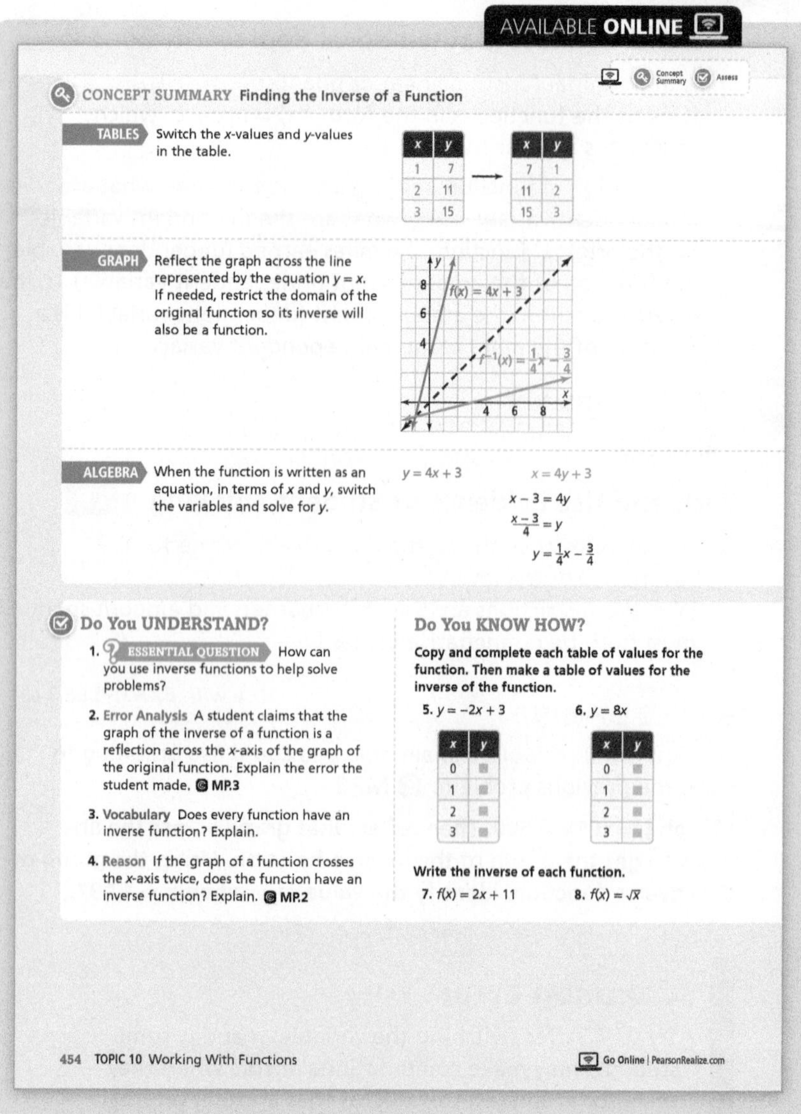

AVAILABLE ONLINE

Concept Summary Assess

CONCEPT SUMMARY Finding the Inverse of a Function

TABLES Switch the *x*-values and *y*-values in the table.

x	y
1	7
2	11
3	15

→

x	y
7	1
11	2
15	3

GRAPH Reflect the graph across the line represented by the equation $y = x$. If needed, restrict the domain of the original function so its inverse will also be a function.

y
8
6
4
f(x) = 4x + 3
f⁻¹(x) = 1/4 x − 3/4
x
4
6
8

ALGEBRA When the function is written as an equation, in terms of *x* and *y*, switch the variables and solve for *y*.

$y = 4x + 3$

$x = 4y + 3$

$x - 3 = 4y$

$\frac{x-3}{4} = y$

$y = \frac{1}{4}x - \frac{3}{4}$

Do You UNDERSTAND?

1. ESSENTIAL QUESTION How can you use inverse functions to help solve problems?
2. **Error Analysis** A student claims that the graph of the inverse of a function is a reflection across the *x*-axis of the graph of the original function. Explain the error the student made. MP.3
3. **Vocabulary** Does every function have an inverse function? Explain.
4. **Reason** If the graph of a function crosses the *x*-axis twice, does the function have an inverse function? Explain. MP.2

Do You KNOW HOW?

Copy and complete each table of values for the function. Then make a table of values for the inverse of the function.

5. $y = -2x + 3$

x	y
0	■
1	■
2	■
3	■

6. $y = 8x$

x	y
0	■
1	■
2	■
3	■

Write the inverse of each function.

7. $f(x) = 2x + 11$ 8. $f(x) = \sqrt{x}$

454 TOPIC 10 Working With Functions Go Online | PearsonRealize.com

10. The student switched $-x$ and *y* instead of *x* and *y*. The correct answer is $f^{-1}(x) = -x + 4$.
11. **b.** No; restrict the domain to nonnegative numbers.

    c. No; restrict the domain to nonnegative numbers.
12. Yes; for example, the relation $y = \pm\sqrt{x}$ has $y = x^2$ as its inverse, which is a function.
13. $f^{-1}(x) = 0.5(x^2 + 1), x \geq 0$; I found my answer by writing the equation represented by the graph and then finding its inverse algebraically.
14. $f^{-1}(x) = -x$; If you reflect $y = -x$ across the line $y = x$, you get $y = -x$.

15.

x	y
11	0
15	1
19	2
23	3

16.

x	y
3	0
4	1
7	2
12	3

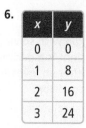

PRACTICE & PROBLEM SOLVING

AVAILABLE ONLINE

Lesson Practice You may opt to have students complete the automatically scored Practice and Problem Solving items online powered by MathXL for School.

Choose from: **Lesson Practice**

Adaptive Practice

You may also take advantage of the bank of exercises for assigning additional practice.

Assignment Guide

Basic	Advanced
9–24, 27–35	9–15, 18–35

Item Analysis

Example	Items	DOK
1	15, 16	2
	9, 12	3
2	17–20	2
	13, 14, 27, 28	3
3	21–26	2
	10, 11, 33, 34	3
4	29–32, 35	3

Answers

See answers for Exercises 9–16 on previous page.

17.

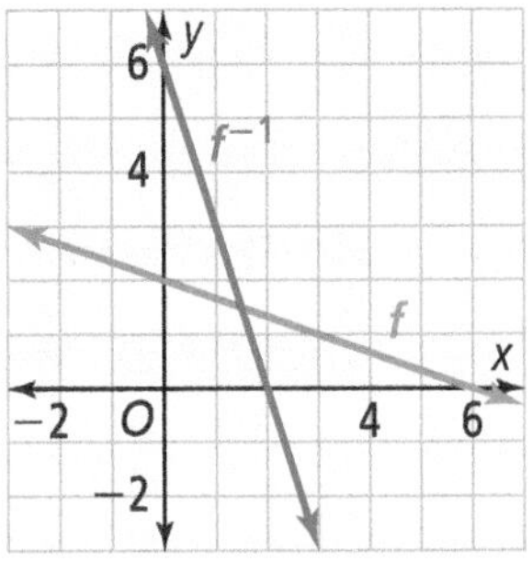

18.

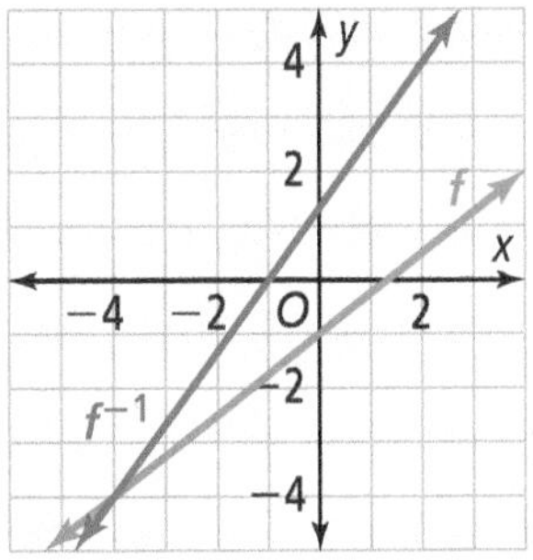

19.

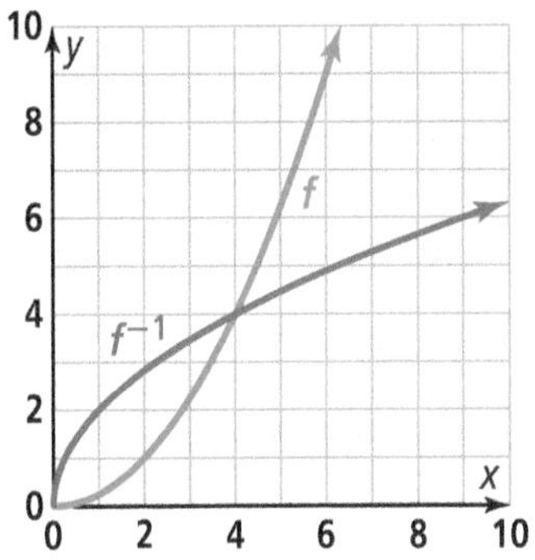

20.

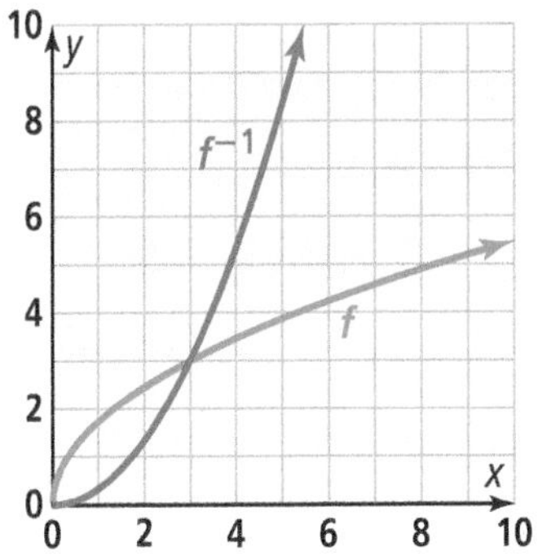

AVAILABLE ONLINE

PRACTICE & PROBLEM SOLVING

Scan for Multimedia | Practice | Tutorial | Additional Exercises Available Online

UNDERSTAND

9. Mathematical Connections How is the inverse of a function similar to inverse operations? How is it different? Explain.

10. Error Analysis Describe and correct the error a student made finding the inverse of $f(x) = -x + 4$. MP.3

$y = -x + 4$
$-x = y + 4$
$-x - 4 = y$
The inverse of the function is
$f^{-1}(x) = -x - 4$.
X

11. Reason Does each function have an inverse function? If so, write the inverse function. If not, explain how you could restrict the domain so that function f does have an inverse function. MP.2

a. $f(x) = 5x$ yes; $f^{-1}(x) = \frac{x}{5}$

b. $f(x) = 5x^2$

c. $f(x) = |5x|$

12. Construct Arguments Can a relation that is not a function have a function as its inverse? Give an example to support your answer. MP.3

13. Use Structure What is the inverse of the function graphed below? Describe how you found your answer. MP.7

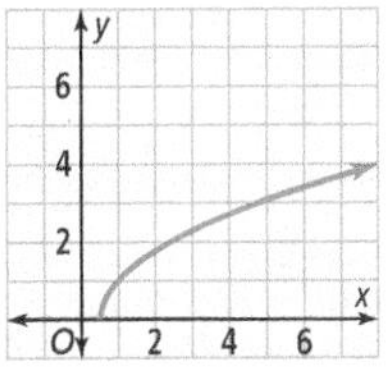

14. Higher Order Thinking What is the inverse of $f(x) = -x$? Use a graph of the function to support your answer.

PRACTICE

For each table, create a table of values for the inverse function. SEE EXAMPLE 1

15.

x	y
0	11
1	15
2	19
3	23

16.

x	y
0	3
1	4
2	7
3	12

Graph each function and its inverse. SEE EXAMPLE 2

17. $f(x) = -\frac{1}{3}x + 2$

18. $f(x) = \frac{3}{4}x - 1$

19. $f(x) = 0.25x^2, x \geq 0$

20. $f(x) = \sqrt{3x}$

Tell whether the functions f and g are inverses or not. SEE EXAMPLE 2

21.

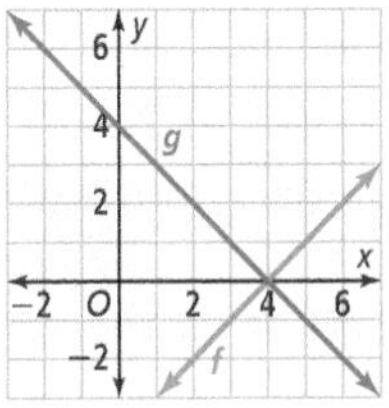

no

22.

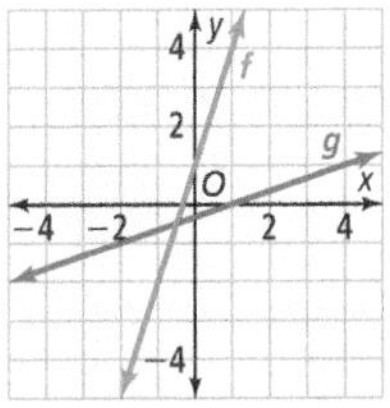

yes

Find the inverse of each function. SEE EXAMPLE 3

23. $f(x) = -5x - 11$
$f^{-1}(x) = -0.2x - 2.2$

24. $f(x) = 0.7x + 4$
$f^{-1}(x) = \frac{10}{7}x - \frac{40}{7}$

25. $f(x) = 7x + 12$
$f^{-1}(x) = \frac{x - 12}{7}$

26. $f(x) = 9x^2, x \geq 0$
$f^{-1}(x) = \frac{\sqrt{x}}{3}$

27. $f(x) = x^2 + 7, x \geq 0$
$f^{-1}(x) = \sqrt{x - 7}$

28. $f(x) = \sqrt{4x + 1}$
$f^{-1}(x) = \frac{x^2 - 1}{4}, x \geq 0$

29. Camilla has \$100 in her savings account. She will put 25% of her salary in her account every time she gets paid at work. Camilla wants to save \$1,250 to go on vacation this summer. Write and evaluate the inverse function to find the amount of money Camilla must earn at work to reach her savings goal. SEE EXAMPLE 4
$y = 4x - 400$; \$4,600

Answers

30. $s = \frac{P}{4}$; you could answer a question about the side length of a square based on its perimeter.

31. a. $f(x) = 50 - 4x$

b. $f^{-1}(x) = -0.25x + 12.5$

c.

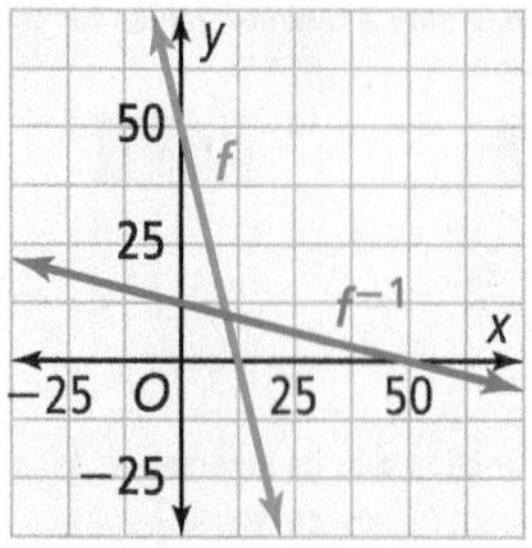
y
50
f
25
f^{-1}
x
−25
O
25
50
−25

d. f^{-1}; The inverse function gives the number of games played as a function of the amount of money left on the card.

32. a. The radius and area of a circle must be positive numbers, so the domain is restricted to $r > 0$ for the area function, and $A > 0$ for the inverse.

b. $r = \sqrt{\frac{A}{\pi}}$

c. about 4 inches

AVAILABLE **ONLINE**

PRACTICE & PROBLEM SOLVING

Practice Tutorial

Mixed Review Available Online

APPLY

30. Reason The perimeter P of a square is given by the equation $P = 4s$, where s is a side length of the square. What is the inverse of $P = 4s$? What type of question could you answer by using the inverse function? **MP.2**

31. Model With Mathematics A raffle has a $50 gift card to a miniature golf course as a prize. **MP.4**

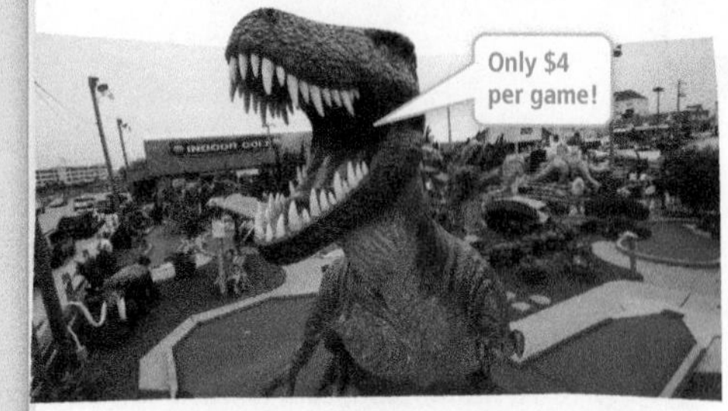
Only $4 per game!

a. Write a function f that represents the amount of money that will be left on the gift card after x games.

b. What is the inverse of the function from part (a)?

c. Graph the functions from parts (a) and (b) on the same grid. Label each graph.

d. Which function would you use to find how many games were played when $10 was left on the card? Explain.

32. Make Sense and Persevere The area A of a circle in terms of the circle's radius r is $A = \pi r^2$. **MP.1**

a. Explain the restrictions on the domain of the function $A = \pi r^2$ and the inverse function in this context.

b. Write the inverse function of $A = \pi r^2$.

c. Use the inverse function you wrote in part (b) to find the radius of a circle that has an area of 50.25 in.^{2}. Round your answer to the nearest inch.

ASSESSMENT PRACTICE

33. Match each function with its inverse.

I. $f(x) = 4x - 8$ A. $f(x)^{-1} = \frac{1}{2}\sqrt{x}$

II. $f(x) = 0.25x - 2$ B. $f(x)^{-1} = 0.25x + 2$

III. $f(x) = 4x^2, x \geq 0$ C. $f(x)^{-1} = 4x + 8$

IV. $f(x) = 2x^2, x \geq 0$ D. $f(x)^{-1} = \sqrt{\frac{1}{2}x}$

34. SAT/ACT What is the inverse of the function $f(x) = -\sqrt{2x}$?

Ⓐ $f(x)^{-1} = 0.5x^2, x \geq 0$

Ⓑ $f(x)^{-1} = 0.5x^2, x \leq 0$

Ⓒ $f(x)^{-1} = 0.5x^2$

Ⓓ $f(x)^{-1} = -0.5x^2$

35. Performance Task A health club advertises a new family membership plan, as shown in the advertisement.

Family Plan:
Additional Members:
HEALTH CLUB
$90 to join
$25 to join
$75 per month for the first member
$40 per month for each additional member

Part A Write two functions, one that gives the total cost of a membership for the first member and one that gives the total cost for each additional member. Write each function, y, in terms of the number of months, x, a member belongs to the health club.
$y = 75x + 90$; $y = 40x + 25$

Part B Write a combined function for the total cost on the family membership for a family of three members. Then write the inverse of the function. $y = 155x + 140$; $y = \frac{x - 140}{155}$

Part C Find the approximate number of months that a family of three will be members of the health club if they spend a total of $1,380.
8 months

SavvasRealize.com

Assess Tutorials Worksheets

LESSON QUIZ

Use the Lesson Quiz to assess students' understanding of the mathematics in the lesson.

Students can take the Lesson Quiz online or you can download a printable copy from **SavvasRealize.com**. The Lesson Quiz is also available in the *Assessment Resources* book.

Item Analysis

Item	DOK	Standards
1	2	HSF.BF.B.4.A
2	1	HSF.BF.B.4.A
3	1	HSF.BF.B.4.A
4	1	HSF.BF.B.4.A
5	2	HSF.BF.B.4.A

RtI Use the student scores on the Lesson Quiz to prescribe differentiated assignments.

If students take the Lesson Quiz online, it will be automatically scored and appropriate differentiated practice will be assigned based on student performance.

I Intervention	0–3 points	• Reteach to Build Understanding • Mathematical Literacy and Vocabulary • Additional Practice
O On-Level	4 points	• Mathematical Literacy and Vocabulary • Additional Practice • Enrichment
A Advanced	5 points	• Enrichment

AVAILABLE **ONLINE**

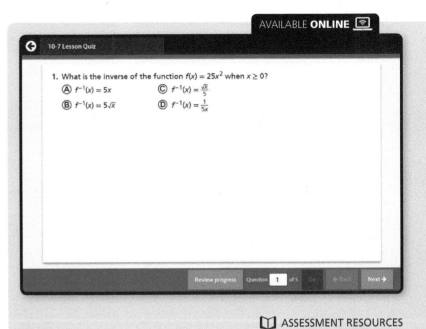

10-7 Lesson Quiz

1. What is the inverse of the function $f(x) = 25x^2$ when $x \geq 0$?

Ⓐ $f^{-1}(x) = 5x$ Ⓒ $f^{-1}(x) = \frac{\sqrt{x}}{5}$

Ⓑ $f^{-1}(x) = 5\sqrt{x}$ Ⓓ $f^{-1}(x) = \frac{1}{5x}$

Review progress Question 1 of 5 Go ←Back Next →

ASSESSMENT RESOURCES

Name ______________________

enVision Algebra 1

PearsonRealize.com

10-7 Lesson Quiz

Inverse Functions

1. What is the inverse of the function $f(x) = 25x^2$ when $x \geq 0$?

Ⓐ $f^{-1}(x) = 5x$ Ⓒ $f^{-1}(x) = \frac{\sqrt{x}}{5}$

Ⓑ $f^{-1}(x) = 5\sqrt{x}$ Ⓓ $f^{-1}(x) = \frac{1}{5x}$

2. What is the slope of the graph of the inverse of the function $f(x) = \frac{1}{3}x + 4$?

Ⓐ $-\frac{1}{3}$ Ⓑ $\frac{1}{4}$ Ⓒ $\frac{1}{3}$ Ⓓ 3

3. A table of values for function $f(x) = 5x - 8$ is shown. Complete the table of values for the inverse of function f. Then write an equation for the inverse.

Function f

x	0	1	2	3
y	−8	−3	2	7

Inverse of function f

x	−8	−3	2	7
y	0	1	2	3

Equation: $f^{-1}(x) = \frac{1}{5}x + \frac{8}{5}$

4. The graph of $f(x) = 2x + 4$ is shown. Graph the inverse of f in the same coordinate plane.

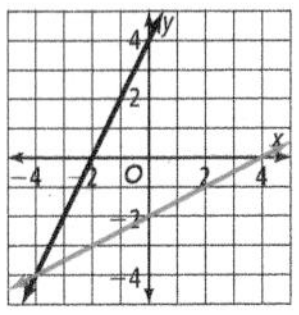

5. A store offers a rewards program where shoppers earn 1 point for every \$5 they spend plus 100 bonus points on their first purchase. If function f represents the number of points earned as a function of the total amount spent x, which function represents the total amount spent as a function of the number of points earned?

Ⓐ $f^{-1}(x) = 5x + 500$

Ⓑ $f^{-1}(x) = 5x - 500$

Ⓒ $f^{-1}(x) = -5x + 100$

Ⓓ $f^{-1}(x) = -5x - 100$

enVision™ **Algebra 1** • Assessment Resources

SavvasRealize.com

Assess Tutorials Worksheets

DIFFERENTIATED RESOURCES

I = Intervention O = On-Level A = Advanced

= This activity is available as a digital assignment powered by MathXL® for School.

AVAILABLE ONLINE

Reteach to Build Understanding I

Provides scaffolded reteaching for the key lesson concepts.

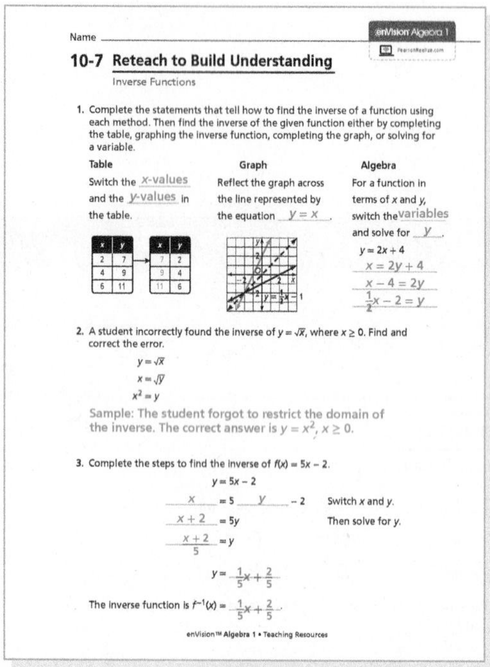
Name

enVision Algebra 1

10-7 Reteach to Build Understanding

Inverse Functions

1. Complete the statements that tell how to find the inverse of a function using each method. Then find the inverse of the given function either by completing the table, graphing the inverse function, completing the graph, or solving for a variable.

Table: Switch the x-values and the y-values in the table.

Graph: Reflect the graph across the line represented by the equation $y = x$.

Algebra: For a function in terms of x and y, switch the variables and solve for y.

$y = 2x + 4$

$x = 2y + 4$

$x - 4 = 2y$

$\frac{1}{2}x - 2 = y$

2. A student incorrectly found the inverse of $y = \sqrt{x}$, where $x \geq 0$. Find and correct the error.

$y = \sqrt{x}$

$x = \sqrt{y}$

$x^2 = y$

Sample: The student forgot to restrict the domain of the inverse. The correct answer is $y = x^2$, $x \geq 0$.

3. Complete the steps to find the inverse of $f(x) = 5x - 2$.

$y = 5x - 2$

$x = 5y - 2$ Switch x and y.

$x + 2 = 5y$ Then solve for y.

$\frac{x+2}{5} = y$

$y = \frac{1}{5}x + \frac{2}{5}$

The inverse function is $f^{-1}(x) = \frac{1}{5}x + \frac{2}{5}$.

enVision™ Algebra 1 • Teaching Resources

Additional Practice I O

Provides extra practice for each lesson.

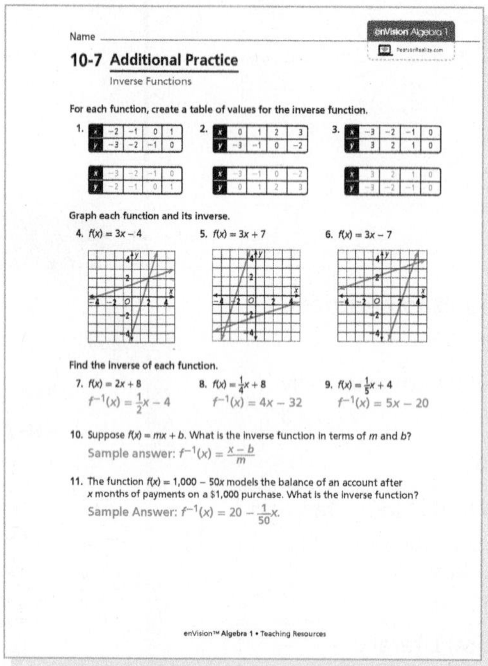
Name

enVision Algebra 1

10-7 Additional Practice

Inverse Functions

For each function, create a table of values for the inverse function.

Graph each function and its inverse.

4. $f(x) = 3x - 4$ 5. $f(x) = 3x + 7$ 6. $f(x) = 3x - 7$

Find the inverse of each function.

7. $f(x) = 2x + 8$ $f^{-1}(x) = \frac{1}{2}x - 4$

8. $f(x) = \frac{1}{4}x + 8$ $f^{-1}(x) = 4x - 32$

9. $f(x) = \frac{1}{5}x + 4$ $f^{-1}(x) = 5x - 20$

10. Suppose $f(x) = mx + b$. What is the inverse function in terms of m and b? Sample answer: $f^{-1}(x) = \frac{x-b}{m}$

11. The function $f(x) = 1{,}000 - 50x$ models the balance of an account after x months of payments on a $1,000 purchase. What is the inverse function? Sample Answer: $f^{-1}(x) = 20 - \frac{1}{50}x$.

enVision™ Algebra 1 • Teaching Resources

Enrichment O A

Presents engaging problems and activities that extend the lesson concepts.

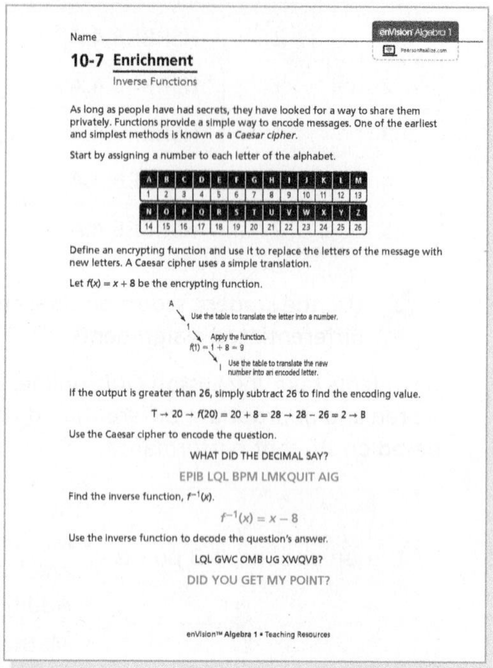
Name

enVision Algebra 1

10-7 Enrichment

Inverse Functions

As long as people have had secrets, they have looked for a way to share them privately. Functions provide a simple way to encode messages. One of the earliest and simplest methods is known as a *Caesar cipher*.

Start by assigning a number to each letter of the alphabet.

A	B	C	D	E	F	G	H	I	J	K	L	M
1	2	3	4	5	6	7	8	9	10	11	12	13
N	O	P	Q	R	S	T	U	V	W	X	Y	Z
14	15	16	17	18	19	20	21	22	23	24	25	26

Define an encrypting function and use it to replace the letters of the message with new letters. A Caesar cipher uses a simple translation.

Let $f(x) = x + 8$ be the encrypting function.

If the output is greater than 26, simply subtract 26 to find the encoding value.

T → 20 → f(20) = 20 + 8 = 28 → 28 − 26 = 2 → B

Use the Caesar cipher to encode the question.

WHAT DID THE DECIMAL SAY?

EPIB LQL BPM LMKQUIT AIG

Find the inverse function, $f^{-1}(x)$.

$f^{-1}(x) = x - 8$

Use the inverse function to decode the question's answer.

LQL GWC OMB UG XWQVB?

DID YOU GET MY POINT?

enVision™ Algebra 1 • Teaching Resources

Mathematical Literacy and Vocabulary I O

Helps students develop and reinforce understanding of key terms and concepts.

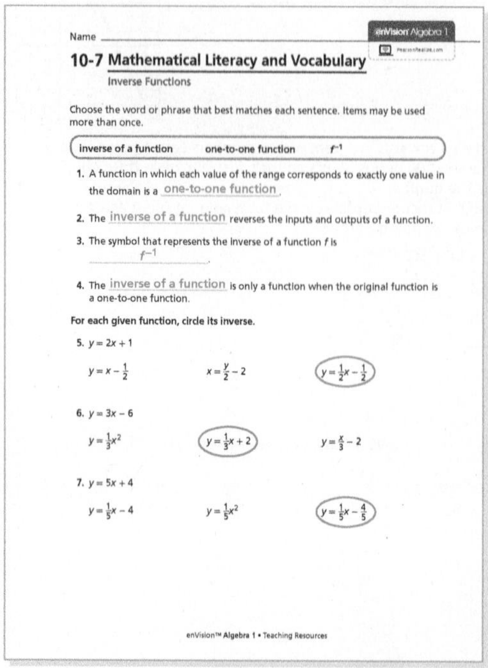
Name

enVision Algebra 1

10-7 Mathematical Literacy and Vocabulary

Inverse Functions

Choose the word or phrase that best matches each sentence. Items may be used more than once.

inverse of a function one-to-one function f^{-1}

1. A function in which each value of the range corresponds to exactly one value in the domain is a one-to-one function.

2. The inverse of a function reverses the inputs and outputs of a function.

3. The symbol that represents the inverse of a function f is f^{-1}.

4. The inverse of a function is only a function when the original function is a one-to-one function.

For each given function, circle its inverse.

5. $y = 2x + 1$: $y = x - \frac{1}{2}$ $x = \frac{y}{2} - 2$ $y = \frac{1}{2}x - \frac{1}{2}$

6. $y = 3x - 6$: $y = \frac{1}{3}x^2$ $y = \frac{1}{3}x + 2$ $y = \frac{x}{3} - 2$

7. $y = 5x + 4$: $y = \frac{1}{5}x - 4$ $y = \frac{1}{5}x^2$ $y = \frac{1}{5}x - \frac{4}{5}$

enVision™ Algebra 1 • Teaching Resources

Digital Resources and Video Tutorials I O A

The **Reteach to Build Understanding**, **Additional Practice**, and **Enrichment** activities are available as digital assignments powered by MathXL for School. These activities are automatically assigned when students complete the lesson quiz online and are automatically scored.

Students can access instructional tutorials using the **Virtual Nerd app**.

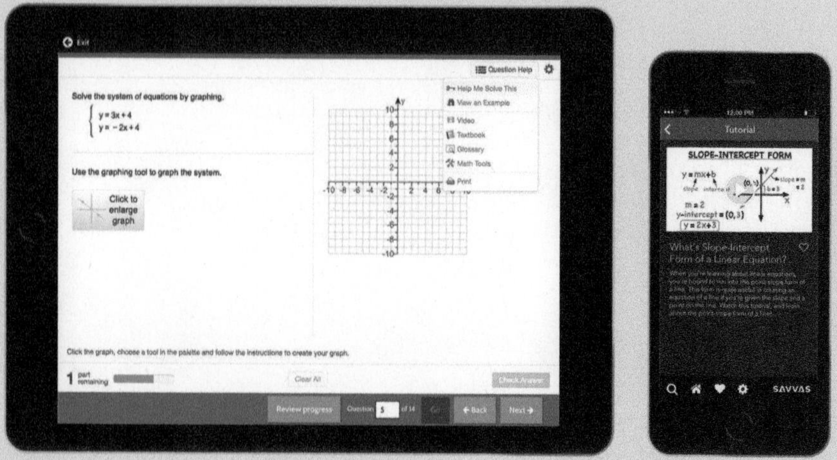

Students can also access Virtual Nerd videos using the **BouncePages app** to scan exercise pages marked with this icon. Students can download both apps for free in their mobile devices' app store.

Glossary Tutorials Math Tools

TOPIC 10
Working With Functions

TOPIC REVIEW

TOPIC ESSENTIAL QUESTION

What are some operations on functions that you can use to create models and solve problems?

As students answer the Essential Question in writing, encourage them to include examples that support their answers. Look for the following points while discussing students' answers.

- You can add, subtract, and multiply functions.
- You can translate, stretch, and compress functions.
- You can find the inverse of a function.

Answers

2. cube root function

3. inverse of a function

4. square root function

5. The graph of g is a vertical translation of 4 units up of the graph of f.

6. The graph of g is a horizontal translation of 8 units right of the graph of f.

7. The graph of g is a horizontal translation of 1 unit right and a vertical translation of 5 units down of the graph of f.

8. The graph of g is a horizontal translation of 2 units left and a vertical translation of 8 units down of the graph of f.

9. $g(x) = \sqrt{x} - 5$

10. $h(x) = \sqrt{x + 2}$

11.

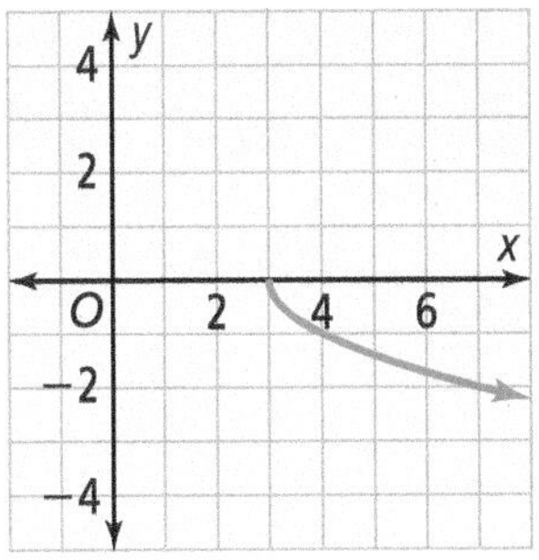

y
4
2
x
O
2
4
6
−2
−4

The domain is $x \geq 3$. The range is $y \leq 0$.

12. about 9 knots

AVAILABLE ONLINE

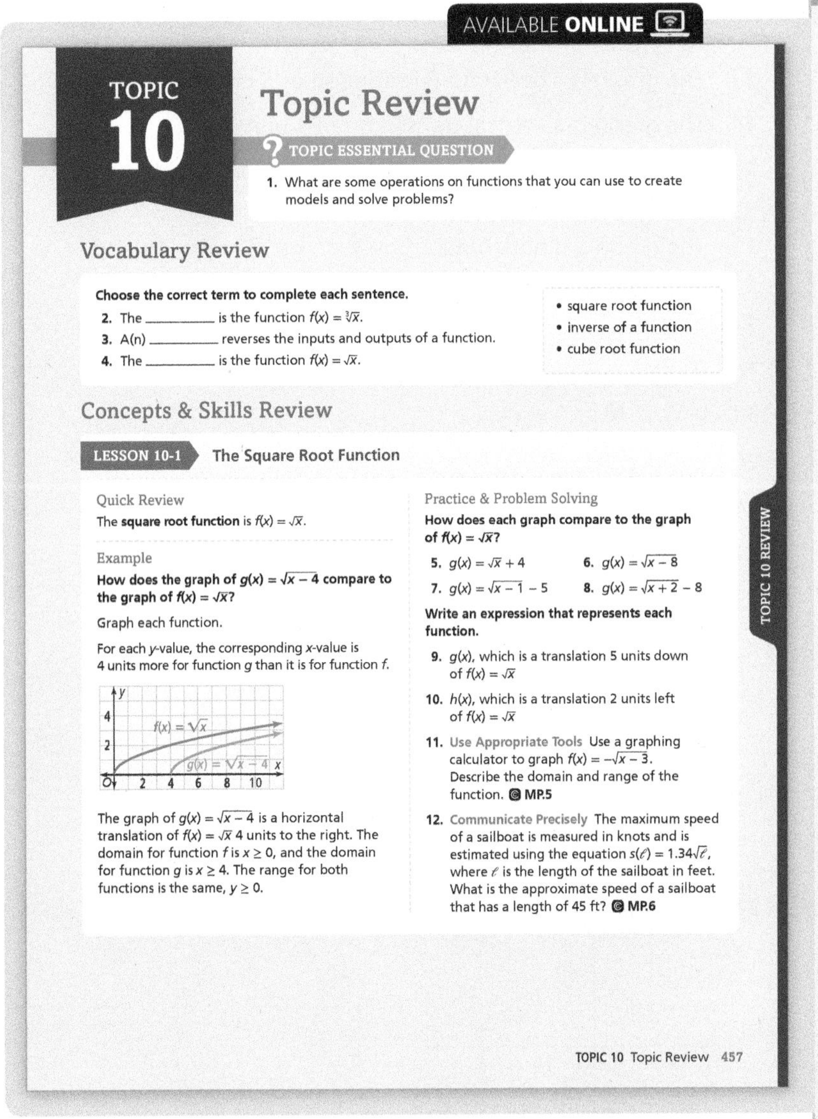

TOPIC 10

Topic Review

TOPIC ESSENTIAL QUESTION

1. What are some operations on functions that you can use to create models and solve problems?

Vocabulary Review

Choose the correct term to complete each sentence.

2. The _______ is the function $f(x) = \sqrt[3]{x}$.
3. A(n) _______ reverses the inputs and outputs of a function.
4. The _______ is the function $f(x) = \sqrt{x}$.

- square root function
- inverse of a function
- cube root function

Concepts & Skills Review

LESSON 10-1 The Square Root Function

Quick Review

The **square root function** is $f(x) = \sqrt{x}$.

Example

How does the graph of $g(x) = \sqrt{x-4}$ compare to the graph of $f(x) = \sqrt{x}$?

Graph each function.

For each y-value, the corresponding x-value is 4 units more for function g than it is for function f.

y
4
2
O
2
4
6
8
10
x
f(x) = √x
g(x) = √x − 4

The graph of $g(x) = \sqrt{x-4}$ is a horizontal translation of $f(x) = \sqrt{x}$ 4 units to the right. The domain for function f is $x \geq 0$, and the domain for function g is $x \geq 4$. The range for both functions is the same, $y \geq 0$.

Practice & Problem Solving

How does each graph compare to the graph of $f(x) = \sqrt{x}$?

5. $g(x) = \sqrt{x} + 4$
6. $g(x) = \sqrt{x-8}$
7. $g(x) = \sqrt{x-1} - 5$
8. $g(x) = \sqrt{x+2} - 8$

Write an expression that represents each function.

9. $g(x)$, which is a translation 5 units down of $f(x) = \sqrt{x}$
10. $h(x)$, which is a translation 2 units left of $f(x) = \sqrt{x}$
11. Use Appropriate Tools Use a graphing calculator to graph $f(x) = -\sqrt{x-3}$. Describe the domain and range of the function. MP.5
12. Communicate Precisely The maximum speed of a sailboat is measured in knots and is estimated using the equation $s(\ell) = 1.34\sqrt{\ell}$, where ℓ is the length of the sailboat in feet. What is the approximate speed of a sailboat that has a length of 45 ft? MP.6

TOPIC 10 REVIEW

TOPIC 10 Topic Review 457

AVAILABLE ONLINE

Go online at **SavvasRealize.com** for additional practice and mixed review.

TOPIC REVIEW

Answers

13. The graph is a horizontal translation of 5 units left.

14. The graph is a vertical translation of 4 units up.

15. The graph is a horizontal translation of 1 unit right and a vertical translation of 2 units up.

16. The graph is a horizontal translation of 1.5 units left and a vertical translation of 2.5 units down.

17. 0.09

18. 0.12

19. 0.63, 0.18

20. $x = 12\sqrt[3]{\frac{C}{5}}$

21.

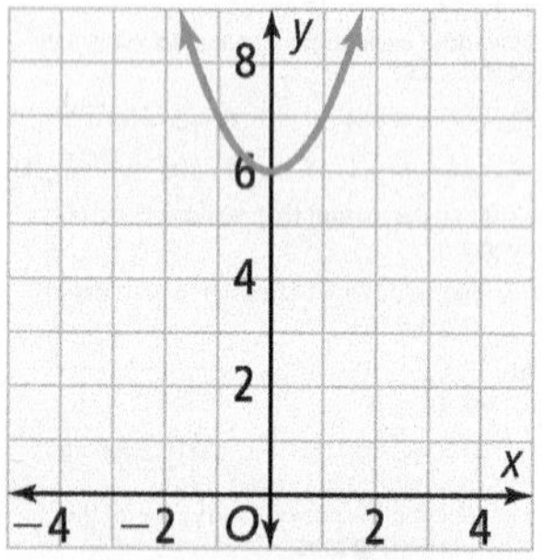

y
8
6
4
2
x
−4
−2
O
2
4

The domain is the set of all real numbers; the range is all real numbers greater than or equal to 6.

22.

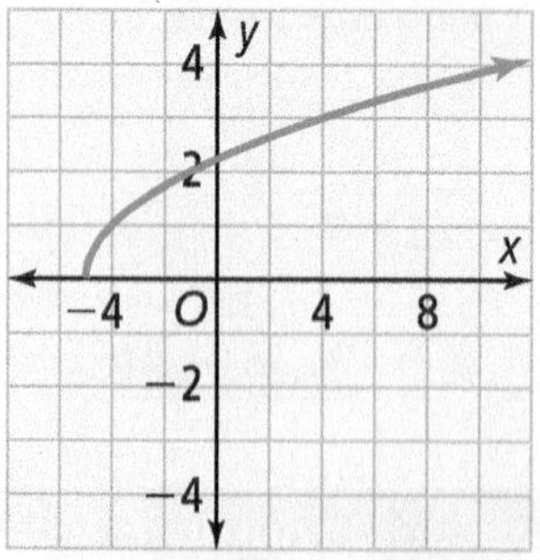

y
4
2
x
−4
O
4
8
−2
−4

The domain is the set of all real numbers greater than or equal to −5; the range is all real numbers greater than or equal to 0.

23. As $x \to \infty$, $j(x) \to -\infty$, and as $x \to -\infty$, $j(x) \to 0$.

24. As $x \to \infty$, $d(x) \to \infty$, and as $x \to -\infty$, $d(x) \to \infty$.

25. f is a quadratic function that opens upward. As $x \to \infty$, $f(x) \to \infty$, and as $x \to -\infty$, $f(x) \to \infty$.

26. The maximum value for h is 116 feet. The axis of symmetry is $x = 1.5$. The maximum value for g is 170 feet. The axis of symmetry is $x = 3.06$.

AVAILABLE **ONLINE**

LESSON 10-2 The Cube Root Function

Quick Review

The **cube root function** is $f(x) = \sqrt[3]{x}$.

Example

For the function $f(x) = \sqrt[3]{x+2}$, how does the average rate of change from $2 \le x \le 4$ compare to the average rate of change from $6 \le x \le 8$?

Evaluate the function for each x-value.

Interval: $2 \le x \le 4$

$f(2) = \sqrt[3]{2+2} \approx 1.59$ $\quad f(4) = \sqrt[3]{4+2} \approx 1.82$

Interval: $6 \le x \le 8$

$f(6) = \sqrt[3]{6+2} = 2$ $\quad f(8) = \sqrt[3]{8+2} \approx 2.15$

Find the average rate of change over each interval.

From $2 \le x \le 4$: $\frac{1.82 - 1.59}{4 - 2} \approx 0.12$

From $6 \le x \le 8$: $\frac{2.15 - 2}{8 - 6} \approx 0.08$

The average rate of change of the function $f(x) = \sqrt[3]{x+2}$ decreases as the x-values of the interval increase.

Practice and Problem Solving

Describe translations that transform the graph of $f(x) = \sqrt[3]{x}$ into the graph of the given function.

13. $g(x) = \sqrt[3]{x+5}$
14. $h(x) = \sqrt[3]{x} + 4$
15. $j(x) = \sqrt[3]{x-1} + 2$
16. $p(x) = \sqrt[3]{x+1.5} - 2.5$

Calculate the average rate of change for each function over the given interval.

17. $f(x) = \sqrt[3]{x}$ for $5 \le x \le 9$
18. $g(x) = \sqrt[3]{x+6}$ for $-3 \le x \le 0$
19. **Look for Relationships** Compare the average rates of change for $f(x) = \sqrt[3]{x}$ and $g(x) = \sqrt[3]{x-3}$ for $-2 \le x \le 2$. **MP.7**
20. **Communicate Precisely** A fish store needs more cube-shaped fish tanks for its display shelves. Each fish requires 1 ft^3 of water, and it costs \$5 per ft^3 for the tanks. Write a cube root function that gives the side lengths of the container x in inches for a given cost C. **MP.6**

LESSON 10-3 Analyzing Functions Graphically

Quick Review

If you know the algebraic structure of a function, you can often use its graph to determine key features of the function.

Example

For the function $f(x) = \sqrt{x-5}$, identify the domain and range, maximum and minimum values, and axis of symmetry, and describe the end behavior.

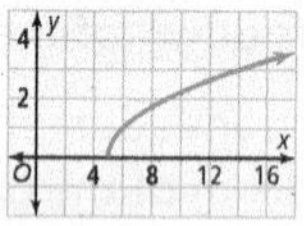

y
4
2
x
O
4
8
12
16

First graph the function.
The domain is $x \ge 5$, and the range is $y \ge 0$.
The minimum is 0 when $x = 5$.
There is no axis of symmetry.
As $x \to \infty$, $f(x) \to \infty$, and as $x \to 5$, $f(x) \to 0$.

Practice & Problem Solving

Sketch the graph of each function and identify its domain and range.

21. $f(x) = x^2 + 6$
22. $g(x) = \sqrt{x+5}$

Describe the end behavior of each function.

23. $j(x) = -5^x$
24. $d(x) = |x - 4| - 2$
25. **Look for Relationships** Without sketching the graph, how can you identify the end behavior of $f(x) = x^2 - 5x + 8$? **MP.7**
26. **Model With Mathematics** The height of a ball thrown from the top of a building is modeled by $h(t) = -16t^2 + 48t + 80$, where $h(t)$ is the height of the ball in feet after t seconds. The height of another ball hit by a bat on a small hill is modeled by $g(t) = -16t^2 + 98t + 20$. Give the maximum values and the axes of symmetry for both functions. **MP.4**

Go Online | PearsonRealize.com

TOPIC 10
Working With Functions

TOPIC REVIEW

Answers

27.

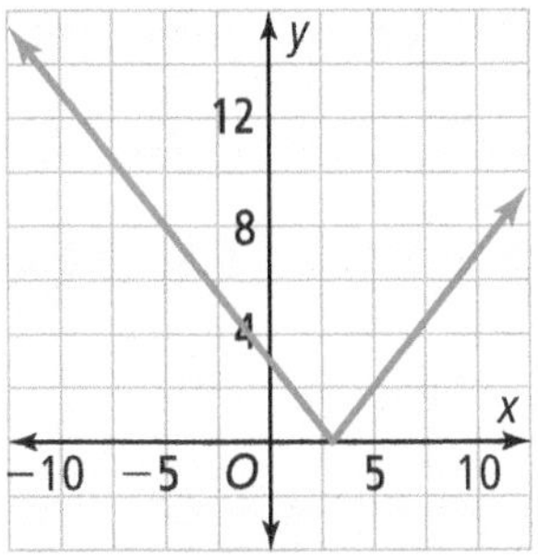

28.

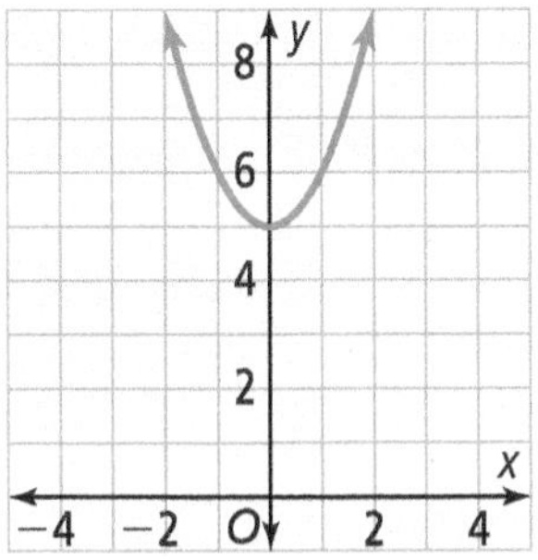

29. $g(x) = (x - 5)^2$

30. Since the graph of f is a horizontal line, the graph is not affected by horizontal translations. So, the value of h has no affect on the graph. The value of k shifts the graph up or down k units.

31. $g(x) = -x^2 - 5$

32. $g(x) = -|2x - 1|$

33. vertical stretch

34. horizontal stretch

35. horizontal compression

36. vertical stretch

37.

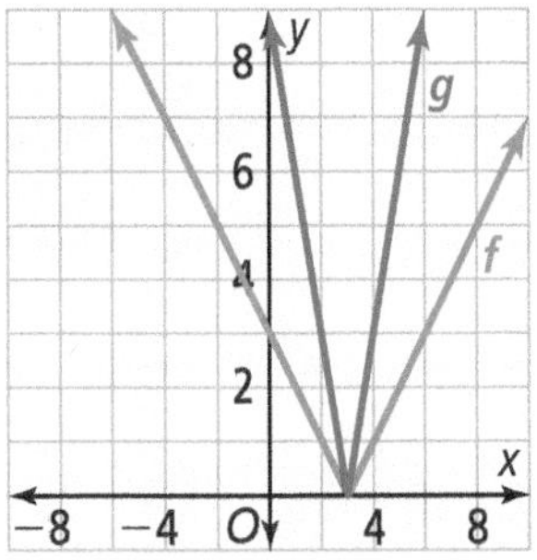

The graph of g is a vertical stretch and a horizontal compression of f. If a graph is vertically stretched, then it is also horizontally compressed.This horizontal compression is in relation to the axis of symmetry rather than the y-axis. Conversely, if a graph is vertically compressed, then it is also horizontally stretched.

AVAILABLE ONLINE

LESSON 10-4 Translations of Functions

Quick Review

The graph of $g(x) = f(x) + k$ is the graph of f shifted up $|k|$ units when $k > 0$ or translated down $|k|$ units when $k < 0$.

The graph of $g(x) = f(x - h)$ is the graph of f shifted right $|h|$ units when $h > 0$ or translated left $|h|$ units when $h < 0$.

Example

Given $f(x) = 3^x$, how does the graph of g compare with the graph of f if $g(x) = f(x) + 4$?

Graph both equations.

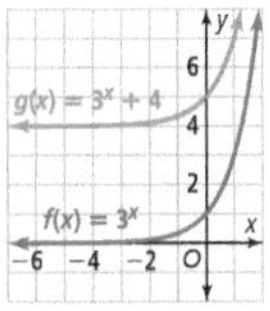

The graph of g translates the graph of f 4 units up.

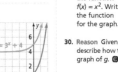

Practice & Problem Solving

Sketch the graph of each function.

27. $g(x) = |x - 3|$ **28.** $g(x) = x^2 + 5$

29. The graph shown is a translation of the function $f(x) = x^2$. Write the function for the graph.

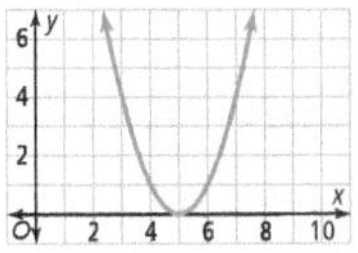

30. Reason Given $f(x) = -3$ and $g(x) = f(x - h) + k$, describe how the constants h and k affect the graph of g. MP.2

LESSON 10-5 Compressions and Stretches of Functions

Quick Review

The graph of $g(x) = kf(x)$ is the graph of f stretched away from the x-axis when $|k| > 1$ and compressed toward the x-axis when $0 < |k| < 1$.

The graph of $g(x) = f(kx)$ is the graph of f stretched away from the y-axis when $0 < |k| < 1$ and compressed toward the y-axis when $|k| > 1$.

Example

Given $f(x) = \sqrt[3]{x + 2}$, how does the graph of g compare with the graph of f if $g(x) = 2f(x)$?

Graph both functions.

The graph of g stretches the graph of f vertically away from the x-axis by a factor of 2.

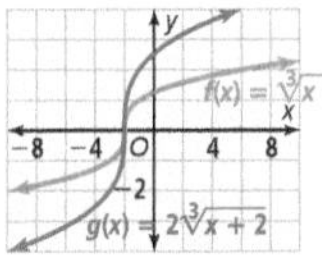

Practice & Problem Solving

Write a function with a graph that is the reflection of the graph of f across the x-axis.

31. $f(x) = x^2 + 5$ **32.** $f(x) = |2x - 1|$

For each pair, tell whether the graph of g is a vertical or horizontal compression or stretch of the graph of f.

33. $f(x) = |2x - 5|$, $g(x) = 2|2x - 5|$ **34.** $f(x) = x^2 + 9$, $g(x) = 0.25x^2 + 9$

35. $f(x) = \sqrt{x - 4}$, $g(x) = \sqrt{4x - 4}$ **36.** $f(x) = 2x - 9$, $g(x) = 6x - 27$

37. Look for Relationships Graph $f(x) = |x - 3|$ and $g(x) = 3|x - 3|$. Is the graph of g a vertical stretch or a horizontal compression of the graph of f? Explain. MP.7

38. Make Sense and Persevere A T-shirt designer uses the function $f(x) = x^2 - 3$ to sew parabolas on his clothing. What are two ways the function could be altered to make the parabolas wider? Explain. MP.1

TOPIC 10 REVIEW

TOPIC 10 Topic Review 459

38. He could vertically compress the graph using the function $g(x) = kf(x)$, where $|k| < 1$. For example, he could use the function $g(x) = 0.5(x^2 - 3)$. He could horizontally stretch the graph using the function $g(x) = f(kx)$, where $|k| < 1$. For example, he could use the function $g(x) = (0.5x^2) - 3$.

Answers

39. $(f+g)(x) = 3x^2 + 7x - 8$

40. $(f+g)(x) = 4x^2 - 13x - 2$

41. $(f+g)(x) = -x + \sqrt{2x} + 4$

42. $(f+g)(x) = 2x^2 + 5x + 4^x - 4$

43. $(f \cdot g)(x) = 15x^3 + x^2 - 2x$

44. $(f \cdot g)(x) = x^3 - 2x^2 - 13x + 20$

45. $(f \cdot g)(x) = 6\sqrt{3}x^{\frac{3}{2}} - 5\sqrt{3x}$

46. $(f \cdot g)(x) = 2^{x+2}x^2 - 3x(2^x) - 2^{x+3}$

47. Answers may vary. Sample: $f(x) = 2x$, $g(x) = 3x$, $(f \cdot g)(x) = 6x^2$

48. $(R - C)(x) = -5x^2 + 21x - 9$; \$9

AVAILABLE **ONLINE**

LESSON 10-6 Operations With Functions

Quick Review

You can add, subtract, and multiply functions to form new functions.

Example

What is the product of the two functions $f(x) = 3x - 5$ and $g(x) = 4x - 1$? Determine the domain and range of $f \cdot g$.

Use the Distributive Property when multiplying polynomials.

$$f(x) \cdot g(x) = (3x - 5) \cdot (4x - 1)$$
$$= 3x(4x) + 3x(-1) + (-5)(4x) + (-5)(-1)$$
$$= 12x^2 - 3x - 20x + 5$$
$$(f \cdot g)(x) = 12x^2 - 23x + 5$$

The domain and range of the original functions are all real numbers. The domain of $f \cdot g$ is all real numbers. The range of $f \cdot g$ is all real numbers greater than or equal to approximately −6.02.

Practice & Problem Solving

Find $f + g$.

39. $f(x) = 3x^2 + 5x$
$g(x) = 2x - 8$

40. $f(x) = 3x^2 - 5x + 1$
$g(x) = x^2 - 8x - 3$

41. $f(x) = \sqrt{2x}$
$g(x) = 4 - x$

42. $f(x) = 4^x - 1$
$g(x) = 2x^2 + 5x - 3$

Find $f \cdot g$.

43. $f(x) = 5x^2 + 2x$
$g(x) = 3x - 1$

44. $f(x) = x^2 + 2x - 5$
$g(x) = x - 4$

45. $f(x) = \sqrt{3x}$
$g(x) = 6x - 5$

46. $f(x) = 2^x$
$g(x) = 4x^2 - 3x - 8$

47. Look for Relationships Write two functions that, when combined by multiplying, have a different range than at least one of the functions. MP.7

48. Make Sense and Persevere A clothing company has determined that the revenue function for selling x thousands of hats is $R(x) = -5x^2 + 23x$. The cost function for producing those hats is $C(x) = 2x + 9$. Write a combined function that represents the profit for selling x thousands of hats, and determine the clothing company's profit from selling 3,000 hats. MP.1

Go Online | PearsonRealize.com

A-Z Glossary | Tutorials | Math Tools

TOPIC 10
Working With Functions

TOPIC REVIEW

Answers.

49.

x	y
3	0
5	1
8	2
11	3

50.

x	y
2	0
4	2
8	2
16	3

51. $f^{-1}(x) = \frac{x+7}{4}$

52. $f^{-1}(x) = \sqrt{\frac{x+8}{3}}, x \geq -8$

53. $f^{-1}(x) = \frac{x^2+3}{2}$

54. $f^{-1}(x) = \frac{x-5}{2}$

55. The student added 3 when solving the equation, instead of subtracting 3.

$f^{-1}(x) = \sqrt{\frac{x-3}{2}}$

56. $s = \sqrt{\frac{A}{6}}$; you could use this equation to find the side length of a cube where you know the surface area of the cube.

AVAILABLE **ONLINE**

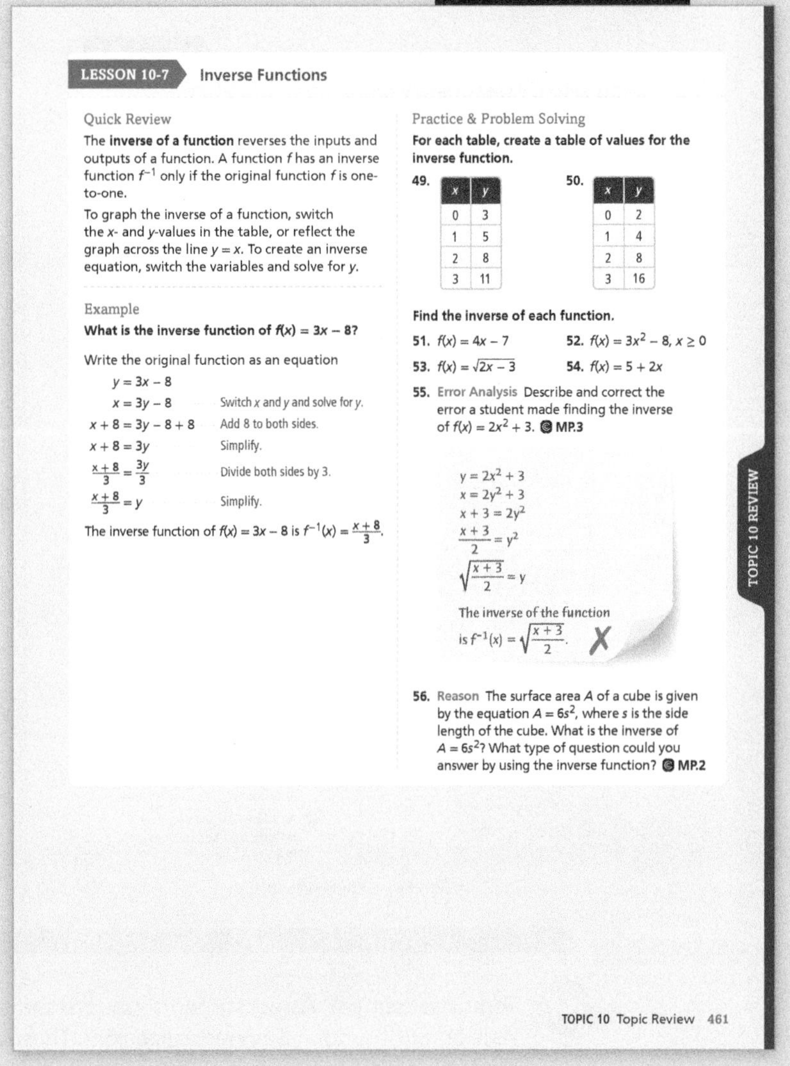
LESSON 10-7 Inverse Functions

Quick Review

The **inverse of a function** reverses the inputs and outputs of a function. A function f has an inverse function f^{-1} only if the original function f is one-to-one.

To graph the inverse of a function, switch the x- and y-values in the table, or reflect the graph across the line $y = x$. To create an inverse equation, switch the variables and solve for y.

Example

What is the inverse function of $f(x) = 3x - 8$?

Write the original function as an equation

$y = 3x - 8$

$x = 3y - 8$ Switch x and y and solve for y.

$x + 8 = 3y - 8 + 8$ Add 8 to both sides.

$x + 8 = 3y$ Simplify.

$\frac{x+8}{3} = \frac{3y}{3}$ Divide both sides by 3.

$\frac{x+8}{3} = y$ Simplify.

The inverse function of $f(x) = 3x - 8$ is $f^{-1}(x) = \frac{x+8}{3}$.

Practice & Problem Solving

For each table, create a table of values for the inverse function.

49.

x	y
0	3
1	5
2	8
3	11

50.

x	y
0	2
1	4
2	8
3	16

Find the inverse of each function.

51. $f(x) = 4x - 7$

52. $f(x) = 3x^2 - 8, x \geq 0$

53. $f(x) = \sqrt{2x-3}$

54. $f(x) = 5 + 2x$

55. Error Analysis Describe and correct the error a student made finding the inverse of $f(x) = 2x^2 + 3$. MP.3

$y = 2x^2 + 3$
$x = 2y^2 + 3$
$x + 3 = 2y^2$
$\frac{x+3}{2} = y^2$
$\sqrt{\frac{x+3}{2}} = y$

The inverse of the function is $f^{-1}(x) = \sqrt{\frac{x+3}{2}}$. ✗

56. Reason The surface area A of a cube is given by the equation $A = 6s^2$, where s is the side length of the cube. What is the inverse of $A = 6s^2$? What type of question could you answer by using the inverse function? MP.2

TOPIC 10 REVIEW

TOPIC 10 Topic Review 461

AVAILABLE ONLINE

Name ______

enVision Algebra 1
PearsonRealize.com

10 Topic Assessment Form A

1. Consider $f(x) = 2x^2 + 1$ and $g(x) = 3x - 6$. Which statement about $f + g$ is true?

Ⓐ It is a linear function.
Ⓑ It is a quadratic function.
Ⓒ The domain is $x \geq -3$.
Ⓓ The range is all real numbers.

2. Which function is graphed?

Ⓐ $f(x) = \sqrt[3]{x+2} - 3$
Ⓑ $f(x) = \sqrt[3]{x-2} - 3$
Ⓒ $f(x) = \sqrt[3]{x+3} - 2$
Ⓓ $f(x) = \sqrt[3]{x-3} - 2$

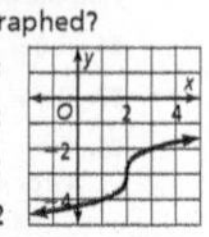
y
x
O
2
4
−2
−4

3. What is the inverse of the function $f(x) = 64x^2$ when $x \geq 0$?

Ⓐ $f^{-1}(x) = \frac{\sqrt{x}}{8}$
Ⓒ $f^{-1}(x) = 8x$
Ⓑ $f^{-1}(x) = 8\sqrt{x}$
Ⓓ $f^{-1}(x) = \frac{1}{8x}$

4. Complete: For the function $f(x) = \sqrt{x+4}$, the average rate of change to the nearest hundredth over the interval $2 \leq x \leq 6$ is 0.18.

5. The graph of $f(x) = -|x + 5| + 6$ models a mountain in a computer drawing for $-11 \leq x \leq 1$. Which function(s) model a mountain with steeper sides? Select all that apply.

Ⓐ $g(x) = -|2x + 5| + 6$
Ⓑ $g(x) = -2|x + 5| + 6$
Ⓒ $g(x) = -\frac{1}{2}|x + 5| + 6$
Ⓓ $g(x) = \left|-\frac{1}{2x} + 5\right| + 6$

6. Complete the sentence, using >, <, ≥, or ≤ and the correct value: The range of $f(x) = \sqrt{x-3} - 1$ is $f(x)$ ≥ -1.

7. Complete the following to describe the end behavior of the exponential function f graphed here.

As $x \to \infty$, $f(x) \to$ ∞.
As $x \to -\infty$, $f(x) \to$ 3.

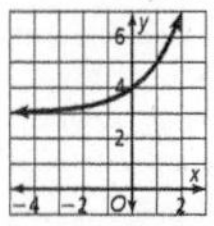
y
6
4
2
x
−4
−2
O
2

8. If $f(x) = 4x - 6$ and $g(x) = 6x - 4$, what is $f \cdot g$?

Ⓐ $f(x) \cdot g(x) = 10x - 10$
Ⓑ $f(x) \cdot g(x) = 24x + 24$
Ⓒ $f(x) \cdot g(x) = 24x^2 - 52x + 24$
Ⓓ $f(x) \cdot g(x) = 10x^2 - 20x - 10$

9. Which statement(s) about the graph of $f(x) = x^2 + 2x - 4$ are true? Select all that apply.

Ⓐ f has an axis of symmetry at $x = -1$.
Ⓑ The maximum value of f is −5 when $x = -1$.
Ⓒ As x approaches infinity, $f(x)$ approaches negative infinity.
Ⓓ As x approaches negative infinity, $f(x)$ approaches infinity.

enVision™ **Algebra 1** • Assessment Resources

10. The graph of $f(x) = \frac{1}{2}x + 2$ is shown. Graph the inverse of f.

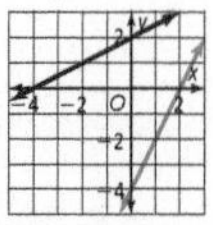
y
2
x
−4
−2
O
2
−2
−4

11. Which function's graph is a vertical stretch of the graph of $f(x) = \sqrt[3]{x+4}$?

Ⓐ $g(x) = \frac{1}{2}\sqrt[3]{x+4}$
Ⓑ $g(x) = 2\sqrt[3]{x+4}$
Ⓒ $g(x) = \sqrt[3]{\frac{1}{2}x+4}$
Ⓓ $g(x) = \sqrt[3]{2x+4}$

12. The graph of g is a translation 1 unit down of the graph of $f(x) = 3|x| - 4$.
Complete: The rate of change of g over the interval $2 \leq x \leq 5$ is 3.

13. The graph of g is a translation 2 units up and 6 units right of the graph of $f(x) = \sqrt{x}$. What is an equation for g?
$g(x) = \sqrt{x-6} + 2$

14. The function $f(x) = 1.25x^2$ models the packaging costs, in cents, for a box shaped like a rectangular prism. The side lengths are $2x$ in., $2x$ in., and $0.5x$ in. What are reasonable domain and range values for this function, if the longest side length of the box can be no greater than 20 in.?

Domain: (0, 10]
Range: (0, 125]

15. Sketch the graph of the function $f(x) = \sqrt{x} - 1$.

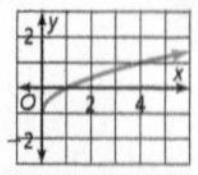
y
2
x
O
2
4
−2

16. At a restaurant, diners earn 1 point for every $2 they spend, plus 25 bonus points on their first meal. Function f represents the number of points earned as a function of the total amount spent x. Which function represents the total amount spent as a function of the number of points earned?

Ⓐ $f^{-1}(x) = 2x - 50$
Ⓑ $f^{-1}(x) = 2x + 50$
Ⓒ $f^{-1}(x) = 0.5x - 50$
Ⓓ $f^{-1}(x) = 0.5x + 50$

17. The surface area of a cylinder with height 2 in. is given by the function $f(x) = 2\pi x^2 + 4\pi x$, where x is the radius. If $g(x) = 4\pi x$ gives the surface area of the side of the cylinder, which combined function gives the total surface area of the two circular bases?

Ⓐ $f + g$
Ⓒ $f - g$
Ⓑ $g - f$
Ⓓ $f \cdot g$

18. Complete: For the function $f(x) = \sqrt[3]{x+3}$, the average rate of change to the nearest hundredth over the interval $-1 \leq x \leq 3$ is 0.14.

19. The graph of g is a translation 3 units down of the graph of $f(x) = x^2 + 1$. What is the range of g?

Ⓐ all real numbers
Ⓒ $g(x) \geq -2$
Ⓑ $g(x) \geq -3$
Ⓓ $g(x) \geq -1$

enVision™ **Algebra 1** • Assessment Resources

AVAILABLE ONLINE

Topic Assessment Assess students' understanding of topic concepts and skills using the Topic Assessment found at **SavvasRealize.com.** These auto-scored online assessments provide students with a breadth of technology-enhanced item types.

There are two versions of the Topic Assessment, Form A and Form B. These two versions, available in print and at **SavvasRealize.com,** are parallel tests that assess the same content item for item. The Item Analysis chart on the next page can be used for both versions.

TOPIC ASSESSMENT Form B

AVAILABLE ONLINE

Name ______

10 Topic Assessment Form B

enVision Algebra 1
PearsonRealize.com

1. Consider $f(x) = 4x^2 - 5$ and $g(x) = 2x + 5$. Which statement about $f + g$ is true?
   - (A) The domain is $x \geq -0.25$.
   - (B) The range is $y \geq -5$.
   - (C) The range is all real numbers.
   - (D) It is a quadratic function.

2. Which function is graphed?
   - (A) $f(x) = \sqrt[3]{x+4} - 1$
   - (B) $f(x) = \sqrt[3]{x+1} + 4$
   - (C) $f(x) = \sqrt[3]{x+4} + 1$
   - (D) $f(x) = \sqrt[3]{x-1} + 4$

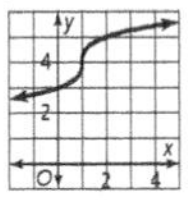

y
4
2
x
O
2
4

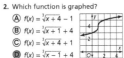

3. What is the inverse of the function $f(x) = 121x^2$ when $x \geq 0$?
   - (A) $f^{-1}(x) = 11\sqrt{x}$
   - (C) $f^{-1}(x) = 11x$
   - (B) $f^{-1}(x) = \frac{\sqrt{x}}{11}$
   - (D) $f^{-1}(x) = \frac{1}{11x}$

4. Complete: For the function $f(x) = \sqrt{x-1}$, the average rate of change to the nearest hundredth over the interval $3 \leq x \leq 6$ is 0.27.

5. The graph of $f(x) = -|x-2| + 1$ models a mountain in a computer drawing for $-4 \leq x \leq 8$. Which function(s) model a mountain with steeper sides? Select all that apply.
   - (A) $g(x) = -\frac{1}{4}|x-2| + 1$
   - (B) $g(x) = -\left|\frac{1}{3}x - 2\right| + 1$
   - (C) $g(x) = -|3x-1| + 2$
   - (D) $g(x) = -|4x-2| + 1$

6. Complete the sentence, using $>$, $<$, $\geq$, or $\leq$ and the correct value: The range of $f(x) = \sqrt{x-3} + 2$ is $f(x)$ ≥ 2.

7. Complete the following to describe the end behavior of the exponential function f graphed here.

   As $x \to \infty$, $f(x) \to$ 2.

   As $x \to -\infty$, $f(x) \to$ ∞.

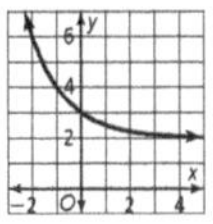

y
6
4
2
x
−2
O
2
4

8. If $f(x) = 3x - 4$ and $g(x) = 4x - 3$, what is $f \cdot g$?
   - (A) $f(x) \cdot g(x) = 7x - 7$
   - (B) $f(x) \cdot g(x) = 12x + 12$
   - (C) $f(x) \cdot g(x) = 7x^2 - 14x - 7$
   - (D) $f(x) \cdot g(x) = 12x^2 - 25x + 12$

9. Which statement(s) about the graph of $f(x) = x^2 - 2x + 3$ are true? Select all that apply.
   - (A) The range of f is $f(x) \geq 3$.
   - (B) The maximum value of f is 2 when $x = 1$.
   - (C) As x approaches infinity, $f(x)$ approaches infinity.
   - (D) As x approaches negative infinity, $f(x)$ approaches infinity.

10. The graph of $f(x) = 2x - 2$ is shown. Graph the inverse of f.

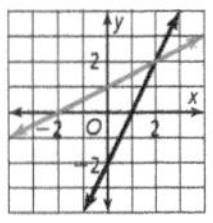

y
2
x
−2
O
2
−2

11. Which function's graph is a vertical compression of the graph of $f(x) = \sqrt[3]{x+4}$?
    - (A) $g(x) = \frac{1}{2}\sqrt[3]{x+4}$
    - (B) $g(x) = 2\sqrt[3]{x+4}$
    - (C) $g(x) = \sqrt[3]{\frac{1}{2}x + 4}$
    - (D) $g(x) = \sqrt[3]{2x+4}$

12. The graph of g is a translation 1 unit down of the graph of $f(x) = 3|x| - 4$.

    Complete: The rate of change of g over the interval $2 \leq x \leq 5$ is 3.

13. The graph of g is a translation 2 units down and 6 units left of the graph of $f(x) = \sqrt{x}$. What is an equation for g?

    $g(x) = \sqrt{x+6} - 2$

14. The function $f(x) = 1.5x^2$ models the packaging costs, in cents, for a box shaped like a rectangular prism. The side lengths are x in., $2x$ in., and $0.5x$ in. What are reasonable domain and range values for this function, if the longest side length of the box can be no greater than 12 in.?

    Domain: (0, 6]

    Range: (0, 54]

15. Sketch the graph of the function $f(x) = \sqrt{x} + 1$.

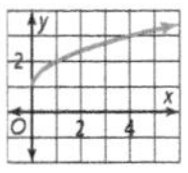

y
2
x
O
2
4

16. At a store, shoppers earn 1 point for every $4 they spend, plus 10 bonus points on their first purchase. If function f represents the number of points earned as a function of the total amount spent x, which function represents the total amount spent as a function of the number of points earned?
    - (A) $f^{-1}(x) = 4x + 40$
    - (B) $f^{-1}(x) = 4x - 40$
    - (C) $f^{-1}(x) = 0.25x + 40$
    - (D) $f^{-1}(x) = 0.25x - 40$

17. The combined surface area of the two bases of a cylinder with height 2 in. is given by the function $f(x) = 2\pi x^2$, where x is the radius, and the function $g(x) = 4\pi x$ gives the surface area of the side of the cylinder. Which combined function gives the total surface area of the cylinder?
    - (A) $f + g$
    - (C) $g - f$
    - (B) $f - g$
    - (D) $f \cdot g$

18. Complete: For $f(x) = \sqrt[3]{x-1}$, the average rate of change to the nearest hundredth over the interval $-2 \leq x \leq 2$ is 0.61.

19. The graph of g is a translation 2 units up of the graph of $f(x) = x^2 - 4$. What is the range of g?
    - (A) $g(x) \geq -4$
    - (C) $g(x) \geq 2$
    - (B) $g(x) \geq -2$
    - (D) all real numbers

Item Analysis

Item	DOK	Standard	Item	DOK	Standard	Item	DOK	Standard
1	1	HSF.BF.A.1.B	8	1	HSF.BF.A.1.B	15	2	HSF.IF.B.5
2	1	HSF.IF.C.7.B	9	1	HSF.IF.B.4	16	2	HSF.IF.C.7.B
3	2	HSF.BF.B.4.A	10	3	HSF.BF.B.4.A	17	3	HSF.BF.B.4.A
4	2	HSF.IF.B.6	11, 12	1	HSF.BF.B.3	18	3	HSF.BF.A.1.B
5	2	HSF.BF.B.3	13	1	HSF.IF.B.6	19	2	HSF.IF.B.6
6, 7	1	HSF.IF.B.4	14	1	HSF.IF.C.7.B, HSF.BF.B.3	20	2	HSF.IF.B.4, HSF.BF.B.3

AVAILABLE ONLINE

Name ______________________

enVision Algebra 1

PearsonRealize.com

10 Performance Assessment Form A

How fast did dinosaurs travel? Scientists analyzed fossilized dinosaur tracks and measured the distance between successive footprints in a series of tracks dated from the Cretaceous Period. This distance is the dinosaur's *stride length*. The maximum walking speed of a dinosaur can be estimated using the dinosaur's stride length.

1. The maximum walking speed of large dinosaurs can be modeled approximately by $w(L) = \sqrt{gL}$, where $w(L)$ represents the walking speed (ft/s), L represents the stride length (ft), and g is the gravitational constant, equal to 32 ft/s^2. The function w can be written $w(L) = \sqrt{32L}$.

Part A

Graph function w. Label the axes and choose an appropriate scale for each axis.

Graphs will vary in scale. Sample:

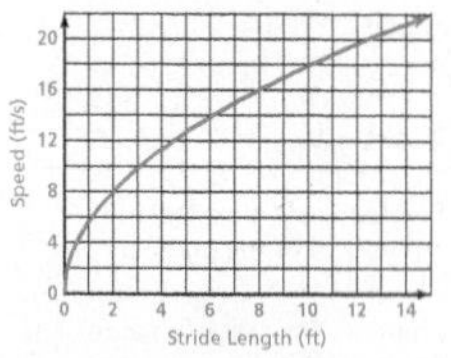

Speed (ft/s)
20
16
12
8
4
0
0 2 4 6 8 10 12 14
Stride Length (ft)

Part B

Use the graph of the function in Part A to identify a maximum and minimum value for the function, if they exist. What are the intercept(s) for the function and what is their meaning in this context? What restrictions might you suggest for the domain and range of the function in context? Explain.

minimum: 0; no maximum; intercept (0, 0); Sample: The intercepts of the function are both 0. If the stride length is 0 ft, the speed must be 0 ft/s. Restrict the domain to $L \geq 0$ because a negative stride length does not make sense. The range is $w(L) \geq 0$, because the square root function returns nonnegative values.

Part C

From Part A, how does the average rate of change of $w(L)$ from $L = 8$ to $L = 10$ compare to the average rate of change of $w(L)$ from $L = 10$ to $L = 12$? Show your work.

The average rate of change over the interval $8 \leq L \leq 10$ is greater than the average rate of change over the interval $10 \leq L \leq 12$.

$w(8) = \sqrt{32(8)} = 16.0$, $w(10) = \sqrt{32(10)} \approx 17.9$, $w(12) = \sqrt{32(12)} \approx 19.6$.

From $L = 8$ to $L = 10$: $\frac{17.9 - 16.0}{10 - 8} \approx 0.95$. From $L = 10$ to $L = 12$: $\frac{19.6 - 17.9}{12 - 10} \approx 0.85$. $0.95 > 0.85$.

enVision™ **Algebra 1** • Assessment Resources

2. A scientific journal includes a table of values for the maximum walking speeds for different dinosaurs in the Cretaceous Period. Calculate the inverse of $w(L)$ algebraically, so you can find the stride length that goes with each of the speeds. If necessary, state any limitations on the domain of the inverse. Show your work.

$w^{-1}(L) = \frac{L^2}{32}$ for $L \geq 0$

$w = \sqrt{32L}$

$L = \sqrt{32w}$

$L^2 = 32w$

$\frac{L^2}{32} = w$ for $L \geq 0$

3. Suppose you want to determine the maximum walking speeds of dinosaurs from the Triassic Period. From Item 1, remember that $w(L) = \sqrt{gL}$ represents the maximum walking speed for dinosaurs living in the more recent Cretaceous Period.

Part A

If $f(L) = \frac{2\sqrt{gL}}{3}$ represents the maximum walking speed for dinosaurs in the Triassic Period, what is $r = w - f$, the resultant function that represents the difference in maximum walking speeds between the two periods? Show your work.

$r(L) = \frac{\sqrt{gL}}{3}$

$w(L) - f(L) = \sqrt{gL} - \frac{2\sqrt{gL}}{3} = \frac{\sqrt{gL}}{3}$

Part B

Identify the transformation of the graph of w in Item 1 that would result in the graph of r in Item 3, Part A.

The graph of r is a vertical compression of w.

enVision™ **Algebra 1** • Assessment Resources

AVAILABLE ONLINE

Topic Performance Assessment Assess students' ability to apply the topic concepts and skills using the Topic Performance Assessments found at **SavvasRealize.com.** These online assessments include a breadth of technology-enhanced item types.

Item Analysis and Scoring Guide

Item	DOK	2-Point Responses	1-Point Responses	Standards
1A	2	Correct graph	Partially correct graph	HSF.IF.C.7.B
1B	2	Correct answer and explanation	Partially correct answer	HSF.IF.B.4, HSF.IF.B.5
1C	2	Correct answer and explanation	Incomplete explanation	HSF.IF.B.6
2	2	Correct answer and solution steps	Incomplete solution steps	HSF.BF.B.4.A
3A	2	Correct answer and solution steps	Correct answer only	HSF.BF.A.1.B
3B	2	Correct explanation	Partially correct explanation	HSF.BF.B.3

TOPIC 10
Working With Functions

TOPIC PERFORMANCE ASSESSMENT Form B

AVAILABLE ONLINE

Name ______________________ enVision Algebra 1 PearsonRealize.com

10 Performance Assessment Form B

If the ground or water on Earth's surface is colder than the air above it, a dense layer of air forms close to the surface, causing light rays to refract downward. The reverse happens if Earth's surface is warmer than the air above it. Refraction affects the amount of Earth's curved surface that you can see.

1. If you ignore the effect of refraction, the distance to the horizon for a person standing on a beach looking out to sea is only affected by the curvature of Earth and the height of the person's eye. The function $d(h) = \sqrt{1.5h}$ models the approximate distance d, in miles, to the horizon for a person whose eye level is h feet above Earth's surface.

Part A

Graph d. Label the axes and use an appropriate scale for each axis.

Graphs will vary. Sample:

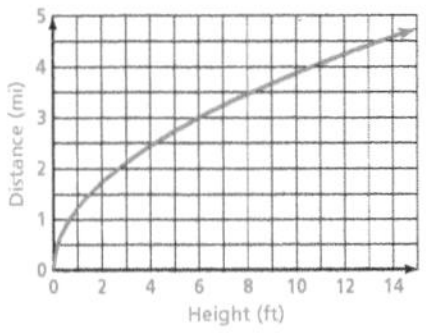
Distance (mi)
Height (ft)
0
2
4
6
8
10
12
14
1
2
3
4
5

Part B

Identify a maximum and minimum value for the function in Part A, if they exist. What are the intercept(s), and what is their meaning in this context? What restrictions do you suggest for the domain and range? (*Hint:* The elevation of Mt. Everest is 29,059 ft.) Explain.

minimum: 0; no maximum; intercept: (0, 0); Sample: If the observer's eye is at ground level, the horizon is 0 ft away. Domain: $0 \leq h \leq 29{,}065$ ft, because only nonnegative numbers have a real square root. A 6-ft-tall observer's eye level at the top of Mt. Everest is a reasonable maximum. The range is then $0 \leq d \leq 208.80$ mi.

Part C

From Part A, how does the average rate of change of $d(h)$ from $h = 2$ to $h = 4$ compare to the average rate of change of $d(h)$ from $h = 4$ to $h = 6$? What does the difference mean in the context? Show your work.

Sample: The average rate of change over $2 \leq h \leq 4$ is greater than over $4 \leq h \leq 6$. The distance to the horizon increases less when the observer's eye level rises from 4 ft to 6 ft than it does when the eye level rises from 2 ft to 4 ft.

$d(2) = \sqrt{1.5(2)} \approx 1.73$ mi, $d(4) = \sqrt{1.5(4)} \approx 2.45$ mi, $d(6) = \sqrt{1.5(6)}$ ≈ 3.00 mi; $\frac{2.45 - 1.73}{4 - 2} \approx 0.36$; $\frac{3 - 2.45}{6 - 4} \approx 0.28$. $0.36 > 0.28$.

2. On a certain day, a scientist decides to account for atmospheric refraction when viewing the horizon looking out to sea from the beach. The refraction function r increases the value for d in Item 1 by a factor of about 1.1.

Part A

Describe the effect, or transformation, on the graph of d of multiplying the function by 1.1. Then graph function r.

Graphs will vary. Sample shown. The graph of $r(h) = 1.1\sqrt{1.5h}$ is a vertical stretch of $d(h) = \sqrt{1.5h}$ away from the horizontal axis.

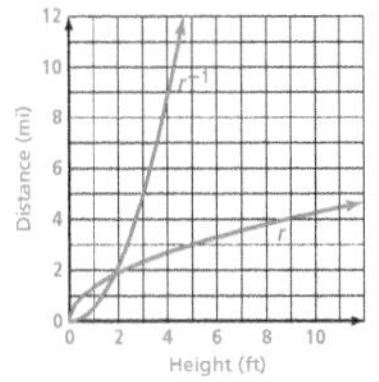
Distance (mi)
Height (ft)
r^{-1}
r
0
2
4
6
8
10
12

Part B

Suppose an island lighthouse is 2.5 mi from shore. Find the inverse of the function r from Part A algebraically. Use the inverse to find the minimum eye level required to see the base of the lighthouse. If necessary, state any limitations on the domain of the inverse function. Show your work.

$r^{-1}(h) \approx \frac{h^2}{1.82}$ for $h \geq 0$; $\frac{(2.5)^2}{1.82} \approx 3.4$ ft is the minimum eye level required.

$r = 1.1\sqrt{1.5h}$

$h = 1.1\sqrt{1.5r}$

$\frac{h}{1.1} = \sqrt{1.5r}$

$\frac{h^2}{1.21} = 1.5r$

$\frac{h^2}{1.82} \approx r$ for $h \geq 0$

Part C

Graph and label r^{-1} on the coordinate plane in Part A, so you can quickly find minimum eye levels required to see landmarks at different distances from shore. How does the graph of r^{-1} compare to the graph of r?

Graphs will vary. Sample shown on graph in Part A. For $h \geq 0$, the graph of r^{-1} is a reflection of the graph of r across the line with equation $r = h$.

AVAILABLE ONLINE

Topic Performance Assessment Assess students' ability to apply the topic concepts and skills using the Topic Performance Assessments found at **SavvasRealize.com.** These online assessments include a breadth of technology-enhanced item types.

Item Analysis and Scoring Guide

Item	DOK	2-Point Responses	1-Point Responses	Standards
1A	2	Correct graph	Partially correct graph	HSF.IF.C.7.B
1B	2	Correct answer and explanation	Partially correct answer	HSF.IF.B.4, HSF.IF.B.5
1C	2	Correct answer and explanation	Incomplete explanation	HSF.IF.B.6
2A	3	Correct graph and description	Correct graph only	HSF.BF.B.3, HSF.IF.C.7.B
2B	2	Correct answer and solution steps	Incomplete solution steps	HSF.BF.B.4.A
2C	3	Correct graph and explanation	Incomplete explanation	HSF.IF.C.7.A

MATH BACKGROUND FOCUS

Topic 11 focuses on extending students' knowledge of dot plots, box plots, and histograms. Students identify that standard deviation is used to compare a specific value to other values. Students understand how to find joint, marginal, and relative frequencies. Students learn methods to interpret data displays and create inferences based on the data.

Data Displays

Dot Plots, Box Plots, and Histograms In Lesson 11-1, students learn that dot plots, box plots, and histograms provide different information about the data sets they represent. Dot plots show the frequency of data and clearly show clusters, gaps, and outliers. Box plots show the center and spread of a distribution. Histograms show the distribution and the shape of the data.

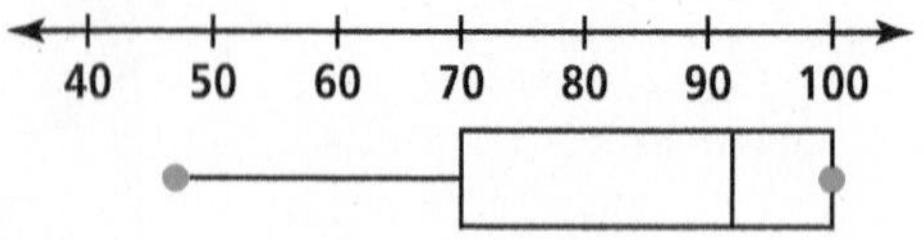

40
50
60
70
80
90
100

Measures of Center and Variability In Lesson 11-2, students understand that measures of center and measures of variability are used to compare data sets displayed in dot plots, box plots, and histograms. Dot plots show how much the data vary. Box plots show the minimum, maximum, and center of the data. Histograms show the ranges of data.

Histograms In Lesson 11-3, students discover that when the shape of a histogram is symmetric, the mean is equal, or approximately equal, to the median. When the shape of the histogram is skewed left, the mean is less than the median. When the shape of the histogram is skewed right, the mean is greater than the median.

Cost of City Parking
n = 250
The mean is $25 per day.
Number of Cars
0
10
20
30
40
50
60
18–19 20–21 22–23 24–25 26–27 28–29 30–31 32–33
Cost per Day ($)

Analyze Data

Standard Deviation In Lesson 11-4, students identify that standard deviation is used to compare a specific value to other values in the data set and to determine the percent of values that fall within a specific interval from the mean.

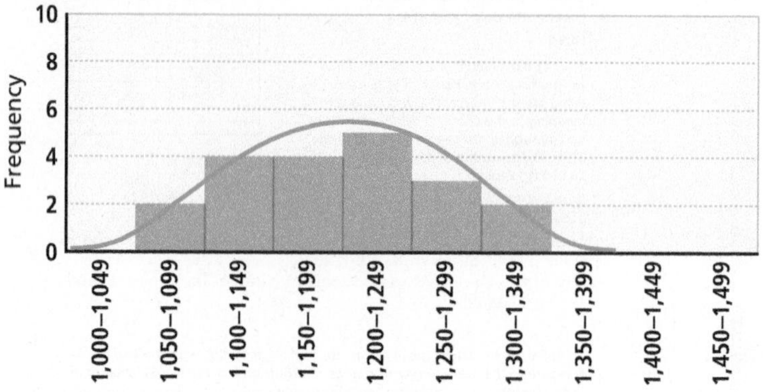

Frequency
0
2
4
6
8
10
1,000–1,049
1,050–1,099
1,100–1,149
1,150–1,199
1,200–1,249
1,250–1,299
1,300–1,349
1,350–1,399
1,400–1,449
1,450–1,499

Frequencies In Lesson 11-5, students comprehend that entries in two-way frequency tables show the frequency of each event, or the joint frequencies, and that the totals for each row or column show the marginal frequencies. Relative frequencies are the ratios between the frequencies or between the frequencies and the total.

	Veggie Burger	Veggie Pizza
Male	$\frac{50}{110} \approx 45\%$	$\frac{40}{115} \approx 35\%$
Female	$\frac{60}{110} \approx 55\%$	$\frac{75}{115} \approx 65\%$
Totals	$\frac{110}{110} = 100\%$	$\frac{115}{115} = 100\%$

TOPIC 11
Statistics

MATH BACKGROUND COHERENCE

Students learn best when concepts are connected through the curriculum. This coherence is achieved within topics, across topics, across domains, and across grade levels.

MAKING MATHEMATICAL CONNECTIONS
Looking Back

How does Topic 11 connect to what students learned earlier?

GRADE 8

- **Dot Plots, Box Plots, and Histograms** Students used dot plots, box plots, and histograms to represent data. In Topic 11, students use these data displays to interpret and compare data.
- **Calculate Measures of Center** Students learned how to calculate measures of center and spread, including mean, median, mean absolute deviation (MAD), and interquartile range (IQR). In Topic 11, students continue to calculate these measures and use them to make inferences based on the data.

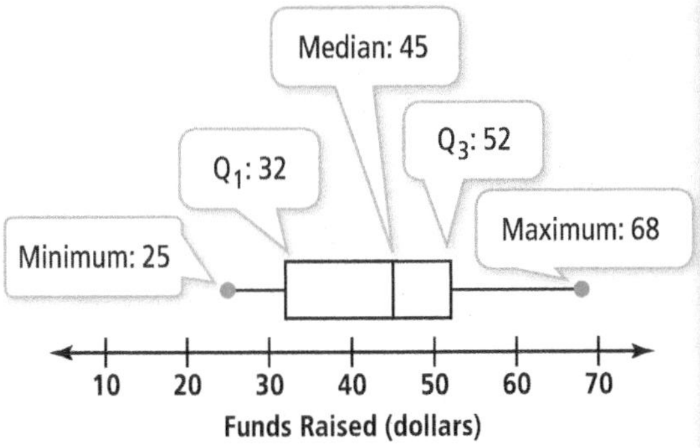

Median: 45
Q_1: 32
Q_3: 52
Minimum: 25
Maximum: 68
10
20
30
40
50
60
70
Funds Raised (dollars)

IN THIS TOPIC

How is content connected within Topic 11?

- **Compare Data** In Lesson 11-1, students represent data using dot plots, box plots, and histograms and use them to make inferences about the data. In Lesson 11-2, students use measures of center and variability to interpret and compare data displayed in dot plots, histograms, and box plots. In Lesson 11-3, students relate the shape of data displays to measures such as mean, median, and MAD.
- **Analyze Data** In Lesson 11-4, students use standard deviation to quantify and analyze the spread of data. In Lesson 11-5, students calculate measures of frequency to analyze and interpret categorical data using two-way frequency tables.

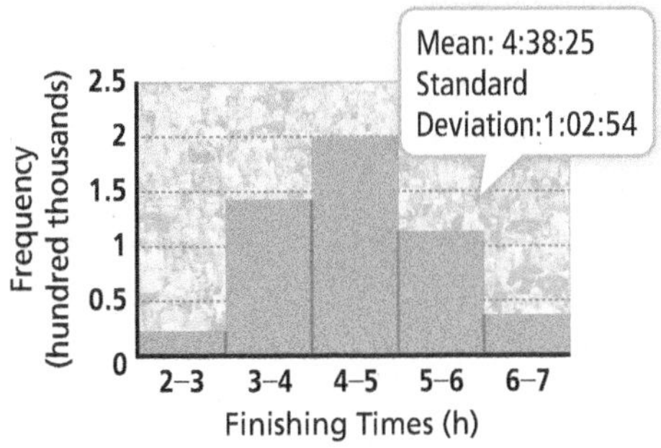

Mean: 4:38:25
Standard
Deviation:1:02:54
Frequency
(hundred thousands)
2.5
2
1.5
1
0.5
0
2–3
3–4
4–5
5–6
6–7
Finishing Times (h)

MAKING MATHEMATICAL CONNECTIONS
Looking Ahead

How does Topic 11 connect to what students will learn later?

ALGEBRA 2

- **Data Analysis and Statistics** In Topic 11, students interpret samples of data based on the shape of the data display and measures of mean, median, and MAD. In Algebra 2, students continue to use sampling methods to study data distributions, normal distributions, margins of error, and to test hypothesis from experiments.
- **Frequency Tables** In Topic 11, students interpret categorical data using two-way frequency tables. In Algebra 2, students will expand this knowledge to approximate conditional probabilities.

STATISTICS

- **Distribution of Graphs** In Topic 11, students use dot plots, box plots, and histograms to represent the mean, median, and range of data samples. In Statistics, students will continue to use these graphs, along with stem and leaf plots and scatter plots to analyze normal distributions, uniform distributions, and skewed distributions.

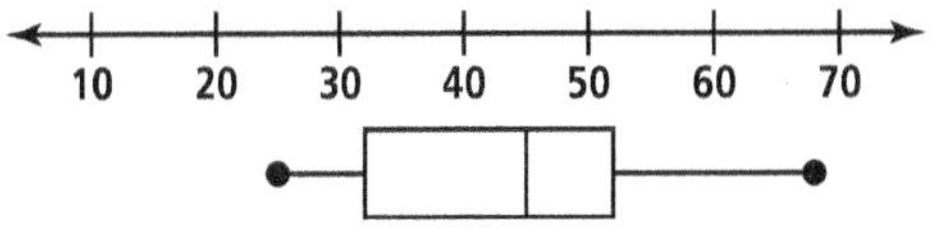

10
20
30
40
50
60
70

- **Deviation** In Topic 11, students use standard deviation to analyze the spread of data. In Statistics, students will find the variance, standard score, and the moment of deviation from the mean. Students will also use paired *t*-tests to determine whether the means of two samples vary considerably and statistical tests to determine the statistical importance of observation.

MATH BACKGROUND RIGOR

A rigorous curriculum emphasizes conceptual understanding, procedural skill and fluency, and applications.

Conceptual Understanding

- **Data Display Representation** Students understand that different data displays can be used to highlight and interpret data in different ways. Dot plots show frequency, histograms show distribution and shape, and box plots show center and spread.

- **Shape of Data** Students understand that when the shape of the data display is symmetric, the mean is approximately equal to the median. When the shape of the data is skewed right or left, the mean and median are not equal.

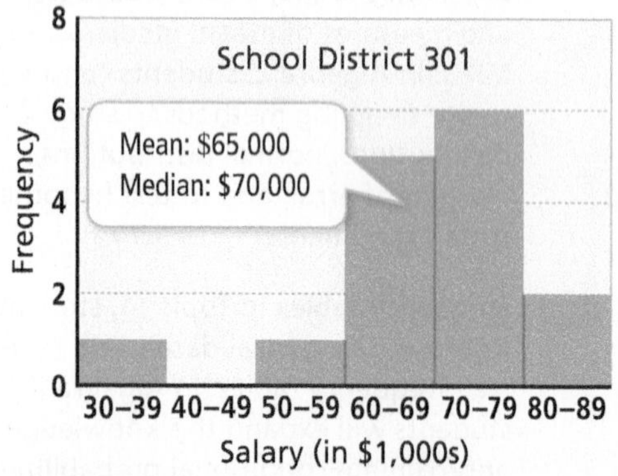
School District 301
Mean: $65,000
Median: $70,000
Frequency
0
2
4
6
8
30–39 40–49 50–59 60–69 70–79 80–89
Salary (in $1,000s)

- **Standard Deviation** Students understand that standard deviation is a measure of spread or variability that, along with the mean, describes the data set completely when it is normally distributed.

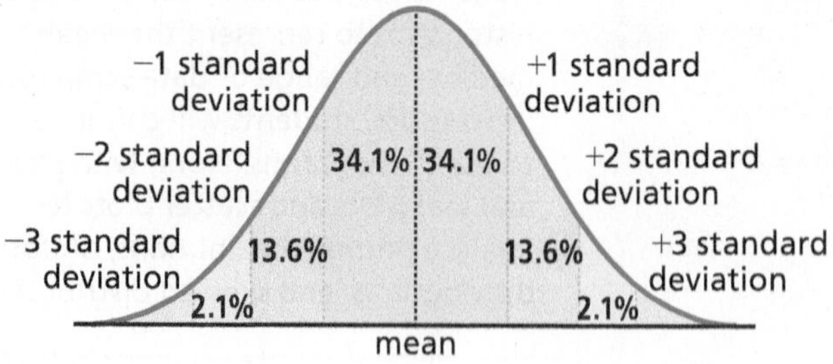
−1 standard deviation
+1 standard deviation
−2 standard deviation
+2 standard deviation
−3 standard deviation
+3 standard deviation
34.1% 34.1%
13.6%
13.6%
2.1%
2.1%
mean

Procedural Skill and Fluency

- **Calculate Standard Deviation** Students calculate the standard deviation by squaring the differences between each data value and the mean, and then taking the square root of the variance.

- **Calculate Conditional Relative Frequency** Students calculate conditional relative frequency by finding the ratio of the joint frequency to the marginal frequency.

A joint frequency is at the joint of a column and a row.

	Veggie Burger	Veggie Pizza	Totals
Male	50	40	90
Female	60	75	135
Totals	110	115	225

A marginal frequency is at the margin, or edge of a column or row.

Applications

- **Interpret Dot Plots, Box Plots, and Histograms** Students interpret dot plots, box plots, and histograms within the context of real-world data, such as when a marketing team decides whether to advertise their product during a particular show based on data about the age ranges of viewers.

- **Interpret Data Displays** Students interpret data displays within the context of real-world problems, such as comparing the fuel efficiency of different cars.

- **Interpret the Shape of Distribution of Data** Students interpret the shape of the distribution of data within the context of real-world data, such as deciding if the process of making bagels needs to be changed based on the weight of samples of bagels.

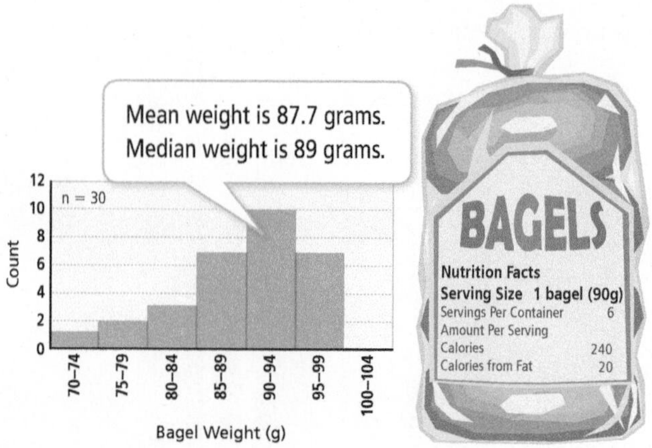
Mean weight is 87.7 grams.
Median weight is 89 grams.
n = 30
Count
0
2
4
6
8
10
12
70–74 75–79 80–84 85–89 90–94 95–99 100–104
Bagel Weight (g)
BAGELS
Nutrition Facts
Serving Size 1 bagel (90g)
Servings Per Container 6
Amount Per Serving
Calories 240
Calories from Fat 20

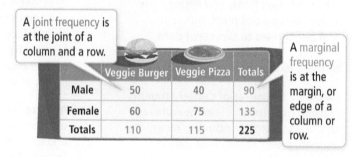

TOPIC 11
Statistics

MATH PRACTICES & PROCESSES

Math Practices Within Topic 11 Lessons

The math practices describe the behaviors and habits of mind that mathematically proficient students demonstrate when actively engaged in mathematics work. Opportunities to develop expertise with these important behaviors and thinking habits exist throughout the topic and program. Here we focus on *reasoning* and *using structure*.

As students present and analyze data, look for the following behaviors to assess and identify students who demonstrate proficiency with these math practices.

Highlighted Math Practices Within Topic 11 Lessons

Reason Abstractly and Quantitatively MP.2	Look For and Make Use of Structure MP.7
Mathematically proficient students:	Mathematically proficient students:
• Create logical representations of data, such as dot plots, box plots, and histograms as a way to analyze data and solve problems.	• Recognize how the overall structure of a box plot represents the interquartile range (IQR) by using a box to highlight the middle 50% of the data.
• Attend to the meaning of quantities when they consider how sample size affects the inferences that can be made about the entire population.	• Look for the overall structure in mathematics when they notice the relationships between the shape of the data displayed in a histogram and the mean, median, and standard deviation of the data.
• Contextualize quantitative relationships when they make inferences using statistical measures, such as the mean, median, and standard deviation.	• See the frequencies in the rows and columns of two-way frequency tables as single objects and recognize that the relative frequencies that are calculated for rows and the relative frequencies that are calculated for columns are interpreted in different ways.
• Assess the reasonableness of inferences made about preferences using frequencies in a two-way frequency table.	• Determine the best data display to use—a dot plot, a box plot, or a histogram—depending on which information they wish to highlight.

Help students become more proficient with reasoning and using structure.

If students do not understand how to identify and use appropriate strategies for understanding and solving problems involving statistics, then use these questioning strategies to help them develop their proficiency with reasoning and using structure as they solve problems throughout the topic.

Q: How do you decide which data display represents the data most clearly?

Q: How does sample size affect the inferences that can be made about a population?

Q: What is the relationship between statistical measures and real-world implications?

Q: How reasonable are the inferences made about preferences using frequencies?

Q: How does a box plot represent the IQR?

Q: What do you notice about the shape of the data displayed in a histogram and the statistical measures?

Q: How are the calculations of relative frequencies of rows interpreted differently from the relative frequencies of columns?

Q: What observations can you make about the relationship between the shapes of data displays?

TOPIC PLANNER

Lesson	New Vocabulary	Objective	Essential Understanding	Standards
11-1 2 DAYS Analyzing Data Displays	none	• Represent data using dot plots, box plots, and histograms. • Interpret the data displayed in dot plots, box plots, and histograms within the context of the data that it represents.	Dot plots, histograms, and box plots provide different information about the data sets they represent. Dot plots show the frequency of data and clearly show clusters, gaps, and outliers. Histograms show the distribution of values within a data set and shape of the data. Box plots show the center and spread of a distribution.	HSS.ID.A.1 **Mathematical Practices** MP.3, MP.5, MP.7
11-2 2 DAYS Comparing Data Sets	none	• Use measures of center to interpret and compare data sets displayed in dot plots, box plots, and histograms. • Explain and account for the effect of outliers on measures of center and variability. • Use measures of variability, such as the MAD and IQR, to interpret and compare data sets.	Measures of center and variability are used to compare data sets displayed in dot plots, box plots, and histograms. Dot plots show how much the data vary. Box plots show the minimum, maximum, and center of the data. Histograms show ranges of data.	HSS.ID.A.1, HSS.ID.A.2, HSS.ID.A.3 **Mathematical Practices** MP.2, MP.6, MP.7
11-3 2 DAYS Interpreting the Shapes of Data Displays	none	• Interpret and compare differences in the shape, center, and spread of data of different data sets. • Determine the relationship between the mean and median of a data set when the shape of the data is evenly spread, skewed right, or skewed left.	When the shape of the data display is symmetric, the mean is equal (or approximately equal) to the median. When the shape of the data display is skewed right or skewed left, the mean and median are not equal.	HSS.ID.A.2, HSA.ID.A.3 **Mathematical Practices** MP.2, MP.7, MP.8

Lesson Resources

Digital / Print

Student Edition

Student Companion

Assessment Resource Book

- Lesson Quiz

Digital

Digital Lesson Courseware

- Examples with Embedded Interactives
- Additional Examples
- Online Practice powered by MathXL for School
- Virtual Nerd Tutorials
- English/Spanish Glossary
- Digital Math Tools
- Mathematical Modeling in 3 Acts

Teaching Resources

- Reteach to Build Understanding
- Mathematical Literacy and Vocabulary
- Additional Practice
- Enrichment

Lesson Support for Teachers

- Professional Development Video
- Lesson Plans

The suggested pacing for each lesson is shown for a 45-minute class.
In addition, allow 1 day for the Topic Review and 1 day for the Topic Assessment.

TOPIC PLANNER

Lesson	New Vocabulary	Objective	Essential Understanding	Standards
11-4 2 DAYS Standard Deviation	• normal distribution, standard deviation, variance	• Interpret differences in the variability or spread in the context of a data set. • Calculate the standard deviation of a data set and use it to compare and interpret data sets.	Standard deviation is a measure of spread, or variability. It indicates by how much the values in a data set deviate from the mean.	HSS.ID.A.2, HSS.ID.A.3 **Mathematical Practices** MP.3, MP.7, MP.8
11-5 2 DAYS Two-Way Frequency Tables	• conditional relative frequency, joint frequency, joint relative frequency, marginal frequency, marginal relative frequency	• Organize and summarize categorical data by creating two-way frequency tables. • Calculate and interpret joint and marginal frequencies, joint and marginal relative frequencies, and conditional relative frequencies, and use them to make inferences about a population.	Two-way frequency tables show relationships between two sets of categorical data. Entries in the table can be frequency counts or relative frequency. Two-way frequency tables are used to analyze data and make inferences about a population.	HSS.ID.B.5 **Mathematical Practices** MP.2, MP.3, MP.7
Mathematical Modeling in 3 Acts: 1 DAY	none	• Use mathematical modeling to represent a problem situation and to propose a solution. • Test and verify the appropriateness of the math model. • Explain why the results from the mathematical model might not align exactly with the problem situation.	Many real-world problem situations can be represented with a mathematical model, but that model might not represent the real-world situation exactly.	HSS.ID.A.2, HSS.ID.A.3 **Mathematical Practices** MP.4

Topic Resources

Digital

Print

Student Edition
- enVision STEM
- Mathematical Modeling in 3 Acts
- Topic Review

Digital Lesson Courseware
- Topic Readiness Assessment
- Topic Assessment
- Topic Performance Assessment

Digital

Teaching Resources
- enVision STEM
- Graphing Technology Activities

Topic Support for Teachers
- Mathematical Modeling in 3 Acts
- ExamView
- Answers and Solutions

TOPIC READINESS ASSESSMENT

AVAILABLE **ONLINE**

Name ______________________ enVision Algebra 1 PearsonRealize.com

11 Readiness Assessment

1. Complete using *increase, decrease,* or *remain constant*: A scatter plot shows a negative association if, as the *x*-values increase, the *y*-values decrease.

2. Which best describes a weak correlation of data?
   - Ⓐ There is no association between the *x*- and *y*-values.
   - Ⓑ There is a negative association between *x*- and *y*-values.
   - Ⓒ The data are grouped closely together in one area on the coordinate plane.
   - Ⓓ There is a data point that lies far away from other data points.

3. Which ordered pair would be classified as an outlier of the data in the table? (2.5, 93)

x	1	1.5	2	2.5	3	4	5	5.5
y	63	64	65	93	70	72	74	78

4. A line of best fit for a data set has equation $y = 3x - 4$. What *y*-value would you predict for an *x*-value of 8 in this data set?
   - Ⓐ 4
   - Ⓑ 8
   - Ⓒ 16
   - Ⓓ 20

5. Which of the lines could be used to predict other values for the data shown in the scatter plot?

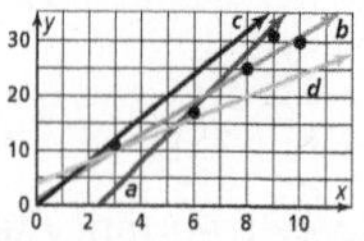

   - Ⓐ Line *a*
   - Ⓑ Line *b*
   - Ⓒ Line *c*
   - Ⓓ Line *d*

Use this data set for Items 6 and 7: 1, 3, 5, 6, 8, 12, 14.

6. What is the mean of the data? 7
7. What is the median of the data? 6
8. What is the range of the data? 13

9. What advantage does a scatter plot have over a table of values? Select all that apply.
   - Ⓐ The scatter plot visually shows any positive or negative association.
   - Ⓑ The scatter plot shows any linear association.
   - Ⓒ The scatter plot easily identifies duplicate data values.
   - Ⓓ The scatter plot visually shows any outliers of the data.

10. Which equation represents a line of best fit for the set of ordered pairs? {(1, 16), (2, 20), (3, 24), (4, 30), (5, 36)}
    - Ⓐ $y = 5x + 10$
    - Ⓑ $y = 10x + 5$
    - Ⓒ $y = -5x + 10$
    - Ⓓ $y = -10x + 5$

11. What is true about a line of best fit for the data in the scatter plot?

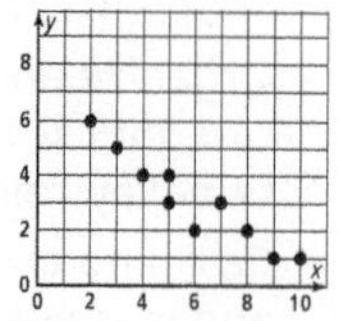

    - Ⓐ The slope is undefined.
    - Ⓑ The slope is negative.
    - Ⓒ The slope is positive.
    - Ⓓ The slope is zero.

12. Which statement best describes a scatter plot with a linear association?
    - Ⓐ Most data points are grouped in a small area of the plane.
    - Ⓑ There is a data point that lies far away from other data.
    - Ⓒ A line could be drawn so that most data points are close to the line.
    - Ⓓ The data points approximate a U-shaped curve.

13. If the outlier were removed from this data set, would the mean increase or decrease?
    39, 68, 72, 81, 86, 88, 91, 95
    increase

14. What is the median of the data?
    53, 47, 61, 73, 39 53

15. What is the definition of the median of a data set?
    - Ⓐ The median is the average of the data values.
    - Ⓑ The median is the value in the middle of an ordered data set.
    - Ⓒ The median is the most frequently occurring data value.
    - Ⓓ The median is the most likely data value.

16. How far is 80 from the mean of this data set?
    110, 130, 100, 120, 150, 80 35

17. The line plots display data from 2 classes. Which measure would best compare the centers of the data?

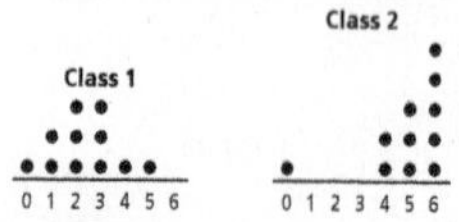

Class 1
Class 2
0 1 2 3 4 5 6
0 1 2 3 4 5 6

median

18. If the mean of this set of data is 8, what is *x*?

4	8	11	14
10	6	8	*x*

    - Ⓐ $x = 1$
    - Ⓒ $x = 8$

be any

AVAILABLE **ONLINE**

Topic Readiness Assessment Assess students' understanding of prerequisite concepts and skills using the Topic Readiness Assessment found at **SavvasRealize.com.** These auto-scored online assessments provide students with a breadth of technology-enhanced item types.

Individualized Study Plan Based on their performance, students will be assigned a study plan tailored to their specific learning needs.

RtI Item Analysis for Diagnosis and Intervention

Item	DOK	Standard	Item	DOK	Standard
1	1	8.SP.A.1	9	2	8.SP.A.2
2	1	8.SP.A.1	10	2	8.SP.A.3
3	1	8.SP.A.1	11	1	6.SP.B.5.C
4	1	8.SP.A.1	12	1	6.SP.B.5.C
5	2	8.SP.A.2	13	1	6.SP.B.5.C
6	2	7.SP.B.4	14	2	6.SP.B.5.C
7	1	8.SP.A.1	15	2	6.SP.B.5.D
8	2	8.SP.A.3	16	2	6.SP.B.5.C

TOPIC OPENER

AVAILABLE ONLINE

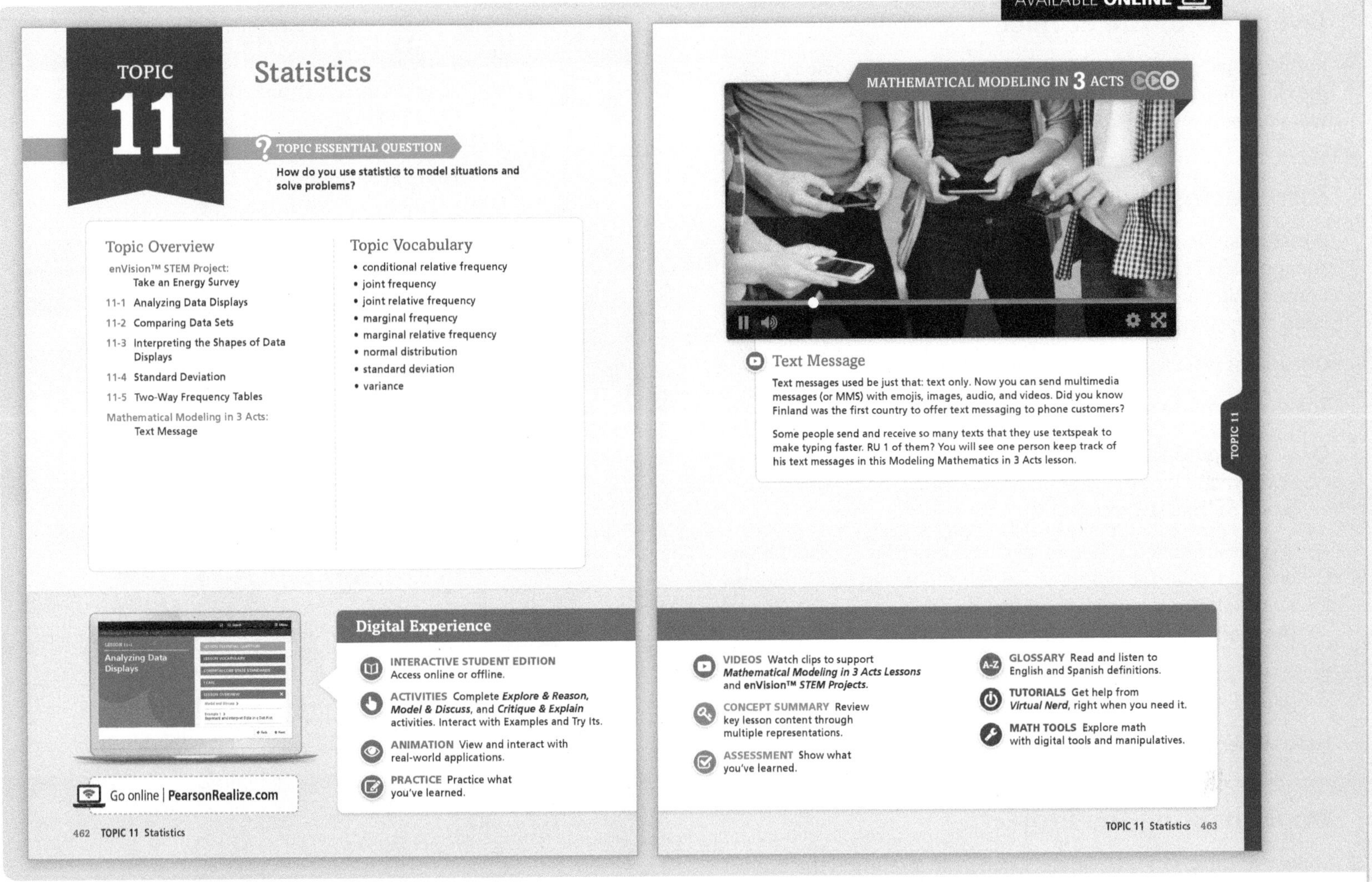

TOPIC 11

Statistics

TOPIC ESSENTIAL QUESTION

How do you use statistics to model situations and solve problems?

Topic Overview

Topic Vocabulary

- conditional relative frequency
- joint frequency
- joint relative frequency
- marginal frequency
- marginal relative frequency
- normal distribution
- standard deviation
- variance

Go online | PearsonRealize.com

Digital Experience

- INTERACTIVE STUDENT EDITION Access online or offline.
- ACTIVITIES Complete *Explore & Reason, Model & Discuss*, and *Critique & Explain* activities. Interact with Examples and Try Its.
- ANIMATION View and interact with real-world applications.
- PRACTICE Practice what you've learned.

MATHEMATICAL MODELING IN 3 ACTS

Text Message

Text messages used be just that: text only. Now you can send multimedia messages (or MMS) with emojis, images, audio, and videos. Did you know Finland was the first country to offer text messaging to phone customers?

Some people send and receive so many texts that they use textspeak to make typing faster. RU 1 of them? You will see one person keep track of his text messages in this Modeling Mathematics in 3 Acts lesson.

- VIDEOS Watch clips to support *Mathematical Modeling in 3 Acts Lessons* and enVision™ *STEM Projects*.
- CONCEPT SUMMARY Review key lesson content through multiple representations.
- ASSESSMENT Show what you've learned.
- GLOSSARY Read and listen to English and Spanish definitions.
- TUTORIALS Get help from *Virtual Nerd*, right when you need it.
- MATH TOOLS Explore math with digital tools and manipulatives.

Topic Essential Question

How do you use statistics to model situations and solve problems?

Revisit the Topic Essential Question throughout the topic. See page 502 (Topic Review) for notes about answering the Topic Essential Question.

Mathematical Modeling in 3 Acts

Generate excitement about the upcoming Mathematical Modeling in 3 Acts lesson by having students read about the math modeling problem for this topic.

See pages 501–501B for notes about how to use the lesson video in your classroom.

Overview of the Project

In this project, students will learn some ways for people to measure their own household energy consumption and suggest ways to reduce it.

Introducing the Project

Present the situation by discussing that energy consumption changes significantly based on local climate and time of year. Consumption increases with extreme temperatures due to the need for heating and cooling.

Discussions will vary depending on your locale.

The questions below can be used to guide the discussion.

Q: Which appliances in your house do you think use the most energy, and why?
[Look for realistic responses.]

Q: If you were told you had to eliminate one of these three high-energy appliances, which would you choose, and why: window air conditioner, washing machine, dryer?
[Answers will vary.]

Q: What could be a reason people try to lower their energy use?
[global resources, finances]

Have students read the task they will be asked to complete.

Implementing the Project

Show the Topic 11 STEM video to generate interest in the project.

You can download blackline masters for use with the project from the Teacher Resource Center.

Students may work in pairs or groups if desired.

Finishing the Project

You may wish to plan a day when students share their completed surveys, data displays, and analyses. Encourage students to explain their process as well as their results.

MAKING MATHEMATICAL CONNECTIONS	
In Topic 7 ...	... you used polynomials to model business decisions.
In this Topic ...	... you gather and analyze data about reducing energy consumption.

AVAILABLE ONLINE

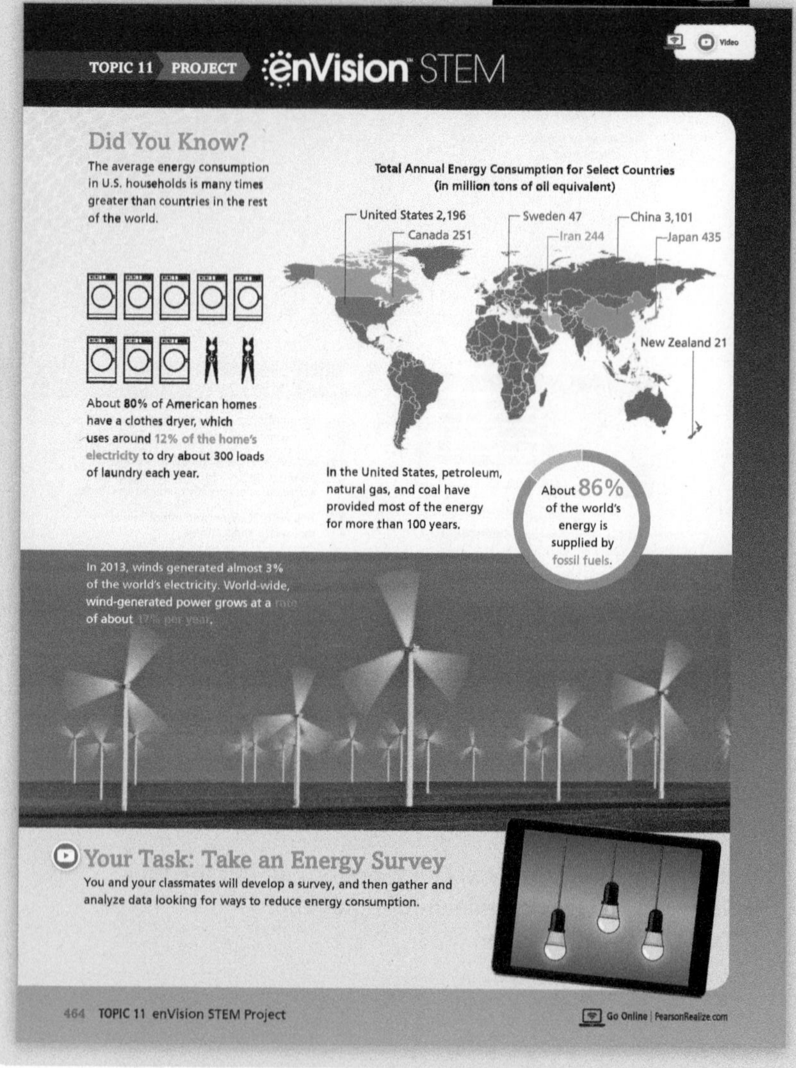

Video
TOPIC 11 PROJECT enVision STEM
Did You Know?
The average energy consumption in U.S. households is many times greater than countries in the rest of the world.
Total Annual Energy Consumption for Select Countries (in million tons of oil equivalent)
United States 2,196
Canada 251
Sweden 47
Iran 244
China 3,101
Japan 435
New Zealand 21
About 80% of American homes have a clothes dryer, which uses around 12% of the home's electricity to dry about 300 loads of laundry each year.
In the United States, petroleum, natural gas, and coal have provided most of the energy for more than 100 years.
About 86% of the world's energy is supplied by fossil fuels.
In 2013, winds generated almost 3% of the world's electricity. World-wide, wind-generated power grows at a rate of about 17% per year.
Your Task: Take an Energy Survey
You and your classmates will develop a survey, and then gather and analyze data looking for ways to reduce energy consumption.
464 TOPIC 11 enVision STEM Project
Go Online | PearsonRealize.com

Common Core Standards HSS.ID.A.1, HSS.ID.A.3, HSS.ID.B.5, HSS.ID.B.6

Mathematical Practices MP.2, MP.4

SavvasRealize.com

A-Z Glossary

LESSON 11-1
Analyzing Data Displays

Lesson Overview

FOCUS

Objective

Students will be able to:

✔ Represent data using dot plots, box plots, and histograms.

✔ Interpret the data displayed in dot plots, box plots, and histograms within the context it represents.

Essential Understanding

Dot plots, histograms, and box plots provide different information about the data sets they represent. Dot plots show the frequency of data and clearly indicate clusters, gaps, and outliers. Histograms show the distribution of values within a data set and shape of the data. Box plots show the center and spread of a distribution.

COHERENCE

In previous courses, students:

- Used dot plots, box plots, and histograms to represent data.

In this lesson, students:

- Represent data using dot plots, box plots, and histograms and use them to interpret data displays within the given data's context.

Later in this topic, students will:

- Interpret measures of center and variability for data displayed in dot pots, box plots, and histograms.

RIGOR

This lesson emphasizes a blend of *conceptual understanding* and *application*.

- Students understand that dot plots, box plots, and histograms are data displays that represent data in different ways. Dot plots show frequency, histograms show distribution and shape, and box plots show center and spread.
- Students interpret dot plots, box plots, and histograms within the context of the real-world data they represent, such as dance competition scores and fundraiser amounts.

Vocabulary Builder

REVIEW VOCABULARY — **English** | *Spanish*

- **bar graph** | *gráfico de barras*
- **box plot** | *gráfica de cajas*
- **cluster** | *cluster*
- **dot plot** | *trama de punto*
- **histogram** | *histograma*
- **interquartile range** | *interval intercuartil*
- **outlier** | *valor extremo*

VOCABULARY ACTIVITY

Review the terms dot plot, box plot, and histogram. Have students identify each definition with the term it describes.

Shows the frequency of data within data sets using dots above a number line [dot plot]

Shows the distribution of values within a data set in ranges or intervals [histogram]

Summarizes the data on a number line, showing the minimum and maximum values, as well as the quartiles [box plot]

Student Companion

Students can do their in-class work for the lesson on pages 249–252 of their *Student Companion* or in Savvas Realize.

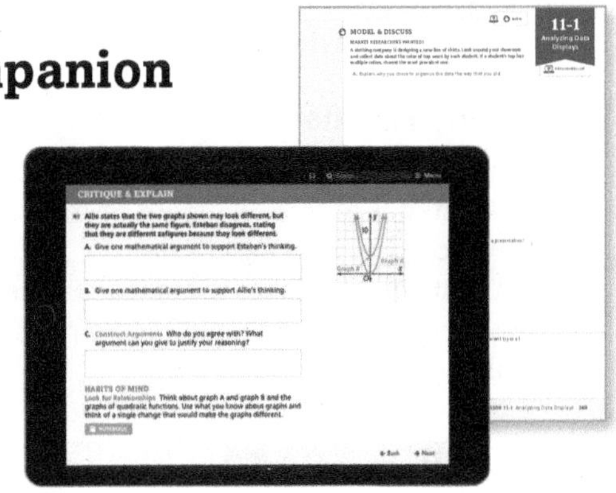

Mathematics Overview — COMMON CORE STANDARDS

Content Standards

In this lesson, students focus on this standard:

HSS.ID.A.1 Represent data with plots on the real number line (dot plots, histograms, and box plots).

Mathematical Practice Standards

These standards are highlighted in this lesson:

MP.3 Construct Viable Arguments and Critique the Reasoning of Others

Students justify arguments mathematically when they construct an explanation about why one type of data display is best for showing a particular aspect of the data, such as using a dot plot to show individual values.

MP.5 Use Appropriate Tools Strategically

Students understand it is helpful to use a histogram to show distribution of data values in intervals or a box plot to show the center and spread of a distribution.

MODEL & DISCUSS

INSTRUCTIONAL FOCUS Students consider methods for collecting, organizing, and displaying categorical data about shirt colors. Thinking about the usefulness of different kinds of data displays prepares students to choose the kinds of displays, such as dot plots, histograms, and box plots, that are helpful for displaying numerical data.

STUDENT COMPANION Students can complete the *Model & Discuss* activity on page 249 of their *Student Companion*.

Before WHOLE CLASS

Implement Tasks that Promote Reasoning and Problem Solving ETP

Q: What tools could you use for recording and displaying the data you collect?
[tally chart, bar graph, circle graph]

During SMALL GROUP

Support Productive Struggle in Learning Mathematics ETP

Q: What should you consider when thinking about how to display the data?
[the kind of data (numerical/categorical), the range of the data, how the data will be used]

For Early Finishers

Q: Choose a second way to display the data. What are the advantages or disadvantages of this display compared to the one you chose for Part C?
[A circle graph makes it easy to see the preferences as a percent of the whole, but would not show the exact counts for each color.]

After WHOLE CLASS

Facilitate Meaningful Mathematical Discourse ETP

Q: If you worked for the marketing research company, what decisions would you make based on the data collected?
[More than half of the students are wearing black shirts, so make more black shirts than other colors.]

Q: How might your choice of data display differ if you collected data on the cost of each shirt?
[Because the data would be numerical instead of categorical, a box plot or histogram may be a better choice for displying the data.]

HABITS OF MIND *Use with* **MODEL & DISCUSS**

Reason What other information could you collect about the different types of shirts in your classroom? How could you organize these data? MP.2

[You could collect data on the lengths of sleeves students are wearing. You could sort the students' shirts by long sleeve, short sleeve, and sleeveless.]

AVAILABLE **ONLINE**

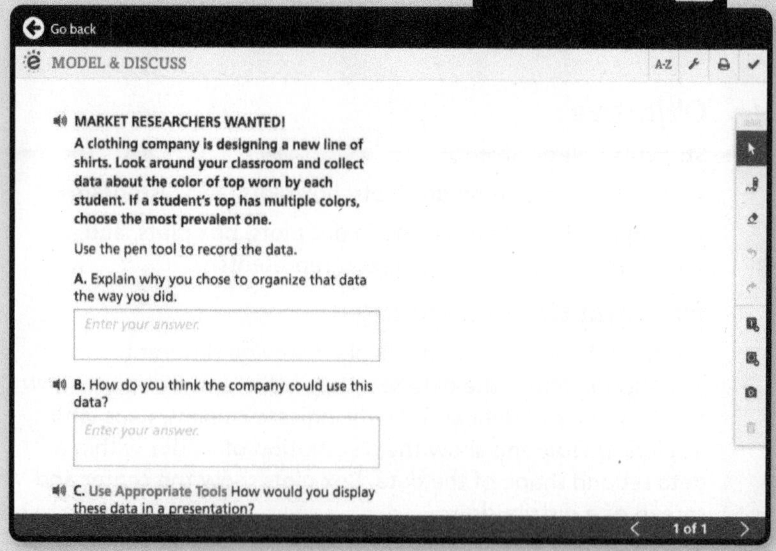
Go back
MODEL & DISCUSS
MARKET RESEARCHERS WANTED!
A clothing company is designing a new line of shirts. Look around your classroom and collect data about the color of top worn by each student. If a student's top has multiple colors, choose the most prevalent one.
Use the pen tool to record the data.
A. Explain why you chose to organize that data the way you did.
Enter your answer.
B. How do you think the company could use this data?
Enter your answer.
C. Use Appropriate Tools How would you display these data in a presentation?
1 of 1

STUDENT EDITION, PAGE 465

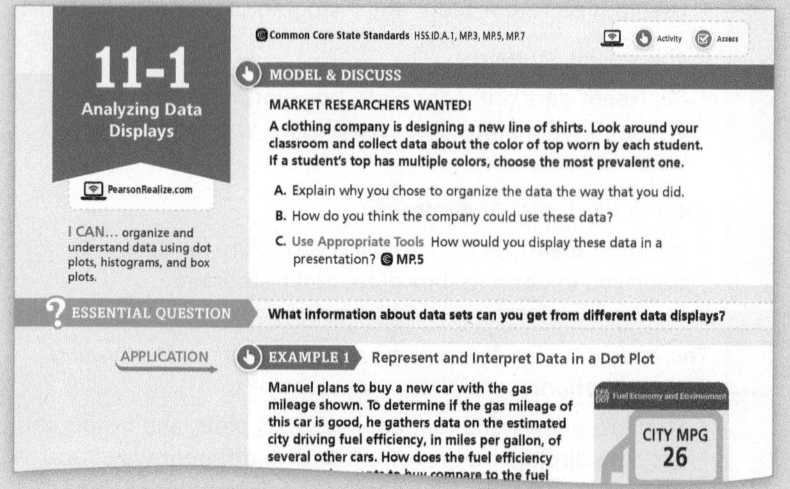
11-1 Analyzing Data Displays
PearsonRealize.com
I CAN… organize and understand data using dot plots, histograms, and box plots.
Common Core State Standards HSS.ID.A.1, MP.3, MP.5, MP.7
MODEL & DISCUSS
MARKET RESEARCHERS WANTED!
A clothing company is designing a new line of shirts. Look around your classroom and collect data about the color of top worn by each student. If a student's top has multiple colors, choose the most prevalent one.
A. Explain why you chose to organize the data the way that you did.
B. How do you think the company could use these data?
C. Use Appropriate Tools How would you display these data in a presentation? MP.5
ESSENTIAL QUESTION What information about data sets can you get from different data displays?
APPLICATION
EXAMPLE 1 Represent and Interpret Data in a Dot Plot
Manuel plans to buy a new car with the gas mileage shown. To determine if the gas mileage of this car is good, he gathers data on the estimated city driving fuel efficiency, in miles per gallon, of several other cars. How does the fuel efficiency
CITY MPG
26

SAMPLE STUDENT WORK

A. I chose to organize my data in a tally chart because it enabled me to easily count the number of students wearing a top of each color.

B. You could advise the company to manufacture shirts in colors that are proportional to the frequencies of the colors in your observations, and they could use the most popular colors in advertising.

C. The variable of shirt color is categorical, so the data could be represented in a frequency table or a bar graph.

INTRODUCE THE ESSENTIAL QUESTION

Establish Mathematics Goals to Focus Learning ETP

Introduce students to analyzing information represented in data displays such as dot plots, box plots, and histograms. Students learn that dot plots show individual values, histograms show the distribution of values within a data set, and box plots show the center and spread of a distribution.

EXAMPLE 1 Represent and Interpret Data in a Dot Plot

Pose Purposeful Questions ETP

Q: What is an outlier? How is it identified on a dot plot?
[An outlier is a point in a sample widely separated from the main cluster of points. It is identified on a dot plot as a point well outside of the range of most of the other points.]

Q: In what situations is it best to display data in a dot plot?
[A dot plot is the best display option for showing individual values and where most of the values are clustered. It is not easy to identify the center of the data using a dot plot.]

Try It! Answer

1. The car could be a hybrid or electric car while the others are gas vehicles.

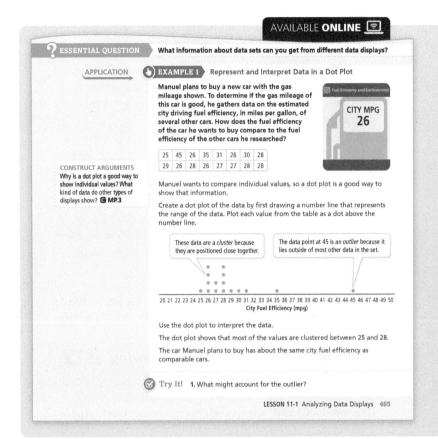

AVAILABLE ONLINE

ESSENTIAL QUESTION What information about data sets can you get from different data displays?

APPLICATION

EXAMPLE 1 Represent and Interpret Data in a Dot Plot

Manuel plans to buy a new car with the gas mileage shown. To determine if the gas mileage of this car is good, he gathers data on the estimated city driving fuel efficiency, in miles per gallon, of several other cars. How does the fuel efficiency of the car he wants to buy compare to the fuel efficiency of the other cars he researched?

Fuel Economy and Environment
CITY MPG
26

25	45	26	35	31	26	30	28
29	26	28	26	27	27	28	28

CONSTRUCT ARGUMENTS
Why is a dot plot a good way to show individual values? What kind of data do other types of displays show? MP.3

Manuel wants to compare individual values, so a dot plot is a good way to show that information.

Create a dot plot of the data by first drawing a number line that represents the range of the data. Plot each value from the table as a dot above the number line.

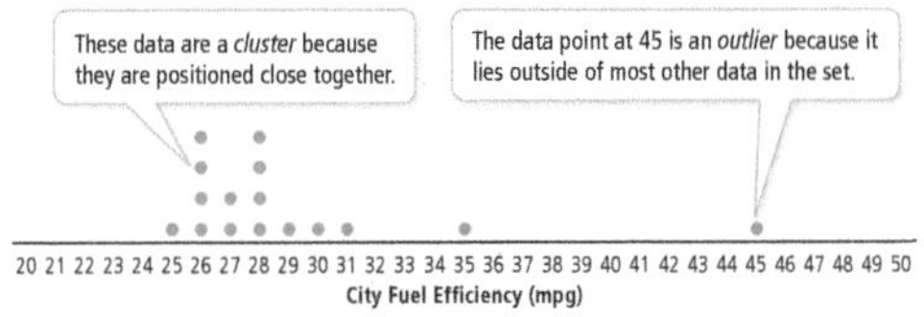
These data are a *cluster* because they are positioned close together.
The data point at 45 is an *outlier* because it lies outside of most other data in the set.
20 21 22 23 24 25 26 27 28 29 30 31 32 33 34 35 36 37 38 39 40 41 42 43 44 45 46 47 48 49 50
City Fuel Efficiency (mpg)

Use the dot plot to interpret the data.

The dot plot shows that most of the values are clustered between 25 and 28.

The car Manuel plans to buy has about the same city fuel efficiency as comparable cars.

Try It! 1. What might account for the outlier?

LESSON 11-1 Analyzing Data Displays 465

ADDITIONAL EXAMPLES

AVAILABLE ONLINE

Go back
ADDITIONAL EXAMPLE 1 ESSENTIAL QUESTION ES A-Z

A teacher gave her students a 10-point quiz. The dot plot shows the scores. How can the teacher use the dot plot to help her summarize the scores?

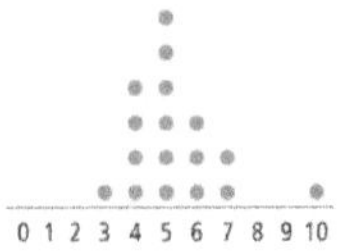
0 1 2 3 4 5 6 7 8 9 10

There is a cluster of scores around 5 points, so most of the students answered only about half of the questions correctly.

There was one student who scored a perfect 10 points, but 10 is an outlier, so it should not affect the teacher's assessment that her students didn't do very well on the quiz.

1 of 2

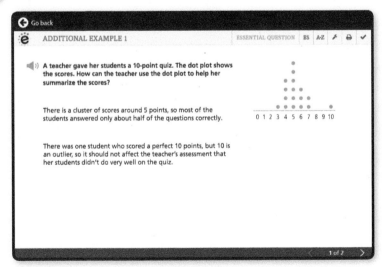

Example 1 Students summarize the data shown by a dot plot.

Q: Why would this data display be helpful for a student who wants to compare his or her score to the scores of the other students in the class?
[The student can see all of the individual scores, which makes it easy to see how one score relates to each of the others.]

Go back
ADDITIONAL EXAMPLE 4 ESSENTIAL QUESTION ES A-Z

A botanist planted 20 seeds. She collected data on the number of days that it took before the seeds produced a flowering plant. She wants to compare the middle 50% of her data to the data she collected for other sets of seeds. Should she use a dot plot, histogram, or box plot?

A box plot uses a box to highlight the IQR which shows the median and the middle 50% of the data.

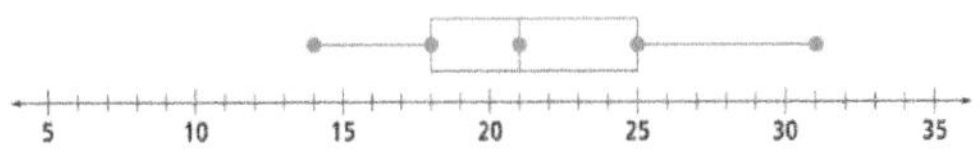
5 10 15 20 25 30 35

The box plot shows that 50% of the seeds produced a flowering plant within 18–25 days.

1 of 2

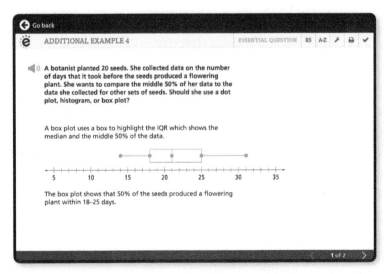

Example 4 Students choose a data display that indicates the center of the data.

Q: What other questions could be answered using the data shown in the box plot?
[What is the shortest amount of time that it took for one of the plants to flower?]

Activity Assess

EXAMPLE 2 Represent and Interpret Data in a Histogram

Pose Purposeful Questions ETP

Q: How are intervals chosen for a data set?
[There should be multiple data points that fall within consistent intervals, but there should be enough intervals with data points in them to show variation.]

Q: What are other possible intervals? How would a different interval change the way the histogram displays the data?
[Choose intervals of 10. There would be fewer bars and the histogram would show less variation. It would show more data values from 20–29 than from 10–19; however, it would not show that most of the data values from 10–19 were 15 or greater and most of the data values from 20–29 were 24 or less.]

Try It! Answer

2. 15 to 25 years; Answers may vary. Sample: Viewers aged 15 to 25 represent 20 out of 30 viewers, or about 67% of the viewers.

Elicit and Use Evidence of Student Thinking ETP

Q: What should you look at in the histogram to decide whether a particular age group would be a good match?
[the interval(s) with the highest bars (most frequency)]

HABITS OF MIND

Use with **EXAMPLES 1 & 2**

Look for Relationships How is interpreting a histogram similar to interpreting a dot plot? How is it different? MP.7

[Histograms and dot plots both show the frequency of specific quantities. Histograms group values into ranges, while dot plots show single values.]

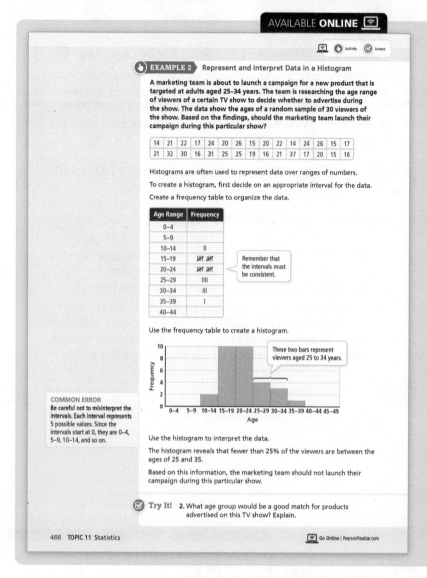

AVAILABLE ONLINE

Activity Assess

EXAMPLE 2 Represent and Interpret Data in a Histogram

A marketing team is about to launch a campaign for a new product that is targeted at adults aged 25–34 years. The team is researching the age range of viewers of a certain TV show to decide whether to advertise during the show. The data show the ages of a random sample of 30 viewers of the show. Based on the findings, should the marketing team launch their campaign during this particular show?

14	21	22	17	24	20	26	15	20	22	14	24	26	15	17
21	32	30	16	31	25	25	19	16	21	37	17	20	15	16

Histograms are often used to represent data over ranges of numbers.

To create a histogram, first decide on an appropriate interval for the data.

Create a frequency table to organize the data.

Age Range	Frequency
0–4	
5–9	
10–14	ll
15–19	~~llll~~ ~~llll~~
20–24	~~llll~~ ~~llll~~
25–29	llll
30–34	lll
35–39	l
40–44	

Remember that the intervals must be consistent.

Use the frequency table to create a histogram.

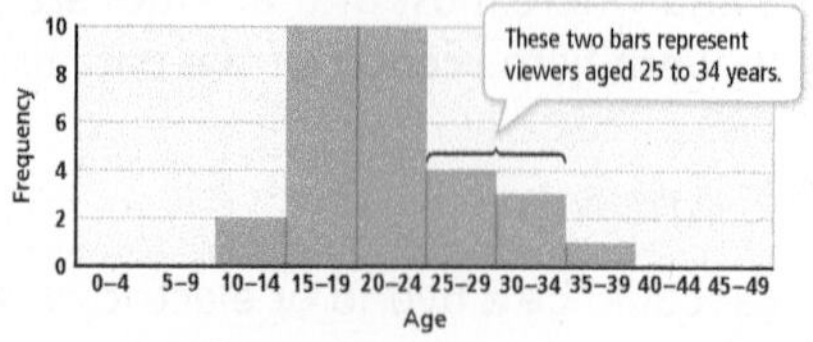

10
8
6
4
2
0
Frequency
0–4 5–9 10–14 15–19 20–24 25–29 30–34 35–39 40–44 45–49
Age
These two bars represent viewers aged 25 to 34 years.

COMMON ERROR
Be careful not to misinterpret the intervals. Each interval represents 5 possible values. Since the intervals start at 0, they are 0–4, 5–9, 10–14, and so on.

Use the histogram to interpret the data.

The histogram reveals that fewer than 25% of the viewers are between the ages of 25 and 35.

Based on this information, the marketing team should not launch their campaign during this particular show.

Try It! **2.** What age group would be a good match for products advertised on this TV show? Explain.

466 TOPIC 11 Statistics

Go Online | PearsonRealize.com

Struggling Students

USE WITH EXAMPLE 2 Students may need extra practice determining what intervals to use for a histogram.

- Have students make frequency tables using two different intervals for organizing the data shown.

12	8	20	25	35	37	46	25	17	62
30	39	26	33	37	41	15	24	50	25

Q: How do you decide which intervals to try?
[Look at the range of the values. Because they are between 8 and 62, make one histogram with intervals of 5 and one with intervals of 10.]

Q: What are the advantages and disadvantages of each interval you chose?
[When using intervals of 5, there are only a few values in each interval, so it is easier to see how the data are spread out. However, there are more bars in the histogram when using intervals of 5 rather than 10, so it is harder to see any trends in the data.]

STEP 2 Understand & Apply

Activity Assess

EXAMPLE 3 Represent and Interpret Data in a Box Plot

Use and Connect Mathematical Representations ETP

Q: What does the interquartile range represent in a box plot?
[IQR represents the range of the middle 50% of the data.]

Q: What can you determine about the data by looking at the size and shape of the box that represents the IQR?
[The range of the data surrounding the median is fairly spread out. There is more variation in the data values that are less than the median than the data values that are greater than the median.]

Q: Can you use the box plot to determine what percentage of students collected more than $50?
[No, the box plot shows that 50% of students collected more than $45 and 25% of students collected more than $52, but the percentage that collected more than $50 cannot be determined.]

Q: Explain why a box plot is the best way to represent the data and support or refute Kaitlyn's claim.
[A box plot shows clearly that half the data are below the median value and half the data are above the median value.]

Try It! Answer

3. $52; The third quartile is 52, so 75% of the data are less than 52 and 25% of the data are greater than 52.

Common Error

Try It! 3 Some students may think that 25% of the data are outside of the box, and therefore over $53. Have students use the terms less than or equal to or greater than or equal to when referring to quartile values so they understand that the values can be included in descriptions of the data.

AVAILABLE **ONLINE**

Activity Assess

EXAMPLE 3 Represent and Interpret Data in a Box Plot

Students at a local high school organized a fundraiser for charity. Kaitlyn, the student council president, announces that more than half of the students raised over $50 each. The amounts of money raised by a random sample of 24 students is shown. Do the data support Kaitlyn's claim?

$59	$42	$25	$38	$45	$54	$68	$32
$26	$54	$50	$45	$42	$48	$50	$25
$45	$36	$55	$27	$31	$32	$49	$54

Kaitlyn's claim is about the distribution of values, so a box plot will reveal the information needed.

A *box plot* shows the distribution of data using a 5-number summary.

The *minimum* value is the least value in the set.

The *maximum* value is the greatest value in the set.

The *median* is the middle value in the set when the numbers are arranged from least to greatest.

The *first quartile* is the middle number between the minimum value and the median. The *third quartile* is the middle number between the median and the maximum value.

List the data from least to greatest to identify each of these values.

25 25 26 27 31 32 32 36 38 42 42 45 45 45 48 49 50 50 54 54 54 55 59 68

The first quartile Is 32. The median is 45. The third quartile Is 52.

The minimum value is 25. The maximum value is 68.

Create a box plot of the data.

VOCABULARY
The interquartile range, *IQR*, represents the range of the middle 50% of the data. Subtract the Q_1 value from the Q_3 value to find the IQR. In this example the IQR is 52 – 32, or 20.

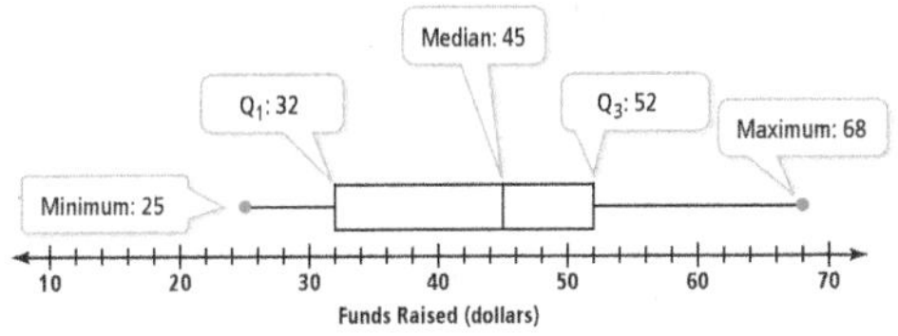
Median: 45
Q1: 32
Q3: 52
Maximum: 68
Minimum: 25
10
20
30
40
50
60
70
Funds Raised (dollars)

Use the box plot to interpret the data. The box plot shows that, based on the sample, the median amount of money collected was $45. Since half of this population collected $45 or less, the data do not support Kaitlyn's claim.

Try It! **3.** Suppose Kaitlyn wants to make the statement that 25% of the students raised over a certain amount. What is that amount? Explain.

LESSON 11-1 Analyzing Data Displays 467

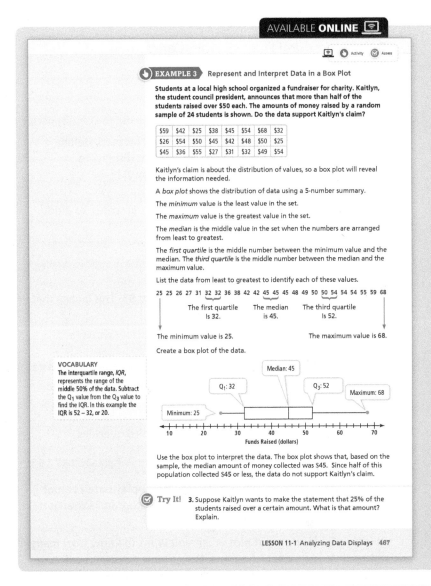

ELL English Language Learners *(Use with* **EXAMPLE 3***)*

READING BEGINNING Have students read the example and identify the first sentence that uses the term *distribution*. Display the following meanings for the term distribution for the class to read.

a) the action or process of supplying goods to stores or businesses that sell to consumers

b) the action of sharing something among a number of recipients

c) the action of displaying data and how it is spread out

Q: Which of these definitions is the correct usage for the word *distribution* in the example? [c]

Display for students to read: Tina makes sure the distribution of apples to the children was fair.

Q: Which of the definitions is the correct usage for the word *distribution*? [b]

LISTENING INTERMEDIATE Read the introduction to the problem aloud as students listen.

Q: What type of sample does Kaitlyn use to collect the data? [random]

Discuss the definition of the word *random*. Read the following sentences and ask students to raise their hand if they think the action in the sentence is random.

Q: The students choose the class president by selecting a name out of a hat. [random]

Q: Geraldo's family choose a vet based on recommendations from friends. [not random]

Q: The computer generates a list of phone numbers for the polling company to use. [random]

SPEAKING ADVANCED Discuss with students the characteristics of a *charity organization*. Explain that a charity organization typically relies on volunteers and donations to help in its mission to aid those in need.

Q: What are some charity organizations in your community?
[soup kitchens, shelters]

Q: What types of problems can charity organizations help out with?
[homelessness, poverty, fires, flooding]

Activity Assess

EXAMPLE 4 Choose a Data Display

Build Procedural Fluency From Conceptual Understanding ETP

Part A

Q: Should Helena consider the values of the data when she decides what kind of data display to use?
[No, all three types of data displays could be used. Helena needs to compare the features of the data displays to determine which data display is most helpful.]

Q: What would be the best data display for Helena?
[Helena is interested in displaying individual scores, so a dot plot is the best choice.]

Part B

Q: What other observations could Helena make about the scores by looking at the dot plot?
[A cluster of scores occurs between 79 and 83. This means that most of the scores lie between 79 and 83.]

Q: Look at the cluster of data from 79 to 83. How would a histogram display this data differently?
[If the histogram uses intervals of 5 or 10, the gaps in the data would not be as evident.]

Try It! Answer

4. Box plot; Box plots reveal the first and third quartiles.

HABITS OF MIND

Use with **EXAMPLES 3 & 4**

Use Appropriate Tools When is it useful to display data as a dot plot? When is it useful to display data as a histogram? When is it useful to display data as a box plot? MP.5

[It is helpful to use a dot plot when you want to know how many data points have a specific value. Histograms are useful when you want to group data into intervals. Box plots are useful when you want to know the distribution of values.]

AVAILABLE ONLINE

Activity Assess

CONCEPTUAL UNDERSTANDING

EXAMPLE 4 Choose a Data Display

Helena's dance team scores 68 points at a competition. The scores for all of the teams that competed are shown.

66	89	81	75
90	79	82	68
80	82	65	80
81	66	81	83

A. Helena wants to know what place her team finished. Should Helena use a dot plot, histogram, or box plot to display the data?

Compare the features of the three types of data displays.

- A dot plot has dots for each value in the data. It shows clusters of data and outliers.
- A histogram groups values in a data set into ranges or intervals. Individual values are not displayed but trends are observable.
- A box plot shows center and spread of a data set. A box plot does not show individual data but summarizes the data using 5 key pieces of information.

Helena is interested in displaying individual scores. A dot plot will display the data in a way that is most helpful to Helena.

CONSTRUCT ARGUMENTS What would be a good display choice if Helena wanted to compare her team's score with the median? MP.3

B. What place did Helena's team finish in the competition?

Create and analyze a dot plot of the data.

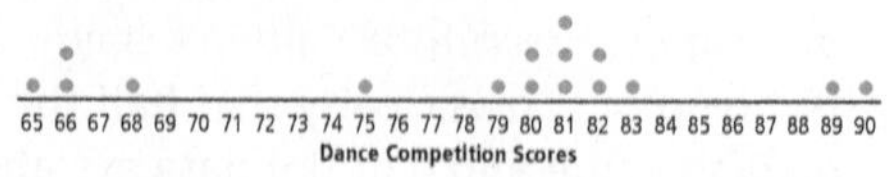

65 66 67 68 69 70 71 72 73 74 75 76 77 78 79 80 81 82 83 84 85 86 87 88 89 90
Dance Competition Scores

A dot plot reveals that Helena's team score was low compared to the other teams. Only three teams scored lower, so Helena's team placed 13th out of 16.

Try It! 4. Which data display should Helena use if she wants to know what percent of the teams scored higher than her team? Explain.

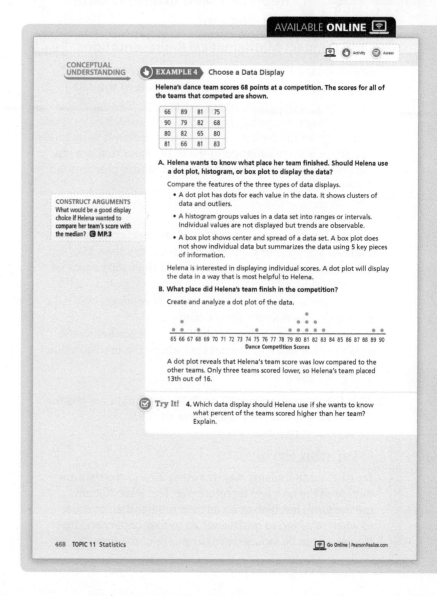

RtI Advanced Students

USE WITH EXAMPLE 4 Extend students' understanding of the usefulness of different data displays by having them make both a box plot and a histogram using the data from Example 4. Ask students to create a list of questions that could be answered using each of the data displays.

Q: What can you see in the box plot that you cannot see in the other displays?
[The median is obvious in a box plot, but not in the other displays. The minimum and maximum scores are also easy to see in the box plot, but not in the histogram.]

Q: Which display makes it appear as if Helena's dance team does just as well as the other teams?
[A box plot reveals that the score of Helena's dance team is near the low end of the IQR, making it appear to be almost as good as the middle 50% of the scores.]

CONCEPT SUMMARY Data Displays

Q: What information about data sets can you get from each kind of data display?
[A dot plot shows frequency and clearly shows clusters, gaps, and outliers. A histogram shows the distribution of values within a data set in intervals. Box plots show the median and spread of a distribution.]

Do You UNDERSTAND? | Do You KNOW HOW?

Common Error

Exercise 5 Some students may think that you can use a histogram to find the minimum and maximum values of a data set because they misinterpret the numbers at the far ends of the intervals as the minimum and maximum values. Write the following list of values: 2, 3, 3, 5, 8, 11, 13 and have students create a histogram using a range of 5 for each interval. Then ask students to compare the minimum and maximum values of the data set (2 and 13) to the numbers at the far ends of the intervals (0 and 15).

AVAILABLE **ONLINE**

Concept Summary   Assess

CONCEPT SUMMARY Data Displays

	Dot Plots	Histograms	Box Plots
WORDS	Dot plots display each data value from a set of data. They show clusters, gaps, and outliers in a data set.	Histograms do not show individual values, but show clearly the shape of the data. The data are organized into intervals. The bars show the frequency, or number of times, that the data within that interval occur.	Box plots show the center (median) and spread of a distribution. Box plots provide the following information about a data set: minimum, maximum, and median values, and the first and third quartile.

GRAPHS

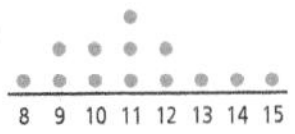
8 9 10 11 12 13 14 15

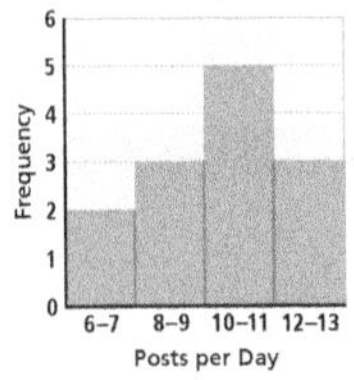
Frequency
0 1 2 3 4 5 6
6–7 8–9 10–11 12–13
Posts per Day

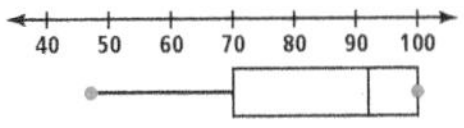
40 50 60 70 80 90 100

Do You UNDERSTAND?

1. ESSENTIAL QUESTION What information about data sets can you get from different data displays?

2. Communicate Precisely How is a dot plot different from a box plot? How are they similar? MP.6

3. Use Appropriate Tools If you want to see data values grouped in intervals, which data display should you choose? Explain. MP.5

4. Error Analysis Taylor says you can determine the mean of a data set from its box plot. Is Taylor correct? Explain your reasoning. MP.3

5. Use Structure Can you determine the minimum and maximum values of a data set simply by looking at its dot plot? Histogram? Box plot? Explain. MP.7

Do You KNOW HOW?

Use the data set shown for exercises 6–11.

7	5	8	15	4
9	10	1	12	8
13	7	11	8	10

6. Make a dot plot for the data. What information does the display reveal about the data set?

7. Make a histogram for the data. What information does the display reveal about the data set?

8. Make a box plot for the data. What information does the display reveal about the data set?

Identify the most appropriate data display to answer each question about the data set. Justify your response.

9. What is the median of the data set?

10. How many data values are greater than 7?

11. How many values fall in the interval 10 to 12?

LESSON 11-1 Analyzing Data Displays 469

Answers

1. Dot plots, histograms, and box plots all show the spread of a data set. Dot plots reveal individual data values, histograms reveal frequencies organized by intervals, and box plots reveal the median, quartiles, minimum, and maximum.

2. A dot plot reveals individual values, while a box plot does not. Both displays reveal the distribution of the data set.

3. Histogram; A histogram groups data values into bins, or intervals, before displaying frequencies.

4. No; you can determine the median from a box plot, but individual values are not revealed, so you cannot determine the mean.

5. Yes; no; yes; You can tell maximum and minimum values from a dot plot because individual values are displayed, and a box plot shows maximum and minimum values. You cannot tell in a histogram because individual values are not displayed within each bar.

6.

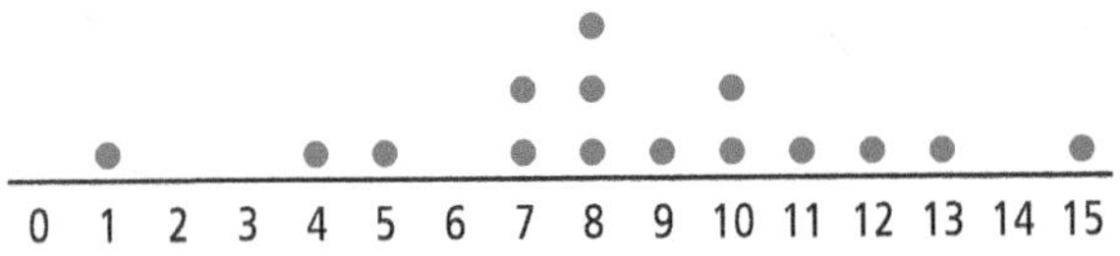
0 1 2 3 4 5 6 7 8 9 10 11 12 13 14 15

Most of the data are clustered between 7 and 10.

7.

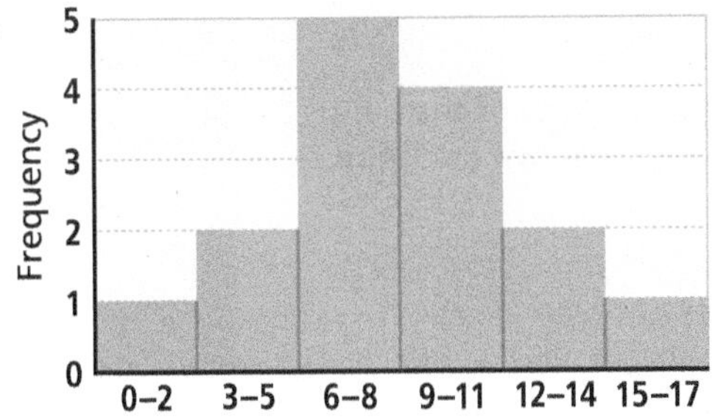
Frequency
0 1 2 3 4 5
0–2 3–5 6–8 9–11 12–14 15–17

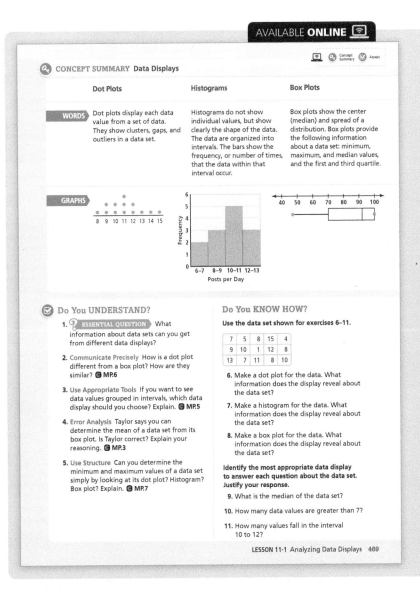

The data are fairly evenly distributed.

8.

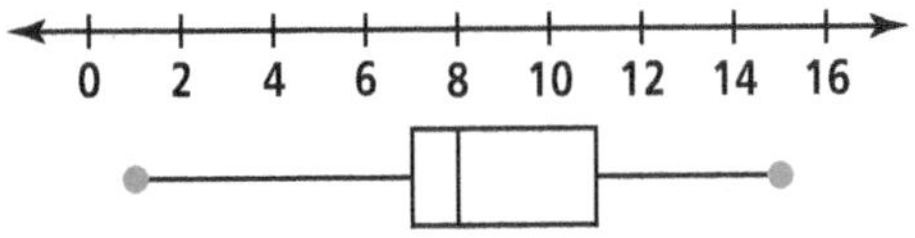
0 2 4 6 8 10 12 14 16

The median is 8, and 50% of the data are between 7 and 11.

9. box plot; 8

10. dot plot; 10

11. histogram; 4

PRACTICE & PROBLEM SOLVING

AVAILABLE **ONLINE**

Lesson Practice You may opt to have students complete the automatically scored Practice and Problem Solving items online powered by MathXL for School.

Choose from: **Lesson Practice**

Adaptive Practice

You may also take advantage of the bank of exercises for assigning additional practice.

Assignment Guide

Basic	Advanced
12–29	12–29

Item Analysis

Example	Items	DOK
1	13	2
	17, 26	3
2	14	2
	18, 25	3
3	12, 27	1
	15, 16, 24	3
4	19–23, 28	2
	29	3

AVAILABLE **ONLINE**

PRACTICE & PROBLEM SOLVING

Scan for Multimedia

Practice Tutorial

Additional Exercises Available Online

UNDERSTAND

12. Reason A data set is represented by the box plot shown. Between which two values would the middle 50% of the data be found? Explain. MP.2

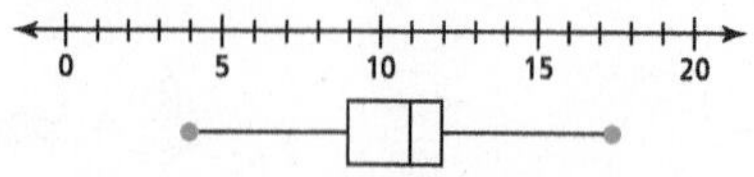

0
5
10
15
20

13. Generalize Write a scenario for which a dot plot would be the best display for a data set. Explain your thinking. MP.8

14. Error Analysis Describe and correct the errors a student made in analyzing the histogram shown. MP.3

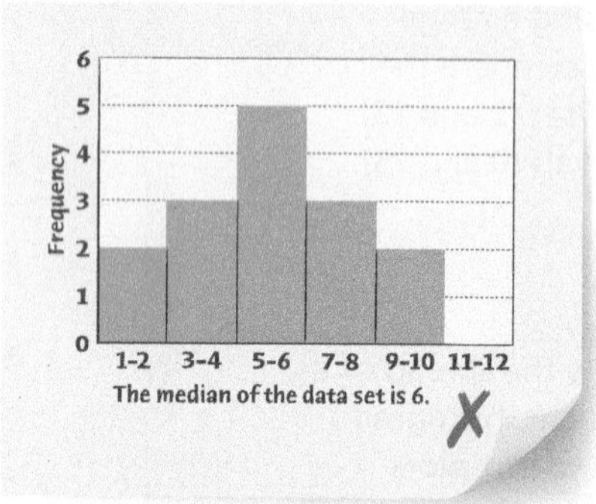

Frequency
0
1
2
3
4
5
6
1-2
3-4
5-6
7-8
9-10
11-12
The median of the data set is 6.
X

15. Higher Order Thinking The box plot represents a data set with 12 values. The minimum, first quartile, median, third quartile, and maximum values are 6, 8, 10, 12, and 14, respectively. MP.7

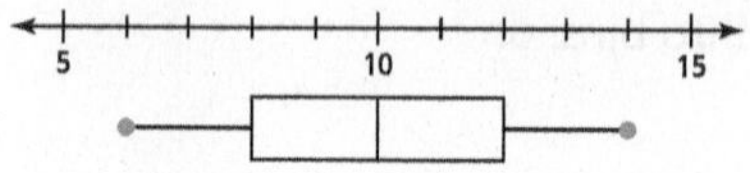

5
10
15

a. Is it possible to create a dot plot for the data set using just the box plot and the values given? Explain.

b. Is it possible to create a histogram using just the box plot and the values given? Explain.

PRACTICE

For each data set, create the data display that best reveals the answer to the question. Explain your reasoning. SEE EXAMPLES 1–4

16. What is the median value of the data set?

40	47	43	35
42	32	40	47
49	46	50	42
48	43	34	45

17. What is the frequency of the data value 83?

85	81	83	84	83	80
84	86	76	83	82	83
82	82	84	89	85	83

18. How many data values are between 7 and 9?

9.6	5.5	8.4	9.1	6.7
7.2	11.5	9.2	5.2	7.6
11.1	6.1	7.2	14.8	12.5
8.4	10.5	10.2	8.4	13.5

Choose whether a dot plot, histogram, or box plot is the most appropriate data display to answer each question about a data set. Explain. SEE EXAMPLE 4

19. How many data values are greater than any given value in the data set?

20. What are the frequencies for each interval of 5 points?

21. 25% of the data values are less than which value?

Consider the data set represented by the dot plot. Create a different data display that better reveals the answer to each question. SEE EXAMPLES 1–4

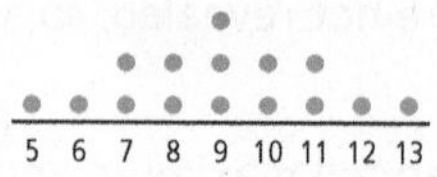

5 6 7 8 9 10 11 12 13

22. How many data values are in the interval between 8 and 10 inclusive?

23. What is the first quartile of the data set?

Go Online | PearsonRealize.com

Answers

12. 9 and 12; The middle 50% of the data values are between the first and third quartiles.

13. Answers may vary. Sample: test scores for a class; Since dot plots reveal individual data values, you would choose a dot plot if you wanted see how many people got a specific test score.

14. The median cannot be determined from the histogram because individual values are not displayed within each bar.

15. a. No, individual values are not displayed in the box plot.

b. No, individual values are not displayed in the box plot, so there is not a way to determine the frequencies for each bin in a histogram.

16. 43; A box plot shows the median.

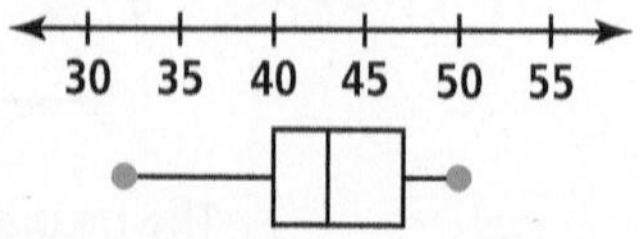

30 35 40 45 50 55

17. 5; A dot plot shows individual data values.

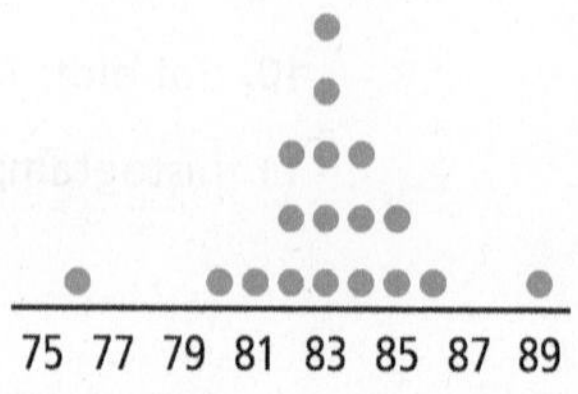

75 77 79 81 83 85 87 89

18. 6; A histogram organizes uses intervals.

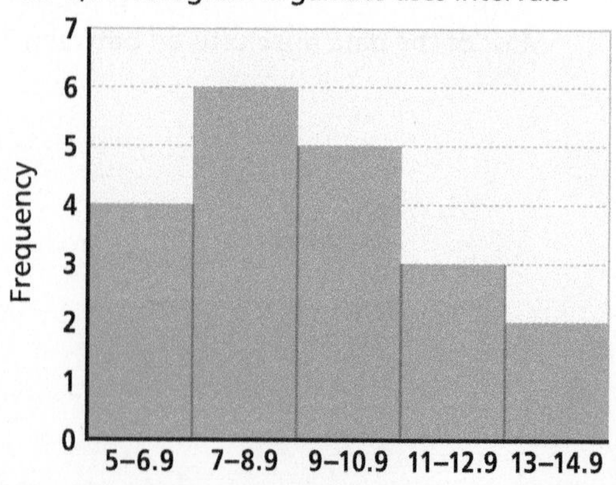

Frequency
0
1
2
3
4
5
6
7
5–6.9
7–8.9
9–10.9
11–12.9
13–14.9

Answers

19–23. See back of book.

24. between \$39 and \$98

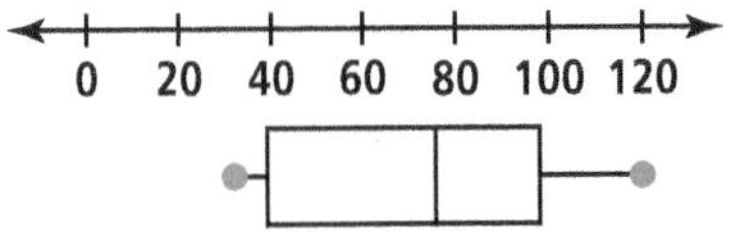
0 20 40 60 80 100 120

25.

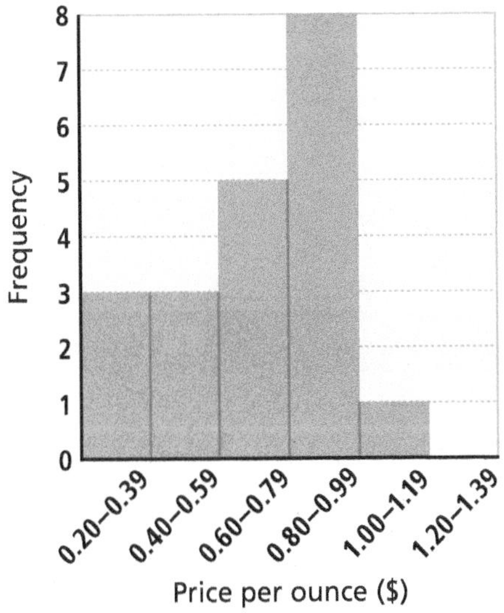
Frequency
0
1
2
3
4
5
6
7
8
0.20–0.39
0.40–0.59
0.60–0.79
0.80–0.99
1.00–1.19
1.20–1.39
Price per ounce ($)

Lucy's price is lower than 70% of the other prices.

26. 8 competitors scored higher than Aaron did.

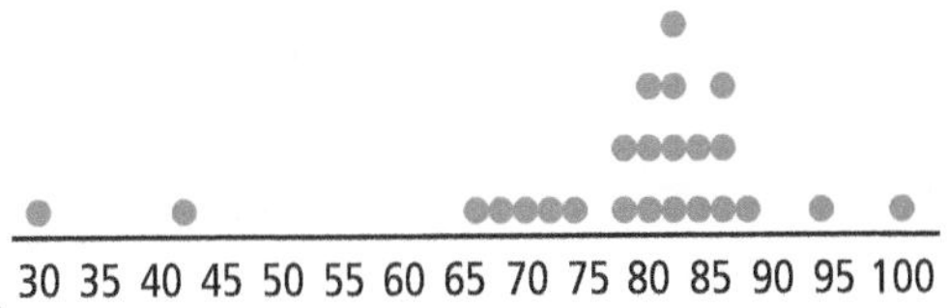
30 35 40 45 50 55 60 65 70 75 80 85 90 95 100

29. Part A Dot plots and histograms are best for displaying the shape of a distribution. For these data, a dot plot will be too spread out, so use a histogram.

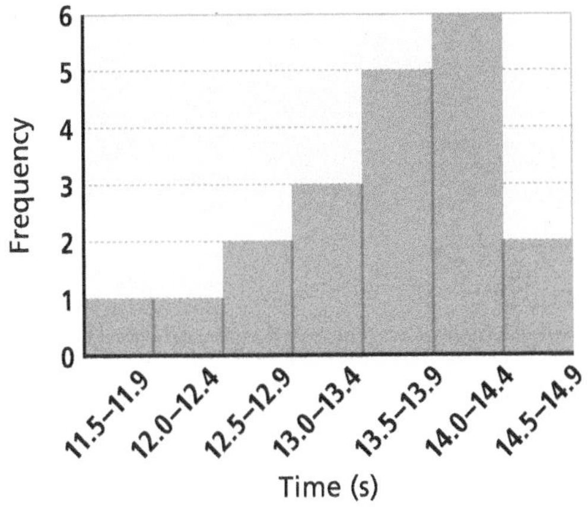
Frequency
0
1
2
3
4
5
6
11.5–11.9
12.0–12.4
12.5–12.9
13.0–13.4
13.5–13.9
14.0–14.4
14.5–14.9
Time (s)

AVAILABLE ONLINE

PRACTICE & PROBLEM SOLVING

Practice Tutorial
Mixed Review Available Online

APPLY

24. Model With Mathematics Isabel knits scarves and sells them online. The table shows the prices of the scarves she sold last month. At what prices were the middle 50% of the scarves sold? Create a data display that will reveal the answer. MP.4

Prices of Scarves ($)				
35	32	60	80	36
90	45	76	96	92
100	120	60	38	75
36	36	100	100	100
95	58	100	85	40

25. Make Sense and Persevere Lucy usually pays between \$0.40 and \$0.60 per ounce for her favorite shampoo. She gathers prices of the same shampoo at different stores near her home. Prices are shown in dollars in the table. Create a data display that allows Lucy to easily compare the price she is paying to the other prices. How does the price she is currently paying compare? MP.1

Shampoo Pricing Comparison				
0.55	0.95	0.29	0.65	0.39
0.99	0.42	1.10	0.99	0.75
0.65	0.99	0.34	0.85	0.99
0.95	0.75	0.95	0.50	0.75

26. Use Structure Aaron scores 82 points at his karate tournament. He wants to compare his score to the others in the competition to see how many competitors scored higher than he did. The table shows all scores for the competition. What type of data display is appropriate to answer his question? Create the data display and analyze Aaron's performance. MP.7

Karate Scores					
78	66	82	86	72	70
74	86	30	80	89	80
82	68	100	84	84	42
86	82	80	94	78	82

ASSESSMENT PRACTICE

27. Consider a box plot. Does a box plot display the features of a data set listed below? Select Yes or No.

	Yes	No
Median of the data set	☑	☐
Individual values in the data set	☐	☑
Outliers	☐	☑
Minimum of the data set	☑	☐

28. SAT/ACT From which display(s) can the median of a data set be determined?

Ⓐ Dot plot only
Ⓑ Box plot only
Ⓒ Dot plot and box plot
Ⓓ Histogram and box plot
Ⓔ Dot plot, histogram, and box plot

29. Performance Task A group of students use a stopwatch to record times for a 100-yard dash. Tell whether each student should choose a dot plot, a histogram, or a box plot to display the data. Explain your reasoning. Then create the display.

12.5	13.5	14.1	12.8	13.4
14.0	11.5	14.2	13.9	14.4
13.3	14.5	13.2	13.6	12.0
14.5	13.5	14.4	14.1	13.9

Part A Neil wants a data display that clearly shows the shape of the data distribution.

Part B Yuki wants a display that shows the spread of data above and below the median.

Part C Thato wants a display that groups the data by intervals.

Part D Edwin wants a display that he could use to find the mean of the data set.

LESSON 11-1 Analyzing Data Displays 471

Part B A box plot is best for displaying the spread of data above and below the median.

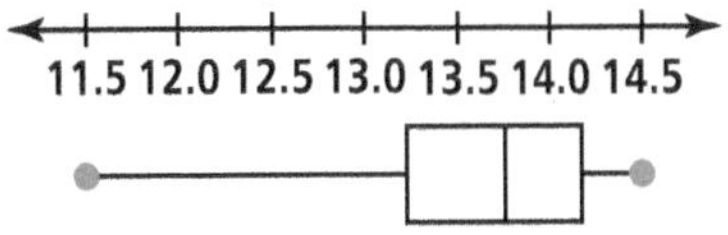
11.5 12.0 12.5 13.0 13.5 14.0 14.5

Part C A histogram is best for grouping data by intervals; see Part A.

Part D A dot plot is the best display to use; to find the mean, he must know the individual data values.

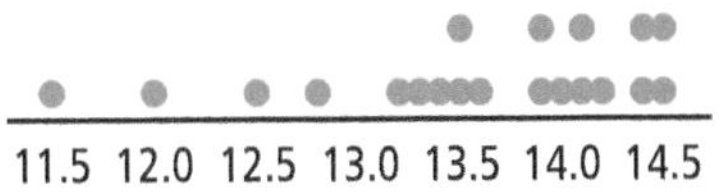
11.5 12.0 12.5 13.0 13.5 14.0 14.5

LESSON QUIZ

Use the Lesson Quiz to assess students' understanding of the mathematics in the lesson.

Students can take the Lesson Quiz online or you can download a printable copy from **SavvasRealize.com**. The Lesson Quiz is also available in the *Assessment Resources* book.

Item Analysis

Item	DOK	Standards
1	1	HSS.ID.A.1
2	1	HSS.ID.A.3
3	2	HSS.ID.A.3
4	1	HSS.ID.A.3
5	1	HSS.ID.A.3

RtI Use the student scores on the Lesson Quiz to prescribe differentiated assignments.

If students take the Lesson Quiz online, it will be automatically scored and appropriate differentiated practice will be assigned based on student performance.

I Intervention	0–3 points	• Reteach to Build Understanding • Mathematical Literacy and Vocabulary • Additional Practice
O On-Level	4 points	• Mathematical Literacy and Vocabulary • Additional Practice • Enrichment
A Advanced	5 points	• Enrichment

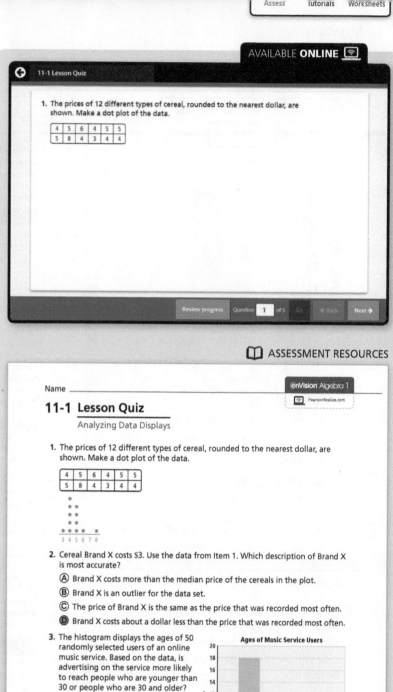

AVAILABLE **ONLINE**

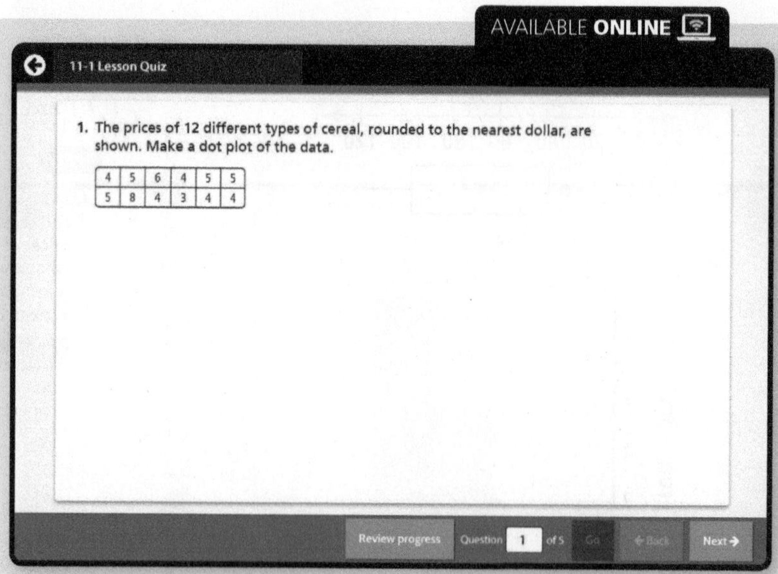
11-1 Lesson Quiz
1. The prices of 12 different types of cereal, rounded to the nearest dollar, are shown. Make a dot plot of the data.
4 5 6 4 5 5
5 8 4 3 4 4
Review progress
Question 1 of 5
Go
Back
Next

ASSESSMENT RESOURCES

Name ______________________ enVision Algebra 1 PearsonRealize.com

11-1 Lesson Quiz

Analyzing Data Displays

1. The prices of 12 different types of cereal, rounded to the nearest dollar, are shown. Make a dot plot of the data.

4	5	6	4	5	5
5	8	4	3	4	4

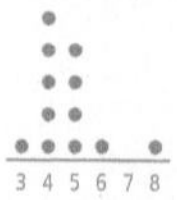
3 4 5 6 7 8

2. Cereal Brand X costs $3. Use the data from Item 1. Which description of Brand X is most accurate?
   Ⓐ Brand X costs more than the median price of the cereals in the plot.
   Ⓑ Brand X is an outlier for the data set.
   Ⓒ The price of Brand X is the same as the price that was recorded most often.
   Ⓓ Brand X costs about a dollar less than the price that was recorded most often.

3. The histogram displays the ages of 50 randomly selected users of an online music service. Based on the data, is advertising on the service more likely to reach people who are younger than 30 or people who are 30 and older?
   younger than 30

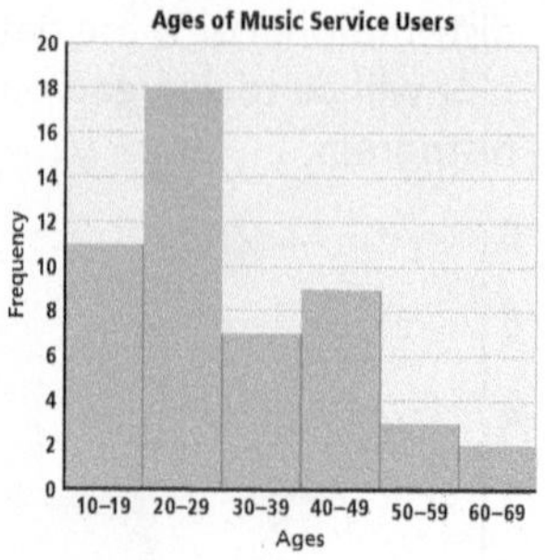
Ages of Music Service Users
Frequency
0
2
4
6
8
10
12
14
16
18
20
10–19
20–29
30–39
40–49
50–59
60–69
Ages

4. The box plot shows the ages of people at a movie screening. What percent of the people are between 20 and 37 years old?

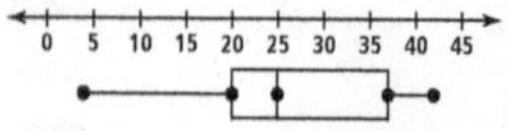
0 5 10 15 20 25 30 35 40 45

50%

5. Which of the following data displays does not show individual data values but rather shows the number of values that fall within a series of specified ranges?
   Ⓐ histogram Ⓑ box plot Ⓒ dot plot Ⓓ scatter plot

enVision™ **Algebra 1** • Assessment Resources

DIFFERENTIATED RESOURCES

I = Intervention   O = On-Level   A = Advanced

= This activity is available as a digital assignment powered by MathXL® for School.

AVAILABLE ONLINE

Reteach to Build Understanding I

Provides scaffolded reteaching for the key lesson concepts.

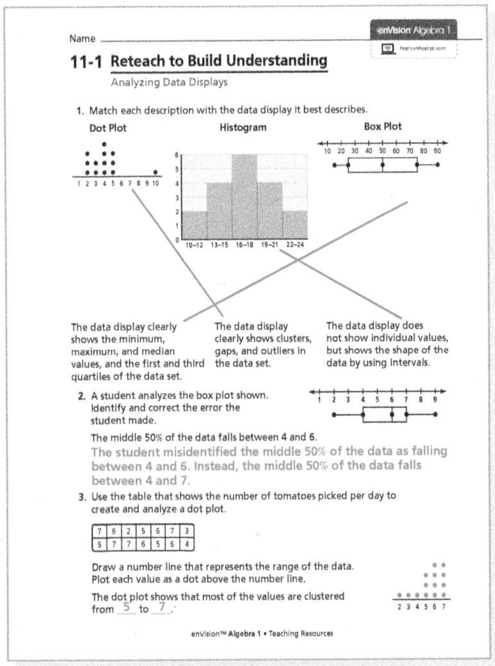
Name

11-1 Reteach to Build Understanding

Analyzing Data Displays

1. Match each description with the data display it best describes.

Dot Plot | Histogram | Box Plot

The data display clearly shows the minimum, maximum, and median values, and the first and third quartiles of the data set.

The data display clearly shows clusters, gaps, and outliers in the data set.

The data display does not show individual values, but shows the shape of the data by using intervals.

2. A student analyzes the box plot shown. Identify and correct the error the student made.

The middle 50% of the data falls between 4 and 6.

The student misidentified the middle 50% of the data as falling between 4 and 6. Instead, the middle 50% of the data falls between 4 and 7.

3. Use the table that shows the number of tomatoes picked per day to create and analyze a dot plot.

7	6	2	5	6	7	3
5	7	7	6	5	6	4

Draw a number line that represents the range of the data. Plot each value as a dot above the number line.

The dot plot shows that most of the values are clustered from 5 to 7.

enVision™ Algebra 1 • Teaching Resources

Additional Practice I O

Provides extra practice for each lesson.

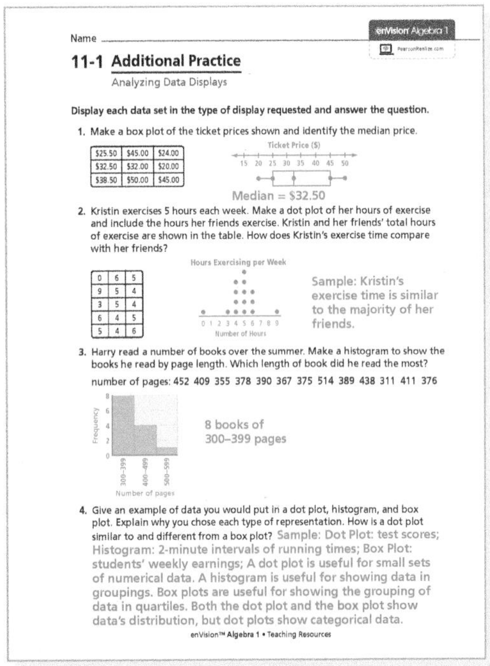
Name

11-1 Additional Practice

Analyzing Data Displays

Display each data set in the type of display requested and answer the question.

1. Make a box plot of the ticket prices shown and identify the median price.

$25.50	$45.00	$24.00
$32.50	$32.00	$20.00
$38.50	$50.00	$45.00

Median = $32.50

2. Kristin exercises 5 hours each week. Make a dot plot of her hours of exercise and include the hours her friends exercise. Kristin and her friends' total hours of exercise are shown in the table. How does Kristin's exercise time compare with her friends?

0	6	5
9	5	4
3	5	4
6	4	5
5	4	6

Sample: Kristin's exercise time is similar to the majority of her friends.

3. Harry read a number of books over the summer. Make a histogram to show the books he read by page length. Which length of book did he read the most?

number of pages: 452 409 355 378 390 367 375 514 389 438 311 411 376

8 books of 300–399 pages

4. Give an example of data you would put in a dot plot, histogram, and box plot. Explain why you chose each type of representation. How is a dot plot similar to and different from a box plot? Sample: Dot Plot: test scores; Histogram: 2-minute intervals of running times; Box Plot: students' weekly earnings; A dot plot is useful for small sets of numerical data. A histogram is useful for showing data in groupings. Box plots are useful for showing the grouping of data in quartiles. Both the dot plot and the box plot show data's distribution, but dot plots show categorical data.

enVision™ Algebra 1 • Teaching Resources

Enrichment O A

Presents engaging problems and activities that extend the lesson concepts.

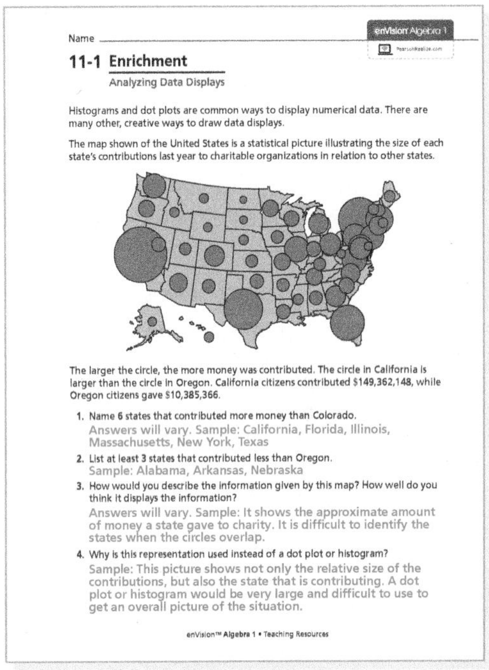
Name

11-1 Enrichment

Analyzing Data Displays

Histograms and dot plots are common ways to display numerical data. There are many other, creative ways to draw data displays.

The map shown of the United States is a statistical picture illustrating the size of each state's contributions last year to charitable organizations in relation to other states.

The larger the circle, the more money was contributed. The circle in California is larger than the circle in Oregon. California citizens contributed $149,362,148, while Oregon citizens gave $10,385,366.

1. Name 6 states that contributed more money than Colorado. Answers will vary. Sample: California, Florida, Illinois, Massachusetts, New York, Texas
2. List at least 3 states that contributed less than Oregon. Sample: Alabama, Arkansas, Nebraska
3. How would you describe the information given by this map? How well do you think it displays the information? Answers will vary. Sample: It shows the approximate amount of money a state gave to charity. It is difficult to identify the states when the circles overlap.
4. Why is this representation used instead of a dot plot or histogram? Sample: This picture shows not only the relative size of the contributions, but also the state that is contributing. A dot plot or histogram would be very large and difficult to use to get an overall picture of the situation.

enVision™ Algebra 1 • Teaching Resources

Mathematical Literacy and Vocabulary I O

Helps students develop and reinforce understanding of key terms and concepts.

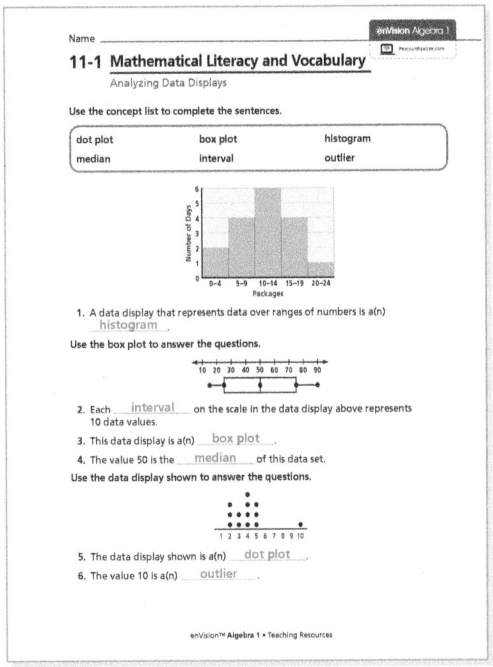
Name

11-1 Mathematical Literacy and Vocabulary

Analyzing Data Displays

Use the concept list to complete the sentences.

dot plot	box plot	histogram
median	interval	outlier

1. A data display that represents data over ranges of numbers is a(n) histogram.

Use the box plot to answer the questions.

2. Each interval on the scale in the data display above represents 10 data values.
3. This data display is a(n) box plot.
4. The value 50 is the median of this data set.

Use the data display shown to answer the questions.

5. The data display shown is a(n) dot plot.
6. The value 10 is a(n) outlier.

enVision™ Algebra 1 • Teaching Resources

Digital Resources and Video Tutorials I O A

The **Reteach to Build Understanding, Additional Practice,** and **Enrichment** activities are available as digital assignments powered by MathXL for School. These activities are automatically assigned when students complete the lesson quiz online and are automatically scored.

Students can access instructional tutorials using the **Virtual Nerd app.**

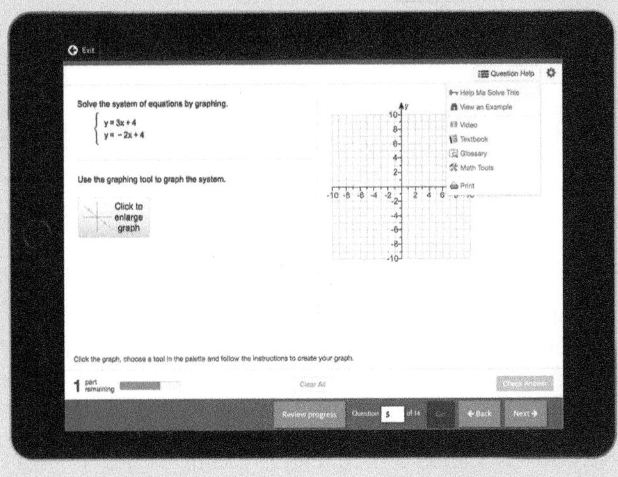
Solve the system of equations by graphing.
y = 3x + 4
y = −2x + 4
Use the graphing tool to graph the system.
Click to enlarge graph
Question Help
Review progress
Back
Next

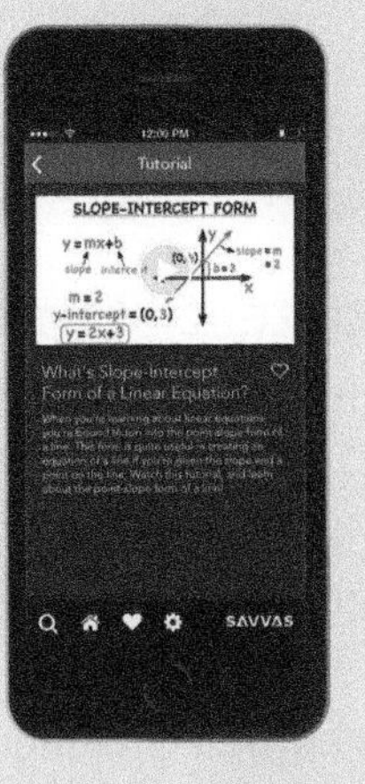
Tutorial
SLOPE-INTERCEPT FORM
What's Slope-Intercept Form of a Linear Equation?
SAVVAS

Students can also access Virtual Nerd videos using the **BouncePages app** to scan exercise pages marked with this icon. Students can download both apps for free in their mobile devices' app store.

Lesson Overview

FOCUS

Objective

Students will be able to:

✔ Use measures of center to interpret and compare data sets displayed in dot plots, box plots, and histograms.

✔ Use measures of variability, such as the MAD and IQR, to interpret and compare data sets.

Essential Understanding

Measures of center and variability are used to compare data sets displayed in dot plots, box plots, and histograms. Dot plots show how much the data vary. Box plots show the minimum, maximum, and center of the data. Histograms show ranges of data.

COHERENCE

Previously in this course, students:

- Represented and interpreted data using dot plots, histograms, and box plots.

In this lesson, students:

- Interpret and compare data sets displayed in dot plots, histograms, and box plots using measures of center and variability.

Later in this topic, students will:

- Relate the shapes of data displays, including dot plots, histograms, and box plots, to the mean and the median.

RIGOR

This lesson emphasizes a blend of *conceptual understanding* and *application*.

- Students understand that different data displays can be used to compare and interpret the data sets in different ways, such as comparing data ranges displayed in histograms.
- Students interpret data sets within the context of real-world situations, such as comparing the fu el efficiency of different cars displayed in dot plots.

A-Z Vocabulary Builder

REVIEW VOCABULARY **English** | *Spanish*

- **interquartile range** | *interval intercuartil*
- **mean** | *media*
- **mean absolute deviation** | *media desviación absoluta*
- **median** | *mediana*
- **variability** | *variabilidad*

VOCABULARY ACTIVITY

Review the difference between measures of *center* and measures of *variability*. Then discuss the terms *mean*, *median*, *interquartile range*, and *mean absolute deviation*, distinguishing between which are measures of center and which are measures of variability. Have students complete the table by sorting the terms mean, median, interquartile range, and mean absolute deviation.

Measures of Center	Measures of Variability
[mean] [median]	[interquartile range] [mean absolute deviation]

Student Companion

Students can do their in-class work for the lesson on pages 253–256 of their *Student Companion* or in Savvas Realize.

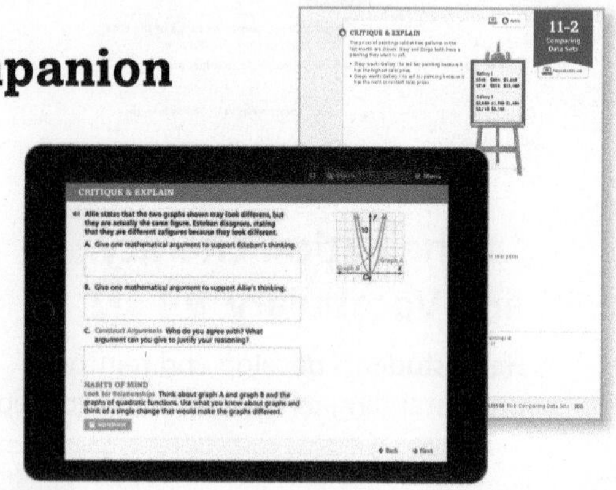

11-2
CRITIQUE & EXPLAIN

Mathematics Overview — COMMON CORE STANDARDS

Content Standards

In this lesson, students focus on these standards:

HSS.ID.A.2 Use statistics appropriate to the shape of the data distribution to compare center (median, mean) and spread (interquartile range, standard deviation) of two or more different data sets.

HSS.ID.A.3 Interpret differences in shape, center, and spread in the context of the data sets, accounting for possible effects of extreme data points (outliers).

They also work with concepts related to this standard:
HSS.ID.A.1

Mathematical Practice Standards

These standards are highlighted in this lesson:

MP.6 Attend to Precision

Students use clear mathematical language to describe the similarities and differences between the mean absolute deviation (MAD) and the interquartile range (IQR).

MP.7 Look For and Make Use of Structure

Students recognize how the overall structure of a box plot represents the interquartile range (IQR).

CRITIQUE & EXPLAIN

INSTRUCTIONAL FOCUS Students examine data sets of sale prices for two galleries. Students make observational comparisons in preparation for learning to compare data sets using different types of data displays.

STUDENT COMPANION Students can complete the *Critique & Explain* activity on page 253 of their *Student Companion*.

Before — WHOLE CLASS

Implement Tasks that Promote Reasoning and Problem Solving — ETP

Q: What do you notice about the sale prices at the different galleries?
[Gallery I has lower sale prices than Gallery II, except for one price that is much higher.]

During — SMALL GROUP

Support Productive Struggle in Learning Mathematics — ETP

Q: What does it mean for the data to be consistent?
[All the values are close together; there is not much variation.]

For Early Finishers

Q: Calculate the mean sale price for Gallery I without the $15,000 outlier. Explain how removing the large-dollar item from the data set changes the interpretation of the situation.
[The mean sale price for Gallery I without the outlier is $760. When the large-dollar item is included, the means of the two galleries are very similar (about $3,133 and $3,030). But when it is removed, the mean selling price at Gallery I is much lower.]

After — WHOLE CLASS

Facilitate Meaningful Mathematical Discourse — ETP

Q: How could you more effectively compare the two data sets?
[Create a data display to analyze and compare the data sets.]

Q: How can a few data points affect the overall data?
[Numbers that are unusually higher or lower than the majority of the data can skew the data.]

HABITS OF MIND — *Use with* **CRITIQUE & EXPLAIN**

Make Sense and Persevere What is the mean sales price for the paintings at Gallery I? What is the mean sales price for the paintings at Gallery II? MP.1

[Gallery I: about $3,133; Gallery II: $3,030]

AVAILABLE **ONLINE**

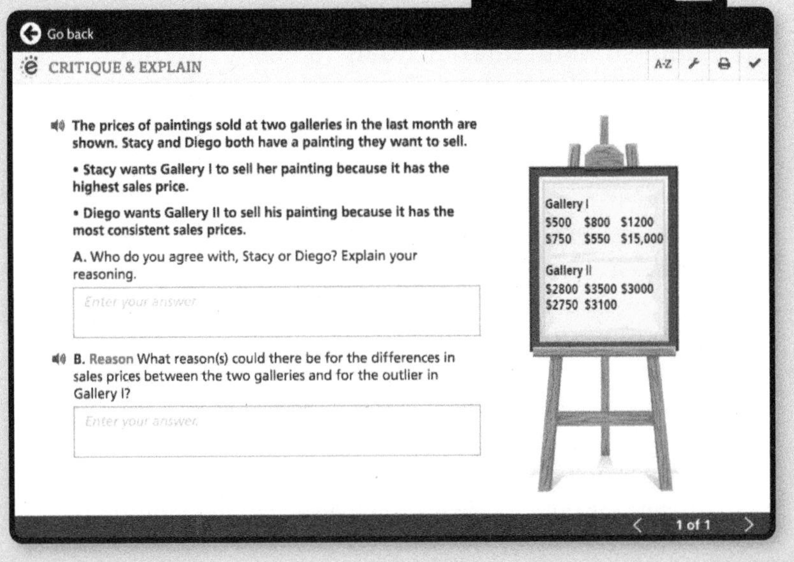
Go back
CRITIQUE & EXPLAIN

The prices of paintings sold at two galleries in the last month are shown. Stacy and Diego both have a painting they want to sell.

- Stacy wants Gallery I to sell her painting because it has the highest sales price.
- Diego wants Gallery II to sell his painting because it has the most consistent sales prices.

A. Who do you agree with, Stacy or Diego? Explain your reasoning.

Enter your answer.

B. Reason What reason(s) could there be for the differences in sales prices between the two galleries and for the outlier in Gallery I?

Enter your answer.

Gallery I
$500 $800 $1200
$750 $550 $15,000
Gallery II
$2800 $3500 $3000
$2750 $3100

1 of 1

STUDENT EDITION, PAGE 472

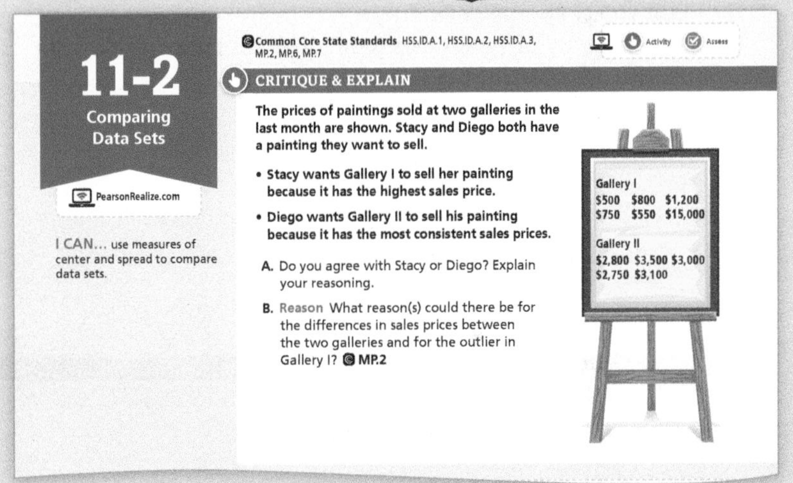
11-2 Comparing Data Sets

PearsonRealize.com

I CAN… use measures of center and spread to compare data sets.

Common Core State Standards HSS.ID.A.1, HSS.ID.A.2, HSS.ID.A.3, MP.2, MP.6, MP.7

CRITIQUE & EXPLAIN

The prices of paintings sold at two galleries in the last month are shown. Stacy and Diego both have a painting they want to sell.

- Stacy wants Gallery I to sell her painting because it has the highest sales price.
- Diego wants Gallery II to sell his painting because it has the most consistent sales prices.

A. Do you agree with Stacy or Diego? Explain your reasoning.

B. Reason What reason(s) could there be for the differences in sales prices between the two galleries and for the outlier in Gallery I? MP.2

Gallery I
$500 $800 $1,200
$750 $550 $15,000
Gallery II
$2,800 $3,500 $3,000
$2,750 $3,100

SAMPLE STUDENT WORK

A. Diego; The average price is about the same, while the distribution of prices varies greatly for Gallery I and very little for Gallery II. I would choose Gallery II because the prices of paintings sold there are consistently higher than the prices at Gallery I.

B. Gallery I could sell paintings by up-and-coming artists, while Gallery II could sell paintings by better-known artists. The outlier at Gallery I could be a painting made by a more famous artist.

INTRODUCE THE ESSENTIAL QUESTION

Establish Mathematics Goals to Focus Learning ETP

Introduce students to statistical comparisons. Explain that data sets can be compared using displays and calculations that describe attributes of the data, such as spread and center.

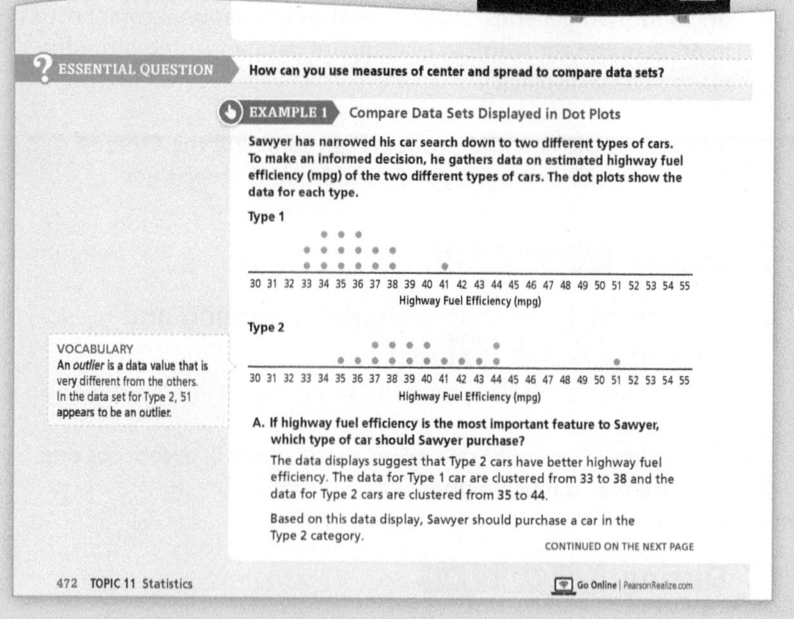
AVAILABLE ONLINE

ESSENTIAL QUESTION How can you use measures of center and spread to compare data sets?

EXAMPLE 1 Compare Data Sets Displayed in Dot Plots

Sawyer has narrowed his car search down to two different types of cars. To make an informed decision, he gathers data on estimated highway fuel efficiency (mpg) of the two different types of cars. The dot plots show the data for each type.

Type 1
30 31 32 33 34 35 36 37 38 39 40 41 42 43 44 45 46 47 48 49 50 51 52 53 54 55
Highway Fuel Efficiency (mpg)
Type 2
30 31 32 33 34 35 36 37 38 39 40 41 42 43 44 45 46 47 48 49 50 51 52 53 54 55
Highway Fuel Efficiency (mpg)

VOCABULARY
An *outlier* is a data value that is very different from the others. In the data set for Type 2, 51 appears to be an outlier.

A. If highway fuel efficiency is the most important feature to Sawyer, which type of car should Sawyer purchase?

The data displays suggest that Type 2 cars have better highway fuel efficiency. The data for Type 1 car are clustered from 33 to 38 and the data for Type 2 cars are clustered from 35 to 44.

Based on this data display, Sawyer should purchase a car in the Type 2 category.

CONTINUED ON THE NEXT PAGE

472 TOPIC 11 Statistics

Go Online | PearsonRealize.com

EXAMPLE 1 Compare Data Sets Displayed in Dot Plots

Use and Connect Mathematical Representations ETP

Part A

Q: What do you notice about the spread of the data points in the two dot plots?
[The data for Type 1 is spread across 6 values with 1 outlier, while the data for Type 2 is spread across 10 values with 1 outlier.]

Q: How do the data displayed in the dot plots help determine the best choice for fuel efficiency?
[The majority of Type 2 cars get higher gas mileage than all but one Type 1 car.]

ADDITIONAL EXAMPLES

AVAILABLE ONLINE

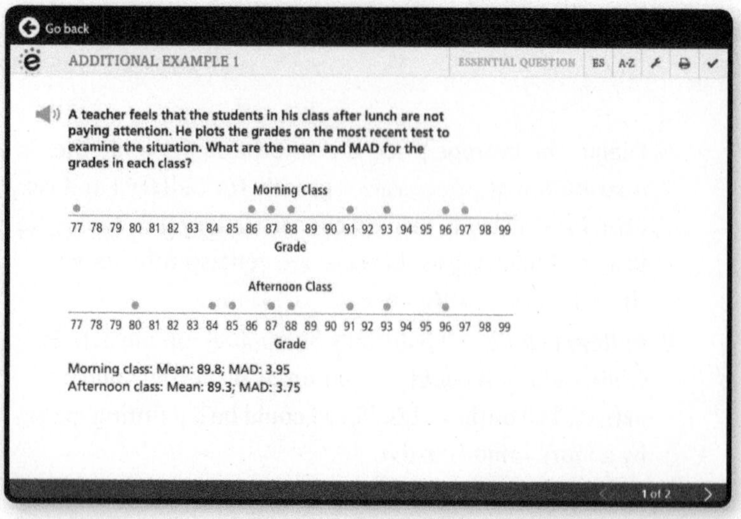
Go back

ADDITIONAL EXAMPLE 1

ESSENTIAL QUESTION ES A-Z

A teacher feels that the students in his class after lunch are not paying attention. He plots the grades on the most recent test to examine the situation. What are the mean and MAD for the grades in each class?

Morning Class
77 78 79 80 81 82 83 84 85 86 87 88 89 90 91 92 93 94 95 96 97 98 99
Grade
Afternoon Class
77 78 79 80 81 82 83 84 85 86 87 88 89 90 91 92 93 94 95 96 97 98 99
Grade

Morning class: Mean: 89.8; MAD: 3.95
Afternoon class: Mean: 89.3; MAD: 3.75

1 of 2

Example 1 Students practice calculating the mean and MAD from a dot plot modeling a real-world situation.

Q: Do the dot plots and calculations support the teacher's concern?
[No, the means and the MADs of the two classes are very close.]

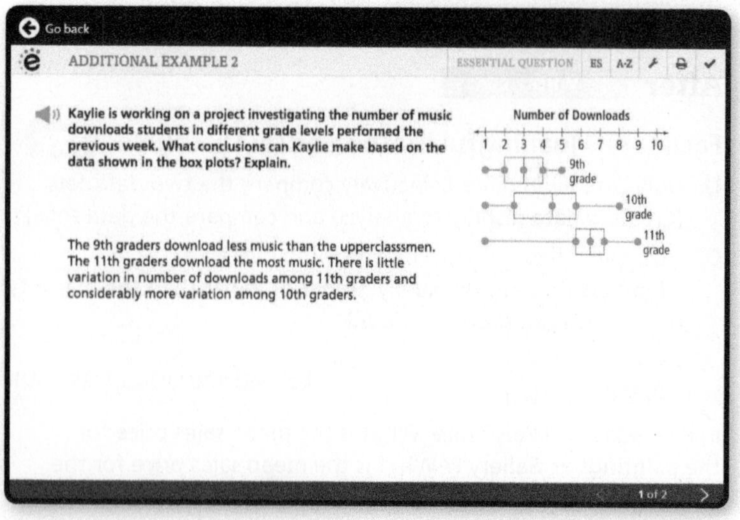
Go back

ADDITIONAL EXAMPLE 2

ESSENTIAL QUESTION ES A-Z

Kaylie is working on a project investigating the number of music downloads students in different grade levels performed the previous week. What conclusions can Kaylie make based on the data shown in the box plots? Explain.

Number of Downloads
1 2 3 4 5 6 7 8 9 10
9th grade
10th grade
11th grade

The 9th graders download less music than the upperclasssmen. The 11th graders download the most music. There is little variation in number of downloads among 11th graders and considerably more variation among 10th graders.

1 of 2

Example 2 Students practice interpreting and comparing box plots from a real-world situation.

Q: How does the plot of Kaylie's data help her to draw conclusions?
[The box plot shows that the average number of downloads increases by grade. The length of the rectangles shows the differences in variability among the grade levels.]

Part B

Q: How does the mean help determine relative fuel efficiency of the two car types?
[It shows that a Type 2 car is likely to have higher fuel efficiency than a Type 1 car.]

Q: How does the value of the mean absolute deviation impact the usefulness of the mean to compare data sets?
[A lower MAD indicates that the data are more consistent and the mean is more reliable.]

Try It! Answer

1. The outlier increases the mean from about 39.53 to 40.25 and the MAD from about 2.3 to 2.94.

Common Error

Try It! 1 Some students may assume that any outlier will significantly affect the mean and the MAD, which will then affect the comparison with the other data set. Have students compute the mean and the MAD without using the outlier to see that it does not significantly change the results.

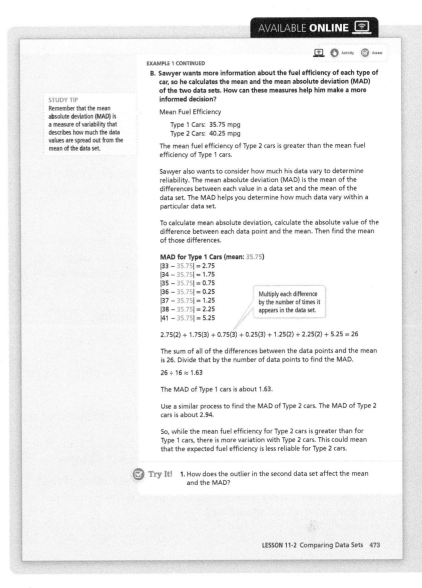

AVAILABLE **ONLINE**

Activity Assess

EXAMPLE 1 CONTINUED

B. Sawyer wants more information about the fuel efficiency of each type of car, so he calculates the mean and the mean absolute deviation (MAD) of the two data sets. How can these measures help him make a more informed decision?

Mean Fuel Efficiency

Type 1 Cars: 35.75 mpg
Type 2 Cars: 40.25 mpg

The mean fuel efficiency of Type 2 cars is greater than the mean fuel efficiency of Type 1 cars.

Sawyer also wants to consider how much his data vary to determine reliability. The mean absolute deviation (MAD) is the mean of the differences between each value in a data set and the mean of the data set. The MAD helps you determine how much data vary within a particular data set.

To calculate mean absolute deviation, calculate the absolute value of the difference between each data point and the mean. Then find the mean of those differences.

STUDY TIP
Remember that the mean absolute deviation (MAD) is a measure of variability that describes how much the data values are spread out from the mean of the data set.

MAD for Type 1 Cars (mean: 35.75)

$|33 - 35.75| = 2.75$
$|34 - 35.75| = 1.75$
$|35 - 35.75| = 0.75$
$|36 - 35.75| = 0.25$
$|37 - 35.75| = 1.25$
$|38 - 35.75| = 2.25$
$|41 - 35.75| = 5.25$

Multiply each difference by the number of times it appears in the data set.

$2.75(2) + 1.75(3) + 0.75(3) + 0.25(3) + 1.25(2) + 2.25(2) + 5.25 = 26$

The sum of all of the differences between the data points and the mean is 26. Divide that by the number of data points to find the MAD.

$26 \div 16 \approx 1.63$

The MAD of Type 1 cars is about 1.63.

Use a similar process to find the MAD of Type 2 cars. The MAD of Type 2 cars is about 2.94.

So, while the mean fuel efficiency for Type 2 cars is greater than for Type 1 cars, there is more variation with Type 2 cars. This could mean that the expected fuel efficiency is less reliable for Type 2 cars.

Try It! 1. How does the outlier in the second data set affect the mean and the MAD?

LESSON 11-2 Comparing Data Sets 473

ELL English Language Learners *(Use with* **EXAMPLE 1***)*

SPEAKING INTERMEDIATE Discuss with students the meaning of the term *cluster*: grouped or gathered together. Ask students to gather in different areas of the room based on their preference of ice cream flavor: vanilla, chocolate, or strawberry.

Q: Which preference of ice cream flavor are most students *clustered* in?
[Answers may vary.]

Repeat the process until each student has a chance to name a category.

Q: On a dot plot, what does a *cluster* indicate?
[the values where the majority of data are located]

WRITING ADVANCED Have students write the definition of *fuel efficiency* in their journals: the amount of fuel used in proportion to the number of miles traveled. Then have them answer the following questions in their journals.

Q: Rewrite the definition in your own words.
[how many miles you can drive on a gallon of gas]

Q: Why is fuel efficiency important to consider when purchasing a vehicle?
[The better the fuel efficiency of the vehicle, the less you have to spend on gas and the less you pollute the environment.]

LISTENING ADVANCED Read the following sentences as students listen.

- The car's *reliability* in the snowy weather was tested during the storm.
- Scientists have little *reliability* in predicting earthquakes.
- His *reliability* as a worker is quite high.

Q: What synonyms could you substitute for *reliability* in each of the sentences?
[dependability, accuracy, achievement]

Q: How is *reliability* interpreted as it relates to the mean absolute deviation?
[The MAD indicates the reliability of the mean to describe the data.]

EXAMPLE 2 Compare Data Sets Displayed in Box Plots

Use and Connect Mathematical Representations ETP

Q: How can you determine the amount of variation in the data set by looking at the box plot?
[A wider box will have a greater variation in the middle 50% of the data.]

Q: Based on the box plots, how do the contributions raised at the two schools compare?
[There is more variation in contribution amounts at Kaitlyn's school, and the contributions generally tended to be lower.]

Try It! Answer

2. The range is the same for both data sets, but the IQR is smaller for Philip's school. The IQR for Kaitlyn's school is larger than the IQR for Philip's school, meaning there is more variability in the money raised by students in Kaitlyn's school.

Elicit and Use Evidence of Student Thinking ETP

Q: How does the value of the IQR help you to understand the data set?
[The smaller the IQR, the closer the middle 50% of the values are to the median.]

HABITS OF MIND

Use with **EXAMPLES 1 & 2**

Use Appropriate Tools Does the information given by a box plot allow you to determine the mean of a set of data? **MP.5**

[No; The vertical line within the box indicates the value of the median. Because individual values cannot be determined from a box plot, neither can the mean.]

AVAILABLE **ONLINE**

Activity Assess

EXAMPLE 2 Compare Data Sets Displayed in Box Plots

Kaitlyn and Philip go to neighboring high schools, and both are sponsoring charity fundraisers. Kaitlyn claims that students at her school are raising more for charity than the students at Philip's school. The amounts raised by a random sample of 30 students at each school are shown in the box plots below. Do the data support Kaitlyn's claim?

Kaitlyn's High School

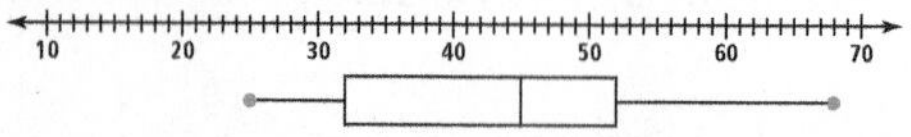
10
20
30
40
50
60
70

Philip's High School

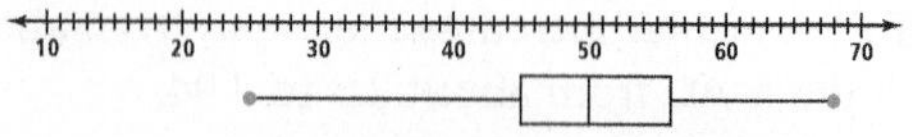
10
20
30
40
50
60
70

Analyze the distribution of values in each data set.

	Kaitlyn's High School	Philip's High School
Minimum Value	25	25
Maximum Value	68	68
First Quartile	32	45
Median	45	50
Third Quartile	52	56
Interquartile Range (IQR)	20	11

USE STRUCTURE
Recall that the interquartile range (IQR) is the difference of the third and first quartiles and represents the spread of the middle 50% of the data values. How does the structure of a box plot represent the IQR? **MP.7**

While the minimum and maximum amount of money raised at each school was the same, the spread of data points between the minimum and maximum values varies.

- The sample data show that 50% of the students at Kaitlyn's school raised between \$32 and \$52. At Philip's school, 50% of the students in the sample raised between \$45 and \$56.
- Based on the data, 50% of the students at Kaitlyn's school raised \$45 or more; At Philip's school, 50% raised \$50 or more.

The data do not support Kaitlyn's claim. Instead, they suggest that individual students at Philip's school raised more money than individual students at Kaitlyn's school.

Try It! **2.** How does the IQR compare to the range for each school?

474 TOPIC 11 Statistics

Go Online | PearsonRealize.com

Activity Assess

EXAMPLE 3 Compare Data Sets Displayed in Histograms

Use and Connect Mathematical Representations ETP

Q: How does a histogram display a data set?
[A histogram shows the distribution of values within a data set by grouping data into intervals.]

Q: Why is the visual display of data in histograms more helpful in analyzing the data than simply knowing the median age of the viewers and the number of viewers in the target age range?
[The median age of the viewers and the number of viewers in the target age range are the same for each show. By looking at the histograms, you can see that Show 1 has no viewers between 20–24. Show 2 has viewers in each subsection of the target range and has viewers just above and just below the target range who are likely to be customers.]

Try It! Answer

3. Show 1;
For Show 1, the total number of viewers age 25–34 is 18, while for Show 2, the total number of viewers age 25–34 is 9.

Elicit and Use Evidence of Student Thinking ETP

Q: What other information shown in the histograms could be useful for making decisions?
[The total number of viewers of each show could help the marketing team decide whether to advertise during that show at all.]

AVAILABLE ONLINE

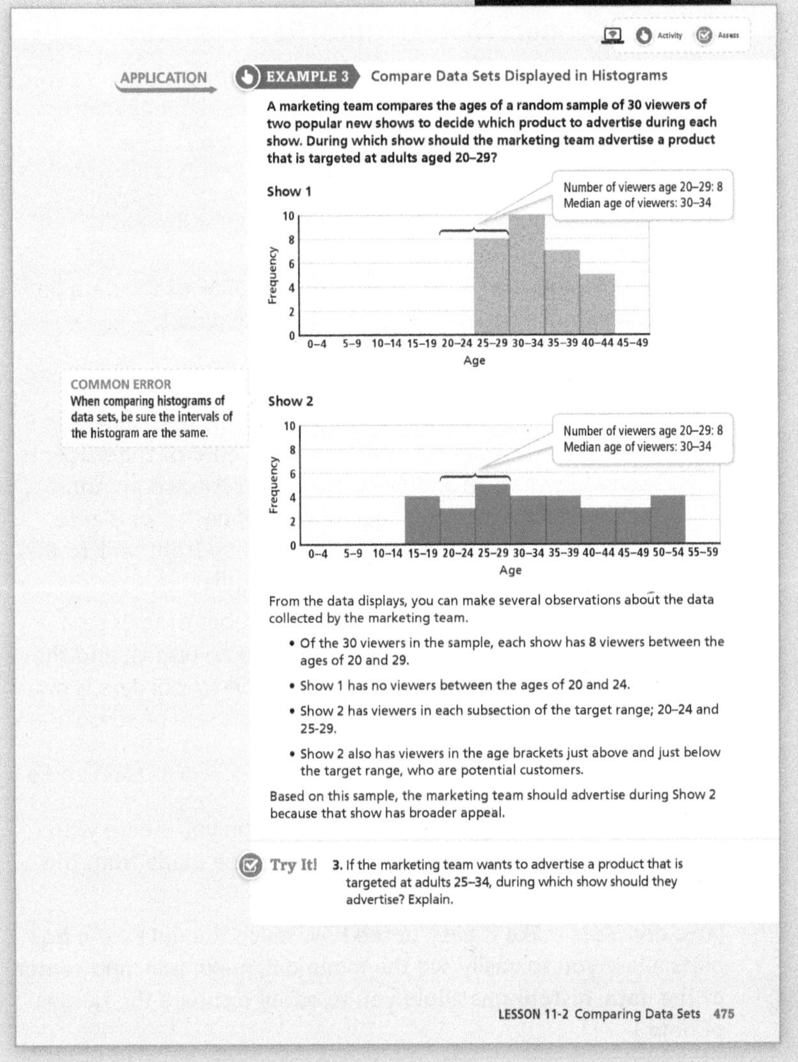
APPLICATION

EXAMPLE 3 Compare Data Sets Displayed in Histograms

A marketing team compares the ages of a random sample of 30 viewers of two popular new shows to decide which product to advertise during each show. During which show should the marketing team advertise a product that is targeted at adults aged 20–29?

COMMON ERROR
When comparing histograms of data sets, be sure the intervals of the histogram are the same.

Show 1
Number of viewers age 20–29: 8
Median age of viewers: 30–34
Frequency
Age
Show 2
Number of viewers age 20–29: 8
Median age of viewers: 30–34
Frequency
Age

From the data displays, you can make several observations about the data collected by the marketing team.

- Of the 30 viewers in the sample, each show has 8 viewers between the ages of 20 and 29.
- Show 1 has no viewers between the ages of 20 and 24.
- Show 2 has viewers in each subsection of the target range; 20–24 and 25-29.
- Show 2 also has viewers in the age brackets just above and just below the target range, who are potential customers.

Based on this sample, the marketing team should advertise during Show 2 because that show has broader appeal.

Try It! 3. If the marketing team wants to advertise a product that is targeted at adults 25–34, during which show should they advertise? Explain.

LESSON 11-2 Comparing Data Sets 475

Struggling Students

USE WITH EXAMPLE 3 Some students need additional practice comparing data sets displayed in histograms.

- The histograms show number of days within given temperature ranges for two different locations.

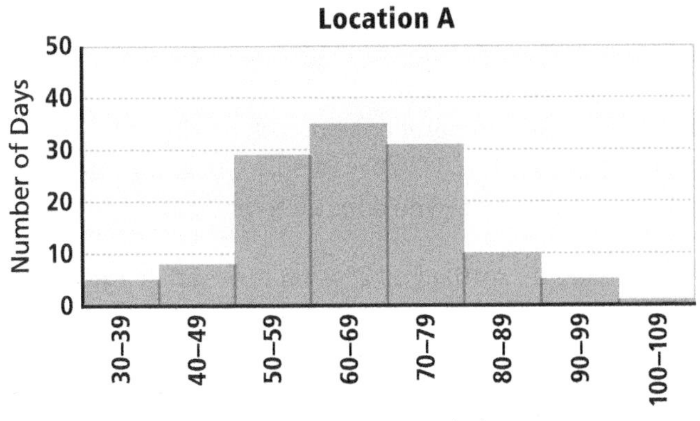

Location A
Number of Days
Temperature (°F)

Q: Which location would be best if the optimal growth temperature of a crop is 70–89 °F?
[Location B has more days within the range.]

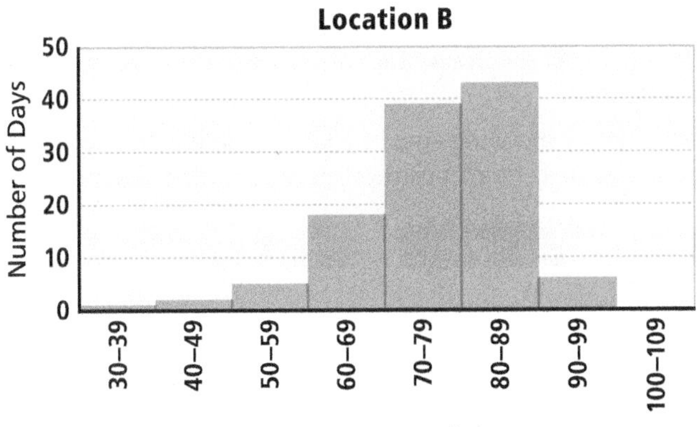

Location B
Number of Days
Temperature (°F)

EXAMPLE 4 Make Observations With Data Displays

Use and Connect Mathematical Representations ETP

Q: How can you use the tables to make observations that cannot be made from the box plots?
[You can calculate means from the tables. You cannot determine a means from a box plot.]

Q: How do box plots provide information that is not easily determined by looking at the tables?
[The box plots display where the middle 50% of the data lie and how much variability there is in those data.]

Try It! Answers

4. **a.** On school days, 50% of the students only send between 9 and 22 texts, but on non-school days, 50% of the students send between 40 and 60 texts. The box shown on non-school days is longer. The minimum of each plot is zero, but on the non-school days plot, the line from zero to the box is very long, so zero is likely an outlier.

   b. Answers may vary. The maximum number of texts sent in either group does not appear to be an outlier, and the maximum number of texts sent on non-school days is more than triple the maximum number of texts sent on school days.

HABITS OF MIND

Use with **EXAMPLES 3 & 4**

Use Appropriate Tools Does the type of graph you create with given data change the observations that can be made from the data display? Explain. **MP.5**

[Yes, dot plots make it easy to see how much the data vary; box plots allow you to easily see the minimum, maximum, and center of the data; histograms allow you to easily compare the ranges of data.]

AVAILABLE **ONLINE**

Activity Assess

CONCEPTUAL UNDERSTANDING

EXAMPLE 4 Make Observations With Data Displays

Nadia collected data from 15 classmates about the number of text messages they send on school days and the number of text messages they send on non-school days. Nadia organized her data in the tables below. How can you use a box plot to compare the data that she collected?

Average # of texts sent on school days		
14	23	18
17	19	26
4	9	0
19	22	25
8	15	16

Average # of texts sent on non-school days		
80	45	50
50	60	75
20	40	0
75	50	60
30	40	50

USE APPROPRIATE TOOLS You may want to enter the data into a spreadsheet so you can easily sort and perform calculations. MP.5

Step 1: Calculate the five-number summary for each set of data.

School Day Texts
Minimum: 0
Maximum: 26
Q1: 9
Median: 17
Q3: 22
IQR: 13

Non-School Day Texts
Minimum: 0
Maximum: 80
Q1: 40
Median: 50
Q3: 60
IQR: 20

Step 2: Use the information to create a box plot to represent each set of data.

Average # of texts sent on school days

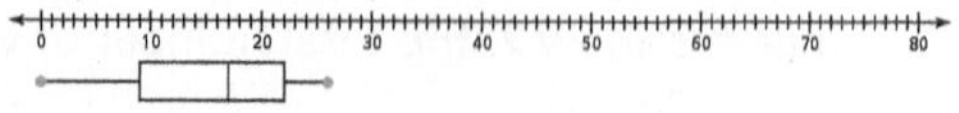
0
10
20
30
40
50
60
70
80

Average # of texts sent on non-school days

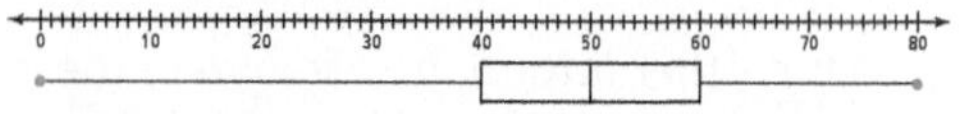
0
10
20
30
40
50
60
70
80

Step 3: Use the data displays to make observations about the data sets.

- Students send far more texts on non-school days than on school days.
- There is more variation in the number of texts sent on non-school days than on school days.
- One person does not send any texts on non-school days. This represents an outlier because it is far from the other data values.

Try It! **4. a.** Provide a possible explanation for each of the observations that was made.

b. Make 2 more observations about the data that Nadia collected.

476 TOPIC 11 Statistics

Go Online | PearsonRealize.com

ADV Advanced Students

USE WITH EXAMPLE 4 Have students explore constructing their own data displays.

- The tables below show the ages of youths signed up for two sports at the community center. Construct box plots for the given data.

Ages of Volleyball Players			
10	14	15	18
12	14	14	18
16	20	20	16
19	17	18	17

Ages of Softball Players			
11	12	16	10
10	8	18	9
14	11	9	16
12	13	15	15

Q: What do the box plots tell you about the spread of the data for the two sports?
[Softball has a slightly greater appeal, with an IQR of 5, compared to the IQR for volleyball of 4.]

Q: What do the box plots tell you about the center of the data?
[The median age for softball is 12, while the median age for volleyball is 16.5.]

CONCEPT SUMMARY Comparing Data Sets

Q: How is the information shown in each of the displays similar? How is it different?
[All three displays show the range and the variability of the data, however only the box plot gives an actual value for variability. All three displays also indicate the central tendency, however only the box plot provides actual values. The box plot does not indicate frequency of a specific value or range of values, but the dot plot and histogram do.]

Do You UNDERSTAND? | Do You KNOW HOW?

Common Error

Exercise 5 Some students may compare the medians, both of which are 87, rather than the means. Have students add all of the data values and divide by the total number of values to calculate the mean. Point out the difference between the means and the medians.

Answers

1. Measures of center show how closely a data set is clustered, while measures of spread show the amount of variability in a data set. Both types of measures should be considered when comparing data sets.
2. Answers may vary. Sample: The MAD and the IQR both measure the spread of a data set. The MAD measures the spread around the mean, while the IQR measures the spread around the median.
3. Since the mean calculates the average value, it is affected by outliers. The MAD shows how closely the data are clustered about the mean, so it can indicate the existence of values that are far from the mean.
4. No, the median is the middle value of an ordered set of data. Unless there are only two values in both sets of data, it is unlikely that the medians of the sets would be the same just because the maximums and minimums are the same.
5. Data Set A: 87; Data Set B: 83.2
6. Data Set A: about 3.47; Data Set B: about 4.96
7. Data Set A: 87; Data Set B: 87
8. Data Set A: 6; Data Set B: 8
9. The ranges and IQRs are very close and the medians are equal, so medians, IQRs, and ranges are better measures of center and spread for comparing data sets A and B.

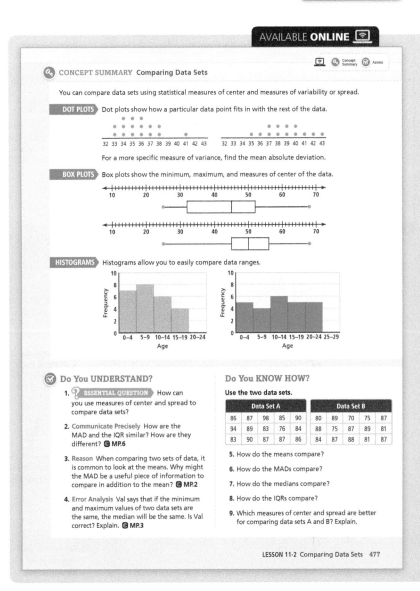

AVAILABLE **ONLINE**

Concept Summary Assess

CONCEPT SUMMARY Comparing Data Sets

You can compare data sets using statistical measures of center and measures of variability or spread.

DOT PLOTS Dot plots show how a particular data point fits in with the rest of the data.

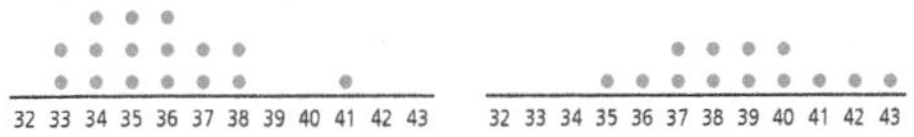
32 33 34 35 36 37 38 39 40 41 42 43
32 33 34 35 36 37 38 39 40 41 42 43

For a more specific measure of variance, find the mean absolute deviation.

BOX PLOTS Box plots show the minimum, maximum, and measures of center of the data.

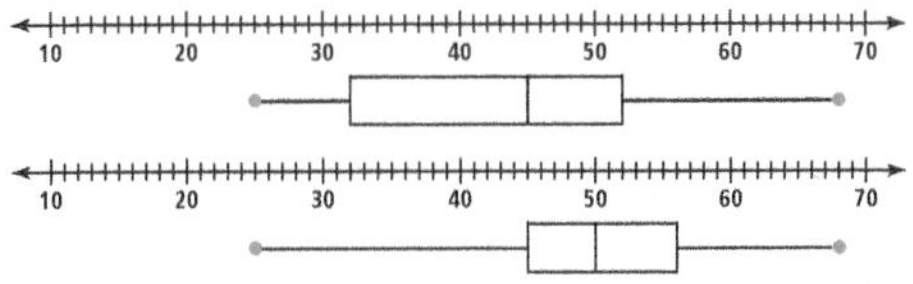
10 20 30 40 50 60 70
10 20 30 40 50 60 70

HISTOGRAMS Histograms allow you to easily compare data ranges.

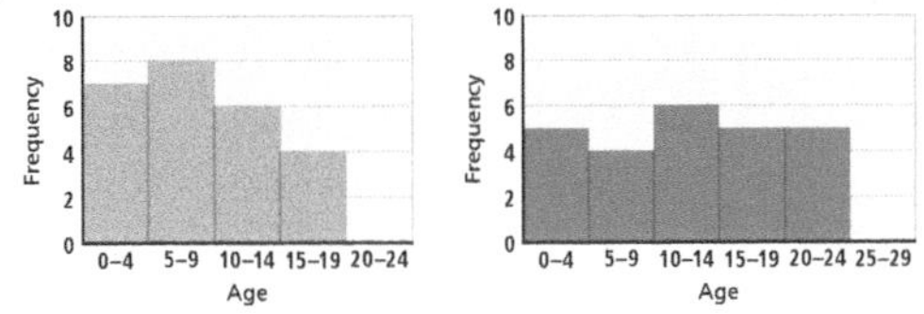
Frequency
0 2 4 6 8 10
0–4 5–9 10–14 15–19 20–24
Age
Frequency
0 2 4 6 8 10
0–4 5–9 10–14 15–19 20–24 25–29
Age

Do You UNDERSTAND?

1. ESSENTIAL QUESTION How can you use measures of center and spread to compare data sets?
2. Communicate Precisely How are the MAD and the IQR similar? How are they different? MP.6
3. Reason When comparing two sets of data, it is common to look at the means. Why might the MAD be a useful piece of information to compare in addition to the mean? MP.2
4. Error Analysis Val says that if the minimum and maximum values of two data sets are the same, the median will be the same. Is Val correct? Explain. MP.3

Do You KNOW HOW?

Use the two data sets.

Data Set A				
86	87	98	85	90
94	89	83	76	84
83	90	87	87	86

Data Set B				
80	89	70	75	87
88	75	87	89	81
84	87	88	81	87

5. How do the means compare?
6. How do the MADs compare?
7. How do the medians compare?
8. How do the IQRs compare?
9. Which measures of center and spread are better for comparing data sets A and B? Explain.

LESSON 11-2 Comparing Data Sets 477

PRACTICE & PROBLEM SOLVING

AVAILABLE ONLINE

Lesson Practice You may opt to have students complete the automatically scored Practice and Problem Solving items online powered by MathXL for School.

Choose from: **Lesson Practice**

Adaptive Practice

You may also take advantage of the bank of exercises for assigning additional practice.

Assignment Guide

Basic	Advanced
10–24	10–24

Item Analysis

Example	Items	DOK
1	12	1
	19, 21	2
2	13	1
	11, 18	2
	14, 20	3
3	10	2
	15–17	3
4	22–24	2

AVAILABLE ONLINE

PRACTICE & PROBLEM SOLVING

Scan for Multimedia

Practice Tutorial

Additional Exercises Available Online

UNDERSTAND

10. Reason The mean of the data set represented by the histogram is 12. What is a reasonable estimate for the median? Explain your reasoning. MP.2

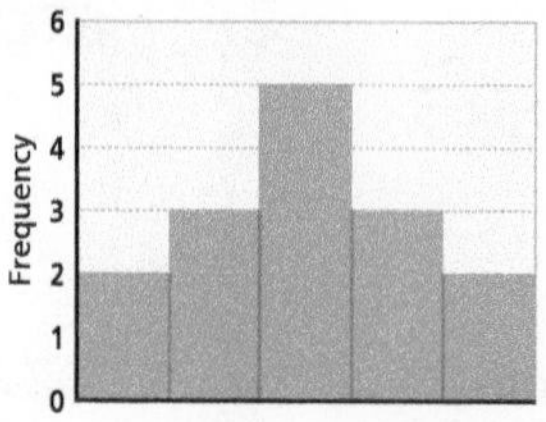
Frequency
0
1
2
3
4
5
6

11. Construct Arguments The means of two data sets are the same, but the median of one data set is much smaller than the median of the other data set. What conclusions can you make about the sets from this information? MP.3

12. Error Analysis Describe and correct the errors a student made when making a statement based on the data set represented by the dot plot. MP.3

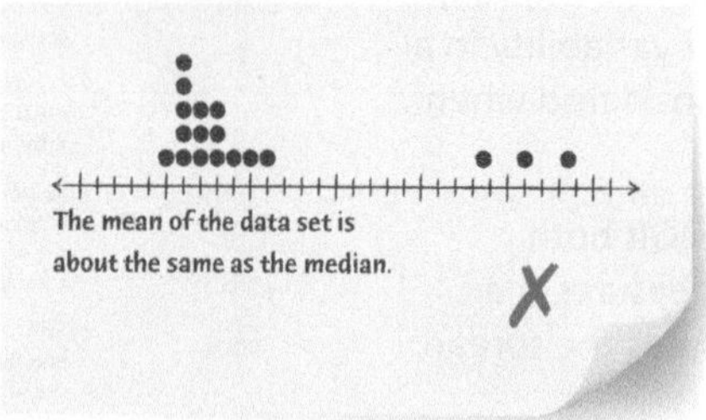
The mean of the data set is about the same as the median.
✗

13. Communicate Precisely How are the IQR and the range of a data set similar in terms of comparing data sets? How are they different? MP.6

14. Higher Order Thinking Two data sets each have a median of 10. The first data set has an IQR of 22 and the second data set has an IQR of 8.

a. What conclusions can you make about the data sets? Explain.

b. Is it possible to also make a prediction about the MADs from the information given? Explain.

PRACTICE

For each pair of data sets, compare the means and the MADs, and then the medians and the IQRs. Decide which measures are better for comparing the data sets. Explain your reasoning.

SEE EXAMPLES 1–4

15.

Data Set A			
5	6	5	4
5	4	5	6
6	5	4	5
4	5	6	5

Data Set B			
5	9	2	5
6	1	5	8
3	5	5	4
5	7	4	6

16.

Data Set A				
3.0	2.8	3.2	3.3	3.2
3.4	3.3	2.9	3.0	4.5
4.8	3.1	3.2	4.9	3.1

Data Set B				
1.9	3.3	1.5	3.2	3.1
3.4	3.0	3.2	3.4	1.6
3.2	3.6	3.5	3.1	3.3

17. Data Set A

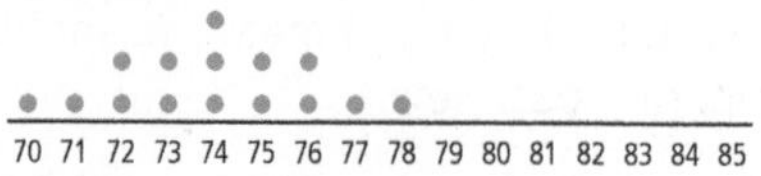
70 71 72 73 74 75 76 77 78 79 80 81 82 83 84 85

Data Set B

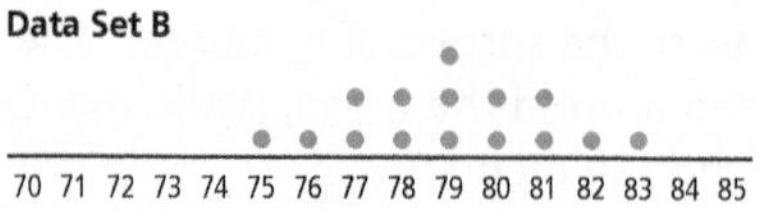
70 71 72 73 74 75 76 77 78 79 80 81 82 83 84 85

18. A researcher claims that students tend to have more apps on their smart phones than adults. Do the data support the researcher's claim? Explain. SEE EXAMPLE 2

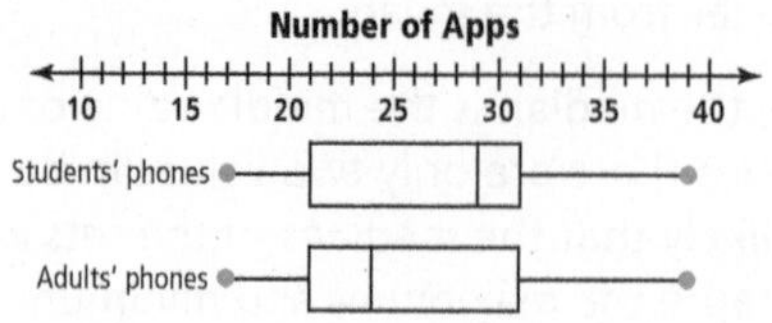
Number of Apps
10 15 20 25 30 35 40
Students' phones
Adults' phones

Answers

10. 12; The data are symmetrical and are centered about the mean, so the mean and median are about the same.

11. Since the means are the same but the median is much smaller in one data set, that data set must include some large values that pull the mean higher.

12. The data are skewed right so the mean is greater than the median.

13. Both are measures of spread. The IQR measures the spread of the middle 50% of data values about the median, while the range measures the spread of the entire data set.

14. a. The first data set is more spread out from the median while the second data set is more clustered about the median.

b. No, all the individual data values are needed.

15. Data Set A Mean: 5; MAD: 0.5; Median: 5; IQR: 1

Data Set B Mean: 5; MAD: 1.375; Median: 5; IQR: 2

The means are the same, but the MAD for set B is larger, so set B is more spread out around the mean.

The medians are the same, but the IQR for set B is larger, so the middle 50% of data set B is more spread out.

The mean and MAD are better measures; the mean is generally preferred over the median when both data sets are evenly spread about the mean.

16. Data Set A Mean: 3.4; MAD: 0.5; Median: 3.2; IQR: 0.4

Data Set B Mean: 3; MAD: 0.5; Median: 3.2; IQR: 0.4

The mean is not equal to the median in either set, so the data are not evenly distributed for either set. The MADs and the IQRs are the same for both sets, so they have similar variance. The median and IQR are better measures because the data sets are not centered about the mean.

Answers

17. Data Set A Mean: 74; MAD: 1.73; Median: 74; IQR: 4

Data Set B Mean: 79; MAD: 1.73; Median: 79; IQR: 4

For both sets, the mean is equal to the median; the data are evenly distributed. The mean and median of Set B is 5 units greater than the mean and median of Set A, but the MADs and IQRs are the same; the sets have similar variance.

The mean and MAD are better measures because the mean is generally preferred over the median when the data are centered about the mean.

18. The data somewhat support the claim. The minimum and maximum number of apps are the same for both groups, and 50% of both groups have between 21 and 31 apps. However, the median number of apps on students' phones is 5 greater than the median number of apps on adults' phones. The researcher could argue that, on average, students have more apps on their phones than adults have.

19. The mean score on this year's exam was 85, with a mean average deviation of 4.9. The mean score was higher than last year's score, but there was also greater spread about the mean this year.

20. Parker's team has a median of 75 points per player, with an IQR of 54 points. The opposing team has a median of 74 points per player, with an IQR of 3 points. Parker's team has a greater median number of points, but the spread around the median number of points is much bigger. There is a lot of variability in the points Parker's team may score.

21. The data for the second machine are not centered about the mean, so use the median and IQR to compare. Machine A has a median of 12.0, with an IQR of 0.25. Machine B has a median of 11.95, with an IQR of 0.4. The median weights are either equal to or very close to the advertised weight, but the high variability in Machine B indicates that it may have a problem.

24. Part A Rounded to the tenth: Phone A Mean: 12.4; MAD: 2.5; Phone B Mean: 13.9; MAD: 0.8

Part B Phone A Median: 14.1; IQR: 4.1; Phone B Median: 14.0; IQR: 2

AVAILABLE **ONLINE**

PRACTICE & PROBLEM SOLVING

Practice Tutorial
Mixed Review Available Online

APPLY

19. Model With Mathematics The mean score on last year's math final exam was 82, with MAD of 3.5 points. Scores for this year's exam are shown in the table. How do the scores for the two years compare? MP.4

Math Final Exam Scores				
85	82	88	84	85
84	86	70	95	86
99	71	85	92	79
88	85	91	82	85
86	75	84	78	100

20. Make Sense and Persevere The points of each player on Parker's basketball team for the season are shown in the table. The points of an opposing team are represented by the box plot. How does Parker's team compare? MP.1

Points per Player				
35	32	60	80	36
90	45	76	96	92
100	120	60	38	75

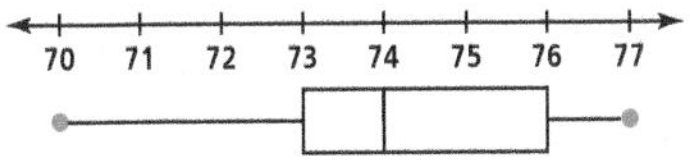
70 71 72 73 74 75 76 77

21. Use Structure The label on the cereal box says the weight is 12 ounces. The dot plots show weights of two random samples of 16 boxes packaged on two different machines. How can you compare the data sets to see if there is a problem with one of the machines? MP.7

Machine A

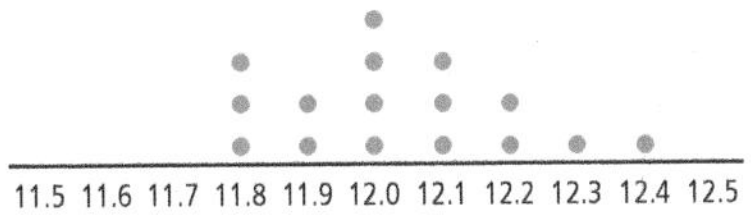
11.5 11.6 11.7 11.8 11.9 12.0 12.1 12.2 12.3 12.4 12.5

Machine B

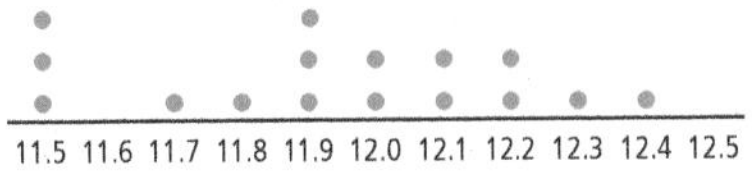
11.5 11.6 11.7 11.8 11.9 12.0 12.1 12.2 12.3 12.4 12.5

ASSESSMENT PRACTICE

22. The table shows the number of minutes Dylan and Kyle spent on their homework each night over the past 5 nights.

Dylan	Kyle
45	30
40	35
80	50
60	70
20	30

Based on this data, which of the following statements are true? Select all that apply.

Ⓐ The median of Kyle's data is greater than the median of Dylan's data.
Ⓑ On average, Dylan spends more time on homework than Kyle.
Ⓒ The mean is greater than the median in both groups.
Ⓓ The IQR of the data is greater for Kyle.

23. SAT/ACT The histograms that correspond to two data sets look identical. What conclusion can you make about the data sets?

Ⓐ The data points in each set are the same.
Ⓑ The mean of each of the data sets is the same.
Ⓒ The median of each of the data sets is the same.
Ⓓ none of these

24. Performance Task A consumer group tested battery life times for two different smart phones. Results are shown in the tables below.

Phone A				
10.0	14.2	12.0	15.1	16.0
14.0	0.9	14.2	9.5	15.0
14.2	15.0	9.5	12.5	14.2
13.0	15.0	14.2	11.0	9.0

Phone B				
12.5	13.0	14.0	13.5	15.0
14.0	14.0	12.0	15.0	12.8
12.8	15.0	13.0	15.2	16.0
14.0	13.6	14.2	13.8	15.1

Part A Find the mean and MAD for each data set.

Part B Find the median and IQR for each data set.

Part C Create data displays that will allow you to compare the two data sets.

Part D Which cell phone battery is likely to last longer? Explain your reasoning.

Part C

Phone A

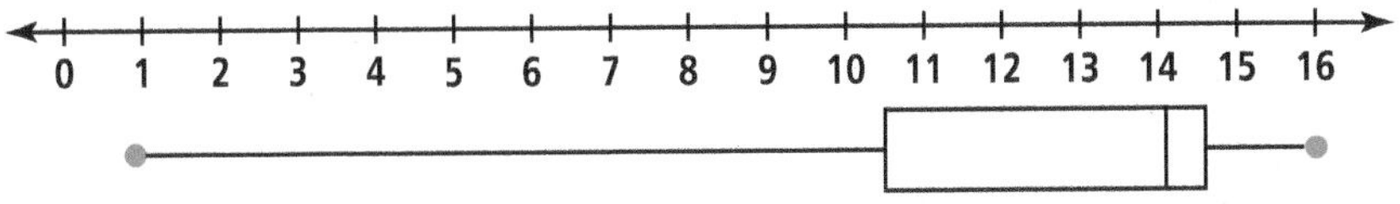
0 1 2 3 4 5 6 7 8 9 10 11 12 13 14 15 16

Phone B

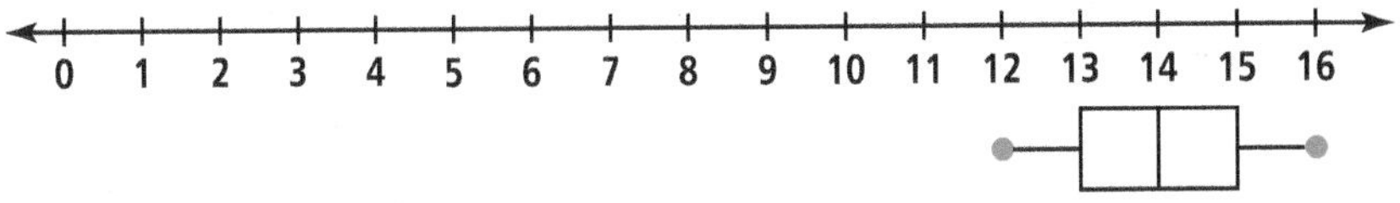
0 1 2 3 4 5 6 7 8 9 10 11 12 13 14 15 16

Part D Phone B; The median battery life for phone A is greater by only 0.1 hours or 6 minutes. The mean for phone B is greater by 1.5 hours. In addition, there is less spread in hours of battery life for phone B.

LESSON QUIZ

Use the Lesson Quiz to assess students' understanding of the mathematics in the lesson.

Students can take the Lesson Quiz online or you can download a printable copy from **SavvasRealize.com**. The Lesson Quiz is also available in the *Assessment Resources* book.

Item Analysis

Item	DOK	Standards
1	1	HSS.ID.A.1, HSS.ID.A.2
2	2	HSS.ID.A.2, HSS.ID.A.3
3	1	HSS.ID.A.3
4	1	HSS.ID.A.2, HSS.ID.A.3
5	2	HSS.ID.A.3

RtI Use the student scores on the Lesson Quiz to prescribe differentiated assignments.

If students take the Lesson Quiz online, it will be automatically scored and appropriate differentiated practice will be assigned based on student performance.

I Intervention	0–3 points	• Reteach to Build Understanding • Mathematical Literacy and Vocabulary • Additional Practice
O On-Level	4 points	• Mathematical Literacy and Vocabulary • Additional Practice • Enrichment
A Advanced	5 points	• Enrichment

AVAILABLE **ONLINE**

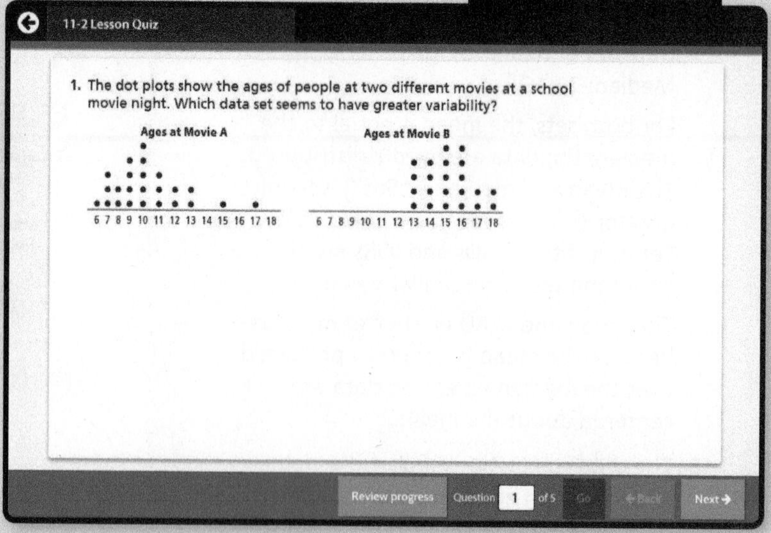
11-2 Lesson Quiz
1. The dot plots show the ages of people at two different movies at a school movie night. Which data set seems to have greater variability?
Ages at Movie A
Ages at Movie B
Review progress
Question 1 of 5
Go
Back
Next

ASSESSMENT RESOURCES

Name ______

enVision Algebra 1
PearsonRealize.com

11-2 Lesson Quiz

Comparing Data Sets

1. The dot plots show the ages of people at two different movies at a school movie night. Which data set seems to have greater variability?

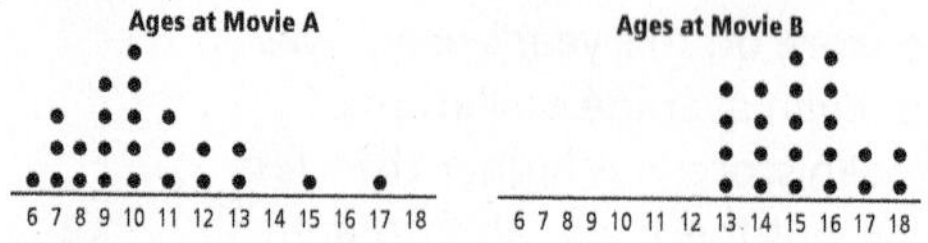
Ages at Movie A
Ages at Movie B
6 7 8 9 10 11 12 13 14 15 16 17 18
6 7 8 9 10 11 12 13 14 15 16 17 18

Movie A

2. Use the data sets in Item 1. What is the mean absolute deviation of the ages at Movie B?

Ⓐ 0 Ⓑ 1.125 Ⓒ 1.4 Ⓓ 16

3. The box plots display the data from Item 1.

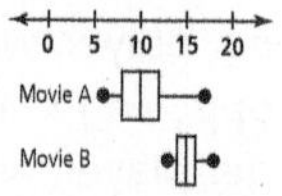
0 5 10 15 20
Movie A
Movie B

Complete: The box plots show that __75__ % of the people at Movie A are younger than the youngest person at Movie B.

4. A reporter wants to interview an employee who works fewer than 30 hours per week. Is the reporter more likely to find such a person at Company A or at Company B?

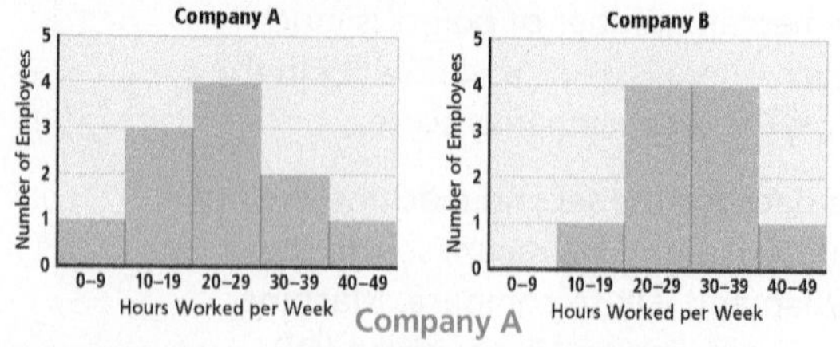
Company A
Company B
Number of Employees
Hours Worked per Week
0–9 10–19 20–29 30–39 40–49

Company A

5. Use the histograms in Item 4 to decide which statement is true.

Ⓐ The mean number of hours worked at Company B is less than 25.

Ⓑ The median number of hours worked at Company A is less than 35.

Ⓒ The standard deviation for the number of hours worked at Company A is less than the standard deviation for the number of hours worked at Company B.

Ⓓ The IQR for the number of hours worked at Company B is greater than the IQR for the number of hours worked at Company A.

enVision™ Algebra 1 • Assessment Resources

DIFFERENTIATED RESOURCES

I = Intervention O = On-Level A = Advanced

⚙ = This activity is available as a digital assignment powered by MathXL® for School.

AVAILABLE ONLINE

Reteach to Build Understanding I ⚙

Provides scaffolded reteaching for the key lesson concepts.

Name ______ enVision Algebra 1 PearsonRealize.com

11-2 Reteach to Build Understanding

Comparing Data Sets

1. For each type of data display or measure, complete each sentence with *variability* or *center*.

   A dot plot shows how a particular data point fits in with the rest of the data. This data display is most useful for comparing measures of variability.

   A box plot compares the minimum, maximum, and measure of center of the data.

   A histogram allows you to easily compare data ranges. This data display is most useful for comparing measures of variability.

   Calculate the Mean Absolute Deviation (MAD) to find a more specific measure of variability.

2. Complete the table for the two data sets shown in the box plots.

   Data Set A

   Data Set B

	Data Set A	Data Set B
Minimum value	2	1
Maximum value	8	9
First quartile	3	4
Median	4	5
Third quartile	5	7
IQR	2	3

3. Josh made an incorrect statement when comparing the two dot plots. Put an X next to the incorrect statement. Correct the error.

   The mean for both data sets is greater than the median.

   The range of Data Set A is greater.

   Data Set B has no outliers.

   The median value of Data Set B is greater than the median of Data Set A. X

   Josh incorrectly identified the median value of Data Set B as being greater than the median value of Data Set A. Actually, both data sets have a median value of 3.

   Data Set A

   Data Set B

enVision™ Algebra 1 • Teaching Resources

Additional Practice I O ⚙

Provides extra practice for each lesson.

Name ______ enVision Algebra 1 PearsonRealize.com

11-2 Additional Practice

Comparing Data Sets

1. The Sullivan family is comparing two neighborhood blocks for the purchase of a new home. The dot plots shown represent the number of children in each household on each block. Which block should the Sullivan family choose if they want their children to connect with new friends in the neighborhood? Use the mean and the MAD to make an informed decision.

   Block A Block B

   Sample:
   Block A: Mean = 1.13, MAD = 1.07
   Block B: Mean = 2.33, MAD = 1.33
   The family should choose Block B, as the mean number of children is higher. There is no significant difference in the MAD.

2. The box plots show recent results of an algebra test from two different classes.

   Based on the data shown, which class performed better on the test? Explain, using the IQRs and the medians.

   Test Scores; 1st Period; 6th Period

   Sample: Although the 6th period performed a little better, the difference between the classes is not great. The IQR for both classes is 16 and the median for both classes is 86. In the 1st period, 50% of the class scored between 76 and 92, but in the 6th period, 50% of the class scored between 80 and 96, which is higher than the 1st period.

3. Is it possible to compare the mean and MAD given two histograms? Is it possible to compare median and IQR? Explain.

   Sample: No, since histogram bars represent a range of values, there is not enough information to determine the individual values necessary for the mean, median, MAD, and IQR.

4. A company needs to know whether the packages it is shipping meet the requirements of being no less than 100 ounces and no greater than 125 ounces. The shipping department weighs 50 boxes and organizes the data in a table. Which data display would you use to display this information and determine whether packaging procedures should be revised? Explain.

   Sample: A histogram would be the most appropriate display, because it would show the shape or distribution of the data and compare the data ranges.

enVision™ Algebra 1 • Teaching Resources

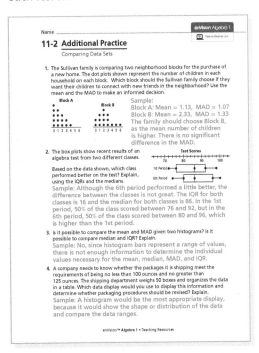

Enrichment O A ⚙

Presents engaging problems and activities that extend the lesson concepts.

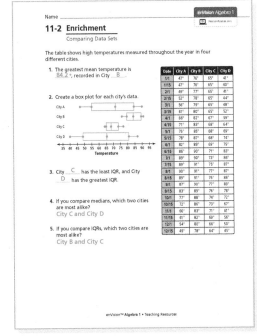

Name ______ enVision Algebra 1 PearsonRealize.com

11-2 Enrichment

Comparing Data Sets

The table shows high temperatures measured throughout the year in four different cities.

1. The greatest mean temperature is 84.2°, recorded in City B.

2. Create a box plot for each city's data.

   City A; City B; City C; City D; Temperature

3. City C has the least IQR, and City D has the greatest IQR.

4. If you compare medians, which two cities are most alike?
   City C and City D

5. If you compare IQRs, which two cities are most alike?
   City B and City C

Date	City A	City B	City C	City D
1/1	47°	76°	65°	41°
1/15	47°	76°	65°	40°
2/1	49°	77°	65°	41°
2/15	52°	78°	65°	44°
3/1	56°	79°	65°	48°
3/15	61°	80°	65°	52°
4/1	66°	82°	67°	59°
4/15	71°	83°	68°	64°
5/1	75°	85°	68°	69°
5/15	78°	87°	68°	74°
6/1	82°	89°	69°	79°
6/15	86°	90°	71°	83°
7/1	89°	90°	73°	86°
7/15	89°	91°	75°	87°
8/1	90°	91°	77°	87°
8/15	89°	91°	76°	86°
9/1	87°	90°	77°	83°
9/15	83°	89°	76°	78°
10/1	77°	88°	74°	72°
10/15	72°	86°	73°	67°
11/1	66°	83°	71°	61°
11/15	61°	82°	69°	56°
12/1	54°	80°	66°	50°
12/15	49°	78°	64°	45°

enVision™ Algebra 1 • Teaching Resources

Mathematical Literacy and Vocabulary I O

Helps students develop and reinforce understanding of key terms and concepts.

Name ______ enVision Algebra 1 PearsonRealize.com

11-2 Mathematical Literacy and Vocabulary

Comparing Data Sets

Concept List

mean	median
quartiles	range of a data set
mean absolute deviation (MAD)	interquartile range (IQR)

Choose the concept from the list that best represents the item in each box.

1. 34, 72, 29, 25, 13, 81, 56 81 − 13 = 68 range of a data set	2. 29, 7, 35, 29, 56, 12, 75, 26, 39, 8 $Q_3 - Q_1 = 39 - 12 = 27$ interquartile range (IQR)	3. 15, 17, 17, 19, 21, 23, 24 median
4. 44, 15, 76, 34, 91 44 + 15 + 76 + 34 + 91 = 260 260 ÷ 5 = 52 mean	5. 44, 15, 76, 34, 91 44 + 15 + 76 + 34 + 91 = 260 260 ÷ 5 = 52 |44 − 52| = 8 |15 − 52| = 37 |76 − 52| = 24 |34 − 52| = 18 |91 − 52| = 39 8 + 37 + 24 + 18 + 39 = 126 126 ÷ 5 = 25.2 mean absolute deviation (MAD)	6. 7, 9, 17, 26, 38, 40, 45, 53, 55, 62 Q1 = 17 Q2 = 39 Q3 = 53 Q4 = 62 quartiles

enVision™ Algebra 1 • Teaching Resources

Digital Resources and Video Tutorials I O A ⚙

The **Reteach to Build Understanding, Additional Practice**, and **Enrichment** activities are available as digital assignments powered by MathXL for School. These activities are automatically assigned when students complete the lesson quiz online and are automatically scored.

Students can access instructional tutorials using the **Virtual Nerd app**.

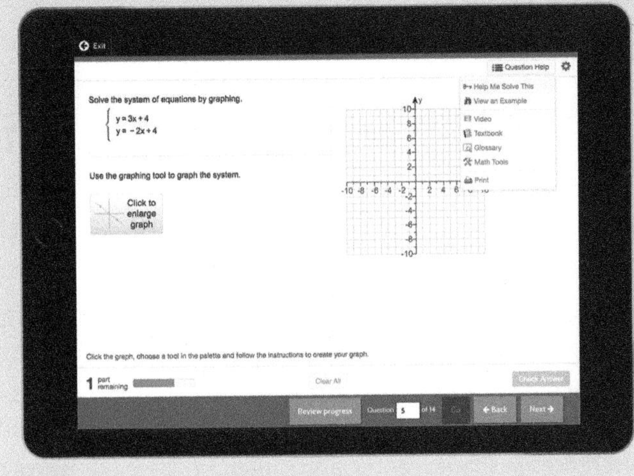
Exit
Question Help
Help Me Solve This
View an Example
Video
Textbook
Glossary
Math Tools
Print
Solve the system of equations by graphing.
y = 3x + 4
y = −2x + 4
Use the graphing tool to graph the system.
Click to enlarge graph
Click the graph, choose a tool in the palette and follow the instructions to create your graph.
1 part remaining
Clear All
Check Answer
Review progress
Back
Next

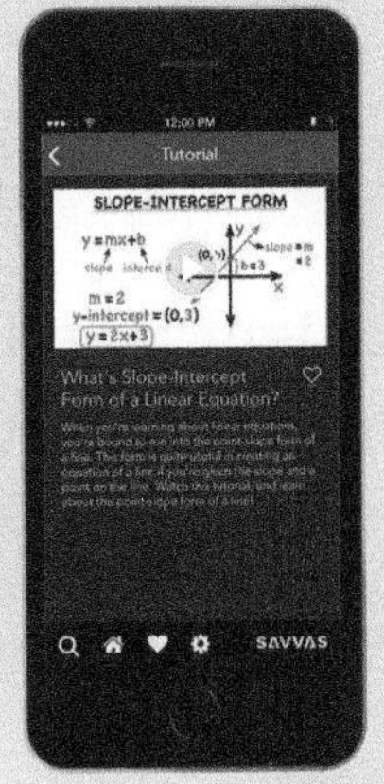
Tutorial
SLOPE-INTERCEPT FORM
What's Slope-Intercept Form of a Linear Equation?
SAVVAS

Students can also access Virtual Nerd videos using the **BouncePages app** to scan exercise pages marked with this icon. Students can download both apps for free in their mobile devices' app store.

Interpreting the Shapes of Data Displays

Glossary

Lesson Overview

FOCUS

Objective

Students will be able to:

✔ Interpret and compare differences in the shape, center, and spread of different data sets.

✔ Determine the relationship between the mean and median of a data set when the shape of the data display is evenly spread, skewed right, or skewed left.

Essential Understanding

When the shape of the data display is symmetric, the mean is approximately equal to the median. When the shape of the data display is skewed, the mean and median are not equal.

COHERENCE

Previously in this topic, students:

- Represented data using dot plots, histograms, and box plots.
- Interpreted measures of center and spread to compare data sets.

In this lesson, students:

- Interpret the shapes of a data displays, including dot plots, histograms, and box plots.
- Relate the shape of a data display to measures such as the mean, median, and MAD.

Later in this topic, students will:

- Interpret the variability of a data set using standard deviation.

RIGOR

This lesson emphasizes a blend of *conceptual understanding* and *application*.

- Students understand that the mean and median are approximately equal when the data are symmetric, and not equal when the data are skewed.
- Students interpret the shape of the distribution of real-world data, such as the weights of bagels created by a new process.

Vocabulary Builder

A-Z

REVIEW VOCABULARY — **English** | *Spanish*

- **histogram** | *histograma*
- **skewed** | *sesgada*

VOCABULARY ACTIVITY

Review the terms *histogram* and *skewed*. Discuss what it would mean if the data were skewed left or skewed right. Students may be confused by the use of the terms left or right and the appearance of the data display. Have students identify whether the histogram is skewed left or skewed right. Then, have them describe what a histogram skewed in the other direction would look like.

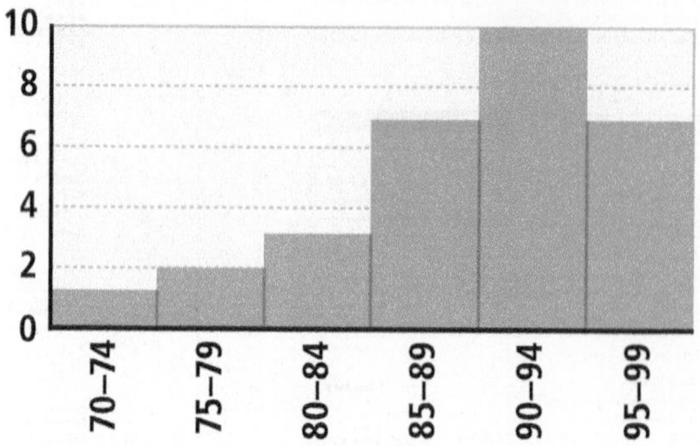
10
8
6
4
2
0
70–74
75–79
80–84
85–89
90–94
95–99

[skewed left; A histogram skewed right would have higher bars on the left and lower bars on the right.]

Student Companion

Students can do their in-class work for the lesson on pages 257–260 of their *Student Companion* or in Savvas Realize.

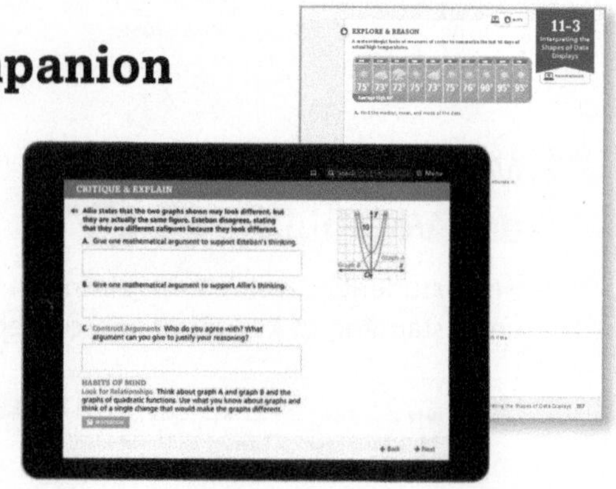

Mathematics Overview — COMMON CORE STANDARDS

Content Standards

In this lesson, students focus on these standards:

HSS.ID.A.2 Use statistics appropriate to the shape of the data distribution to compare center (median, mean) and spread (interquartile range, standard deviation) of two or more different data sets.

HSS.ID.A.3 Interpret differences in shape, center, and spread in the context of the data sets, accounting for possible effects of extreme data points (outliers).

Mathematical Practice Standards

These standards are highlighted in this lesson:

MP.2 Reason Abstractly and Quantitatively
Students attend to the meaning of quantities when they consider how sample size affects the inferences that can be made about the entire population.

MP.8 Look For and Express Regularity in Repeated Reasoning
Students generalize that when data are evenly distributed, the mean can be used to make an inference and when the data are skewed, they need to consider other measures.

SavvasRealize.com

Activity

EXPLORE & REASON

INSTRUCTIONAL FOCUS Students explore how to describe data using its mean, median, and mode. This leads them to make inferences about evenly distributed and skewed data based upon means and medians.

STUDENT COMPANION Students can complete the *Explore & Reason* activity on page 257 of their *Student Companion*.

Before — WHOLE CLASS

Implement Tasks that Promote Reasoning and Problem Solving ETP

Q: Describe the temperature of the last 10 days.
[The temperature is in the 70s for the first 7 days and then it spikes to the 90s for the last 3 days.]

During — SMALL GROUP

Support Productive Struggle in Learning Mathematics ETP

Q: What is one strategy to help remember the measures of center?
[Use key words to connect: mean-average, median-middle, mode-most.]

For Early Finishers

Q: Make a chart of 10 days of low temperatures in your area. Find the mean, median, and mode of your data.
[Check students' work.]

After — WHOLE CLASS

Facilitate Meaningful Mathematical Discourse ETP

Q: What do the mean and median tell you about data?
[Knowing the mean and median of a data set can help determine whether the data are evenly distributed or not.]

Q: What does the mode tell you about data?
[The mode tells you which data value occurs most often.]

HABITS OF MIND

Use with **EXPLORE & REASON**

Reason Explain how the central tendencies of the data would shift if the temperatures 90°, 95°, and 95° were not included. MP.2

[The mean would decrease and the median would stay the same. The mean would become about 74.1° and the median would stay at 75°.]

AVAILABLE **ONLINE**

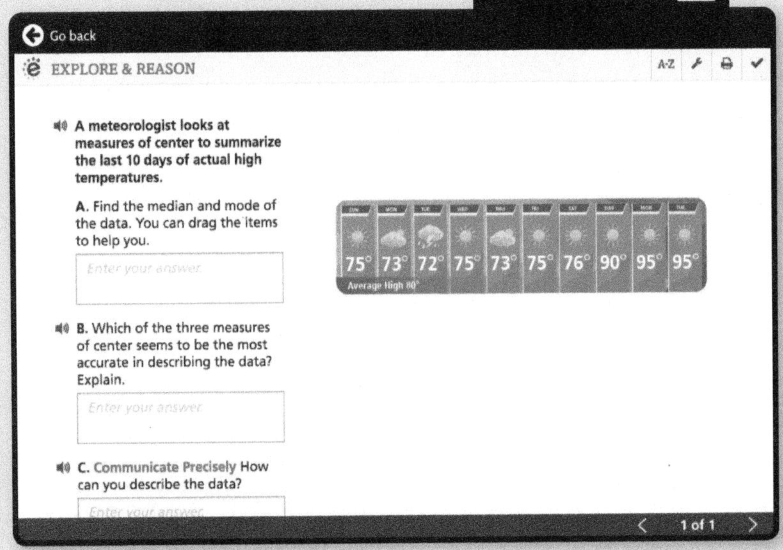

Go back
EXPLORE & REASON
A meteorologist looks at measures of center to summarize the last 10 days of actual high temperatures.
A. Find the median and mode of the data. You can drag the items to help you.
Enter your answer.
B. Which of the three measures of center seems to be the most accurate in describing the data? Explain.
Enter your answer.
C. Communicate Precisely How can you describe the data?
Enter your answer.
75° 73° 72° 75° 73° 75° 76° 90° 95° 95°
1 of 1

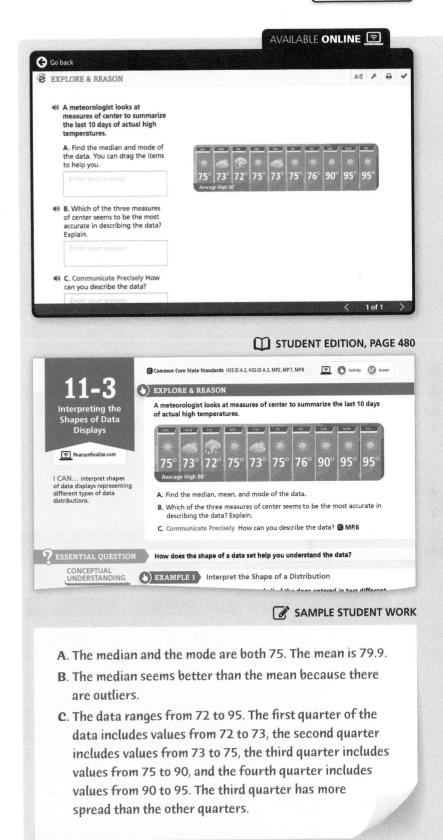

STUDENT EDITION, PAGE 480

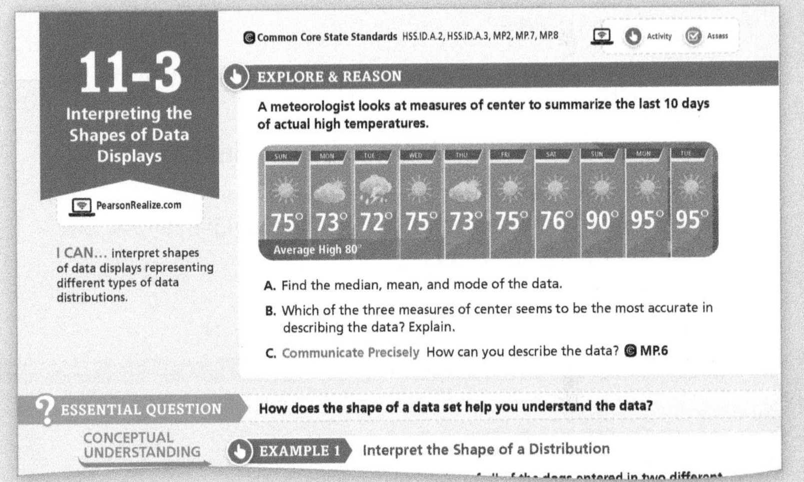

11-3
Interpreting the Shapes of Data Displays
PearsonRealize.com
I CAN… interpret shapes of data displays representing different types of data distributions.
Common Core State Standards HSS.ID.A.2, HSS.ID.A.3, MP.2, MP.7, MP.8
EXPLORE & REASON
A meteorologist looks at measures of center to summarize the last 10 days of actual high temperatures.
SUN MON TUE WED THU FRI SAT SUN MON TUE
75° 73° 72° 75° 73° 75° 76° 90° 95° 95°
Average High 80°
A. Find the median, mean, and mode of the data.
B. Which of the three measures of center seems to be the most accurate in describing the data? Explain.
C. Communicate Precisely How can you describe the data? MP.6
ESSENTIAL QUESTION How does the shape of a data set help you understand the data?
CONCEPTUAL UNDERSTANDING
EXAMPLE 1 Interpret the Shape of a Distribution

SAMPLE STUDENT WORK

A. The median and the mode are both 75. The mean is 79.9.

B. The median seems better than the mean because there are outliers.

C. The data ranges from 72 to 95. The first quarter of the data includes values from 72 to 73, the second quarter includes values from 73 to 75, the third quarter includes values from 75 to 90, and the fourth quarter includes values from 90 to 95. The third quarter has more spread than the other quarters.

Activity Assess

INTRODUCE THE ESSENTIAL QUESTION

Establish Mathematics Goals to Focus Learning ETP

Introduce students to interpreting and comparing histograms. Explain that histograms can be evenly distributed or skewed to the right or left, depending on the median and the mean.

EXAMPLE 1 Interpret the Shape of a Distribution

Build Procedural Fluency From Conceptual Understanding ETP

Q: When is a histogram symmetric?
[when the data are evenly distributed around the center]

Q: What does it mean that the mean and median are different in the second graph?
[Because the mean is greater than the median, the histogram shows data skewed to the right. This means that the data are not evenly distributed around the center.]

Try It! Answer

1. The histogram will be skewed right because the mean is greater than the median.

Elicit and Use Evidence of Student Thinking ETP

Q: What information is helpful in making your inference?
[The mean and median are in separate weight ranges, but they are both above 30.]

AVAILABLE ONLINE

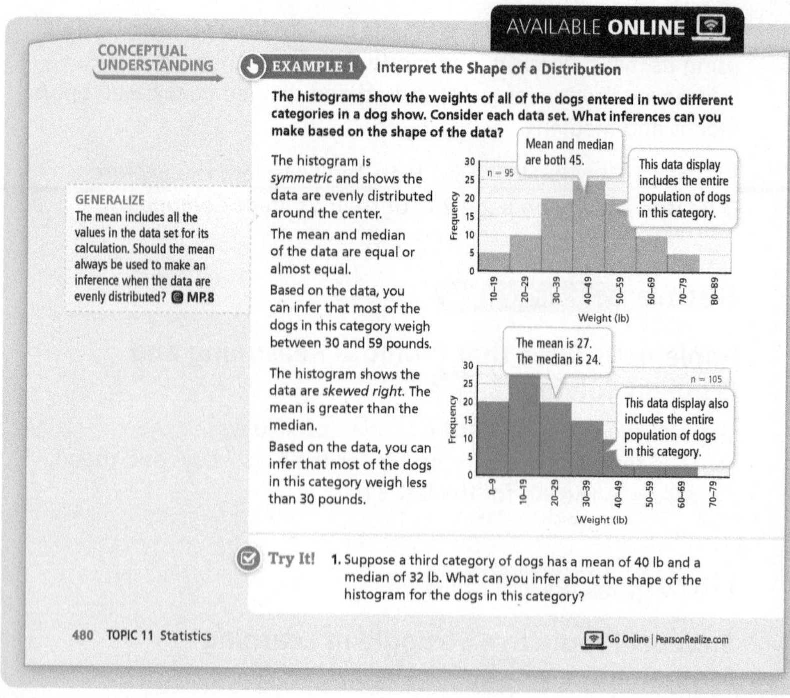
CONCEPTUAL UNDERSTANDING

EXAMPLE 1 Interpret the Shape of a Distribution

The histograms show the weights of all of the dogs entered in two different categories in a dog show. Consider each data set. What inferences can you make based on the shape of the data?

GENERALIZE The mean includes all the values in the data set for its calculation. Should the mean always be used to make an inference when the data are evenly distributed? MP.8

The histogram is *symmetric* and shows the data are evenly distributed around the center.

The mean and median of the data are equal or almost equal.

Based on the data, you can infer that most of the dogs in this category weigh between 30 and 59 pounds.

Mean and median are both 45.
n = 95
This data display includes the entire population of dogs in this category.
Frequency
30
25
20
15
10
5
0
10–19
20–29
30–39
40–49
50–59
60–69
70–79
80–89
Weight (lb)

The histogram shows the data are *skewed right*. The mean is greater than the median.

Based on the data, you can infer that most of the dogs in this category weigh less than 30 pounds.

The mean is 27.
The median is 24.
n = 105
This data display also includes the entire population of dogs in this category.
Frequency
30
25
20
15
10
5
0
0–9
10–19
20–29
30–39
40–49
50–59
60–69
70–79
Weight (lb)

Try It! 1. Suppose a third category of dogs has a mean of 40 lb and a median of 32 lb. What can you infer about the shape of the histogram for the dogs in this category?

480 TOPIC 11 Statistics

Go Online | PearsonRealize.com

Common Error

Try It! 1 Students may think that data *skewed right* means that most of the data is to the right of the mean or median. Have students create a list of sample data with a mean of 40 and a median of 32 and make a histogram for the data to check their reasoning.

AVAILABLE ONLINE

ADDITIONAL EXAMPLES

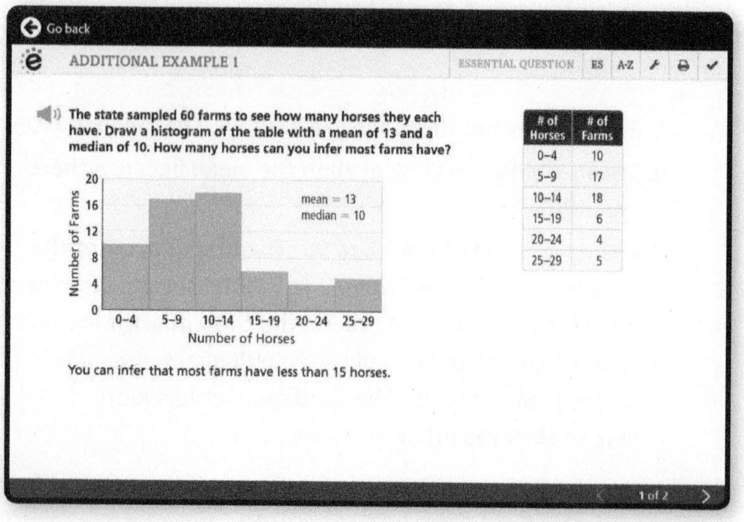
Go back
ADDITIONAL EXAMPLE 1
ESSENTIAL QUESTION ES A-Z
The state sampled 60 farms to see how many horses they each have. Draw a histogram of the table with a mean of 13 and a median of 10. How many horses can you infer most farms have?
# of Horses
# of Farms
0–4 10
5–9 17
10–14 18
15–19 6
20–24 4
25–29 5
Number of Farms
20
16
12
8
4
0
mean = 13
median = 10
0–4
5–9
10–14
15–19
20–24
25–29
Number of Horses
You can infer that most farms have less than 15 horses.
1 of 2

Example 1 Have students draw a histogram based on a table and interpret the shape.

Q: What do you notice about the shape of the histogram?
[The histogram is skewed to the right, so the mean is greater than the median.]

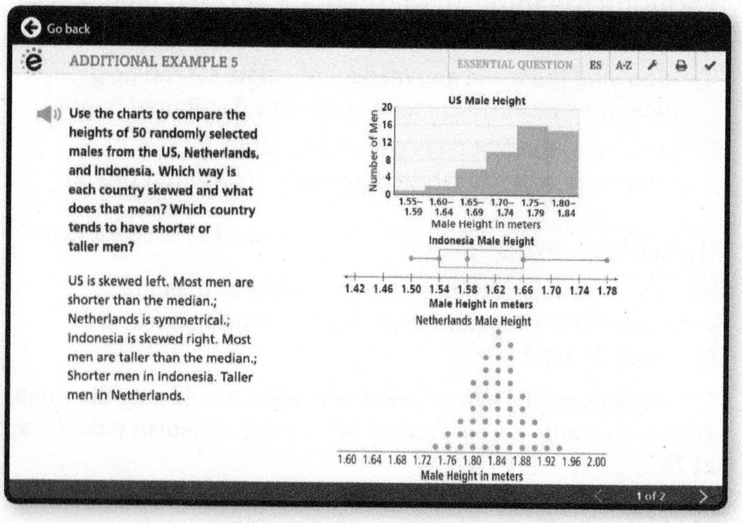
Go back
ADDITIONAL EXAMPLE 5
ESSENTIAL QUESTION ES A-Z
Use the charts to compare the heights of 50 randomly selected males from the US, Netherlands, and Indonesia. Which way is each country skewed and what does that mean? Which country tends to have shorter or taller men?
US is skewed left. Most men are shorter than the median.; Netherlands is symmetrical.; Indonesia is skewed right. Most men are taller than the median.; Shorter men in Indonesia. Taller men in Netherlands.
US Male Height
Number of Men
20
16
12
8
4
0
1.55–1.59
1.60–1.64
1.65–1.69
1.70–1.74
1.75–1.79
1.80–1.84
Male Height in meters
Indonesia Male Height
1.42 1.46 1.50 1.54 1.58 1.62 1.66 1.70 1.74 1.78
Male Height in meters
Netherlands Male Height
1.60 1.64 1.68 1.72 1.76 1.80 1.84 1.88 1.92 1.96 2.00
Male Height in meters
1 of 2

Example 5 Have students compare the shapes of data sets when the displays are different—box plots, dot plots, and histograms.

Q: Is height easily comparable?
[Yes, it is obvious which country has taller and shorter men. However, if you are asked questions about the exact number of men at a certain height, that would be difficult to determine for the U.S. and Indonesia.]

EXAMPLE 2 Interpret the Shape of a Skewed Data Display

Pose Purposeful Questions ETP

Q: When is the shape of the data display skewed left?
[The mean weight is less than the median weight.]

Q: Why is sample size important when making a conclusion?
[When a sample size is too small, it is not a good representation of the entire population.]

Try It! Answer

2. In this context, skewed data reduce the value of the mean.

HABITS OF MIND

Use with **EXAMPLES 1 & 2**

Construct Arguments A student reasons that because most of the data in a histogram lies on the right side of the graph, the data must be skewed right. Is this student correct? Justify your answer. **MP.3**

[No, the student is not correct. When more of the data lie on the right side of a graph, the data are skewed left, meaning the mean is less than the median.]

EXAMPLE 3 Compare Shapes of Skewed Data Displays

Use and Connect Mathematical Representations ETP

Q: Why does the mean weight change from the previous sample but the median weight stays the same?
[The middle value in both samples is the same, so the median weight is the same. The mean weight changes since each graph is skewed. The mean is lower when the graph is skewed left, and higher when skewed right.]

Q: Why does the manager not recommend changes based on this data?
[The mean from this data sample differs from the mean of the data from the first sample. Because the results are not consistent, the manager needs more samples.]

AVAILABLE ONLINE

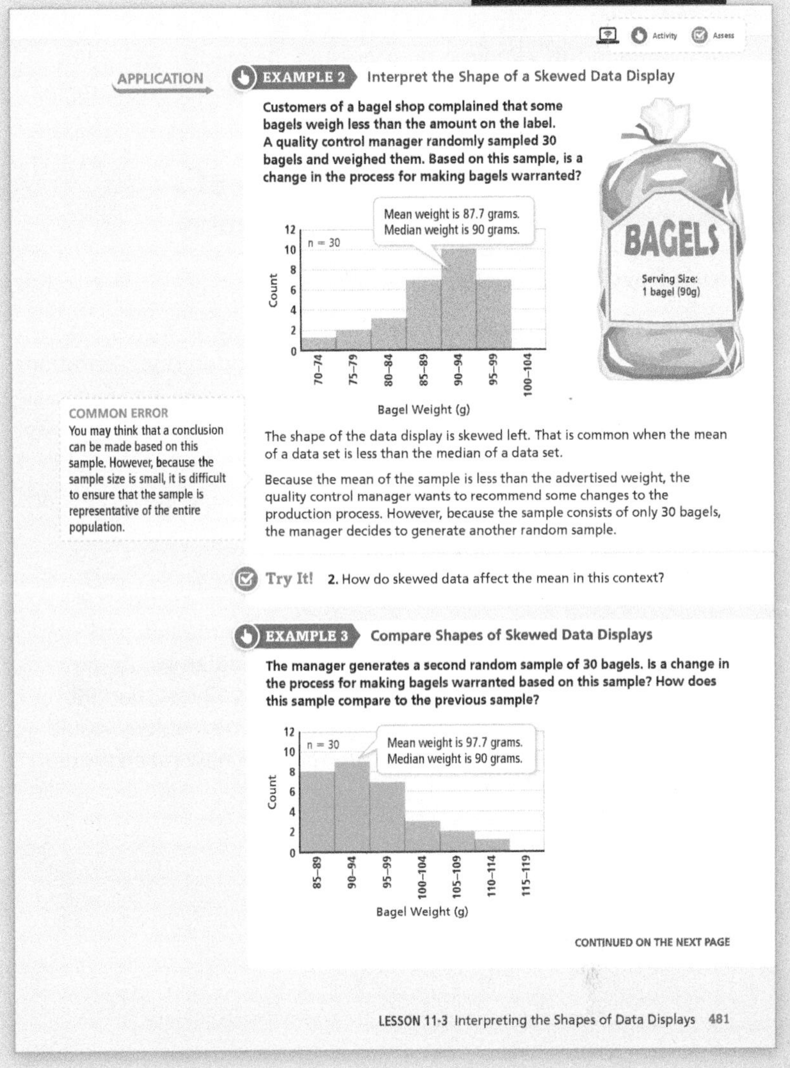
Activity Assess

APPLICATION

EXAMPLE 2 Interpret the Shape of a Skewed Data Display

Customers of a bagel shop complained that some bagels weigh less than the amount on the label. A quality control manager randomly sampled 30 bagels and weighed them. Based on this sample, is a change in the process for making bagels warranted?

Mean weight is 87.7 grams.
Median weight is 90 grams.
n = 30
Count
70–74
75–79
80–84
85–89
90–94
95–99
100–104
Bagel Weight (g)
BAGELS
Serving Size: 1 bagel (90g)

COMMON ERROR
You may think that a conclusion can be made based on this sample. However, because the sample size is small, it is difficult to ensure that the sample is representative of the entire population.

The shape of the data display is skewed left. That is common when the mean of a data set is less than the median of a data set.

Because the mean of the sample is less than the advertised weight, the quality control manager wants to recommend some changes to the production process. However, because the sample consists of only 30 bagels, the manager decides to generate another random sample.

Try It! 2. How do skewed data affect the mean in this context?

EXAMPLE 3 Compare Shapes of Skewed Data Displays

The manager generates a second random sample of 30 bagels. Is a change in the process for making bagels warranted based on this sample? How does this sample compare to the previous sample?

Mean weight is 97.7 grams.
Median weight is 90 grams.
n = 30
Count
85–89
90–94
95–99
100–104
105–109
110–114
115–119
Bagel Weight (g)

CONTINUED ON THE NEXT PAGE

LESSON 11-3 Interpreting the Shapes of Data Displays 481

Struggling Students

USE WITH EXAMPLE 2 Some students may not understand what it means for graphs to be skewed to the right or left. Have students practice interpreting the shapes of data with guidance.

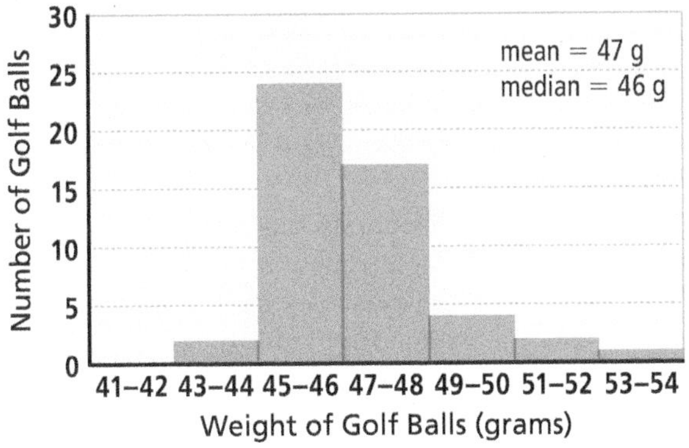
mean = 47 g
median = 46 g
Number of Golf Balls
30
25
20
15
10
5
0
41–42
43–44
45–46
47–48
49–50
51–52
53–54
Weight of Golf Balls (grams)

- A golf retailer is concerned that the golf balls are heavier than the allowed weight of 46 g. The histogram provides you with the weight of 50 randomly selected golf balls.

Q: Is the graph skewed right or left?
[right]

Q: What does this indicate about the mean and median?
[The mean weight of the golf balls is greater than the median weight.]

Q: Can you determine if they need to make manufacturing changes based on this sample?
[No; the sample size is too small and not representative of the entire population.]

Activity Assess

EXAMPLE 3 CONTINUED

Try It! Answers

3. Since the data are skewed right, the average weight of the bagels in this sample is greater than the median weight of the bagels. The average weight of the bagels in this sample is greater than the advertised weight.

EXAMPLE 4 Interpret the Shape of a Symmetric Data Display

Pose Purposeful Questions ETP

Q: Why is using a larger sample size beneficial?
[A larger sample size provides you with a good representation of the entire population.]

Q: What does it mean if the data points are symmetrically distributed around the center?
[The mean and median are the same or close, and the data are evenly distributed around the center.]

Try It! Answer

4. Adding 5 data values that are less than the median and 5 data values that are greater than the median would not affect the median. However, because 78 is 12 less than 90, but 106 is 16 greater than 90, adding the new values would affect the mean by making it greater. The new mean would be about 90.3.

AVAILABLE ONLINE

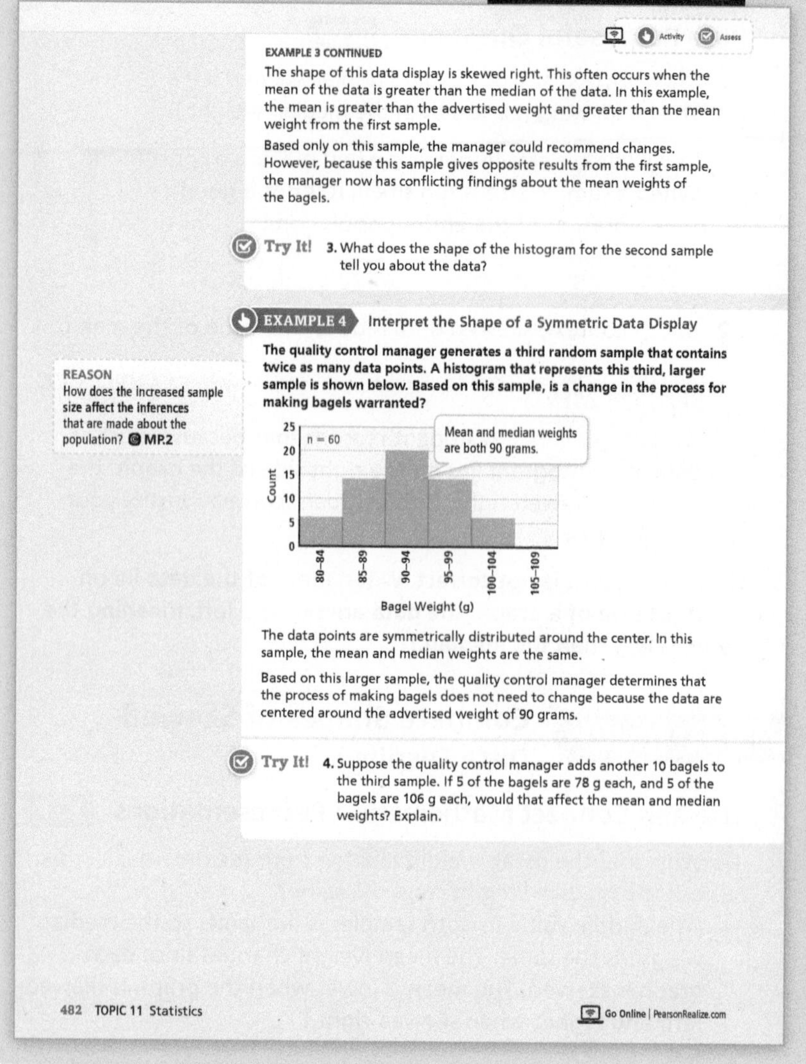
Activity Assess

EXAMPLE 3 CONTINUED

The shape of this data display is skewed right. This often occurs when the mean of the data is greater than the median of the data. In this example, the mean is greater than the advertised weight and greater than the mean weight from the first sample.

Based only on this sample, the manager could recommend changes. However, because this sample gives opposite results from the first sample, the manager now has conflicting findings about the mean weights of the bagels.

Try It! 3. What does the shape of the histogram for the second sample tell you about the data?

EXAMPLE 4 Interpret the Shape of a Symmetric Data Display

The quality control manager generates a third random sample that contains twice as many data points. A histogram that represents this third, larger sample is shown below. Based on this sample, is a change in the process for making bagels warranted?

REASON
How does the increased sample size affect the inferences that are made about the population? MP.2

25
20
15
10
5
0
Count
n = 60
Mean and median weights are both 90 grams.
80–84
85–89
90–94
95–99
100–104
105–109
Bagel Weight (g)

The data points are symmetrically distributed around the center. In this sample, the mean and median weights are the same.

Based on this larger sample, the quality control manager determines that the process of making bagels does not need to change because the data are centered around the advertised weight of 90 grams.

Try It! 4. Suppose the quality control manager adds another 10 bagels to the third sample. If 5 of the bagels are 78 g each, and 5 of the bagels are 106 g each, would that affect the mean and median weights? Explain.

482 TOPIC 11 Statistics

Go Online | PearsonRealize.com

ADV Advanced Students

USE WITH EXAMPLE 3 Students first explore creating a histogram, and then comparing their results to given data.

Q: Create a histogram of the given weights, in grams, of golf balls. [Check students' graph.]

43, 45, 41, 44, 45, 43, 45, 39, 44, 45, 43, 45, 43, 45, 41, 46, 42, 45, 37, 43, 45, 40, 41, 42, 45

Q: What is the mean and median of the histogram you created?
[mean = 43.1 g and median = 43 g]

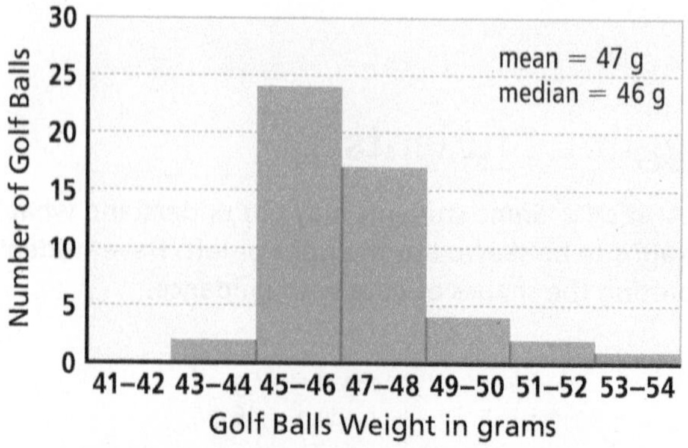

30
25
20
15
10
5
0
Number of Golf Balls
mean = 47 g
median = 46 g
41–42 43–44 45–46 47–48 49–50 51–52 53–54
Golf Balls Weight in grams

Q: How does the information in the histogram you created compare to the given histogram?
[The sample size for the given histogram is greater, so it is difficult to compare the histograms. However, the given histogram is skewed right, so the mean is greater than the median. The mean and the median for the histogram are nearly equal.]

SavvasRealize.com

Activity Assess

EXAMPLE 5 Comparing the Shapes of Data Sets

Build Procedural Fluency From Conceptual Understanding ETP

Q: Would it be better to work for a school district whose salaries are skewed to the right or left?
[Skewed to the left; most teachers have salaries higher than the mean. This indicates that more teachers make a higher salary.]

Q: If Jennifer only looks at the salary of the highest-paid teacher in each district, how is this misleading?
[Although the teacher with the highest salary in School District 201 makes more than the highest-paid teacher in School District 101, the average teacher salary in School District 101 is higher than that in School District 201.]

Try It! Answer

5. No, because the mean is so much greater than the median, it indicates that the teacher's salaries in School District 401 are skewed right. The mean is likely higher than some of the other school districts because there are a couple of teachers at the high end of the salary scale. However, half of the teachers earn below $49,000, so Jennifer should still consider School District 101 or School District 301 instead.

HABITS OF MIND

Use with **EXAMPLES 3–5**

Reason **If the mean and median of a set of data are equal, or nearly equal, are the data necessarily symmetric? Explain. MP.2**

[Yes. In order for the mean and the median to be equal the values above and below the mean must balance each other out, which only happens if the data are symmetric.]

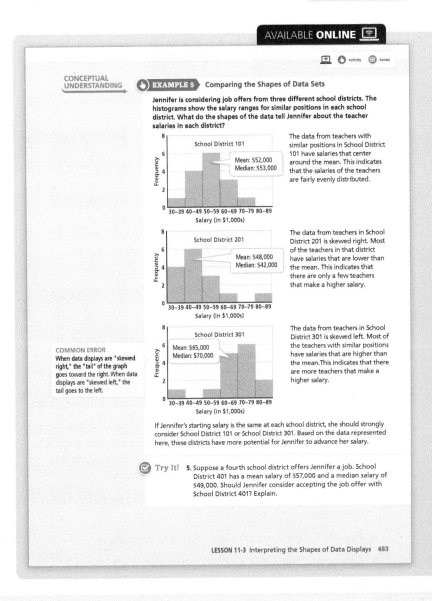

AVAILABLE **ONLINE**

Activity Assess

CONCEPTUAL UNDERSTANDING

EXAMPLE 5 Comparing the Shapes of Data Sets

Jennifer is considering job offers from three different school districts. The histograms show the salary ranges for similar positions in each school district. What do the shapes of the data tell Jennifer about the teacher salaries in each district?

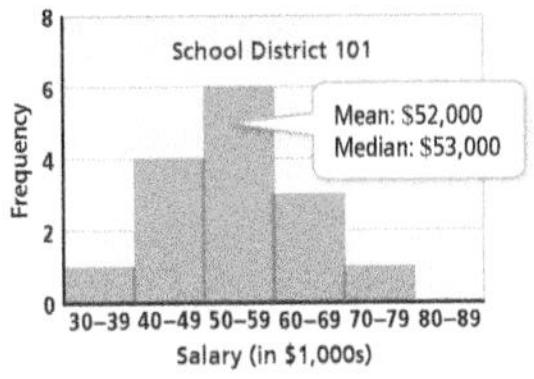
School District 101
Mean: $52,000
Median: $53,000
Frequency
8
6
4
2
0
30–39 40–49 50–59 60–69 70–79 80–89
Salary (in $1,000s)

The data from teachers with similar positions in School District 101 have salaries that center around the mean. This indicates that the salaries of the teachers are fairly evenly distributed.

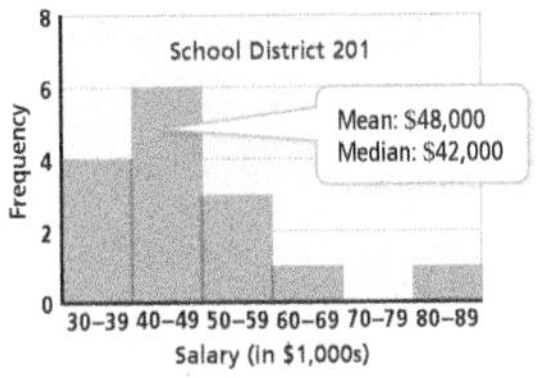
School District 201
Mean: $48,000
Median: $42,000
Frequency
8
6
4
2
0
30–39 40–49 50–59 60–69 70–79 80–89
Salary (in $1,000s)

The data from teachers in School District 201 is skewed right. Most of the teachers in that district have salaries that are lower than the mean. This indicates that there are only a few teachers that make a higher salary.

COMMON ERROR
When data displays are "skewed right," the "tail" of the graph goes toward the right. When data displays are "skewed left," the tail goes to the left.

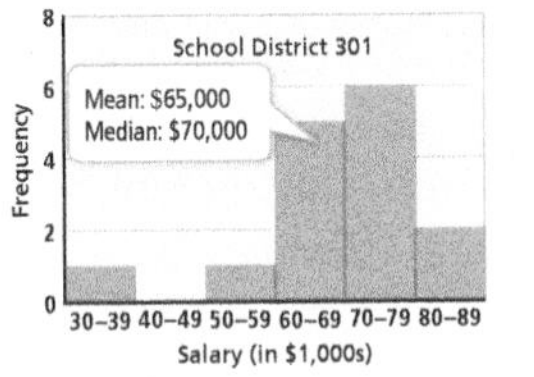
School District 301
Mean: $65,000
Median: $70,000
Frequency
8
6
4
2
0
30–39 40–49 50–59 60–69 70–79 80–89
Salary (in $1,000s)

The data from teachers in School District 301 is skewed left. Most of the teachers with similar positions have salaries that are higher than the mean.This indicates that there are more teachers that make a higher salary.

If Jennifer's starting salary is the same at each school district, she should strongly consider School District 101 or School District 301. Based on the data represented here, these districts have more potential for Jennifer to advance her salary.

Try It! **5. Suppose a fourth school district offers Jennifer a job. School District 401 has a mean salary of $57,000 and a median salary of $49,000. Should Jennifer consider accepting the job offer with School District 401? Explain.**

LESSON 11-3 Interpreting the Shapes of Data Displays 483

ELL English Language Learners *(Use with* **EXAMPLE 5***)*

READING BEGINNING Have students read the last sentence of the example. Then, display two definitions of *advance* for students to read: to move forward; to pay someone a sum of money earlier than arranged.

Q: How does the word *advance*, as used in the example, relate to the definitions you read?
[Jennifer would be moving forward in terms of making more money. And, she may make a larger sum of money earlier in her career than she would working for another district.]

SPEAKING INTERMEDIATE In pairs, have students discuss different meanings of the word *range*.

Q: How is the use of the word *range* as it pertains to statistics different from the use of the word when it pertains to functions?
[The *range* in statitistics is a number that shows how far the data values are spread apart while the *range* of a function includes all the values that can be output.]

Q: Does the word *ranges* in the example align with the statistical definition of range?
[No; in the example, ranges means the intervals over which the data are split.]

WRITING ADVANCED Have students practice their writing skills to explain whether the histograms can help Jennifer predict her future salary.

Q: Are the histograms useful tools for predicting the future?
[No; the histograms only provide a snapshot of the current situation.]

Q: How might the histograms for School District 101 and School District 301 look different 10 years from now?
[As older teachers retire from School District 301 and new teachers are hired, the histogram for this disctrict may be more symmetrical. As the teachers of School District 101 gain seniority, the histogram for this district may become skewed left.]

CONCEPT SUMMARY Interpreting the Shapes of Data Displays

Q: What does it mean if the data are skewed?
[The data values are unevenly spread on either side of the center. The mean and median are not equal.]

Do You UNDERSTAND? | Do You KNOW HOW?

Common Error

Exercise 6 Some students may interpret the graph as being skewed left since the bars are taller on the left. Remind students that shorter bars on the right indicate the data are skewed right. This usually means that the mean is greater than the median.

Answers

1. The shape of a data set can help you understand relationships between measures of center and spread. For example, when the data are symmetrically distributed, the mean and median are about the same. However, the mean is less than the median if the data are skewed left and greater if the data are skewed right.
2. All three displays show the shape of a data set. Dot plots and histograms show the shape, or frequency, vertically; a box plot shows the shape with a box and whiskers.
3. No; the display for a normal distribution is symmetric about the mean.
4. Skewed left; the mean is less than the median.
5. Symmetric; the mean and the median are both about 12.
6. Skewed right; the mean is greater than the median.

AVAILABLE ONLINE

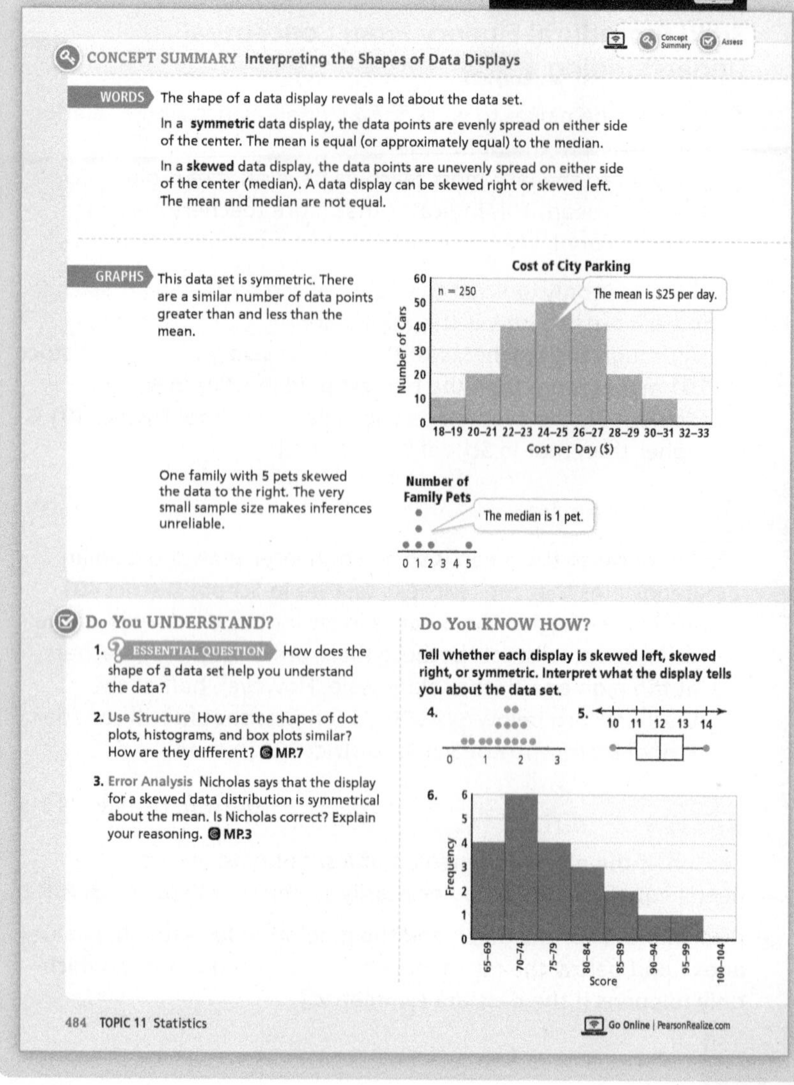

CONCEPT SUMMARY Interpreting the Shapes of Data Displays

WORDS The shape of a data display reveals a lot about the data set.

In a **symmetric** data display, the data points are evenly spread on either side of the center. The mean is equal (or approximately equal) to the median.

In a **skewed** data display, the data points are unevenly spread on either side of the center (median). A data display can be skewed right or skewed left. The mean and median are not equal.

GRAPHS This data set is symmetric. There are a similar number of data points greater than and less than the mean.

Cost of City Parking
n = 250
The mean is $25 per day.
Number of Cars
Cost per Day ($)

One family with 5 pets skewed the data to the right. The very small sample size makes inferences unreliable.

Number of Family Pets
The median is 1 pet.

Do You UNDERSTAND?

1. ESSENTIAL QUESTION How does the shape of a data set help you understand the data?
2. Use Structure How are the shapes of dot plots, histograms, and box plots similar? How are they different? MP.7
3. Error Analysis Nicholas says that the display for a skewed data distribution is symmetrical about the mean. Is Nicholas correct? Explain your reasoning. MP.3

Do You KNOW HOW?

Tell whether each display is skewed left, skewed right, or symmetric. Interpret what the display tells you about the data set.

4.
5.
6.

Frequency
Score

484 TOPIC 11 Statistics

Go Online | PearsonRealize.com

PRACTICE & PROBLEM SOLVING

AVAILABLE ONLINE

Lesson Practice You may opt to have students complete the automatically scored Practice and Problem Solving items online powered by MathXL for School.

Choose from: **Lesson Practice**

Adaptive Practice

You may also take advantage of the bank of exercises for assigning additional practice.

Assignment Guide

Basic	Advanced
7–14, 16–22	7–12, 14–22

Item Analysis

Example	Items	DOK
1	10	3
2	7, 9	3
3	14	1
	8	3
4	13, 20, 21	1
	15, 16	2
	11, 12	3
5	17–19, 22	3

AVAILABLE ONLINE

PRACTICE & PROBLEM SOLVING

Scan for Multimedia

Practice Tutorial

Additional Exercises Available Online

UNDERSTAND

7. Construct Arguments A student in your class does not understand why the mean is less than the median when a data display is skewed left. How can you explain this relationship to the student? MP.3

8. Look for Relationships Two data sets have the same median. If one data set is skewed right and the other is skewed left, how are the means of the two data sets related? MP.7

9. Error Analysis Describe and correct the error(s) a student made in interpreting the shape of a box plot. MP.3

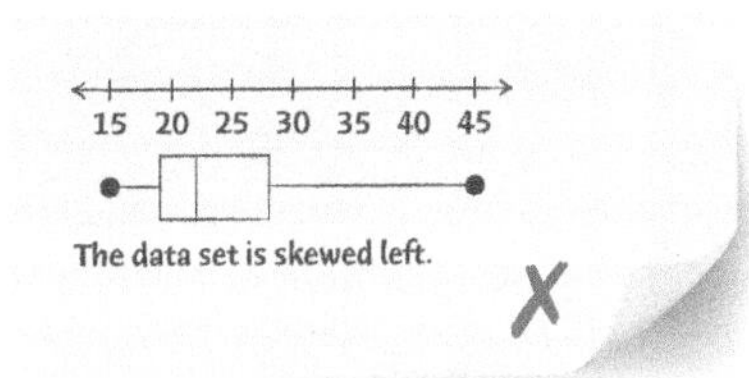
15 20 25 30 35 40 45
The data set is skewed left.

10. Reason Two data sets both have a mean of 10. The first set has a MAD of 1.5, and the second has a MAD of 3. How are the shapes of the data displays similar? How are they different? MP.2

11. Higher Order Thinking Data display A is symmetric with a mean of 50 and a MAD of 5. Data display B is symmetric with a mean of 75 and a MAD of 5.

a. How are the data displays similar? How are they different?

b. If the shapes of the displays are not identical, how could values in data set B be changed so that the displays are exactly the same?

12. Make Sense and Persevere The data represent the average number of hours 12 students spend on homework each night. Create two different data sets that could be represented by the display. MP.1

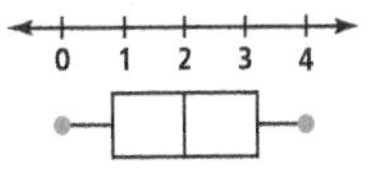
0 1 2 3 4

PRACTICE

Compare each pair of data displays. Tell whether each display is skewed left, skewed right, or symmetric. SEE EXAMPLES 1–3

13. Data Set A

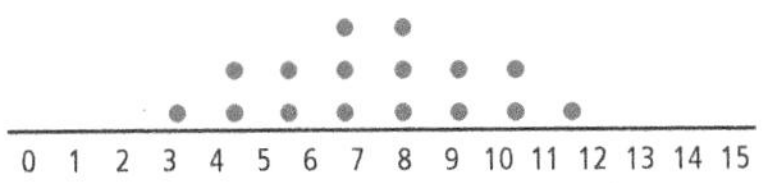
0 1 2 3 4 5 6 7 8 9 10 11 12 13 14 15

Data Set B

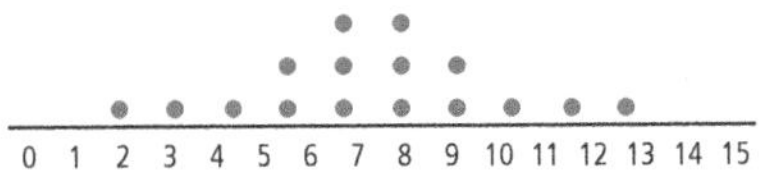
0 1 2 3 4 5 6 7 8 9 10 11 12 13 14 15

14. Data Set A

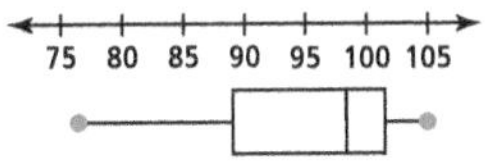
75 80 85 90 95 100 105

Data Set B

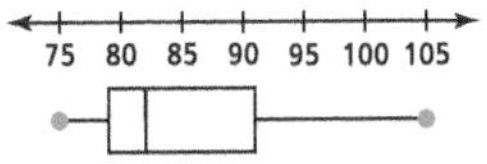
75 80 85 90 95 100 105

Interpret the shape of each display for the given context and make an inference based on a measure of center. SEE EXAMPLES 4 AND 5

15. The data represent amounts raised by students for a charity.

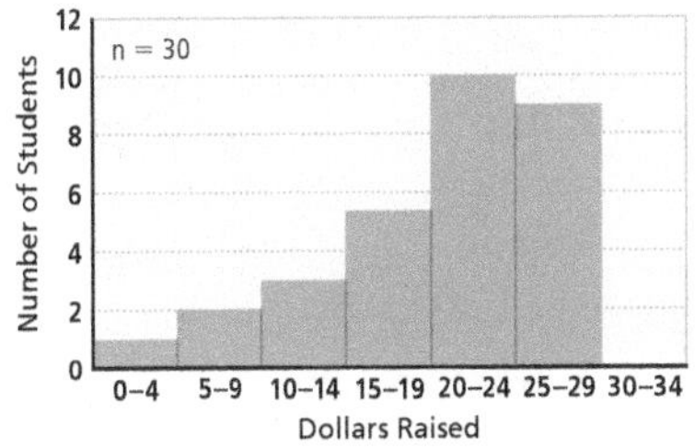
n = 30
Number of Students
0 2 4 6 8 10 12
0–4 5–9 10–14 15–19 20–24 25–29 30–34
Dollars Raised

16. The data represent thousands of points scored in a video game tournament.

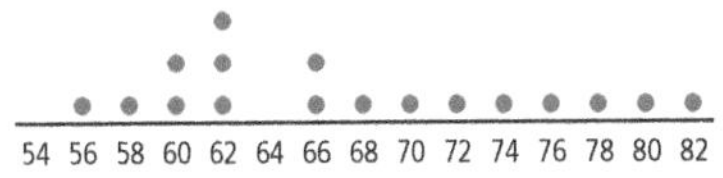
54 56 58 60 62 64 66 68 70 72 74 76 78 80 82

Answers

7. Suppose two data sets have the same mean and median. If a much lower data value is substituted for one of the data values in the lower half of the ordered set, then the median will stay the same, but the mean will decrease.

8. The mean of the first data set is greater than the mean of the second data set.

9. The display represents a data set that is skewed right.

10. On average, the values in the second set deviate more from the mean, so the second display is more spread out than the first.

11. a. Both displays are symmetrical about the mean, and both have the same spread, but display A is 25 units to the left of display B on a number line.

b. Answers may vary. Sample: If set B did not have the same shape as set A, you could form a new set B by subtracting 25 from every data value in set B. Then display B would have the same shape as display A.

12. Answers may vary. Sample:
data set A: 0, 1, 1, 1, 2, 2, 2, 2, 3, 3, 3, 4
data set B: 0, 0, 1, 1, 1, 2, 2, 3, 3, 3, 4, 4

13. Both data sets are symmetric and have the same mean and median, but data set B has a greater MAD.

14. Data set A is skewed left, while data set B is skewed right. The mean of data set A is less than the median, while the mean of data set B is greater than the median.

15. The data display is skewed left. The mean amount raised is less than the median.

16. The graph is skewed right. The mean score is greater than the median score.

Answers

17. The display for year 1 is skewed right, so the mean house price was greater than the median house price. The display for year 2 is close to symmetrical, so the mean house price and the median house price were about the same.

18. Both displays look the same for heights greater than 66 inches. However, the first display is close to being symmetrical about 67 inches because there were more students with heights shorter than 66 in that sample.

19. The display for Test 1 is symmetrical, so the mean and median are close to equal. The median is about 525, Q1 is 400, and Q3 is 600. A student who takes Test 1 is likely to get a score between 400 and 600 and is also likely to score close to the mean score of 525. For Test 2, the median is about 450, Q1 is 400, and Q3 is 525. These are lower than the scores for Test 1, so a person who takes Test 1 is more likely to get a higher score. Also, the display for Test 2 is skewed to the right, so the mean is greater than the median. A student who takes Test 2 is less likely to have a score close to the mean than a student who takes Test 1.

22. Part A Test 1 mean: 1,000; MAD: 40; median: 1,000; IQR: 100;
Test 2 mean: 1,000; MAD: about 16.7; median: 1,000; IQR: 50

Part B The mean and median are the same for each data set, so a box plot will show if the middle 50% of values are in the acceptable range of plus or minus 50 hours.

Test 1

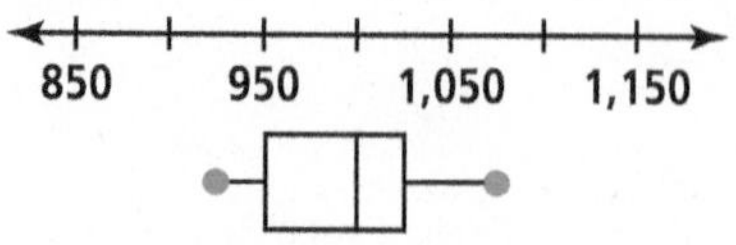
850
950
1,050
1,150

Test 2

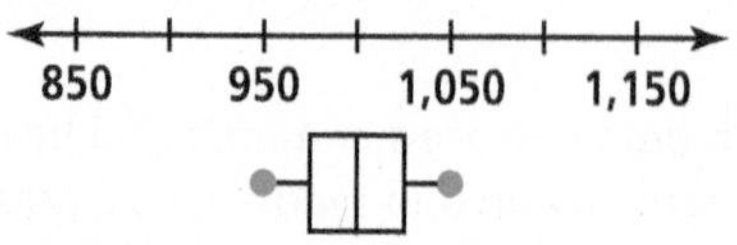
850
950
1,050
1,150

Part C The data from both tests are symmetrical with a median of 1,000. Fifty percent of the lights from Test 1 lasted between 950 and 1,150 hours. So, only 50% of the lights from Test 1 were within the acceptable range of 1,000 hours plus or minus 50 hours. All of the lights from Test 2 were within the acceptable range.

AVAILABLE **ONLINE**

PRACTICE & PROBLEM SOLVING

Practice Tutorial

Mixed Review Available Online

APPLY

17. Mathematical Connections The displays represent house prices in a town over two consecutive years. What do the displays tell you about the change in house prices in the two years?

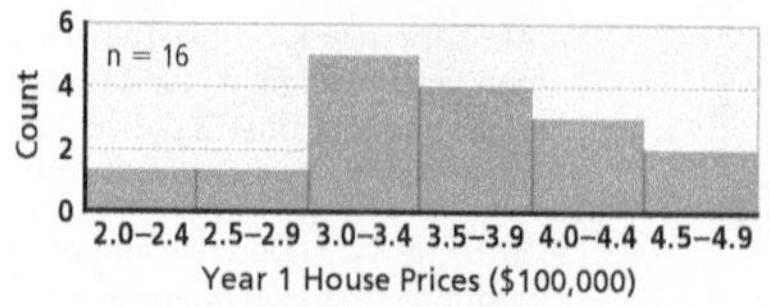
Count
n = 16
0
2
4
6
2.0–2.4 2.5–2.9 3.0–3.4 3.5–3.9 4.0–4.4 4.5–4.9
Year 1 House Prices ($100,000)

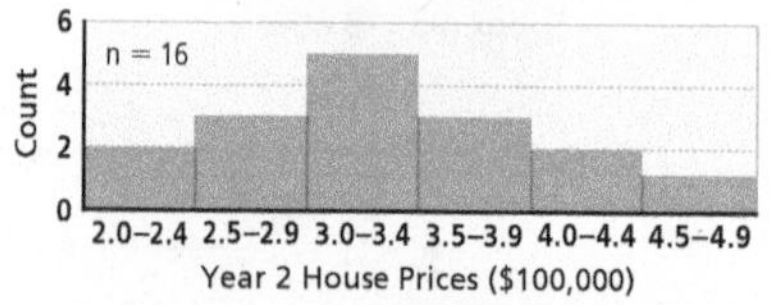
Count
n = 16
0
2
4
6
2.0–2.4 2.5–2.9 3.0–3.4 3.5–3.9 4.0–4.4 4.5–4.9
Year 2 House Prices ($100,000)

18. Make Sense and Persevere Amelia gathered data about the heights of students at her school. Based on the displays, what inferences can you make about each sample? MP.1

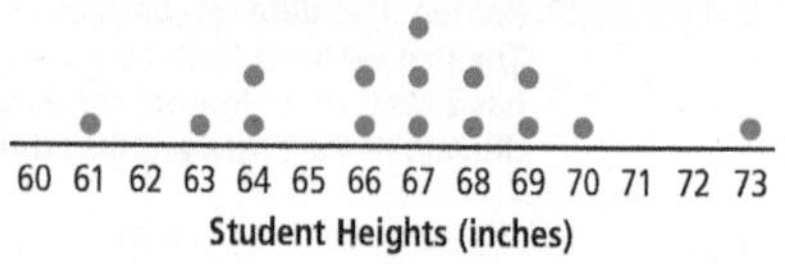
60 61 62 63 64 65 66 67 68 69 70 71 72 73
Student Heights (inches)

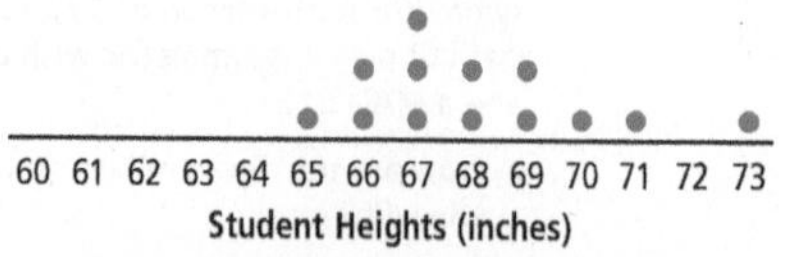
60 61 62 63 64 65 66 67 68 69 70 71 72 73
Student Heights (inches)

19. Make Sense and Persevere The displays show scores on two versions of a test. On which test is a randomly selected student more likely to get a higher score? On which version is a randomly selected student more likely to have a score close to the mean? Explain. MP.1

Test 1

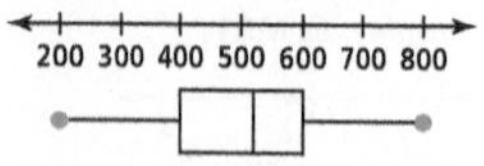
200 300 400 500 600 700 800

Test 2

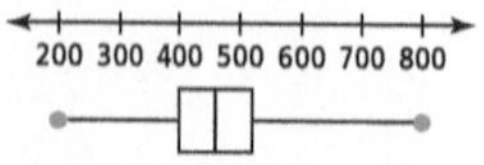
200 300 400 500 600 700 800

ASSESSMENT PRACTICE

20. A data display is symmetrical about the data value 10. Select all that apply.
- Ⓐ The mean is about 10.
- Ⓑ The median is about 10.
- Ⓒ The mean must be greater than the median.
- Ⓓ The median must be greater than the mean.
- Ⓔ The majority of data values in the data set are greater than 10.

21. SAT/ACT The shape of a data set is relatively symmetrical. What does that indicate about the measures of center?
- Ⓐ The mean is less than the median.
- Ⓑ The mean is greater than the median.
- Ⓒ The mean and the median are exactly the same.
- Ⓓ The mean and the median are close in value.

22. Performance Task Strings of decorative mini lights are supposed to last 1,000 hours, with an acceptable error of plus or minus 50 hours. Data from two quality control tests are given.

Mini Lights Lifespan

TEST 1				
975	1,025	950	950	975
1,050	925	1,050	1,025	1,050
1,000	1,075	975	950	1,025

TEST 2				
975	1,000	1,025	1,000	1,000
1,025	1,000	950	975	1,025
1,000	975	1,050	1,000	1,000

Part A Find the mean, MAD, median, and IQR for each data set.

Part B Select the type of data display that you think will best allow you to compare the data sets. Explain your reasoning. Create the data displays.

Part C Interpret and compare the shapes of the data displays. What do the displays tell you about the quality of the mini lights?

Go Online | PearsonRealize.com

LESSON QUIZ

Use the Lesson Quiz to assess students' understanding of the mathematics in the lesson.

Students can take the Lesson Quiz online or you can download a printable copy from **SavvasRealize.com**. The Lesson Quiz is also available in the *Assessment Resources* book.

Item Analysis

Item	DOK	Standards
1	1	HSS.ID.A.3
2	1	HSS.ID.A.3
3	2	HSS.ID.A.2
4	1	HSS.ID.A.3
5	1	HSS.ID.A.2

RtI Use the student scores on the Lesson Quiz to prescribe differentiated assignments.

If students take the Lesson Quiz online, it will be automatically scored and appropriate differentiated practice will be assigned based on student performance.

I Intervention	0–3 points	• Reteach to Build Understanding • Mathematical Literacy and Vocabulary • Additional Practice
O On-Level	4 points	• Mathematical Literacy and Vocabulary • Additional Practice • Enrichment
A Advanced	5 points	• Enrichment

AVAILABLE **ONLINE**

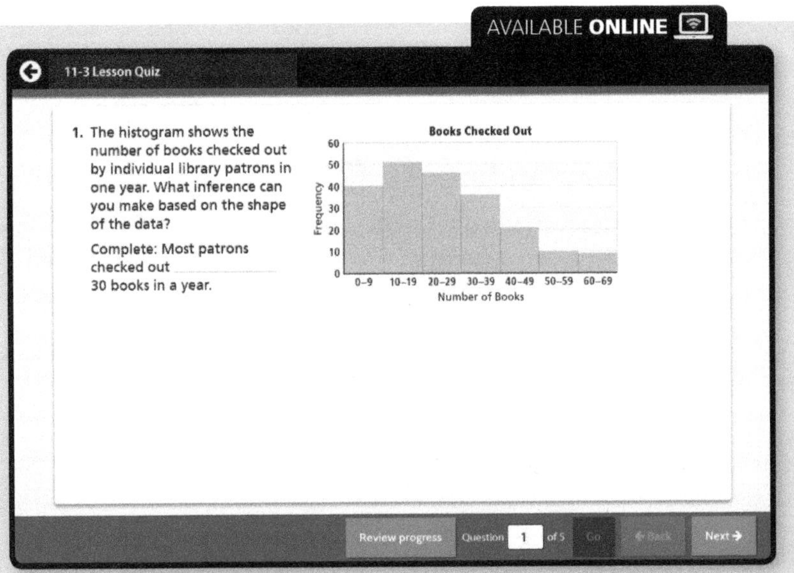
11-3 Lesson Quiz

1. The histogram shows the number of books checked out by individual library patrons in one year. What inference can you make based on the shape of the data?

Complete: Most patrons checked out ______ 30 books in a year.

Books Checked Out
Frequency
Number of Books
0–9 10–19 20–29 30–39 40–49 50–59 60–69
Review progress
Question 1 of 5
Go
Back
Next

ASSESSMENT RESOURCES

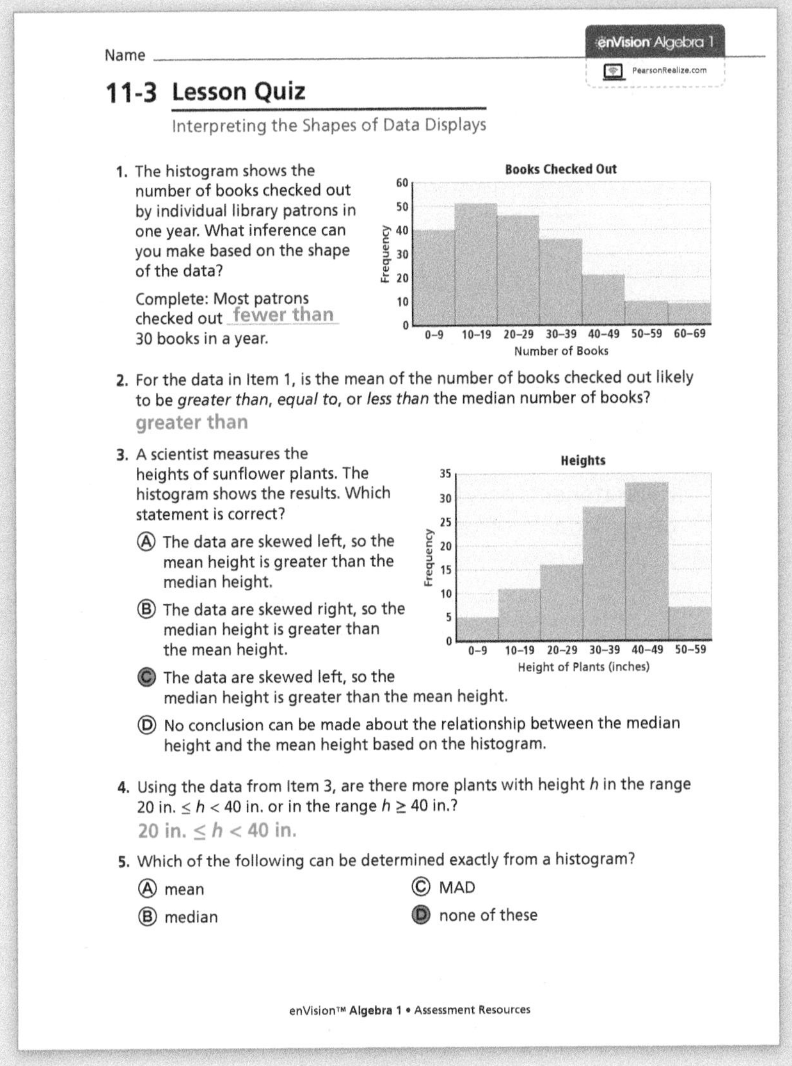
Name ______

enVision Algebra 1

PearsonRealize.com

11-3 Lesson Quiz

Interpreting the Shapes of Data Displays

1. The histogram shows the number of books checked out by individual library patrons in one year. What inference can you make based on the shape of the data?

Complete: Most patrons checked out fewer than 30 books in a year.

Books Checked Out
Frequency
0 10 20 30 40 50 60
0–9 10–19 20–29 30–39 40–49 50–59 60–69
Number of Books

2. For the data in Item 1, is the mean of the number of books checked out likely to be *greater than*, *equal to*, or *less than* the median number of books?

greater than

3. A scientist measures the heights of sunflower plants. The histogram shows the results. Which statement is correct?

Ⓐ The data are skewed left, so the mean height is greater than the median height.

Ⓑ The data are skewed right, so the median height is greater than the mean height.

Ⓒ The data are skewed left, so the median height is greater than the mean height.

Ⓓ No conclusion can be made about the relationship between the median height and the mean height based on the histogram.

Heights
Frequency
0 5 10 15 20 25 30 35
0–9 10–19 20–29 30–39 40–49 50–59
Height of Plants (inches)

4. Using the data from Item 3, are there more plants with height h in the range 20 in. $\leq h < 40$ in. or in the range $h \geq 40$ in.?

20 in. $\leq h < 40$ in.

5. Which of the following can be determined exactly from a histogram?

Ⓐ mean Ⓒ MAD

Ⓑ median Ⓓ none of these

enVision™ Algebra 1 • Assessment Resources

Assess | Tutorials | Worksheets

DIFFERENTIATED RESOURCES

I = Intervention   O = On-Level   A = Advanced

= This activity is available as a digital assignment powered by MathXL® for School.

AVAILABLE ONLINE

Reteach to Build Understanding I ⚙

Provides scaffolded reteaching for the key lesson concepts.

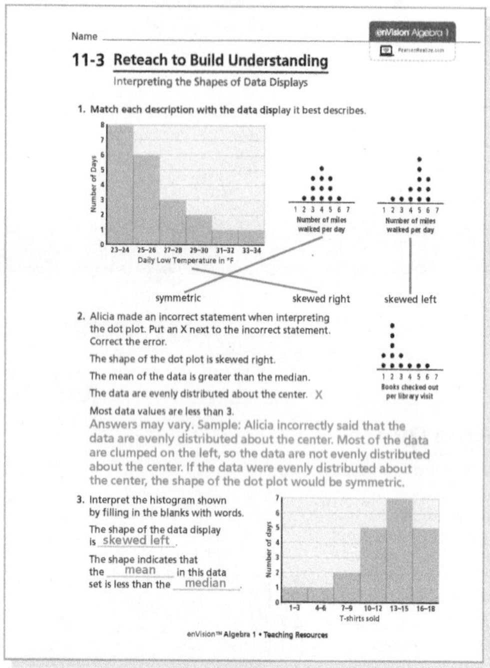

Name
enVision Algebra 1
PearsonRealize.com

11-3 Reteach to Build Understanding
Interpreting the Shapes of Data Displays

1. Match each description with the data display it best describes.

Number of Days; Daily Low Temperature in °F; 23–24, 25–26, 27–28, 29–30, 31–32, 33–34
Number of miles walked per day
Number of miles walked per day

symmetric   skewed right   skewed left

2. Alicia made an incorrect statement when interpreting the dot plot. Put an X next to the incorrect statement. Correct the error.

The shape of the dot plot is skewed right.
The mean of the data is greater than the median.
The data are evenly distributed about the center. X
Most data values are less than 3.

Books checked out per library visit

Answers may vary. Sample: Alicia incorrectly said that the data are evenly distributed about the center. Most of the data are clumped on the left, so the data are not evenly distributed about the center. If the data were evenly distributed about the center, the shape of the dot plot would be symmetric.

3. Interpret the histogram shown by filling in the blanks with words.

The shape of the data display is skewed left.

The shape indicates that the mean in this data set is less than the median.

Number of days; T-shirts sold; 1–3, 4–6, 7–9, 10–12, 13–15, 16–18

enVision™ Algebra 1 • Teaching Resources

Additional Practice I O ⚙

Provides extra practice for each lesson.

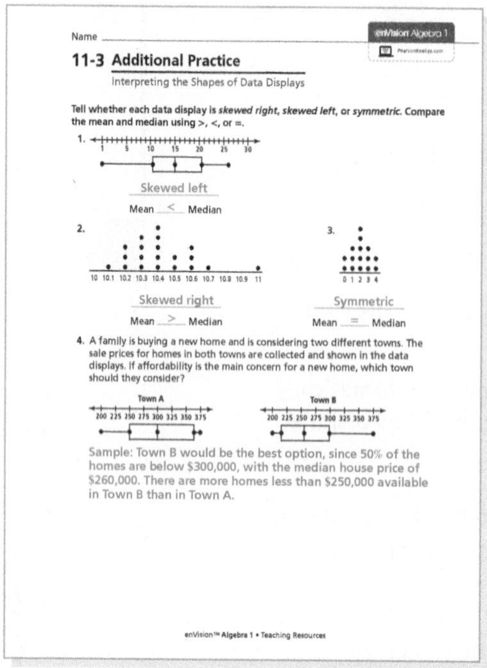

Name
enVision Algebra 1
PearsonRealize.com

11-3 Additional Practice
Interpreting the Shapes of Data Displays

Tell whether each data display is *skewed right, skewed left,* or *symmetric.* Compare the mean and median using >, <, or =.

1. Skewed left
Mean < Median

2. Skewed right
Mean > Median

3. Symmetric
Mean = Median

4. A family is buying a new home and is considering two different towns. The sale prices for homes in both towns are collected and shown in the data displays. If affordability is the main concern for a new home, which town should they consider?

Town A   Town B

Sample: Town B would be the best option, since 50% of the homes are below $300,000, with the median house price of $260,000. There are more homes less than $250,000 available in Town B than in Town A.

enVision™ Algebra 1 • Teaching Resources

Enrichment O A ⚙

Presents engaging problems and activities that extend the lesson concepts.

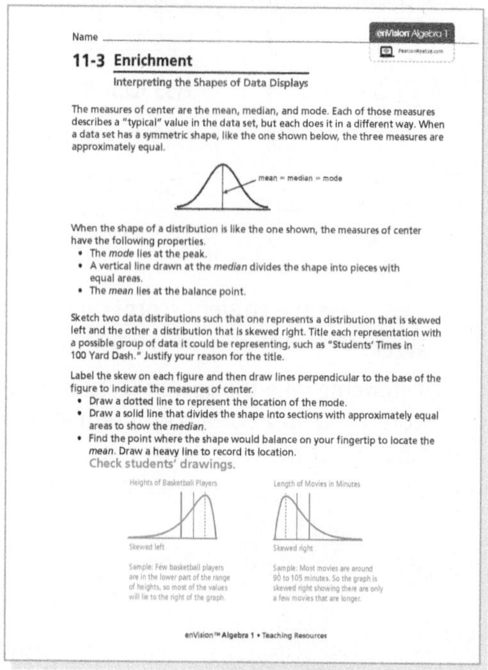

Name
enVision Algebra 1
PearsonRealize.com

11-3 Enrichment
Interpreting the Shapes of Data Displays

The measures of center are the mean, median, and mode. Each of those measures describes a "typical" value in the data set, but each does it in a different way. When a data set has a symmetric shape, like the one shown below, the three measures are approximately equal.

mean = median = mode

When the shape of a distribution is like the one shown, the measures of center have the following properties.
- The *mode* lies at the peak.
- A vertical line drawn at the *median* divides the shape into pieces with equal areas.
- The *mean* lies at the balance point.

Sketch two data distributions such that one represents a distribution that is skewed left and the other a distribution that is skewed right. Title each representation with a possible group of data it could be representing, such as "Students' Times in 100 Yard Dash." Justify your reason for the title.

Label the skew on each figure and then draw lines perpendicular to the base of the figure to indicate the measures of center.
- Draw a dotted line to represent the location of the mode.
- Draw a solid line that divides the shape into sections with approximately equal areas to show the *median*.
- Find the point where the shape would balance on your fingertip to locate the *mean*. Draw a heavy line to record its location.

Check students' drawings.

Heights of Basketball Players — Skewed left
Sample: Few basketball players are in the lower part of the range of heights, so most of the values will lie to the right of the graph.

Length of Movies in Minutes — Skewed right
Sample: Most movies are around 90 to 105 minutes. So the graph is skewed right showing there are only a few movies that are longer.

enVision™ Algebra 1 • Teaching Resources

Mathematical Literacy and Vocabulary I O

Helps students develop and reinforce understanding of key terms and concepts.

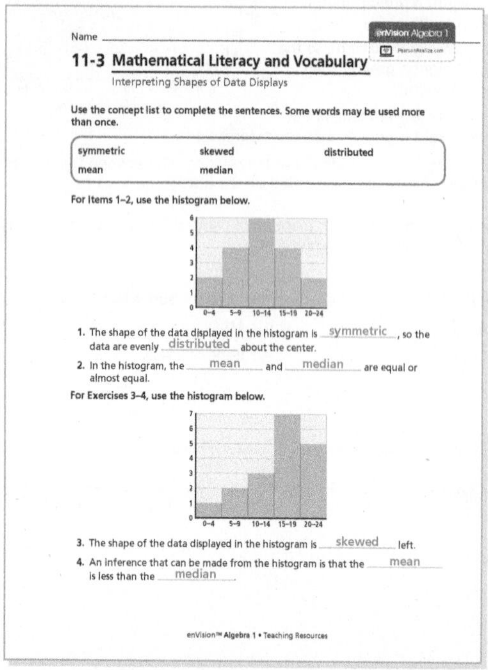

Name
enVision Algebra 1
PearsonRealize.com

11-3 Mathematical Literacy and Vocabulary
Interpreting Shapes of Data Displays

Use the concept list to complete the sentences. Some words may be used more than once.

symmetric	skewed	distributed
mean	median	

For Items 1–2, use the histogram below.

1. The shape of the data displayed in the histogram is symmetric, so the data are evenly distributed about the center.
2. In the histogram, the mean and median are equal or almost equal.

For Exercises 3–4, use the histogram below.

3. The shape of the data displayed in the histogram is skewed left.
4. An inference that can be made from the histogram is that the mean is less than the median.

enVision™ Algebra 1 • Teaching Resources

Digital Resources and Video Tutorials I O A ⚙

The **Reteach to Build Understanding, Additional Practice,** and **Enrichment** activities are available as digital assignments powered by MathXL for School. These activities are automatically assigned when students complete the lesson quiz online and are automatically scored.

Students can access instructional tutorials using the **Virtual Nerd app.**

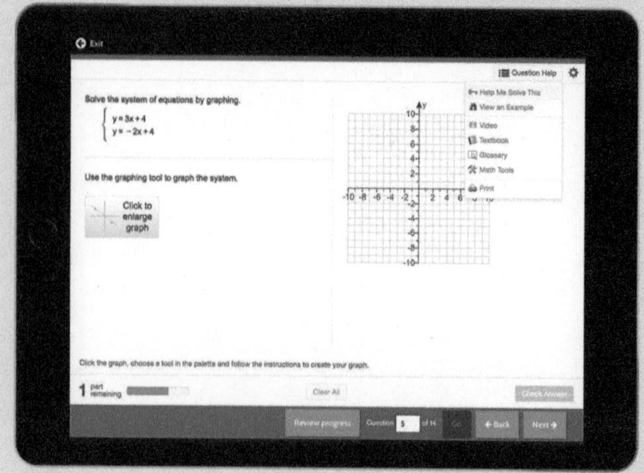
Exit
Question Help
Solve the system of equations by graphing.
Use the graphing tool to graph the system.
Click to enlarge graph
Help Me Solve This
View an Example
Video
Textbook
Glossary
Math Tools
Print
Clear All
Check Answer
Review progress
Back
Next

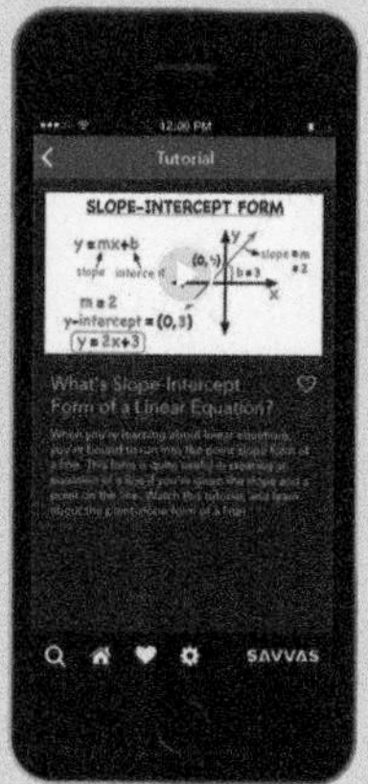
Tutorial
SLOPE-INTERCEPT FORM
What's Slope-Intercept Form of a Linear Equation?
SAVVAS

Students can also access Virtual Nerd videos using the **BouncePages app** to scan exercise pages marked with this icon. Students can download both apps for free in their mobile devices' app store.

A-Z Glossary

LESSON 11-4

Standard Deviation

Lesson Overview

FOCUS

Objective

Students will be able to:

✔ Interpret differences in the variability or spread in the context of a data set.

✔ Calculate the standard deviation of a data set and use it to compare and interpret data sets.

Essential Understanding

Standard deviation is a measure of spread, or variability. It indicates by how much the values in a data set deviate from the mean. The standard deviation is used to compare a specific value to other values in the data set and to determine the percent of values that fall within a specific range from the mean.

COHERENCE

Previously in this course, students:

- Interpreted and compared the spread of data sets using the mean absolute deviation (MAD).

In this lesson, students:

- Use standard deviation to quantify and analyze the spread of data.

In later courses, students will:

- Choose the best measure of spread or variability to describe specific relationships between data sets.

RIGOR

This lesson emphasizes a blend of *conceptual understanding* and *procedural skill and fluency*.

- Students understand that standard deviation is a measure of spread or variability that, along with the mean, describes the data set completely when it is normally distributed.
- Students calculate the standard deviation by squaring the differences between each data value and the mean, and then taking the square root of the variance.

A-Z Vocabulary Builder

REVIEW VOCABULARY — **English** | *Spanish*

- **mean absolute deviation** | *desviación absoluta media*
- **variability** | *variabilidad*

NEW VOCABULARY

- **normal distribution** | *distribución*
- **standard deviation** | *desviación tipica*
- **variance** | *varianza*

VOCABULARY ACTIVITY

Review the term *variability.*

Q: How can you use the meaning of the term *variability* to predict the meaning of the term *variance*?

Next discuss students' experience with *mean absolute deviation.*

Q: How can you use the meaning of the term *mean absolute deviation* to predict the meaning of the term *standard deviation*?

After students make predictions, introduce them to the definitions of the terms *variance* and *mean absolute deviation.* Discuss how their predictions relate to the actual meanings of the terms.

Student Companion

Students can do their in-class work for the lesson on pages 261–264 of their *Student Companion* or in Savvas Realize.

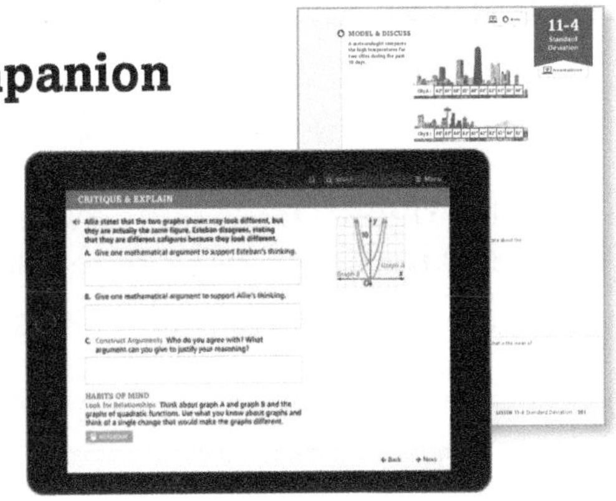
11-4
CRITIQUE & EXPLAIN

Mathematics Overview — COMMON CORE STANDARDS

Content Standards

In this lesson, students focus on these standards:

HSS.ID.A.2 Use statistics appropriate to the shape of the data distribution to compare center (median, mean) and spread (interquartile range, standard deviation) of two or more different data sets.

HSS.ID.A.3 Interpret differences in shape, center, and spread in the context of the data sets, accounting for possible effects of extreme data points (outliers).

Mathematical Practice Standards

These standards are highlighted in this lesson:

MP.3 Construct Viable Arguments and Critique the Reasoning of Others

Students use stated mathematical definitions for *standard deviation*, *mean*, and *median* to refute the incorrect reasoning of a student who says that standard deviation measures how much values in a data set deviate from the median.

MP.8 Look For and Express Regularity in Repeated Reasoning

Students generalize about the relationship between the shape and the mean and standard deviation of a data set.

MODEL & DISCUSS

INSTRUCTIONAL FOCUS Students use what they know about data analysis to create a data display in order to interpret the spread of the data. Students describe the shape of each data display and what it indicates. This prepares students to interpret data that are normally distributed using a measure of spread called standard deviation.

STUDENT COMPANION Students can complete the *Model & Discuss* activity on page 261 of their *Student Companion*.

Before WHOLE CLASS

Implement Tasks that Promote Reasoning and Problem Solving ETP

Q: How can you list the data in order to begin creating the data display?
[It is best to list the data in ascending order to organize and represent the data in a table or graph.]

During SMALL GROUP

Support Productive Struggle in Learning Mathematics ETP

Q: What can you infer from the data that are listed?
[The temperatures from City B have a greater range.]

Q: What type of data display will be suitable for this type of data?
[A histogram or frequency table will show the shape of the data, which can help with analysis.]

For Early Finishers

Use the data from City C to answer the following questions:

69°	63°	64°	64°	64°	74°	70°	69°	68°	74°

Q: Create a data display for the given data. How does the shape of this data display differ from the others? Can you determine the measures of center?
[The shape of this display appears to be random; neither symmetrical nor clearly skewed in either direction. The measures of center are not easily identified from the display.]

After WHOLE CLASS

Facilitate Meaningful Mathematical Discourse ETP

Q: What do the shapes of the displays suggest about the data?
[The shape of the display for City A suggests that the temperatures are fairly consistent and do not vary much from the mean. The shape of the display for City B suggests more fluctuation among the temperatures.]

HABITS OF MIND *Use with* **MODEL & DISCUSS**

Make Sense and Persevere What is the range of each data set? What is the mean of each data set? **MP.1**

[$62 \le x \le 66$; $62 \le x \le 68$; 64; 63.4]

AVAILABLE **ONLINE**

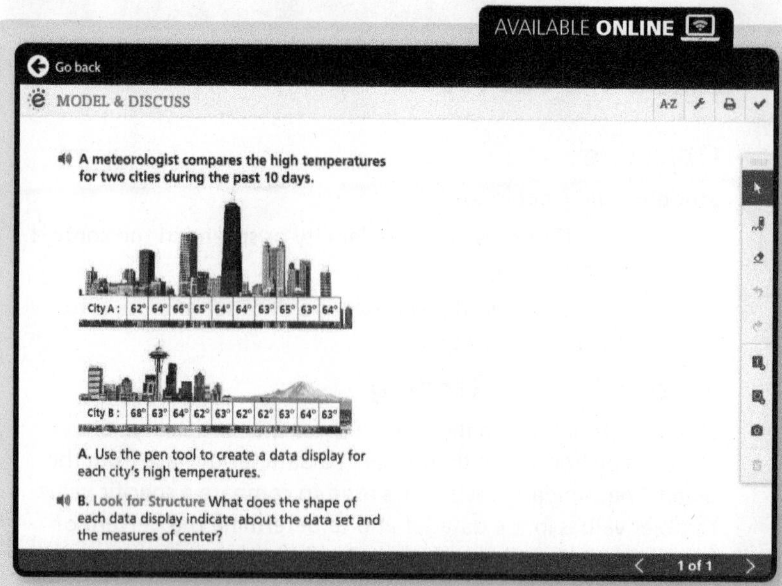
Go back
MODEL & DISCUSS
A meteorologist compares the high temperatures for two cities during the past 10 days.
City A: 62° 64° 66° 65° 64° 64° 63° 65° 63° 64°
City B: 68° 63° 64° 62° 63° 62° 62° 63° 64° 63°
A. Use the pen tool to create a data display for each city's high temperatures.
B. Look for Structure What does the shape of each data display indicate about the data set and the measures of center?
1 of 1

STUDENT EDITION, PAGE 487

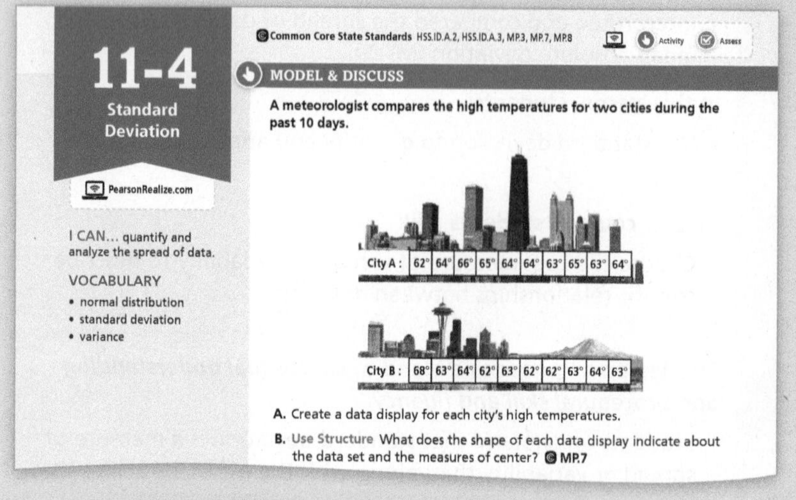
Common Core State Standards HSS.ID.A.2, HSS.ID.A.3, MP.3, MP.7, MP.8
Activity
Assess
11-4
Standard Deviation
PearsonRealize.com
I CAN… quantify and analyze the spread of data.
VOCABULARY
• normal distribution
• standard deviation
• variance
MODEL & DISCUSS
A meteorologist compares the high temperatures for two cities during the past 10 days.
City A: 62° 64° 66° 65° 64° 64° 63° 65° 63° 64°
City B: 68° 63° 64° 62° 63° 62° 62° 63° 64° 63°
A. Create a data display for each city's high temperatures.
B. Use Structure What does the shape of each data display indicate about the data set and the measures of center? MP.7

SAMPLE STUDENT WORK

A.

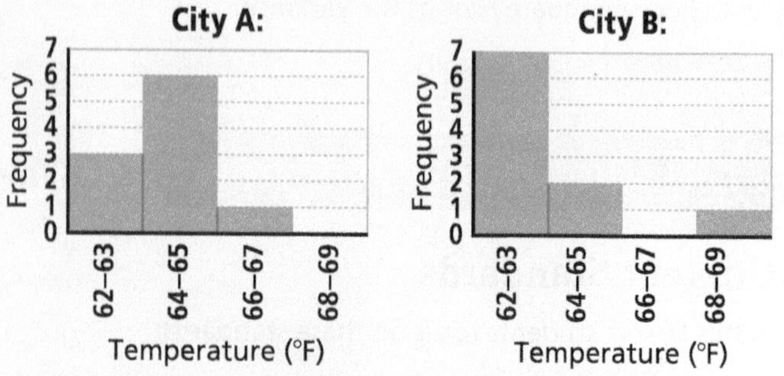
City A:
City B:
Frequency
0
1
2
3
4
5
6
7
62–63
64–65
66–67
68–69
Temperature (°F)

B. For City A, the data appear to be more evenly spread out. The values for the mean and median are likely to be equal or very close. For City B, the outlier causes the data to be skewed right, so the mean value is likely greater than the median value.

INTRODUCE THE ESSENTIAL QUESTION

Establish Mathematics Goals to Focus Learning ETP

Discuss the definition of the range of data sets. Explain that the range is the total spread of data from the least value to the greatest. Remind students that data can be displayed in histograms and frequency tables from which they can interpret how the data are spread. This prepares students to define the variability of data sets.

AVAILABLE ONLINE

ESSENTIAL QUESTION Why does the way in which data are spread out matter?

EXAMPLE 1 Interpret the Variability of a Data Set

The makers of a certain brand of light bulbs claim that the average life of the bulb is 1,200 hours. The life spans, in hours, of a sample of Brand A light bulbs are shown. How close to the claim were the light bulbs in this sample?

1,150	1,231	1,305	1,080	1,125	1,295	1,127	1,184	1,099	1,123
1,204	1,345	1,173	1,126	1,220	1,245	1,283	1,225	1,185	1,275

A. What type of data display will provide the best view of the data?

The numbers in the data set span a large range of numbers. To understand how these numbers relate to the claimed mean, create a histogram.

USE STRUCTURE How does the shape of the distribution help you identify the mean? MP.7

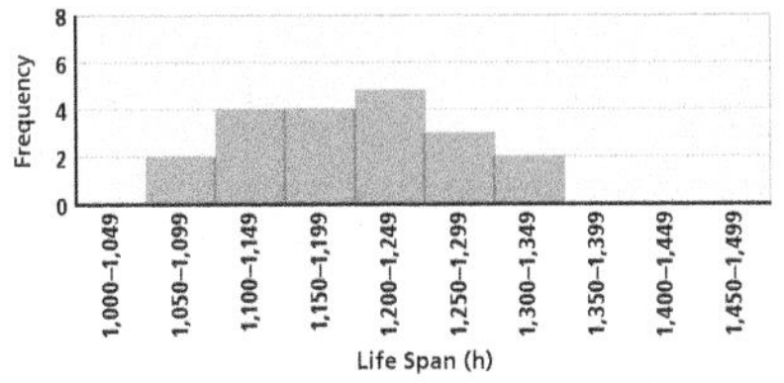
8
6
4
2
0
Frequency
1,000–1,049
1,050–1,099
1,100–1,149
1,150–1,199
1,200–1,249
1,250–1,299
1,300–1,349
1,350–1,399
1,400–1,449
1,450–1,499
Life Span (h)

CONTINUED ON THE NEXT PAGE

LESSON 11-4 Standard Deviation 487

EXAMPLE 1 Interpret the Variability of a Data Set

Pose Purposeful Questions ETP

Part A

Q: Why is data display important when presenting a list of raw data?
[Data displays are helpful when analyzing frequency and range. They should display the data in a way that gives a visual of frequency.]

Q: What does the middle section of the histogram suggest about the data?
[The majority of the data points are listed in the middle of the histogram, which suggests that most of the light bulbs lasted between 1,150 and 1,249 hours.]

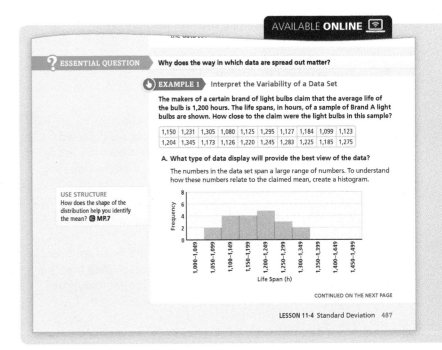

ADDITIONAL EXAMPLES

AVAILABLE ONLINE

Go back

ADDITIONAL EXAMPLE 3 ESSENTIAL QUESTION ES A-Z

Based on the line plot, what data values are within one standard deviation of the mean?
Calculate the mean and standard deviation first.

mean ≈ 5.3 and standard deviation ≈ 1.68.

Data values within one standard deviation are from about 3.62 to 6.98.

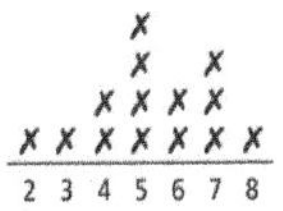
2 3 4 5 6 7 8

1 of 2

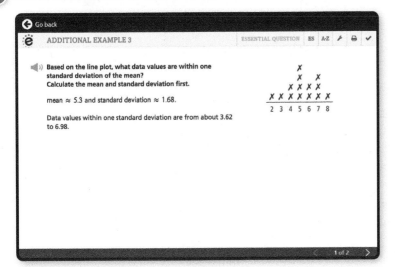

Example 3 Students find the mean, the standard deviation, and the values within 1 standard deviation of the mean using a frequency table.

Q: How is the data display useful when interpreting the standard deviation of a data set? [It is a visual representation of the mean and standard deviation.]

Go back

ADDITIONAL EXAMPLE 4 ESSENTIAL QUESTION ES A-Z

Two fertilizer companies have statistics on their label that describes how using their product will give your tomato garden consistent results. TotalGro claims they have a mean of 28 tomatoes per plant with a standard deviation of 2.68 from a sample of 2,000 plants. REAL-Ripe claims that they have a mean of 36 tomatoes per plant with a standard deviation of 12.85 from a sample of 800 plants. Which product has the best data? Use the approximate number of plants within one standard deviation of the mean to inform your decision.

TotalGro has results within one standard deviation of the mean from about 25 to 31 per plant. REAL-Ripe has results within one standard deviation of the mean from about 23 to 49 per plant. TotalGro has a larger set of data with a smaller standard deviation, which suggests that they have a more consistent rate of growth.

1 of 2

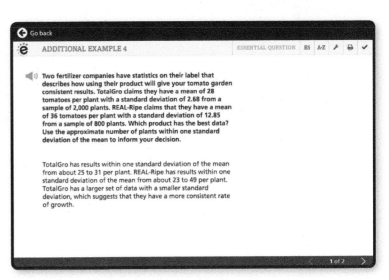

Example 4 Students make informational decisions and arguments from the meaning of sample size, mean, and standard deviation when comparing data sets.

Q: How can you read information about a data set and interpret strong results?
[The larger the sample size and the smaller the standard deviation, the more the data are consistent and the closer the results are to the mean.]

Activity Assess

EXAMPLE 1 CONTINUED

EXAMPLE 1 Interpret the Variability of a Data Set Continued

Pose Purposeful Questions ETP

Part B

Q: What does it mean to have a normal distribution?
[A normal distribution occurs when the data are clustered around the mean. The frequency of the data becomes less as you move farther from the mean in either direction, creating the bell-shaped curve.]

Q: In a normal distribution, what is the difference between data that are 1 standard deviation from the mean and data that are 3 standard deviations from the mean?
[Data that are 1 standard deviation from the mean are closer to the mean and are much more likely to occur. Data that are 3 standard deviations from the mean are further away from the mean and are much less likely to occur.]

Try It! Answers

1. 1,049 to 1,351 hours; 973.5 to 1,426.5 hours

HABITS OF MIND

Use with **EXAMPLE 1**

Use Appropriate Tools Do any of the data from Example 1 fall three standard deviations above or below the mean? In general, is it possible for data to fall more than two standard deviations above or below the mean? Explain. MP.5

[No; Yes; It is possible, although not likely, for data to fall more than 2 standard deviations from the mean. According to the percentages listed under the normal curve, 0.4% of the data may fall more than 3 standard deviations from the mean.]

AVAILABLE **ONLINE**

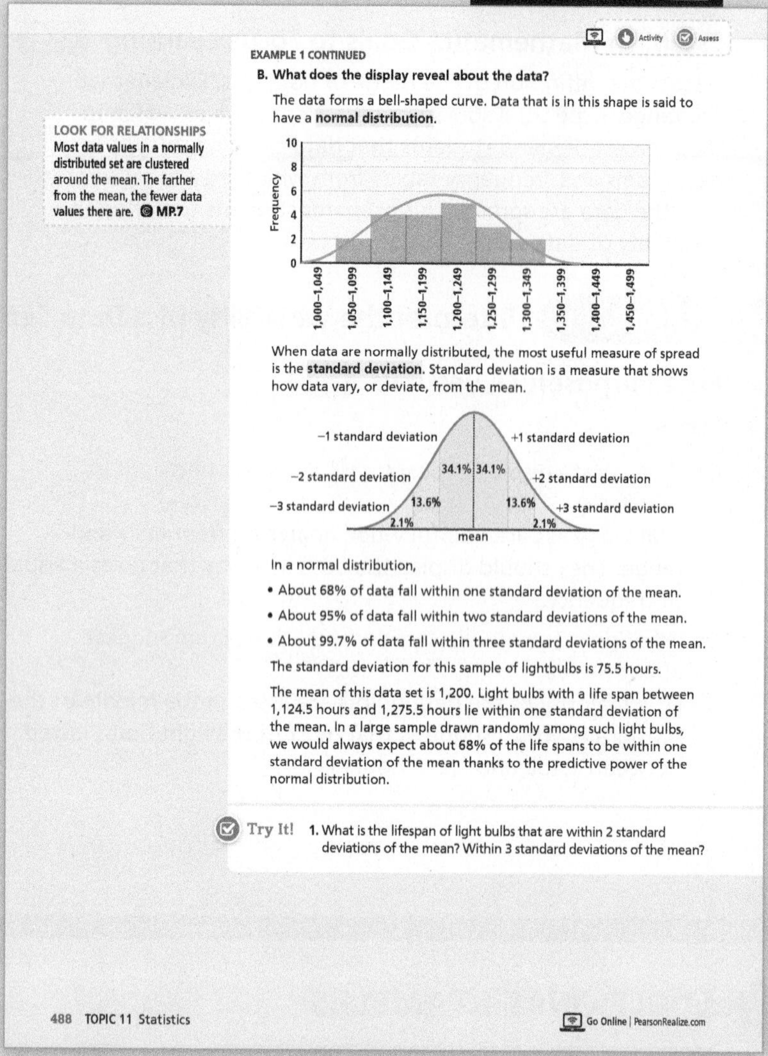

Activity Assess

EXAMPLE 1 CONTINUED

B. What does the display reveal about the data?

The data forms a bell-shaped curve. Data that is in this shape is said to have a **normal distribution**.

LOOK FOR RELATIONSHIPS
Most data values in a normally distributed set are clustered around the mean. The farther from the mean, the fewer data values there are. MP.7

Frequency
0
2
4
6
8
10
1,000–1,049
1,050–1,099
1,100–1,149
1,150–1,199
1,200–1,249
1,250–1,299
1,300–1,349
1,350–1,399
1,400–1,449
1,450–1,499

When data are normally distributed, the most useful measure of spread is the **standard deviation**. Standard deviation is a measure that shows how data vary, or deviate, from the mean.

−1 standard deviation
+1 standard deviation
−2 standard deviation
+2 standard deviation
−3 standard deviation
+3 standard deviation
34.1%
34.1%
13.6%
13.6%
2.1%
2.1%
mean

In a normal distribution,

- About 68% of data fall within one standard deviation of the mean.
- About 95% of data fall within two standard deviations of the mean.
- About 99.7% of data fall within three standard deviations of the mean.

The standard deviation for this sample of lightbulbs is 75.5 hours.

The mean of this data set is 1,200. Light bulbs with a life span between 1,124.5 hours and 1,275.5 hours lie within one standard deviation of the mean. In a large sample drawn randomly among such light bulbs, we would always expect about 68% of the life spans to be within one standard deviation of the mean thanks to the predictive power of the normal distribution.

Try It! 1. What is the lifespan of light bulbs that are within 2 standard deviations of the mean? Within 3 standard deviations of the mean?

488 TOPIC 11 Statistics

Go Online | PearsonRealize.com

ELL English Language Learners *(Use with* **EXAMPLE 1***)*

WRITING BEGINNING The word *range* can have several different meanings. Display three definitions of *range* on the board for students to write in their journals: a stove to cook on; a group of mountains; the difference between the highest and lowest values of a data set.

Have students copy the following sentences in their journals and match each sentence to one of the definitions.

Q: The range of ages of participants in a contest is 10.
[3]

Q: There are splatters of bacon grease all over the range.
[1]

Q: The Appalachian range is majestic.
[2]

LISTENING INTERMEDIATE Read the following sentences to students and have them listen for the word *span*.

- The butterfly has a 2-inch wing*span*.
- The batteries have a short life *span*.
- His career *spanned* over 30 years.
- The bridge *spanned* the river.

Q: Does *span* have the same meaning in each sentence?
[No, in the first and last sentences, *span* means the distance between two points. In the middle two sentences, *span* means to extend over the complete duration of an event.]

Q: Which meaning of *span* is used in the example?
[both]

READING ADVANCED Display the definition for *normal*: regular, common, typical; conforming to the conventions of a group. Then have students read the first two paragraphs of Part B of the example.

Q: Does the use of the term *normal* in the example seem to meet the definition?
[Yes, the normal distribution seems typical, with the majority of values close to the average value.]

Q: Describe the shape of a normal distribution.
[It is in the shape of a bell.]

STEP 2 Understand & Apply

EXAMPLE 2 Calculate the Standard Deviation of a Sample

Build Procedural Fluency From Conceptual Understanding ETP

Q: Within the data set, what do you notice about the majority of the data entries?
[All of them, except 2, are within a difference of 2 from the mean.]

Q: Why do you divide by $n - 1$ rather than n when calculating the variance of a total population?
[n provides too small of an estimate because data points are clustered more around the sample mean than the population mean. Dividing by $n - 1$ gives a slightly larger number, closer to the population variance.]

Try It! Answer

2. The mean for this eight-week period is 16.5 and the standard deviation is about 5.7. The data show more variance for this eight-week period than they did for the last. The associate sells between about 11 and 22 cars for this period.

Elicit and Use Evidence of Student Thinking ETP

Q: What do you notice about this data set before doing any calculations that can help you check your answer for reasonableness?
[The data are spread farther from the mean; therefore there should be a larger measure of spread.]

Common Error

Try It! 2 Some students may neglect to use repeated data results when calculating standard deviation. For example, they may only use the data value 16 once. Explain that when data sets are displayed, first arrange them in order from least to greatest. Then use each data value because every number in the data set represents a specific value from the set and repeated data does occur.

AVAILABLE ONLINE

Activity Assess

CONCEPTUAL UNDERSTANDING

EXAMPLE 2 Calculate the Standard Deviation of a Sample

The table shows the number of cars sold by an auto sales associate over an eight-week period. How much variability do the data show?

18	25	18	10	17	15	18	15

You can find the variability by solving for the standard deviation for a sample, using the formula $s = \sqrt{\frac{\sum(x - \bar{x})^2}{n - 1}}$. To calculate it, follow these steps.

Step 1 Find the mean of the data by finding the sum of the data points and dividing by 8. The notation $\bar{x}$ is used to indicate the mean.

$\bar{x} = 17$

Step 2 Find the difference between each data value, x, and the mean, $\bar{x}$. Then square each difference.

COMMON ERROR
Remember to square the differences between each data value and the mean. Otherwise, the sum of the differences will be zero.

x	18	25	18	10	17	15	18	15
$\bar{x}$	17	17	17	17	17	17	17	17
$x - \bar{x}$	1	8	1	−7	0	−2	1	−2
$(x - \bar{x})^2$	1	64	1	49	0	4	1	4

Step 3 Find the variance.

The **variance** of a total population, often noted σ^2, is the mean of the squares of the differences between each data value and the mean. When finding the variance of a sample, often noted s^2, dividing by n provides too small an estimate of the variance of the population. This is because data points from the sample are likely to cluster more closely around the sample mean than the population mean. If you divide by $n - 1$ instead of n, you get a slightly bigger number that is closer to the true population variance.

$s^2 = \frac{1 + 64 + 1 + 49 + 0 + 4 + 1 + 4}{7}$

$s^2 \approx 17.71$

In this sample, $n = 8$ so we divide by $n - 1$, or 7.

Step 4 Take the square root of the variance to find the standard deviation, s.

$s \approx \sqrt{17.71}$

$s \approx 4.21$

Since only whole cars can be sold, it makes sense to round the standard deviation to 4.

The standard deviation is about 4 cars and the mean is about 17 cars, so there is some variability in the data. The sales associate will sell between 13 and 21 cars about 68% of the time because those values are one standard deviation from the mean.

Try It! 2. The table shows the number of cars sold by the auto sales associate over the next eight-week period. How much variability do the data show?

12	14	29	10	17	16	18	16

LESSON 11-4 Standard Deviation 489

Activity Assess

EXAMPLE 3 Find Standard Deviation of a Sample

Pose Purposeful Questions ETP

Q: What is one strategy to use when organizing your data to calculate the standard deviation?
[You can build a table that shows each piece of information needed for the calculation: the data value, the mean, the difference between each data value and the mean, and the square of this difference.]

Q: Why do you divide by n rather than $n - 1$ when calculating the variance?
[You divide by n because you are working with an entire population of football games.]

Q: Does most of the data cluster around the mean?
[No, the team scored a wide range of scores and the spread shows a large variance.]

Q: When considering the spread, do the majority of the games fall within 1 standard deviation of the mean?
[Yes, the standard deviation is about 7.3, which covers the range of scores from 10 to 25. This accounts for all but three scores.]

Try It! Answer

3. 2 to 32 points

Elicit and Use Evidence of Student Thinking ETP

Q: What does it mean by the range of points that the team scored in 95% of their regular season games?
[About 95% of the data will fall within 2 standard deviations of the mean.]

AVAILABLE ONLINE

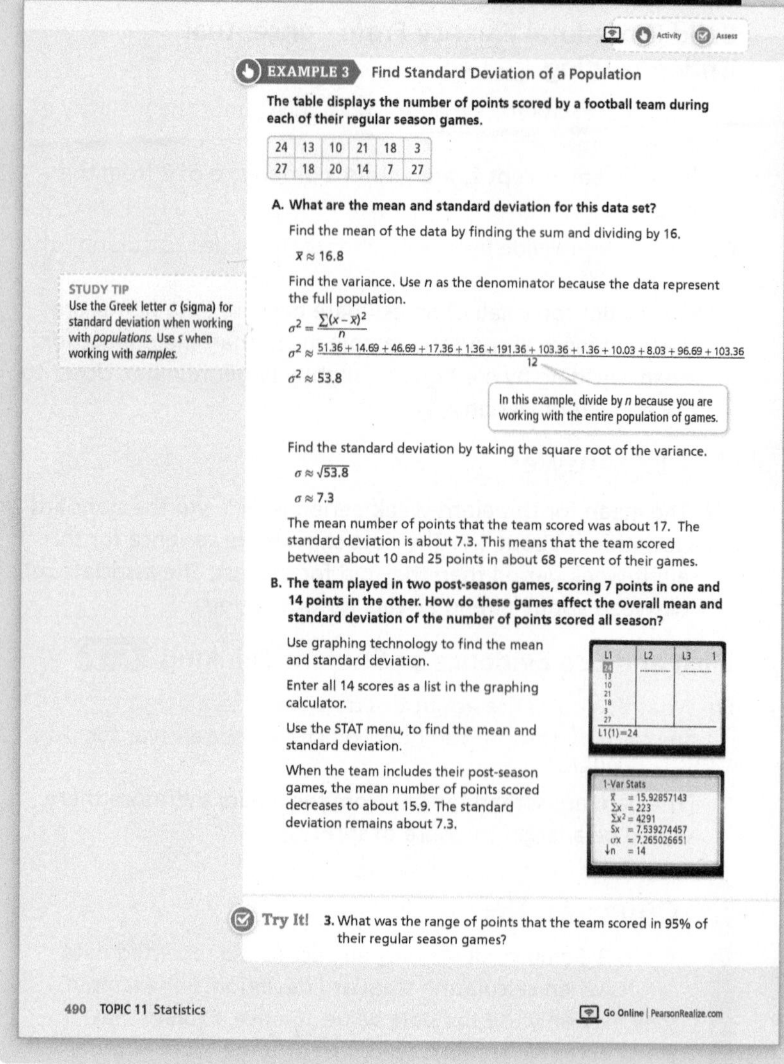

Activity Assess

EXAMPLE 3 Find Standard Deviation of a Population

The table displays the number of points scored by a football team during each of their regular season games.

24	13	10	21	18	3
27	18	20	14	7	27

A. What are the mean and standard deviation for this data set?

Find the mean of the data by finding the sum and dividing by 16.

$\bar{x} \approx 16.8$

Find the variance. Use n as the denominator because the data represent the full population.

$\sigma^2 = \frac{\sum(x - \bar{x})^2}{n}$

$\sigma^2 \approx \frac{51.36 + 14.69 + 46.69 + 17.36 + 1.36 + 191.36 + 103.36 + 1.36 + 10.03 + 8.03 + 96.69 + 103.36}{12}$

$\sigma^2 \approx 53.8$

In this example, divide by n because you are working with the entire population of games.

STUDY TIP
Use the Greek letter σ (sigma) for standard deviation when working with *populations*. Use s when working with *samples*.

Find the standard deviation by taking the square root of the variance.

$\sigma \approx \sqrt{53.8}$

$\sigma \approx 7.3$

The mean number of points that the team scored was about 17. The standard deviation is about 7.3. This means that the team scored between about 10 and 25 points in about 68 percent of their games.

B. The team played in two post-season games, scoring 7 points in one and 14 points in the other. How do these games affect the overall mean and standard deviation of the number of points scored all season?

Use graphing technology to find the mean and standard deviation.

Enter all 14 scores as a list in the graphing calculator.

Use the STAT menu, to find the mean and standard deviation.

When the team includes their post-season games, the mean number of points scored decreases to about 15.9. The standard deviation remains about 7.3.

L1 L2 L3 1
24
13
10
21
18
3
27
L1(1)=24

1-Var Stats
x̄ = 15.92857143
Σx = 223
Σx² = 4291
Sx = 7.539274457
σx = 7.265026651
↓n = 14

Try It! **3.** What was the range of points that the team scored in 95% of their regular season games?

490 TOPIC 11 Statistics

Go Online | PearsonRealize.com

Struggling Students

USE WITH EXAMPLE 3 Some students may need additional support in understanding when to use n versus $n - 1$ when calculating the variance.

- Use the following examples to determine whether the data are a sample of a population ($n - 1$) or a total population (n).

1. A data set of all of your grades for the first semester of school.
[Because this is the total population of grades, use n.]

2. A data set that contains the recorded energy life of three different types of batteries used in a flashlight.
[Because this is a sample of three different types of batteries, use $n - 1$.]

Q: What determines if you have a data set of a sample or the total population?
[If the data set uses every possible piece of data, it is the total population. If the data set uses part of the population to analyze data, it is a sample population.]

EXAMPLE 4 Compare Data Sets Using Standard Deviation

Use and Connect Mathematical Representations ETP

Q: What do you notice about the shapes of the graphs of the two data displays?
[The Brand A data display shows a normal distribution, where the data are clustered more around the mean. The Brand B data display has a larger spread.]

Q: What does the data display for Brand B suggest about the life span of the light bulbs?
[Since the spread is larger, the life span for Brand B is less predictable.]

Try It! Answer

4. The average life span of Brand C light bulbs is greater than the other two brands by 50 h. The standard deviation of Brand C is greater than the standard deviation of Brand A by 8.5 h and less than the standard deviation of Brand B by 7.25 h.

Elicit and Use Evidence of Student Thinking ETP

Q: What do you notice about the mean of Brand C compared to Brands A and B?
[The light bulbs of Brand C have an average life span that is higher than both of the other brands.]

HABITS OF MIND

Use with **EXAMPLES 2–4**

Communicate Precisely When the means of two or more data sets are equal, what does a greater standard deviation indicate? MP.6

[A greater standard deviation indicates that the data from that set show more variability than the other data sets.]

AVAILABLE **ONLINE**

Activity Assess

APPLICATION

EXAMPLE 4 Compare Data Sets Using Standard Deviation

The histograms show the life spans of a sample of light bulbs from 2 companies. The first shows a sample from Brand A and the second from Brand B. The red lines indicate the mean and each standard deviation from the mean. Compare the distributions of life spans for the two light bulb brands.

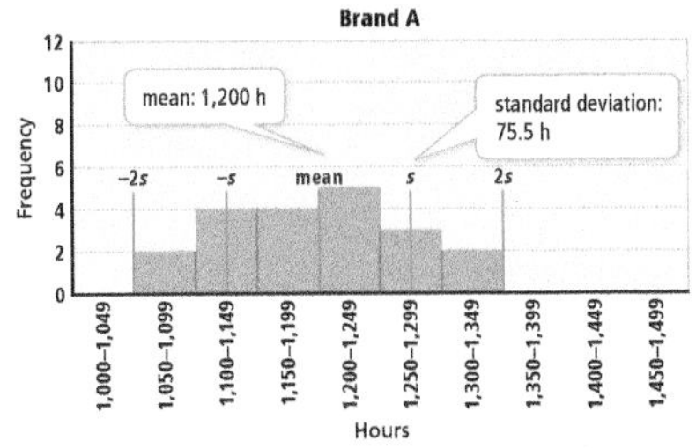
Brand A
mean: 1,200 h
standard deviation: 75.5 h
−2s
−s
mean
s
2s
Frequency
12
10
8
6
4
2
0
1,000–1,049
1,050–1,099
1,100–1,149
1,150–1,199
1,200–1,249
1,250–1,299
1,300–1,349
1,350–1,399
1,400–1,449
1,450–1,499
Hours

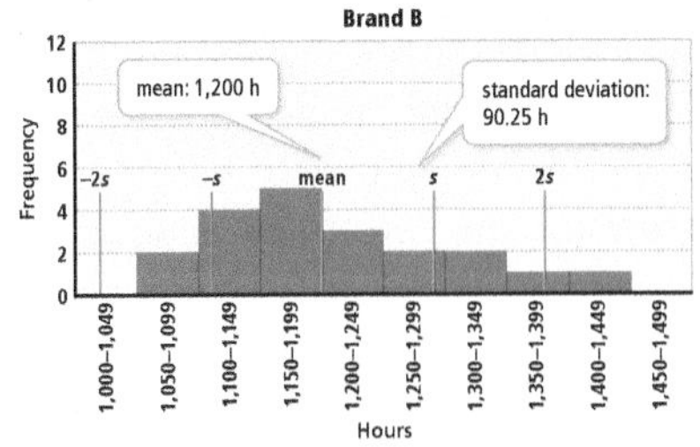
Brand B
mean: 1,200 h
standard deviation: 90.25 h
−2s
−s
mean
s
2s
Frequency
12
10
8
6
4
2
0
1,000–1,049
1,050–1,099
1,100–1,149
1,150–1,199
1,200–1,249
1,250–1,299
1,300–1,349
1,350–1,399
1,400–1,449
1,450–1,499
Hours

USE STRUCTURE
How does the shape of each graph help you compare the standard deviations? MP.7

Both brands of light bulbs have an average life of about 1,200 hours.

The standard deviation for the data set for Brand A is less than the standard deviation for Brand B. This suggests that Brand A light bulbs show less variability in their life spans.

Since their light bulbs are more consistently closer to the mean, Brand A light bulbs are more predictable in their life spans than Brand B.

Try It! 4. Compare Brand C, with mean 1,250 hours and standard deviation 83 hours, to Brands A and B.

LESSON 11-4 Standard Deviation 491

ADV Advanced Students

USE WITH EXAMPLE 4 Have students explore testing their conjectures by simply looking at the data.

- Identify the key features you can use to interpret the data from a display.

1. Describe the features of Brand A.
[Brand A has a stronger normal distribution than Brand B. The data are closer to the mean and the spread is smaller.]

2. Describe the features of Brand B.
[Brand B has a larger spread and the data are distributed farther from the mean than the data for Brand A.]

Q: Is it possible to make informed decisions about the variance and spread of data sets by understanding the bell curve from a normal distribution?
[Yes, when comparing data sets with different shapes, specific features of the curves can be used when interpreting which data set is closest to the mean. If the curve is bell-shaped, it shows how data measures deviate from the mean.]

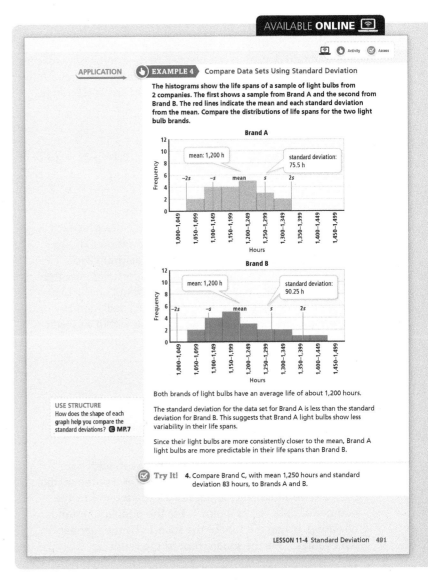

CONCEPT SUMMARY Standard Deviation

Q: How can standard deviation be used to interpret values within a set of data?
[The standard deviation can be used to determine how specific data values deviate from the calculated mean. This shows how specific values within a data set are spread across the range of the entire data.]

Do You UNDERSTAND? | Do You KNOW HOW?

Common Error

Exercise 8 Some students may incorrectly interpret each column of the histogram as standard deviation indicators. Show students the normal distribution diagram and explain that it is a visual for them to understand how the different standard deviations are distributed on the bell curve. Have them use the actual standard deviation to determine the percent of values that fall within a specific range from the mean.

Answers

1. A data set can be analyzed by looking at the difference between the greatest and least values as well as patterns in how close or far data fall from the mean.
2. Find the mean. Find the differences between each data value and the mean. Square the differences. For the sample standard deviation, divide the sum of the squares by the number of data values minus 1. For the population standard deviation, divide the sum of the squares by the number of data values. Take the square root of the result.
3. Marisol is incorrect. Standard deviation measures variation from the mean.
4. The mean increases by 10, while the range and standard deviation stay the same. The variability of a data set is not affected by adding the same amount to each value.
5. Sample A has a range of 5, and Sample B has a range of 6. Sample B has a greater difference between extreme values than Sample A.
6. Sample A: 2; Sample B: 1.92
7. Although the standard deviation for Sample A is greater than the standard deviation for Sample B, the range of Sample A is less than the range of Sample B. Different measures of spread may yield different results when comparing two data sets.
8. 8.65 through 13.45

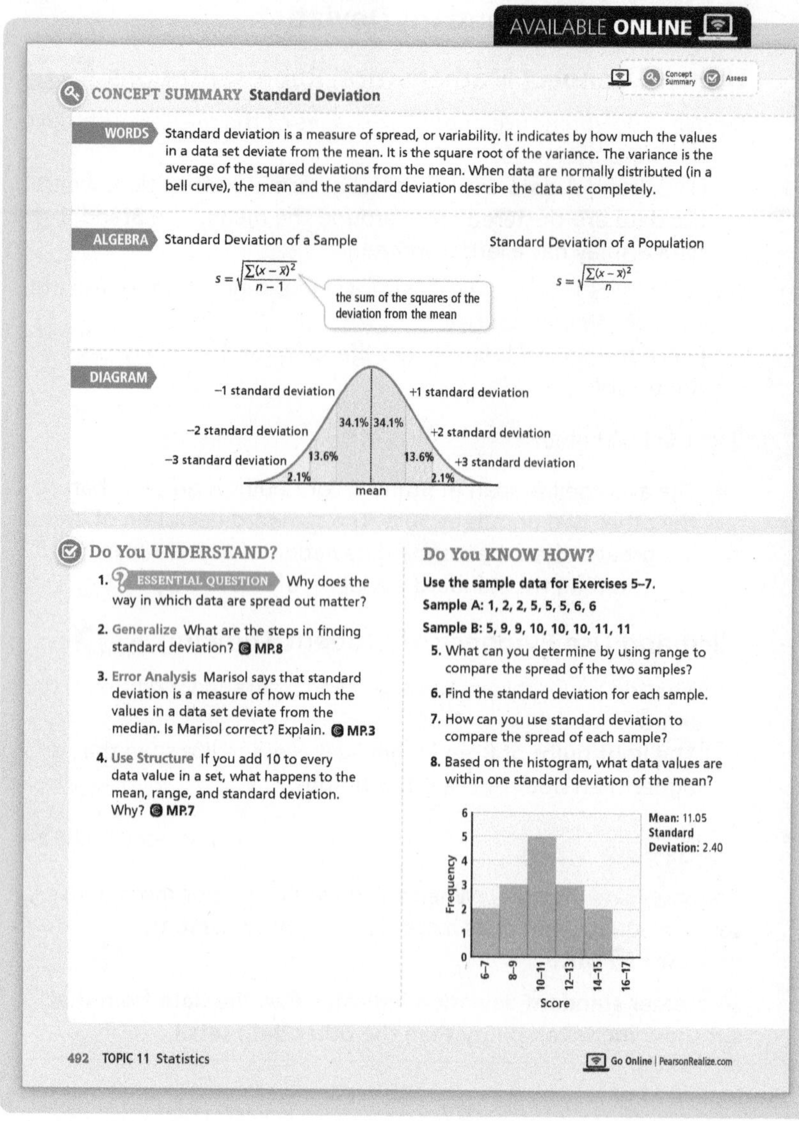
AVAILABLE ONLINE

Concept Summary Assess

CONCEPT SUMMARY Standard Deviation

WORDS Standard deviation is a measure of spread, or variability. It indicates by how much the values in a data set deviate from the mean. It is the square root of the variance. The variance is the average of the squared deviations from the mean. When data are normally distributed (in a bell curve), the mean and the standard deviation describe the data set completely.

ALGEBRA Standard Deviation of a Sample

$$s = \sqrt{\frac{\sum (x - \bar{x})^2}{n - 1}}$$

the sum of the squares of the deviation from the mean

Standard Deviation of a Population

$$s = \sqrt{\frac{\sum (x - \bar{x})^2}{n}}$$

DIAGRAM

−1 standard deviation
+1 standard deviation
−2 standard deviation
+2 standard deviation
−3 standard deviation
+3 standard deviation
34.1% 34.1%
13.6%
13.6%
2.1%
2.1%
mean

Do You UNDERSTAND?

1. ESSENTIAL QUESTION Why does the way in which data are spread out matter?
2. Generalize What are the steps in finding standard deviation? MP.8
3. Error Analysis Marisol says that standard deviation is a measure of how much the values in a data set deviate from the median. Is Marisol correct? Explain. MP.3
4. Use Structure If you add 10 to every data value in a set, what happens to the mean, range, and standard deviation. Why? MP.7

Do You KNOW HOW?

Use the sample data for Exercises 5–7.

Sample A: 1, 2, 2, 5, 5, 5, 6, 6

Sample B: 5, 9, 9, 10, 10, 10, 11, 11

5. What can you determine by using range to compare the spread of the two samples?
6. Find the standard deviation for each sample.
7. How can you use standard deviation to compare the spread of each sample?
8. Based on the histogram, what data values are within one standard deviation of the mean?

Frequency
6
5
4
3
2
1
0
6–7
8–9
10–11
12–13
14–15
16–17
Score
Mean: 11.05
Standard Deviation: 2.40

492 TOPIC 11 Statistics

Go Online | PearsonRealize.com

PRACTICE & PROBLEM SOLVING

AVAILABLE ONLINE

Lesson Practice You may opt to have students complete the automatically scored Practice and Problem Solving items online powered by MathXL for School.

Choose from: **Lesson Practice**

Adaptive Practice

You may also take advantage of the bank of exercises for assigning additional practice.

Assignment Guide

Basic	Advanced
9–17, 19–24	9–12,14–24

Item Analysis

Example	Items	DOK
1	22	1
2	10, 16–18, 23	2
3	11	1
	12, 19, 21	2
4	9, 13–15, 20	2
	24	3

AVAILABLE ONLINE

PRACTICE & PROBLEM SOLVING

Scan for Multimedia

Practice Tutorial

Additional Exercises Available Online

UNDERSTAND

9. Generalize Two data sets have the same number of values. The first data set has a mean of 7.2 and a standard deviation of 1.25. The second data set has a mean of 7.2 and a standard deviation of 2.5.

a. How can you tell which data set is more spread out?

b. How is the shape of a histogram for the first data set different from the shape of a histogram for the second data set? MP.8

10. Error Analysis Describe and correct the errors a student made in calculating the standard deviation of a data set. MP.3

$$\sigma^2 = \frac{(-4) + 2 + (-1) + (-3) + 5 + 1}{6} = \frac{0}{6} = 0$$

$$\sigma = \sqrt{0} = 0$$

✗

11. Use Appropriate Tools The screen shows statistics for a data set that has been entered into a graphing calculator. Does 8.7 fall within 2 standard deviations of the mean of the data set? Explain. MP.5

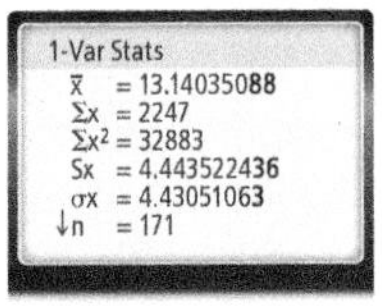
1-Var Stats
x̄ = 13.14035088
Σx = 2247
Σx² = 32883
Sx = 4.443522436
σx = 4.43051063
↓n = 171

12. Higher Order Thinking A data set has data one standard deviation below the mean at 76.2 and data one standard deviation above the mean at 105.4.

a. What is the mean of the data set? 90.8

b. What is the standard deviation of the data set? 14.6

c. What end values of the data are two standard deviations from the mean? 61.6 and 120

PRACTICE

Find and use the mean and the standard deviation to compare the variability of each pair of sample data sets. SEE EXAMPLES 1, 2, AND 4

13. Data Set A: 6, 9, 1, 2, 3, 4, 4, 5

Data Set B: 10, 5, 5, 2, 3, 7, 4, 8

14.

Data Set A	Data Set B
21.25	41.50
42.25	29.25
2.00	39.75
40.50	40.00
19.75	38.25
57.75	51.25
39.25	42.00
78.75	31.00
38.50	37.75
62.25	49.00

15. Find and use the mean and standard deviation to compare the variability of the populations represented in the dot plots. SEE EXAMPLES 3–4

Data Set A

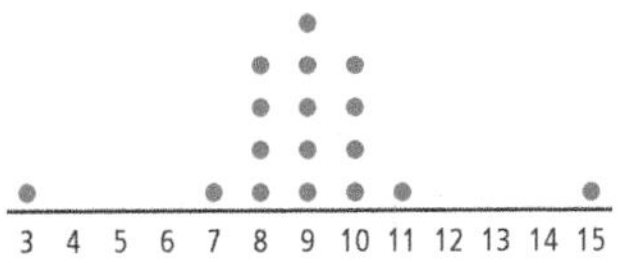
3 4 5 6 7 8 9 10 11 12 13 14 15

Data Set B

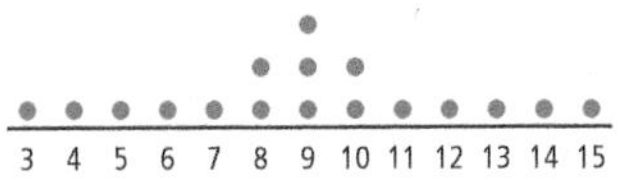
3 4 5 6 7 8 9 10 11 12 13 14 15

Data values in normally distributed data sets A and B are integers from 0 to 30 inclusive. Identify the range of values that satisfies each description. SEE EXAMPLE 2

Data Set A: mean: 12; standard deviation: 2

Data Set B: mean: 18; standard deviation: 3

16. All data values within 2 standard deviations from the mean of data set A 8–16

17. All data values more than 2 standard deviations from the mean of data set A 0–7 and 17–30

18. All data values within 1 standard deviation of the mean of data set B 15–21

LESSON 11-4 Standard Deviation 493

Answers

9. a. Since the means of data sets are equal, you can infer that the data set with the greater standard deviation is more spread out.

b. The shape of the histogram for the second set is wider and flatter.

10. The student forgot to square the differences before finding the sum.

11. Yes; 2 standard deviations below the mean and above the mean includes data values from about 4.28 to about 22. Therefore 8.7 falls within 2 standard deviations of the mean.

13. Data Set A: mean: 4.25, standard deviation: 2.49; Data Set B: mean: 5.50, standard deviation: 2.67; The means and the sample standard deviations of both sets are close to equal, so the sets have similar variability.

14. Data Set A: mean: 40.23, standard deviation: 22.42; Data Set B: mean: 39.98, standard deviation: 6.82; The means are about the same, but the sample standard deviation for Set A is much greater than the sample standard deviation for Set B, so the data from Set A have greater variability.

15. Data Set A: mean: 9, standard deviation: 2.28; Data Set B: mean: 9; standard deviation: 3.29; The means are about the same, but the sample standard deviation for Set B is greater than the sample standard deviation for Set A, so the data from Set B have greater variability. You can also verify this by observing that the data in the dot plot for Set B have a greater spread.

Answers

19. Finishing times under 2:32:37 are more than 2 standard deviations below the mean finishing time. The histogram bar for finishing times between 2 and 3 hours represents about 25,000 runners, so there would be no more than 25,000 runners who had finishing times less than 2 standard deviations below the mean.

20. With the new plant food, the mean number of blooms is about 17, or 3 blooms greater than last year, and the population standard deviation is about 4 blooms, or 2 blooms greater than last year. So both the mean and variability are greater with the new food. Because both the mean and standard deviation are greater, there is a greater chance of having more blooms more of the time, but because the standard deviation is greater, there is also a chance of having less blooms some of the time.

21. greater than 700; about 1,950

24. **Part A** Men: 11.6; Women: 11.4; The spread of the average driving distances is about the same for men and women.

Part B Men: 3.6; Women: 3.3; The variability of average driving distances about the mean is approximately the same for men and women.

Part C The histograms would have similar shapes; however, the histogram for the women would be shifted about 40 units to the left on the number line from the histogram for the men.

AVAILABLE **ONLINE**

PRACTICE & PROBLEM SOLVING

Practice Tutorial
Mixed Review Available Online

APPLY

19. **Make Sense and Persevere** The data display shows the number of runners with finishing times under 7 hours for all marathons run in a given year. How could you estimate the number of runners who had finishing times less than 2 standard deviations below the mean? **MP.1**

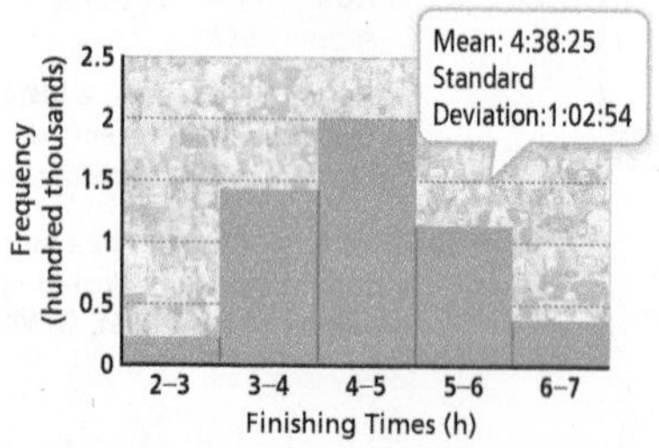
Mean: 4:38:25
Standard Deviation:1:02:54
Frequency (hundred thousands)
2.5
2
1.5
1
0.5
0
2–3
3–4
4–5
5–6
6–7
Finishing Times (h)

20. **Make Sense and Persevere** Last year, twelve hydrangea bushes had a mean of 14 blooms each, with a standard deviation of 2. The dot plot shows the number of blooms on the same bushes this year after a new plant food is used. What conclusions can you draw about the use of the new plant food and the number of blooms? **MP.1**

Hydrangeas with New Plant Food

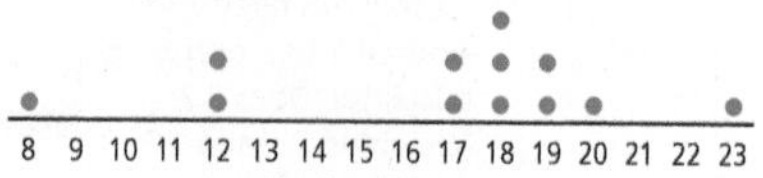
8 9 10 11 12 13 14 15 16 17 18 19 20 21 22 23
Number of Blooms

21. **Make Sense and Persevere** On a standardized test with the given statistics, about 68% of the scores fall within 1 standard deviation of the mean and about 95% of the scores fall within two standard deviations of the mean.

Mean Score: 450 **Standard Deviation:** 125
Total Number of Test Takers: 78,000

What is your score if you can say that you scored above the middle 95% of the people who took the test? How many test takers can say that? **MP.1**

ASSESSMENT PRACTICE

22. Consider a data set with a mean of 5.72 and a standard deviation of 1.55. Are the numbers within one standard deviation of the mean? Select *Yes* or *No*.

	Yes	No
7.51	☐	☑
4.18	☑	☐
4.16	☐	☑
10.00	☐	☑

23. **SAT/ACT** The variance for a data set with 8 items is 144. What is the standard deviation?

Ⓐ 4
Ⓑ 8
● 12
Ⓓ none of these

24. **Performance Task** The table shows the top ten average driving distances in 2015 for male and female professional golfers. The mean for men is 310.9 yards, and the mean for women is 267.2 yards.

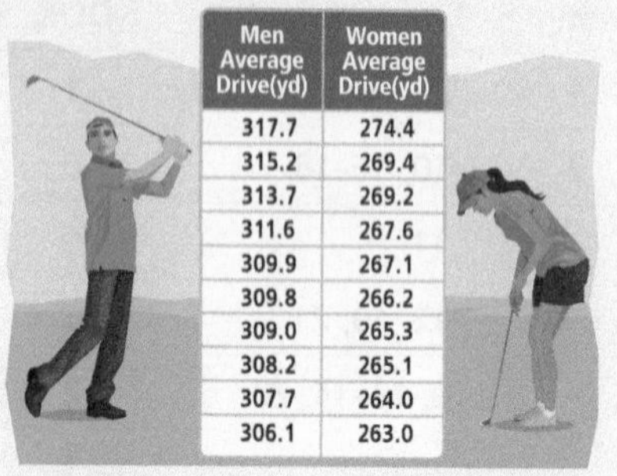

Men Average Drive(yd)	Women Average Drive(yd)
317.7	274.4
315.2	269.4
313.7	269.2
311.6	267.6
309.9	267.1
309.8	266.2
309.0	265.3
308.2	265.1
307.7	264.0
306.1	263.0

Part A Find the range for each data set. What do the ranges tell you about gender and average driving distance?

Part B Calculate the standard deviation for each sample. How can you use standard deviation to better understand the relationship between gender and average driving distance?

Part C How would histograms for the top ten men's and women's average driving distances be similar? How would they be different?

LESSON QUIZ

Use the Lesson Quiz to assess students' understanding of the mathematics in the lesson.

Students can take the Lesson Quiz online or you can download a printable copy from **SavvasRealize.com**. The Lesson Quiz is also available in the *Assessment Resources* book.

Item Analysis

Item	DOK	Standards
1	1	HSS.ID.A.2
2	2	HSS.ID.A.2
3	2	HSS.ID.A.2
4	1	HSS.ID.A.2
5	2	HSS.ID.A.3

RtI Use the student scores on the Lesson Quiz to prescribe differentiated assignments.

If students take the Lesson Quiz online, it will be automatically scored and appropriate differentiated practice will be assigned based on student performance.

I Intervention	0–3 points	• Reteach to Build Understanding • Mathematical Literacy and Vocabulary • Additional Practice
O On-Level	4 points	• Mathematical Literacy and Vocabulary • Additional Practice • Enrichment
A Advanced	5 points	• Enrichment

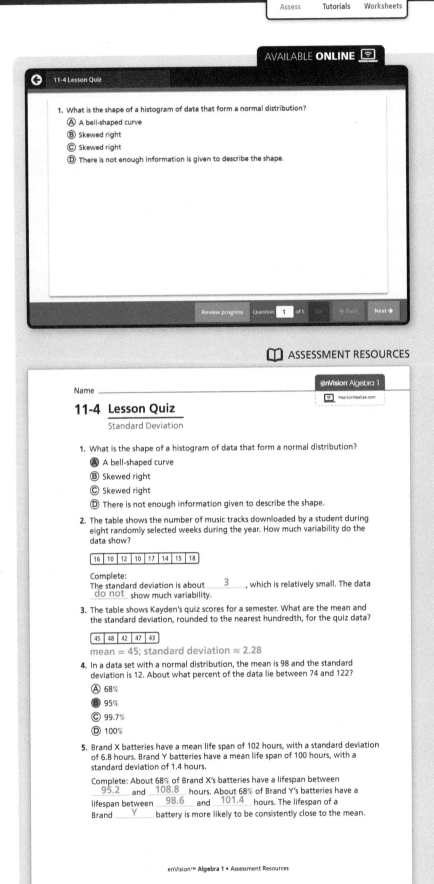

AVAILABLE **ONLINE**

11-4 Lesson Quiz

1. What is the shape of a histogram of data that form a normal distribution?
   Ⓐ A bell-shaped curve
   Ⓑ Skewed right
   Ⓒ Skewed right
   Ⓓ There is not enough information is given to describe the shape.

Review progress Question 1 of 5 Go ← Back Next →

ASSESSMENT RESOURCES

Name ______

enVision Algebra 1

PearsonRealize.com

11-4 Lesson Quiz

Standard Deviation

1. What is the shape of a histogram of data that form a normal distribution?
   Ⓐ A bell-shaped curve
   Ⓑ Skewed right
   Ⓒ Skewed right
   Ⓓ There is not enough information given to describe the shape.

2. The table shows the number of music tracks downloaded by a student during eight randomly selected weeks during the year. How much variability do the data show?

16	10	12	10	17	14	15	18

Complete:
The standard deviation is about __3__, which is relatively small. The data __do not__ show much variability.

3. The table shows Kayden's quiz scores for a semester. What are the mean and the standard deviation, rounded to the nearest hundredth, for the quiz data?

45	48	42	47	43

mean = 45; standard deviation ≈ 2.28

4. In a data set with a normal distribution, the mean is 98 and the standard deviation is 12. About what percent of the data lie between 74 and 122?
   Ⓐ 68%
   Ⓑ 95%
   Ⓒ 99.7%
   Ⓓ 100%

5. Brand X batteries have a mean life span of 102 hours, with a standard deviation of 6.8 hours. Brand Y batteries have a mean life span of 100 hours, with a standard deviation of 1.4 hours.

   Complete: About 68% of Brand X's batteries have a lifespan between __95.2__ and __108.8__ hours. About 68% of Brand Y's batteries have a lifespan between __98.6__ and __101.4__ hours. The lifespan of a Brand __Y__ battery is more likely to be consistently close to the mean.

enVision™ **Algebra 1** • Assessment Resources

DIFFERENTIATED RESOURCES

I = Intervention **O** = On-Level **A** = Advanced

= This activity is available as a digital assignment powered by MathXL® for School.

AVAILABLE ONLINE

Reteach to Build Understanding I

Provides scaffolded reteaching for the key lesson concepts.

Name ____________ enVision Algebra 1 PearsonRealize.com

11-4 Reteach to Build Understanding

Standard Deviation

1. Complete the diagram of a normal distribution by using words or numbers to fill in the blanks.

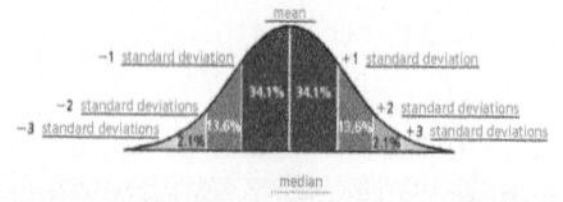
mean
−1 standard deviation
+1 standard deviation
−2 standard deviations
+2 standard deviations
−3 standard deviations
+3 standard deviations
34.1%
34.1%
13.6%
13.6%
2.1%
2.1%
median

2. The table shows sample data of how many minutes students spend on homework each night. Round to the nearest tenth if necessary.

90	75	60	85
65	80	70	75

The mean of the data is $\bar{x} =$ 75.

The variance is $\sigma^2 = \frac{15^2 + 0^2 + 15^2 + 10^2 + 10^2 + 5^2 + 5^2 + 0^2}{8 - 1}$

$= \frac{225 + 0 + 225 + 100 + 100 + 25 + 25 + 0}{8 - 1}$

$=$ 100

The standard deviation is $\sigma = \sqrt{100} =$ 10.

3. A student made an incorrect statement about finding the standard deviation. Put an X next to the incorrect statement. Correct the error.

a. The mean of the data is the sum of all items in the data set divided by the number of items n in the data set.

b. The variance of the data is found by taking the sum of $(x - \bar{x})$ for all values x and then dividing by $n - 1$. X

c. To find the standard deviation, take the square root of the variance.

d. When data are normally distributed, about 68% of data fall within one standard deviation of the mean.

Sample: The student forgot to state that the difference of the mean from the data value should be squared before dividing it by $(n - 1)$.

enVision™ Algebra 1 • Teaching Resources

Additional Practice I O

Provides extra practice for each lesson.

Name ____________ enVision Algebra 1 PearsonRealize.com

11-4 Additional Practice

Standard Deviation

A sample of computer tablet batteries has a mean battery life of 28 months and standard deviation of 4 months. What is the lifespan of batteries that are within the given standard deviations of the mean?

1. 1 standard deviation
24 to 32 months

2. 2 standard deviations
20 to 36 months

3. 3 standard deviations
16 to 40 months

Find the mean and standard deviation of the following data sets.

4.

28	12	15	17	22
25	19	23	15	26

Mean: 20.2
Standard Dev.: 5.39

5.

4.0	2.7	3.0	3.3	3.3
3.7	3.7	4.0	3.0	2.3

Mean: 3.3
Standard Dev.: 0.56

6.

49	67	58	55	62
70	52	65	60	58

Mean: 59.6
Standard Dev.: 6.62

7. Under what conditions might you use standard deviation to understand a situation?
Sample: Standard deviation is useful when determining how consistent or predictable data are. For example, if you were comparing the life of batteries, you would want to see a low standard deviation, because that would indicate less variability in the batteries' performance.

8. The table shows the points scored by a community football team during two seasons. Use the mean and standard deviation to determine during which season the team scored more consistently.

Last Season	10	3	20	27	35	17	20	13	17
This Season	23	17	28	16	23	16	16	10	13

Sample: During this season, the mean number of points scored was 18, and standard deviation was 9.3. During the last season, the mean number of points scored was also 18, and the standard deviation was 5.6. The standard deviation helps us see that scores were closer to the mean in this season, so the team's scores were more consistent during this season.

enVision™ Algebra 1 • Teaching Resources

Enrichment O A

Presents engaging problems and activities that extend the lesson concepts.

Name ____________ enVision Algebra 1 PearsonRealize.com

11-4 Enrichment

Standard Deviation

Background
On the fourteenth of last month, a shocking crime was committed. An evil individual attacked the very foundation of Mathtropolis. The villain stated that π is equal to *exactly* 3.14. Fortunately, the Mathtropolis Police Department (MPD) has 10 suspects under investigation and is sure one of them is the culprit.

Goal:
Help the MPD determine which of the suspects is the villain. The table shows the suspects' responses to a series of questions with population mean and standard deviation that are given.

Instructions:
- Begin by identifying the five suspects whose responses to Question 1 are more than 1.5 standard deviations from the mean. Suspects B, D, E, G, J
- Of the five, identify the suspects whose responses to Questions 2 and 3 are *both* more than 1.7 standard deviations from the mean. Suspects D, G, J
- Of the remaining three, identify the suspect whose responses to Questions 4, 5, and 6 are all at least 2 standard deviations from the mean.
This is the mathematical criminal! Who is it? Suspect G

	A	B	C	D	E	F	G	H	I	J
Q1	14	7	21	28	2	9	5	25	22	27
Q2	0	9	1	8	5	4	2	5	10	1
Q3	77%	96%	89%	66%	59%	32%	100%	92%	86%	60%
Q4	13	1	2	16	12	52	4	13	7	18
Q5	3	4	1	2	2	5	6	3	4	5
Q6	3	5	4	7	3	4	3	5	4	3

Question 1: How many waffles did you eat during this past week?
mean = 17
standard deviation = 6

Question 2: How many calculators do you and your family own?
mean = 5.1
standard deviation = 1.3

Question 3: What was your high school algebra average?
mean = 83.2%
standard deviation = 9.5%

Question 4: How many weeks ago did you last see an action movie?
mean = 10.3
standard deviation = 2.7

Question 5: How many times a day do you brush your teeth?
mean = 3.9
standard deviation = 0.8

Question 6: How many digits of π can you recite from memory?
mean = 5.2
standard deviation = 1.1

enVision™ Algebra 1 • Teaching Resources

Mathematical Literacy and Vocabulary I O

Helps students develop and reinforce understanding of key terms and concepts.

Name ____________ enVision Algebra 1 PearsonRealize.com

11-4 Mathematical Literacy and Vocabulary

Standard Deviation

Rita was studying for a quiz on standard deviation. She wrote the steps to find standard deviation on a set of note cards, but the cards got mixed up. Help Rita write the steps on how to find the standard deviation in order.

Calculate the variance of the sample set by finding the mean of the squares.

Square each difference $(x - \bar{x})^2$.

Find the mean $\bar{x}$ of the n values in the data set.

Take the square root of the variance to find the standard deviation.

Find the difference $x - \bar{x}$ between each value x and the mean.

Use the note cards to write the steps in order.

1. First, find the mean $\bar{x}$ of the n values in the data set.
2. Second, find the difference $x - \bar{x}$ between each value x and the mean.
3. Next, square each difference $(x - \bar{x})^2$.
4. Then, calculate the variance of the sample set by finding the mean of the squares.
5. Finally, take the square root of the variance to find the standard deviation.

enVision™ Algebra 1 • Teaching Resources

Digital Resources and Video Tutorials I O A

The **Reteach to Build Understanding, Additional Practice,** and **Enrichment** activities are available as digital assignments powered by MathXL for School. These activities are automatically assigned when students complete the lesson quiz online and are automatically scored.

Students can access instructional tutorials using the **Virtual Nerd app.**

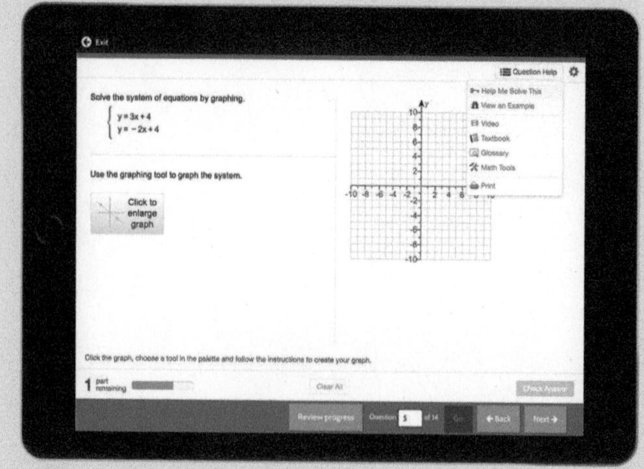
Solve the system of equations by graphing.
y = 3x + 4
y = −2x + 4
Use the graphing tool to graph the system.
Click to enlarge graph
Question Help
Help Me Solve This
View an Example
Video
Textbook
Glossary
Math Tools
Print
Clear All
Check Answer
Review progress
Back
Next

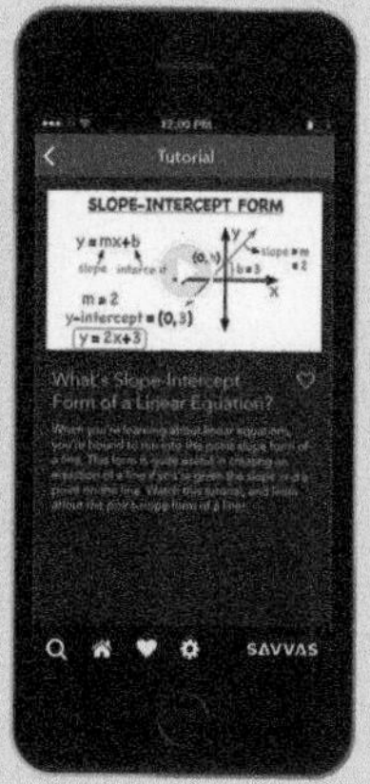
Tutorial
SLOPE-INTERCEPT FORM
SAVVAS

Students can also access Virtual Nerd videos using the **BouncePages app** to scan exercise pages marked with this icon. Students can download both apps for free in their mobile devices' app store.

A-Z Glossary

LESSON 11-5

Two-Way Frequency Tables

Lesson Overview

FOCUS

Objective

Students will be able to:

✓ Organize and summarize categorical data by creating two-way frequency tables.

✓ Calculate and interpret joint and marginal frequencies, joint and marginal relative frequencies and conditional relative frequencies, and use them to make inferences about a population.

Essential Understanding

Two-way frequency tables show relationships between two sets of categorical data. Entries in the table can be frequency counts or relative frequency. Two-way frequency tables are used to analyze data and make inferences about a population.

COHERENCE

Previously in this course, students:

- Calculated and interpreted statistical measures of center and spread to analyze and interpret data sets.

In this lesson, students:

- Calculate and use measures of frequency to analyze and interpret categorical data using two-way frequency tables.

In Algebra II, students will:

- Use two-way frequency tables to approximate conditional probabilities.

RIGOR

This lesson emphasizes *procedural skill and fluency* and *application*.

- Students calculate conditional relative frequency by finding the ratio of the joint frequency to the marginal frequency.
- Students interpret relative frequencies within the context of real-world situations, such as interpreting the results of a survey about food preferences.

Vocabulary Builder

NEW VOCABULARY

English | *Spanish*

- **conditional relative frequency** | *frequencia relativa condicionada*
- **joint frequency** | *frecuencia conjunta*
- **joint relative frequency** | *frequencia relative conjunta*
- **marginal frequency** | *frecuencia marginal*
- **marginal relative frequency** | *frequencia relativa marginal*

VOCABULARY ACTIVITY

Discuss with students the meanings of the terms *frequency, joint, relative,* and *marginal*. Some definitions of the terms, as used in daily life, do not relate to how they are used in this context. Have students match each relative frequency to the correct ratio.

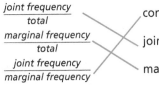

$\dfrac{\textit{joint frequency}}{\textit{total}}$	conditional relative frequency
$\dfrac{\textit{marginal frequency}}{\textit{total}}$	joint relative frequency
$\dfrac{\textit{joint frequency}}{\textit{marginal frequency}}$	marginal relative frequency

Student Companion

Students can do their in-class work for the lesson on pages 265–268 of their *Student Companion* or in Savvas Realize.

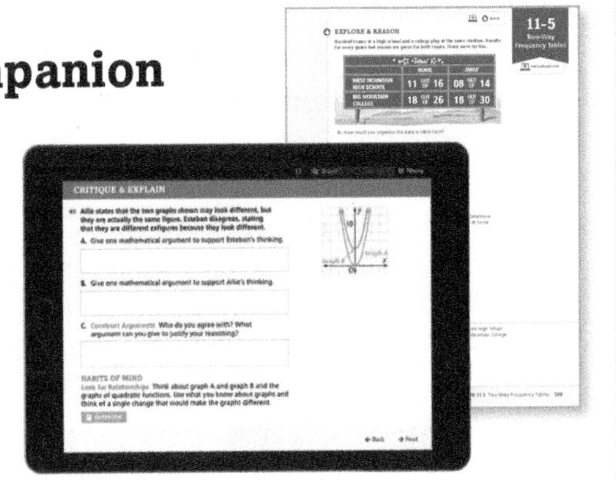

Mathematics Overview

COMMON CORE STANDARDS

Content Standards

In this lesson, students focus on this standard:

HSS.ID.B.5 Summarize categorical data for two categories in two-way frequency tables. Interpret relative frequencies in the context of the data (including joint, marginal, and conditional relative frequencies). Recognize possible associations and trends in the data.

Mathematical Practice Standards

These standards are highlighted in this lesson:

MP.2 Reason Abstractly and Quantitatively

Students attend to the meaning of quantities when they determine the reasonableness of inferences made from two-way frequency tables that represent real-world situations, such as the lunch preferences of juniors and seniors in high school.

MP.7 Look For and Make Use of Structure

Students observe the frequencies in the rows and columns of the tables as single objects and recognize that the relative frequencies that are calculated for rows and the relative frequencies that are calculated for columns are interpreted in different ways.

Activity

EXPLORE & REASON

INSTRUCTIONAL FOCUS Students explore organizing given data in a table and analyzing claims made about the data. This prepares students to make and interpret two-way frequency tables.

STUDENT COMPANION Students can complete the *Explore & Reason* activity on page 265 of their *Student Companion.*

Before WHOLE CLASS

Implement Tasks that Promote Reasoning and Problem Solving ETP

Q: What do you notice about the information in the picture? [The college team plays more games than the high school team. The high school team plays more home games than away games and the college team plays more away games than home games.]

During SMALL GROUP

Support Productive Struggle in Learning Mathematics ETP

Q: Is there more than one correct way to set up a table to organize the data?
[Yes, the rows can represent the different teams and the columns can represent the number of wins at home and away, or vice versa.]

For Early Finishers

Q: Use the given information and reorganize the data in table form using the number of losses for each team. Analyze the data. What conclusions can you make about the number of losses for each team versus games played at home or away?
[See students' tables. Answers may vary.]

After WHOLE CLASS

Facilitate Meaningful Mathematical Discourse ETP

Q: What information not listed could you determine using the given information?
[You can determine the number of losses for each team at home and away. You can determine the total number of games each team played.]

Q: How could you make a table that displays the wins and losses for West Mountain High School? [Create a table with two rows, labeled wins and losses, and two columns, labeled home and away.]

HABITS OF MIND

Use with **EXPLORE & REASON**

Make Sense and Persevere What percentage of the West Mountain High School team's total games are home wins? What percentage of the Big Mountain College team's total games are away losses? MP.1

[about 37%; about 20%]

AVAILABLE **ONLINE**

Go back

EXPLORE & REASON

A-Z

Baseball teams at a high school and a college play at the same stadium. Results for every game last season are given for both teams. There were no ties.

A. How could you organize the data in table form?

Enter your answer.

B. Look for Relationships How would you analyze the data to determine whether the data support the claim that the team that plays at home is more likely to win?

Enter your answer.

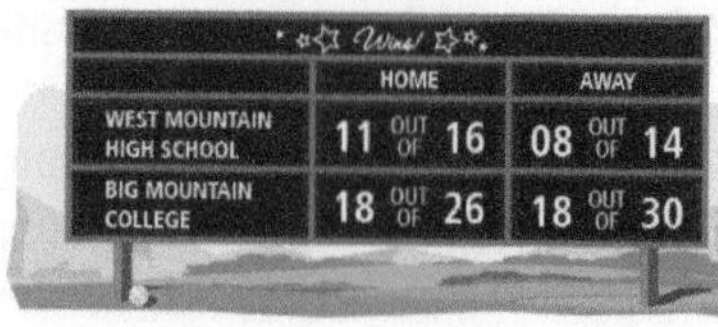

Wins!
HOME
AWAY
WEST MOUNTAIN HIGH SCHOOL
11 OUT OF 16
08 OUT OF 14
BIG MOUNTAIN COLLEGE
18 OUT OF 26
18 OUT OF 30

1 of 1

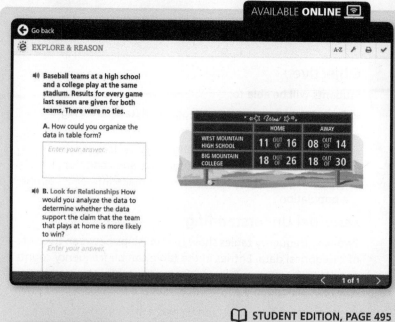

STUDENT EDITION, PAGE 495

11-5 Two-Way Frequency Tables

PearsonRealize.com

Common Core State Standards HSS.ID.B.5, MP.2, MP.3, MP.7

Activity Assess

EXPLORE & REASON

Baseball teams at a high school and a college play at the same stadium. Results for every game last season are given for both teams. There were no ties.

Baseball Season Results at Mountain View Stadium

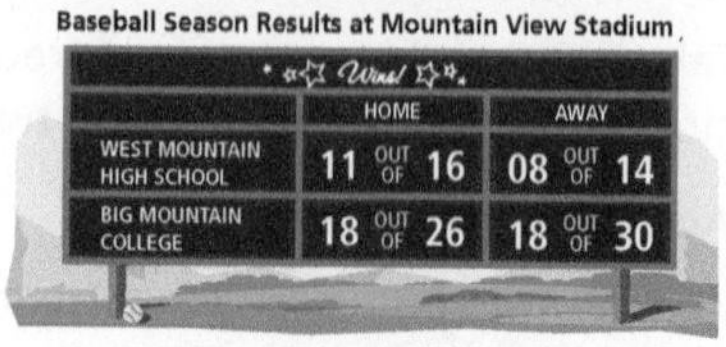

Wins!
HOME
AWAY
WEST MOUNTAIN HIGH SCHOOL
11 OUT OF 16
08 OUT OF 14
BIG MOUNTAIN COLLEGE
18 OUT OF 26
18 OUT OF 30

A. How could you organize the data in table form?

B. Look for Relationships How would you analyze the data to determine whether the data support the claim that the team that plays at home is more likely to win? MP.7

I CAN… organize data in two-way frequency tables and use them to make inferences.

VOCABULARY
- conditional relative frequency
- joint frequency
- joint relative frequency
- marginal frequency
- marginal relative frequency

ESSENTIAL QUESTION How can you use two-way frequency tables to analyze data?

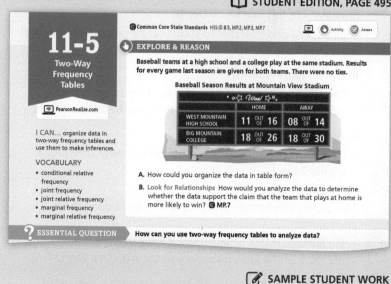

SAMPLE STUDENT WORK

A. You could create a two-way frequency table with rows for high school and college teams and columns for games won at home and away.

B. You could compare the percentage of games won at home and away for high school and college teams to see if both have significantly more wins at home than away.

Activity Assess

INTRODUCE THE ESSENTIAL QUESTION

Establish Mathematics Goals to Focus Learning ETP

Introduce students to two-way frequency tables. Remind students that they have previously used tables to display and analyze data. Explain that they can use a two-way frequency table to interpret a data set and make inferences.

EXAMPLE 1 Interpret a Two-Way Frequency Table

Pose Purposeful Questions ETP

Q: What do you notice about the relationship between the joint frequencies and the marginal frequencies?
[The sum of the joint frequencies in a row or column is equal to the marginal frequency for that row or column.]

Try It! Answer

1. The marginal frequencies show that 90 male and 135 female customers were surveyed.

Common Error

Try It! 1 Students may use marginal frequencies for burgers and pizza instead of males and females. Have students cover up the rows for "Female" and "Totals" and ask them how many total males are in the table.

AVAILABLE ONLINE

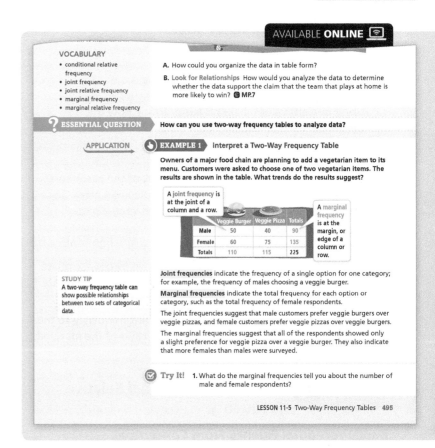

VOCABULARY
- conditional relative frequency
- joint frequency
- joint relative frequency
- marginal frequency
- marginal relative frequency

A. How could you organize the data in table form?

B. Look for Relationships How would you analyze the data to determine whether the data support the claim that the team that plays at home is more likely to win? MP.7

ESSENTIAL QUESTION How can you use two-way frequency tables to analyze data?

APPLICATION

EXAMPLE 1 Interpret a Two-Way Frequency Table

Owners of a major food chain are planning to add a vegetarian item to its menu. Customers were asked to choose one of two vegetarian items. The results are shown in the table. What trends do the results suggest?

A joint frequency is at the joint of a column and a row.

	Veggie Burger	Veggie Pizza	Totals
Male	50	40	90
Female	60	75	135
Totals	110	115	225

A marginal frequency is at the margin, or edge of a column or row.

STUDY TIP
A two-way frequency table can show possible relationships between two sets of categorical data.

Joint frequencies indicate the frequency of a single option for one category; for example, the frequency of males choosing a veggie burger.

Marginal frequencies indicate the total frequency for each option or category, such as the total frequency of female respondents.

The joint frequencies suggest that male customers prefer veggie burgers over veggie pizzas, and female customers prefer veggie pizzas over veggie burgers.

The marginal frequencies suggest that all of the respondents showed only a slight preference for veggie pizza over a veggie burger. They also indicate that more females than males were surveyed.

Try It! 1. What do the marginal frequencies tell you about the number of male and female respondents?

LESSON 11-5 Two-Way Frequency Tables 495

ADDITIONAL EXAMPLES

AVAILABLE ONLINE

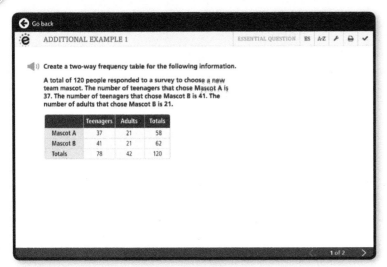

Go back
ADDITIONAL EXAMPLE 1 ESSENTIAL QUESTION ES A-Z

Create a two-way frequency table for the following information.

A total of 120 people responded to a survey to choose a new team mascot. The number of teenagers that chose Mascot A is 37. The number of teenagers that chose Mascot B is 41. The number of adults that chose Mascot B is 21.

	Teenagers	Adults	Totals
Mascot A	37	21	58
Mascot B	41	21	62
Totals	78	42	120

1 of 2

Go back
ADDITIONAL EXAMPLE 5 ESSENTIAL QUESTION ES A-Z

A basketball team has two uniforms, a blue uniform and a white uniform. The table shows the number of wins and losses the team has wearing the different uniforms.

	Wins	Losses	Total
Blue Uniform	27	15	42
White Uniform	13	22	35
Total	40	37	77

What does the marginal relative frequency $\frac{42}{77}$ mean in this context?

The marginal relative frequency is the ratio of games the team wears the blue uniforms to the total number of games.

1 of 2

Example 1 Students create a two-way frequency table.

Q: How can you create a two-way frequency table if you are given the total number of values and one of the joint frequencies is missing?
[Add the given joint frequencies in either a row or column and subtract from the total number in that row or column to find the missing frequency.]

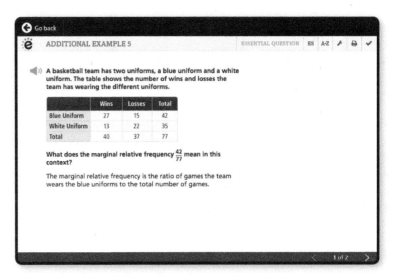

Example 5 Students determine what a given marginal relative frequency means in the context of the problem.

Q: How can you interpret a given marginal relative frequency?
[Find the value of the numerator of the marginal relative frequency in the two-way frequency table. Use the label of the row or column that value appears in to describe what the value means.]

Activity Assess

EXAMPLE 2 Interpret a Two-Way Relative Frequency Table

Pose Purposeful Questions ETP

Q: Why is a two-way relative frequency table easier to use than a two-way frequency table to interpret the data?
[Using percent values makes it easier to see how the categorical data compare to each other.]

Try It! Answer

2. The marginal frequencies show that 49% of the customers selected veggie burger and 51% selected veggie pizza. So, a greater percentage of customers selected veggie pizza.

HABITS OF MIND

Use with **EXAMPLES 1 & 2**

Communicate Precisely How does joint relative frequency relate to joint frequency? How does marginal relative frequency relate to marginal frequency? **MP.6**

[Joint relative frequency is the ratio of the joint frequency to the total, and marginal relative frequency is the ratio of the marginal frequency to the total.]

EXAMPLE 3 Calculate Conditional Relative Frequency

Build Procedural Fluency From Conceptual Understanding ETP

Q: What is a difference between the conditional relative frequencies and the joint and marginal relative frequencies?
[The joint and marginal relative frequencies in the table are all related to the total number of data. The sum of the relative frequencies is 1. The conditional relative frequencies are only related to the row total. There is no relationship across rows.]

Q: How does conditional relative frequency relate to joint frequency and marginal frequency?
[Conditional relative frequency is the ratio of the joint frequency and the related marginal frequency.]

AVAILABLE **ONLINE**

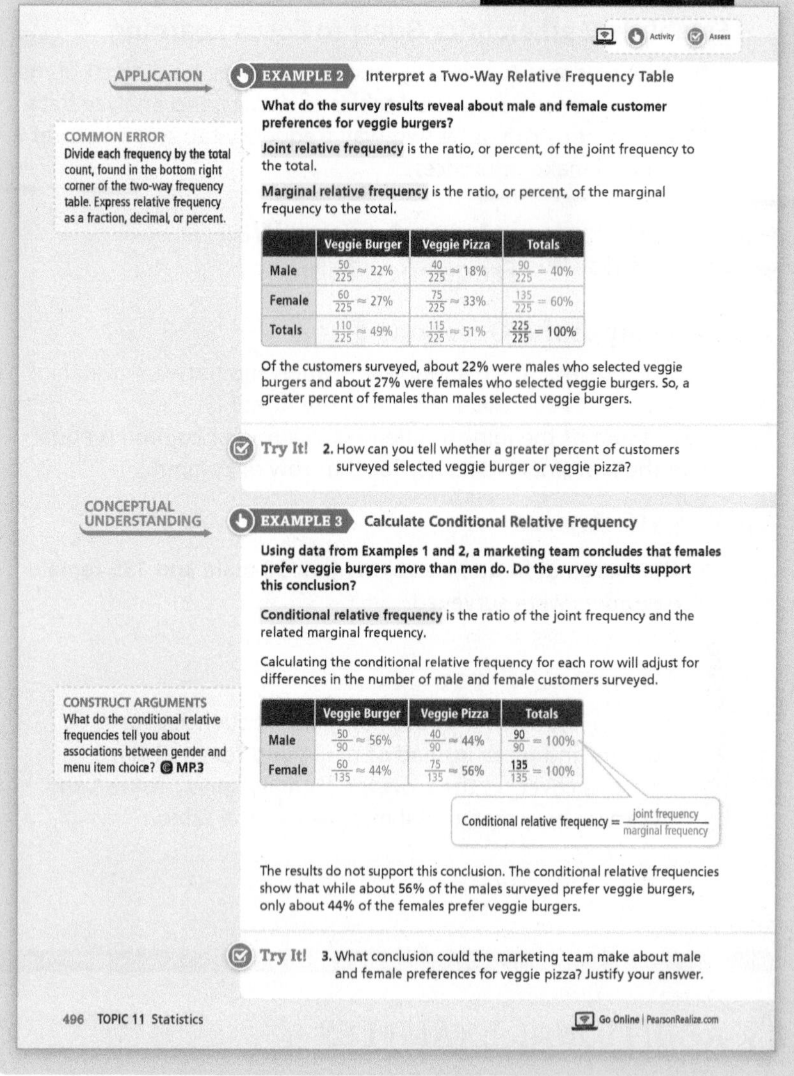
Activity Assess

APPLICATION

EXAMPLE 2 Interpret a Two-Way Relative Frequency Table

What do the survey results reveal about male and female customer preferences for veggie burgers?

COMMON ERROR
Divide each frequency by the total count, found in the bottom right corner of the two-way frequency table. Express relative frequency as a fraction, decimal, or percent.

Joint relative frequency is the ratio, or percent, of the joint frequency to the total.

Marginal relative frequency is the ratio, or percent, of the marginal frequency to the total.

	Veggie Burger	Veggie Pizza	Totals
Male	$\frac{50}{225} \approx 22\%$	$\frac{40}{225} \approx 18\%$	$\frac{90}{225} = 40\%$
Female	$\frac{60}{225} \approx 27\%$	$\frac{75}{225} \approx 33\%$	$\frac{135}{225} = 60\%$
Totals	$\frac{110}{225} \approx 49\%$	$\frac{115}{225} \approx 51\%$	$\frac{225}{225} = 100\%$

Of the customers surveyed, about 22% were males who selected veggie burgers and about 27% were females who selected veggie burgers. So, a greater percent of females than males selected veggie burgers.

Try It! 2. How can you tell whether a greater percent of customers surveyed selected veggie burger or veggie pizza?

CONCEPTUAL UNDERSTANDING

EXAMPLE 3 Calculate Conditional Relative Frequency

Using data from Examples 1 and 2, a marketing team concludes that females prefer veggie burgers more than men do. Do the survey results support this conclusion?

Conditional relative frequency is the ratio of the joint frequency and the related marginal frequency.

Calculating the conditional relative frequency for each row will adjust for differences in the number of male and female customers surveyed.

CONSTRUCT ARGUMENTS
What do the conditional relative frequencies tell you about associations between gender and menu item choice? MP.3

	Veggie Burger	Veggie Pizza	Totals
Male	$\frac{50}{90} \approx 56\%$	$\frac{40}{90} \approx 44\%$	$\frac{90}{90} = 100\%$
Female	$\frac{60}{135} \approx 44\%$	$\frac{75}{135} \approx 56\%$	$\frac{135}{135} = 100\%$

$$\text{Conditional relative frequency} = \frac{\text{joint frequency}}{\text{marginal frequency}}$$

The results do not support this conclusion. The conditional relative frequencies show that while about 56% of the males surveyed prefer veggie burgers, only about 44% of the females prefer veggie burgers.

Try It! 3. What conclusion could the marketing team make about male and female preferences for veggie pizza? Justify your answer.

496 TOPIC 11 Statistics

Go Online | PearsonRealize.com

Try It! Answer

3. Females prefer veggie pizza more than males do. Conditional relative frequencies show that while 56% of the females surveyed prefer veggie pizza, only 44% of the males do. This difference could be statistically significant.

ADV Advanced Students

USE WITH EXAMPLE 2 Have students explore finding the joint relative frequencies and marginal relative frequencies, given a description of the data.

Q: Males and females are surveyed to see whether they prefer watching movies or TV shows. Of the males, 54 prefer movies and 40 prefer TV shows. Of the females, 44 prefer movies and 62 prefer TV shows. Find the joint relative frequencies and marginal relative frequencies of the data set.
[Joint relative frequencies: Males who prefer movies: 27%; Males who prefer TV: 20%; Females who prefer movies: 22%; Females who prefer TV: 31%. Marginal relative frequencies: Males: 47%, Females: 53%; Movies: 49%, TV: 51%.]

RtI Struggling Students

USE WITH EXAMPLE 3 Some students may struggle writing the conditional relative frequencies as percents.

- Have students practice finding percent.

1. What percent of 64 is 24?
[37.5%]
2. What percent of 88 is 66?
[75%]
3. What percent of 60 is 21?
[35%]
4. What percent of 250 is 80?
[32%]

EXAMPLE 4 Interpret Conditional Relative Frequency

Pose Purposeful Questions ETP

Q: Why is it important to know the total number of people that chose veggie burgers and the total number of people that chose veggie pizza? [The total numbers of customers that chose each type of food are the values that are used as the denominators of the conditional relative frequencies.]

Try It! Answer

4. Of the customers who prefer veggie pizza, there is no significant difference between males and females when compared to the customers who prefer veggie burgers.

HABITS OF MIND

Use with **EXAMPLES 3 & 4**

Look for Relationships Why can there be multiple values for the conditional relative frequency? MP.7

[Conditional relative frequency is the ratio of the joint frequency to the related marginal frequency, so depending on which parameter you are using, different marginal frequencies can be used.]

EXAMPLE 5 Interpret Data Frequencies

Pose Purposeful Questions ETP

Q: How can you compare the number of males and females cheering for Bears using conditional relative frequencies? [Divide each joint frequency in the Cheering for Bears column by the marginal frequency in the Cheering for Bears column. Then compare the ratios.]

Try It! Answer

5. The number $\frac{72}{137}$ represents the ratio of male Bears fans to the number of males surveyed.

AVAILABLE ONLINE

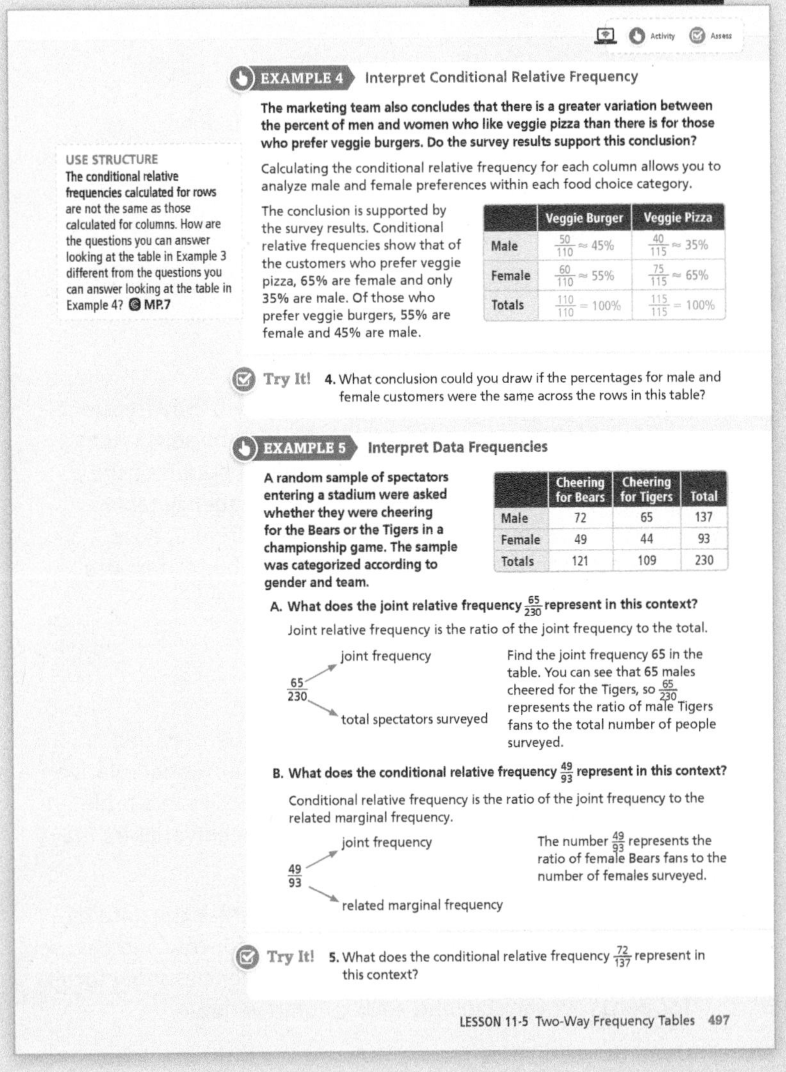
Activity Assess

EXAMPLE 4 Interpret Conditional Relative Frequency

The marketing team also concludes that there is a greater variation between the percent of men and women who like veggie pizza than there is for those who prefer veggie burgers. Do the survey results support this conclusion?

USE STRUCTURE
The conditional relative frequencies calculated for rows are not the same as those calculated for columns. How are the questions you can answer looking at the table in Example 3 different from the questions you can answer looking at the table in Example 4? **MP.7**

Calculating the conditional relative frequency for each column allows you to analyze male and female preferences within each food choice category.

The conclusion is supported by the survey results. Conditional relative frequencies show that of the customers who prefer veggie pizza, 65% are female and only 35% are male. Of those who prefer veggie burgers, 55% are female and 45% are male.

	Veggie Burger	Veggie Pizza
Male	$\frac{50}{110} \approx 45\%$	$\frac{40}{115} \approx 35\%$
Female	$\frac{60}{110} \approx 55\%$	$\frac{75}{115} \approx 65\%$
Totals	$\frac{110}{110} = 100\%$	$\frac{115}{115} = 100\%$

Try It! 4. What conclusion could you draw if the percentages for male and female customers were the same across the rows in this table?

EXAMPLE 5 Interpret Data Frequencies

A random sample of spectators entering a stadium were asked whether they were cheering for the Bears or the Tigers in a championship game. The sample was categorized according to gender and team.

	Cheering for Bears	Cheering for Tigers	Total
Male	72	65	137
Female	49	44	93
Totals	121	109	230

A. What does the joint relative frequency $\frac{65}{230}$ represent in this context?

Joint relative frequency is the ratio of the joint frequency to the total.

$\frac{65}{230}$ → joint frequency / total spectators surveyed

Find the joint frequency 65 in the table. You can see that 65 males cheered for the Tigers, so $\frac{65}{230}$ represents the ratio of male Tigers fans to the total number of people surveyed.

B. What does the conditional relative frequency $\frac{49}{93}$ represent in this context?

Conditional relative frequency is the ratio of the joint frequency to the related marginal frequency.

$\frac{49}{93}$ → joint frequency / related marginal frequency

The number $\frac{49}{93}$ represents the ratio of female Bears fans to the number of females surveyed.

Try It! 5. What does the conditional relative frequency $\frac{72}{137}$ represent in this context?

LESSON 11-5 Two-Way Frequency Tables 497

ELL English Language Learners *(Use with* **EXAMPLE 4***)*

LISTENING BEGINNING Review the terms *row* and *column* with students. Provide colored game chips and give students directions to arrange the chips in rows and columns. For example, "Make an arrangement with three rows and 2 columns. Each row should have two different colored chips, and each column should have the same colored chips."

Q: In the example, what information is shown in the rows of the table? In the columns? [people surveyed; food choice]

Q: How can any one value in a table be described? [You can name it by the intersection of its row and its column.]

READING INTERMEDIATE The phrase *conditional relative frequency* can be better understood when each word in the phrase is looked at separately. First have students read the definition of the noun *frequency*. Then have students read the definitions for *relative* and *conditional*.

Q: Based on the definitions of each word, define *conditional relative frequency*. [the number of times something occurs that is related to something else and controlled by or tied to another thing]

Q: How does that relate to the definition in the example? [It is a ratio of the number of times something occurs (joint frequency) and the marginal frequency.]

WRITING ADVANCED Have students write the meaning of the term *survey* in their journals. Have students include the purpose of a survey and the qualities of a good survey question. Challenge students to write a good survey question. First, brainstorm a list of possible topics, writing some key terms to use on the board.

Q: Why might someone use a survey? [to find out people's preferences for different items]

Q: How are survey questions different from some other types of questions? [Survey questions cannot be open-ended; they have a specific number of choices for the responder to pick from.]

CONCEPT SUMMARY Two-Way Frequency Tables

Q: Would you use joint and marginal relative frequencies or conditional relative frequencies to compare all values in the table?
[You would use joint and marginal relative frequencies to compare all values in the table. Conditional relative frequencies only compare items in the same row or column.]

AVAILABLE **ONLINE**

Concept Summary Assess

CONCEPT SUMMARY Two-Way Frequency Tables

WORDS Two-way frequency tables show relationships between two sets of categorical data. Entries can be frequency counts or relative frequencies. Entries in the body of the table are **joint frequencies** (counts) or **joint relative frequencies** (ratios). Entries in the totals column or row are **marginal frequencies** or **marginal relative frequencies**.

Conditional relative frequencies show the frequency of responses for a given condition, or the ratio of the joint frequencies to the corresponding marginal frequency.

TABLES

Movie Time Preferences

	Afternoon	Evening	Totals
Student	$\frac{90}{200} = 45\%$	$\frac{50}{200} = 25\%$	$\frac{140}{200} = 70\%$
Adult	$\frac{20}{200} = 10\%$	$\frac{40}{200} = 20\%$	$\frac{60}{200} = 30\%$
Totals	$\frac{110}{200} = 55\%$	$\frac{90}{200} = 45\%$	$\frac{200}{200} = 100\%$

20 of the 200 respondents, or 10%, were adults who prefer the afternoon show.

70% of the respondents were students.

Conditional Relative Frequency

	Afternoon	Evening	Totals
Student	$\frac{90}{140} \approx 64\%$	$\frac{50}{140} \approx 36\%$	$\frac{140}{140} = 100\%$
Adult	$\frac{20}{60} \approx 33\%$	$\frac{40}{60} \approx 67\%$	$\frac{60}{60} = 100\%$

Of all of the adult respondents, 33% prefer afternoon shows.

Conditional Relative Frequency

	Afternoon	Evening
Student	$\frac{90}{110} \approx 82\%$	$\frac{50}{90} \approx 56\%$
Adult	$\frac{20}{110} \approx 18\%$	$\frac{40}{90} \approx 44\%$
Totals	$\frac{110}{110} = 100\%$	$\frac{90}{90} = 100\%$

Of all of the respondents that prefer evening shows, 44% were adults.

Do You UNDERSTAND?

1. ESSENTIAL QUESTION How can you use two-way frequency tables to analyze data?
2. **Communicate Precisely** How are joint frequencies and marginal frequencies similar? How are they different? MP.6
3. **Look for Relationships** How are conditional relative frequencies related to joint frequencies and marginal frequencies? MP.7
4. **Error Analysis** Zhang says that the marginal relative frequency for a given variable is 10. Could Zhang be correct? Explain your reasoning. MP.3

Do You KNOW HOW?

In a survey, customers select Item A or Item B. Item A is selected by 20 males and 10 females. Of 20 customers who select Item B, five are males.

5. Make a two-way frequency table to organize the data.
6. Make a two-way relative frequency table to organize the data.
7. Calculate conditional relative frequencies for males and females. Is it reasonable to conclude that males prefer Item A more than females do?
8. Calculate conditional relative frequencies for Item A and Item B. Is it reasonable to conclude that a customer who prefers Item B is more likely to be a female than a male?

498 TOPIC 11 Statistics

Go Online | PearsonRealize.com

Do You UNDERSTAND? | Do You KNOW HOW?

Common Error

Exercise 5 Some students may create a two-way frequency table with 20 as the number of females who select item B. Have students carefully read the given details of the problem before making the two-way frequency table. Since 5 males out of 20 customers select Item B, have students use subtraction to find the number of females who select Item B.

Answers

1. You can calculate joint and marginal frequencies, joint and marginal relative frequencies, and conditional relative frequencies. If conditional relative frequencies in a table are not all about the same, associations between variables may be statistically significant.
2. Joint and marginal frequencies both organize the data by categories. Joint frequencies show totals for row and column variables combined, while marginal frequencies show totals for each row variable and each column variable.
3. Conditional relative frequencies are the ratio of a joint frequency and the marginal frequency of the corresponding row or column, depending on which parameter, or condition, you are using.
4. Zhang cannot be correct. A marginal relative frequency is a decimal between 0 and 1. She may be confusing marginal relative frequency and marginal frequency, which could have a value of 10.

5.

	Item A	Item B	Totals
Male	20	5	25
Female	10	15	25
Totals	30	20	50

6.

	Item A	Item B	Totals
Male	0.4	0.1	0.5
Female	0.2	0.3	0.5
Totals	0.6	0.4	1.0

7.

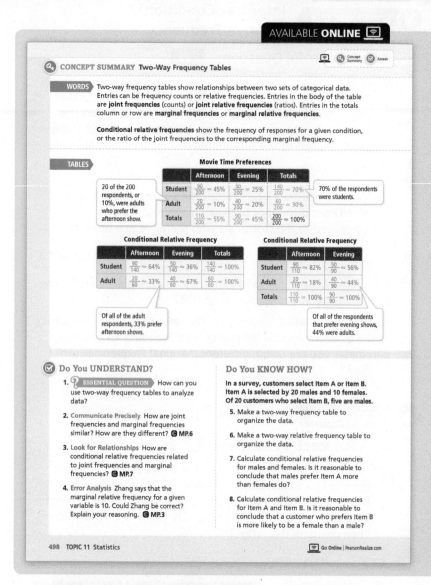

	Item A	Item B	Totals
Male	0.8	0.2	1.0
Female	0.4	0.6	1.0

Yes; it is reasonable to conclude that males prefer Item A more than females do because 80% of males prefer Item A, while only 40% of females prefer Item A.

8.

	Item A	Item B
Male	0.67	0.25
Female	0.33	0.75
Totals	1.0	1.0

Yes; it is reasonable to conclude that a customer who prefers Item B is more likely to be female because of the customers who prefer Item B, 75% are female, while only 25% are male.

PRACTICE & PROBLEM SOLVING

AVAILABLE ONLINE

Lesson Practice You may opt to have students complete the automatically scored Practice and Problem Solving items online powered by MathXL for School.

Choose from: **Lesson Practice**

Adaptive Practice

You may also take advantage of the bank of exercises for assigning additional practice.

Assignment Guide

Basic	Advanced
9–18, 21–27	9–13, 16–27

Item Analysis

Example	Items	DOK
1	25	1
	10, 13, 14, 23	2
2	17, 26	1
	11	2
3	18, 19	1
4	9, 15, 16	2
5	20–22, 24	2
	12, 27	3

Answers

9. Yes; an equal number of juniors and seniors were surveyed, so percentages can be compared without calculating conditional relative frequencies. The table shows that a greater percentage of juniors prefer Item B and a greater percentage of seniors prefer Item A.

10. The student did not take into account that more male than female students were surveyed. The student should have calculated conditional relative frequencies to find that the same percentage (50%) of each group of students prefers math.

11. Each marginal relative frequency is the sum of the joint relative frequencies in the corresponding row or column.

AVAILABLE ONLINE

PRACTICE & PROBLEM SOLVING

Scan for Multimedia

Practice Tutorial

Additional Exercises Available Online

UNDERSTAND

9. Reason An equal number of juniors and seniors were surveyed about whether they prefer lunch item A or B. Is it reasonable to infer from the table that more juniors prefer lunch item B while more seniors prefer lunch item A? Explain. MP.2

	Item A	Item B	Totals
Junior	0.1	0.4	0.5
Senior	0.3	0.2	0.5
Totals	0.6	0.4	1.0

10. Error Analysis Describe and correct the errors a student made when making a generalization based on a two-way frequency table. MP.3

Which subject do you prefer?

	Math	Language Arts	Totals
Male	45	45	90
Female	30	30	60
Totals	75	75	150

Male students prefer math more than female students do. ✗

11. Look for Relationships In a two-way relative frequency table, how are joint relative frequencies and marginal relative frequencies related? MP.7

12. Higher Order Thinking Students are surveyed to see how long they studied for a test.
- 10% of the students who studied 3 hours or more failed the test.
- 40% of the students who studied less than 3 hours passed the test.
- 2 students who studied 3 hours or more failed the test.
- 4 students who studied less than 3 hours passed the test.

a. Make a two-way frequency table that shows the association between hours spent studying and passing the test.

b. Does the association appear to be significant? Explain.

PRACTICE

In a survey, music club members select their preference between Song A or Song B. Song A is selected by 30 teens and 10 adults. Of 20 members who select Song B, five are teens. SEE EXAMPLES 1–4

Make a two-way frequency table to organize the data.

13. Is it reasonable to say that more people surveyed prefer Song A? Explain.

14. Is it reasonable to say that more adults than teens participated in the survey? Explain.

Calculate conditional relative frequencies.

15. Is it reasonable to say that teens prefer Song A more than adults do? Explain.

16. Is a member who prefers Song B significantly more likely to be an adult than a teen? Explain.

In the two-way frequency table, frequencies are shown on the top of each cell in blue, and relative frequencies are shown at the bottom in red. Most of the frequencies are missing. SEE EXAMPLES 1–5

High School Graduate?	Choice A	Choice B	Totals
Yes	16 0.08	___ ___	___ 0.56
No	___ ___	24 ___	___ ___
Totals	___ ___	___ ___	___ ___

17. Complete the table.

18. Calculate conditional relative frequencies for yes and no.

19. Calculate conditional relative frequencies for Choices A and B.

20. Is a high school graduate more likely to prefer Choice A or B? Explain.

21. Is someone who prefers Choice A more likely to be a high school graduate than not? Explain.

22. What does the joint relative frequency $\frac{64}{200}$ represent in this context?

23. What does the conditional relative frequency $\frac{96}{120}$ represent in this context?

LESSON 11-5 Two-Way Frequency Tables 499

12. a.

	Pass	Fail	Totals
< 3 h	4	6	10
≥ 3 h	18	2	20
Totals	22	8	30

b. Yes; the association appears to be significant because the conditional relative frequencies for rows are all different.

	Pass	Fail	Totals
< 3 h	0.4	0.6	1.0
≥ 3 h	0.9	0.1	1.0

13–21. See back of book.

22–23. See next page.

Answers

22. the ratio of non-graduates who prefer Choice A to the total number of respondents

23. the ratio of graduates who prefer Choice B to the overall number of respondents who chose B

24. No; calculating conditional relative frequencies for rows shows that 80% of voters support the referendum regardless of income.

Do you support the referendum?			
Income	Yes	No	Totals
≤ $100,000	0.8	0.2	1.00
> $100,000	0.8	0.2	1.00

25.

Blooms?	No Plant Food	Plant Food	Totals
< 14	5	3	8
≥ 14	7	9	16
Totals	12	12	24

Blooms?	No Plant Food	Plant Food
< 14	0.42	0.25
≥ 14	0.58	0.75
Totals	1.00	1.00

Calculating the conditional relative frequencies by columns shows that, of the 12 plants grown without the new food, 58% had satisfactory blooms. Of the 12 plants grown with the new food, 76% had satisfactory blooms. It is reasonable to infer that there is a significant association between using the plant food and the number of blooms the plant will produce.

26. Yes; calculating conditional relative frequencies for rows shows that 29% of respondents between 18 and 24 years old have never flown on a commercial airline, while only 15% of respondents 25 years or older have flown on a commercial airline.

Have you ever flown on a commercial airline?			
Age	Yes	No	Totals
18–24 yrs	0.71	0.29	1.00
25^+ yrs	0.85	0.15	1.00

AVAILABLE ONLINE

Practice Tutorial
Mixed Review Available Online

PRACTICE & PROBLEM SOLVING

APPLY

24. Construct Arguments Is there a significant association between income and whether or not a voter supports the referendum? Justify your answer. MP.3

Do you support the referendum?			
Income	Yes	No	Totals
≤ $100,000	80	20	100
> $100,000	40	10	50
Totals	120	30	150

25. Make Sense and Persevere A gardener is only satisfied when a hydrangea bush has at least 14 blooms. How can you organize the data shown in the dot plots into two-way frequency tables to make inferences about the new plant food and the number of blooms? MP.1

Hydrangeas Without New Plant Food

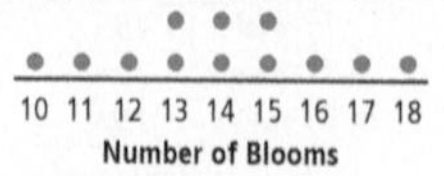
10 11 12 13 14 15 16 17 18
Number of Blooms

Hydrangeas with New Plant Food

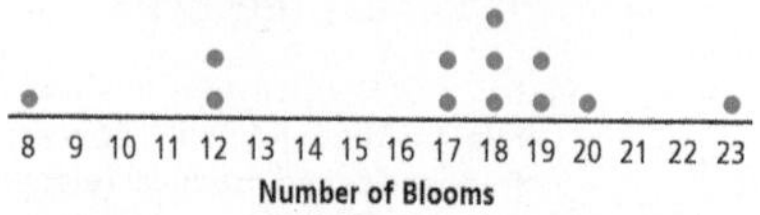
8 9 10 11 12 13 14 15 16 17 18 19 20 21 22 23
Number of Blooms

26. Construct Arguments Based on the survey data below, a marketing team for an airline concludes that someone between 18 and 24 years of age is more likely never to have flown on a commercial airliner than someone 25 years or older. Do you agree with this conclusion? Justify your answer. MP.3

Terminal

Have you ever flown on a commercial airline?			
	Yes	No	Totals
18-24 yrs	198	81	279
25+ yrs	2,539	448	2,987
Totals	2,737	529	3,266

ASSESSMENT PRACTICE

27. Consider a two-way frequency table. Select all that apply.

Ⓐ The sum of all joint frequencies equals the total frequency.
Ⓑ The sum of all marginal frequencies equals the total frequency.
Ⓒ The sum of all marginal frequencies in a row equals the total frequency.
Ⓓ The sum of all joint frequencies in a column equals the marginal frequency at the bottom of the column.
Ⓔ A relative frequency is the ratio of a joint frequency and a marginal frequency.

28. SAT/ACT In a two-way frequency table, the joint frequency in a cell is 8 and the marginal frequency in the same row is 32. What is the conditional relative frequency for the cell?

Ⓐ 0.12
Ⓑ 0.20
Ⓒ 0.25
Ⓓ 0.40
Ⓔ 0.50

29. Performance Task A high school offers a prep course for students who are taking a retest for a college entrance exam.

- Of 25 students who took the prep course, 20 scored at least 50 points higher on the retest than on the original exam.
- Overall, 100 students took the retest and 50 students scored at least 50 points higher on the retest than on the original exam.

Part A Create a two-way frequency table to organize the data.

Part B Funding for the prep course may be cut because more students scored at least 50 points higher on the retest without taking the prep course. Do you agree with this decision? If not, how could you use a two-way frequency table to construct an argument to keep the funding?

500 TOPIC 11 Statistics

Go Online | PearsonRealize.com

29. See back of book.

SavvasRealize.com

Assess Tutorials Worksheets

LESSON QUIZ

Use the Lesson Quiz to assess students' understanding of the mathematics in the lesson.

Students can take the Lesson Quiz online or you can download a printable copy from **SavvasRealize.com**. The Lesson Quiz is also available in the *Assessment Resources* book.

Item Analysis

Item	DOK	Standards
1	2	HSS.ID.B.5
2	1	HSS.ID.B.5
3	2	HSS.ID.B.5
4	1	HSS.ID.B.5
5	2	HSS.ID.B.5

RtI Use the student scores on the Lesson Quiz to prescribe differentiated assignments.

If students take the Lesson Quiz online, it will be automatically scored and appropriate differentiated practice will be assigned based on student performance.

I Intervention	0–3 points	• Reteach to Build Understanding • Mathematical Literacy and Vocabulary • Additional Practice
O On-Level	4 points	• Mathematical Literacy and Vocabulary • Additional Practice • Enrichment
A Advanced	5 points	• Enrichment

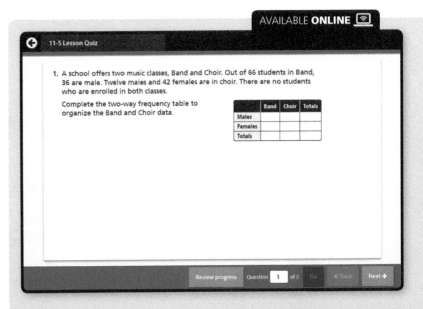

AVAILABLE **ONLINE**

11-5 Lesson Quiz

1. A school offers two music classes, Band and Choir. Out of 66 students in Band, 36 are male. Twelve males and 42 females are in choir. There are no students who are enrolled in both classes.

Complete the two-way frequency table to organize the Band and Choir data.

	Band	Choir	Totals
Males			
Females			
Totals			

Review progress Question 1 of 5 Go ← Back Next →

ASSESSMENT RESOURCES

Name ______

enVision Algebra 1 PearsonRealize.com

11-5 Lesson Quiz

Two-Way Frequency Tables

1. A school offers two music classes, Band and Choir. Out of 66 students in Band, 36 are male. Twelve males and 42 females are in choir. There are no students who are enrolled in both classes.

Complete the two-way frequency table to organize the Band and Choir data.

	Band	Choir	Totals
Males	36	12	48
Females	30	42	72
Totals	66	54	120

2. Use the table in Item 1. Which of these statements is true?

Ⓐ Of the students in music, 10% are males in Choir, and 35% are females in Choir.

Ⓑ Of the students in music, 55% are males, and 45% are females.

Ⓒ Of the students in music, 25% are males in Choir, and 75% are males in Band.

Ⓓ Of the students in music, 25% are females in Choir, and 30% are males in Choir.

3. The table shows the number of athletes in sports at a school in the fall. No students belong in more than one of the groups shown. Complete the table and find the percent of the JV athletes in the cross-country program and the soccer program. Round all percents to the nearest whole percent.

	Soccer	Cross-country	Totals
JV	22	32	54
Varsity	18	24	42
Totals	40	56	96

Percent of JV athletes in soccer: 41%

Percent of JV athletes in cross-country: 59%

4. Use the data in Item 3, and round your answer to the nearest whole percent. What percent of the athletes are in cross-country? What percent of the athletes are varsity athletes?

58% in cross-country

44% varsity athletes

5. Use the data in Item 3. What does the conditional frequency $\frac{18}{40}$ represent in this context?

Ⓐ the percent of soccer players who are JV athletes

Ⓑ the percent of varsity athletes who are in the cross-country program

Ⓒ the percent of soccer players who are varsity athletes

Ⓓ the percent of athletes in the cross-country program who are varsity athletes

enVision™ Algebra 1 • Assessment Resources

DIFFERENTIATED RESOURCES

I = Intervention **O** = On-Level **A** = Advanced

⚙ = This activity is available as a digital assignment powered by MathXL® for School.

AVAILABLE ONLINE

Reteach to Build Understanding I ⚙

Provides scaffolded reteaching for the key lesson concepts.

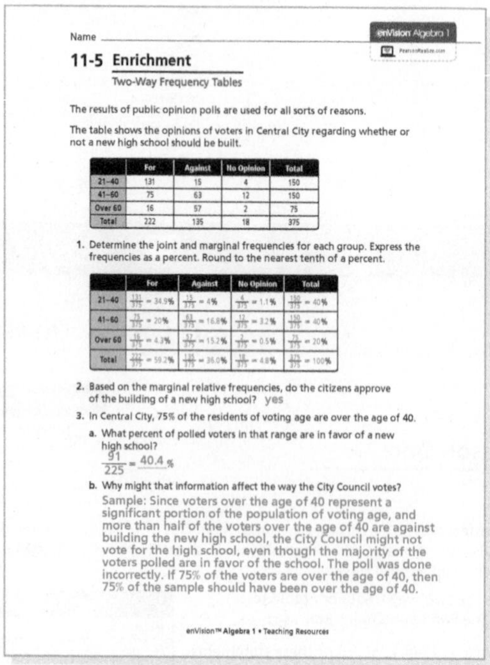

Name

11-5 Enrichment

Two-Way Frequency Tables

The results of public opinion polls are used for all sorts of reasons.

The table shows the opinions of voters in Central City regarding whether or not a new high school should be built.

	For	Against	No Opinion	Total
21–40	131	15	4	150
41–60	75	63	12	150
Over 60	16	57	2	75
Total	222	135	18	375

1. Determine the joint and marginal frequencies for each group. Express the frequencies as a percent. Round to the nearest tenth of a percent.

	For	Against	No Opinion	Total
21–40	$\frac{131}{375}\approx 34.9\%$	$\frac{15}{375}=4\%$	$\frac{4}{375}\approx 1.1\%$	$\frac{150}{375}=40\%$
41–60	$\frac{75}{375}=20\%$	$\frac{63}{375}=16.8\%$	$\frac{12}{375}=3.2\%$	$\frac{150}{375}=40\%$
Over 60	$\frac{16}{375}\approx 4.3\%$	$\frac{57}{375}=15.2\%$	$\frac{2}{375}\approx 0.5\%$	$\frac{75}{375}=20\%$
Total	$\frac{222}{375}\approx 59.2\%$	$\frac{135}{375}=36.0\%$	$\frac{18}{375}=4.8\%$	$\frac{375}{375}=100\%$

2. Based on the marginal relative frequencies, do the citizens approve of the building of a new high school? yes
3. In Central City, 75% of the residents of voting age are over the age of 40.
   a. What percent of polled voters in that range are in favor of a new high school? $\frac{91}{225}=40.4\%$
   b. Why might that information affect the way the City Council votes? Sample: Since voters over the age of 40 represent a significant portion of the population of voting age, and more than half of the voters over the age of 40 are against building the new high school, the City Council might not vote for the high school, even though the majority of the voters polled are in favor of the school. The poll was done incorrectly. If 75% of the voters are over the age of 40, then 75% of the sample should have been over the age of 40.

enVision™ Algebra 1 • Teaching Resources

Additional Practice I O ⚙

Provides extra practice for each lesson.

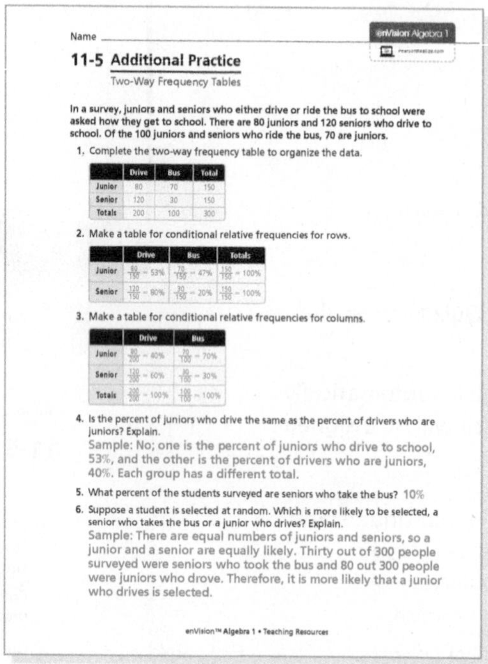

Name

11-5 Additional Practice

Two-Way Frequency Tables

In a survey, juniors and seniors who either drive or ride the bus to school were asked how they get to school. There are 80 juniors and 120 seniors who drive to school. Of the 100 juniors and seniors who ride the bus, 70 are juniors.

1. Complete the two-way frequency table to organize the data.

	Drive	Bus	Total
Junior	80	70	150
Senior	120	30	150
Totals	200	100	300

2. Make a table for conditional relative frequencies for rows.

	Drive	Bus	Totals
Junior	$\frac{80}{150}\approx 53\%$	$\frac{70}{150}\approx 47\%$	$\frac{150}{150}=100\%$
Senior	$\frac{120}{150}=80\%$	$\frac{30}{150}=20\%$	$\frac{150}{150}=100\%$

3. Make a table for conditional relative frequencies for columns.

	Drive	Bus
Junior	$\frac{80}{200}=40\%$	$\frac{70}{100}=70\%$
Senior	$\frac{120}{200}=60\%$	$\frac{30}{100}=30\%$
Totals	$\frac{200}{200}=100\%$	$\frac{100}{100}=100\%$

4. Is the percent of juniors who drive the same as the percent of drivers who are juniors? Explain. Sample: No; one is the percent of juniors who drive to school, 53%, and the other is the percent of drivers who are juniors, 40%. Each group has a different total.
5. What percent of the students surveyed are seniors who take the bus? 10%
6. Suppose a student is selected at random. Which is more likely to be selected, a senior who takes the bus or a junior who drives? Explain. Sample: There are equal numbers of juniors and seniors, so a junior and a senior are equally likely. Thirty out of 300 people surveyed were seniors who took the bus and 80 out 300 people were juniors who drove. Therefore, it is more likely that a junior who drives is selected.

enVision™ Algebra 1 • Teaching Resources

Enrichment O A ⚙

Presents engaging problems and activities that extend the lesson concepts.

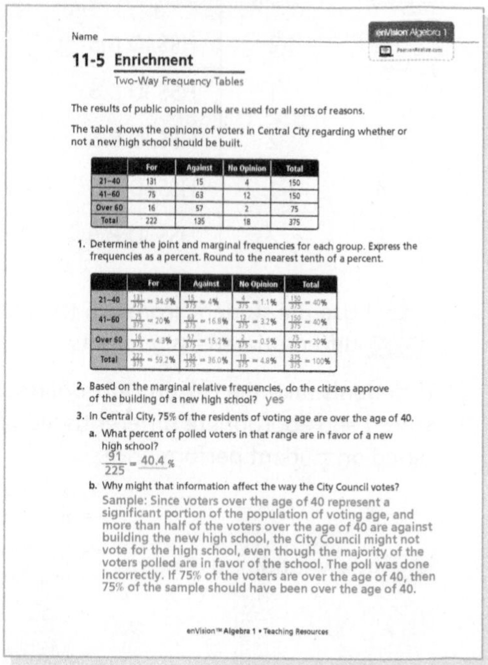

Name

11-5 Enrichment

Two-Way Frequency Tables

The results of public opinion polls are used for all sorts of reasons.

The table shows the opinions of voters in Central City regarding whether or not a new high school should be built.

	For	Against	No Opinion	Total
21–40	131	15	4	150
41–60	75	63	12	150
Over 60	16	57	2	75
Total	222	135	18	375

1. Determine the joint and marginal frequencies for each group. Express the frequencies as a percent. Round to the nearest tenth of a percent.

	For	Against	No Opinion	Total
21–40	$\frac{131}{375}\approx 34.9\%$	$\frac{15}{375}=4\%$	$\frac{4}{375}\approx 1.1\%$	$\frac{150}{375}=40\%$
41–60	$\frac{75}{375}=20\%$	$\frac{63}{375}=16.8\%$	$\frac{12}{375}=3.2\%$	$\frac{150}{375}=40\%$
Over 60	$\frac{16}{375}\approx 4.3\%$	$\frac{57}{375}=15.2\%$	$\frac{2}{375}\approx 0.5\%$	$\frac{75}{375}=20\%$
Total	$\frac{222}{375}\approx 59.2\%$	$\frac{135}{375}=36.0\%$	$\frac{18}{375}=4.8\%$	$\frac{375}{375}=100\%$

2. Based on the marginal relative frequencies, do the citizens approve of the building of a new high school? yes
3. In Central City, 75% of the residents of voting age are over the age of 40.
   a. What percent of polled voters in that range are in favor of a new high school? $\frac{91}{225}=40.4\%$
   b. Why might that information affect the way the City Council votes? Sample: Since voters over the age of 40 represent a significant portion of the population of voting age, and more than half of the voters over the age of 40 are against building the new high school, the City Council might not vote for the high school, even though the majority of the voters polled are in favor of the school. The poll was done incorrectly. If 75% of the voters are over the age of 40, then 75% of the sample should have been over the age of 40.

enVision™ Algebra 1 • Teaching Resources

Mathematical Literacy and Vocabulary I O

Helps students develop and reinforce understanding of key terms and concepts.

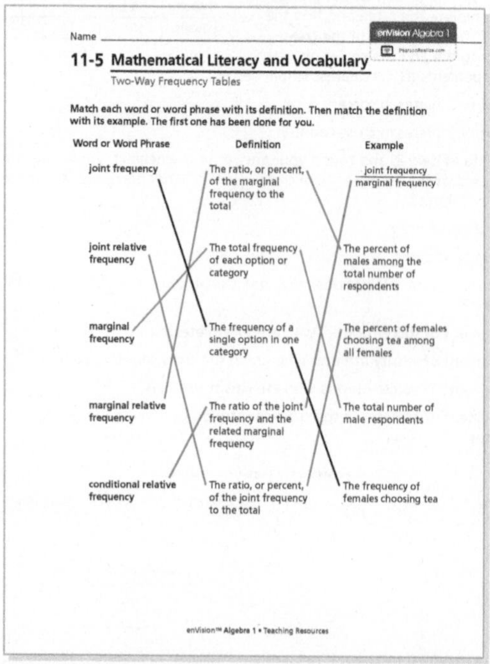

Name

11-5 Mathematical Literacy and Vocabulary

Two-Way Frequency Tables

Match each word or word phrase with its definition. Then match the definition with its example. The first one has been done for you.

Word or Word Phrase	Definition	Example
joint frequency	The ratio, or percent, of the marginal frequency to the total	joint frequency / marginal frequency
joint relative frequency	The total frequency of each option or category	The percent of males among the total number of respondents
marginal frequency	The frequency of a single option in one category	The percent of females choosing tea among all females
marginal relative frequency	The ratio of the joint frequency and the related marginal frequency	The total number of male respondents
conditional relative frequency	The ratio, or percent, of the joint frequency to the total	The frequency of females choosing tea

enVision™ Algebra 1 • Teaching Resources

Digital Resources and Video Tutorials I O A ⚙

The **Reteach to Build Understanding, Additional Practice,** and **Enrichment** activities are available as digital assignments powered by MathXL for School. These activities are automatically assigned when students complete the lesson quiz online and are automatically scored.

Students can access instructional tutorials using the **Virtual Nerd app.**

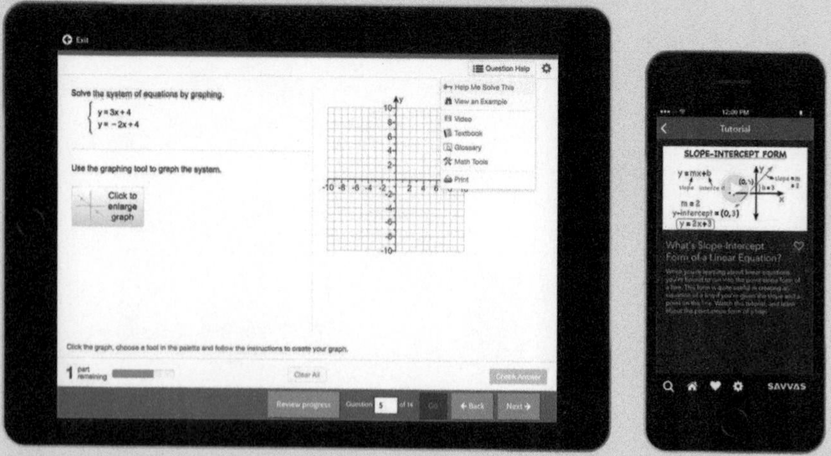
Solve the system of equations by graphing.
y = 3x + 4
y = −2x + 4
Use the graphing tool to graph the system.
Click to enlarge graph
Question Help
Tutorial
SLOPE-INTERCEPT FORM
What's Slope-Intercept Form of a Linear Equation?
SAVVAS

Students can also access Virtual Nerd videos using the **BouncePages app** to scan exercise pages marked with this icon. Students can download both apps for free in their mobile devices' app store.

SavvasRealize.com

Video

TOPIC 11
Mathematical Modeling in 3 Acts: Text Message

Lesson Overview

FOCUS

Objective

Students will be able to:

✓ Use mathematical modeling to represent a problem situation and to propose a solution.

✓ Test and verify the appropriateness of their math models.

✓ Explain why the results from their mathematical models might not align exactly with the problem situation.

Essential Understanding

Many real-world problem situations can be represented with a mathematical model, but that model might not represent the real-world situation exactly.

COHERENCE

Earlier in this topic, students:

- Interpreted data using data plots and statistical measures of center and dispersion.

In this lesson, students:

- Develop a mathematical model to represent and propose a solution to a problem situation involving statistics.

In later courses, students will:

- Refine their mathematical modeling skills.

RIGOR

This mathematical modeling lesson focuses on application of both math content and math practices and processes.

- Students draw on their understanding of concepts related to statistics to develop a representative model.
- Students apply their mathematical model to test and validate its applicability to similar problem situations.

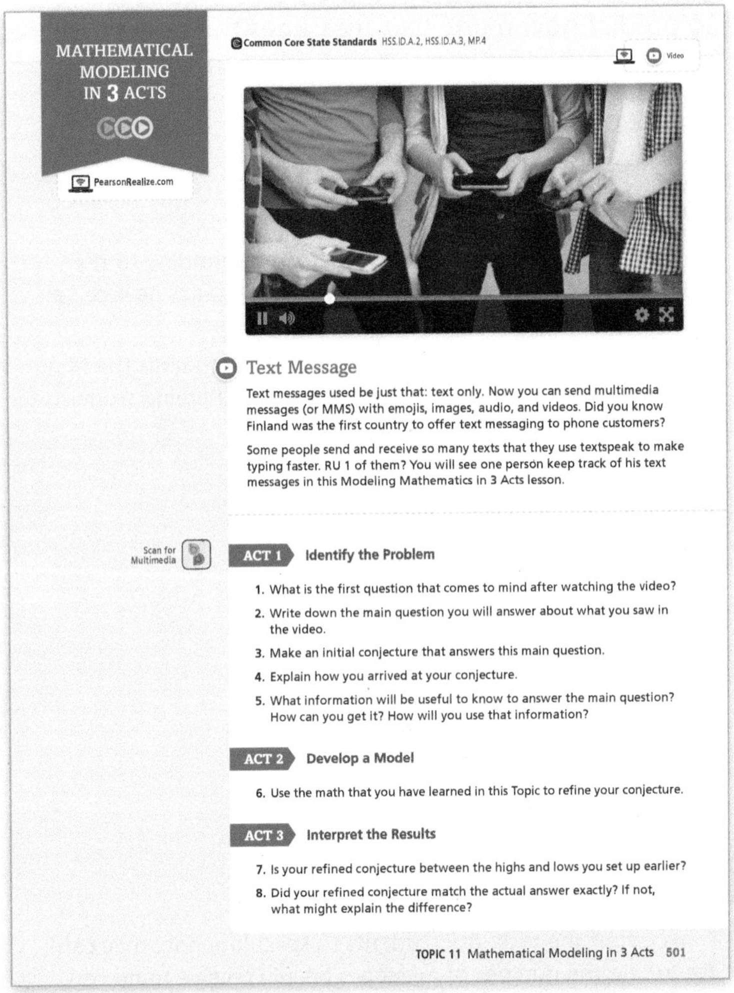

MATHEMATICAL MODELING IN 3 ACTS

PearsonRealize.com

Common Core State Standards HSS.ID.A.2, HSS.ID.A.3, MP.4

Video

Text Message

Text messages used be just that: text only. Now you can send multimedia messages (or MMS) with emojis, images, audio, and videos. Did you know Finland was the first country to offer text messaging to phone customers?

Some people send and receive so many texts that they use textspeak to make typing faster. RU 1 of them? You will see one person keep track of his text messages in this Modeling Mathematics in 3 Acts lesson.

Scan for Multimedia

ACT 1 **Identify the Problem**

1. What is the first question that comes to mind after watching the video?
2. Write down the main question you will answer about what you saw in the video.
3. Make an initial conjecture that answers this main question.
4. Explain how you arrived at your conjecture.
5. What information will be useful to know to answer the main question? How can you get it? How will you use that information?

ACT 2 **Develop a Model**

6. Use the math that you have learned in this Topic to refine your conjecture.

ACT 3 **Interpret the Results**

7. Is your refined conjecture between the highs and lows you set up earlier?
8. Did your refined conjecture match the actual answer exactly? If not, what might explain the difference?

TOPIC 11 Mathematical Modeling in 3 Acts 501

Student Companion

Students can do their work for the task on pages 269–270 of their *Student Companion* or on **SavvasRealize.com**.

Mathematics Overview COMMON CORE STANDARDS

Content Standards

In this lesson, students apply concepts and skills related to Common Core Standards **HSS.ID.A.2** and **HSS.ID.A.3**.

HSS.ID.A.2 Use statistics appropriate to the shape of the data distribution to compare center (median, mean) and spread (interquartile range, standard deviation) of two or more different data sets.

HSS.ID.A.3 Interpret differences in shape, center, and spread in the context of the data sets, accounting for possible effects of extreme data points (outliers).

Mathematical Practice Standards

MP.4 Model With Mathematics

To solve the problem presented, students identify variables and the relationship among them, develop a model that represents the situation, and use the model to propose a solution. Students interpret their solutions and propose explanations for why their answer may not match the real-world answer.

Students also engage in sense-making (**MP.1**), abstract and quantitative reasoning (**MP.2**), and mathematical communication and argumentation (**MP.3**). In testing their models, students look for patterns in the structure of their models (**MP.7, MP.8**).

Video

Text Message

In this mathematical modeling task, students analyze sample data of the numbers of text messages one person receives over several days. They need to predict how many text messages the person will receive tomorrow. To do so, they apply concepts they studied in Topic 11.

ACT 1 The Hook

Play the video. The video shows a person responding to text messages and wondering how many text messages he receives each day. Very little data are provided in this act.

After the question brainstorming, present to students the Main Question they will be tasked with answering. Remind students to write down their questions and conjectures.

MAIN QUESTION

How many messages will he get tomorrow?

ACT 2 Modeling With Math

Think about the task. Ask students to speculate how they can determine the number of messages he will receive tomorrow. Then have them think about what information they need.

Reveal the information. The images show sample data represented in different plots. You can download a blackline master with the data plots from SavvasRealize.com.

What's the connection? Give students time to struggle as they think about how to connect their ideas to what they learned in this topic about statistics. What information can you infer from each graph? How can you interpret the center and spread of each plot, and how can you use that information?

Before showing the answers, find out where there is disagreement. Allow students to argue their cases and update their conjectures.

INTERESTING MOMENTS WITH STUDENTS

There are many different ways to interpret the data plots. You can discuss the different measures of center and dispersion. Ask students which measures are appropriate for each plot. Look for students to mention how the shape of each distribution may influence these measures.

Necessary Information

Data Plots (see image gallery)

- Histogram: December-February
- Dot plot: April
- Box plot: Weekdays in March & April

Texts also include a video message, audio message, image, or emoji.

ACT 3 The Solution

Play the video. The final video shows the number of texts he gets the following day. Offer praise to the students whose conjectures are closest to the actual answer.

MAIN QUESTION ANSWER

217 texts

Do the "post-game" analysis. Help students understand why the actual result might differ, even slightly, from the mathematical answer. Students should mention that they made a prediction from the statistics given and cannot know for certain what the actual result will be. There may have been an important event that day, or he may have been trying to make plans with friends.

ONE POSSIBLE SOLUTION

The histogram shows that the greatest frequency is 120–130. The data are skewed to the right.

The histogram collects the greatest number of data points but is the least recent data. It is more useful to understand the shape of the data distribution but may not be a good predictor for the number of texts he'll receive tomorrow.

The dot plot is skewed to the right. The greatest frequency is 118. Most of the data are clustered between 99 and 118. There is an outlier at 20.

The dot plot has the least number of data points but is the most recent data. It is more useful to predict the number of texts he'll receive tomorrow.

The median of the box-and-whisker plot is 102, and the IQR is 24. The number tends to be between 88 and 126 texts. The left whisker is very long, so there is an outlier.

The box plot is neither the most recent data nor the most data points. It is the least reliable data display.

The data show that he most often receives about 120 texts on a school day. The data suggest that he will receive about 160 texts tomorrow.

INTERESTING MOMENTS WITH STUDENTS

The day of the week may affect the answer. Students may discuss whether they typically send more texts on a weekend day or a weekday. Ask them how different days of the week might show up in the data plots.

SEQUEL

As students finish, ask them to explain which data plot is most helpful to solve the problem. Tell them to make a list of pros and cons for each data plot. [Students' descriptions should include whether the plot shows outliers, which measures of center and dispersion are most useful, and which plot best displays the shape of the data. (You may have already discussed how the data sets are different sizes and come from different months.)]

TOPIC ESSENTIAL QUESTION

How do you use statistics to model situations and solve problems?

As students answer the Essential Question in writing, encourage them to include examples that support their answers. Look for the following points to come out while discussing students' answers.

- Dot plots show the frequency of data and clearly show clusters, gaps, and outliers. Histograms show the distribution of values within a data set and shape of the data. Box plots show the center and spread of a distribution.
- Measures of center and variability are used to compare data sets displayed in dot plots, box plots, and histograms. Dot plots show how much the data vary. Box plots show the minimum, maximum, and center of the data. Histograms show the ranges of data.
- When the shape of the data display is symmetric, the mean is equal (or approximately equal) to the median. When the shape of the data display is skewed left, the mean is less than the median. When the shape of the data display is skewed right, the mean is greater than the median. This information helps to make inferences about the data.
- Standard deviation indicates by how much the values in a data set deviate from the mean.
- Two-way frequency tables show relationships between two sets of categorical data.

Answers

2. standard deviation
3. joint frequencies
4. normal distribution
5. conditional relative frequency
6. Answers may vary. Sample: You would use a box plot when you want to know the median of the data, as well as the maximum and minimum values.
7. You would use a dot plot when you want to know individual data values or see clusters, gaps, and outliers.
8. A dot plot is a good display to use when you want to know how many times a specific value occurs in a set of data; the value 35 occurs 4 times.

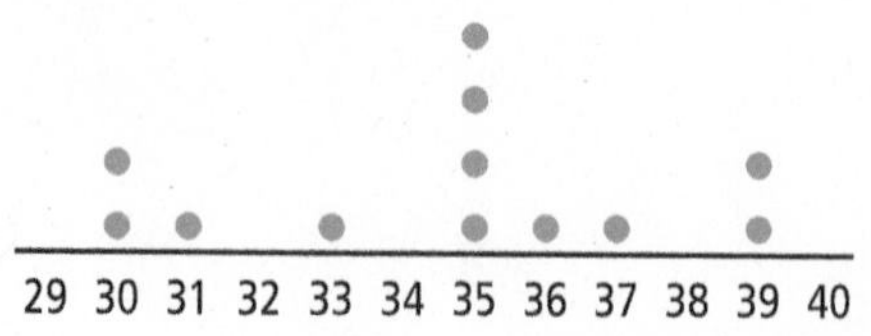

29 30 31 32 33 34 35 36 37 38 39 40

AVAILABLE **ONLINE**

TOPIC 11

Topic Review

TOPIC ESSENTIAL QUESTION

1. How do you use statistics to model situations and solve problems?

Vocabulary Review

Choose the correct term to complete each sentence.

2. ________ is a measure of spread that reflects how the data vary from the mean.
3. ________ indicate the frequency of a single option for one category.
4. A(n) ________ is a data distribution that forms a bell-shaped curve.
5. ________ is the ratio of the joint frequency and the related marginal frequency.

- conditional relative frequency
- joint frequencies
- normal distribution
- standard deviation
- joint relative frequency

Concepts & Skills Review

LESSON 11-1 **Analyzing Data Displays**

Quick Review

Dot plots show counts of values within data sets. **Histograms** show the distribution of values within a data set in ranges or intervals. **Box plots** show the center and spread of a distribution using a five-number summary.

Example

The table below shows a class's math test scores. Create a histogram of the data.

83	92	56	63	80	91	78	59
75	79	62	85	81	90	82	74
60	95	88	82	77	74	68	82

Break the scores into intervals of 10.

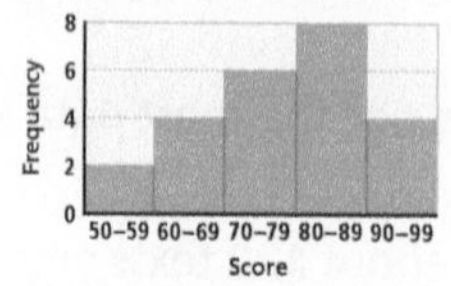

8
6
4
2
0
Frequency
50–59 60–69 70–79 80–89 90–99
Score

Practice & Problem Solving

6. Generalize In what situations would a box plot be the best display for a data set? MP.8
7. In what situations would a dot plot be the best display for a data set?

For the data set below, create the data display that best reveals the answer to the question. Explain your reasoning.

8. What is the frequency of the data value 35?

30	33	35	39
37	35	31	36
39	30	35	35

Choose the most appropriate data display to answer each question about a data set. Explain.

9. What are the frequencies for each interval of 2 points?
10. How many data values are less than any given value in the data set?

502 TOPIC 11 Statistics

Go Online | PearsonRealize.com

AVAILABLE **ONLINE**

Go online at **SavvasRealize.com** for additional practice and mixed review.

9. A histogram because it shows the frequency of data values within an interval.
10. A dot plot because it shows the frequency of specific values.

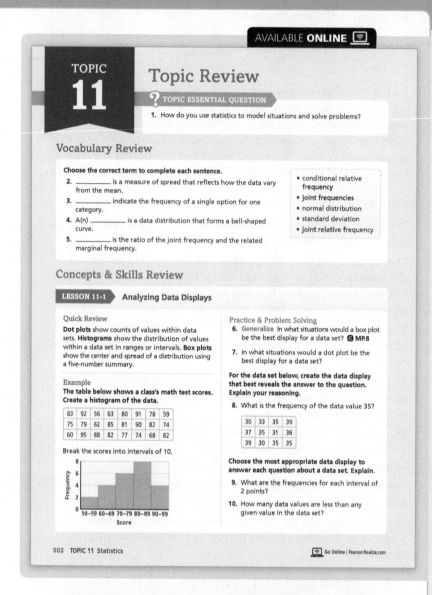

TOPIC 11
Statistics

TOPIC REVIEW

Answers

11. The data are skewed right.

12. Data Set A: mean ≈ 4.563, MAD ≈ 1.883;
Data Set B: mean ≈ 5.313, MAD ≈ 2.023

Data Set B has a higher mean, but there is more variance from the mean than Data Set A.

Data Set A: median = 4, IQR = 3.5; Data Set B: median = 6, IQR = 4.5

Data Set B has a higher median. The middle 50% of data in Data Set A is closer to the median than in Data Set B.

The median is the best way to compare the data sets as most of the values are close to the median.

13. This year's mean is 80.2 points and the MAD is 5.67. This year's team had a higher average score but last year's team was more consistent in its scoring near the mean.

AVAILABLE **ONLINE**

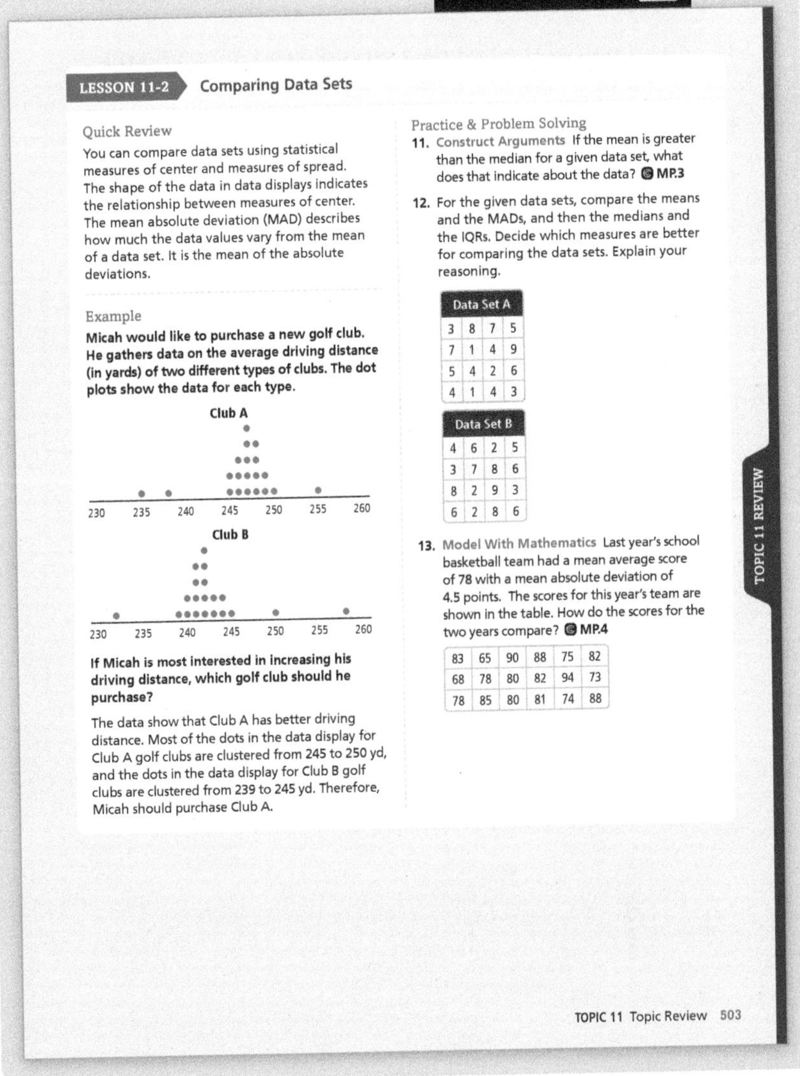

LESSON 11-2 **Comparing Data Sets**

Quick Review

You can compare data sets using statistical measures of center and measures of spread. The shape of the data in data displays indicates the relationship between measures of center. The mean absolute deviation (MAD) describes how much the data values vary from the mean of a data set. It is the mean of the absolute deviations.

Example

Micah would like to purchase a new golf club. He gathers data on the average driving distance (in yards) of two different types of clubs. The dot plots show the data for each type.

Club A
230
235
240
245
250
255
260
Club B
230
235
240
245
250
255
260

If Micah is most interested in increasing his driving distance, which golf club should he purchase?

The data show that Club A has better driving distance. Most of the dots in the data display for Club A golf clubs are clustered from 245 to 250 yd, and the dots in the data display for Club B golf clubs are clustered from 239 to 245 yd. Therefore, Micah should purchase Club A.

Practice & Problem Solving

11. **Construct Arguments** If the mean is greater than the median for a given data set, what does that indicate about the data? MP.3

12. For the given data sets, compare the means and the MADs, and then the medians and the IQRs. Decide which measures are better for comparing the data sets. Explain your reasoning.

Data Set A			
3	8	7	5
7	1	4	9
5	4	2	6
4	1	4	3

Data Set B			
4	6	2	5
3	7	8	6
8	2	9	3
6	2	8	6

13. **Model With Mathematics** Last year's school basketball team had a mean average score of 78 with a mean absolute deviation of 4.5 points. The scores for this year's team are shown in the table. How do the scores for the two years compare? MP.4

83	65	90	88	75	82
68	78	80	82	94	73
78	85	80	81	74	88

TOPIC 11 REVIEW

TOPIC 11 Topic Review 503

TOPIC REVIEW

Answers

14. The graph of the first data set is skewed right, and the graph of the second data set is skewed left.

15. Skewed left

16. Symmetric

17. The distance from the minimum value to the middle 50% of the data is greater than the distance from the middle 50% to the maximum value of the data. This indicates that a small value skewed the data to the left and that the mean is smaller than the median.

18. The graph for the first month is more symmetric than the graph for the second month. There were more cars priced over $25,000 sold in the first month, and there was an increase in cars priced between $20,000 to $24,000 in the second month.

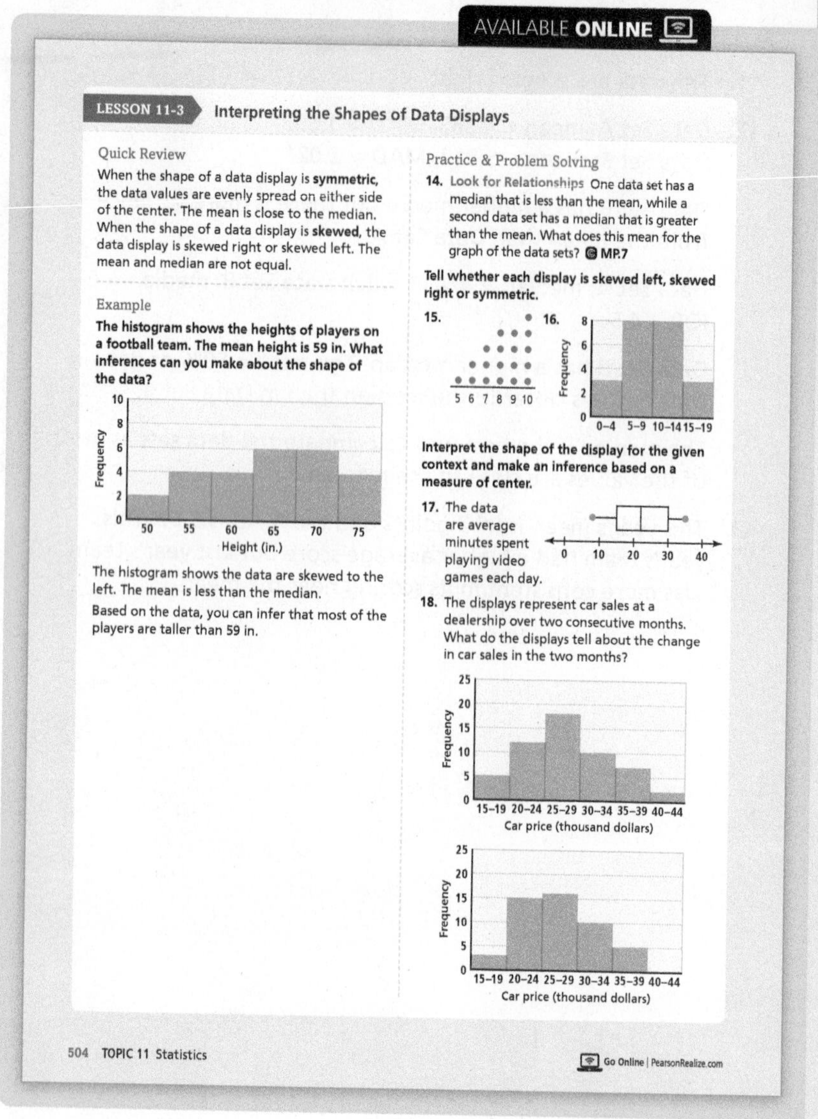
AVAILABLE ONLINE

LESSON 11-3 Interpreting the Shapes of Data Displays

Quick Review

When the shape of a data display is **symmetric,** the data values are evenly spread on either side of the center. The mean is close to the median. When the shape of a data display is **skewed**, the data display is skewed right or skewed left. The mean and median are not equal.

Example

The histogram shows the heights of players on a football team. The mean height is 59 in. What inferences can you make about the shape of the data?

Frequency
10
8
6
4
2
0
50
55
60
65
70
75
Height (in.)

The histogram shows the data are skewed to the left. The mean is less than the median.

Based on the data, you can infer that most of the players are taller than 59 in.

Practice & Problem Solving

14. Look for Relationships One data set has a median that is less than the mean, while a second data set has a median that is greater than the mean. What does this mean for the graph of the data sets? MP.7

Tell whether each display is skewed left, skewed right or symmetric.

15. 16.

5 6 7 8 9 10
Frequency
8
6
4
2
0
0–4 5–9 10–14 15–19

Interpret the shape of the display for the given context and make an inference based on a measure of center.

17. The data are average minutes spent playing video games each day.

0 10 20 30 40

18. The displays represent car sales at a dealership over two consecutive months. What do the displays tell about the change in car sales in the two months?

Frequency
25
20
15
10
5
0
15–19 20–24 25–29 30–34 35–39 40–44
Car price (thousand dollars)
Frequency
25
20
15
10
5
0
15–19 20–24 25–29 30–34 35–39 40–44
Car price (thousand dollars)

504 TOPIC 11 Statistics

Go Online | PearsonRealize.com

TOPIC REVIEW

Answers

19. No; 70.5 is greater than 50.5 + 9.6 + 9.6.

20. **A:** mean = 13.25, sample standard deviation ≈ 3.24;
B: mean ≈ 12.38, sample standard deviation ≈ 3.85;
Data Set A shows less variability from the mean.

21. more than $24,550; 2.5% of accounts would meet the requirement

22.

	Action	Comedy	Totals
Male	40	10	50
Female	10	20	30
Totals	50	30	80

Yes, as there were 50 people who preferred action movies and only 30 who preferred comedies.

23.

Where do you get most of your news?			
Age	TV	Internet	Totals
≤30	25%	40%	65%
>30	15%	20%	35%
Totals	40%	60%	100%

No, most people from each age group prefer to get their news from the Internet compared to TV (60% vs. 40%).

AVAILABLE **ONLINE**

LESSON 11-4 Standard Deviation

Quick Review

Standard deviation indicates by how much the values in a data set deviate from the mean. It is the square root of the **variance**, the mean of the squared deviations from the mean.

Example

The table shows the number of hot dogs sold per day by a street vendor over a two-week period. How much variability do the sample data show?

40	28	18	36	52	41	29
24	30	27	51	34	42	35

Mean: $\bar{x} \approx 35$; variance: $s^2 \approx 95.41$; standard deviation: $s \approx 9.77$

The standard deviation is relatively large, so the data show quite a bit of variability. Typically, the vendor sells between 25 and 45 hot dogs per day.

Practice & Problem Solving

19. **Reason** The mean of a data set is 50.5 and the standard deviation is about 9.6. Does 70.5 fall within 2 standard deviations of the mean of the data set? Explain. MP.2

Find and use the mean and the standard deviation to compare the variability of the data sets.

20. **Sample A:** 15, 12, 8, 18, 16, 13, 14, 10;
Sample B: 16, 19, 11, 9, 8, 10, 15, 11

21. **Make Sense and Persevere** A normally distributed sample of bank accounts shows a mean of $22,000 and a standard deviation of $1,275. How much money would be in an account that contains more than the middle 95% of the accounts? How many accounts would meet that requirement? MP.1

LESSON 11-5 Two-Way Frequency Tables

Quick Review

Two-way frequency tables show relationships between two sets of categorical data. **Joint frequencies** indicate the frequency of one category. **Marginal frequencies** indicate the total frequency for each category.

Example

A teacher asked her students to choose between the museum or the zoo for a class trip. The results are shown in the table. What trends do the results suggest?

	Museum	Zoo	Totals
Male	5	7	12
Female	12	6	18
Totals	17	13	30

The joint frequencies suggest that males prefer the zoo and females prefer the museum. The marginal frequencies suggest that all respondents showed a slight preference for going to the museum.

Practice & Problem Solving

In a survey, TV viewers can choose between two movies. 40 men and 10 women choose the action movie that is featured. Of the 30 people who chose the comedy, 20 are women and 10 are men.

22. Make a two-way frequency table to organize the data. Is it reasonable to say that more people surveyed prefer action movies? Explain.

23. **Construct Arguments** According to the data below, is there a significant association between age and a person's news source? Justify your answer. MP.3

Where do you get most of your news?			
Age	TV	Internet	Totals
≤ 30	50	80	130
> 30	30	40	70
Totals	80	120	200

TOPIC 11 REVIEW

TOPIC 11 Topic Review 505

AVAILABLE **ONLINE**

Name ______________________ enVision Algebra 1 PearsonRealize.com

11 Topic Assessment Form A

For Items 1 and 2, use this data set: 2, 4, 6, 9, 14. If necessary, round your answer to the nearest tenth of a unit.

1. Find the mean absolute deviation. 3.6
2. Find the standard deviation. 4.2

Use these box plots for Items 3 and 4.

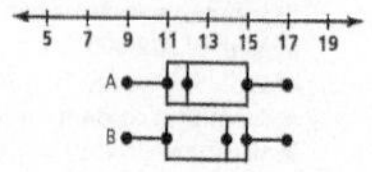

5 7 9 11 13 15 17 19
A
B

3. Which data set has more of its values less than 13? A
4. In which data set is the mean less than the median? B

Use this two-way frequency table for Items 5–7.

	Rock	Rap	Totals
Grade 9	4	6	10
Grade 10	30	10	40
Totals	34	16	50

5. How many 9th graders like rock? 4
6. What percent of the students in the survey are 10th graders? B

   Ⓐ 90% Ⓑ 80% Ⓒ 20% Ⓓ 10%
7. Complete the table for the conditional relative frequencies.

	Rock	Rap	Totals
Grade 9	40%	60%	100%
Grade 10	75%	25%	100%
Totals	68%	32%	100%

8. Which of the following best describe the box plot? Select all that apply.

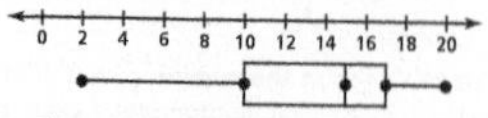

0 2 4 6 8 10 12 14 16 18 20

   Ⓐ The data set is skewed to the right.
   Ⓑ The data set is skewed to the left.
   Ⓒ About 50% of the values are between 10 and 17.
   Ⓓ About 50% of the values are between 2 and10.

9. In a data set, the mean is less than the median. What does that indicate about the data?

   Ⓐ It is skewed to the right.
   Ⓑ It is skewed to the left.
   Ⓒ It is symmetric.
   Ⓓ It is bell-shaped.

10. Data Set A is a normal distribution with mean 10 and mean absolute deviation 2. Data Set B is a normal distribution with mean 10 and a mean absolute deviation 5. Which best describes the data sets? Select all that apply.

   Ⓐ They both have the same shape.
   Ⓑ The both have the same median.
   Ⓒ They are both symmetric about the mean.
   Ⓓ Data Set A is more spread out than Data Set B.

11. Which box plot represents the data set 1, 1, 4, 4, 4, 9, 10, 10, 10, 14, 14?

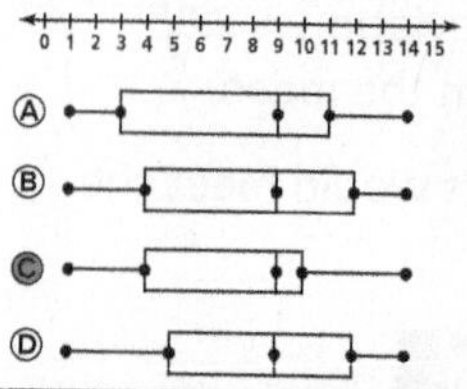

0 1 2 3 4 5 6 7 8 9 10 11 12 13 14 15
Ⓐ
Ⓑ
Ⓒ
Ⓓ

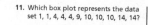

Use the histogram for Items 12–14.

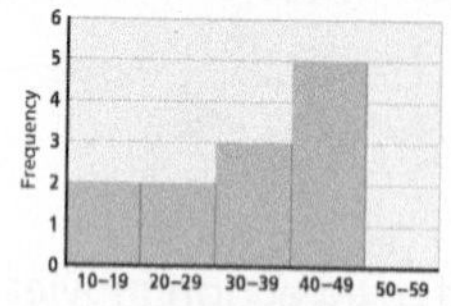

Frequency
0 1 2 3 4 5 6
10–19 20–29 30–39 40–49 50–59

12. How many values are in the data set? 12
13. What percent of the values are between 10 and 30? Round to the nearest tenth of a percent. 33.3%
14. The median value of the data set is 39. What could be the mean of the data set?

   Ⓐ 48.5 Ⓒ 39.0
   Ⓑ 45.2 Ⓓ 32.5

Use this dot plot for Items 15–17.

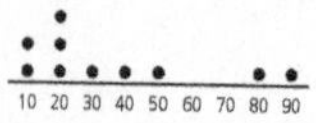

10 20 30 40 50 60 70 80 90

15. What is the mean of the data in the dot plot? 37
16. What is the standard deviation of the data? Round to the nearest tenth. 26.8
17. Will the median value be to the right or to the left of the mean? left

A survey of birds in Forests A and B counted the number of robins and sparrows. Use the resulting frequency table for Items 18–20.

	Robins	Sparrows	Totals
Forest A	9	16	25
Forest B	36	64	100
Totals	45	80	125

18. What percent of the robins are in Forest A? 20%
19. What percent of the birds in Forest A are robins? 36%
20. What percent of the birds are robins? 36%
21. During one month, the mean high temperature in Boise, Idaho, was 52.1° F with a standard deviation of 6.5° F. During the same month, the mean high temperature in Death Valley, California, was 81.9° F with a standard deviation of 6.4° F. Which of the following are true? Select all that apply.

   Ⓐ About 95% of the high temperatures measured in Boise ranged from 45.6° to 58.6°.
   Ⓑ The average high temperature in Death Valley was greater than the average in Boise.
   Ⓒ The variation of high temperatures in Death Valley was about the same as the variation in Boise.

AVAILABLE **ONLINE**

Topic Assessment Assess students' understanding of topic concepts and skills using the Topic Assessment found at **SavvasRealize.com.** These auto-scored online assessments provide students with a breadth of technology-enhanced item types.

There are two versions of the Topic Assessment, Form A and Form B. These two versions, available in print and at **SavvasRealize.com,** are parallel tests that assess the same content item for item. The Item Analysis chart on the next page can be used for both versions.

TOPIC 11
Statistics

TOPIC ASSESSMENT Form B

AVAILABLE ONLINE

enVision Algebra 1

PearsonRealize.com

Name ______________________

11 Topic Assessment Form B

For Items 1 and 2, use this data set: 2, 4, 6, 7, 8, 9. If necessary, round your answer to the nearest tenth of a unit.

1. Find the mean absolute deviation. 2
2. Find the standard deviation. 2.4

Use the box plots for Items 3 and 4.

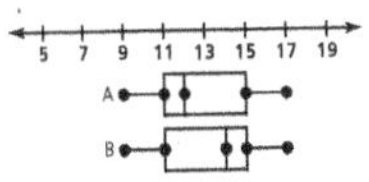

3. Which data set has a greater percent of its values less than 12? A
4. In which data set is the median less than the mean? A

Use the two-way frequency table for Items 5–7.

	Rock	Rap	Totals
Grade 9	4	6	10
Grade 10	30	10	40
Totals	34	16	50

5. How many 10th graders like rock? 30
6. What percent of the students in the survey are 9th graders?
   Ⓐ 90% Ⓑ 80% Ⓒ 20% Ⓓ 10%
7. Complete the table for the conditional relative frequencies.

	Rock	Rap	Totals
Grade 9	40%	60%	100%
Grade 10	75%	25%	100%
Totals	68%	32%	100%

8. Which of the following best describe the box plot? Select all that apply.

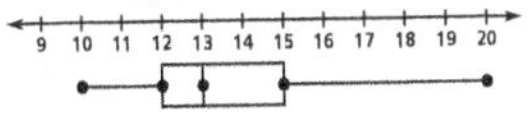

   Ⓐ The data set is skewed to the right.
   Ⓑ The data set is skewed to the left.
   Ⓒ About 50% of the values are between 13 and 20.
   Ⓓ About 25% of the values are between 10 and 12.

9. In a data set, the mean is equal to the median. What does that indicate about the data?
   Ⓐ It is skewed to the right.
   Ⓑ It is skewed to the left.
   Ⓒ It is symmetric.
   Ⓓ It is bell-shaped.

10. Data Set A is a normal distribution with mean 20 and mean absolute deviation 2. Data Set B is a normal distribution with mean 10 and a mean absolute deviation 2. Which best describes the data sets? Select all that apply.
   Ⓐ While they are not identical, they have the same shape.
   Ⓑ The both have the same median.
   Ⓒ They are both symmetric about the mean.
   Ⓓ Data Set A is more spread out than Data Set B.

11. Which box plot represents the data set 1, 4, 4 ,9, 10, 10, 14?

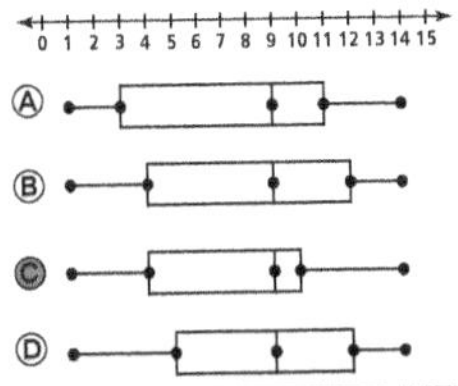

Use the histogram for Items 12–14.

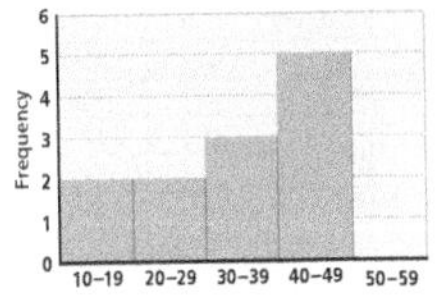
Frequency
10–19
20–29
30–39
40–49
50–59

12. How many values are between 30 and 50? 8
13. What percent of the values are between 10 and 20? 17%
14. The mean value of the data set is 32.9. What could be the median value of the data set?
   Ⓐ 39.0
   Ⓑ 32.5
   Ⓒ 30.5
   Ⓓ 30.0

Use this dot plot for Items 15–17.

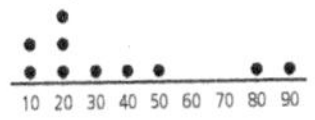

15. What is the median of the data in the dot plot? 25
16. What is the mean absolute deviation of the data in the dot plot? 22.4
17. Will the mean value be to the right or to the left of the median? right

A survey of birds in Forests A and B counted the number of robins and sparrows. Use the resulting frequency table for Items 18–20.

	Robins	Sparrows	Totals
Forest A	9	16	25
Forest B	36	64	100
Totals	45	80	125

18. What percent of the sparrows are in Forest A? 20%
19. What percent of the birds in Forest A are sparrows? 64%
20. What percent of the birds surveyed are sparrows? 64%
21. During one month, the mean high temperature in Stowe, Vermont, was 56.0° F with a standard deviation of 3.6° F. During the same month, the mean high temperature in Bend, Oregon, was 56.2° F with a standard deviation of 2.4° F. Which of the following are true? Select all that apply.
   Ⓐ About 95% of the high temperatures measured in Stowe ranged from 48.8° to 63.2°.
   Ⓑ The variation of high temperatures in Stowe was greater than the variation in Bend.
   Ⓒ The average high temperature in Stowe was about the same as in Bend.

Item Analysis

Item	DOK	Standard	Item	DOK	Standard	Item	DOK	Standard
1	2	HSS.ID.A.2	8	2	HSS.ID.A.3	15	2	HSS.ID.A.1, HSS.ID.A.2
2	2	HSS.ID.A.2	9	2	HSS.ID.A.3	16	2	HSS.ID.A.1, HSS.ID.A.2
3	2	HSS.ID.A.3	10	2	HSS.ID.A.3	17	2	HSS.ID.A.2
4	2	HSS.ID.A.3	11	2	HSS.ID.A.1, HSS.ID.A.2	18	2	HSS.ID.B.5
5	1	HSS.ID.B.5	12	1	HSS.ID.A.1	19	2	HSS.ID.B.5
6	2	HSS.ID.B.5	13	2	HSS.ID.A.2	20	2	HSS.ID.B.5
7	3	HSS.ID.B.5	14	3	HSS.ID.A.3	21	2	HSS.ID.A.3

AVAILABLE ONLINE

Name ______________________

enVision Algebra 1
PearsonRealize.com

11 Performance Assessment Form A

Amelia collects and analyzes weather data. Here is part of her presentation for an environmental science class.

1. On May 3, 1999, fifty-nine tornadoes hit Oklahoma in the largest tornado outbreak ever recorded in the state. The data in the table show sixteen of those tornadoes that were classified as strong (F2 or F3) or violent (F4 or F5).

Major Tornadoes in Oklahoma, May 3, 1999

Time	Length of path (miles)	Intensity
5:20 pm	6	F3
5:46 pm	9	F3
6:12 pm	4	F2
6:26 pm	37	F5
7:53 pm	7	F2
9:41 pm	12	F3
9:48 pm	8	F2
10:05 pm	7	F2
10:10 pm	15	F4
10:25 pm	39	F4
10:57 pm	1	F2
11:03 pm	22	F3
11:10 pm	15	F3
11:18 pm	8	F2
11:56 pm	13	F3
12:33 am	2	F2

Part A

Create a dot plot of the data for length of the path of each tornado. List any outliers by their length.

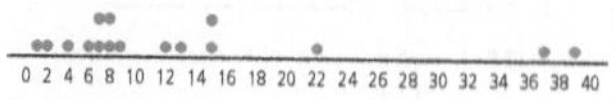
0 2 4 6 8 10 12 14 16 18 20 22 24 26 28 30 32 34 36 38 40

22, 37, and 39

Part B

Make a box plot of the data for length of path. Amelia was asked if more than half of the tornadoes had a path length of at least 15 mi. How should she respond?

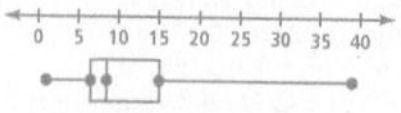
0 5 10 15 20 25 30 35 40

Answers will vary. Sample: No, the box plot shows that only 25% of the paths are at least 15 miles.

Part C

Remove the outliers from the data set given in Parts A and B, and make a revised box plot. How does the removal of the outliers affect the box plot? How does it affect the median of the data set?

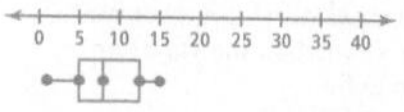
0 5 10 15 20 25 30 35 40

Answers may vary. Sample: The box is shifted left, and the new median, 8, moves almost to the center of the range.

2. Amelia researches average rainfall data for two nearby cities during a twelve-month period from January to December. The data are recorded in the table below.

Inches of Rainfall

	J	F	M	A	M	J	J	A	S	O	N	D
City A	3.2	3.1	4.5	5.0	4.1	2.9	1.8	0.8	2.2	2.3	3.1	3.0
City B	4.2	4.0	4.7	4.8	4.5	4.3	4.0	3.9	4.3	4.4	4.6	4.5

Part A

Amelia displayed the data to show values grouped into ranges or intervals *without* showing any individual values. Do you think she used a dot plot, histogram, or box plot to display the data? Create a data display for each city with the type of display that gives the clearest picture of the information.

histogram; Histograms will vary. Sample:

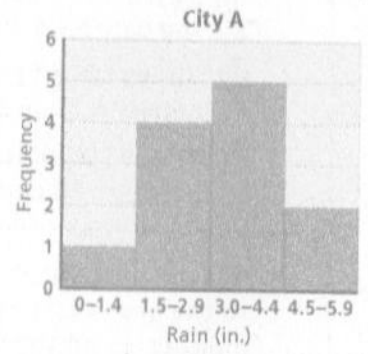
City A
Frequency
0 1 2 3 4 5 6
0–1.4 1.5–2.9 3.0–4.4 4.5–5.9
Rain (in.)

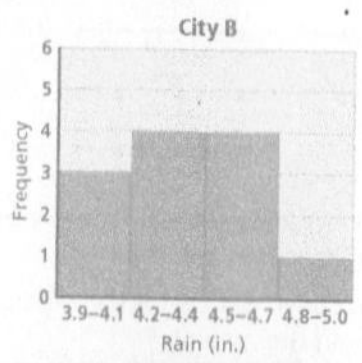
City B
Frequency
0 1 2 3 4 5 6
3.9–4.1 4.2–4.4 4.5–4.7 4.8–5.0
Rain (in.)

Part B

The consensus opinion of the class is that, because City A had the greatest amount of rain in April, 5.0 in., City A had more rainfall during the year. Analyze the distribution of values in each data set by completing the table. Tell the class whether the data support the consensus. Also tell them whether the data sets appear to be influenced by outliers.

Box Plot Values

Data Measures (in.)	City A	City B
Minimum	0.8	3.9
First Quartile	2.25	4.1
Median	3.05	4.35
Third Quartile	3.65	4.55
Maximum	5	4.8
Interquartile Range	1.40	0.45

Answers may vary. Sample: No. Based on the data, the median and interquartile range of rainfall for City B are both greater. The data for City A seem to be affected by an outlier in August of 0.8 in.

Part C

Amelia discusses the predictability of rainfall amounts in both cities with her class. State the mean and the standard deviation to compare the variability of the data sets. Use those measures to discuss the predictability of rainfall in each city.

City A: mean = 3.0 in., standard deviation = 1.16 in. City B: mean = 4.35 in., standard deviation = 0.28 in. Sample: The standard deviation for City A is greater than the standard deviation for City B. The amount of rainfall in City A is less predictable than the amount of rainfall for City B.

AVAILABLE ONLINE

Topic Performance Assessment Assess students' ability to apply the topic concepts and skills using the Topic Performance Assessments found at **SavvasRealize.com.** These online assessments include a breadth of technology-enhanced item types.

Item Analysis and Scoring Guide

Item	DOK	2-Point Responses	1-Point Responses	Standards
1A	2	Correct plot and outliers	Partially correct answers	HSS.ID.A.1
1B	2	Correct plot and explanation	Incomplete explanation	HSS.ID.A.1
1C	2	Correct plot and explanation	Incomplete explanation	HSS.ID.A.1
2A	3	Correct answer and histograms	One correct histogram	HSS.ID.A.1
2B	2	Correct table and explanation	Correct table values only	HSS.ID.A.2, HSS.ID.A.3
2C	3	Correct answer and explanation	Incomplete explanation	HSS.ID.A.2

Statistics

SavvasRealize.com

Assess

TOPIC PERFORMANCE ASSESSMENT Form B

AVAILABLE ONLINE

Name ______________________

enVision Algebra 1
PearsonRealize.com

11 Performance Assessment Form B

The data in the table show the bowling averages for 20 players in each of two different leagues. Bowling officials want to organize and display averages for each league using various methods of data analysis.

League 1	League 2
158	172
99	141
178	160
157	68
119	103
125	81
74	126
133	117
179	144
133	105
157	141
134	123
176	121
118	121
135	119
158	139
178	64
129	143
178	122
99	92

1. Create a box plot of the data for League 1.

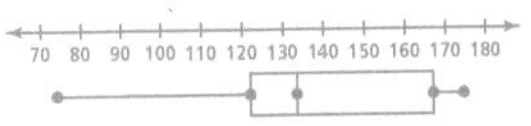

70 80 90 100 110 120 130 140 150 160 170 180

2. Create a box plot of the data for League 2.

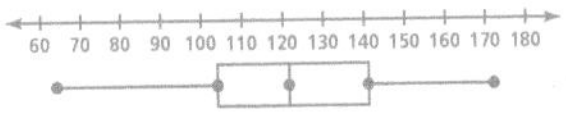

60 70 80 90 100 110 120 130 140 150 160 170 180

3. Use the data displays in Items 1 and 2 and the data in the table above.

   Make observations and comparisons about the data sets in terms of the following:

   - ability of the bowlers in each league
   - how the data are affected by any outliers
   - key pieces of information in the box plots (median, first quartile, third quartile, interquartile range)
   - spread of data based on standard deviation

   Answers will vary. Sample: Bowlers in League 1, in general, are better bowlers than bowlers in League 2 because they have higher averages. That can be seen in the fact that the League 1 values for Q_1, median, and Q_3 (122, 134.5, and 167) are greater than the League 2 values for Q_1, median, and Q_3 (104, 121.5, 141). The standard deviation for League 1 is 29.59, which is greater than the standard deviation for League 2, 27.72. So the players' averages in League 1 are slightly more diverse than in League 2.

enVision™ Algebra 1 • Assessment Resources

4. Create a histogram for each set of data. Describe each data distribution. What does the shape of the distribution tell you?

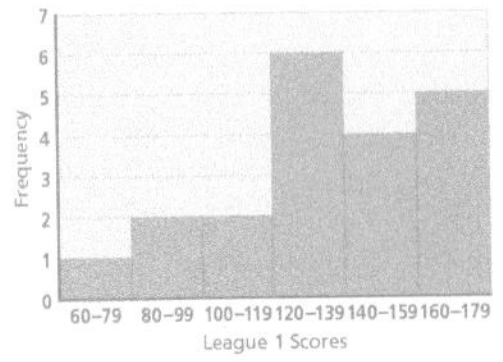

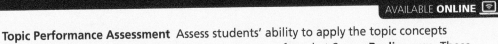

Frequency
7
6
5
4
3
2
1
0
60–79
80–99
100–119
120–139
140–159
160–179
League 1 Scores

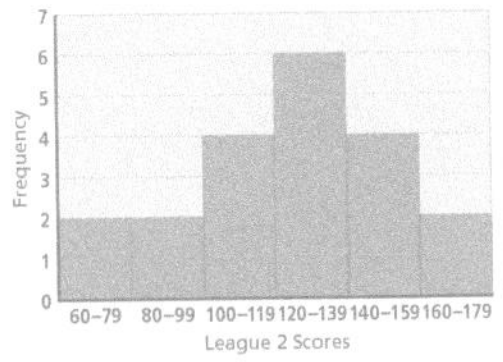

Frequency
7
6
5
4
3
2
1
0
60–79
80–99
100–119
120–139
140–159
160–179
League 2 Scores

   Answers will vary. Sample: The shape of the data for League 2 appears to be a normal distribution because the mean, 120.1, is about the same as the median, 121.5. In the histogram for League 1, there is one extra interval to the left of the interval with the mean, but it contains only one bowler. So the distribution for League 1 is probably not skewed left. The fact that the mean of 140.9 is greater than the median of 134.5 confirms that the data are not skewed left.

5. Both leagues want to create a third league for the most skilled players. They will start a separate league if there are 20 players who average at least 140. Complete the two-way frequency table below. What trends do the results suggest with respect to joint and marginal frequencies? Should there be a separate league for players who average 140 or more? Explain.

	Below 140	Above 140	Totals
League 1	11	9	20
League 2	14	6	20
Totals	25	15	40

   Sample: The joint frequencies show that about half the bowlers in League 1 average at least 140. However, League 2 only has less than a third of its players who average at least 140. The marginal frequencies show that averages below 140 are much more the norm for the combined leagues, so there may not be enough skilled players for a separate league.

6. Complete the table that shows the joint relative frequencies and marginal relative frequencies from the data in Item 5. What suggestions would you give for new members who want to join League 1? League 2?

	Below 140	Above 140	Totals
League 1	$\frac{11}{40} = 27.5\%$	$\frac{9}{40} = 22.5\%$	$\frac{20}{40} = 50\%$
League 2	$\frac{14}{40} = 35\%$	$\frac{6}{40} = 15\%$	$\frac{20}{40} = 50\%$
Totals	$\frac{25}{40} = 62.5\%$	$\frac{15}{40} = 37.5\%$	$\frac{40}{40} = 100\%$

   Answers may vary. Sample:
   New players who average below 140 should join League 2 so they match the skill level of the league, and new players who average at least 140 should join League 1.

enVision™ Algebra 1 • Assessment Resources

AVAILABLE ONLINE

Topic Performance Assessment Assess students' ability to apply the topic concepts and skills using the Topic Performance Assessments found at **SavvasRealize.com.** These online assessments include a breadth of technology-enhanced item types.

Item Analysis and Scoring Guide

Item	DOK	2-Point Responses	1-Point Responses	Standards
1	2	Correct plot	Partially correct quartiles	HSS.ID.A.1
2	2	Correct plot	Partially correct quartiles	HSS.ID.A.1
3	3	Correct data measures and analysis	Correct data measures only	HSS.ID.A.2, HSS.ID.A.3
4	4	Correct histograms and explanation	Correct histograms only	HSS.ID.A.1, HSS.ID.A.2
5	3	Correct table values and explanation	Correct table values only	HSS.ID.B.5
6	2	Correct table and explanation	Correct table only	HSS.ID.B.5

Visual Glossary

English	Spanish

A

Absolute value function $f(x) = |x|$

Función de valor absoluto $f(x) = |x|$

Example

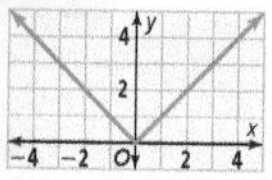

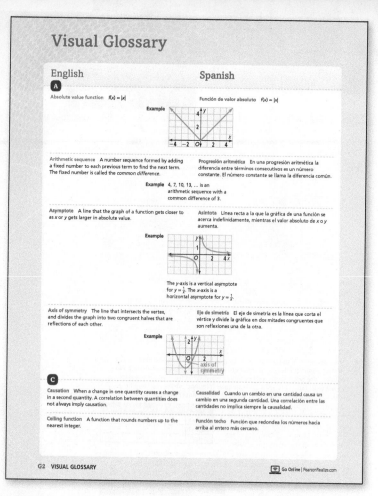

Arithmetic sequence A number sequence formed by adding a fixed number to each previous term to find the next term. The fixed number is called the *common difference*.

Progresión aritmética En una progresión aritmética la diferencia entre términos consecutivos es un número constante. El número constante se llama la diferencia común.

Example 4, 7, 10, 13, … is an arithmetic sequence with a common difference of 3.

Asymptote A line that the graph of a function gets closer to as x or y gets larger in absolute value.

Asíntota Línea recta a la que la gráfica de una función se acerca indefinidamente, mientras el valor absoluto de x o y aumenta.

Example

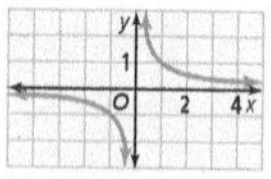

The y-axis is a vertical asymptote for $y = \frac{1}{x}$. The x-axis is a horizontal asymptote for $y = \frac{1}{x}$.

Axis of symmetry The line that intersects the vertex, and divides the graph into two congruent halves that are reflections of each other.

Eje de simetría El eje de simetría es la línea que corta el vértice y divide la gráfica en dos mitades congruentes que son reflexiones una de la otra.

Example

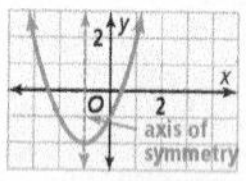
axis of symmetry

C

Causation When a change in one quantity causes a change in a second quantity. A correlation between quantities does not always imply causation.

Causalidad Cuando un cambio en una cantidad causa un cambio en una segunda cantidad. Una correlación entre las cantidades no implica siempre la causalidad.

Ceiling function A function that rounds numbers up to the nearest integer.

Función techo Función que redondea los números hacia arriba al entero más cercano.

English	Spanish

Closure property A set of numbers is closed under an operation when the result of the operation is also part of the same set of numbers.

Propiedad de cerradura Un conjunto de números está cerrado bajo una operación cuando el resultado de la operación también forma parte del mismo conjunto de números.

Example The set of integers is closed under addition because the sum of two integers is always an integer.

Common difference The difference between consecutive terms of an arithmetic sequence.

Diferencia común La diferencia común es la diferencia entre los términos consecutivos de una progresión aritmética.

Example The common difference is 3 in the arithmetic sequence 4, 7, 10, 13, …

Completing the square The process of adding $\left(\frac{b}{2}\right)^2$ to $x^2 + bx$ to form a perfect-square trinomial.

Completar el cuadrado El proceso de sumar $\left(\frac{b}{2}\right)^2$ a $x^2 + bx$ para formar un trinomio cuadrado perfecto.

Example $x^2 + 6x - 7 = 9$ is rewritten as $(x + 3)^2 = 25$ by completing the square.

Compound inequalities Two inequalities that are joined by *and* or *or*.

Desigualdades compuestas Dos desigualdades que están enlazadas por medio de una *y* o una *o*.

Examples $5 < x$ and $x < 10$
$14 < x$ or $x \leq -3$

Compound interest Interest paid on both the principal and the interest that has already been paid.

Interés compuesto Interés calculado tanto sobre el capital como sobre los intereses ya pagados.

Example For an initial deposit of $1,000 at a 6% interest rate with interest compounded quarterly, the function $y = 1000\left(\frac{0.06}{4}\right)^{4x}$ gives the account balance y after x years.

Conditional relative frequency The ratio of the joint frequency and the related marginal frequency.

Frecuencia relativa condicional La razón de la frecuencia conjunta y la frecuencia marginal relacionada.

Example

	Afternoon	Evening	Totals
Student	$\frac{90}{140} = 64\%$	$\frac{50}{140} = 36\%$	$\frac{140}{140} = 100\%$
Adult	$\frac{20}{60} = 33\%$	$\frac{40}{60} = 67\%$	$\frac{60}{60} = 100\%$

Constant ratio The number that an exponential function repeatedly multiplies an initial amount by.

Razón constante El número por el que una función exponencial multiplica repetidamente a una cantidad inicial.

Example In an exponential function of the form $f(x) = ab^x$, b is the constant ratio.

English	Spanish

Continuous A graph that is unbroken.

Continua Una gráfica continua es una gráfica ininterrumpida.

Example

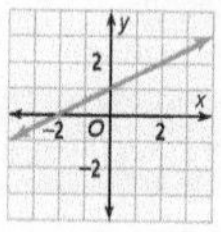

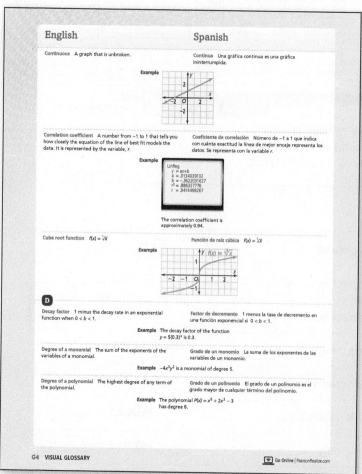

Correlation coefficient A number from −1 to 1 that tells you how closely the equation of the line of best fit models the data. It is represented by the variable, r.

Coeficiente de correlación Número de −1 a 1 que indica con cuánta exactitud la línea de mejor encaje representa los datos. Se representa con la variable r.

Example

LinReg
y = ax+b
a = .0134039132
b = −.3622031627
r² = .886327776
r = .9414498267

The correlation coefficient is approximately 0.94.

Cube root function $f(x) = \sqrt[3]{x}$

Función de raíz cúbica $f(x) = \sqrt[3]{x}$

Example

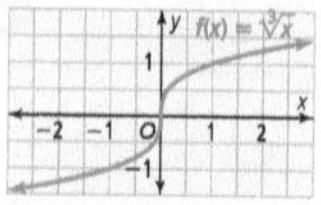
f(x) = ∛x

D

Decay factor 1 minus the decay rate in an exponential function when $0 < b < 1$.

Factor de decremento 1 menos la tasa de decremento en una función exponencial si $0 < b < 1$.

Example The decay factor of the function $y = 5(0.3)^x$ is 0.3.

Degree of a monomial The sum of the exponents of the variables of a monomial.

Grado de un monomio La suma de los exponentes de las variables de un monomio.

Example $-4x^3y^2$ is a monomial of degree 5.

Degree of a polynomial The highest degree of any term of the polynomial.

Grado de un polinomio El grado de un polinomio es el grado mayor de cualquier término del polinomio.

Example The polynomial $P(x) = x^6 + 2x^3 - 3$ has degree 6.

English	Spanish

Difference of two squares A difference of two squares is an expression of the form $a^2 - b^2$. It can be factored as $(a + b)(a - b)$.

Diferencia de dos cuadrados La diferencia de dos cuadrados es una expresión de la forma $a^2 - b^2$. Se puede factorizar como $(a + b)(a - b)$.

Examples $25a^2 - 4 = (5a + 2)(5a - 2)$
$m^6 - 1 = (m^3 + 1)(m^3 - 1)$

Discrete A graph composed of isolated points.

Discreta Una gráfica discreta es compuesta de puntos aislados.

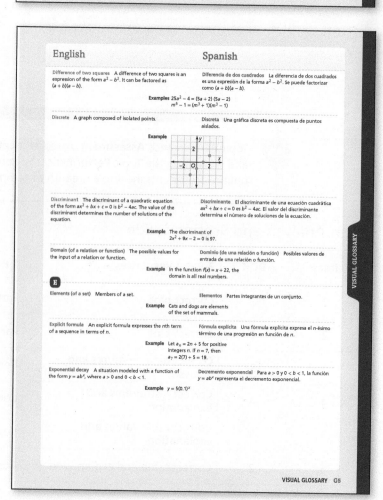

Example

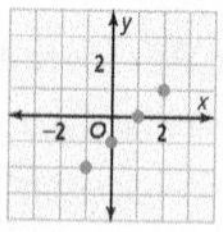

Discriminant The discriminant of a quadratic equation of the form $ax^2 + bx + c = 0$ is $b^2 - 4ac$. The value of the discriminant determines the number of solutions of the equation.

Discriminante El discriminante de una ecuación cuadrática $ax^2 + bx + c = 0$ es $b^2 - 4ac$. El valor del discriminante determina el número de soluciones de la ecuación.

Example The discriminant of $2x^2 + 9x - 2 = 0$ is 97.

Domain (of a relation or function) The possible values for the input of a relation or function.

Dominio (de una relación o función) Posibles valores de entrada de una relación o función.

Example In the function $f(x) = x + 22$, the domain is all real numbers.

E

Elements (of a set) Members of a set.

Elementos Partes integrantes de un conjunto.

Example Cats and dogs are elements of the set of mammals.

Explicit formula An explicit formula expresses the nth term of a sequence in terms of n.

Fórmula explícita Una fórmula explícita expresa el n-ésimo término de una progresión en función de n.

Example Let $a_n = 2n + 5$ for positive integers n. If $n = 7$, then $a_7 = 2(7) + 5 = 19$.

Exponential decay A situation modeled with a function of the form $y = ab^x$, where $a > 0$ and $0 < b < 1$.

Decremento exponencial Para $a > 0$ y $0 < b < 1$, la función $y = ab^x$ representa el decremento exponencial.

Example $y = 5(0.1)^x$

English / Spanish

Exponential function The function $f(x) = b^x$, where $b > 0$ and $b \neq 1$.

Función exponencial La función $f(x) = b^x$, donde $b > 0$ y $b \neq 1$.

Example

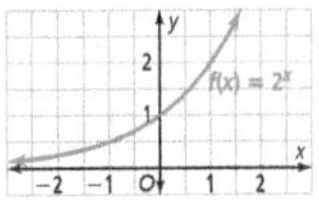
y
2
f(x) = 2^x
1
x
−2
−1
O
1
2

Exponential growth A situation modeled with a function of the form $y = ab^x$, where $a > 0$ and $b > 1$.

Incremento exponencial Para $a > 0$ y $b > 1$, la función $y = ab^x$ representa el incremento exponencial.

Example $y = 100(2)^x$

Extrapolation The process of predicting a value outside the range of known values.

Extrapolación Proceso que se usa para predecir un valor por fuera del ámbito de los valores dados.

F

Family of functions A group of functions that use the same common operation in their equation forms.

Familia de funciones Un grupo de funciones que usan la misma operación común en su forma de ecuación.

Example $f(x) = 3x + 7$ and $f(x) = \frac{2}{3}x - 9$ are members of the linear family of functions.

Floor function The floor function rounds numbers down to the nearest integer.

Función piso La función piso redondea los números hacia abajo al entero más cercano.

Formula An equation that states a relationship among quantities.

Fórmula Ecuación que establece una relación entre cantidades.

Example The formula for the volume V of a cylinder is $V = \pi r^2 h$, where r is the radius of the cylinder and h is its height.

Function A relation in which each element of the domain corresponds with exactly one element in the range.

Función Una relación en la cual cada elemento del dominio se corresponde con exactamente un elemento del rango.

Example Earned income is a function of the number of hours worked. If you earn \$4.50/h, then your income is expressed by the function $f(h) = 4.5h$.

Function notation A method for writing variables as a function of other variables.

Notación de una función Un método para escribir variables como una función de otras variables.

Example $f(x) = 3x - 8$ is in function notation.

English / Spanish

G

Geometric sequence A number sequence formed by multiplying a term in a sequence by a fixed number to find the next term.

Progresión geométrica Tipo de sucesión numérica formada al multiplicar un término de la secuencia por un número constante, para hallar el siguiente término.

Example 9, 3, 1, $\frac{1}{3}$, ... is an example of a geometric sequence.

Growth factor 1 plus the growth rate in an exponential function when $b > 1$.

Factor incremental 1 más la tasa de incremento en una función exponencial si $b > 1$.

Example The growth factor of $y = 7(1.3)^x$ is 1.3.

I

Identity An equation that is true for every value.

Identidad Una ecuación que es verdadera para todos los valores.

Example $5 - 14x = 5\left(1 - \frac{14}{5}x\right)$ is an identity because it is true for any value of x.

Interpolation The process of estimating a value between two known quantities.

Interpolación Proceso que se usa para estimar el valor entre dos cantidades dadas.

Inverse function If function f pairs a value b with a, then its inverse, denoted f^{-1}, pairs the value a with b. If f^{-1} is also a function, then f and f^{-1} are inverse functions.

Funcion inversa Si la función f empareja un valor b con a, entonces su inversa, cuya notación es f^{-1}, empareja el valor a con b. Si f^{-1} también es una función, entonces f y f^{-1} son funciones inversas.

Example If $f(x) = x + 3$, then $f^{-1}(x) = x - 3$.

J

Joint frequency The frequency of a single option for one category.

Frecuencia conjunta La frecuencia de una única opción por categoría.

Example

	Afternoon	Evening	Totals
Student	90	50	140
Adult	20	40	60
Totals	110	90	200

90, 50, 20, and 40 are joint frequencies.

Joint relative frequency The ratio, or percent, of the joint frequency to the total.

Frecuencia relativa conjunta La razón, o porcentaje, de la frecuencia conjunta al total.

Example

	Afternoon	Evening	Totals
Student	$\frac{90}{200} = 45\%$	$\frac{50}{200} = 25\%$	$\frac{140}{200} = 70\%$
Adult	$\frac{20}{200} = 10\%$	$\frac{40}{200} = 20\%$	$\frac{60}{200} = 30\%$
Totals	$\frac{110}{200} = 55\%$	$\frac{90}{200} = 45\%$	$\frac{200}{200} = 100\%$

45%, 25%, 10%, and 20% are joint relative frequencies.

English / Spanish

L

Linear function A function whose graph is a line is a linear function. You can represent a linear function with a linear equation.

Función lineal Una función cuya gráfica es una recta es una función lineal. La función lineal se representa con una ecuación lineal.

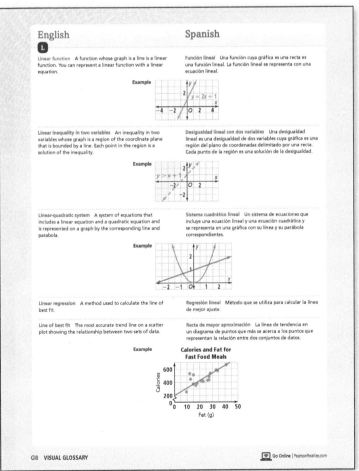

Example

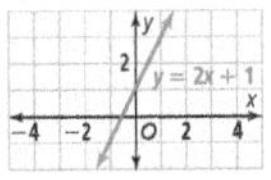
y
2
y = 2x + 1
x
−4
−2
O
2
4

Linear inequality in two variables An inequality in two variables whose graph is a region of the coordinate plane that is bounded by a line. Each point in the region is a solution of the inequality.

Desigualdad lineal con dos variables Una desigualdad lineal es una desigualdad de dos variables cuya gráfica es una región del plano de coordenadas delimitado por una recta. Cada punto de la región es una solución de la desigualdad.

Example

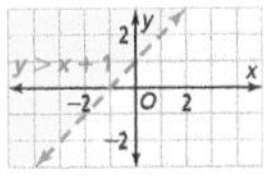
2
y
y > x + 1
x
−2
O
2
−2

Linear-quadratic system A system of equations that includes a linear equation and a quadratic equation and is represented on a graph by the corresponding line and parabola.

Sistema cuadrático lineal Un sistema de ecuaciones que incluye una ecuación lineal y una ecuación cuadrática y se representa en una gráfica con su línea y su parábola correspondientes.

Example

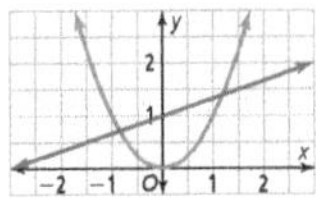
y
2
1
x
−2
−1
O
1
2

Linear regression A method used to calculate the line of best fit.

Regresión lineal Método que se utiliza para calcular la línea de mejor ajuste.

Line of best fit The most accurate trend line on a scatter plot showing the relationship between two sets of data.

Recta de mayor aproximación La línea de tendencia en un diagrama de puntos que más se acerca a los puntos que representan la relación entre dos conjuntos de datos.

Example

Calories and Fat for Fast Food Meals

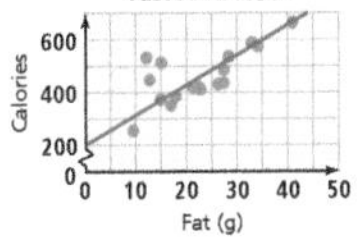
Calories
600
400
200
0
0
10
20
30
40
50
Fat (g)

English / Spanish

Literal equation An equation expressed in variables.

Ecuación literal Ecuación que se expresa con variables.

Example $4x + 2y = 18$ is a literal equation.

M

Marginal frequency The total frequency for each option or category.

Frecuencia marginal La frecuencia total para cada opción o categoría.

Example

	Afternoon	Evening	Totals
Student	90	50	140
Adult	20	40	60
Totals	110	90	200

140, 60, 110, and 90 are marginal frequencies.

Marginal relative frequency The ratio, or percent, of the marginal frequency to the total.

Frecuencia relativa marginal La razón, o porcentaje, de la frecuencia marginal al total.

Example

	Afternoon	Evening	Totals
Student	$\frac{90}{200} = 45\%$	$\frac{50}{200} = 25\%$	$\frac{140}{200} = 70\%$
Adult	$\frac{20}{200} = 10\%$	$\frac{40}{200} = 20\%$	$\frac{60}{200} = 30\%$
Totals	$\frac{110}{200} = 55\%$	$\frac{90}{200} = 45\%$	$\frac{200}{200} = 100\%$

70%, 30%, 55%, and 45% are marginal relative frequencies.

Monomial A real number, a variable, or a product of a real number and one or more variables with whole-number exponents.

Monomio Número real, variable o el producto de un número real y una o más variables con números enteros como exponentes.

Example 9, n, and $-5xy^2$ are examples of monomials.

N

Negative association When y-values tend to decrease as x-values increase, the two data sets have a negative association.

Asociación negativa Cuando los valores de y tienden a disminuir a medida que los valores de x aumentan, los dos conjuntos de datos tienen una asociación negativa.

Example

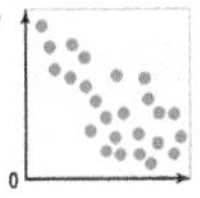
0

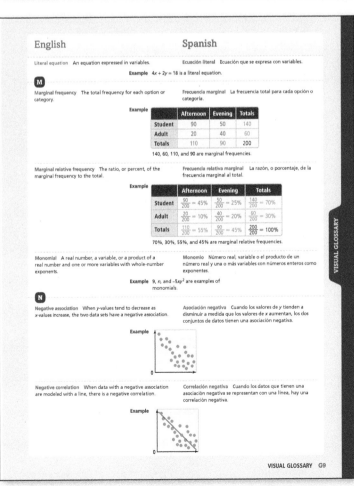

Negative correlation When data with a negative association are modeled with a line, there is a negative correlation.

Correlación negativa Cuando los datos que tienen una asociación negativa se representan con una línea, hay una correlación negativa.

Example

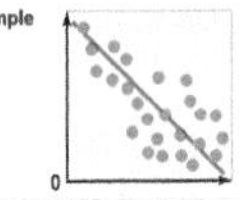
0

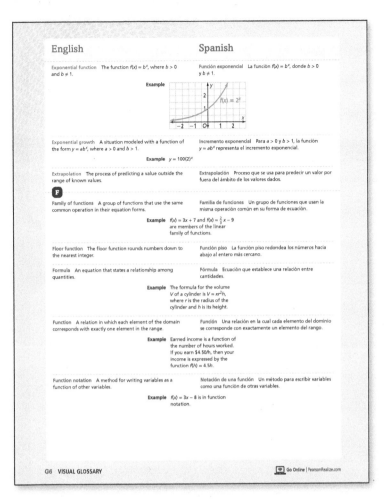

English | Spanish

No association When there is no general relationship between *x*-values and *y*-values, the two data sets have no association.

Sin asociación Cuando no existe ninguna relación general entre los valores de *x* y los valores de *y*, los dos conjuntos de datos no tienen ninguna asociación.

Example

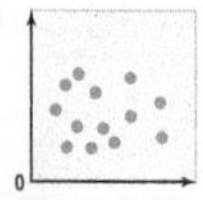
0

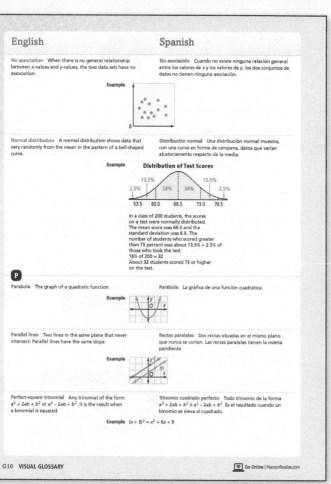

Normal distribution A normal distribution shows data that vary randomly from the mean in the pattern of a bell-shaped curve.

Distribución normal Una distribución normal muestra, con una curva en forma de campana, datos que varían alcatoriamento respecto de la media.

Example

Distribution of Test Scores

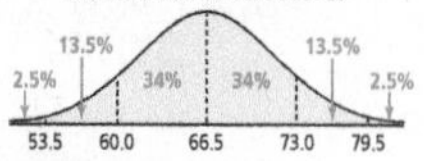
13.5%
13.5%
2.5%
34%
34%
2.5%
53.5
60.0
66.5
73.0
79.5

In a class of 200 students, the scores on a test were normally distributed. The mean score was 66.5 and the standard deviation was 6.5. The number of students who scored greater than 73 percent was about 13.5% + 2.5% of those who took the test.
16% of 200 = 32
About 32 students scored 73 or higher on the test.

P

Parabola The graph of a quadratic function.

Parábola La gráfica de una función cuadrática.

Example

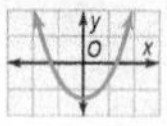
y
O
x

Parallel lines Two lines in the same plane that never intersect. Parallel lines have the same slope.

Rectas paralelas Dos rectas situadas en el mismo plano que nunca se cortan. Las rectas paralelas tienen la misma pendiente.

Example

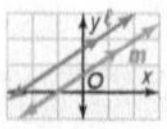
y
ℓ
m
O
x

Perfect-square trinomial Any trinomial of the form $a^2 + 2ab + b^2$ or $a^2 - 2ab + b^2$. It is the result when a binomial is squared.

Trinomio cuadrado perfecto Todo trinomio de la forma $a^2 + 2ab + b^2$ ó $a^2 - 2ab + b^2$. Es el resultado cuando un binomio se eleva al cuadrado.

Example $(x + 3)^2 = x^2 + 6x + 9$

English | Spanish

Perpendicular lines Lines that intersect to form right angles. Two lines are perpendicular if the product of their slopes is −1.

Rectas perpendiculares Rectas que forman ángulos rectos en su intersección. Dos rectas son perpendiculares si el producto de sus pendientes es −1.

Example

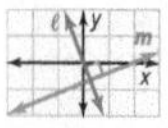
ℓ
y
m
x

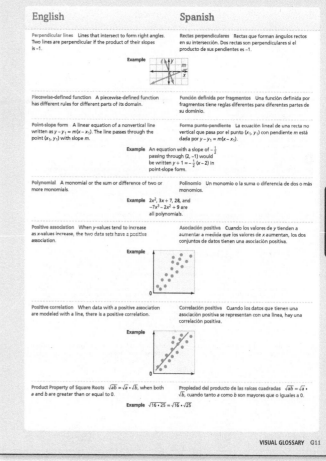

Piecewise-defined function A piecewise-defined function has different rules for different parts of its domain.

Función definida por fragmentos Una función definida por fragmentos tiene reglas diferentes para diferentes partes de su dominio.

Point-slope form A linear equation of a nonvertical line written as $y - y_1 = m(x - x_1)$. The line passes through the point (x_1, y_1) with slope *m*.

Forma punto-pendiente La ecuación lineal de una recta no vertical que pasa por el punto (x_1, y_1) con pendiente *m* está dada por $y - y_1 = m(x - x_1)$.

Example An equation with a slope of $-\frac{1}{2}$ passing through (2, −1) would be written $y + 1 = -\frac{1}{2}(x - 2)$ in point-slope form.

Polynomial A monomial or the sum or difference of two or more monomials.

Polinomio Un monomio o la suma o diferencia de dos o más monomios.

Example $2x^2$, $3x + 7$, 28, and $-7x^3 - 2x^2 + 9$ are all polynomials.

Positive association When *y*-values tend to increase as *x*-values increase, the two data sets have a positive association.

Asociación positiva Cuando los valores de *y* tienden a aumentar a medida que los valores de *x* aumentan, los dos conjuntos de datos tienen una asociación positiva.

Example

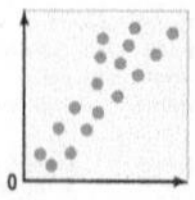
0

Positive correlation When data with a positive association are modeled with a line, there is a positive correlation.

Correlación positiva Cuando los datos que tienen una asociación positiva se representan con una línea, hay una correlación positiva.

Example

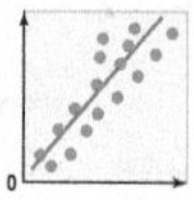
0

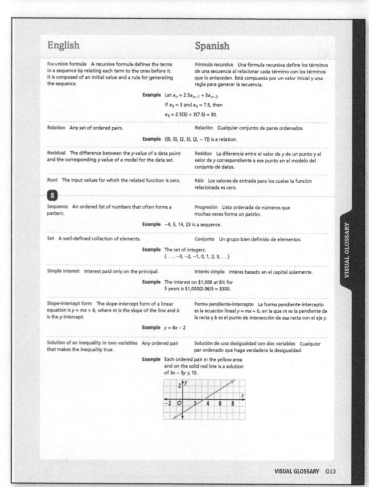

Product Property of Square Roots $\sqrt{ab} = \sqrt{a} \cdot \sqrt{b}$, when both *a* and *b* are greater than or equal to 0.

Propiedad del producto de las raíces cuadradas $\sqrt{ab} = \sqrt{a} \cdot \sqrt{b}$, cuando tanto *a* como *b* son mayores que o iguales a 0.

Example $\sqrt{16 \cdot 25} = \sqrt{16} \cdot \sqrt{25}$

English | Spanish

Q

Quadratic equation An equation of the second degree.

Ecuación cuadrática Una ecuación de segundo grado.

Example $4x^2 + 9x - 5 = 0$

Quadratic formula If $ax^2 + bx + c = 0$ and $a \neq 0$, then $x = \frac{-b \pm \sqrt{b^2 - 4ac}}{2a}$.

Fórmula cuadrática Si $ax^2 + bx + c = 0$ y $a \neq 0$, entonces $x = \frac{-b \pm \sqrt{b^2 - 4ac}}{2a}$.

Example

$$2x^2 + 10x + 12 = 0$$
$$x = \frac{-b \pm \sqrt{b^2 - 4ac}}{2a}$$
$$x = \frac{-10 \pm \sqrt{10^2 - 4(2)(12)}}{2(2)}$$
$$x = \frac{-10 \pm \sqrt{4}}{4}$$
$$x = \frac{-10 + 2}{4} \text{ or } \frac{-10 - 2}{4}$$
$$x = -2 \text{ or } -3$$

Quadratic function A function of the form $y = ax^2 + bx + c$, where $a \neq 0$. The graph of a quadratic function is a parabola, a U-shaped curve that opens up or down.

Función cuadrática La función $y = ax^2 + bx + c$, en la que $a \neq 0$. La gráfica de una función cuadrática es una parábola, o curva en forma de U que se abre hacia arriba o hacia abajo.

Example $y = 5x^2 - 2x + 1$ is a quadratic function.

Quadratic parent function The simplest quadratic function $f(x) = x^2$ or $y = x^2$.

Función cuadrática madre La función cuadrática más simple $f(x) = x^2$ ó $y = x^2$.

Example $y = x^2$ is the parent function for the family of quadratic equations of the form $y = ax^2 + bx + c$.

Quadratic regression A method used to find the quadratic function that best fits a data set.

Regresión cuadrática Método que se utiliza para hallar la función cuadrática que se ajusta mejor a un conjunto de datos.

R

Range (of a relation or function) The possible values of the output, or dependent variable, of a relation or function.

Rango (de una relación o función) El conjunto de todos los valores posibles de la salida, o variable dependiente, de una relación o función.

Example In the function $y = |x|$, the range is the set of all nonnegative numbers.

Rational exponent Another way to express radicals.

Exponente racional Otra forma de expresar los radicales.

Example $\sqrt[3]{x} = x^{\frac{1}{3}}$

$\frac{1}{3}$ is the rational exponent.

Reciprocal The reciprocal of a number is 1 divided by that number.

Recíproco El recíproco de un número es 1 dividido entre ese número.

Example $\frac{2}{5}$ and $\frac{5}{2}$ are reciprocals because $1 \div \frac{2}{5} = \frac{5}{2}$.

English | Spanish

Recursive formula A recursive formula defines the terms in a sequence by relating each term to the ones before it. It is composed of an initial value and a rule for generating the sequence.

Fórmula recursiva Una fórmula recursiva define los términos de una secuencia al relacionar cada término con los términos que lo anteceden. Está compuesta por un valor inicial y una regla para generar la secuencia.

Example Let $a_n = 2.5a_{n-1} + 3a_{n-2}$.
If $a_5 = 3$ and $a_4 = 7.5$, then
$a_6 = 2.5(3) + 3(7.5) = 30$.

Relation Any set of ordered pairs.

Relación Cualquier conjunto de pares ordenados.

Example {(0, 0), (2, 3), (2, − 7)} is a relation.

Residual The difference between the *y*-value of a data point and the corresponding *y*-value of a model for the data set.

Residuo La diferencia entre el valor de *y* de un punto y el valor de *y* correspondiente a ese punto en el modelo del conjunto de datos.

Root The input values for which the related function is zero.

Ráiz Los valores de entrada para los cuales la función relacionada es cero.

S

Sequence An ordered list of numbers that often forms a pattern.

Progresión Lista ordenada de números que muchas veces forma un patrón.

Example −4, 5, 14, 23 is a sequence.

Set A well-defined collection of elements.

Conjunto Un grupo bien definido de elementos.

Example The set of integers: {. . . , −3, −2, −1, 0, 1, 2, 3, . . .}

Simple interest Interest paid only on the principal.

Interés simple Intéres basado en el capital solamente.

Example The interest on \$1,000 at 6% for 5 years is \$1,000(0.06)5 = \$300.

Slope-intercept form The slope-intercept form of a linear equation is $y = mx + b$, where *m* is the slope of the line and *b* is the *y*-intercept.

Forma pendiente-intercepto La forma pendiente-intercepto es la ecuación lineal $y = mx + b$, en la que *m* es la pendiente de la recta y *b* es el punto de intersección de esa recta con el eje *y*.

Example $y = 8x - 2$

Solution of an inequality in two variables Any ordered pair that makes the inequality true.

Solución de una desigualdad con dos variables Cualquier par ordenado que haga verdadera la desigualdad.

Example Each ordered pair in the yellow area and on the solid red line is a solution of $3x - 5y \leq 10$.

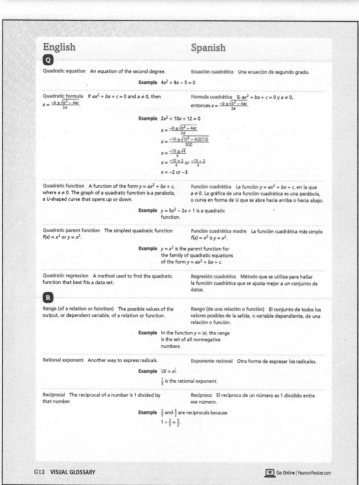

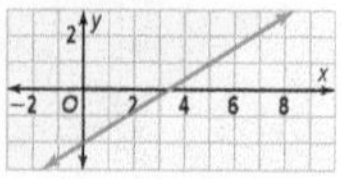
2
y
x
−2
O
2
4
6
8

English | Spanish

Solution of a system of linear inequalities Any ordered pair that makes all of the inequalities in the system true.

Solución de un sistema de desigualdades lineales Todo par ordenado que hace verdaderas todas las desigualdades del sistema.

Example

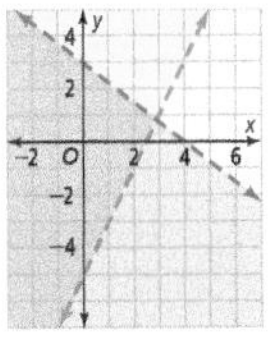
y
4
2
x
−2
O
2
4
6
−2
−4

The shaded green area shows the solution of the system $\begin{matrix} y > 2x - 5 \\ 3x + 4y < 12 \end{matrix}$.

Square root function A function that contains the independent variable in the radicand.

Función de raíz cuadrada Una función que contiene la variable independiente en el radicando.

Example $y = \sqrt{2x}$ is a square root function.

Standard deviation A measure of how data varies, or deviates, from the mean.

Desviación típica Medida de cómo los datos varían, o se desvían, de la media.

Example Use the following formula to find the standard deviation.

$\sigma = \sqrt{\frac{\Sigma(x - \bar{x})^2}{n}}$

Standard form of a linear equation The standard form of a linear equation is $Ax + By = C$, where A, B, and C are real numbers and A and B are not both zero.

Forma normal de una ecuación lineal La forma normal de una ecuación lineal es $Ax + By = C$, donde A, B y C son números reales, y donde A y B no son iguales a cero.

Example $6x - y = 12$

Standard form of a polynomial The form of a polynomial that places the terms in descending order by degree.

Forma normal de un polinomio Cuando el grado de los términos de un polinomio disminuye de izquierda a derecha, está en forma normal, o en orden descendente.

Example $15x^3 + x^2 + 3x + 9$

Standard form of a quadratic equation The standard form of a quadratic equation is $ax^2 + bx + c = 0$, where $a \neq 0$.

Forma normal de una ecuación cuadrática Cuando una ecuación cuadrática se expresa de forma $ax^2 + bx + c = 0$.

Example $-x^2 + 2x - 9 = 0$

Standard form of a quadratic function The standard form of a quadratic function is $f(x) = ax^2 + bx + C$, where $a \neq 0$.

Forma normal de una función cuadrática La forma normal de una función cuadrática es $f(x) = ax^2 + bx + C$, donde $a \neq 0$.

Example $f(x) = 2x^2 - 5x + 2$

Step-function A step-function pairs every number in an interval with a single value. The graph of a step function can look like the steps of a staircase.

Función escalón Una función escalón empareja cada número de un intervalo con un solo valor. La gráfica de una función escalón se puede parecer a los peldaños de una escalera.

English | Spanish

Subset A subset of a set consists of elements from the given set.

Subconjunto Un subconjunto de un conjunto consiste en elementos del conjunto dado.

Example If $B = \{1, 2, 3, 4, 5, 6, 7\}$ and $A = \{1, 2, 5\}$, then A is a subset of B.

System of linear inequalities Two or more linear inequalities using the same variables.

Sistema de desigualdades lineales Dos o más desigualdades lineales que usen las mismas variables.

Example $y \leq x + 11$
$y < 5x$

T

Term of a sequence A term of a sequence is any number in a sequence.

Término de una progresión Un término de una secuencia es cualquier número de una secuencia.

Example −4 is the first term of the sequence −4, 5, 14, 23.

Transformation A transformation of a function maps each point of its graph to a new location.

Transformación Una transformación de una función desplaza cada punto de su gráfica a una ubicación nueva.

Example Transformations can be translations, rotations, reflections, or dilations.

Translation A transformation that shifts the graph of a function the same distance horizontally, vertically, or both.

Translación Proceso de mover una gráfica horizontalmente, verticalmente o en ambos sentidos.

Example

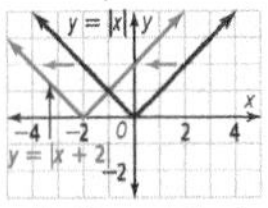
y = |x|
y
x
−4
−2
O
2
4
y = |x + 2|
−2

$y = |x + 2|$ is a translation of $y = |x|$.

Trend line A line that models the data in a scatter plot by showing the general direction of the data.

Línea de tendencia Una línea que representa los datos en un diagrama de puntos y muestra la dirección general de los datos.

Example

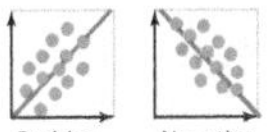

Positive Negative

V

Variance The mean of the squares of the difference between each data value and the mean.

Varianza La media de los cuadrados de la diferencia entre cada valor de los datos y la media.

Example

x	18	25	18	10	17	15	18	15
$\bar{x}$	17	17	17	17	17	17	17	17
$x - \bar{x}$	1	8	1	−7	0	−2	1	−2
$(x - \bar{x})^2$	1	64	1	49	0	4	1	4

The variance is $s^2 = \frac{1 + 64 + 1 + 49 + 0 + 4 + 1 + 4}{7}$.

English | Spanish

Vertex The highest or lowest point on the graph of a function.

Vértice El punto más alto o más bajo de la gráfica de una función.

Example

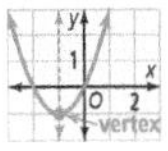
y
1
x
O
2
vertex

Vertex form of a quadratic function The function $f(x) = a(x - h)^2 + k$, where $a \neq 0$. The vertex of the graph is at (h, k).

Forma canónica de una función cuadrática La función $f(x) = a(x - h)^2 + k$, donde $a \neq 0$. El vértice de la gráfica está en (h, k).

Example If the vertex form of a function is $f(x) = 5(x + 3)^2 + 7$, the vertex of the graph is $(-3, 7)$.

Vertical motion model The vertical motion model is the quadratic function $h(t) = -16t^2 + v_0t + h_0$. The variable h represents the height of an object, in feet, t seconds after it is launched into the air. The term v_0 is the object's initial velocity and h_0 is its initial height.

Modelo de movimiento vertical El modelo de movimiento vertical es la función cuadrática $h(t) = -16t^2 + v_0t + h_0$. La variable h representa la altura en pies de un objeto t segundos después de lanzarlo al aire. El término v_0 es la velocidad inicial del objeto y h_0 es su altura inicial.

Example If an object is launched from a height of 10 ft with an initial velocity of 8 ft/s, then the equation of the object's height over time is $h(t) = -16t^2 + 8t + 10$.

Y

y-intercept The y-coordinate of a point where a graph crosses the y-axis.

Intercepto en y Coordenada y por donde la gráfica cruza el eje de las y.

Example The y-intercept of $y = 5x + 2$ is 2.

Z

Zero-Product Property For all real numbers a and b, if $ab = 0$, then $a = 0$ or $b = 0$.

Propiedad del producto cero Para todos los números reales a y b, si $ab = 0$, entonces $a = 0$ ó $b = 0$.

Example $x(x + 3) = 0$

$x = 0$ or $x + 3 = 0$

$x = 0$ or $x = -3$

Zero of a function An x-intercept of the graph of a function.

Cero de una función Intercepto x de la gráfica de una función.

Example The zeros of $y = x^2 - 4$ are ± 2.

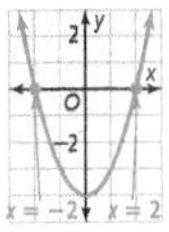
2
y
x
O
−2
x = −2
x = 2

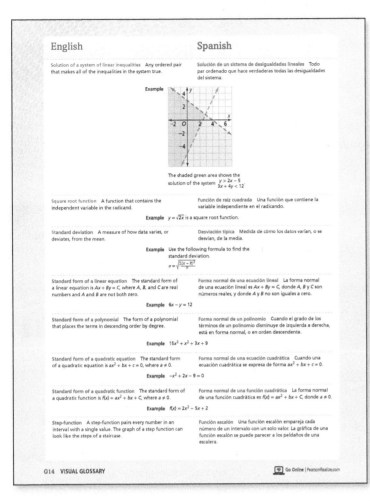

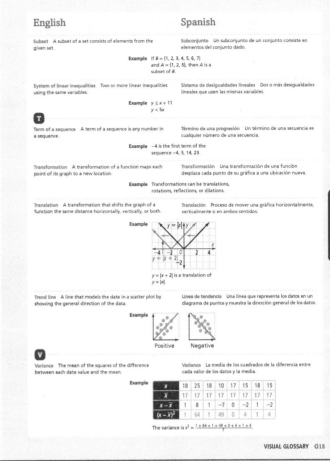

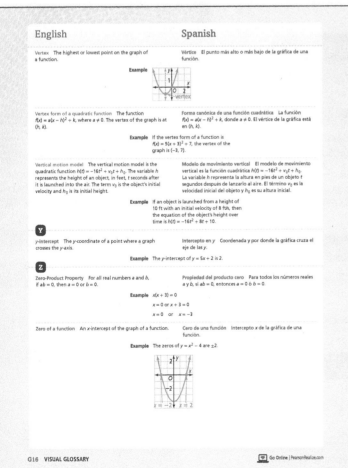

Topic 10

Lesson 10-3

Practice and Problem-Solving Exercises **page 431**

36. Part A

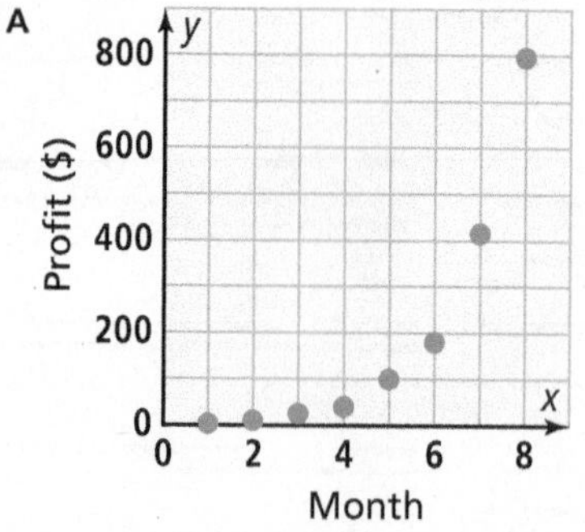

y
800
600
400
200
0
Profit ($)
0
2
4
6
8
x
Month

Jack's business growth so far is roughly exponential.

Part B The growth of the exponential function begins slowly but then increases more and more rapidly. The function has no maximum, but this may not be relevant, because Jack's profits will likely begin to level off.

Part C Let x = number of months in business. $P(x) = 2.4^x$ predicts $P(20) = 2.4^{20} = 40{,}199{,}887$/month. This is not likely—the fast growth at the beginning will probably level out rather than continue.

Lesson 10-4

Practice and Problem-Solving Exercises **page 436**

29.

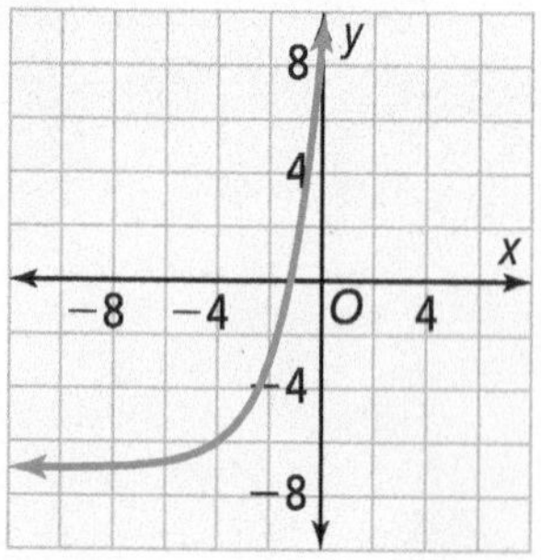

8
y
4
x
−8
−4
O
4
−4
−8

30.

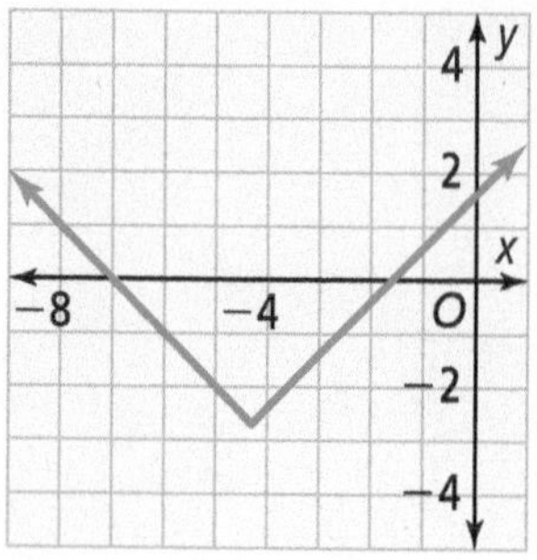

4
y
2
x
−8
−4
O
−2
−4

Topic 11

Lesson 11-1

Practice and Problem-Solving Exercises **page 470**

19. dot plot; You need to see individual data values to count how many are greater than any given value.

20. histogram; A histogram organizes data by equal-sized intervals.

21. box plot; A box plot reveals quartiles.

22. 7

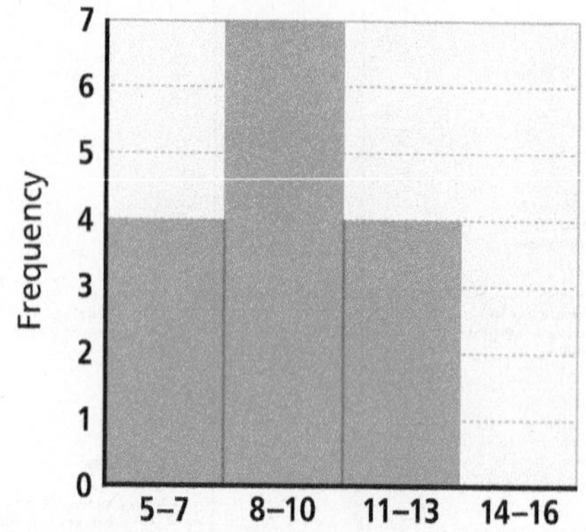

Frequency
7
6
5
4
3
2
1
0
5–7
8–10
11–13
14–16

23. 7

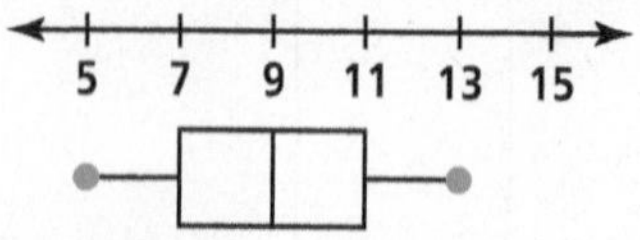

5
7
9
11
13
15

Lesson 11-5

Practice and Problem-Solving Exercises **page 499**

13.

	Song A	Song B	Totals
Teen	30	5	35
Adult	10	15	25
Totals	40	20	60

Yes; the marginal frequencies show that more people surveyed prefer Song A.

14. No; the marginal frequencies show that 35 teens were surveyed and 25 adults were surveyed. So, more teens participated in the survey.

15.

	Song A	Song B	Totals
Teen	0.86	0.14	1.00
Adult	0.40	0.60	1.00

Yes; 86% of teens prefer Song A while only 40% of adults do.

16.

	Song A	Song B
Teen	0.75	0.25
Adult	0.25	0.75
Totals	1.00	1.00

Yes; 75% of the members who prefer Song B are adults.

17.

High School Graduate?	Choice A	Choice B	Totals
Yes	16 0.08	96 0.48	112 0.56
No	64 0.32	24 0.12	88 0.44
Totals	80 0.40	120 0.60	200 1.00

18.

High School Graduate?	Choice A	Choice B	Totals
Yes	0.14	0.86	1.00
No	0.73	0.27	1.00

19.

High School Graduate?	Choice A	Choice B
Yes	0.2	0.8
No	0.8	0.2
Totals	1.00	1.00

20. Choice B; Of the high school graduates, 14% prefer Choice A and 86% prefer Choice B.

21. No; of those who prefer Choice A, only 20% are high school graduates.

29. Part A

By how many points did your score increase?			
	< 50	≥ 50	Totals
Prep Course	5	20	25
No Prep Course	45	30	75
Totals	50	50	100

Part B No; you could calculate conditional relative frequencies by rows to show that 80% of students who took the prep course scored 50 points or higher on the retest, compared to only 40% of students who did not take the prep course.

By how many points did your score increase?			
	< 50	≥ 50	Totals
Prep Course	0.20	0.80	1.00
No Prep Course	0.60	0.40	1.00

Index

INDEX

INDEX

INDEX | N1 | INDEX

INDEX

INDEX

N

O

P

Q

INDEX | N5 | INDEX

Acknowledgments

Topic 07:
259 Agencja Fotograficzna Caro/Alamy Stock Photo; **265** Paul White/UK Industries/Alamy Stock Photo; **273** Gunter Marx/BI/Alamy Stock Photo; **282T** Vittorio Valletta/Agf Srl/Alamy Stock Photo; **282B** Asiapics/Alamy Stock Photo; **284** Monkey Business/Fotolia; **285** Redsnapper/Alamy Stock Photo; **288** Design56/123RF; **297** Brian Kinney/Shutterstock; **302** Jose Luis Stephens/Alamy Stock Photo

Topic 08:
315 Larry w. Smith/epa/Newscom; **321** Larry w. Smith/epa/Newscom; **323** Studio Source/Alamy Stock Photo; **333** Wdg Photo/Shutterstock;

Topic 09:
383 Mario Hagen/Shutterstock; **386** Floresco Productions/Cultura RM/Alamy Stock Photo;

Topic 10:
413 Marco Diaz Segura/Shutterstock; **416** Joern Sackermann/Alamy Stock Photo; **419** Jason Edwards/National Geographic/Getty Images; **419** Efrain Padro/Alamy Stock Photo; **422** Double Photo Studio/Shutterstock; **433** DariosStudio/Alamy Stock Photo; **445** Konstantin Trubavin/123RF; **449** Frederic Cirou/PhotoAlto/Alamy Stock Photo; **452L** Apopium/Fotolia; **452R** Marc Xavier/Fotolia; **455** Erick Nguyen/Alamy Stock Photo; **458** World Foto/Alamy Stock Photo;

Topic 11:
490T MaxyM/Shutterstock; **490B** Kanonsky/Fotolia;

STEM
258 1r1ska/Shutterstock; **258** Robuart/Shutterstock; **258** Pedro Alexandre Teixeira/Shutterstock; **258** Veronchick84/Shutterstock; **258** Sean Pavone/Shutterstock; **258** Stockbroker/Alamy Stock Photo; **258** Hand Idea/Shutterstock; **314** Jeff Gilbert/Alamy Stock Photo; **314** Hero Images Inc./Alamy Stock Photo; **314** Marcin Balcerzak/Shutterstock; **356** Somchai Som/Shutterstock; **356** Claudio Divizia/Shutterstock; **356** NASA Images/Shutterstock; **356** Martin Rickett/PA Images/Alamy Stock Photo; **356** Eugene Onischenko/Shutterstock; **356** Vadim Sadovski/Shutterstock; **410** Dikobraziy/Shutterstock; **410** Greens87/Shutterstock; **410** Greens87/Shutterstock; **410** Greens87/Shutterstock; **410** Razvan Sera/Shutterstock; **410** Stockshoppe/Shutterstock; **464** Ganibal/Shutterstock; **464** Kaissa/Shutterstock; **464** okili77/Shutterstock; **464** Kris Tan/Shutterstock; **464** Porojnicu Stelian/Shutterstock;